PART ONE: MATHEMATICAL ANALYSIS OF BIOLOGIC DATA

statistical tech~~~~~~ ~lysis

~~~~~~ ques

~~~~~~ control

PART TWO: BIOCHEMISTRY — THEORY AND DATA

PART THREE: BIOPHYSICS — THEORY AND DATA

THE HANDBOOK OF BIOCHEMISTRY AND BIOPHYSICS

COMPANION TO THIS BOOK:

METHODS AND REFERENCES IN BIOCHEMISTRY AND BIOPHYSICS

THE HANDBOOK OF BIOCHEMISTRY AND BIOPHYSICS

EDITOR
HENRY C. DAMM, PH.D.
WESTERN RESERVE UNIVERSITY

ASSOCIATE EDITOR AND
CHAIRMAN OF ADVISORY BOARD
PAIGE K. BESCH, PH.D.
THE OHIO STATE UNIVERSITY

DIRECTOR OF DOCUMENTATION
ALVIN J. GOLDWYN, M.A.
WESTERN RESERVE UNIVERSITY

THE WORLD PUBLISHING COMPANY
CLEVELAND AND NEW YORK

Published by The World Publishing Company
2231 West 110th Street, Cleveland, Ohio 44102

Published simultaneously in Canada by
Nelson, Foster & Scott Ltd.

First Printing 1966

Library of Congress Catalog Card Number: 65-25773

Printed in the United States of America

PREFACE

Biochemistry and biophysics are two vital, dynamic, enormously expanding areas. Biology, physiology, medicine, microbiology, nutrition—these and numerous other fields are now part of the responsibility of the biochemist and the biophysicist. Professionals engaged in research or in academic pursuits have long felt and voiced the need for an up-to-date source of materials and references to keep abreast of the rapidly advancing and changing technology of these disciplines. The purpose of *The Handbook of Biochemistry and Biophysics,* and of its companion volume, *Methods and References in Biochemistry and Biophysics,* is to fill this increasingly urgent need.

The logarithmic growth of published research articles, the active exchange of information at national meetings and conferences, the endless outpouring of data, the nearly infinite number of books and monographs published in the field have long necessitated a coalescing of new knowledge in biochemistry and biophysics into one usable and *current* book. This publication was designed to answer that call. In any such undertaking, however, some omissions are inevitable. For example, in keeping with the philosophy of the publisher, editor, and board members, it was the intent to include all pertinent and useful references in the fields of biochemistry and biophysics. But, despite a herculean attempt, this goal of completeness and perfection was not fully attained. Along the same lines, our commitment to timeliness required that content be updated virtually to the point of publication. The few inconsistencies in content and cross-referencing that resulted from these changes were felt to be more than offset by the value of the new information presented. Future editions will be produced on this same principle of updating, so that ultimately this handbook will contain all important material and references in the fields of biochemistry and biophysics.

Future editions will also be guided by the response of the users of the present volume. Accordingly, the editors solicit and will appreciate statements regarding the accuracy of material and completeness of coverage and we welcome suggestions for the incorporation of new material in subsequent editions.

Credit for the success of this book is due to competent and conscientious editorial and advisory boards and to the many persons involved in compiling, typing, and proofreading. The publisher and editors extend sincere thanks to these dedicated and loyal individuals.

15 July 1966   THE EDITORS
Cleveland, Ohio

CONTENTS

CONTRIBUTORS

G. ACKERS, Johns Hopkins University, Baltimore, Maryland, *Protein Chemistry*.

W. F. ANDERSON, National Institutes of Health, Bethesda, Maryland, *Genetic Code and Protein Synthesis*.

W. C. BALL, Jr., Johns Hopkins Hospital, Baltimore, Maryland, *Computer Techniques*.

J. S. BENDAT, Measurement Analysis Corporation, Los Angeles, California, *Statistical Techniques*.

W. S. CAUGHEY, The Johns Hopkins University School of Medicine, Baltimore, Maryland, *Physical Constants of Porphyrins*.

P. CHERIATHUNDAM, Mt. Sinai Hospital, Cleveland, Ohio, *Nucleoproteins, Metabolism of Nucleic Acids*.

C. COHEN, Western Reserve University, Cleveland, Ohio, *Methods of Immunization*.

R. DAGIRMANJIAN, The Ohio State University, Columbus, Ohio, *Biogenic Amines*.

H. C. DAMM, Western Reserve University, Cleveland, Ohio, *Nucleoproteins, Metabolism of Nucleic Acids*.

J. T. DICKMAN, Chemical Abstracts Service, Columbus, Ohio, *Abstracting, Indexing, and Alerting Services*.

T. DOWNS, Western Reserve University, Cleveland, Ohio, *Quality Control*.

F. DUNN, University of Illinois, Urbana, Illinois, *Ultrasound*.

J. G. ERDMAN, Phillips Petroleum Company, Bartlesville, Oklahoma, *Chemistry of Dipyrryl Compounds.*

J. E. FALK, Commonwealth Science and Industrial Research Organization, Canberra, Australia, *Chemistry of Hemoproteins.*

P. G. GASSMAN, The Ohio State University, Columbus, Ohio, *Instrumentation.*

W. B. GEHO, Western Reserve University, Cleveland, Ohio, *Oxidation-Reduction.*

E. GOLD, Cleveland Metropolitan General Hospital, Cleveland, Ohio, *Viruses.*

K. E. GUYER, Medical College of Virginia, Richmond, Virginia, *Phospholipids and Glycolipids.*

R. J. HENRY, Bio Science Laboratories, Los Angeles, California, *The Selection and Evaluation of Analytical Clinical Chemical Methods.*

L. HORROCKS, Cleveland Psychiatric Institute, Cleveland, Ohio, *Lipids, References to Methods.*

D. HORTON, The Ohio State University, Columbus, Ohio, *Carbohydrates; Introduction, Natural Monosaccharides.*

H. A. HUNSCHER, Western Reserve University, Cleveland, Ohio, *Nutrition.*

E. L. KEAN, Western Reserve University, Cleveland, Ohio, *Carbohydrate Esters.*

W. H. KO, Case Institute of Technology, Cleveland, Ohio, *Telemetering of Biological Signals: Bio-Telemetry.*

J. S. KROHMER, Roswell Park Memorial Institute, Buffalo, New York, *Shielding and Attenuation of Ionizing Radiation.*

F. A. KRUGER, The Ohio State University, Columbus, Ohio, *Protein Metabolism.*

S. McCOY, The Johns Hopkins University School of Medicine, Baltimore, Maryland, *Physical Constants of Porphyrins.*

J. H. MILSUM, McGill University, Montreal, Canada, *Control and Regulation.*

D. B. MORELL, Institute of Medical Research, New South Wales, Australia, *Chemistry of Hemoproteins.*

J. NEVILLE, Western Reserve University, Cleveland, Ohio, *Nutrition.*

M. NIRENBERG, National Institutes of Health, Bethesda, Maryland, *Genetic Code and Protein Synthesis.*

D. L. OXENDER, University of Michigan, Ann Arbor, Michigan, *Chemistry of Amino Acids.*

W. R. PASTERCZYK, DePaul University, Chicago, Illinois, *Purification Procedures.*

A. E. POWELL, Western Reserve University, Cleveland, Ohio, *Extinction Coefficients of Biological Substances.*

L. E. REICHERT, JR., Emory University, Atlanta, Georgia, *Amino Acid and Protein Hormones.*

R. D. SAGERS, Brigham Young University, Provo, Utah, *Amino Acid Metabolism.*

M. SCHUBERT, New York University School of Medicine, New York, N.Y., *Natural Oligosaccharides, Polysaccharides.*

B. SHAPIRO, Albert Einstein Medical Center, Philadelphia, Pennsylvania, *Radiation Biochemistry.*

E. M. SMITH, The Hospital for Special Surgery, Cornell University Medical College, New York, N.Y., *Radiation Absorbed Dose from Internally Deposited Radionuclides.*

A. SOKOLLU, Western Reserve University, Cleveland, Ohio, *Ultrasound.*

H. M. SPRECHER, The Ohio State College of Medicine, Columbus, Ohio, *Fatty Acids and Glycerides.*

R. F. STEINER, Naval Medical Research Institute, Bethesda, Maryland, *Chemistry of the Purines and Pyrimidines.*

H. STIFFLER, Western Reserve University, Cleveland, Ohio, *Nutrition.*

L. TADDEINI, University of Minnesota, Minneapolis, Minnesota, *Porphyrins; Introduction.*

O. TOUSTER, Vanderbilt University, Nashville, Tennessee, *Pathways of Carbohydrate Metabolism.*

C. J. WATSON, University of Minnesota Hospital, Minneapolis, Minnesota, *Porphyrins; Introduction.*

G. N. WEBB, The Johns Hopkins School of Medicine, Baltimore, Maryland, *Computer Techniques.*

J. J. WEISS, The University, Newcastle-upon-Tyne, England, *Radiation Chemistry.*

R. WINSLOW, The Polyclinic Hospital, Cleveland, Ohio, *General Procedures.*

D. A. WOLFE, U. S. Bureau of Commercial Fisheries, Beaufort, North Carolina, *Pigments, Vitamins, Hormones.*

R. WU, Stanford University School of Medicine, Palo Alto, California, *Enzymes.*

G. ZBINDEN, Hoffmann-LaRoche, Inc., Nutley, New Jersey, *Toxicology of New Drugs.*

H. ZIMMER, University of Cincinnati, Cincinnati, Ohio, *Analytical Methods.*

I. PROBABILITY FUNDAMENTALS

Probability theory and statistics are concerned with providing a mathematical model for the description and interpretation of observed physical phenomena. The underlying concept in probability theory is a set, S, which is a class of objects such that it is possible to determine whether or not a particular object belongs to the set. For example, the people in a particular city, or the collection of positive integers, constitute finite and infinite sets, respectively. The objects in sets may be called *points* and these points may be grouped in various ways called *events*, A.

A *probability function* P(A) is defined for events A in S if the following three properties hold.

$$0 \leq P(A) \leq 1 \tag{1}$$
$$P(\phi) = 0 \text{ and } P(S) = 1 \tag{2}$$
$$P(\cup_n A_n) = \Sigma_n P(A_n) \tag{3}$$

In these expressions, ϕ = null set (impossible event), S = whole set (certain event), and $\cup_n A_n$ is any set of mutually disjoint events in S. The term *mutually disjoint* means that the events have no points in common. The notation $\cup_n A_n$ stands for the *union* of the events A_n and is the set containing points which lie in any of the events A_n.

For situations where two events may have overlapping points, the probability of their union event $(A \cup B)$ is given by

$$P(A \cup B) = P(A) + P(B) - P(A \cap B) \tag{4}$$

where $(A \cap B)$ represents the *intersection* of the event A with B and is the set containing points which belong both to A and to B. Equation (4) is known as the *addition rule* of probability theory, and may be extended to handle cases of three or more events. When A and B are disjoint, or *mutually exclusive*, their interaction is the null set ϕ and

$$P(A \cup B) = P(A) + P(B) \tag{5}$$

The *conditional probability* of A, given that B has occurred, is denoted by P(A|B). Similarly, P(B|A) is the conditional probability of B, given that A has occurred. For two intersecting events A and B, the probability of their intersection set (A ∩ B) is given by

$$P(A \cap B) = P(A \mid B)P(B) \qquad (6)$$
$$= P(B \mid A)P(A)$$

Equation (6) is known as the *multiplication rule* of probability theory. When $P(A) \neq 0$ and $P(B) \neq 0$, one obtains

$$P(A \mid B) = \frac{P(A \cap B)}{P(B)}; \; P(B \mid A) = \frac{P(A \cap B)}{P(A)} \qquad (7)$$

Two events A and B are said to be statistically independent if

$$P(A \cap B) = P(A) P(B) \qquad (8)$$

It follows from Eqs. (7) and (8) that for statistically independent events,

$$P(A \mid B) = P(A); \; P(B \mid A) = P(B) \qquad (9)$$

Consider Eq. (6) with $P(B) \neq 0$. Then

$$P(A \mid B) = \frac{P(B \mid A) \, P(A)}{P(B)} \qquad (10)$$

This formula, or its extensions, is known as *Bayes Theorem*. In applying this result, one calculates the probability of A after observing that B has occurred, i.e., the *a posteriori probability* of A. For example, suppose that *a priori probability* of A is $P(A) = 0.4$, the probability of B is $P(B) = 0.8$ and $P(B \mid A) = 0.6$. Then, for this case, one calculates $P(A \mid B) = 0.3$ so that observation of B has reduced the probability that A is true. On the other hand, if $P(B) = 0.4$ and $P(B \mid A) = 0.8$, then $P(A \mid B) = 0.8$. Here, observation of B has increased the probability that A is true.

II. RANDOM VARIABLES AND DISTRIBUTION FUNCTIONS

Consider a set of points, called a *sample space*, representing the possible outcomes of a particular experiment (or measurement). A *random variable* $x(k)$ is a real number between $-\infty$ and ∞ which is assigned to each sample point k that might occur. Consider the set of possible sample points k such that $x(k) \leq x$, where x is an arbitrary fixed real number. One may define a (first-order) *cumulative probability distribution function* $P(x)$ as the probability associated with the set of points k satisfying $x(k) \leq x$, namely,

$$P(x) = \text{Prob} \, [x(k) \leq x] \qquad (11)$$

Properties of $P(x)$ are

$$P(-\infty) = 0 \qquad P(\infty) = 1 \qquad (12)$$
$$P(a) \leq P(b) \text{ if } a \leq b \qquad (13)$$

If the random variable assumes a continuous range of values, then a (first-order) *probability density function* p(x) may be defined by the differential relation

$$p(x) \, dx = dP(x) = \text{Prob} \, [x < x(k) \leq x + dx] \tag{14}$$

Properties of p(x) are

$$p(x) \geq 0 \tag{15}$$

$$P(x) = \int_{-\infty}^{x} p(\xi) \, d(\xi) \tag{16}$$

For discrete distributions, the probability density function is permitted to include delta functions.

The *mean value* (also called *expected value* or *average value*) of x(k) is given by

$$E[x(k)] = \int_{-\infty}^{\infty} x \, p(x) \, dx = \mu_x \tag{17}$$

where E[ ] denotes the expected value of the term inside the brackets. For finite sets, expected values are obtained by summations rather than integrals.

The *variance* of x(k) is defined by the mean square value of x(k) about its mean value,

$$E[(x(k) - \mu_x)^2] = \int_{-\infty}^{\infty} (x - \mu_x)^2 \, p(x) \, dx = \sigma_x^2 \tag{18}$$

By definition, the standard deviation of x(k), denoted by σ_x, is the positive square root of the variance. The standard deviation is measured in the same units as the mean value.

One possible method for estimating the mean value and variance of x(k) based upon N independent observed values x_i, i = 1,2, . . . ,N, is as follows

$$\bar{x} = \hat{\mu}_x = \frac{1}{N} \sum_{i=1}^{N} x_i \tag{19}$$

$$s^2 = \hat{\sigma}_x^2 = \frac{1}{N} \sum_{i=1}^{N} (x_i - \hat{\mu}_x)^2 \tag{20}$$

The hats over $\hat{\mu}_x$ and $\hat{\sigma}_x^2$ indicate that these quantities are *estimates (sample values)* of the true values. The number of values N used to compute the estimates is called the *sample size*.

III. IMPORTANT DISTRIBUTION FUNCTIONS

Several examples of important distribution functions are listed below. They are the normal (Gaussian) distribution, the χ^2 distribution, the "t" distribution, the F distribution, and the Tchebycheff distribution. Applications for each of these distributions are discussed in the references.

Normal (Gaussian) Distribution. The *normal (Gaussian) probability density function* is given by

$$p(x) = \frac{1}{\sigma_x \sqrt{2\pi}} \exp\left[\frac{-(x - \mu_x)^2}{2\sigma_x^2}\right] \tag{21}$$

and is completely specified by μ_x and σ_x. This is probably the most important distribution in physical problems where many effects are producing the observed results. It is usually tabulated in terms of a standardized variable $z(k)$ where

$$z(k) = \frac{x(k) - \mu_x}{\sigma_x} \tag{22}$$

Thus $\mu_z = 0$, $\sigma_z = 1$, and $p(x)$ is replaced by

$$p(z) = \frac{1}{\sqrt{2\pi}} \exp\left[\frac{-z^2}{2}\right] \tag{23}$$

The corresponding normal probability distribution function is

$$P(z) = \frac{1}{\sqrt{2\pi}} \int_{-\infty}^{z} \exp\left(\frac{-\xi^2}{2}\right) d\xi \tag{24}$$

Let z_α be the value of z such that $P(z_\alpha) = (1 - \alpha)$, where $0 < \alpha < 1$. That is

$$P(z_\alpha) = \int_{-\infty}^{z_\alpha} p(z)\, dz = \text{Prob}\,[z(k) \leq z_\alpha] = 1 - \alpha \tag{25}$$

The value z_α is called the *100α Percentage Point*. Observe that

$$1 - P(z_\alpha) = \int_{z_\alpha}^{\infty} p(z)\, dz = \text{Prob}\,[z(k) > z_\alpha] = \alpha \tag{26}$$

For the standardized normal distribution,

$$\text{Prob}\,[\,|z_k| \leq 3] \approx 0.997 \tag{27}$$

This corresponds to

$$\text{Prob}\,[\,|x(k) - \mu_x| \leq 3\sigma_x] \approx 0.997 \tag{28}$$

Chi-Square Distribution. Let $z_1(k)$, $z_2(k)$, . . . , $z_n(k)$ be n independent random variables, each of which has a normal distribution with zero mean and unit variance. Let the sum of the squared standardized variables be denoted by

$$\chi_n^2 = z_1^2(k) + \cdots + z_n^2(k) \tag{29}$$

Then the distribution for χ_n^2 is called the *chi-square distribution* with n degrees-of-freedom.

The chi-square distribution is a special case of the more general gamma distribution. For two degrees-of-freedom, the chi-square distribution defines a *Rayleigh distribution function,* while for three degrees-of-freedom, it defines a *Maxwell distribution.*

Student "t" Distribution. Let y(k) and z(k) be independent random variables such that y(k) has a χ_n^2 distribution function, and z(k) has a normal distribution function with zero mean and unit variance. Define the random variable

$$t_n = \frac{z(k)}{\sqrt{y(k)/n}} \tag{30}$$

Then the distribution for t_n is called the *student "t" distribution* with n degrees-of-freedom. The "t" distribution approaches a standardized normal distribution as n becomes large, say n > 30.

The F Distribution. Let $y_1(k)$ and $y_2(k)$ be independent random variables such that $y_1(k)$ has a $\chi_{n_1}^2$ distribution and $y_2(k)$ has a $\chi_{n_2}^2$ distribution. Define the random variable

$$F_{n_1, n_2} = \frac{y_1(k)/n_1}{y_2(k)/n_2} \tag{31}$$

Then the distribution for F_{n_1, n_2} is called the F distribution with n_1 and n_2 degrees-of-freedom.

Tchebycheff Distribution (Nonparametric). Suppose that x(k) is an arbitrary random variable with a mean value μ_x and variance σ_x^2. Suppose that the probability density function p(x) is unknown. Then, a nonparametric distribution, i.e., one which is not restricted to a particular distribution function, is given by the *Tchebycheff Distribution.* This states for any constant c > 0, that

$$\text{Prob}\,[\,|\,x(k) - \mu_x| \leq c\sigma_x] \geq 1 - \frac{1}{c^2} \tag{32}$$

For example, when c = 3

$$\text{Prob}\,[\,|\,x(k) - \mu_x| \leq 3\sigma_x] \geq 0.89 \tag{33}$$

Note that this result is not as strong as the corresponding relation for the normal distribution in Eq. (28).

IV. SAMPLING DISTRIBUTIONS AND ILLUSTRATIONS

Consider a random variable $x(k)$ with a probability distribution function $P(x)$. Let $x_1, x_2, \ldots, x_N$ be a sample of N observed values of $x(k)$. Any quantity computed from these sample values will also be a random variable. For example, consider the mean value $\bar{x}$ for the sample. If a series of different samples of size N were selected from the same random variable $x(k)$, the value of $\bar{x}$ computed from each sample would generally be different. Hence, the sample mean value $\bar{x}$ is also a random variable which has some probability distribution function $P(\bar{x})$. This probability distribution function is called the *sampling distribution* for the same mean $\bar{x}$.

Distribution for Sample Mean with Known Variance. Consider the mean value of a sample of N independent observations from a random variable $x(k)$ as in Eq. (19), namely,

$$\bar{x} = \frac{1}{N} \sum_{i=1}^{N} x_i \tag{34}$$

Assume that the random variable $x(k)$ is normally distributed with a mean value of μ_x and a known variance of σ_x^2. From basic theoretical considerations, it is known that the sampling distribution for the sample mean $\bar{x}$ will also be normally distributed. The mean value for the sampling distribution of $\bar{x}$ is

$$\mu_{\bar{x}} = \mu_x \tag{35}$$

The variance for the sampling distribution of $\bar{x}$ is

$$\sigma_{\bar{x}}^2 = \mathrm{Var}\left[\frac{1}{N} \sum_{i=1}^{N} x_i \right] = \frac{1}{N^2} \sum_{i=1}^{N} \sigma_x^2 = \frac{\sigma_x^2}{N} \tag{36}$$

Hence, in terms of standardized normal distribution, the following sampling distribution applies for the sample mean $\bar{x}$.

$$\frac{(\bar{x} - \mu_x) \sqrt{N}}{\sigma_x} = z(k) \tag{37}$$

Here, $z(k)$ has a standardized normal distribution, as defined in Eq. (22).

It follows that a probability statement concerning the value of a sample mean *prior* to collecting the sample may be made as follows:

$$\mathrm{Prob}\left[\bar{x} > \left(\frac{\sigma_x z_\alpha}{\sqrt{N}} + \mu_x \right) \right] = \alpha \tag{38}$$

where z_α is defined in Eq. (25). Note that the probability statement in Eq. (38) is valid only prior to collecting the sample, since after a sample is collected, the probability of $\bar{x}$ being greater than any given value is either zero or one. This point will be further clarified when confidence intervals are discussed in the next section.

Distribution for Sample Mean with Unknown Variance. Consider the mean value of a sample of N independent observations from a random variable x(k), as given by Eq. (34). If the variable x(k) is normally distributed with a mean value of μ_x and an unknown variance, the following sampling distribution applies for the sample mean $\bar{x}$ and sample standard deviation s.

$$\frac{(\bar{x} - \mu_x) \sqrt{N}}{s} = t_n; \; n = N - 1 \tag{39}$$

Here, t_n has a student "t" distribution with $n = N - 1$ degrees-of-freedom. It follows that a probability statement concerning the value of the sample mean $\bar{x}$ *prior* to collecting the sample may be made as follows:

$$\text{Prob}\left[\bar{x} > \left(\frac{st_{n; \, \alpha}}{\sqrt{N}} + \mu_x\right)\right] = \alpha \tag{40}$$

where $t_{n; \, \alpha}$ is the 100α Percentage Point of the t distribution.

V. CONFIDENCE INTERVALS AND ILLUSTRATION

The use of sample values as estimators for parameters of random variables is shown in Eqs. (19) and (20). However, those procedures result only in point estimates for a parameter of interest. No indication is provided as to how closely a sample value estimates the parameter. A more complete and meaningful procedure for estimating parameters of random variables involves the estimation of an interval, as opposed to a single point value, which will include the parameter being estimated with a known degree of uncertainty. For example, consider the case where the mean value $\bar{x}$ for a sample of size N from a random variable x(k) is being used as an estimator for the true mean value μ_x. It is far more meaningful if the true mean value μ_x is estimated in terms of some interval, such as $\bar{x} \pm d$, where there is some measure of the uncertainty that the true mean value μ_x falls within that interval. Such intervals can be established if the sampling distribution is known for the sample value being used as an estimator.

Continuing with the example of a mean value estimate, it is shown in the previous section that probability statements can be made concerning the value of a sample mean $\bar{x}$ prior to collecting the sample. For the case of a normally distributed random variable with an unknown mean value and unknown variance, a probability statement is obtained from Eq. (40) as follows:

$$\text{Prob}\left[t_{n;\,(1-\alpha/2)} < \frac{(\bar{x} - \mu_x)\sqrt{N}}{s} \leq t_{n;\,\alpha/2} \right] = 1 - \alpha \tag{41}$$

$$n = N - 1$$

Now, *after* the sample has been collected, the values $\bar{x}$ and s are fixed numbers rather than random variables. Hence, the above probability statement no longer applies since the quantity $(\bar{x} - \mu_x)\sqrt{N}/s$ either *does* or *does not* fall within the noted limits. In other words, after a sample has been collected, a technically correct probability statement would be as follows.

$$\text{Prob}\left[t_{n;\,(1-\alpha/2)} < \frac{(\bar{x} - \mu_x)\sqrt{N}}{s} \leq t_{n;\,\alpha/2} \right] = \begin{cases} 0 \\ 1 \end{cases} \tag{42}$$

Whether the correct probability is zero or unity is usually not known. However, as the value α becomes small (as the interval $t_{n;\,(1-\alpha/2)}$ to $t_{n;\,\alpha/2}$ becomes wide), one would guess that the probability is more likely to be unity than zero. In slightly different terms, if many different samples were repeatedly collected and values for $\bar{x}$ and s were computed for each sample, one would expect the quantity in Eq. (41) to fall within the noted interval for about $(1 - \alpha)$ portion of the samples.

In this context, a statement can be made about an interval within which one would expect to find the quantity $(\bar{x} - \mu_x)\sqrt{N}/s$ with a small degree of uncertainty. Such statements are called *confidence statements*. The interval associated with a confidence statement is called a *confidence interval*. The degree of trust associated with the confidence statement is called the *confidence coefficient*.

For the case of the mean value estimate, a confidence interval can be established for the mean value μ_x based upon sample values $\bar{x}$ and s by rearranging terms in Eq. (41) as follows:

$$\left[\left(\bar{x} - \frac{s t_{n;\,\alpha/2}}{\sqrt{N}} \leq \mu_x < \bar{x} + \frac{s t_{n;\,\alpha/2}}{\sqrt{N}} \right) \right]; n = N - 1 \tag{43}$$

Equation (43) uses the fact that $t_{n;\,(1-\alpha/2)} = -t_{n;\,\alpha/2}$. The confidence coefficient associated with the above interval is $(1 - \alpha)$. Hence, the confidence statement would be as follows: "The true mean value μ_x falls within the noted interval with a confidence coefficient of $(1 - \alpha)$," or in more common terminology, "with a confidence of $100(1 - \alpha)\%$." Similar confidence statements can be established for any parameter estimates where proper sampling distributions are known.

VI. HYPOTHESIS TESTS

Consider the case where some estimator $\hat{\Phi}$ is computed from a sample of N independent observations of a random variable X(k). Assume that there is reason to believe that the true parameter Φ being estimated has a specific value Φ_0. Now, even if $\Phi = \Phi_0$, the sample value $\hat{\Phi}$ will probably not come out exactly equal to Φ_0 because of the sampling variability associated with $\hat{\Phi}$. Hence, the following question arises. If it is hypothesized that $\Phi = \Phi_0$, how much difference between $\hat{\Phi}$ and Φ_0 must occur before the hypothesis should be rejected as being invalid? This question can be answered in statistical terms by considering the probability of any noted difference between $\hat{\Phi}$ and Φ_0 based upon the sampling distribution for $\hat{\Phi}$. If the probability of a given difference is small, the difference would be considered significant and the hypothesis that $\Phi = \Phi_0$ would be rejected. If the probability of a given difference is not small, the difference would be accepted as normal statistical variability and the hypothesis that $\Phi = \Phi_0$ would be accepted.

There are two possible errors which can occur when a hypothesis test is performed. First, the hypothesis might be rejected when in fact it is true. This possible error is called a *Type I Error*. Second, the hypothesis might be accepted when in fact it is false. This possible error is called a *Type II Error*. The only way to reduce both of these errors simultaneously is to increase the sample size N.

BIBLIOGRAPHY

Bendat, J. S., and A. G. Piersol, *Measurement and Analysis of Random Data*, 1966.
Bowker, A. H., and G. J. Lieberman, *Engineering Statistics*, 1959.
Cramer, C., *The Elements of Probability Theory*, 1955.
Kendall, M. G., and A. Stuart, *The Advanced Theory of Statistics*, 2nd Ed., Vol. 1, 1963.

I. INTRODUCTION

Two recent volumes anthologizing a representative group of essays on *Computers in Biomedical Research*[1] cover an interesting range of subjects, from the analysis of bioelectric signals to the "automation" of hospital functions. The variety of subject matter available is more overwhelming when one considers the fact that many areas are either not touched in these books (*e.g.*, computer-based procedures for bibliographic or subject control of the medical literature—"information retrieval"), or are touched upon with necessary brevity. To realize this is to accept the fact that in the present *Handbook* there is room for only the briefest and most preliminary remarks on computer techniques.

A computer is a device which accepts information, processes it by the application of specified logical routines, and offers as output the result of such processing. Physical modes of input and output are now almost unlimited. The application of a so-called light pen to the face of a cathode-ray tube can now effect instructions to a computer with speed and ease that would amaze those who worked with early punched-card systems. Output has gone far beyond early on-line typewriters to computer-driven photocomposition systems which prepare camera-ready copy almost instantaneously, selecting type-faces from a variety of fonts. Indeed, the question in current computer technology is not "what can the machines do?" but rather, "how can I define my problem in such a clear and elegant way that I can best take advantage of the variety of instruments available?" Problem definition, in this sense, is the main challenge facing the researcher in biophysics and biochemistry in the computer age.

II. THE DIGITAL COMPUTER

The computer consists of input-output devices, a memory or storage unit, and a processor. The input devices may be one or more typewriters, punch card or tape readers, magnetic tape drives, or connections accepting electrical inputs in digital form. Input devices may be closely connected with the processor, or may be many miles away. The output devices may be one or more typewriters, on-line printers, card or tape punches[2], magnetic tape recorders, oscilloscopes or graphic plotters. But as suggested above, a list such as this can only suggest the range of equipment available.

Programming. Within the computer *memory*, data and instructions are stored in coded form. The location of each unit of information (character or word), consisting of a group of binary digits, is designated by a storage *address*. A machine *instruction*, which consists of a word or a string of characters, designates to the processor the nature of the basic operation to be carried out, and specifies the addresses of any data involved. The *processor* normally executes the stored instructions in sequence, but provision is made for *branching*, or transferring control to one or another of a sequence of instructions, depending upon the result of a comparison made by the processor.

A machine instruction may direct the mechanical operation of one of the input-output devices or may cause the processor to perform one or more *basic* operations upon the stored data. These basic operations consist of 1) addition or subtraction, and in some instances multiplication and division, of digit configurations within the stored data or in an accumulator (special storage area in the processor), 2) transfer of data, and 3) comparison of digits.

A series of complex operations may be specified by a program, which is a logical sequence of instructions, introduced into the computer memory through one of the input devices. *Programming* is the technique of constructing a sequence of machine instructions which will carry out a desired set of operations. A program may be written in machine-coded form, but for complex data-processing or numerical computation this is usually too tedious. In practice, the machine-coded program is generated by a *compiler*, which is a computer program capable of translating to machine form instructions written in some language more convenient for the programmer.

Many computer languages are available. These languages represent the usual contact between programmer and machine, and although they differ greatly from each other in format, complexity, and intended application, they allow the programmer 1) to specify operations by means of *mnemonics*, English words or algebraic symbols, 2) to refer to stored data and instructions by arbitrary labels rather than by machine addresses, and 3) to introduce and recover data in the form of decimal numbers or strings of letters and symbols rather than in binary form. Most compilers also test for and report certain types of errors in the source program as an aid to the programmer in making corrections.

Some languages (*e.g.*, Fortran,[3] Algol[4]) permit complex operations to be specified by a single source program instruction (see Table I). In other languages (*e.g.*, FAP, Autocoder), each step of a complex operation must be specified, thus requiring more lines of program code.

Table 1.   Examples of Program Instruction

Fortran Statement

X(1) = LOGF (AMT) + A * B

"Calculate the natural logarithm of the number s stored in the location named AMT, add the product of the numbers stored at A and B, and place the result in the location allocated for the value X_1."

Manipulator Statement

JBMRX   6,REC,1,=VECTOR,INST5

"Scan right from the first character of a string labelled REC looking for the 6-character word "VECTOR", and branch to instruction INST5 if the word is found, otherwise execute the next instruction."

Autocoder Statement

RT   5,INFO

"Read a record from tape unit 5 into storage starting at the location labelled INFO."

FAP Statement

ADD   VT

"Add the number at location VT to the contents of the accumulator."

A	B	C	D	E	F
12	2048	4095	0.0245%	2048	0
11	1024	2047	0.0489%	1024	0
10	512	1023	0.0976%	512	1
9	256	511	0.195%	756	0
8	128	255	0.392%	640	0
7	64	127	0.787%	576	0
6	32	63	1.59%	544	1
5	16	31	3.23%	560	1
4	8	15	6.67%	568	0
3	4	7	14.3%	564	0
2	2	3	33.3%	562	1
1	1	1	100%	563	1

In general, programs written in a "lower" type of language cannot be used on any but the original type of machine because of variations in construction. Although programs written in "higher" types of language, such as Fortran, are basically the same for most machines, the total program may not be readily interchangeable between installations because of local compiler variations. Ordinarily, however, only minor adjustments need be made.

The programmer's choice of a language[5, 6, 7, 8] will be limited by the type of equipment and compiler programs available to him. The best choice for a specific problem is further determined by 1) the nature and complexity of the operations to be performed, 2) the skill of the programmer and his familiarity with the languages available, 3) the relative importance of time and effort required to write, test and correct a program as balanced against the speed of execution, and 4) the availability of a "library" of subroutines.

Analog to Digital Conversion for Computer Input.[9, 10, 11] Data which is to be entered into a computer obviously must be in a form which the computer can accept. Input information often exists in the form of values of voltage, current, or mechanical position. These quantities can be converted to a digital form by reading values from a scale or meter, scaling a graphical record, etc., and subsequently inserting into a computer program by means of punched cards or punched tape. Where a great deal of data is to be manipulated, automatic means can be used. The "analog to digital converter"[12, 13] describes an instrument which performs the digitizing function by electrical means, while the "shaft encoder"[14] or "position encoder" is used for mechanical conversion. The human, electrical, or mechanical converter samples the continuous single-valued function and writes a digital value in a code representing the number of basic units of measurement to the nearest unit (*e.g.*, to within $\pm \frac{1}{2}$ unit).

Relationships for a binary counting system are shown in columns A and B of Figure 1. If a six-bit code is to be used, the highest ordered bit will have a value of 32. These six bits can represent levels up to and including a value of 63; the least significant bit will have a resolution value of 1.589% of the maximum value expressible with 6 binary bits. A string of binary digits representing 58 would be written as 111010, with the least significant digit at the right.

It is the function of the analog to digital converter to create the proper digit pattern representing the sampled value, for transmission to the digital computer. When data will ultimately enter a digital computer, it is generally wise to convert it to digital form at the earliest stage possible.

There are three major specifications of performance of the A–D converter.[15, 16, 17, 18] 1) *Sample Rate.* The number of samples taken per unit interval is determined by the accuracy to which each frequency component is to be determined. For complex waveforms, a first approximation

Figure 1

Some binary digit relationships

A. The index or order of the binary digits.
B. The numerical value of the digit indexed by column A.
C. The maximum numerical value for the number of digits given in column A.
D. The value of the lowest ordered digit expressed as a percentage of the value in column C.
E. Values of A, for an analog-to-digital conversion of the amplitude 563 for sequential value programming.
F. Binary digits set to represent 563.

Example: The 6th digit of a 6 digit code has a value of 32, a total count of 63 can be made by 6 digits and the lowest ordered digit will be 1.59% of full scale.

of the sample rate calls for two samples for each cycle of the highest frequency which is to be detected but about which no amplitude information is required. 2) *Sample Resolution.* The number of units used in a sample must be such that the least significant change in the variable will be larger than the basic measuring unit or value of the least significant bit. Figure 1, column D, illustrates the resolution obtained by different numbers of binary digits. 3) *Sample Aperture Time.* Where the analog signal is changing rapidly, the sample taken for conversion must be obtained in a time that is shorter than the interval in which the signal varies by the equivalent of the least significant digit. If the conversion cannot be accomplished in the "aperture time," then the value sampled must be stored while the conversion is being made. 4) *Multiplexing.* When more than one analog signal is to be converted to digital form, a switch is used to sequentially connect the A–D converter to the various signals. The multiplexing rate will be the sample rate per channel times the number of channels.

BIBLIOGRAPHY

References:

1. Stacy, Ralph W., and B. D. Waxman (eds.), *Computers in Biomedical Research,* 2 vols., 1965.
2. Gannon, W. A., "Perforated Tape Readers," *Computer Design,* 4(2):14, 1965; and W. A. Gannon, "Paper Tape Punches," *Computer Design,* 4(7):18, 1965.
3. McCracken, D. D., *A Guide to Fortran Programmers,* 1962.
4. Bauman, R., et al, *Introduction to ALGOL,* 1964.
5. Galler, B. A., *Language of Computers,* 1962.
6. Special Issue in Computer Languages. *IEEE Transactions on Electronic Computers,* Vol. EC-13(4), 1964.
7. Wegner, P. (ed.), *Introduction to System Programming,* 1964, (ALGOL).
8. *Kwic Index to Computer Applications in Science, Research, and Engineering,* I.B.M., 1964.
9. Staff, Computer Control Co., *Data Conversion Circuits and Subsystems,* 1964.
10. Stephenson, B. W., *Analog-Digital Conversion Handbook,* 1964.
11. Susskind, A. K. (ed.), *Notes on Analog-Digital Conversion Techniques,* 1958.
12. Gaines, W. M., and P. P. Fischer, "Terminology for Functional Characteristics of Analog-to-Digital Converters," *Control Engineering,* 8:97, 1961.
13. Friauf, W. S., "Dynamic Characteristics of Analog-Digital Converters," *Instruments & Control Systems,* 38(1):111, 1965.
14. Product Reference File: Shaft-angle Encoders. *Computer Design,* 2(11):16, 1963.
15. Blackman, R. B., and J. W. Tukey, *The Measurement of Power Spectra,* 1959.
16. Ralston, A., and H. Wilf (eds.), *Mathematical Methods for Digital Computers,* 1960.
17. Pierce, John R., *Symbols, Signals and Noise,* 1962.
18. Schroeder, R., "Input Data Source Limitations for Real-Time Operation of Digital Computers," *J. Association of Computing Machinery,* 11(2):152, 1964.

I. INTRODUCTION

Whenever a sequence of measurements is observed over time, the mean value may gradually or suddenly depart from what the mean value is supposed to be. Suppose a colloidal suspension is required to have a specific constant pH value, and portions of this suspension are used daily in some chemical analysis. The pH may gradually increase (or decrease) due to evaporation of the suspension liquid. The results or measurements of the chemical analysis might then gradually drift away from their expected values. In this case the evaporation is an *assignable cause* of the departure. The techniques of quality control form a set of statistical methods for determining whether a sequence of measurements is departing significantly from their specified mean values. When a significant departure occurs, *action* is taken in the form of halting the measuring process and searching for an assignable cause of the departure. In the case at hand, an assignable cause would be the change in pH due to evaporation. After the cause has been discovered and corrective action taken, the measuring process may be resumed. It may happen that a significant departure from the expected mean value is purely due to chance (*i.e.*, there is no assignable cause for the departure). In this event, time and effort will be spent in a fruitless search for an assignable cause. Quality control techniques may be used to make the frequency of occurrence of such "false positives" arbitrarily small.

II. THE QUALITY CONTROL CHART

A quality control chart is a graph of the observed measurements as ordinates plotted against time as the abscissa. The use of quality control methods is much facilitated by maintaining an up-to-date quality control chart.

The mean value curve is a graph of the expected values of the observed measurements plotted against time as the abscissa. If the measurements are supposed to have a constant mean value over time, then the mean value curve will be a horizontal line whose distance from the time

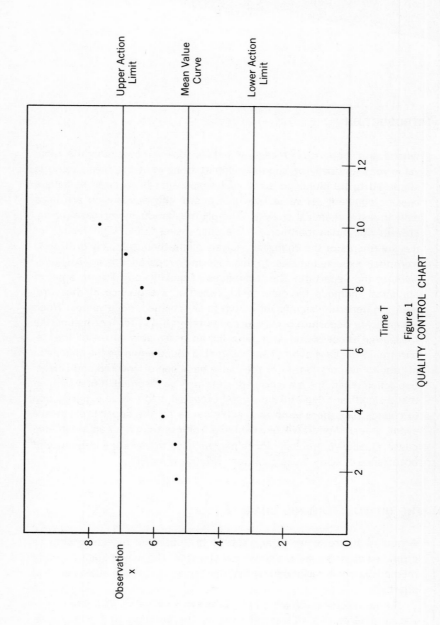

Figure 1
QUALITY CONTROL CHART

axis is the constant mean value. The mean value curve should be drawn on the quality control chart at the beginning of the experiment.

Action limits are values of the observations beyond which the measuring process is halted and a search for an assignable cause begun. Action limits should be determined and drawn on the quality control chart at the beginning of the experiment. Methods for obtaining the mean value curve and action limits are described below. Figure 1 illustrates a quality control chart with mean value curve constantly 5 over time, and action limits 5 ± 2, or 3 and 7. In this case 3 is the *lower action limit* and 7 is the *upper action limit*. The dots in Figure 1 represent observations. At time T = 10 an observation X = 8 exceeds the upper action limit 7, so the measurement process should be halted at that time and a search for an assignable cause begun. Actually, the upward trend beginning at about T = 4 and continuing steadily thereafter should have aroused the investigator's suspicions by time T = 8, and he might well have stopped the process after the observation for T = 9, even though the action limits were not exceeded.

The observed X's in Figure 1 may represent single observations or means of observations all taken at the same time. Alternatively, several observations taken at the same time may be plotted as separate points.

III. DETERMINATION OF MEAN VALUE CURVE AND ACTION LIMITS

The mean value curve. If a mean value of say, 5, is specified *a priori* at the beginning of an experiment, and if values more than 2 units from the mean value are intolerable while values less than 2 units are not, then the mean value curve is 5 and the action limits are 3 and 7.

If the mean value is unknown and is constant over time, then a *sample* of the measurements must be taken at the beginning of the experiment. The arithmetic mean of the sample observations is then taken for the mean value. The number of observations to be taken in this sample, or the *sample size*, is an important consideration, and will depend on availability of money, materials, etc., and the exactness desired in fixing the standard mean value curve. As a rule of thumb, a sample size of at least 15 should be taken. The smaller the sample size, the less reliable the estimated standard mean value curve. If a mean value curve is based on a small sample, then succeeding observations over time may fall outside the action limits distressingly often. The consequent searches for assignable causes might well be fruitless, and the estimated mean value would have to be revised.

The Action Limits. When the action limits are not specifiable *a priori*, they may be determined empirically from the same sample used to estimate the mean value curve. Usually the estimated action limits are based on the *sample variance* of this sample. If n observations are taken in the initial sample for determining the standard mean value curve and action limits, and if the values obtained are $X_1, \cdots, X_n$, then the *arithmetic mean* is

$$\overline{X} = (X_1 + \cdots + X_n)/n$$

and the *sample variance* is

$$S^2 = [(X_1 - \overline{X})^2 + \cdots + (X_n - \overline{X})^2]/(n - 1)$$

The *standard deviation* of the sample is then

$$S = +\sqrt{S^2}$$

The mean value curve is then estimated by $\overline{X}$, and empirical action limits may be taken as $\overline{X} \pm 2s$, or $\overline{X} \pm 3s$, etc., depending on the accuracy required and the amount of time the investigator is willing to spend looking for "false positive" causes. The higher the accuracy required, the closer together the action limits. The smaller the time spent looking for "false positive" causes, the farther apart the action limits.

If the observations plotted on the quality control chart are *means* instead of individual observations, then the action limits should be $\overline{X} \pm 2 \dfrac{s}{\sqrt{m}}$, or $\overline{X} \pm 3 \dfrac{s}{\sqrt{m}}$, etc., where m is the number of individual observations used for the plotted mean.

In general, if an investigator wants only a proportion p of values to exceed the action limits because of pure chance alone (*i.e.*, a proportion p of values will exceed the action limits and be "false positives"), then the action limits will be

$$\overline{X} \pm t\left(1 - \frac{p}{2}\right) \cdot \frac{s}{\sqrt{m}}$$

where $\overline{X}$ is the standard mean value, s is the standard deviation based on the original sample of n, m is the number of observations used in calculating the observed mean, and $t\left(1 - \dfrac{p}{2}\right)$ is the $\left(1 - \dfrac{p}{2}\right)$ 100 percentile of the "t" distribution with $n - 1$ degrees of freedom. The percentiles of the t distribution for various degrees of freedom are shown in the *t* Table.

Example. Suppose that the mean value curve is constant but unknown, and that only 1% of values should exceed the action limits because of chance alone. Suppose that an initial sample of $n = 20$ yields a sample mean $\overline{X} = 5.0$ and a sample variance $S^2 = 9$. Then $p = .01$, $1 - \dfrac{p}{2} = .995$, the number of degrees of freedom is $n - 1 = 19$, and the 99.5 percentile of the "t" distribution with 19 degrees of freedom is t (.995) = 2.861. If the plotted observations on the quality control chart are to be means, each based on M = 4 observations, then the mean value curve is $\bar{X}$ = 5.0 and the action limits are $\bar{X} \pm$ t(.995) $\dfrac{s}{\sqrt{m}}$ =

5.0 $\pm$ 2.861 $\dfrac{3}{\sqrt{4}}$ = 5.0 $\pm$ 4.29. The lower action limit is .71 and the upper is 9.29.

Suppose further that at time T = 1 we observe the four observations: 3,7,6,3. The mean of these observations at time T = 1 is

$$\bar{X}_1 = (3 + 7 + 5 + 3)/4 = 4.5$$

and their sample variance is

$$S_1{}^2 = [(3{-}4.5)^2 + (7{-}4.5)^2 + (5{-}4.5)^2 + (3{-}4.5)^2]/3 = \frac{11}{3} = 3.67.$$

The mean, $\bar{X}$, lies well within the action limits. The variances are supposed to be the same for the initial sample and for the sample at time T = 1. We may check equality of variances by the "F" test. We compute

$$F (n - 1, m - 1) = \frac{s^2}{s_1{}^2} = \frac{3.9}{11} = 2.45$$

which has the F distribution with n − 1 and m − 1 degrees of freedom. The greater variance is taken as the numerator. Significance points for the F distribution are given in the *F* table. Since the calculated value of 2.45 does not exceed the 5% point (8.66) for the F distribution with 3 and 19 degrees of freedom, we accept equality of variances at the 5% significance level.

DISTRIBUTION OF t

n.	P=·9	·8.	·7.	·6.	·5.	·4.	·3.	·2.	·1.	·05.	·02.	·01.
1	·158	·325	·510	·727	1·000	1·376	1·963	3·078	6·314	12·706	31·821	63·657
2	·142	·289	·445	·617	·816	1·061	1·386	1·886	2·920	4·303	6·965	9·925
3	·137	·277	·424	·584	·765	·978	1·250	1·638	2·353	3·182	4·541	5·841
4	·134	·271	·414	·569	·741	·941	1·190	1·533	2·132	2·776	3·747	4·604
5	·132	·267	·408	·559	·727	·920	1·156	1·476	2·015	2·571	3·365	4·032
6	·131	·265	·404	·553	·718	·906	1·134	1·440	1·943	2·447	3·143	3·707
7	·130	·263	·402	·549	·711	·896	1·119	1·415	1·895	2·365	2·998	3·499
8	·130	·262	·399	·546	·706	·889	1·108	1·397	1·860	2·306	2·896	3·355
9	·129	·261	·398	·543	·703	·883	1·100	1·383	1·833	2·262	2·821	3·250
10	·129	·260	·397	·542	·700	·879	1·093	1·372	1·812	2·228	2·764	3·169
11	·129	·260	·396	·540	·697	·876	1·088	1·363	1·796	2·201	2·718	3·106
12	·128	·259	·395	·539	·695	·873	1·083	1·356	1·782	2·179	2·681	3·055
13	·128	·259	·394	·538	·694	·870	1·079	1·350	1·771	2·160	2·650	3·012
14	·128	·258	·393	·537	·692	·868	1·076	1·345	1·761	2·145	2·624	2·977
15	·128	·258	·393	·536	·691	·866	1·074	1·341	1·753	2·131	2·602	2·947
16	·128	·258	·392	·535	·690	·865	1·071	1·337	1·746	2·120	2·583	2·921
17	·128	·257	·392	·534	·689	·863	1·069	1·333	1·740	2·110	2·567	2·898
18	·127	·257	·392	·534	·688	·862	1·067	1·330	1·734	2·101	2·552	2·878
19	·127	·257	·391	·533	·688	·861	1·066	1·328	1·729	2·093	2·539	2·861
20	·127	·257	·391	·533	·687	·860	1·064	1·325	1·725	2·086	2·528	2·845
21	·127	·257	·391	·532	·686	·859	1·063	1·323	1·721	2·080	2·518	2·831
22	·127	·256	·390	·532	·686	·858	1·061	1·321	1·717	2·074	2·508	2·819
23	·127	·256	·390	·532	·685	·858	1·060	1·319	1·714	2·069	2·500	2·807
24	·127	·256	·390	·531	·685	·857	1·059	1·318	1·711	2·064	2·492	2·797
25	·127	·256	·390	·531	·684	·856	1·058	1·316	1·708	2·060	2·485	2·787
26	·127	·256	·390	·531	·684	·856	1·058	1·315	1·706	2·056	2·479	2·779
27	·127	·256	·389	·531	·684	·855	1·057	1·314	1·703	2·052	2·473	2·771
28	·127	·256	·389	·530	·683	·855	1·056	1·313	1·701	2·048	2·467	2·763
29	·127	·256	·389	·530	·683	·854	1·055	1·311	1·699	2·045	2·462	2·756
30	·127	·256	·389	·530	·683	·854	1·055	1·310	1·697	2·042	2·457	2·750
∞	·12566	·25335	·38532	·52440	·67449	·84162	1·03643	1·28155	1·64485	1·95996	2·32634	2·57582

Reproduced by permission from *Statistical Methods for Research Workers*, by R. A. Fisher, 10th Edition, Oliver and Boyd, Ltd., Edinburgh.

Distribution of F 5% (Roman Type) and 1% (Bold Face Type)

f^1 degrees of freedom (for greater mean square)

f^2	1	2	3	4	5	6	7	8	9	10	11	12	14	16	20	24	30	40	50	75	100	200	500	∞
1	161 / **4,052**	200 / **4,999**	216 / **5,403**	225 / **5,625**	230 / **5,764**	234 / **5,859**	237 / **5,928**	239 / **5,981**	241 / **6,022**	242 / **6,056**	243 / **6,082**	244 / **6,106**	245 / **6,142**	246 / **6,169**	248 / **6,208**	249 / **6,234**	250 / **6,258**	251 / **6,286**	252 / **6,302**	253 / **6,323**	253 / **6,334**	254 / **6,352**	254 / **6,361**	254 / **6,366**
2	18.51 / **98.49**	19.00 / **99.00**	19.16 / **99.17**	19.25 / **99.25**	19.30 / **99.30**	19.33 / **99.33**	19.36 / **99.34**	19.37 / **99.36**	19.38 / **99.38**	19.39 / **99.40**	19.40 / **99.41**	19.41 / **99.42**	19.42 / **99.43**	19.43 / **99.44**	19.44 / **99.45**	19.45 / **99.46**	19.46 / **99.47**	19.47 / **99.48**	19.47 / **99.48**	19.48 / **99.49**	19.49 / **99.49**	19.49 / **99.49**	19.50 / **99.50**	19.50 / **99.50**
3	10.13 / **34.12**	9.55 / **30.82**	9.28 / **29.46**	9.12 / **28.71**	9.01 / **28.24**	8.94 / **27.91**	8.88 / **27.67**	8.84 / **27.49**	8.81 / **27.34**	8.78 / **27.23**	8.76 / **27.13**	8.74 / **27.05**	8.71 / **26.92**	8.69 / **26.83**	8.66 / **26.69**	8.64 / **26.60**	8.62 / **26.50**	8.60 / **26.41**	8.58 / **26.35**	8.57 / **26.27**	8.56 / **26.23**	8.54 / **26.18**	8.54 / **26.14**	8.53 / **26.12**
4	7.71 / **21.20**	6.94 / **18.00**	6.59 / **16.69**	6.39 / **15.98**	6.26 / **15.52**	6.16 / **15.21**	6.09 / **14.98**	6.04 / **14.80**	6.00 / **14.66**	5.96 / **14.54**	5.93 / **14.45**	5.91 / **14.37**	5.87 / **14.24**	5.84 / **14.15**	5.80 / **14.02**	5.77 / **13.93**	5.74 / **13.83**	5.71 / **13.74**	5.70 / **13.69**	5.68 / **13.61**	5.66 / **13.57**	5.65 / **13.52**	5.64 / **13.48**	5.63 / **13.46**
5	6.61 / **16.26**	5.79 / **13.27**	5.41 / **12.06**	5.19 / **11.39**	5.05 / **10.97**	4.95 / **10.67**	4.88 / **10.45**	4.82 / **10.27**	4.78 / **10.15**	4.74 / **10.05**	4.70 / **9.96**	4.68 / **9.89**	4.64 / **9.77**	4.60 / **9.68**	4.56 / **9.55**	4.53 / **9.47**	4.50 / **9.38**	4.46 / **9.29**	4.44 / **9.24**	4.42 / **9.17**	4.40 / **9.13**	4.38 / **9.07**	4.37 / **9.04**	4.36 / **9.02**
6	5.99 / **13.74**	5.14 / **10.92**	4.76 / **9.78**	4.53 / **9.15**	4.39 / **8.75**	4.28 / **8.47**	4.21 / **8.26**	4.15 / **8.10**	4.10 / **7.98**	4.06 / **7.87**	4.03 / **7.79**	4.00 / **7.72**	3.96 / **7.60**	3.92 / **7.52**	3.87 / **7.39**	3.84 / **7.31**	3.81 / **7.23**	3.77 / **7.14**	3.75 / **7.09**	3.72 / **7.02**	3.71 / **6.99**	3.69 / **6.94**	3.68 / **6.90**	3.67 / **6.88**
7	5.59 / **12.25**	4.74 / **9.55**	4.35 / **8.45**	4.12 / **7.85**	3.97 / **7.46**	3.87 / **7.19**	3.79 / **7.00**	3.73 / **6.84**	3.68 / **6.71**	3.63 / **6.62**	3.60 / **6.54**	3.57 / **6.47**	3.52 / **6.35**	3.49 / **6.27**	3.44 / **6.15**	3.41 / **6.07**	3.38 / **5.98**	3.34 / **5.90**	3.32 / **5.85**	3.29 / **5.78**	3.28 / **5.75**	3.25 / **5.70**	3.24 / **5.67**	3.23 / **5.65**
8	5.32 / **11.26**	4.46 / **8.65**	4.07 / **7.59**	3.84 / **7.01**	3.69 / **6.63**	3.58 / **6.37**	3.50 / **6.19**	3.44 / **6.03**	3.39 / **5.91**	3.34 / **5.82**	3.31 / **5.74**	3.28 / **5.67**	3.23 / **5.56**	3.20 / **5.48**	3.15 / **5.36**	3.12 / **5.28**	3.08 / **5.20**	3.05 / **5.11**	3.03 / **5.06**	3.00 / **5.00**	2.98 / **4.96**	2.96 / **4.91**	2.94 / **4.88**	2.93 / **4.86**
9	5.12 / **10.56**	4.26 / **8.02**	3.86 / **6.99**	3.63 / **6.42**	3.48 / **6.06**	3.37 / **5.80**	3.29 / **5.62**	3.23 / **5.47**	3.18 / **5.35**	3.13 / **5.26**	3.10 / **5.18**	3.07 / **5.11**	3.02 / **5.00**	2.98 / **4.92**	2.93 / **4.80**	2.90 / **4.73**	2.86 / **4.64**	2.82 / **4.56**	2.80 / **4.51**	2.77 / **4.45**	2.76 / **4.41**	2.73 / **4.36**	2.72 / **4.33**	2.71 / **4.31**
10	4.96 / **10.04**	4.10 / **7.56**	3.71 / **6.55**	3.48 / **5.99**	3.33 / **5.64**	3.22 / **5.39**	3.14 / **5.21**	3.07 / **5.06**	3.02 / **4.95**	2.97 / **4.85**	2.94 / **4.78**	2.91 / **4.71**	2.86 / **4.60**	2.82 / **4.52**	2.77 / **4.41**	2.74 / **4.33**	2.70 / **4.25**	2.67 / **4.17**	2.64 / **4.12**	2.61 / **4.05**	2.59 / **4.01**	2.56 / **3.96**	2.55 / **3.93**	2.54 / **3.91**
11	4.84 / **9.65**	3.98 / **7.20**	3.59 / **6.22**	3.36 / **5.67**	3.20 / **5.32**	3.09 / **5.07**	3.01 / **4.88**	2.95 / **4.74**	2.90 / **4.63**	2.86 / **4.54**	2.82 / **4.46**	2.79 / **4.40**	2.74 / **4.29**	2.70 / **4.21**	2.65 / **4.10**	2.61 / **4.02**	2.57 / **3.94**	2.53 / **3.86**	2.50 / **3.80**	2.47 / **3.74**	2.45 / **3.70**	2.42 / **3.66**	2.41 / **3.62**	2.40 / **3.60**
12	4.75 / **9.33**	3.88 / **6.93**	3.49 / **5.95**	3.26 / **5.41**	3.11 / **5.06**	3.00 / **4.82**	2.92 / **4.65**	2.85 / **4.50**	2.80 / **4.39**	2.76 / **4.30**	2.72 / **4.22**	2.69 / **4.16**	2.64 / **4.05**	2.60 / **3.98**	2.54 / **3.86**	2.50 / **3.78**	2.46 / **3.70**	2.42 / **3.61**	2.40 / **3.56**	2.36 / **3.49**	2.35 / **3.46**	2.32 / **3.41**	2.31 / **3.38**	2.30 / **3.36**
13	4.67 / **9.07**	3.80 / **6.70**	3.41 / **5.74**	3.18 / **5.20**	3.02 / **4.86**	2.92 / **4.62**	2.84 / **4.44**	2.77 / **4.30**	2.72 / **4.19**	2.67 / **4.10**	2.63 / **4.02**	2.60 / **3.96**	2.55 / **3.85**	2.51 / **3.78**	2.46 / **3.67**	2.42 / **3.59**	2.38 / **3.51**	2.34 / **3.42**	2.32 / **3.37**	2.28 / **3.30**	2.26 / **3.27**	2.24 / **3.21**	2.22 / **3.18**	2.21 / **3.16**

Reproduced by permission from Statistical Methods by George Snedecor, 5th Edition, 1956, by The Iowa State University Press.

Distribution of F (continued)

Each cell shows the 5% point (upper) / 1% point (lower).

f^2	1	2	3	4	5	6	7	8	9	10	11	12	14	16	20	24	30	40	50	75	100	200	500	x	f^2
14	4.60 / 8.86	3.74 / 6.51	3.34 / 5.56	3.11 / 5.03	2.96 / 4.69	2.85 / 4.46	2.77 / 4.28	2.70 / 4.14	2.65 / 4.03	2.60 / 3.94	2.56 / 3.86	2.53 / 3.80	2.48 / 3.70	2.44 / 3.62	2.39 / 3.51	2.35 / 3.43	2.31 / 3.34	2.27 / 3.26	2.24 / 3.21	2.21 / 3.14	2.19 / 3.11	2.16 / 3.06	2.14 / 3.02	2.13 / 3.00	14
15	4.54 / 8.68	3.68 / 6.36	3.29 / 5.42	3.06 / 4.89	2.90 / 4.56	2.79 / 4.32	2.70 / 4.14	2.64 / 4.00	2.59 / 3.89	2.55 / 3.80	2.51 / 3.73	2.48 / 3.67	2.43 / 3.56	2.39 / 3.48	2.33 / 3.36	2.29 / 3.29	2.25 / 3.20	2.21 / 3.12	2.18 / 3.07	2.15 / 3.00	2.12 / 2.97	2.10 / 2.92	2.08 / 2.89	2.07 / 2.87	15
16	4.49 / 8.53	3.63 / 6.23	3.24 / 5.29	3.01 / 4.77	2.85 / 4.44	2.74 / 4.20	2.66 / 4.03	2.59 / 3.89	2.54 / 3.78	2.49 / 3.69	2.45 / 3.61	2.42 / 3.55	2.37 / 3.45	2.33 / 3.37	2.28 / 3.25	2.24 / 3.18	2.20 / 3.10	2.16 / 3.01	2.13 / 2.96	2.09 / 2.89	2.07 / 2.86	2.04 / 2.80	2.02 / 2.77	2.01 / 2.75	16
17	4.45 / 8.40	3.59 / 6.11	3.20 / 5.18	2.96 / 4.67	2.81 / 4.34	2.70 / 4.10	2.62 / 3.93	2.55 / 3.79	2.50 / 3.68	2.45 / 3.59	2.41 / 3.52	2.38 / 3.45	2.33 / 3.35	2.29 / 3.27	2.23 / 3.16	2.19 / 3.08	2.15 / 3.00	2.11 / 2.92	2.08 / 2.86	2.04 / 2.79	2.02 / 2.76	1.99 / 2.70	1.97 / 2.67	1.96 / 2.65	17
18	4.41 / 8.28	3.55 / 6.01	3.16 / 5.09	2.93 / 4.58	2.77 / 4.25	2.66 / 4.01	2.58 / 3.85	2.51 / 3.71	2.46 / 3.60	2.41 / 3.51	2.37 / 3.44	2.34 / 3.37	2.29 / 3.27	2.25 / 3.19	2.19 / 3.07	2.15 / 3.00	2.11 / 2.91	2.07 / 2.83	2.04 / 2.78	2.00 / 2.71	1.98 / 2.68	1.95 / 2.62	1.93 / 2.59	1.92 / 2.57	18
19	4.38 / 8.18	3.52 / 5.93	3.13 / 5.01	2.90 / 4.50	2.74 / 4.17	2.63 / 3.94	2.55 / 3.77	2.48 / 3.63	2.43 / 3.52	2.38 / 3.43	2.34 / 3.36	2.31 / 3.30	2.26 / 3.19	2.21 / 3.12	2.15 / 3.00	2.11 / 2.92	2.07 / 2.84	2.02 / 2.76	2.00 / 2.70	1.96 / 2.63	1.94 / 2.60	1.91 / 2.54	1.90 / 2.51	1.88 / 2.49	19
20	4.35 / 8.10	3.49 / 5.85	3.10 / 4.94	2.87 / 4.43	2.71 / 4.10	2.60 / 3.87	2.52 / 3.71	2.45 / 3.56	2.40 / 3.45	2.35 / 3.37	2.31 / 3.30	2.28 / 3.23	2.23 / 3.13	2.18 / 3.05	2.12 / 2.94	2.08 / 2.86	2.04 / 2.77	1.99 / 2.69	1.96 / 2.63	1.92 / 2.56	1.90 / 2.53	1.87 / 2.47	1.85 / 2.44	1.84 / 2.42	20
21	4.32 / 8.02	3.47 / 5.78	3.07 / 4.87	2.84 / 4.37	2.68 / 4.04	2.57 / 3.81	2.49 / 3.65	2.42 / 3.51	2.37 / 3.40	2.32 / 3.31	2.28 / 3.24	2.25 / 3.17	2.20 / 3.07	2.15 / 2.99	2.09 / 2.88	2.05 / 2.80	2.00 / 2.72	1.96 / 2.63	1.93 / 2.58	1.89 / 2.51	1.87 / 2.47	1.84 / 2.42	1.82 / 2.38	1.81 / 2.36	21
22	4.30 / 7.94	3.44 / 5.72	3.05 / 4.82	2.82 / 4.31	2.66 / 3.99	2.55 / 3.76	2.47 / 3.59	2.40 / 3.45	2.35 / 3.35	2.30 / 3.26	2.26 / 3.18	2.23 / 3.12	2.18 / 3.02	2.13 / 2.94	2.07 / 2.83	2.03 / 2.75	1.98 / 2.67	1.93 / 2.58	1.91 / 2.53	1.87 / 2.46	1.84 / 2.42	1.81 / 2.37	1.80 / 2.33	1.78 / 2.31	22
23	4.28 / 7.88	3.42 / 5.66	3.03 / 4.76	2.80 / 4.26	2.64 / 3.94	2.53 / 3.71	2.45 / 3.54	2.38 / 3.41	2.32 / 3.30	2.28 / 3.21	2.24 / 3.14	2.20 / 3.07	2.14 / 2.97	2.10 / 2.89	2.04 / 2.78	2.00 / 2.70	1.96 / 2.62	1.91 / 2.53	1.88 / 2.48	1.84 / 2.41	1.82 / 2.37	1.79 / 2.32	1.77 / 2.28	1.76 / 2.26	23
24	4.26 / 7.82	3.40 / 5.61	3.01 / 4.72	2.78 / 4.22	2.62 / 3.90	2.51 / 3.67	2.43 / 3.50	2.36 / 3.36	2.30 / 3.25	2.26 / 3.17	2.22 / 3.09	2.18 / 3.03	2.13 / 2.93	2.09 / 2.85	2.02 / 2.74	1.98 / 2.66	1.94 / 2.58	1.89 / 2.49	1.86 / 2.44	1.82 / 2.36	1.80 / 2.33	1.76 / 2.27	1.74 / 2.23	1.73 / 2.21	24
25	4.24 / 7.77	3.38 / 5.57	2.99 / 4.68	2.76 / 4.18	2.60 / 3.86	2.49 / 3.63	2.41 / 3.46	2.34 / 3.32	2.28 / 3.21	2.24 / 3.13	2.20 / 3.05	2.16 / 2.99	2.11 / 2.89	2.06 / 2.81	2.00 / 2.70	1.96 / 2.62	1.92 / 2.54	1.87 / 2.45	1.84 / 2.40	1.80 / 2.32	1.77 / 2.29	1.74 / 2.23	1.72 / 2.19	1.71 / 2.17	25
26	4.22 / 7.72	3.37 / 5.53	2.98 / 4.64	2.74 / 4.14	2.59 / 3.82	2.47 / 3.59	2.39 / 3.42	2.32 / 3.29	2.27 / 3.17	2.22 / 3.09	2.18 / 3.02	2.15 / 2.96	2.10 / 2.86	2.05 / 2.77	1.99 / 2.66	1.95 / 2.58	1.90 / 2.50	1.85 / 2.41	1.82 / 2.36	1.78 / 2.28	1.76 / 2.25	1.72 / 2.19	1.70 / 2.15	1.69 / 2.13	26

f^1 degrees of freedom (for greater mean square)

Distribution of F (continued)

									f^1 degrees of freedom (for greater mean square)																
f^2	1	2	3	4	5	6	7	8	9	10	11	12	14	16	20	24	30	40	50	75	100	200	500	∞	f^2
27	4.21 / 7.68	3.35 / 5.49	2.96 / 4.60	2.73 / 4.11	2.57 / 3.79	2.46 / 3.56	2.37 / 3.39	2.30 / 3.26	2.25 / 3.14	2.20 / 3.06	2.16 / 2.98	2.13 / 2.93	2.08 / 2.83	2.03 / 2.74	1.97 / 2.63	1.93 / 2.55	1.88 / 2.47	1.84 / 2.38	1.80 / 2.33	1.76 / 2.25	1.74 / 2.21	1.71 / 2.16	1.68 / 2.12	1.67 / 2.10	27
28	4.20 / 7.64	3.34 / 5.45	2.95 / 4.57	2.71 / 4.07	2.56 / 3.76	2.44 / 3.53	2.36 / 3.36	2.29 / 3.23	2.24 / 3.11	2.19 / 3.03	2.15 / 2.95	2.12 / 2.90	2.06 / 2.80	2.02 / 2.71	1.96 / 2.60	1.91 / 2.52	1.87 / 2.44	1.81 / 2.35	1.78 / 2.30	1.75 / 2.22	1.72 / 2.18	1.69 / 2.13	1.67 / 2.09	1.65 / 2.06	28
29	4.18 / 7.60	3.33 / 5.42	2.93 / 4.54	2.70 / 4.04	2.54 / 3.73	2.43 / 3.50	2.35 / 3.33	2.28 / 3.20	2.22 / 3.08	2.18 / 3.00	2.14 / 2.92	2.10 / 2.87	2.05 / 2.77	2.00 / 2.68	1.94 / 2.57	1.90 / 2.49	1.85 / 2.41	1.80 / 2.32	1.77 / 2.27	1.73 / 2.19	1.71 / 2.15	1.68 / 2.10	1.65 / 2.06	1.64 / 2.03	29
30	4.17 / 7.56	3.32 / 5.39	2.92 / 4.51	2.69 / 4.02	2.53 / 3.70	2.42 / 3.47	2.34 / 3.30	2.27 / 3.17	2.21 / 3.06	2.16 / 2.98	2.12 / 2.90	2.09 / 2.84	2.04 / 2.74	1.99 / 2.66	1.93 / 2.55	1.89 / 2.47	1.84 / 2.38	1.79 / 2.29	1.76 / 2.24	1.72 / 2.16	1.69 / 2.13	1.66 / 2.07	1.64 / 2.03	1.62 / 2.01	30
32	4.15 / 7.50	3.30 / 5.34	2.90 / 4.46	2.67 / 3.97	2.51 / 3.66	2.40 / 3.42	2.32 / 3.25	2.25 / 3.12	2.19 / 3.01	2.14 / 2.94	2.10 / 2.86	2.07 / 2.80	2.02 / 2.70	1.97 / 2.62	1.91 / 2.51	1.86 / 2.42	1.82 / 2.34	1.76 / 2.25	1.74 / 2.20	1.69 / 2.12	1.67 / 2.08	1.64 / 2.02	1.61 / 1.98	1.59 / 1.96	32
34	4.13 / 7.44	3.28 / 5.29	2.88 / 4.42	2.65 / 3.93	2.49 / 3.61	2.38 / 3.38	2.30 / 3.21	2.23 / 3.08	2.17 / 2.97	2.12 / 2.89	2.08 / 2.82	2.05 / 2.76	2.00 / 2.66	1.95 / 2.58	1.89 / 2.47	1.84 / 2.38	1.80 / 2.30	1.74 / 2.21	1.71 / 2.15	1.67 / 2.08	1.64 / 2.04	1.61 / 1.98	1.59 / 1.94	1.57 / 1.91	34
36	4.11 / 7.39	3.26 / 5.25	2.86 / 4.38	2.63 / 3.89	2.48 / 3.58	2.36 / 3.35	2.28 / 3.18	2.21 / 3.04	2.15 / 2.94	2.10 / 2.86	2.06 / 2.78	2.03 / 2.72	1.98 / 2.62	1.93 / 2.54	1.87 / 2.43	1.82 / 2.35	1.78 / 2.26	1.72 / 2.17	1.69 / 2.12	1.65 / 2.04	1.62 / 2.00	1.59 / 1.94	1.56 / 1.90	1.55 / 1.87	36
38	4.10 / 7.35	3.25 / 5.21	2.85 / 4.34	2.62 / 3.86	2.46 / 3.54	2.35 / 3.32	2.26 / 3.15	2.19 / 3.02	2.14 / 2.91	2.09 / 2.82	2.05 / 2.75	2.02 / 2.69	1.96 / 2.59	1.92 / 2.51	1.85 / 2.40	1.80 / 2.32	1.76 / 2.22	1.71 / 2.14	1.67 / 2.08	1.63 / 2.00	1.60 / 1.97	1.57 / 1.90	1.54 / 1.86	1.53 / 1.84	38
40	4.08 / 7.31	3.23 / 5.18	2.84 / 4.31	2.61 / 3.83	2.45 / 3.51	2.34 / 3.29	2.25 / 3.12	2.18 / 2.99	2.12 / 2.88	2.07 / 2.80	2.04 / 2.73	2.00 / 2.66	1.95 / 2.56	1.90 / 2.49	1.84 / 2.37	1.79 / 2.29	1.74 / 2.20	1.69 / 2.11	1.66 / 2.05	1.61 / 1.97	1.59 / 1.94	1.55 / 1.88	1.53 / 1.84	1.51 / 1.81	40
42	4.07 / 7.27	3.22 / 5.15	2.83 / 4.29	2.59 / 3.80	2.44 / 3.49	2.32 / 3.26	2.24 / 3.10	2.17 / 2.96	2.11 / 2.86	2.06 / 2.77	2.02 / 2.70	1.99 / 2.64	1.94 / 2.54	1.89 / 2.46	1.82 / 2.35	1.78 / 2.26	1.73 / 2.17	1.68 / 2.08	1.64 / 2.02	1.60 / 1.94	1.57 / 1.91	1.54 / 1.85	1.51 / 1.80	1.49 / 1.78	42
44	4.06 / 7.24	3.21 / 5.12	2.82 / 4.26	2.58 / 3.78	2.43 / 3.46	2.31 / 3.24	2.23 / 3.07	2.16 / 2.94	2.10 / 2.84	2.05 / 2.75	2.01 / 2.68	1.98 / 2.62	1.92 / 2.52	1.88 / 2.44	1.81 / 2.32	1.76 / 2.24	1.72 / 2.15	1.66 / 2.06	1.63 / 2.00	1.58 / 1.92	1.56 / 1.88	1.52 / 1.82	1.50 / 1.78	1.48 / 1.75	44
46	4.05 / 7.21	3.20 / 5.10	2.81 / 4.24	2.57 / 3.76	2.42 / 3.44	2.30 / 3.22	2.22 / 3.05	2.14 / 2.92	2.09 / 2.82	2.04 / 2.73	2.00 / 2.66	1.97 / 2.60	1.91 / 2.50	1.87 / 2.42	1.80 / 2.30	1.75 / 2.22	1.71 / 2.13	1.65 / 2.04	1.62 / 1.98	1.57 / 1.90	1.54 / 1.86	1.51 / 1.80	1.48 / 1.76	1.46 / 1.72	46
48	4.04 / 7.19	3.19 / 5.08	2.80 / 4.22	2.56 / 3.74	2.41 / 3.42	2.30 / 3.20	2.21 / 3.04	2.14 / 2.90	2.08 / 2.80	2.03 / 2.71	1.99 / 2.64	1.96 / 2.58	1.90 / 2.48	1.86 / 2.40	1.79 / 2.28	1.74 / 2.20	1.70 / 2.11	1.64 / 2.02	1.61 / 1.96	1.56 / 1.88	1.53 / 1.84	1.50 / 1.78	1.47 / 1.73	1.45 / 1.70	48

Distribution of F (continued)

f^2	1	2	3	4	5	6	7	8	9	10	11	12	14	16	20	24	30	40	50	75	100	200	500	∞	f^2
50	4.03 7.17	3.18 5.06	2.79 4.20	2.56 3.72	2.40 3.41	2.29 3.18	2.20 3.02	2.13 2.88	2.07 2.78	2.02 2.70	1.98 2.62	1.95 2.56	1.90 2.46	1.85 2.39	1.78 2.26	1.74 2.18	1.69 2.10	1.63 2.00	1.60 1.94	1.55 1.86	1.52 1.82	1.48 1.76	1.46 1.71	1.44 1.68	50
55	4.02 7.12	3.17 5.01	2.78 4.16	2.54 3.68	2.38 3.37	2.27 3.15	2.18 2.98	2.11 2.85	2.05 2.75	2.00 2.66	1.97 2.59	1.93 2.53	1.88 2.43	1.83 2.35	1.76 2.23	1.72 2.15	1.67 2.06	1.61 1.96	1.58 1.90	1.52 1.82	1.50 1.78	1.46 1.71	1.43 1.66	1.41 1.64	55
60	4.00 7.08	3.15 4.98	2.76 4.13	2.52 3.65	2.37 3.34	2.25 3.12	2.17 2.95	2.10 2.82	2.04 2.72	1.99 2.63	1.95 2.56	1.92 2.50	1.86 2.40	1.81 2.32	1.75 2.20	1.70 2.12	1.65 2.03	1.59 1.93	1.56 1.87	1.50 1.79	1.48 1.74	1.44 1.68	1.41 1.63	1.39 1.60	60
65	3.99 7.04	3.14 4.95	2.75 4.10	2.51 3.62	2.36 3.31	2.24 3.09	2.15 2.93	2.08 2.79	2.02 2.70	1.98 2.61	1.94 2.54	1.90 2.47	1.85 2.37	1.80 2.30	1.73 2.18	1.68 2.09	1.63 2.00	1.57 1.90	1.54 1.84	1.49 1.76	1.46 1.71	1.42 1.64	1.39 1.60	1.37 1.56	65
70	3.98 7.01	3.13 4.92	2.74 4.08	2.50 3.60	2.35 3.29	2.23 3.07	2.14 2.91	2.07 2.77	2.01 2.67	1.97 2.59	1.93 2.51	1.89 2.45	1.84 2.35	1.79 2.28	1.72 2.15	1.67 2.07	1.62 1.98	1.56 1.88	1.53 1.82	1.47 1.74	1.45 1.69	1.40 1.62	1.37 1.56	1.35 1.53	70
80	3.96 6.96	3.11 4.88	2.72 4.04	2.48 3.56	2.33 3.25	2.21 3.04	2.12 2.87	2.05 2.74	1.99 2.64	1.95 2.55	1.91 2.48	1.88 2.41	1.82 2.32	1.77 2.24	1.70 2.11	1.65 2.03	1.60 1.94	1.54 1.84	1.51 1.78	1.45 1.70	1.42 1.65	1.38 1.57	1.35 1.52	1.32 1.49	80
100	3.94 6.90	3.09 4.82	2.70 3.98	2.46 3.51	2.30 3.20	2.19 2.99	2.10 2.82	2.03 2.69	1.97 2.59	1.92 2.51	1.88 2.43	1.85 2.36	1.79 2.26	1.75 2.19	1.68 2.06	1.63 1.98	1.57 1.89	1.51 1.79	1.48 1.73	1.42 1.64	1.39 1.59	1.34 1.51	1.30 1.46	1.28 1.43	100
125	3.92 6.84	3.07 4.78	2.68 3.94	2.44 3.47	2.29 3.17	2.17 2.95	2.08 2.79	2.01 2.65	1.95 2.56	1.90 2.47	1.86 2.40	1.83 2.33	1.77 2.23	1.72 2.15	1.65 2.03	1.60 1.94	1.55 1.85	1.49 1.75	1.45 1.68	1.39 1.59	1.36 1.54	1.31 1.46	1.27 1.40	1.25 1.37	125
150	3.91 6.81	3.06 4.75	2.67 3.91	2.43 3.44	2.27 3.14	2.16 2.92	2.07 2.76	2.00 2.62	1.94 2.53	1.89 2.44	1.85 2.37	1.82 2.30	1.76 2.20	1.71 2.12	1.64 2.00	1.59 1.91	1.54 1.83	1.47 1.72	1.44 1.66	1.37 1.56	1.34 1.51	1.29 1.43	1.25 1.37	1.22 1.33	150
200	3.89 6.76	3.04 4.71	2.65 3.88	2.41 3.41	2.26 3.11	2.14 2.90	2.05 2.73	1.98 2.60	1.92 2.50	1.87 2.41	1.83 2.34	1.80 2.28	1.74 2.17	1.69 2.09	1.62 1.97	1.57 1.88	1.52 1.79	1.45 1.69	1.42 1.62	1.35 1.53	1.32 1.48	1.26 1.39	1.22 1.33	1.19 1.28	200
400	3.86 6.70	3.02 4.66	2.62 3.83	2.39 3.36	2.23 3.06	2.12 2.85	2.03 2.69	1.96 2.55	1.90 2.46	1.85 2.37	1.81 2.29	1.78 2.23	1.72 2.12	1.67 2.04	1.60 1.92	1.54 1.84	1.49 1.74	1.42 1.64	1.38 1.57	1.32 1.47	1.28 1.42	1.22 1.32	1.16 1.24	1.13 1.19	400
1000	3.85 6.66	3.00 4.62	2.61 3.80	2.38 3.34	2.22 3.04	2.10 2.82	2.01 2.64	1.95 2.53	1.88 2.43	1.84 2.34	1.80 2.26	1.76 2.20	1.70 2.09	1.65 2.01	1.58 1.89	1.53 1.81	1.47 1.71	1.41 1.61	1.36 1.54	1.30 1.44	1.26 1.38	1.19 1.28	1.13 1.19	1.08 1.11	1000
∞	3.84 6.64	2.99 4.60	2.60 3.78	2.37 3.32	2.21 3.02	2.09 2.80	2.01 2.64	1.94 2.51	1.88 2.41	1.83 2.32	1.79 2.24	1.75 2.18	1.69 2.07	1.64 1.99	1.57 1.87	1.52 1.79	1.46 1.69	1.40 1.59	1.35 1.52	1.28 1.41	1.24 1.36	1.17 1.25	1.11 1.15	1.00 1.00	∞

f^1 degrees of freedom (for greater mean square)

χ^2 Distribution

n.	P = ·99.	·98.	·95.	·90.	·80.	·70.	·50.	·30.	·20.	·10.	·05.	·02.	·01.
1	·000157	·000628	·00393	·0158	·0642	·148	·455	1·074	1·642	2·706	3·841	5·412	6·635
2	·0201	·0404	·103	·211	·446	·713	1·386	2·408	3·219	4·605	5·991	7·824	9·210
3	·115	·185	·352	·584	1·005	1·424	2·366	3·665	4·642	6·251	7·815	9·837	11·345
4	·297	·429	·711	1·064	1·649	2·195	3·357	4·878	5·989	7·779	9·488	11·668	13·277
5	·554	·752	1·145	1·610	2·343	3·000	4·351	6·064	7·289	9·236	11·070	13·388	15·086
6	·872	1·134	1·635	2·204	3·070	3·828	5·348	7·231	8·558	10·645	12·592	15·033	16·812
7	1·239	1·564	2·167	2·833	3·822	4·671	6·346	8·383	9·803	12·017	14·067	16·622	18·475
8	1·646	2·032	2·733	3·490	4·594	5·527	7·344	9·524	11·030	13·362	15·507	18·168	20·090
9	2·088	2·532	3·325	4·168	5·380	6·393	8·343	10·656	12·242	14·684	16·919	19·679	21·666
10	2·558	3·059	3·940	4·865	6·179	7·267	9·342	11·781	13·442	15·987	18·307	21·161	23·209
11	3·053	3·609	4·575	5·578	6·989	8·148	10·341	12·899	14·631	17·275	19·675	22·618	24·725
12	3·571	4·178	5·226	6·304	7·807	9·034	11·340	14·011	15·812	18·549	21·026	24·054	26·217
13	4·107	4·765	5·892	7·042	8·634	9·926	12·340	15·119	16·985	19·812	22·362	25·472	27·688
14	4·660	5·368	6·571	7·790	9·467	10·821	13·339	16·222	18·151	21·064	23·685	26·873	29·141
15	5·229	5·985	7·261	8·547	10·307	11·721	14·339	17·322	19·311	22·307	24·996	28·259	30·578
16	5·812	6·614	7·962	9·312	11·152	12·624	15·338	18·418	20·465	23·542	26·296	29·633	32·000
17	6·408	7·255	8·672	10·085	12·002	13·531	16·338	19·511	21·615	24·769	27·587	30·995	33·409
18	7·015	7·906	9·390	10·865	12·857	14·440	17·338	20·601	22·760	25·989	28·869	32·346	34·805
19	7·633	8·567	10·117	11·651	13·716	15·352	18·338	21·689	23·900	27·204	30·144	33·687	36·191
20	8·260	9·237	10·851	12·443	14·578	16·266	19·337	22·775	25·038	28·412	31·410	35·020	37·566
21	8·897	9·915	11·591	13·240	15·445	17·182	20·337	23·858	26·171	29·615	32·671	36·343	38·932
22	9·542	10·600	12·338	14·041	16·314	18·101	21·337	24·939	27·301	30·813	33·924	37·659	40·289
23	10·196	11·293	13·091	14·848	17·187	19·021	22·337	26·018	28·429	32·007	35·172	38·968	41·638
24	10·856	11·992	13·848	15·659	18·062	19·943	23·337	27·096	29·553	33·196	36·415	40·270	42·980
25	11·524	12·697	14·611	16·473	18·940	20·867	24·337	28·172	30·675	34·382	37·652	41·566	44·314
26	12·198	13·409	15·379	17·292	19·820	21·792	25·336	29·246	31·795	35·563	38·885	42·856	45·642
27	12·879	14·125	16·151	18·114	20·703	22·719	26·336	30·319	32·912	36·741	40·113	44·140	46·963
28	13·565	14·847	16·928	18·939	21·588	23·647	27·336	31·391	34·027	37·916	41·337	45·419	48·278
29	14·256	15·574	17·708	19·768	22·475	24·577	28·336	32·461	35·139	39·087	42·557	46·693	49·588
30	14·953	16·306	18·493	20·599	23·364	25·508	29·336	33·530	36·250	40·256	43·773	47·962	50·892

For larger values of n, the expression $\sqrt{2\chi^2} - \sqrt{2n - 1}$, may be used as a normal deviate with unit variance.

Reproduced by permission from Statistical Methods for Research Workers by R. A. Fisher, 10th Edition,
Oliver and Boyd, Ltd., Edinburgh.

THE CUMULATIVE NORMAL DISTRIBUTION FUNCTION

$$\Phi(u) = \frac{1}{\sqrt{2\pi}} \int_{-\infty}^{u} e^{-\frac{x^2}{2}}\, dx \text{ FOR } 0 \cdot 00 \le u \le 4 \cdot 99.$$

u	·00	·01	·02	·03	·04	·05	·06	·07	·08	·09
·0	·5000	·5040	·5080	·5120	·5160	·5199	·5239	·5279	·5319	·5359
·1	·5398	·5438	·5478	·5517	·5557	·5596	·5636	·5675	·5714	·5753
·2	·5793	·5832	·5871	·5910	·5948	·5987	·6026	·6064	·6103	·6141
·3	·6179	·6217	·6255	·6293	·6331	·6368	·6406	·6443	·6480	·6517
·4	·6554	·6591	·6628	·6664	·6700	·6736	·6772	·6808	·6844	·6879
·5	·6915	·6950	·6985	·7019	·7054	·7088	·7123	·7157	·7190	·7224
·6	·7257	·7291	·7324	·7357	·7389	·7422	·7454	·7486	·7517	·7549
·7	·7580	·7611	·7642	·7673	·7703	·7734	·7764	·7794	·7823	·7852
·8	·7881	·7910	·7939	·7967	·7995	·8023	·8051	·8078	·8106	·8133
·9	·8159	·8186	·8212	·8238	·8264	·8289	·8315	·8340	·8365	·8389
1·0	·8413	·8438	·8461	·8485	·8508	·8531	·8554	·8577	·8599	·8621
1·1	·8643	·8665	·8686	·8708	·8729	·8749	·8770	·8790	·8810	·8830
1·2	·8849	·8869	·8888	·8907	·8925	·8944	·8962	·8980	·8997	·90147
1·3	·90320	·90490	·90658	·90824	·90988	·91149	·91309	·91466	·91621	·91774
1·4	·91924	·92073	·92220	·92364	·92507	·92647	·92785	·92922	·93056	·93189
1·5	·93319	·93448	·93574	·93699	·93822	·93943	·94062	·94179	·94295	·94408
1·6	·94520	·94630	·94738	·94845	·94950	·95053	·95154	·95254	·95352	·95449
1·7	·95543	·95637	·95728	·95818	·95907	·95994	·96080	·96164	·96246	·96327
1·8	·96407	·96485	·96562	·96638	·96712	·96784	·96856	·96926	·96995	·97062
1·9	·97128	·97193	·97257	·97320	·97381	·97441	·97500	·97558	·97615	·97670
2·0	·97725	·97778	·97831	·97882	·97932	·97982	·98030	·98077	·98124	·98169
2·1	·98214	·98257	·98300	·98341	·98382	·98422	·98461	·98500	·98537	·98574
2·2	·98610	·98645	·98679	·98713	·98745	·98778	·98809	·98840	·98870	·98899
2·3	·98928	·98956	·98983	·$9^2$0097	·$9^2$0358	·$9^2$0613	·$9^2$0863	·$9^2$1106	·$9^2$1344	·$9^2$1576
2·4	·$9^2$1802	·$9^2$2024	·$9^2$2240	·$9^2$2451	·$9^2$2656	·$9^2$2857	·$9^2$3053	·$9^2$3244	·$9^2$3431	·$9^2$3613
2·5	·$9^2$3790	·$9^2$3963	·$9^2$4132	·$9^2$4297	·$9^2$4457	·$9^2$4614	·$9^2$4766	·$9^2$4915	·$9^2$5060	·$9^2$5201
2·6	·$9^2$5339	·$9^2$5473	·$9^2$5604	·$9^2$5731	·$9^2$5855	·$9^2$5975	·$9^2$6093	·$9^2$6207	·$9^2$6319	·$9^2$6427
2·7	·$9^2$6533	·$9^2$6636	·$9^2$6736	·$9^2$6833	·$9^2$6928	·$9^2$7020	·$9^2$7111	·$9^2$7197	·$9^2$7282	·$9^2$7365
2·8	·$9^2$7445	·$9^2$7523	·$9^2$7599	·$9^2$7673	·$9^2$7744	·$9^2$7814	·$9^2$7882	·$9^2$7948	·$9^2$8012	·$9^2$8074
2·9	·$9^2$8134	·$9^2$8193	·$9^2$8250	·$9^2$8305	·$9^2$8359	·$9^2$8411	·$9^2$8462	·$9^2$8511	·$9^2$8559	·$9^2$8605
3·0	·$9^2$8650	·$9^2$8694	·$9^2$8736	·$9^2$8777	·$9^2$8817	·$9^2$8856	·$9^2$8893	·$9^2$8930	·$9^2$8965	·$9^2$8999
3·1	·$9^3$0324	·$9^3$0646	·$9^3$0957	·$9^3$1260	·$9^3$1553	·$9^3$1836	·$9^3$2112	·$9^3$2378	·$9^3$2636	·$9^3$2886
3·2	·$9^3$3129	·$9^3$3363	·$9^3$3590	·$9^3$3810	·$9^3$4024	·$9^3$4230	·$9^3$4429	·$9^3$4623	·$9^3$4810	·$9^3$4991
3·3	·$9^3$5166	·$9^3$5335	·$9^3$5499	·$9^3$5658	·$9^3$5811	·$9^3$5959	·$9^3$6103	·$9^3$6242	·$9^3$6376	·$9^3$6505
3·4	·$9^3$6631	·$9^3$6752	·$9^3$6869	·$9^3$6982	·$9^3$7091	·$9^3$7197	·$9^3$7299	·$9^3$7398	·$9^3$7493	·$9^3$7585
3·5	·$9^3$7674	·$9^3$7759	·$9^3$7842	·$9^3$7922	·$9^3$7999	·$9^3$8074	·$9^3$8146	·$9^3$8215	·$9^3$8282	·$9^3$8347
3·6	·$9^3$8409	·$9^3$8469	·$9^3$8527	·$9^3$8583	·$9^3$8637	·$9^3$8689	·$9^3$8739	·$9^3$8787	·$9^3$8834	·$9^3$8879
3·7	·$9^3$8922	·$9^3$8964	·$9^4$0039	·$9^4$0426	·$9^4$0799	·$9^4$1158	·$9^4$1504	·$9^4$1838	·$9^4$2159	·$9^4$2468
3·8	·$9^4$2765	·$9^4$3052	·$9^4$3327	·$9^4$3593	·$9^4$3848	·$9^4$4094	·$9^4$4331	·$9^4$4558	·$9^4$4777	·$9^4$4988
3·9	·$9^4$5190	·$9^4$5385	·$9^4$5573	·$9^4$5753	·$9^4$5926	·$9^4$6092	·$9^4$6253	·$9^4$6406	·$9^4$6554	·$9^4$6696
4·0	·$9^4$6833	·$9^4$6964	·$9^4$7090	·$9^4$7211	·$9^4$7327	·$9^4$7439	·$9^4$7546	·$9^4$7649	·$9^4$7748	·$9^4$7843
4·1	·$9^4$7934	·$9^4$8022	·$9^4$8106	·$9^4$8186	·$9^4$8263	·$9^4$8338	·$9^4$8409	·$9^4$8477	·$9^4$8542	·$9^4$8605
4·2	·$9^4$8665	·$9^4$8723	·$9^4$8778	·$9^4$8832	·$9^4$8882	·$9^4$8931	·$9^4$8978	·$9^5$0226	·$9^5$0655	·$9^5$1066
4·3	·$9^5$1460	·$9^5$1837	·$9^5$2199	·$9^5$2545	·$9^5$2876	·$9^5$3193	·$9^5$3497	·$9^5$3788	·$9^5$4066	·$9^5$4332
4·4	·$9^5$4587	·$9^5$4831	·$9^5$5065	·$9^5$5288	·$9^5$5502	·$9^5$5706	·$9^5$5902	·$9^5$6089	·$9^5$6268	·$9^5$6439
4·5	·$9^5$6602	·$9^5$6759	·$9^5$6908	·$9^5$7051	·$9^5$7187	·$9^5$7318	·$9^5$7442	·$9^5$7561	·$9^5$7675	·$9^5$7784
4·6	·$9^5$7888	·$9^5$7987	·$9^5$8081	·$9^5$8172	·$9^5$8258	·$9^5$8340	·$9^5$8419	·$9^5$8494	·$9^5$8566	·$9^5$8634
4·7	·$9^5$8699	·$9^5$8761	·$9^5$8821	·$9^5$8877	·$9^5$8931	·$9^5$8983	·$9^6$0320	·$9^6$0789	·$9^6$1235	·$9^6$1661
4·8	·$9^6$2067	·$9^6$2453	·$9^6$2822	·$9^6$3173	·$9^6$3508	·$9^6$3827	·$9^6$4131	·$9^6$4420	·$9^6$4696	·$9^6$4958
4·9	·$9^6$5208	·$9^6$5446	·$9^6$5673	·$9^6$5889	·$9^6$6094	·$9^6$6289	·$9^6$6475	·$9^6$6652	·$9^6$6821	·$9^6$6981

Example: $\Phi(3 \cdot 57) = \cdot 9^3 8215 = 0 \cdot 9998215$.

Reproduced by permission from *Statistical Tables and Formulas* by A. Hald 1952 by John Wiley and Sons.

THE CUMULATIVE NORMAL DISTRIBUTION FUNCTION

$$\Phi(u) = \frac{1}{\sqrt{2\pi}} \int_{-\infty}^{u} e^{-\frac{x^2}{2}}\, dx \text{ FOR } -4\cdot99 \le u \le 0\cdot00.$$

u	·00	·01	·02	·03	·04	·05	·06	·07	·08	·09
− ·0	·5000	·4960	·4920	·4880	·4840	·4801	·4761	·4721	·4681	·4641
− ·1	·4602	·4562	·4522	·4483	·4443	·4404	·4364	·4325	·4286	·4247
− ·2	·4207	·4168	·4129	·4090	·4052	·4013	·3974	·3936	·3897	·3859
− ·3	·3821	·3783	·3745	·3707	·3669	·3632	·3594	·3557	·3520	·3483
− ·4	·3446	·3409	·3372	·3336	·3300	·3264	·3228	·3192	·3156	·3121
− ·5	·3085	·3050	·3015	·2981	·2946	·2912	·2877	·2843	·2810	·2776
− ·6	·2743	·2709	·2676	·2643	·2611	·2578	·2546	·2514	·2483	·2451
− ·7	·2420	·2389	·2358	·2327	·2297	·2266	·2236	·2206	·2177	·2148
− ·8	·2119	·2090	·2061	·2033	·2005	·1977	·1949	·1922	·1894	·1867
− ·9	·1841	·1814	·1788	·1762	·1736	·1711	·1685	·1660	·1635	·1611
−1·0	·1587	·1562	·1539	·1515	·1492	·1469	·1446	·1423	·1401	·1379
−1·1	·1357	·1335	·1314	·1292	·1271	·1251	·1230	·1210	·1190	·1170
−1·2	·1151	·1131	·1112	·1093	·1075	·1056	·1038	·1020	·1003	·09853
−1·3	·09680	·09510	·09342	·09176	·09012	·08851	·08691	·08534	·08379	·08226
−1·4	·08076	·07927	·07780	·07636	·07493	·07353	·07215	·07078	·06944	·06811
−1·5	·06681	·06552	·06426	·06301	·06178	·06057	·05938	·05821	·05705	·05592
−1·6	·05480	·05370	·05262	·05155	·05050	·04947	·04846	·04746	·04648	·04551
−1·7	·04457	·04363	·04272	·04182	·04093	·04006	·03920	·03836	·03754	·03673
−1·8	·03593	·03515	·03438	·03362	·03288	·03216	·03144	·03074	·03005	·02938
−1·9	·02872	·02807	·02743	·02680	·02619	·02559	·02500	·02442	·02385	·02330
−2·0	·02275	·02222	·02169	·02118	·02068	·02018	·01970	·01923	·01876	·01831
−2·1	·01786	·01743	·01700	·01659	·01618	·01578	·01539	·01500	·01463	·01426
−2·2	·01390	·01355	·01321	·01287	·01255	·01222	·01191	·01160	·01130	·01101
−2·3	·01072	·01044	·01017	$\cdot0^29903$	$\cdot0^29642$	$\cdot0^29387$	$\cdot0^29137$	$\cdot0^28894$	$\cdot0^28656$	$\cdot0^28424$
−2·4	$\cdot0^28198$	$\cdot0^27976$	$\cdot0^27760$	$\cdot0^27549$	$\cdot0^27344$	$\cdot0^27143$	$\cdot0^26947$	$\cdot0^26756$	$\cdot0^26569$	$\cdot0^26387$
−2·5	$\cdot0^26210$	$\cdot0^26037$	$\cdot0^25868$	$\cdot0^25703$	$\cdot0^25543$	$\cdot0^25386$	$\cdot0^25234$	$\cdot0^25085$	$\cdot0^24940$	$\cdot0^24799$
−2·6	$\cdot0^24661$	$\cdot0^24527$	$\cdot0^24396$	$\cdot0^24269$	$\cdot0^24145$	$\cdot0^24025$	$\cdot0^23907$	$\cdot0^23793$	$\cdot0^23681$	$\cdot0^23573$
−2·7	$\cdot0^23467$	$\cdot0^23364$	$\cdot0^23264$	$\cdot0^23167$	$\cdot0^23072$	$\cdot0^22980$	$\cdot0^22890$	$\cdot0^22803$	$\cdot0^22718$	$\cdot0^22635$
−2·8	$\cdot0^22555$	$\cdot0^22477$	$\cdot0^22401$	$\cdot0^22327$	$\cdot0^22256$	$\cdot0^22186$	$\cdot0^22118$	$\cdot0^22052$	$\cdot0^21988$	$\cdot0^21926$
−2·9	$\cdot0^21866$	$\cdot0^21807$	$\cdot0^21750$	$\cdot0^21695$	$\cdot0^21641$	$\cdot0^21589$	$\cdot0^21538$	$\cdot0^21489$	$\cdot0^21441$	$\cdot0^21395$
−3·0	$\cdot0^21350$	$\cdot0^21306$	$\cdot0^21264$	$\cdot0^21223$	$\cdot0^21183$	$\cdot0^21144$	$\cdot0^21107$	$\cdot0^21070$	$\cdot0^21035$	$\cdot0^21001$
−3·1	$\cdot0^39676$	$\cdot0^39354$	$\cdot0^39043$	$\cdot0^38740$	$\cdot0^38447$	$\cdot0^38164$	$\cdot0^37888$	$\cdot0^37622$	$\cdot0^37364$	$\cdot0^37114$
−3·2	$\cdot0^36871$	$\cdot0^36637$	$\cdot0^36410$	$\cdot0^36190$	$\cdot0^35976$	$\cdot0^35770$	$\cdot0^35571$	$\cdot0^35377$	$\cdot0^35190$	$\cdot0^35009$
−3·3	$\cdot0^34834$	$\cdot0^34665$	$\cdot0^34501$	$\cdot0^34342$	$\cdot0^34189$	$\cdot0^34041$	$\cdot0^33897$	$\cdot0^33758$	$\cdot0^33624$	$\cdot0^33495$
−3·4	$\cdot0^33369$	$\cdot0^33248$	$\cdot0^33131$	$\cdot0^33018$	$\cdot0^32909$	$\cdot0^32803$	$\cdot0^32701$	$\cdot0^32602$	$\cdot0^32507$	$\cdot0^32415$
−3·5	$\cdot0^32326$	$\cdot0^32241$	$\cdot0^32158$	$\cdot0^32078$	$\cdot0^32001$	$\cdot0^31926$	$\cdot0^31854$	$\cdot0^31785$	$\cdot0^31718$	$\cdot0^31653$
−3·6	$\cdot0^31591$	$\cdot0^31531$	$\cdot0^31473$	$\cdot0^31417$	$\cdot0^31363$	$\cdot0^31311$	$\cdot0^31261$	$\cdot0^31213$	$\cdot0^31166$	$\cdot0^31121$
−3·7	$\cdot0^31078$	$\cdot0^31036$	$\cdot0^39961$	$\cdot0^49574$	$\cdot0^49201$	$\cdot0^48842$	$\cdot0^48496$	$\cdot0^48162$	$\cdot0^47841$	$\cdot0^47532$
−3·8	$\cdot0^47235$	$\cdot0^46948$	$\cdot0^46673$	$\cdot0^46407$	$\cdot0^46152$	$\cdot0^45906$	$\cdot0^45669$	$\cdot0^45442$	$\cdot0^45223$	$\cdot0^45012$
−3·9	$\cdot0^44810$	$\cdot0^44615$	$\cdot0^44427$	$\cdot0^44247$	$\cdot0^44074$	$\cdot0^43908$	$\cdot0^43747$	$\cdot0^43594$	$\cdot0^43446$	$\cdot0^43304$
−4·0	$\cdot0^43167$	$\cdot0^43036$	$\cdot0^42910$	$\cdot0^42789$	$\cdot0^42673$	$\cdot0^42561$	$\cdot0^42454$	$\cdot0^42351$	$\cdot0^42252$	$\cdot0^42157$
−4·1	$\cdot0^42066$	$\cdot0^41978$	$\cdot0^41894$	$\cdot0^41814$	$\cdot0^41737$	$\cdot0^41662$	$\cdot0^41591$	$\cdot0^41523$	$\cdot0^41458$	$\cdot0^41395$
−4·2	$\cdot0^41335$	$\cdot0^41277$	$\cdot0^41222$	$\cdot0^41168$	$\cdot0^41118$	$\cdot0^41069$	$\cdot0^41022$	$\cdot0^59774$	$\cdot0^59345$	$\cdot0^58934$
−4·3	$\cdot0^58540$	$\cdot0^58163$	$\cdot0^57801$	$\cdot0^57455$	$\cdot0^57124$	$\cdot0^56807$	$\cdot0^56503$	$\cdot0^56212$	$\cdot0^55934$	$\cdot0^55668$
−4·4	$\cdot0^55413$	$\cdot0^55169$	$\cdot0^54935$	$\cdot0^54712$	$\cdot0^54498$	$\cdot0^54294$	$\cdot0^54098$	$\cdot0^53911$	$\cdot0^53732$	$\cdot0^53561$
−4·5	$\cdot0^53398$	$\cdot0^53241$	$\cdot0^53092$	$\cdot0^52949$	$\cdot0^52813$	$\cdot0^52682$	$\cdot0^52558$	$\cdot0^52439$	$\cdot0^52325$	$\cdot0^52216$
−4·6	$\cdot0^52112$	$\cdot0^52013$	$\cdot0^51919$	$\cdot0^51828$	$\cdot0^51742$	$\cdot0^51660$	$\cdot0^51581$	$\cdot0^51506$	$\cdot0^51434$	$\cdot0^51366$
−4·7	$\cdot0^51301$	$\cdot0^51239$	$\cdot0^51179$	$\cdot0^51123$	$\cdot0^51069$	$\cdot0^51017$	$\cdot0^69680$	$\cdot0^69211$	$\cdot0^68765$	$\cdot0^68339$
−4·8	$\cdot0^67933$	$\cdot0^67547$	$\cdot0^67178$	$\cdot0^66827$	$\cdot0^66492$	$\cdot0^66173$	$\cdot0^65869$	$\cdot0^65580$	$\cdot0^65304$	$\cdot0^65042$
−4·9	$\cdot0^64792$	$\cdot0^64554$	$\cdot0^64327$	$\cdot0^64111$	$\cdot0^63906$	$\cdot0^63711$	$\cdot0^63525$	$\cdot0^63348$	$\cdot0^63179$	$\cdot0^63019$

Example: $\Phi(-3\cdot57) = \cdot0^31785 = 0\cdot0001785.$

RANDOM SAMPLING NUMBERS

```
69 10 64 95 40    16 65 81 29 11    22 99 84    00 04    36 77 66 58 71    49 14 34 07 11
01 20 90 51 77    40 09 86 94 58    00 99 02    94 20    46 11 28 22 26    17 69 34 12 66
47 40 35 40 15    16 08 45 33 69    84 92 48    62 60    13 23 93 57 28    83 41 24 68 86
20 87 69 85 33    11 46 17 15 86    55 16 70    57 71    60 01 33 05 17    91 79 32 99 23
26 47 55 13 10    81 16 16 40 54    99 16 34    74 59    19 59 48 85 03    00 34 71 74 38

77 74 26 55 18    67 94 21 18 46    01 56 13    13 46    29 87 89 92 30    30 57 57 38 62
67 48 31 89 06    73 44 03 47 59    17 97 98    42 23    36 15 60 22 36    00 29 32 55 28
45 36 53 50 05    99 60 21 72 63    20 99 84    54 81    12 22 97 06 82    62 02 25 47 91
44 05 68 65 46    39 99 51 89 90    26 14 73    87 94    15 97 37 25 79    23 52 66 33 88
31 59 59 31 91    15 70 46 14 92    55 74 21    94 69    71 82 13 82 73    40 56 63 88 87

08 13 15 79 23    34 38 02 16 96    31 91 21    80 12    36 57 95 98 96    68 69 52 79 15
21 00 67 88 25    30 24 30 43 39    87 39 31    75 81    36 79 45 10 09    40 11 49 50 85
99 09 08 61 32    22 88 77 52 42    92 89 71    43 54    02 50 55 97 48    07 21 16 07 14
05 40 44 44 84    68 84 85 04 05    34 68 98    65 21    69 08 97 23 10    12 00 47 42 36
24 94 27 13 78    48 82 19 38 91    98 49 04    03 56    05 43 97 40 66    16 73 25 75 49

18 88 98 60 25    71 07 03 53 92    92 15 17    13 45    25 97 58 73 65    34 98 16 39 06
94 84 16 40 41    94 12 04 73 20    45 16 18    93 26    25 36 49 10 00    92 03 33 02 57
25 46 76 97 60    93 17 07 17 62    16 61 94    11 60    27 18 99 56 80    76 47 25 89 37
55 84 80 86 89    23 49 53 14 17    39 34 94    93 14    97 38 21 78 00    92 92 48 28 70
44 69 90 42 25    20 58 47 83 83    93 66 56    21 99    72 50 08 62 64    51 11 90 32 73

98 91 71 34 90    21 05 95 67 31    35 04 57    60 64    15 34 45 30 72    63 92 62 07 57
08 62 84 48 70    38 21 27 77 12    57 12 15    47 34    68 06 46 80 46    17 99 43 25 46
75 82 17 44 87    02 50 26 21 92    05 61 41    59 82    16 60 46 83 99    12 14 32 36 40
24 56 39 87 22    59 34 70 08 69    80 38 61    01 67    21 48 32 13 63    15 32 57 59 81
55 76 34 17 18    69 64 07 82 51    46 41 75    65 85    46 69 04 55 58    52 87 59 71 89

89 44 23 53 80    74 49 86 96 31    88 85 09    12 13    48 81 98 70 82    64 25 90 80 15
26 48 96 95 82    12 93 24 42 06    70 91 14    31 79    21 47 54 03 58    38 13 21 99 74
76 86 45 97 20    54 55 19 79 72    18 10 10    15 54    32 01 55 43 71    43 20 08 90 34
71 19 69 74 43    40 61 99 84 63    48 82 43    94 27    83 67 08 45 91    73 36 59 60 33
58 35 36 89 25    92 06 96 63 54    66 39 70    77 34    51 94 59 81 68    57 27 14 92 49

99 29 89 90 60    88 50 42 63 93    84 48 30    82 20    17 49 50 98 19    64 12 75 27 48
89 14 89 10 00    78 52 34 04 70    33 59 24    96 03    15 98 72 56 74    14 30 75 95 71
81 38 52 53 49    53 27 04 74 15    21 11 83    59 22    32 83 68 84 19    87 37 64 65 99
22 86 65 38 45    98 91 40 64 14    70 41 88    99 71    43 83 20 20 25    66 25 06 33 12
83 67 47 88 56    00 77 49 74 89    62 11 05    90 57    08 84 38 90 23    11 10 85 42 84

17 41 88 33 30    84 23 95 25 20    32 84 72    81 97    77 46 72 16 71    37 43 38 89 69
50 08 96 43 68    29 28 68 23 77    02 90 33    58 08    90 65 31 09 07    29 29 61 33 37
69 24 39 08 92    07 06 88 66 67    52 81 04    07 29    76 45 89 19 01    96 61 78 31 37
12 99 26 93 56    11 37 42 98 72    34 39 97    40 38    07 03 99 20 36    06 42 07 87 99
98 46 67 27 00    77 60 51 29 90    89 62 82    63 30    72 98 92 98 41    18 24 99 85 31

38 99 86 44 42    78 90 60 30 25    43 78 23    79 33    22 48 87 16 83    19 72 82 35 56
26 13 59 85 80    50 97 11 65 68    02 29 30    74 92    84 43 83 31 84    29 87 46 33 16
35 25 63 14 44    08 43 06 06 51    31 81 73    45 37    40 31 67 55 80    17 68 56 14 68
35 88 62 59 65    86 75 17 00 06    63 15 20    86 55    49 34 89 90 19    34 58 27 09 48
90 94 94 40 98    27 29 21 08 47    19 60 89    94 07    63 22 94 64 75    30 62 91 25 57
```

As the investigation of biological phenomena has focused more sharply upon the interacting molecules in living organisms, the metabolism of amino acids has assumed an increasingly important role, not only in terms of nutrition, but also in terms of structure and function. Amino acids play a vital part in the interconversion of proteins, carbohydrates and lipids; in the formation of certain essential vitamins; and in the synthesis of several antibiotics. Of great interest within recent years has been the elucidation of the genetic code by which amino acids are precisely arranged and incorporated into the fascinating biological catalysts, the enzymes, and into other functional proteins.

The following material, while not encyclopedic, furnishes some essential information concerning the amino acids, and provides the investigator with some pertinent references, both to original works, and to review articles. The references are not intended to be all-inclusive.

Table I. Amino Acid Metabolism

Amino Acid	Product of Oxidative Deamination or Transamination	Product of Decarboxylation	Pathways of Metabolism
1. L-Alanine	Pyruvic acid		1. Synthesis: Aspartic acid → alanine + CO_2 Pyruvate + NH_3 → alanine Kynurenine → anthranilic acid + alanine Degradation: Alanine → propionic acid + acetic acid + NH_3
2. L-Arginine	α-Keto-δ-guanidovaleric acid	Agmatine	2. Synthesis: Glutamic acid + acetyl Co A → N-acetyl glutamic acid → N-acetyl glutamic semialdehyde → N-acetyl ornithine → ornithine → arginine Glutamic acid semialdehyde + amino acid → ornithine + keto acid Ornithine → arginine Degradation: Arginine → ornithine + urea Arginine → citrulline + NH_3 Arginine → agmatine + CO_2 Arginine + glycine ⇌ guanidoacetic acid + ornithine
3. L-Asparagine	α-Ketosuccinamic acid		3. Synthesis: α-Ketosuccinamic acid ⇌ asparagine Degradation: Asparagine ⇌ aspartic acid + NH_3 Asparagine → α-ketosuccinamic acid → NH_3 + oxalacetic acid
4. L-Aspartic acid	Oxalacetic acid	α-Alanine, β-alanine	4. Synthesis: Fumaric acid + NH_3 → aspartic acid Degradation: Aspartic acid + carbamylphosphate → $PO_4^{\equiv}$ + carbamylaspartic acid → pyrimidines Aspartic acid ⇌ fumaric acid + NH_3 Aspartic acid ⇌ homoserine threonine → isoleucine methionine → homoserine

5. L-Citrulline   α-Keto-δ-carbamidovaleric acid

5. Synthesis:

Arginine → citrulline + NH_3

Degradation:

Citrulline + aspartic acid + ATP → AMP + PP + arginosuccinic acid ⇌ arginine + fumaric acid

Citrulline + PO_4 ⇌ ornithine + carbamylphosphate

Citrulline → carbamylphosphate + ADP ⇌ CO_2 + NH_3 + ATP

6. L-Cysteine & L-cystine   β-Mercaptopyruvic acid

6. Synthesis:

Cystathionine → cysteine + homoserine

Serine + H_2S → cysteine

Degradation:

Cysteine → β-mercaptopyruvic acid → pyruvic acid + S

Cysteine → H_2S + NH_3 + pyruvic acid

Cysteine → cysteine sulfinic acid → (i) cysteic acid → taurine, (ii) hypotaurine, or (iii) via transamination → β-sulfinylpyruvate → pyruvate + SO_3 (2 cysteine ⇌ cystine)

Cysteine + ethanolamine → S-aminoethylcysteine → serine + 2-mercaptoethylamine

Cysteine + formaldehyde → thiazolidine carboxylic acid → N-formyl cysteine

7. L-Glutamic acid   α-Ketoglutaric acid   γ-Aminobutyric acid

7. Synthesis:

From α-ketoglutaric acid by transamination

Histidine → formiminoglutamic acid → glutamic acid

Degradation:

Glutamic acid → γ-aminobutyric acid + CO_2

Ornithine ⇌ glutamic acid

Proline ⇌ glutamic acid

Histidine → urocanic acid → glutamic acid + NH_3 + formate

Glutamine ⇌ glutamic acid + NH_3

Glutamic acid → β-methyl aspartate → mesaconate → citramalate → acetate + pyruvate

Table I. Amino Acid Metabolism (continued)

Amino Acid	Product of Oxidative Deamination or Transamination	Product of Decarboxylation	Pathways of Metabolism
8. L-Glutamine	α-Ketoglutaramic acid		8. Synthesis: Glutamic acid + $NH_3 \rightleftharpoons$ glutamine Degradation: Glutamine $\rightleftharpoons$ glutamic acid + NH_3 Glutamine $\rightarrow \alpha$-ketoglutaramic acid $\rightarrow NH_3 + \alpha$-ketoglutaric acid
9. Glycine	Glyoxylic acid		9. Synthesis: Serine + tetrahydrofolate $\rightleftharpoons$ glycine + 5, 10-methylene-tetrahydro-folate Purines $\rightarrow$ forminimoglycine $\rightarrow$ glycine + NH_3 + formate Degradation: Glycine + $N^{5,10}$-methylenetetrahydrofolate$\rightleftharpoons$serine + tetrahydrofolate Glycine + glyoxylic acid $\rightarrow$ formate + CO_2 Glycine + succinyl-CoA $\rightarrow \delta$-aminolevulinate $\rightarrow$ porphyrins Glycine + 5'-phospho-β-D-ribosamine $\rightarrow$ purines Glycine $\rightleftharpoons$ betaine Glycine $\rightarrow$ acetate + CO_2 + NH_3 Glycine $\rightarrow$ amino-acetone
10. L-Histidine	β-Imidazolepyruvic acid	Histamine	10. Synthesis: First step: ATP + 5-phosphoribosyl pyrophosphate $\rightarrow$ N-1-5' (phos-phoribosyl)-ATP Imidazoleglycerolphosphate $\rightarrow$ imidazoleacetol phosphate + glutamic acid $\rightarrow$ histidinol phosphate $\rightarrow$ histidinal $\rightarrow$ histidine Degradation: Histidine $\rightarrow$ urocanic acid $\rightarrow$ glutamic acid + NH_3 + formate Histidine $\rightarrow$ carnosine Histidine $\rightarrow$ anserine Histidine $\rightarrow$ histamine $\rightarrow$ imidazoleacetic acid $\rightarrow NH_3$ + formylaspartic acid
11. L-Hydroxyproline	α-Keto-γ-hydroxy-δ-aminovaleric acid		11. Synthesis: Glutamic acid $\rightarrow$ glutamic semialdehyde $\rightarrow$ ^{1}-pyrroline-5-carboxylic acid $\rightarrow$ proline $\rightarrow$ hydroxyproline Degradation: Hydroxypyrroline $\rightarrow$ Δ^1-proline-4-hydroxy-2-carboxylate $\rightarrow$ pyrolle-2-carboxylate Hydroxypyrroline $\rightarrow$ glutamate Hydroxypyrroline $\rightarrow \gamma$-hydroxyglutamic acid $\rightarrow \gamma$-hydroxy-α-keto glutaric acid $\rightarrow$ glyoxylate + pyruvate

12. L-Isoleucine — d-α-Keto-β-methylvaleric acid

Synthesis:

Degradation:
Isoleucine → α-keto-β-methylvaleric acid → CO_2 + α-methyl-butyryl-CoA ⇌ tiglyl-CoA ⇌ α-methyl-β-hydroxybutyryl-CoA α-methyl aceto-acetyl-CoA ⇌ acetyl-CoA + propionyl-CoA

13. L-Leucine — α-Ketoisocaproic acid

Synthesis:
α-Ketoisovaleric acid → β-hydroxy-β-carboxyisocaproic acid → di-methyl citraconic acid → carboxyisocaproic acid → α-keto-isocaproic acid → leucine

Degradation:
Leucine → α-ketoisocaproic acid → CO_2 + isovaleryl-CoA ⇌ senecioyl-CoA + CO_2 ⇌ β-methylglutaconyl-CoA ⇌ β-hydroxy-β-methyl glutaryl-CoA ⇌ acetoacetic acid + acetyl-CoA

14. L-Lysine — α-Keto-ε-aminocaproic acid — Cadaverine

Synthesis:
α, -Diaminopimelic acid → lysine or (ii) α-aminoadipic acid → lysine

Degradation:
Lysine → α-keto-ε-aminocaproic acid → ¹-piperidine-2-carboxylic acid → pipecolic acid → Δ⁶-piperidine-2-carboxylic acid → α-aminoadipic-ε-semialdehyde → t-α-aminoadipic acid → α-ketoadipic acid → glutaric acid → α-keto glutaric acid → glutamic acid
Glutaryl-CoA → β-hydroxyisovaleryl-CoA → malonyl-CoA
Lysine → acetate + butyrate

15. L-Methionine — α-Keto-γ-methiolbutyric acid

Synthesis:
Methylcobalamin or methyl tetrahydrofolate + homocysteine → methionine

Degradation:
Methionine → labile CH_3 + homocysteine → (i) homocysteic acid (ii) H_2S + NH_3 + α-ketobutyric acid, or (iii) serine → cystathionine → cysteine + NH_3 → α-ketobutyric acid

16. L-Ornithine — Glutamic-γ-semialdehyde, or α-keto-δ-aminovaleric acid — Putrescine

Synthesis:
Arginine → ornithine + urea

Degradation:
Ornithine ⇌ proline
Ornithine ⇌ glutamic acid
Ornithine + carbamylphosphate → citrulline
Citrulline + PO_4 ⇌ ornithine + carbamylphosphate

Table I. Amino Acid Metabolism (continued)

Amino Acid	Product of Oxidative Deamination or Transamination	Product of Decarboxylation	Pathways of Metabolism
17. L-Phenylalanine	Phenylpyruvic acid	Phenylethylamine	17. Synthesis: Quinic acid → shikimic acid → prephenic acid → phenylpyruvic acid → phenylalanine Degradation: Phenylalanine → tyrosine Phenylalanine → phenylpyruvic acid → phenylacetic and phenyllactic acids Tyrosine → p-hydroxyphenylpyruvic acid → CO_2 + homogentisic acid + maleylacetoacetic acid → fumarylacetoacetic acid → fumaric acid + acetoacetic acid
18. L-Proline	Glutamic-γ-semialdehyde, or α-keto-δ-aminovaleric acid		18. Synthesis: Glutamic acid → glutamic semialdehyde → Δ^1-pyrroline-5-carboxylic acid → proline Degradation: Proline ⇌ ornithine Proline ⇌ glutamic acid Proline → hydroxyproline
19. L-Serine	β-Hydroxypyruvic acid	Ethanolamine	19. Synthesis: 3-Phosphoglycerate → phosphohydroxy pyruvate → phosphoserine → serine Glycine + 5, 10-methylenetetrahydrofolate → serine + tetrahydrofolate Degradation: Serine → NH_3 + H_2O + pyruvic acid Serine + indole-3-glycerol phosphate ⇌ tryptophan Glycine + $N^{5, 10}$-methenyl-tetrahydrofolate ⇌ serine + tetrahydrofolate

20. L-Threonine | d-α-Keto-β-hydroxybutyric acid

Synthesis:
Aspartic semialdehyde → homoserine → phosphohomoserine → threonine

Degradation:
Threonine → NH_3 + H_2O + α-ketobutyric acid
Threonine → glycine + acetaldehyde
Threonine → α-keto-β-hydroxybutyric acid
Threonine → aminoacetone

Aspartic acid ⇌ homoserine ↗ threonine → isoleucine ↘ methionine

21. L-Tryptophan | β-Indolepyruvic acid | Tryptamine

Synthesis:
Anthranilic acid + 5-phosphoribosyl pyrophosphate → N-O-carboxyphenyl-D-ribosylamine-5'-phosphate → indole glycerol-3-phosphate → indole + glyceraldehyde phosphate
Indole + serine → tryptophan

Degradation:
Tryptophan → formylkynurenine → formate + kynurenine → (i) kynurenic acid (ii) anthranilic acid + alanine, or (iii) 3-hydroxykynurenine → 3-hydroxyanthranilic acid → 2-acroleyl-3-aminofumaric acid → quinolinic acid → nicotinic acid ribonucleotide
Tryptophan → 5-hydroxytryptophan → 5-hydroxytryptamine → 5-hydroxyindoleacetic acid

22. L-Tyrosine | p-Hydroxyphenylpyruvic acid | Tyramine

Synthesis:
Phenylalanine → tyrosine
Prephenic acid → tyrosine

Degradation:
Tyrosine → p-hydroxyphenylpyruvic acid → CO_2 + homogentisic acid + maleylacetoacetic acid → fumarylacetoacetic acid → fumaric acid + acetoacetic acid

23. L-Valine | α-Ketoisovaleric acid

Synthesis:
2 Pyruvate → acetolactate → α, β-dihydroxyisovalerate → α-ketoisovalerate → valine

Degradation:
Valine → α-ketoisovaleric acid → CO_2 + isobutyryl-CoA ⇌ methacrylyl-CoA ⇌ β-hydroxyisobutyryl-CoA ⇌ β-hydroxyisobutyric acid ⇌ methylmalonic acid semialdehyde ⇌ β-aminoisobutyric acid

Genetic Code

Amino Acid		RNA Codewords		
1. Alanine	CCG	UCG*	ACG*	
2. Arginine	CGC	AGA	UGC*	CGA*
3. Asparagine	ACA	AUA	ACU*	
4. Aspartic acid	GUA	GCA*	GAA*	
5. Cysteine	UUG			
6. Glutamic acid	GAA	GAU*	GAC*	
7. Glutamine	AAC	AGA	AGU*	
8. Glycine	UGG	AGG	CGG	
9. Histidine	ACC	ACU*		
10. Isoleucine	UAU	UAA		
11. Leucine	UUG	UUC	UCC	UUA
12. Lysine	AAA	AAU		
13. Methionine	UGA			
14. Phenylalanine	UUU	CUU		
15. Proline	CCC	CCU	CCA	CCG*
16. Serine	UCU	UCC	UCG*	ACG
17. Threonine	CAC	CAA		
18. Tryptophan	GGU			
19. Tyrosine	AUU			
20. Valine	UGU	UGA*		

*Probable codeword

Reproduced by permission from *Biology Data Book* by Altman, P. and D. Dittmer, 1964, by The Federation of American Societies for Experimental Biology.

BIBLIOGRAPHY

1. Adams, E., "Amino Acid Metabolism," *Ann. Rev. Biochem.*, 31:173, 1962.
2. Adams, E., and A. Goldstone, "Hydroxyproline Metabolism," *J. Biol. Chem.*, 235:3499, 1960.
3. Adelberg, E. A., C. A. Coughlin and R. W. Baratt, "The Biosynthesis of Isoleucine and Valine. II. Independence of the Biosynthetic Pathways in Neurospora," *J. Biol. Chem.*, 216:425, 1955.
4. Ames, B. N., R. G. Martin, and B. J. Garry, "The First Step of Histidine Biosynthesis," *J. Biol. Chem.*, 236:2019, 1961.
5. Bagchi, S. P. and B. C. Guha, "Glutamate Labelling Pattern Obtained from Acetate 1–C14 and Sodium Bicarbonate C14 by Incubation with Rat Liver Slices," *Naturwissenschaften* 45:521, 1958.
6. Barker, H. A., H. Weissbach, and G. D. Smyth, *Proc. Nat. Acad. Sci. U. S.*, 45:521, 1959.
7. Barker, H. A. and B. P. Cardon, "Amino Acid Fermentations by *Clostridium propionicum* and *Diplococcus glycinophilus*," *Arch. Biochem.*, 12:165, 1947.
8. Bessman, S. P., J. Rossen, and E. C. Layne, "γ-Aminobutyric Acid—Glutamic Acid Transamination in Brain," *J. Biol. Chem.*, 201:385, 1953.
9. Black, S. and N. C. Wright, "β-Aspartokinase and β-Aspartyl Phosphate," "Aspartic β-Semialdehyde Dehydrogenase and Aspartic β-Semialdehyde," "Homoserine Dehydrogenase," *J. Biol. Chem.*, 213:29, 39, 51, 1955.
10. Borek, B. A. and H. Waelsh, "The Enzymatic Degradation of Histidine," *J. Biol. Chem.*, 205:459, 1953.
11. Borsoo, H., C. L. Deasy, A. J. Haagen-Smit, G. Keighley and P. H. Lowy, "The Degradation of 1-lysine in Guinea Pig Liver Homogenate: Formation of α-Aminoadipic Acid," "The Degradation of α-Aminoadipic Acid in Guinea Pig Liver Homogenate," *J. Biol. Chem.*, 176:1383, 1395, 1948.

12. Cavallini, D., B. Mondovi, and C. DeMarco, "A Preliminary Report on the Metabolism of S-Aminoethyl Cysteine by the Rat in Vivo," *Biochem. et Biophys. Acta*, 18:122, 1955.

13. Challenger, F. and J. M. Walshe, "Methyl Mercaptan in Relation to Factor Hepaticus," *Biochem. J.*, 59:372, 1955.

14. Chatagner, F., B. Bergeret, T. Sejourne, and C. Fromageot, "Transamination et Desulfination de L'Acide L-Cysteine-sulfinique," *Biochem. Biophys. Acta*," 9:340, 1952.

15. Coon, M. J., "The Metabolic Fate of the Isopropyl Group of Leucine," *J. Biol. Chem.*, 187:71, 1950.

16. Coon, M. J. and W. G. Robinson, "Amino Acid Metabolism" *Ann. Rev. Biochem.*, 27:561, 1958.

17. Davis, B. D., "Intermediates in Amino Acid Biosynthesis," *Advan. in Enzymol.*, 16:247, 1955.

18. Davis, B. D., "Some Aspects of Amino Acid Biosynthesis in Microorganisms," *Federation Proc.*, 14:691, 1955.

19. Eldjarn, L., A. Phil and A. Sverdrup, "The Synthesis of S^{35}-labeled Hypotaurine and its Metabolism in Rats and Mice," *J. Biol. Chem.*, 223:353, 1956.

20. Ellfolk, N., *Ann. Acad. Sci. Finnicae*, (Ser. 2) 79:74, 1956.

21. Foster, M. A., M. J. Dilworth and D. D. Woods, "Cobalamin and the Synthesis of Methionine by *Escherichia coli*," *Nature*, 201:37, 1964.

22. Greenberg, D. M., A. E. Bagot and O. A. Roholt, "Liver Arginase III. Properties of Highly Purified Argenase," *Arch. Biochem. Biophys.*, 62:446, 1956.

23. Hamilton, P. B., "Clutamine: A Major Constituent of Free α-Amino Acids in Animal Tissues and Blood Plasma," *J. Biol. Chem.*, 158:397, 1945.

24. Huennekens, F. M. and M. J. Osborn, "Folic Acid Co-Enzymes and Carbon Metabolism," *Advan. in Enzymol.*, 21:369, 1959.

25. Jakoby, W. B., and D. M. Bonner, "Kynureininase from Neurospora: Purification and Properties," *J. Biol. Chem.*, 205:699, 1953.

26. Jungwirth, C., S. R. Gross, P. Margolin and H. E. Umbarger, "The Biosynthesis of Leucine," *Biochemistry*, 2:1, 1963.

27. Kaufman, S. and B. Levenberg, "A New Cofactor Required for the Enzymatic Conversion of Phenylalanine to Tyrosine," *J. Biol. Chem.*, 230:931, 1958, 234:2677, 1959.

28. Kinnory, D. S., T. Takeda, and D. M. Greenberg, "Isotope Studies on the Metabolism of Valine," *J. Biol. Chem.*, 212:385, 1955.

29. Lang, K. and V. Mayer, "Uber Bildung und Abbau von L-Oxyprolin," *Biochemistry*, 324:237, 1953.

30. Lin, S. C. and D. M. Greenberg, *J. Gen. Physiol.*, 38:181, 1954.

31. Lukens, L. N. and J. M. Buchanan, "Further Intermediates in the Biosynthesis of Inosinic Acid," *J. Am. Chem. Soc.*, 79:1511, 1957.

32. Mackenzie, C. G., "Production of Active Formaldehyde in the Mitochondrial Oxidation of Sarcosine—CD_3," *J. Biol. Chem.*, 222:145, 1956.

33. Magasanik, B., and H. R. Bowser, "The Degradation of Histidine by *Aerobacter aerogenes*," *J. Biol. Chem.*, 213:571, 1955.

34. Maas, W. K., G. D. Novelli and F. Lipmann, "Acetylation of Glutamic Acid by Extracts of *Escherichia coli*.," *Proc. Nat. Acad. Sci.*, 39:1004, 1953.

35. Matsuo, Y. and D. M. Greenberg, "Metabolic Formation of Homoserine and α-Aminobutyric Acid from Methionine," *J. Biol. Chem.*, 215:547, 1955.

36. McElroy, W. D. and B. Glass (eds.), *Amino Acid Metabolism*, 1955.

37. Meister, A., *Biochemistry of the Amino Acids*, 2nd ed., 1964.

38. Nakada, H. I., "Pathways of Glysine Catabolism in Rat River," *J. Biol. Chem.*, 216:583, 1955.

39. Nakada, H. I. and L. P. Sund, "Glyoxylic Acid Oxidation by Rat Liver," *J. Biol. Chem.*, 233:8, 1958.

40. Nemeth, A. M., C. S. Russell and D. Shemin, "The Succinate-Glycine Cycle II. Metabolism of α-Aminolevulinic Acid," *J. Biol. Chem.*, 229:415, 1957.

41. Olinsky, E. L. and R. F. Gehring, "The Arginine Dihydrolase System of *Streptococcus faecalis* II. Properties of Arginine Desimidase," *J. Biol. Chem.*, 198: 799, 1952.

42. Pyatnitskaya, I. N., "The Synthesis of Amino Acids from Keto Acids and Ammonia in Rat Kidney," *Biokhimiya*, 25:1981, 1960.

43. Rabinowitz, J. C. and W. E. Pricer, "The Enzymatic Synthesis of N^{10} Formyltetrahydrofolic Acid and its Role in ATP Formalation during Formiminoglycine Degradation," *J. Am. Chem. Soc.*, 78:4176, 1956.

44. Robinson, W. G., B. K. Bachhawat and M. J. Coon, "Tiglyl Coenzyme A and α-Methylacetoacetyl Coenzyme A, Intermediates in the Enzymatic Degradation of Isoleucine," *J. Biol. Chem.*, 218:391, 1956.

45. Romano, A. H. and W. J. Nickerson, "Cystine Reductase of Pea Seeds and Yeasts," *J. Biol. Chem.*, 208:409, 1954.

46. Rothstein, M. and D. M. Greenberg, "Evidence for a New Oxidative Pathway for Tryptophan," *Biochim. Biophys. Acta*, 34:598, 1959.

47. Rudman, D. and A. Meister, "Transaminations in *Escherichia coli*." *J. Biol. Chem.*, 250:591, 1953.

48. Sagers, R. D. and I. C. Gunsalus, "Intermediary Metabolism of *Diplococcus glycinophilus*," *J. Bacteriol.*, 81:541, 1961.

49. Schlossman, K., J. Bruggemann and F. Lynen, "Biosynthesis des Cysteines I. Nachweis und Isolierung der Serinsulfhydrase aus Backerhefe," *Biochem. Z.*, 336:258, 1962.

50. Stadtman, R. C., "Anaerobic Degradation of Lysine," *J. Biol. Chem.*, 238: 2766, 1963.

51. Stadtman, T. C., P. Elliott and L. Tiemann, "Studies on the Enzymic Reduction of Amino Acids. III. Phosphate Esterification Coupled with Glycine Reduction," *J. Biol. Chem.*, 231:961, 1958.

52. Strassman, M. J., "A Generalized Pathway for Leucine and Lysine Biosynthesis," *J. Albert Einstein Medical Center*, 12:9, 1964.

53. Tabachnik, M. and H. Tarver, "The Conversion of Methionine S^{35} to Cystathionine S^{35} and Taurine S^{35} in the Rat," *Arch. Biochem. Biophys.*, 56:115, 1955.

54. Tustanoff, E. R. and J. R. Stern, "Enzymic Carboxylation of Crotonyl-CoA and the Metabolism of Glutaric Acid," *Biochem. Biophys. Res. Commun.*, 3:81, 1960.

55. Umbarger, H. E. and M. A. Umbarger, "The Biosynthetic Pathways of Serine in Salmonella Tuphinurium," *Biochim. Biophys. Acta*, 62:193, 1962.

56. Urata, G. and S. Granick, "Aminoacetone Formation and Decomposition in Liver," *Biochem. Biophys. Res. Commun.*, 4:96, 1961.

57. Vogel, H. J., "On Biochemical Evolution: Lysine Formation in Higher Plants," *Proc. Nat. Acad. Sci. U. S.* 45:1717, 1959.

58. Vogel, H. J. and D. M. Bonner, "Acetylornithinase of *Escherichia coli*: Partial Purification and some Properties," *J. Biol. Chem.*, 218:97, 1956.

59. Wachsman, J. T. and H. A. Barker, "Tracer Experiments on Glutamate Fermentation by *Clostridium tetanomorphum*," *J. Biol. Chem.*, 217:695, 1955.

60. Wood, J. L., and S. L. Cooley, "Detoxication of Cyanide by Cystine," *J. Biol. Chem.*, 218:449, 1956.

61. Wormser, E. H. and A. B. Pardee, "Regulation of Threonine Biosynthesis in *Escherichia coli*," *Arch. Biochem. Biophys.*, 7:416, 1958.

62. Yanofsky, C. J., "An Isotopic Study of the Conversion of Anthranillic Acid to Indole," *J. Biol. Chem.*, 217:345, 1955.

I. DEFINITIONS AND CLASSIFICATIONS

The naturally occuring amino acids may be defined as a small group of organic acids possessing one or more amino groups, one of which is always α to the carboxyl group. Biochemists customarily use a series of trivial names (see Table I) for the amino acids and usually specify the optical configuration of the amino acids by means of small capital letters. There are 23 amino acids which are commonly found in hydrolysates of proteins and the following discussion will be limited to a consideration of these.

The halogenated tyrosines and thyroxine are also known to be present in thyroglobulin but will not be treated here.

Classification of the amino acids is given below in Table I.

II. GENERAL PROPERTIES

A detailed discussion of the properties of the amino acids will not be attempted here. The reader is referred to an extensive coverage of this area by Greenstein and Winitz[1] and by Meister.[2]

Some of the general chemical reactions will be mentioned briefly.

Nitrous Acid. Amino acids with primary amino groups react with nitrous acid giving the corresponding hydroxy acids. This reaction forms the basis for the Van Slyke nitrous acid method for determining amino acids volumetrically[3] and manometrically.[4]

Ninhydrin. (See quantitative section below.)

Carbobenzoxychloride. Bergmann and Zervas[5] introduced the use of this reagent for blocking amino groups during peptide synthesis.

Dinitrophenyl derivatives (DNP). 2,4-dinitrofluorobenzene reacts with the amino group of the amino acids in bicarbonate solutions at ordinary temperature producing N-dinitrophenyl derivatives[6] which are yellow, a useful property for paper chromatography. Melting points of DNP amino acids are listed in Table IV.

Tosyl derivatives. p-Toluenesulfonyl chloride reacts with amino groups to form p-toluenesulfonyl derivatives which have been used for directed synthesis.[7,8] Melting points of these derivatives are listed in Table IV.

Schiff base. Amino acids form Schiff bases with various aldehydes (formaldehyde,[9] aromatic aldehydes,[10] pyridoxal, [11,12] and pyridoxal phosphate.[13])

Other general reactions. Formylation,[9] α-N-phosphate derivatives,[14,15] and copper complexes.[16]

III. STRUCTURAL FORMULA (TABLE I)

General formulas for amino acids of the L and the D optical configuration are:

L-Amino Acid   D-Amino Acid

Except for glycine the α-carbon of amino acids is substituted asymmetrically.

IV. MOLECULAR WEIGHT

The amino acids have relatively low molecular weights in the range of 75–300 (Table I).

V. DECOMPOSITION POINT

The amino acids are white crystalline solids which when heated undergo decomposition (over a range of several degrees) at relatively high temperatures (Table I).

As a characteristic property the decomposition points is of little value.

VI. SOLUBILITY

The solubility of amino acids in water varies from the sparingly soluble cystine and tyrosine to the extremely soluble proline (Table I). Most of the amino acids are only slightly soluble in absolute ethanol with the exception of proline. The hydrochlorides are more soluble in ethanol than the free amino acids. The solubility of amino acids has been considered in detail by Edsall and Scatchard[17] and by Cohn and Edsall.[18]

VII. ISOLATION

The year each amino acid was first isolated from a protein source and the protein from which it was isolated are listed in Table I. References to methods for isolating each amino acid from proteins appear in Table IV.

VIII. pK$_a$

In aqueous solutions the amino acids exist as dipolar ions called zwitterions. They are ampholytes and can react either as acids by releasing protons or as bases by accepting protons. Thus glycine exhibits a titration curve with two points of inflection. The formula for the zwitterion of glycine is:

$$\begin{array}{c} O \\ \diagup \!\!\!\!\diagup \\ C\!-\!O^{\ominus} \\ \vert \\ H_2C\!-\!^{\oplus}NH_3 \end{array}$$

Each functional group has a characteristic dissociation constant, K, whose negative logarithm is called the pK$_a$ value. A majority of measurements of dissociation constants were made at a fixed ionic strength and therefore are "apparent dissociation constants, pK$_a'$." The constant pK$_1'$ usually refers to the most acidic group. The isoelectric point (pI) of an amino acid is the pH value where there is no net charge on the amino acid molecule. The pK' and the pI values of the more common amino acids are listed in Table II.[18,2]

Variations of pK$_a$ value with ionic strength [18,18a]. For the equilibrium $A \rightleftharpoons B + H^+$, the relationship is:

$$K_a = \frac{aHaB}{aA} = a_H \frac{(B)\,\gamma B}{(A)\,\gamma A} = K_a' \frac{\gamma B}{\gamma A} \tag{1}$$

where a refers to activity, and γ to activity coefficient. Defining pH as $-\log aH$, the following is obtained:

$$pH = pK'_a + \log \frac{(B)}{(A)} = pK_a + \log \frac{(B)}{(A)} + \log \frac{\gamma B}{\gamma A} \tag{2}$$

The value of pK_a can be obtained with high precision from measurements on cells without liquid junction. Concentrations of B and A can be determined from the stoichiometry of the system but we must then make a reasonable assumption about the values of $\log \gamma_A$ and $\log \gamma_B$. At moderate ionic strengths, the application of the Debye-Hückel equation, expanded by including a term linear in ionic strength involving a salting out constant K_s, can be used to obtain the activity coefficients of the ions γ_i.

$$-\log \gamma_i = \frac{0.5 \, Z_i^2 \, \sqrt{\omega}}{1 + Qa \, \sqrt{\omega}} - K_s\omega \tag{3}$$

In this equation a is the "collision diameter" in angstroms, $Q \cong 0.33$, and the value of Qa usually lies between 1 and 2. Omega (ω) is ionic strength:

$$1/2 \sum_i Z_i^2 \, C_i$$

If either the acid A or its conjugate base B is a dipolar ion, its net charge is zero. However, its large dipole moment leads to a salting in term K_R proportional to but of opposite sign to K_s. Therefore, for a dipolar ion, the negative logarithim of the activity coefficient takes the following form:

$$-\log \gamma \text{ (dipolar ion)} = (K_R - K_S) \tag{4}$$

at low ionic strengths. Roughly speaking, K_R, the salting in term, is large if the dipole moment of the dipolar ion is large and K_S, the salting out term, is large if the molecule contains large nonpolar residues. For an α amino acid in water, K_R is of the order of 0.32; for a dipeptide, it is 0.6. Assuming the K_S is the same for any acid and its conjugate base, we can use equation (3) for the cation or anion and equation (4) for the dipolar ion, obtaining the expressions for the variation of pK of an amino acid with ionic strength. Class I (exemplified by pK_1 of glycine): As is a cation, B a dipolar ion.

$$pK'_1 = pK_1 + \frac{0.5 \, \sqrt{\omega}}{1 + Qa \, \sqrt{\omega}} - K_R\omega \tag{5}$$

Class II (exemplified by pK_2 of glycine): A is a dipolar ion, B is an anion.

$$pK'_2 = pK_2 - \frac{0.5 \, \sqrt{\omega}}{1 + Qa \, \sqrt{\omega}} + K_R\omega \tag{6}$$

In the absence of a dipolar ion the salting in term is not present.
Class III (exemplified by acetic acid): A is uncharged, B is an anion,

$$pK' = pK_o - \frac{0.5 \, \sqrt{\omega}}{1 + Qa \, \sqrt{\omega}} \tag{7}$$

Class IV (exemplified by ethylammonium ion): A is a cation and B is uncharged.

$$pK' = pK_o + \frac{0.5\sqrt{\omega}}{1 + Qa\sqrt{\omega}} \tag{8}$$

Equations (5–8) have been used by Neuberger[18b] for calculating the pK' values for acids of different charge types including dipolar ions. Setting Qa = 1, his data show general agreement between experimental pH measurements and the expectation from the equations. This and other studies show the usefulness of the concepts of the activity coefficient of individual ions and its calculation at low ionic strengths by application of the Debye-Hückel theory.

The above discussion was taken from Cohn and Edsall [18] and Edsall and Wyman.[18b]

IX. OPTICAL ROTATION

Since all of the amino acids found in proteins with the exception of glycine possess one or more asymmetric carbon atoms, they are optically active. Furthermore, evidence indicates that they have the same configuration about the α-carbon atom, *i.e.*, the L-configuration. The direction of optical rotation is indicated by a ($+$) or ($-$) for rotation to the right or to the left respectively. The small capital letters D and L refer to the configuration about the α-carbon atom, with D-glyceraldehyde being the accepted standard of reference. The specific optical rotation $(\alpha)_D$ and the molecular rotation $(M)_D$ in two different solvents are given in Table II. Rotatory dispersion is the change in angle of rotation upon alteration of the wavelength of polarized light.[19] Measurements of rotatory dispersion of α-amino acids have been published by Otey *et al.*[20] and Greenstein and Winitz,[1] page 116.

X. SPECTRA

A review of the ultraviolet absorption spectra of amino acids is given by Greenstein and Winitz.[1] The infrared absorption spectra of the α-amino acids in the solid state can also be obtained from Greenstein and Winitz.[1] Garfinkel and Edsall[21] have obtained Raman spectra of the amino acids.

XI. CHROMATOGRAPHY

The use of ion exchange resins developed by Moore and Stein[22] has undergone many refinements and improvements by Hamilton.[23] Figures, taken from Hamilton's article,[23] gives the elution pattern of a large number of amino acids and related compounds. Chromatography on paper has been extensively covered in references 24, 25, 26. Some of the common solvents used for paper chromatography are:

1   1-butanol: glacial acetic acid: water (120:30:50) (BuA)

2   Phenol: water (160 gm:40 ml) (Ph)

3   Phenol: Ammonia (200 ml of 2) to 1 ml concentrated ammonia (PhAm)

4   t-Butanol: water: methyl ethylketone: Diethylamine (80:80:40:8) (TBuK)

R_f values for the various amino acids in the above solvents are given in Table III. Solvent systems of the general type ethanol (10 v.): 1-butanol (10 v.): water (5 v.) and 2 v. of either an organic acid or base have been investigated by Hardy and coworkers[27] and R_f's for the various amino acids are given.

R_f values for the DNP amino acids are available in the literature.[28]

Detection of Amino Acids on Paper Chromatograms: Ninhydrin. Blue to purple spots are produced by most amino acids. Proline and hydroxyproline give yellow spots. Dried chromatograms may be sprayed with (a) 0.1–0.25% ninhydrin in acetone, (b) 0.2% ninhydrin in water-saturated n-butanol, or (c) 0.25% ninhydrin in pyridine: water (50:50) (v/v). Prior spraying with 5% cyclohexylamine or addition of 0.1% collidine to sprays (a) or (b) gives a greater variety of colors.[29] Chromatograms can be air dried for 1–2 hours or heated at 80–100°C for 5 min.

Several of the amino acids can be detected by the use of specific sprays. See Table III for references to these methods.

Two-dimensional chromatography on paper for amino acids has been developed by Dent[30] and Redfield.[31] Paper electrophoresis has also been a useful technique.[32, 26] Gas chromatography of the amino acids using the n-amyl esters has been done by Johnson and Polgar and a diagram of a typical chromatogram is given by Meister.[2] Thin layer chromatography of amino acids has been discussed by Stahl.[33]

XII. QUALITATIVE ANALYSIS

Ninhydrin: The amino acids may be detected qualitatively by the blue color developed when 1 ml of a solution of an amino acid (0.5 to 1.0

μmole) is added to 1 ml of a 0.1% aqueous solution of ninhydrin and placed in a boiling water bath for 5 minutes. Proline and hydroxyproline give yellow colors under these conditions. A detailed discussion of qualitative reactions of the amino acids is covered by Meister[2] and Greenstein and Winitz.[1] Some of the more common qualitative tests have been adapted from color reactions which are listed in Table III.

XIII. QUANTITATIVE ANALYSIS

The most important quantitative analytical procedure for the amino acids is the ninhydrin procedure. Of the many procedures developed the most widely used method is that of Rosen.[34] This procedure is detailed in the volume, *Methods and References in Biochemistry and Biophysics.*

Quantitative analytical procedures for specific amino acids are referred to in Table III.

XIV. SYNTHESIS

The common methods of synthesis of the amino acids are the Strecker synthesis, with addition of HCN and NH_4Cl to an aldehyde, and the conversion of the α-halo acid to the amino acid by using ammonia. References to the synthesis of each of the amino acids are listed in Table IV.

XV. RESOLUTION

Since most synthetic methods lead to racemic mixtures, resolution of the amino acids is necessary to obtain the optical isomers. Two methods have been in common practice: chemical resolution, based on the formation and subsequent separation of diastereoisomers, and enzymatic resolution. References to these methods for each of the amino acids are listed in Table IV.

XVI. RACEMIZATION

The interconversion of optical isomers by racemization to obtain maximum yields of a given isomer when resolving a synthetic mixture has been developed. Methods of racemization of various amino acids are referred to in Table IV.

Table I.

Classification	Amino Acid	Formula	M.W.	Decomposition Point (°C)	Solubility in Water g/100 g at 25°C	First Isolation from Protein Year Source
I. Aliphatic A. Monoamino monocarboxylic acids	1. Glycine	$CH_2(NH_3^+)CO_2^-$	75.1	290	24.99	1820 Gelatin
	2. Alanine	$CH_3CH(NH_3^+)CO_2^-$	89.1	297	16.51	1888 Silk fibroin
	3. Valine	$(CH_3)_2CHCH(NH_3^+)CO_2^-$	117.1	315	8.85	1901 Casein
	4. Leucine	$(CH_3)_2CH-CH_2-CH(NH_3^+)CO_2^-$	131.2	337	2.19	1820 Muscle fiber, wool
	5. Isoleucine	$CH_3CH_2CH(CH_3)CH(NH_3^+)CO_2^-$	131.2	284	4.12	1904 Fibrin
B. Hydroxy-monoamino monocarboxylic acids	6. Serine	$CH_2(OH)CH(NH_3^+)CO_2^-$	105.1	228	5.02(DL)	1865 Sericine
	7. Threonine	$CH_3CH(OH)CH(NH_3^+)CO_2^-$	119.1	253	20.5(DL)	1925 Oat protein
C. Monoamino dicarboxylic acids and their amides	8. Aspartic acid	$CH(NH_3^+)CO_2^-$ $\mid$ CH_2CO_2H	133.1	270	0.50	1868 Conglutin, legumin
	9. Glutamic acid	$CH(NH_3^+)CO_2^-$ $\mid$ $CH_2CH_2CO_2H$	147.1	249	0.84	1866 Glutenfibrin
	10. Asparagine	$CH(NH_3^+)CO_2^-$ $\mid$ CH_2CONH_2	132.1	236	3.11(28°)	1932 Edestin
	11. Glutamine	$CH(NH_3^+)CO_2^-$ $\mid$ $CH_2CH_2CONH_2$	146.2	185	3.6(18°)	1932 Gliadin
D. Diamino-monocarboxylic acids	12. Lysine	$CH_2(NH_2)CH_2CH_2CH_2CH(NH_3^+)CO_2^-$	146.2	224		1889 Casein
	13. 5-Hydroxy-lysine	$CH_2(NH_2)CH(OH)CH_2CH_2CH(NH_3^+)CO_2^-$	162.2			1925 Fish gelatin
	14. Arginine	$H_2NC(=NH)NHCH_2CH_2CH_2CH(NH_3^+)CO_2^-$	174.2	238		1895 Horn

Table I.

Classification	Amino Acid	Formula	M.W.	Decomposition Point (°C)	Solubility in Water g/100 g at 25°C	First Isolation from Protein — Year	Source
E. Sulfur containing amino acids	15. Cysteine	$HSCH_2CH(NH_3^+)CO_2^-$	121.2	178		1899	Horn
	16. Cystine	$SCH_2CH(NH_3^+)CO_2^-$ $\|$ $SCH_2CH(NH_3^+)CO_2^-$	240.3	261	0.011	1922	Casein
	17. Methionine	$CH_3SCH_2CH_2CH(NH_3^+)CO_2^-$	149.2	283	3.35(DL)	1849	Casein
II. Aromatic amino acids	18. Phenyl-alanine	⟨benzene⟩$-CH_2CH(NH_3^+)CO_2^-$	165.2	284	2.96	1881	Lupine seedlings
	19. Tyrosine	$HO-$⟨benzene⟩$-CH_2CH(NH_3^+)CO_2^-$	181.2	344	0.045	1849	Casein
III. Hetero-cyclic	20. Tryptophan	⟨indole⟩$-CH_2CH(NH_3^+)CO_2^-$	204.2	282	1.14	1902	Casein
	21. Histidine	$HC=C-CH_2CH(NH_3^+)CO_2^-$ imidazole ring structure	155.2	277	4.29	1896	Sturine
	22. Proline	pyrrolidine ring $CHCO_2^-$ structure	115.1	222	162.3	1901	Casein
	23. Hydroxy-proline	hydroxypyrrolidine ring $CHCO_2^-$ structure	131.1	270	36.11	1902	Gelatin

Table II.

L-Amino Acid	Dissociation Constants (pK'_a) $pK'_1(COOH)$[a]	$pK'_2(NH_3^+)$[a]	pK'_3[a]	pI[a]	Specific Rotation[b] $[\alpha]_D(H_2O)$	$[\alpha]_D$(5N HCl)	Molecular Rotation[b] $[M]_D(H_2O)$	$[M]_D$(5N HCl)
Glycine	2.34	9.60		5.97	—	—	—	—
Alanine	2.34	9.69		6.00	+ 1.8	+14.6	+ 1.6	+13.0
Valine	2.32	9.62		5.96	+ 5.6	+28.3	+ 6.6	+33.1
Leucine	2.36	9.60		5.98	−11.0	+16.0	−14.4	+21.0
Isoleucine	2.36	9.68		6.02	+12.4	+39.5	+16.3	+51.8
Serine	2.21	9.15		5.68	− 7.5	+15.1	− 7.9	+15.9
Threonine	2.71	9.62		6.16	−28.5	−15.0	−33.9	−17.9
Aspartic Acid	1.88	3.65(COOH)	9.60(NH_3^+)	2.77	+ 5.0	+25.4	+ 6.7	+33.8
Asparagine	2.02	8.80		5.41	—	+28.6	− 7.4	+37.8
Glutamic Acid	2.19	4.25(COOH)	9.67(NH_3^+)	3.22	+12.0	+31.8	+17.7	+46.8
Glutamine	2.17	9.13		5.65	+ 6.3	+31.8(1N HCl)	+ 9.2	+46.5
Lysine	2.18	8.95 (α)	10.53(ε—NH_3^+)	9.74	+13.5	+26.0	+19.7	+37.9
5-Hydroxylysine	2.13	8.62 (α)	9.67(ε—NH_3^+)	9.15	+ 9.2	+17.8	+14.9	+28.9
Arginine	2.17	9.04	12.48(Guan)	10.76	+12.5	+27.6	+21.8	+48.1
Cysteine	1.96(30°)	8.18	10.28(SH)	5.07	−16.5	+ 6.5	−20.0	+ 7.9
Cystine	1.00(30°)	1.7(COOH)	pK_3 7.48(NH_3^+) pK_4 9.02(NH_3^+)	4.60	—	−232	—	−509.2(NHCl)
Methionine	2.28	9.21		5.74	−10.0	+23.2	−14.9	+34.6
Phenylalanine	1.83	9.13		5.48	−34.5	− 4.5	−57.0	− 7.4
Tyrosine	2.20	9.11	10.07(OH)	5.66	—	−10.0	—	−18.1
Tryptophan	2.38	9.39		5.89	−33.7	+ 2.8(1N HCl)	−68.8	+ 5.7
Histidine	1.82	6.00 (imidazole)	9.17(NH_3^+)	7.59	−38.5	+11.8	−59.8	+18.3
Proline	1.99	10.96		6.30	−86.2	−60.4	−99.2	−69.5
Hydroxyproline	1.92	9.73		5.83	−76.0	−50.5	−99.6	−66.2

[a] From Edsall, T. J. in "Proteins, Amino Acids and Peptides as Ions and Dipolar Ions" (E. J. Cohn and J. T. Edsall, eds.) p. 75, Reinhold, New York, 1943.
[b] Compounds were obtained by enzymatic resolution. Greenstein, J. P., Adv. Protein Chem. 9:121 (1954). T = 25°, concentration 0.5 to 2.0%.

Table III.

| | References to Specific Analytical Reactions | | Paper Chromatography R_f in Various Solvents[a] | | | |
Amino Acid	Quantitative Method	Paper Chromatogram	BuA	Ph	PhAm	TBuK
Alanine			.30	.58	.58	.20
Arginine	Sakaguchi (35)	Sakaguchi (36)	.15	.83	.86	.05
Asparagine			.12	.40	.40	.12
Aspartic Acid			.23	.20	.17	.06
Cysteine	Hydrazine (37)	Nitroprusside (38)	.08	.22	.11	.05
Cystine	Hydrazine (37)	Nitroprusside (38)	.08	.22	.11	.05
Glutamic Acid			.28	.33	.26	.06
Glutamine			.17	.27	.57	.10
Glycine	Chromotropic acid (52)		.23	.42	.42	.18
Histidine	Pauly (39)	Pauly (40) (41)	.11	.65	.72	.18
Hydroxylysine	Periodate (42)		.11	.28	.58	
Hydroxyproline	Ninhydrin (43)	Isatin (44)	.22	.67	.67	.15
Isoleucine			.67	.85	.85	.45
Leucine			.70	.85	.85	.52
Lysine			.12	.42	.77	.10
Methionine	Iodometric (45)		.50	.82	.82	.39
Phenylalanine			.60	.84	.84	.52
Proline	Ninhydrin (46)	Isatin (44)	.34	.90	.90	.25
Serine	Periodate (47)	Periodate (47)	.22	.35	.35	.30
Threonine	Periodate (47)	Periodate (47)	.26	.48	.48	.50
Tryptophan	Ehrlich (51)	Ehrlich (49)	.50	.77	.77	.50
Tyrosine	Iodometric (45)	Nitrosonaphthol (50) (48)	.45	.60	.60	.30
Valine	Iodometric (45)		.51	.78	.78	.35

[a] See text for composition of solvents.

Table IV.

		Synthesis			Resolution			Derivatives of L-Amino Acid			
Amino Acid	Isolation from Protein	Strecker	α-halo Acid	Other	Enzymatic	Chemical	Racemization	Tosyl- M.P. (°C)	Cbzo-[a] M.P. (°C)	DNP M.W.	DNP M.P. (°C)
Alanine	casein (53)	(69)	(70)		(106)	(117)	p. 1837 ref. (1)	134	87	255	177
Arginine	gelatin (54)			(71)	(107)		(134)	256	175 (α), 190 (ω)	340[d]	260[d]
Asparagine	edestin (55)			(72)	(106)				165	298	180
Aspartic Acid	(56)		(73)	(74)	(106)	(118)	(135)	139	116	299	186
Cysteine				(75)	(108)	(119)	(136)	125	97[b]	377[c]	111[c]
Cystine	hair (57)			(76)	(109)	(120)		204	123[b]	572[b]	109[b]
Glutamic Acid	gluten (58)			(77)	(106)	(118)	(134)	131	120	313	
Glutamine	red beets (59)			(78)				165	135	312	189
Glycine	gelatin (60)	(79)	(80)					149	120	241	203
Histidine	hemoglobin (61)			(81)	(108)	(121)	(137)	202	166	487[b]	232[b]
Hydroxy-lysine											
Hydroxy-proline	gelatin (62)			(82)	(1) (110)		(138)	153 (N), 163 (O)	106	297	174
Isoleucine	casein (63)	(84)	(85)	(83) p. 2063 (1)	(111) (112)	(122) (123)	(139) (112)	135		297	113
Leucine	hemoglobin (64)	(86)	(87)	(88)	(106)	(124)	(109)	124	53 (DL)	297	94
Lysine	gelatin (65)		(89)	(90)	(106)	(125)	(140) (1)	263 (α), 237 (ε)	150 (α), 255 (ε)	478[b]	170[b]
Methionine	casein (66)	(91)	(92)	(93)	(106)	(126)	(107)	104[b]	68		
Phenyl-alanine	hemoglobin (64)	(94)	(95)		(106)	(127)	(134)	164	88	331	189
Proline	casein (53)			(96)	(113)	(128)	(113)	58-60	76	281	138
Serine	hemoglobin (64)	(97)	(98)	(99)	(114) (106)	(129)	(114)	235	121	271	173
Threonine			(100)	(101)	(115) (106)	(130)	(134)	136	103	285	145
Tryptophan	(67)			(102)	(116)	(131)	(141)	176	126	370	221
Tyrosine	casein (68)			(103)	(106)	(132)	(134)	187	101 (N), 215 (O)	513[b]	178[b]
Valine		(104)	(105)		(106)	(133)	ref. (1)	147	66	283	132

[a] Cbzo refers to carbobenzoxy derivatives.
[b] di—derivatives.
[c] S-benzylcysteine.
[d] (α only)

XVII. DERIVATIVES

The second volume of Greenstein and Winitz[1] contains extensive tables of amino acid derivatives. Table IV shows the melting points for three of the common derivatives of amino acids: tosyl, dinitrophenyl and carbo-benzoxy derivatives.

BIBLIOGRAPHY

References:

(1) Greenstein, J. P., and M. Winitz, *Chemistry of the Amino Acids*, 1961.

(2) Meister, A., *Biochemistry of the Amino Acids*, Second Edition, 1965.

(3) Van Slyke, D. D., "The Quantitative Determination of Aliphatic Amino Groups," *J. Biol. Chem.*, 12:275, 1912.

(4) Van Slyke, D. D., "Manometric Determination of Primary Amino Nitrogen and its Application to Blood Analysis," *J. Biol. Chem.*, 83:425, 1929.

(5) Bergmann, M., and L. Zervas, "Uber ein Allgemeines Verfahren der Peptid-Synthese," *Ber.*, 65:1192, 1932.

(6) Rao, K. R., and H. A. Sober, "Preparation and Properties of 2,4-Dinitrophenyl-L-Amino Acids," *J. Am. Chem. Soc.*, 76:1328, 1954.

(7) Harris, J. I., and T. S. Work, "The Synthesis of Peptides Related to Gramiciden S and the Significance of Optical Configuration in Antibiotic Peptides," *Biochem. J.*, 46:582, 1950.

(8) Theodoropoulos, D., and L. C. Craig, "Hydrolytic Behavior of Certain Branches Peptide Derivatives of Lysine," *J. Org. Chem.*, 21:1376, 1956.

(9) French, D., and J. T. Edsall, "The Reactions of Formaldehyde with Amino Acids and Proteins," *Advan. Protein Chem.*, 2:278, 1945.

(10) Bergmann, M., and L. Zervas, "Uber die Aldehydverbindungen der Aminosauren and Ihre Praparative Verwendung," *Z. Physiol. Chem.*, 152:282, 1926.

(11) Heyl, D., E. Luz, S. A. Harris, and K. Folkers,
"The Chemistry of Vitamin B_6. VI. Pyridoxylamino Acids," *J. Am. Chem. Soc.*, 70:3429, 1948.
"The Chemistry of Vitamin B_6. VII. Pyridoxylidenes and Pyridoxylamines," *J. Am. Chem. Soc.*, 70:3669, 1948.
"The Chemistry of Vitamin B_6. VIII. Additional Pyridoxylidene-amines and Pyridoxylamines, *J. Am. Chem. Soc.*, 74:414, 1952.

(12) Metzler, D. E., "Equilibria Between Pyridoxal and Amino Acids and their Imines," *J. Am. Chem. Soc.*, 79:485, 1957.

(13) Matsuo, Y., Formation of Schiff Bases of Pyridoxal Phosphate, Reaction with Metal Ions," *J. Am. Chem. Soc.*, 79:2011, 1957.

(14) Winnick, T., and E. M. Scott, "Phosphorylated Amino Acids," *Arch. Biochem.*, 12:201, 1947.

(15) Zervas, L., and P. G. Katsoyannis, "N-Phosphoroamino Acids and Peptides," *J. Am. Chem. Soc.*, 77:5351, 1955.

(16) Spies, J. R., "An Ultraviolet Spectrophotometric Micromethod for Studying Protein Hydrolysis," *J. Biol. Chem.*, 195:65, 1952.

(17) Edsall, J. T., and G. Scatchard, in E. J. Cohn and J. T. Edsall (Eds.), *Proteins, Amino Acids, and Peptides as Ions and Dipolar Ions*, p. 177, 1943.

(18) Cohn, E. J., and J. T. Edsall (Eds.), *Proteins, Amino Acids, and Peptides as Ions and Dipolar Ions*, p. 196, 1943.

(18a) Edsall, J. T., and J. Wyman, *Biophysical Chemistry*, 1958.

(18b) Neuberger, A., *Proc. Roy. Soc.*, A158:68, 1937.

(19) Djerassi, C., *Optical Rotatory Dispersion*, 1960.

(20) Otey, M. C., J. P. Greenstein, M. Winitz, and S. M. Birnbaum, "Studies on Diastereoisomeric α-Amino Acids and Corresponding α-Hydroxy Acids," *J. Am. Chem. Soc.*, 77:3112, 1955.

(21) Garfinkel, D., and J. T. Edsall, "Raman Spectra of Amino Acids and Related Compounds," *J. Am. Chem. Soc.*, 80:3823, 1958.

(22) Moore, S., and W. H. Stein, "Procedures for the Chromatographic Determination of Amino Acids on Four Percent Cross-linked Sulfonated Polystyrene Resins," *J. Biol. Chem.*, 211:893, 1954. "Modified Ninhydrin Reagents for the Photometric Determination of Amino Acid and Related Compounds," *J. Biol. Chem.*, 211:907, 1954.

(23) Hamilton, P. B., "Ion Exchange Chromatography of Amino Acids," *Anal. Chem.*, 35:2055, 1963.

(24) Consden, R., A. H. Gorden, and A. J. P. Martin, "Qualitative Analysis of Proteins," *Biochem. J.*, 38:224, 1944.

(25) Lederer, E., and M. Lederer, *Chromatography*, 2nd ed., 1957.

(26) Block, R. J., E. L. Durrum, and G. Zweig, *Paper Chromatography and Paper Electrophoresis*, Second Edition, 1958.

(27) Hardy, T. L., D. O. Holland, and J. H. C. Nayler, "One Phase Solvent Mixture for the Separation of Amino Acids," *Anal. Chem.*, 27:971, 1955.

(28) Smith, I., *Chromatographic and Electrophoretic Techniques*, 1960.

(29) Woiwood, A. J., "A Technique for Examining Larger Numbers of Bacterial Culture Filtrates by Partition Chromatography," *J. Gen. Microbiol.*, 3:312, 1949.

(30) Dent, C. E., "A Study of the Behavior of some Sixty Amino Acids and other Ninhydrin-Reacting Substances on Phenol-'Collidine' Filter Paper Chromatograms with Notes as to the Occurrence of some of them in Biological Fluids," *Biochem. J.*, 43:169, 1948.

(31) Redfield, R. R. "Two Dimensional Paper Chromatographic Systems with High Revolving Power for Amino Acids," *Biochim. Biophys. Acta*, 10:344, 1953.

(32) Durrum, E. L., "Two Dimensional Electrophoresis and Ionophoresis," *J. Colloid Sci.*, 6:274, 1961.

(33) Stahl, E., *Thin-Layer Chromatography*, 1965.

(34) Rosen, H., "A Modified Ninhydrin Colorimetric Analysis for Amino Acids," *Arch. Biochem. Biophys.*, 67:10, 1957.

(35) Weber, C. J., "A Modification of Sakaguchi's Reaction for the Quantitative Determination of Arginine," *J. Biol. Chem.*, 86:217, 1930.

(36) Roche, J., N-V. Thoai, and J. L. Hatt, "Metabolisme des Derives Guanidyles," *Biochim. Biophys. Acta*, 14:71, 1954.

(37) Kuratomi, K., K. Ohno, and S. Akabori, "A New Microdetermination of the Total Quantity of Cysteine Plus Cystine in Protein by Hydrazinolysis," *J. Biochem.*, 44:183 1957.

(38) Toennies, G., and J. J. Kolb, "Techniques and Reagents for Paper Chromatography," *Anal. Chem.*, 23:823, 1951.

(39) Weiss, M., and N. Ssobolew, "Uber Ein Colorimetrisches Verfahren Zur Quantitativen Bestimmung Des Histidins," *Biochem. Z.*, 58:119, 1913.

(40) Ames, B. N., and H. K. Mitchell, "The Paper Chromatography of Imidazoles," *J. Am. Chem. Soc.*, 74:252, 1952.

(41) Cowgill, R. W., "Identification of Imidazole Compounds by Paper Chromatography," *Anal. Chem.,* 27:1519, 1955.

(42) Van Slyke, D. D., A. Hiller, and D. A. Mac Fadyen, "The Determination of Hydroxylysine in Proteins," *J. Biol. Chem.,* 141:681, 1941.

(43) Troll, W., and R. K. Cannan, "A Modified Photometric Ninhydrin Method for the Analysis of Amino and Imino Acids," *J. Biol. Chem.,* 200:803, 1953.

(44) Hulme, A. C., and W. Arthington, "New Amino Acids in Young Apple Fruits," *Nature,* 170:659, 1952.

(45) Genevois, L., and J. Baraud, *Chim. Anal.,* 38:87, 1956.

(46) Troll, W., and J. Lindsey, "A Photometric Method for the Determination of Proline," *J. Biol. Chem.,* 215:655, 1955.

(47) Cifonelli, J. A., and F. Smith, "Detection of Amino Acids on Paper Chromatograms," *Anal. Chem.,* 27:1501, 1955.

(48) Jepson, J. B., and I. Smith, "Multiple Dipping Procedures in Paper Chromatography: A Specific Test for Hydroxy-Proline," *Nature,* 172:1100, 1953.

(49) Dalgliesh, C. E., "The Relation Between Pyridoxin and Tryptophan Metabolism," *Biochem. J.,* 52:3, 1952.

(50) Acher, R., and C. Crocker, "Reactions Colorees Specifiques de l'Arginine et de la Tyrosine Realisees Apres Chromatographie sur Papier," *Biochem. Biophys. Acta.,* 9:704, 1952.

(51) Spies, J. R., and D. C. Chambers, "Clinical Determination of Tryptophan in Proteins," *Anal. Chem.,* 21:1249, 1949.

(52) Alexander, B., G. Landwehr, and A. M. Seligman, "A Specific Micromethod for the Colorimetric Determination of Glycine in Blood and Urine," *J. Biol. Chem.,* 160:51, 1945.

(53) Selim, A. S. M., M. E. A. Ramadan, and M. M. El-Sadr, "A New Method for the Isolation of L-Alanine and L-Proline from Protein Hydrolysates," *J. Biol. Chem.,* 227:871, 1957.

(54) Brand, E., and M. Sandberg, "*d*-Arginine Hydrochloride," *Org. Syn.,* 2:49, 1943.

(55) Damodaran, M., "The Isolation of Asparagine from an Enzymatic Digest of Edestin," *Biochem. J.,* 26:235, 1932.

(56) Vickery, H. B., and G. W. Pucher, "L-Aspartic Acid," *Biochem. Preps.,* 2:71, 1952.

(57) Miller, G. L., and V. du Vigneaud, "The Cystine Content of Insulin," *J. Biol. Chem.,* 118:101, 1937.

(58) King, H., "*d*-Glutamic Acid," *Org. Syn.,* 1:286, 1941.

(59) Vickery, H. B., "C^{14} Uniformly Labeled Sucrose," *Biochem. Preps.,* 1:44, 1949.

(60) Stein, W. H., and S. Moore, "L-Alanine and L-Serine," *Biochem. Preps.,* 1:9, 1949.

(61) Foster, G. L., and D. Shemin, "*l*-Histidine Monohydrochloride," *Org. Syn.,* 2:330, 1943.

(62) Neuberger, A., "The Stereochemistry of Hydroxyproline," *J. Chem. Soc.,* 429, 1945.

(63) Ehrlich, F., and A. Wendel, "Zur Kenntnis der Leucinfraktion des Einweibes," *Biochem. Z.,* 8:399, 1908.

(64) Stein, W. H., S. Moore, G. Stamm, C.-Y. Chou, and M. Bergmann, "Aromatic Sulphonic Acid as Reagents for Amino Acids," *J. Biol. Chem.,* 143:121, 1942.

(65)   Kurtz, A. C., "A New Method for Isolating *l*-(+)-Lysine," *J. Biol. Chem.*, 140:705, 1941.

(66)   Hill, E. M., and W. Robson, "The Salting Out of Amino Acids from Protein Hydrolysates," *Biochem. J.*, 28:1008, 1934.

(67)   Hopkins, F. G., and S. W. Cole, "A Contribution to the Chemistry of Proteides," *J. Physiol.*, 29:451, 1903.

(68)   Cox, G. J., and H. King, "*l*-tryptophane," *Org. Syntheses*, 2:612, 1943.

(69)   Kendall, E. C., and B. F. McKenzie, "*dl*-Alanine," *Org. Syntheses*, 1:21, 1941.

(70)   Tobie, W. C., and G. B. Ayres, "Synthesis of *dl*-Alanine in Improved Yield from α-Bromoproionic Acid and Aqueous Ammonia," *J. Am. Chem. Soc.*, 59:950, 1937.

(71)   Kurtz, A. C., "Use of Copper (II) Ion in Making α-Amine Groups of Amino Acids," *J. Biol. Chem.*, 180:1253, 1949.

(72)   Bergmann, M., L. Zervas, and L. Salzmann, "Synthese Von *l*-Asparagin und *d*-Glutamin," *Ber.*, 66:1288, 1933.

(73)   Dunn, M. S., B. W. Smart, *Org. Syn.*, 4:55, 1963.

(74)   Frankel, M., Y. Liwschitz, and Y. Amiel, "Synthesis of DL-Aspartic Acid and DL-Aspargine Via their N-Benzyl Derivatives," *J. Am. Chem. Soc.*, 75:330, 1953.

(75)   Baumann, E., and C. Preusse, "Zur Kenntniss der Synthetischen Prozesse im Thierkorper," *Z. Physiol. Chem.*, 5:309, 1881.

(76)   Farlow, M. W., "A New Synthesis of Cystine," *J. Biol. Chem.*, 176:71, 1948.

(77)   Snyder, H. R., J. F. Shekleton, and C. D. Lewis, "Synthetic Amino Acids, Synthesis from Acetamidomalonic Ester," *J. Am. Chem. Soc.*, 67:310, 1945.

(78)   Akabori, S., and K. Narita, *Proc. Acad. Sci.* (Japan), 29:264, 1953.

(79)   Adams, R., and W. D. Langley, *Org. Syntheses*, 1:355, 1941, and Anslow, W. K., and H. King, *Org. Syntheses*, 1:300, 1941.

(80)   Cheronis, N. D., and K. H. Spitzmueller, "Studies in Ammonolysis. (1) The Ammonolysis of Halogen Fatty Acids and Preparation of α-Amino Acids," *J. Org. Chem.*, 6:349, 1941.

(81)   Albertson, N. F., and S. Archer, "The Use of Ethyl Acetamidomalnate in the Syntheses of Amino Acids. The Preparation of *dl*-histidine, *dl*-phenyl-alanine and *dl*-leucine, *J. Am. Chem. Soc.*, 67:308, 1945.

(82)   Van Zyl, G., E. E. Van Tamelen, and G. D. Zuidema, "A Synthesis of Hydroxylysine," *J. Am. Chem. Soc.*, 73:1765, 1951.

(83)   Gaudry, R., and C. Godin, "New Synthesis of Hydroxyproline," *J. Am. Chem. Soc.*, 76:139, 1954.

(84)   Ehrlich, F., "Uber das Naturliche Isomere des Leucins," *Ber.*, 40:2538, 1907.

(85)   Marvel, C. S., "*dl*-Isoleucine," *Org. Syn.*, 3:495, 1955.

(86)   Ehrlich, F., "Uber das Naturliche Isomere des Leucins," *Ber.*, 37:1809, 1904.
       "Uber das Naturliche Isomere des Leucins," *Ber.*, 40:2538, 1907.

(87)   Marvel, C. S., "*dl*-Leucine," *Org. Syn.*, 3:523, 1955.

(88)   Huang, Y., K. Lin, and L. Li, *J. Chinese Chem. Soc.*, 15:38, 1947.

(89)   Eck, J. C., and C. S. Marvel, "*dl*-Lysine Hydrochlorides." *Org. Syn.*, 2:374, 1943.

(90)   Gaudry, R., *Can. J. Research*, *26B*, pg. 387, 1948.

(91)   Pierson, E., M. Giella, and M. Tishler, "Synthesis of DL-Methionine," *J. Am. Chem. Soc.*, 70:1450, 1948.

(92) Plieninger, H., "Die Aufspaltung des γ-Butyrolactions und α-Amino-γ-Butyrolactions mit Natriummethylmercaptid BZN-Selenid," *Chem. Ber.*, 83:265, 1950.

(93) Barger, G., and T. E. Weichselbaum, "*dl*-Methionine," *Org. Syn.*, 2:384, 1943.

(94) Erlenmeyer, E., and A. Lipp, "Synthesis of Turosins," *Ann.*, 219:161, 179, 1883.

(95) Marvel, C. S., "*dl*-Phenylalanine," *Org. Syn.*, 3:705, 1955.

(96) Albertson, N. F., and J. L. Fillman, "A Synthesis of DL-Proline," *J. Am. Chem. Soc.*, 71:2818, 1949.

(97) Redemann, C. E., and R. N. Icke, "A Commercial Synthesis of *dl*-Serine," *J. Org. Chem.*, 8:159, 1943.

(98) Carter, H. E., and H. D. West, "*dl*-Serine," *Org. Syn.*, 3:774, 1955.

(99) King, J. A., "A New Synthesis of *dl*-Serine," *J. Am. Chem. Soc.*, 69:2738, 1947.

(100) Carter, H. E., and H. D. West, "*dl*-Threonine," *Org. Syn.*, 3:813, 1955.

(101) Pfister, K., C. A. Robinson, A. C. Shabica, and M. Tishler, "The Synthesis of DL-Threnine," *J. Am. Chem. Soc.*, 71:1101, 1949.

(102) Snyder, H. R., and C. W. Smith, "A Convenient Synthesis of *dl*-Tryptophan," *J. Am. Chem. Soc.*, 66:350, 1944.

(103) Borrows, E. T., J. C. Clayton, and B. A. Hems, "The Synthesis of Thyroxine and Related Substances. I. The Preparation of Tyrosine and Some of its Derivatives, and a New Route to Thyroxine," *J. Chem. Soc.*, Suppl. Issue, 1:185, 1949.

(104) Gaudry, R., *Can. J. Research*, 24:301, 1946.

(105) Marvel, C. S., "*dl*-Valine," *Org. Syn.*, 3:848, 1955.

(106) Birnbaum, S. M., L. Levintow, R. B. Kingsley, and J. P. Greenstein, "Specificity of Amino Acid Acylases," *J. Biol. Chem.*, 194:455, 1952.

(107) Bergmann, M., and L. Zervas, "Uber Katalytische Racemisation von Aminosauren Und Peptiden," *Biochem. Z.*, 203:280, 1928.

(108) Birnbaum, S. M., and J. P. Greenstein, "Preparation of the Optical Isomers of Arginine, Histidine and S-Benzylcysteine by Asymmetric Enzymatic Hydrolysis of their Acetyl Derivatives," *Arch. Biochem. Biophys.*, 39:108, 1952.

(109) Marshall, R., M. Winitz, S. M. Birnbaum, and J. P. Greenstein, *J. Am. Chem. Soc.*, 79:4538, 1957.

(110) Fones, W. S., "The Optical Isomers of Hydroxylysine and Allohydroxylysine," *J. Am. Chem. Soc.*, 75:4865, 1953.

(111) Parikh, J. R., J. P. Greenstein, M. Winitz, and S. M. Birnbaum, "The Use of Amino Acid Oxidases for the Small-Scale Preparation of the Optical Isomers of Amino Acids," *J. Am. Chem. Soc.*, 80:953, 1958.

(112) Greenstein, J. P., L. Levintow, C. G. Baker, and J. White, "Preparation of the Four Stereoisomers of Isoleucine," *J. Biol. Chem.*, 188:647, 1951.

(113) Price, V. E., L. Levintow, J. P. Greenstein, and R. B. Kingsley, "The Enzymatic Hydrolysis of L- and D-Amino Acid Amides by Mushroom Reparation," *Arch. Biochem.*, 26:92, 1950.

(114) Akabori, S., T. T. Otani, R. Marshall, M. Winitz, and J. P. Greenstein, "A Synthesis and Resolution of DL-Serine," *Arch. Biochem. Biophys.*, 83:1, 1959.

(115) Price, V. E., J. B. Gilbert, and J. P. Greenstein, *J. Biol. Chem.*, 179:1169, 1949.

(116) Fodor, P. J., V. E. Price and J. P. Greenstein, "Preparation of L- and D-Alanine by Enzymatic Resolution of Acetyl-DL-Alanine,"*J. Biol. Chem.*, 178:503, 1949.

(117) Pope, W. J., and C. S. Gibson, "The Resolution of Benzoylalanine into its optically Active Components," *J. Chem. Soc.*, 101:939, 1912.

(118) Fischer, E., "Uber die Spactungeiniger Racemischer Amidosauren in die Optisch-Activen Components," *Ber.*, 32:2451, 1899.

(119) Wood, J. L., and V. du Vigneaud, "Racemization of Benzyl-I-Cystine with a new Method of Preparing d-Cystine," *J. Biol. Chem.*, 130:109, 1939.

(120) Hollander, L., and V. du Vigneaud, "The Resolution of Inactive Cystine and Isolation of Pure Dextrorotatory Cystine," *J. Biol. Chem.*, 94:243, 1931–32.

(121) Pyman, F. L., "The Synthesis of Histidine," *J. Chem. Soc.*, 99:1386, 1911.

(122) Leuchs, H., and K. Bormann, "Darstellung der Drei mit dem Naturlichen Oxy-Prolin Stereoisomeren Formen," *Ber.*, 52:2086, 1919.

(123) Abderhalden, E., and W. Zeisset, "Spaltung von synthetisch dargestelltem Isoleucin in seine vier optisch-aktiven Komponenten, nahmlich l-(+) und d-(−) Isoleucin, sowie d-(−) und l-(+) Alloisoleucin," *Z. Physiol. Chem.*, 195:121, 1931.

(124) Fisher, E., and O. Warburg, "Spaltung des Leucins in die Optisch-Activen Componenten Mittels der Formylverbindug," *Ber.*, 38:3997, 1905.

(125) Berg, C. P., "The Resolution of *dl*-Lysine," *J. Biol. Chem.*, 115:9, 1936.

(126) Windus, W., and C. S. Marvel, "The Resolution of Synthetic Methionine," *J. Am. Chem. Soc.*, 53:3490, 1931.

(127) Fischer, E., and W. Schoeller, *Ann.*, 357:1, 1907.

(128) Fischer, E., and G. Zemplen, "Synthese der Beiden Optisch-Aktiven Proline," *Ber.*, 42:2989, 1909.

(129) Fischer, E., and W. A. Jacobs, "Spaltung der Racemischen Serins in die Optisch-Activen Componenten," *Ber.*, 39:2942, 1906.

(130) West, H. D., and H. E. Carter, "Synthesis of α-amino-β-Hydroxy-n-Butynic Acids," *J. Biol. Chem.*, 122:611, 1938.

(131) Berg, C. P., "The Resolution of *dl*-Tryptophane," *J. Biol. Chem.*, 100:79, 1933.

(132) Fischer, E., "Spaltung Einiger Racemischer Amidosauren in die Optisch-Activen Componenten," *Ber.*, 2:3638, 1899.

(133) Fischer, E., "Spaltung der α-Aminoisovaleriansaure in die Optisch-Activen Componenten," *Ber.*, 39:2320, 1906.

(134) du Vigneaud, V., and C. E. Meyer, "The Racemization of Amino Acid in Aqueous Solution by Acetic Anhydride," *J. Biol. Chem.*, 98:295, 1932.

(135) Ehrlich, F., "Uber Asymmetrische und Symmetrische Einnirkung von Hefe auf Racemverbindungen Naturlich Vorkommen der Aminosauren," *Biochem. Z.*, 63:379, 1914.

(136) Loring, H. S., and V. du Vigneaud, "The Isolation and Characterization of Mesocystine," *J. Biol. Chem.*, 102:287, 1933.

(137) du Vigneaud, V., and M. Hunt, "The Synthesis of d-Carnosine, the Enantiomorths of the Naturally Occurring form, and a Study of its Depressor Effect on the Blood Pressure," *J. Biol. Chem.*, 115:93, 1936.

(138) Hamilton, P. B., and R. A. Anderson, "Hydroxylysine: Isolation from Gelatin and Resolution of its Diastereoisomers by Ion Exchange Chromatography," *J. Biol. Chem.*, 213:249, 1955.

(139) Robinson, D. S., and J. P. Greenstein, *J. Biol. Chem.*, 195:383, 1954.

(140) Fischer, E., and F. Weigert, "Synthese der α, E-Diaminocapronsaure," *Ber.*, 35:3772, 1902.

(141)   du Vigneaud, V., and R. R. Sealock, "The Racemization of Acetyl-1-Trypto-phane," *J. Biol. Chem.*, 96:511, 1932.

I. INTRODUCTION

Protein synthesis and degradation (peptide bond formation and lysis) are metabolically completely distinct processes, involving separate enzymatic and control mechanisms. The energetics of the interaction of proteins and water favor the formation of amino acids under biological conditions of temperature, pH and concentration. Therefore, enzymes specifically catalyzing this interaction, the peptidases, can only effect net degradation of proteins. Peptide bond formation must involve a more circuitous route utilizing a source of energy to overcome the unfavorable equilibrium. In addition, protein synthesis involves specific ordering of the constituent amino acids, the so-called primary structure which is unique for each protein.

II. PROTEIN SYNTHESIS

Each of the twenty different amino acids is activated by a specific enzyme (the *aminoacyl t-RNA synthetases*) in the presence of ATP and magnesium ions, to form an enzyme-bound aminoacyl adenylate and inorganic pyrophosphate. This reaction is reversible, but the formation of aminoacyl adenylate is favored by the presence of a pyrophosphatase which removes one of the products of the reaction. The adenylate is linked to the amino acid via the phosphate group in anhydride linkage with the carboxyl group. The aminoacyl group is transferred to the *transfer-RNA* (t-RNA) specific for this particular aminoacyl adenylate-enzyme complex. *Transfer RNA's* are polynucleotides with molecular weights of approximately 25,000, containing 70–80 base residues beginning with a 5' phosphorylated guanine and terminating with the sequence -pCpCpA at the free 3'-hydroxyl end. The remainder of the base sequence of each t-RNA is different, determining the specificity for interaction with a particular aminoacyl t-RNA synthetase; in addition, it contains a specific triplet of bases (the *anti-codon*) which is complementary to a messenger-RNA (m-RNA) coding unit (*codon*). The primary structure of the protein being synthesized is encoded in m-RNA as a linear sequence of specific base triplets (codons). The genetic code is given in the accompanying table. The code is degenerate (redundant): there is more than one triplet (as many as six) code for each amino acid. This degeneracy extends also to the transfer-RNA's. Thus, for example, the base sequences ACU, ACC, ACA and ACG all code for threonine. Of the 64 possible permutations, only two, UAA and UAG, do not code for amino acids. These triplets signify the end of a peptide sequence; that is, they represent periods in the language of codeword sentences. In general, the synthesis of more than one protein may be determined by a single messenger RNA strand. The actual translation of base sequence information into amino acid sequence occurs at the locus of attachment of the m-RNA to a third type of RNA which exists in the form of *ribosomes*. These latter particles consist of approximately 50% RNA and 50% protein and vary in size from about a molecular weight of 3 million in bacteria to about 4 million in plants and animals. Initial attachment occurs at the free 5'-hydroxyl end of the m-RNA and actual reading of the code is determined uniquely by grouping triplets from this end. There are no other special punctuation devices to determine to which triplet a given base belongs. An aminoacyl t-RNA whose anticodon region is complementary to the initial m-RNA triplet becomes attached to the ribosome at this locus. A second aminoacyl t-RNA whose anticodon region is complementary to the adjacent m-RNA triplet then lines up next to it and, in the presence of two enzymes, GTP, and glutathione, the alpha-amino group of the second aminoacyl t-RNA displaces the t-RNA from the carboxyl carbon of the first aminoacyl t-RNA to form a peptide bond. At the same time, the m-RNA and the ribosome move one codon relative to each other. Appropriate aminoacyl t-RNA's are repeated until the process is terminated either if the end of the m-RNA is reached, or a triplet signifying the end of a polypeptide (UAA or UAG). After a given ribosome has moved along the m-RNA strand for an appreciable distance (80–100 nucleotides), additional ribosomes may become attached so that for long m-RNA's many ribosomes appear to be associated as polyribosomes, and each will be attached to a growing polypeptide chain in different stages of completion. The rate of protein synthesis may be controlled by many factors: availability of amino acids, ATP, t-RNA's and rate of synthesis and degradation of messenger RNA. Specific control of synthetic rates of particular proteins is determined primarily at the transcription level between DNA encoded information and messenger RNA encoded information. Several antibiotics and antimetabolites have been used in studies of the control of protein synthesis.

Ethionine interferes with protein synthesis by sequestration of the cellular supply of adenine nucleotides. Methionine-activating enzyme, which normally catalyzes the formation of S-adenosyl-methionine from methionine and ATP, also catalyzes the formation of S-adenosyl-ethionine from ethionine and ATP. The ethionine derivative is much more stable biologically than is that of methionine, and hence it accumulates with a resultant diminution in the cell's adenine supply. Ethionine induced inhibition of protein synthesis can be reversed by the addition of adenine.

Actinomycin D inhibits DNA-dependent RNA polymerase activity and thus interferes with the production of messenger-RNA. This antibiotic thus blocks the earliest step in the control of protein synthesis.

Puromycin, by virtue of its structural resemblance to the terminal aminoacylated adenosine group of aminoacyl t-RNA, becomes incorporated into the growing polypeptide chain and causes the release of incompleted chains from the ribosome. By this action, it interferes with the transfer of amino acids from aminoacyl t-RNA to the polypeptide chain.

Cycloheximide (actidione) also inhibits the transfer of amino acids from t-RNA to nascent polypeptide chains, but in this case it appears to do so by inhibiting the enzyme involved in peptide bond formation on the ribosome.

III. PROTEOLYSIS

The literature covering this area is very extensive, and only the briefest survey will be attempted. *Exopeptidases* hydrolyze peptide bonds adjacent to terminal alpha-amino and alpha carboxyl groups. Included in this group are the aminopeptidases, the carboxypeptidases, and the dipeptidases. *Endopeptidases* attack centrally-located peptide bonds as well as terminal peptide bonds. Included in this group are the digestive enzymes, pepsin, trypsin and chymotrypsin, the animal intracellular enzymes known as cathepsins, such plant proteinases as papain and ficin, and bacterial enzymes such as subtilisin. These enzymes differ not only as to specificity for amino acid residues which are linked by the peptide bond being split, but also by the chemical nature of their active sites. The activity of one group, which includes papain, ficin and certain cathepsins, depends on the presence of thiol groups; they are inactivated by reagents which react with these. A second group requires the presence of some divalent cation such as Mg, Mn, Co, Zn or Fe for activity. This group includes carboxypeptidase A, leucine aminopeptidase and prolidase. A third group, the so-called serine group, is characterized by being inhibited by organophosphorus compounds of the diisopropyl fluorophosphate type. Among these are trypsin, chymotrypsin, thrombin and subtilisin.

Genetic Code (August, 1965)

	Uracil		Cytosine		Adenine		Guanine	
U **r** **a** **c** **i** **l**	UUU UUC	Phe	UCU UCC	Ser	UAU UAC	Tyr	UGU UGC	Cys
	UUA UUG	Leu	UCA UCG		UAA UAG	(.)	UGA UGG	Try
C **y** **t** **o** **s** **i** **n** **e**	CUU CUC	Leu	CCU CCC	Pro	CAU CAC	His	CGU CGC	Arg
	CUA CUG		CCA CCG		CAA CAG	Glun	CGA CGG	
A **d** **e** **n** **i** **n** **e**	AUU AUC	Ileu	ACU ACC	Thr	AAU AAC	Aspn	AGU AGC	Ser
	AUA AUG	Met	ACA ACG		AAA AAG	Lys	AGA AGG	Arg
G **u** **a** **n** **i** **n** **e**	GUU GUC	Val	GCU GCC	Ala	GAU GAC	Asp	GGU GGC	Gly
	GUA GUG		GCA GCG		GAA GAG	Glu	GGA GGG	

Ala	alanine		Leu	leucine
Arg	arginine		Lys	lysine
Asp	aspartic acid		Met	methionine
Aspn	asparagine		Phe	phenylalanine
Cys	Cysteine		Pro	proline
Glu	glutamic acid		Ser	serine
Glun	glutamine		Thr	threonine
Gly	glycine		Try	tryptophan
His	histidine		Tyr	tyrosine
Ileu	isoleucine		Val	valine

The best understood proteinases in mammalian metabolism are those secreted into the gastrointestinal tract. Figure 1 summarizes their role in the breakdown of ingested protein to constituent amino acids for absorption.

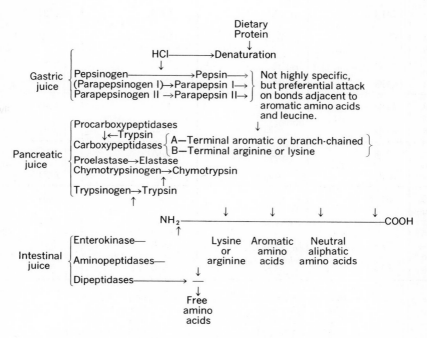

Figure 1. Summary of digestion of protein in the alimentary tract of the nonruminant mammal. (*Reference:* Gitler, Carlos, "Protein Digestion and Absorption in Nonruminants," in H. N. Munro and J. B. Allison (Eds.), *Mammalian Protein Metabolism,* 1964.

BIBLIOGRAPHY

References:

1. Munro, H. N., and J. B. Allison, *Mammalian Protein Metabolism*, Vols. 1, 2, 1964.
2. Harris, R. J. C., *Protein Biosynthesis*, 1961.
3. Fruton, J. S., "Chemical Aspects of Protein Synthesis," *The Proteins*, 1:189, 1963.
4. Moldave, Kivie, "Nucleic Acids and Protein Biosynthesis," *Ann. Rev. Biochem.*, 34:419, 1965.
5. Ames, B. N., and R. G. Martin, "Biochemical Aspects of Genetics: The Operon," *Ann. Rev. Biochem.*, 33:235, 1964.
6. Bennett, J. C., and W. J. Dreyer, "Genetic Coding for Protein Structure," *Ann. Rev. Biochem.*, 33:205, 1964.
7. Peterman, M. L., *The Physical and Chemical Properties of Ribosomes*, 1964.
8. Arnstein, H. R. V., "Mechanism of Protein Biosynthesis," *Brit. Med. Bull.*, 21:217, 1965.
9. Stretton, A. O. W., "The Genetic Code," *Brit. Med. Bull.*, 21:229, 1965.
10. Collins, J. F., "Antibiotics, Proteins and Nucleic Acids," *Brit. Med. Bull.*, 21:223, 1965.
11. Stekol, J. A., "Biochemical Basis for Ethionine Effects on Tissues," *Adv. Enzymol.*, 25:369, 1963.
12. Trakatellis, A. C., M. Montjar, and A. E. Axelrod, "Effect of Cycloheximide on Polysomes and Protein Synthesis in the Mouse Liver," *Biochemistry*, 4:2065, 1965.
13. Dixon, M., and E. C. Webb, *Enzymes*, p. 251, 1958.
14. Boyer, P. D., H. Lardy, and K. Myrback, (eds.), *The Enzymes*, 2nd ed. 4:1, 1960.
15. Cunningham, Leon, "The Structure and Mechanism of Action of Proteolytic Enzymes," *Comprehensive Biochemistry*, 16:85, 1965.
16. Hill, R. L., "Hydrolysis of Proteins," *Advan. Protein Chem.*, 20:37, 1965.
17. Neurath, H., and G. W. Schwert, "The Mode of Action of the Crystalline Pancreatic Proteolytic Enzymes," *Chem. Rev.*, 46:69.

I. DEFINITIONS AND CLASSIFICATION

The proteins constitute an extremely diverse group of naturally occurring macromolecules, each comprised of one or more chains of α-L-amino acid residues in repeating peptide linkage. These compounds have definite composition and are biosynthesized in specific coded sequence under genetic control from about twenty naturally-occurring amino acids. Proteins are traditionally classified according to their solubility and heat stability properties, and conjugate existence with other classes of compounds, such as nucleic acids, carbohydrates, lipids, metal ions and various cofactors.[1] As functional units they exhibit definite levels of structural organization, commonly classified according to the following scheme.

Primary Structure. The sequential arrangement and one-dimensional configuration of covalently-linked residues in the polypeptide chains that comprise the molecule, including cross-linkages that may bind two or more chains together. The basic organizational unit at this level is the planar amide bond[2] (see Figure 1a).

Secondary Structure. Short-range folding of the polypeptide backbone to produce definite, periodic spatial orientations between near-neighbor residues. Much of secondary structure is attributable to hydrogen bonding as in the α-helix[3] (see Figure 1b).

Tertiary Structure. Overall three-dimensional folding of the chain into a compact unit stabilized by interactions between remote segments of the polypeptide chain (principally hydrophobic, hydrogen and salt-linkage bonding). A model for the tertiary structure of myoglobin is found in Kendrew *et al.*[4]

Quaternary Structure. Organization resulting from association of sub-units into a structural unit of definite geometric configuration.

II. PHYSICAL PROPERTIES

Standard methods of macromolecular physical chemistry yield a variety of different kinds of information about protein molecules. These methods and their most common uses are tabulated below. Detailed descriptions of the procedures and limitations for each method can be found in the corresponding reference.

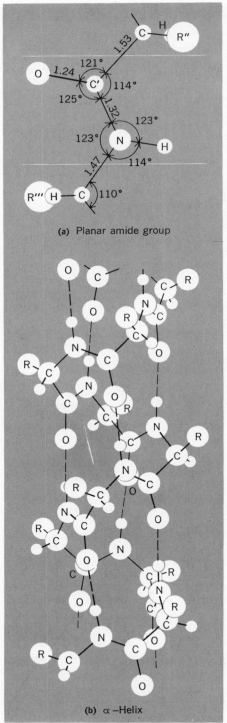

(a) Planar amide group

(b) α–Helix

Figure 1.   Primary (a) and secondary (b) structures of proteins. "R"-groups are amino acid side chains.[2, 3]

Table I. Physical Methods Used For Studies of Proteins

Method	Information Obtainable		Ref.
A. *Static Methods:*			
1. Osmotic pressure	Number ave. molecular weight, $\overline{M}_n$	Degree of heterogeneity by combination of M_n and M_w	(5)
2. Light scattering	Weight ave. mol. wt., $\overline{M}_w$		(6)
3. Low angle x-ray scattering	$\overline{M}_w$, radius of gyration		(7)
4. X-ray diffraction analysis of unit cell dimensions	$\overline{M}_n$ if crystal density and number of molecules per unit cell are known		(8)
5. High resolution x-ray diffraction analysis plus solution of the phase problem	Complete primary, secondary and tertiary structure of globular proteins		(8)
6. Optical Rotatory Dispersion	Helical content, conformational changes		(9)
7. Ultra-violet Difference Spectroscopy	Conformational changes, relative helical content		(10)
8. Titration curve	Charge, number of groups in each pk' class		(11)
9. Deuterium-hydrogen Exchange	Conformational changes, extent of unfolding		(12)
10. Electron microscopy	Size and shape, $\overline{M}_n$		(13)
B. *Dynamic Methods:*			
1. Translational Diffusion	Frictional Coefficient, asymmetry, if hydration is known. Upper limit mol. wt., if $\overline{V}$ is known.		(14)
2. Sedimentation velocity	Same as Diffusion. Combination with diffusion or viscosity gives $\overline{M}_w$		(15)
3. Sedimentation equilibrium	$\overline{M}_w$		(15)
4. Viscosity	Molecular asymmetry if hydration is known		(16)
5. Dielectric dispersion	Relaxation time, assymetry if hydration is known		(17)
6. Flow birefringence	Asymmetry if hydration is known		(18)
7. Depolarization of fluorescence	Asymmetry if hydration is known		(19)
8. Electrophoresis	Relates charge to shape and size		(20)
9. Molecular sieve chromatography	Molecular size and approximate weight		(21)
10. Restricted diffusion through porous membranes	Approximate molecular size		(22)

BIBLIOGRAPHY

References:

1. Desnuelle, P., in Neurath, H. (ed.), *The Proteins*, 1st ed., 1(A):1, 1953.
2. Corey, R. B., and L. Pauling, *Proc. Roy. Soc. London*, B141:10, 1953.
3. Pauling, L., *The Nature of the Chemical Bond*, 3rd ed., 1960.
4. Kendrew, J. C. *et al.*, "A Partial Determination by X-ray Methods, and its Correlation with Chemical Data," *Nature*, 190:666, 1961.
5. Kupke, D. W., "Osmotic Pressure," *Advan. Prot. Chem.*, 15:57, 1960.
6. Stacey, K. A., in Alexander, P. and R. J. Block (eds.), *Analytical Methods of Protein Chemistry*, 3:246, 1961.
7. Anderegg, J. W. *et al.*, "An Investigation of the Size, Shape and Hydration of Serum Albumin by Small-angle X-ray Scattering," *J. Am. Chem. Soc.*, 77:2927, 1955.
8. Dickerson, R. E., in Neurath, H. (ed.), *The Proteins*, 2nd ed., 2:603, 1964.
9. Urnes, P., and P. Doty, "Optical Rotation and the Confrontation of Polypeptides and Proteins," *Advan. Prot. Chem.*, 16:401, 1961.
10. Wetlaufer, D. B., "Ultraviolet Spectra of Proteins and Amino Acids," *Advan. Prot. Chem.*, 17:303, 1962.
11. Tanford, C., "The Interpretation of Hydrogen Ion Titration Curves of Proteins," *Advan. Prot. Chem.*, 17:69, 1962.
12. Scheraga, H. A., *Protein Structure*, p. 192, 1961.
13. Birbeck, M. S. C., in Alexander, P. and R. J. Block (eds.), *Analytical Methods of Protein Chemistry*, 3:1, 1961.
14. Svensson, H., and T. E. Thompson in Alexander, P. and R. J. Block (eds.), *Analytical Methods of Protein Chemistry*, 3:57, 1961.
15. Schachman, H. K., *Ultracentrifugation in Biochemistry*, 1959.
16. Yang, J. T., "The Viscosity of Micro-Macromolecules in Relation to Molecular Conformation," *Advan. Prot. Chem.*, 16:323, 1961.
17. Oncley, J. L. in Cohn, E. J. and J. T. Edsall (eds.), *Proteins, Amino Acids, and Peptides*, p. 543, 1943.
18. Cerf, R., and H. A. Scheraga, "Flow Birefringence in Solutions of Macromolecules," *Chem. Revs.*, 51:185, 1952.
19. Weber, G., "Rotational Brownian Motion and Polarization of the Fluorescence of Solutions," *Advan. Prot. Chem.*, 8:415, 1953.
20. Bier, M., *Electrophoresis*, 1959.
21. Ackers, G. K., and R. L. Steere in Maramorasch, K. and H. Kaprowski (eds.), *Methods in Virology*, 1966.
22. Craig, L. C., T. P. King, and A. Stracher, "Dialysis Studies. II. Some Experiments Dealing with the Problem of Selectivity," *J. Am. Chem. Soc.*, 79:3729, 1957.
23. Edsall, J. T. in Neurath, H. and K. Bailey (eds.), *The Proteins*, 1:549, 1953.
24. Tristram, G. R., and R. H. Smith, "The Amino Acid Composition of Some Purified Proteins," *Advan. Prot. Chem.*, 18:227, 1963.

Table II. Physical Constants of Proteins (23)

Protein	$\overline{V}_{20}$	$S_{20,w} \times 10^{13}$	$D_{20,w} \times 10^7$	$M_{s,d} \times 10^{-3}$	$M_e \times 10^{-3}$	f/f_0
Insulin (dimer)	0.749	1.6	15.0	12.0		1.1
Insulin (tetramer)	0.735	1.95	7.3	24.5		
Ribonuclease	0.728	1.64	11.9	12.4		1.05
Lysozyme	0.688	1.87	10.4	14.1		1.21
Cytochrome c (cow heart)		2.5	13.3	15.6		
Cytochrome c (horse heart)		2.1	13.0	13.4		1.00
Cytochrome c (pig heart)		2.3	12.3	15.5		1.01
Myoglobin	0.741	2.04	11.3	16.9	17.5	1.11
Erythrocruorin (Lampetra)	0.751	1.87	10.7	17.1	19.0	1.17
α-Lactalbumin (cow)	0.751	1.9	10.6	17.4		
Adrenocorticotropic hormone (sheep)	0.75	2.00	9.0	20.0		
Adrenocorticotropic hormone (pig)		2.04		20.0		
Trypsin		1.69	10.95	15.1		1.2
		2.5				
DFP trypsin	0.73	2.50	9.5	23.7		1.18
Trypsinogen	0.737	2.48	9.7	23.7		1.15
α-Chymotrypsin	0.736	2.4	10.2	21.6		
Chymotrypsinogen	0.721	2.54	9.5	23.2		1.19
Carbonic anhydrase	0.749	2.8	9.0	30.0		
		3.80				
Carboxypeptidase	0.75	3.07	8.68			1.16
Prolactin		2.65	7.5	32.0		
Pepsin	0.750	3.3	9.0	35.5	39.0	1.08
		3.0	9.69			
Peroxidase	0.699	3.48	7.05	39.8		1.36
α-Lactoglobulin (dimer)	0.751	3.12	7.30	41.5	38.0	1.26
Concanavalin B	0.73	3.5	7.4	42.0		
Ovalbumin	0.749	3.55	7.76	44.0	40.5	1.16
Growth hormone, pituitary	0.76	3.60	7.36	49.2		
Zein	0.776	1.9	4.0	50.0		2.17
Pyrophosphatase	0.75	4.4	6.8	63.0		
Enolase	0.735	5.59	8.08	63.7		1.01
Serum albumin (cow)	0.730	4.73	6.0	69.4		
Serum albumin (horse)	0.748	4.46	6.1	70.0	68.0	1.27
Serum albumin (man)	0.736	4.67	5.93	72.3		1.30
Hemoglobin (man)	0.749	4.46	6.9	63.0		1.16
Tropomyosin	0.71	2.51	2.22	92.7		3.1
Concanavalin A	0.73	6.0	5.6	96.0		1.25
Hexokinase	0.740	3.1	2.9	96.6		2.37
Glyceraldehyde phosphate dehydrogenase						
Yeast	0.74	6.8	5.19	122		1.24
Rabbit muscle	0.74	7.0	5.46	120		1.19

Table II. (Continued)

Protein	$\overline{V}_{20}$	$S_{20,w} \times 10^{13}$	$D_{20,w} \times 10^{7}$	$M_{s,d} \times 10^{-3}$	$M_e \times 10^{-3}$	f/f_0
Ascorbic acid oxidase	0.75	6.9	4.6	146		
β-Amylase (sweet potato)	0.749	8.9	5.77	152		
γ-Globulin (human)	0.745	7.1	3.84	176		
Aldolase	0.74	7.3	4.63	147		1.31
Fumarase	0.75	8.51	4.05	204		
Catalase	0.73	11.3	4.1	250		1.25
Phycocyan	0.746	11.4	4.05	270	275	
Phycoerythrin (Ceramium)	0.746	12.0	4.00	290	290	1.21
Phosphorylase (rabbit muscle)	0.74	13.7	3.2–3.8	340–400		
Fibrinogen (cow)	0.706	7.9	2.02	330		2.34
Hemocyanin (palinurus)	0.740	16.4	3.4	450	450	1.23
Apoferritin	0.747	17.6	3.61	467		
Urease	0.73	18.6	3.46	480		
Thyroglobulin (pig)	0.72	19.2	2.65	630	650	1.31
Hemocyanin (homarus)	0.740	22.6	2.78	760	800	
Myosin	0.74	7.2	0.87	829–880		4.0
Glutamic acid dehydrogenase (tetramer)	0.75	26.6	2.54	1,000		1.26
β₁-Lipoprotein, serum (man)	0.97	5.9	1.7	2,600		
	0.950	2.9		1,300		1.7
Erythrocruorin (Planorbis)	0.745	33.7	1.96	1,630	1,540	
Erythrocruorin (Lumbricus)	0.740	60.9	1.81	3,150	2,950	
Hemocyanin (Helix pomatia)	0.738	103	1.07	8,900	6,700	1.24
Yellow fever virus	0.87	27–45		2,500		
Turnip yellow mosaic virus	0.666	106	1.55	4,970		1.25
Southern bean mosaic virus	0.696	115	1.39	6,630		1.25
Tomato bushy stunt virus	0.739	146			7,600	1.09
		132	1.15	10,600		1.27
Tobacco mosaic virus	0.743	198	0.46	40,700		2.0
Rabbit papilloma virus	0.756	280	0.51	47,100		1.65

Definitions of Symbols for Table II

$\overline{V}_{20}$ Partial specific volume at 20°C., cc./g.

$S_{20,w}$ Sedimentation coefficient, corrected to water at 20°C., sec.

$D_{20,w}$ Diffusion Coefficient, corrected to water at 20°C., cm²/sec.

$M_{s,d}$ Molecular Weight calculated from sedimentation and diffusion results, g/mole

M_e Molecular weight determined by sedimentation equilibrium, g/mole

f/f_0 Frictional ratio (see ref. 15)

CHEMISTRY OF THE PURINES AND PYRIMIDINES

I. OCCURRENCE AND GENERAL PROPERTIES[1-5]

Purine and pyrimidine bases are heterocyclic, nitrogen-containing ring compounds which occur as constituents of many biological molecules, and in particular as constituents of ribonucleic acid (RNA) and deoxyribonucleic acid (DNA). The pyrimidines are derivitives of the parent 6-membered ring compound *pyrimidine*, whose structure is indicated in figure 1. Ring positions are designated according to the International System.

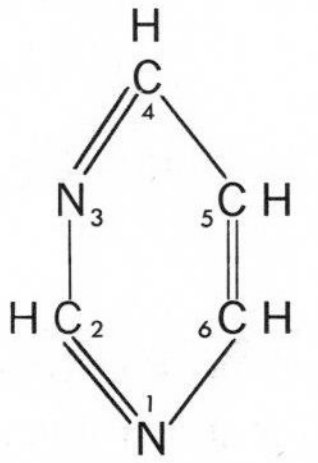

Figure 1.   Pyrimidine

The purines are derivatives of *purine*, which consists of a pyrimidine ring fused with a 5-membered imidazole ring.

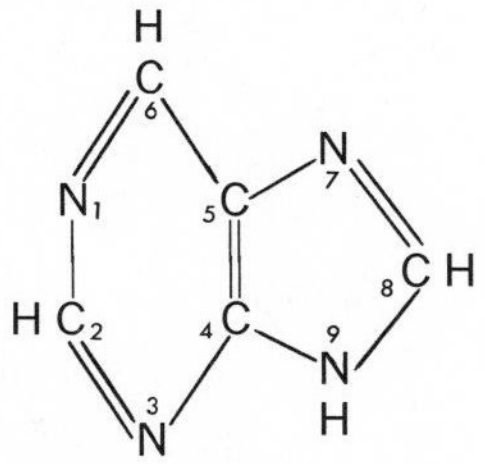

Figure 2.   Purine

Both classes of compound have definite aromatic characteristics, including resistance to oxidation and a planar conformation. Ring positions 2, 6, and 8 in purine and 2, 4, and 6 in pyrimidine are electron-deficient, permitting a wide range of nucleophilic substitution reactions.

The physical properties of purine and pyrimidine derivatives depend upon the nature of the substituents. Halogen and alkyl derivatives have low melting points and are soluble in organic solvents, while amino and hydroxyl substituents have high melting points and are water-soluble.

In nucleic acids, the purines and pyrimidines occur as constituents of nucleotides, being joined to ribose (or deoxyribose) by a C—N β-glycosidic bond between the 1′-position of the sugar and the 1-position for pyrimidines and the 9-position for purines. The two purines of frequent occurrence, adenine and guanine, are common to DNA and RNA.

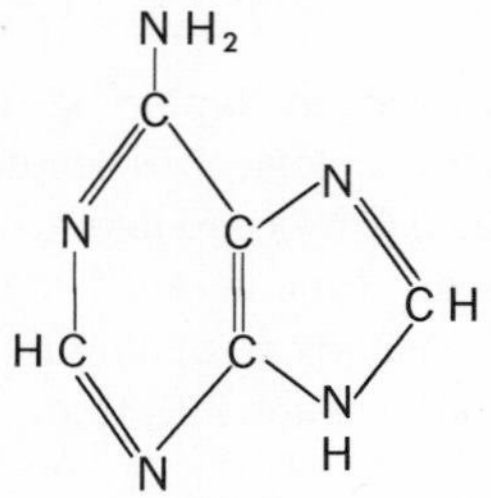

adenine 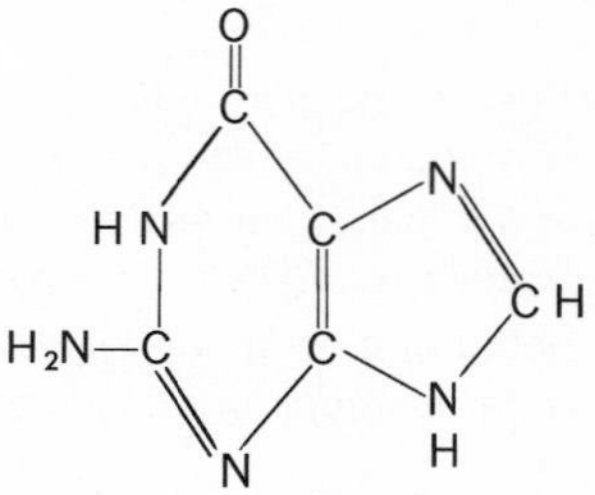   guanine

Figure 3

Of the pyrimidines, cytosine occurs in both types of nucleic acid, while uracil is found in natural RNA and thymine in DNA.

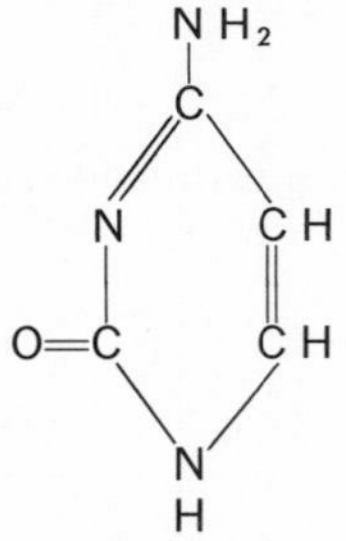

cytosine 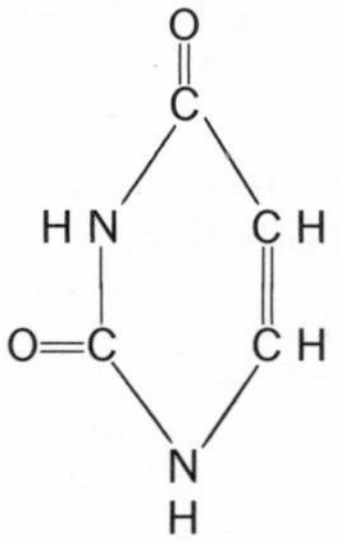   uracil 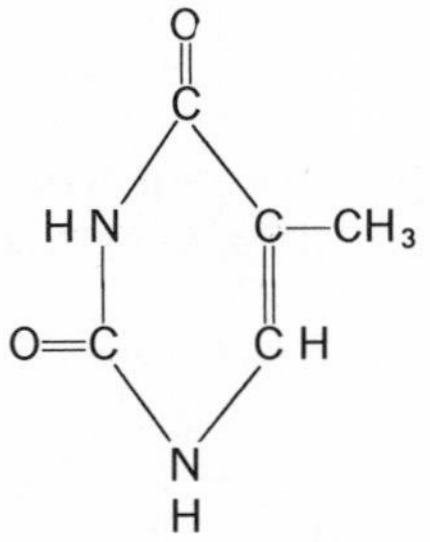   thymine

Figure 4

In addition to the five common bases cited above, others occur with lower frequency or in special cases.[6-13] Only a few unusual bases have been detected in natural DNA. In the T-even bacteriophages of *E. coli*, cytosine is completely replaced by 5-hydroxymethyl cytosine. 5-Methyl-cytosine occurs in small quantities in the DNA of plants, especially in wheat germ, as well as some higher animals.[11] The base 6-methylamino-purine is of general occurrence in bacterial DNA's,[6] its quantity being about 2% of that of adenine in *E. coli*.[7]

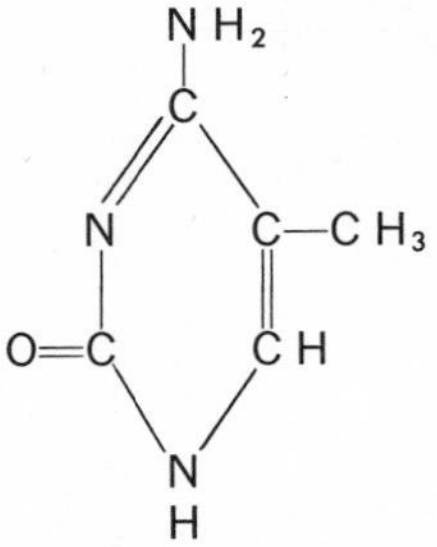

5-methyl-cytosine

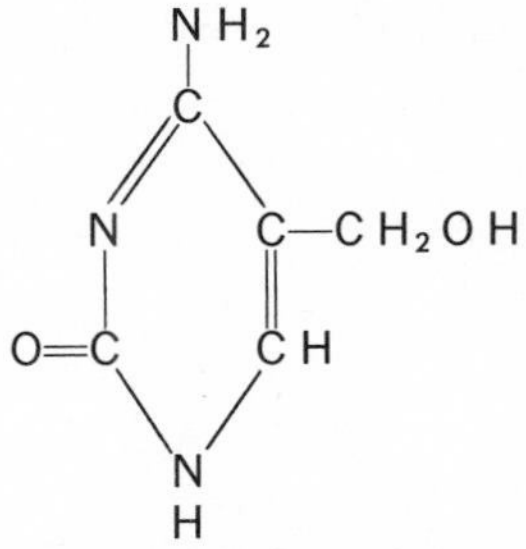

5-hydroxy-methylcytosine

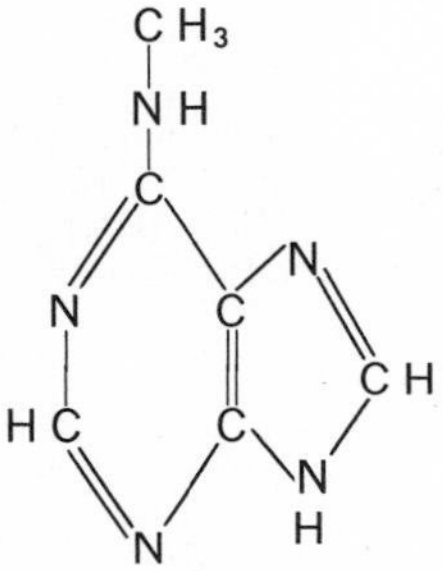

6-methylaminopurine

Figure 5

Unusual bases occur somewhat more frequently in RNA than in DNA and are especially prominent in soluble RNA. These include, in addition to 6-methylaminopurine[8] and 5-methylcytosine,[9] the bases 1-methyl-adenine,[10] 2-methyladenine,[11] 6,6-dimethylaminopurine,[8] 1-methyl-guanine,[12] 2-methylamino-6-hydroxypurine,[12] and 2,2-dimethylamino-6-hydroxypurine.[13]

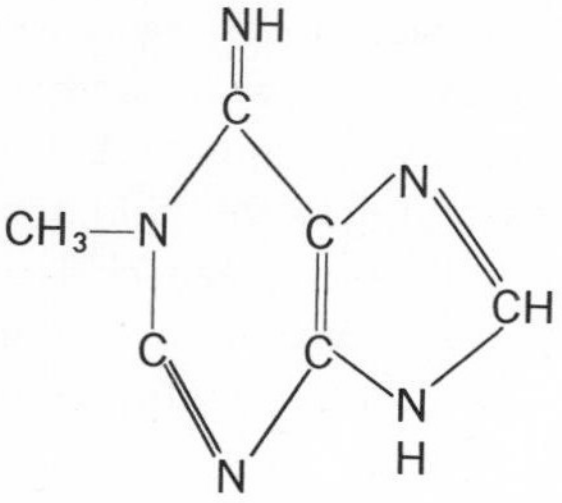

1-methyladenine

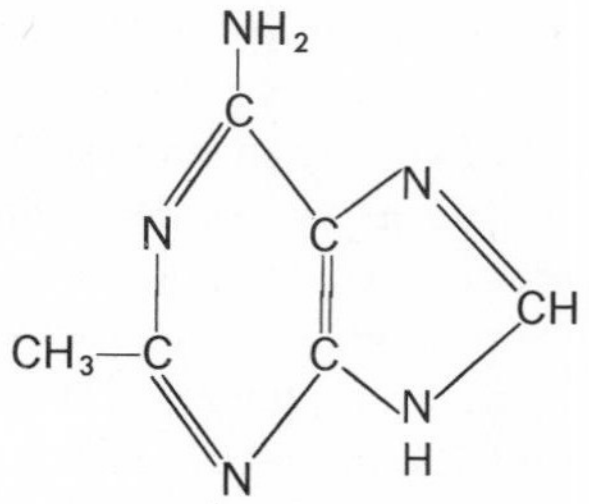

2-methyladenine

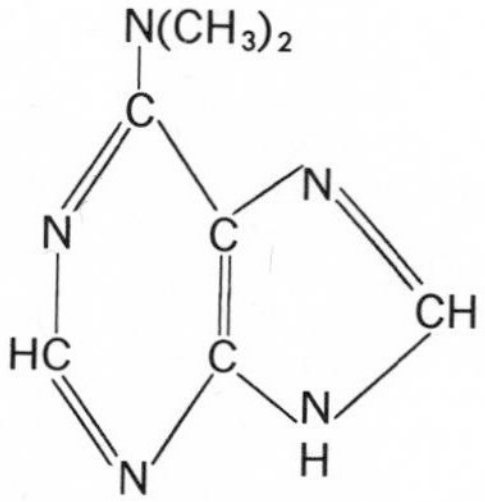

6,6-dimethylamino purine

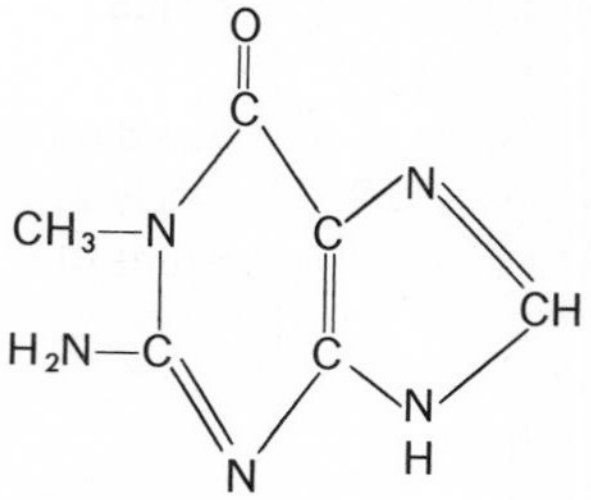

1-methylguanine

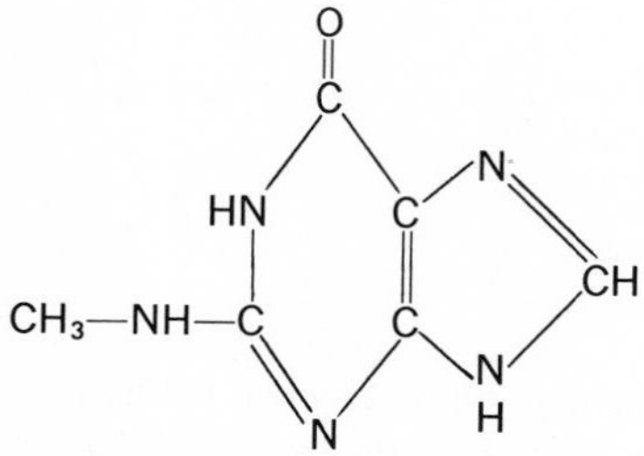

2-methylamino-6-hydroxypurine

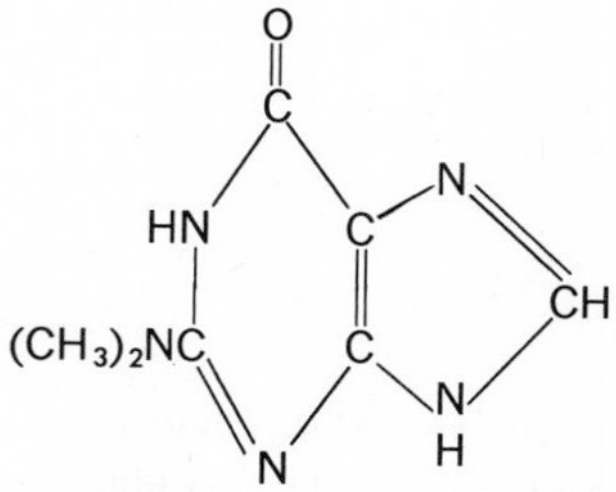

2,2-dimethylamino-6-hydroxypurine

Figure 6

A number of other bases, while not found in natural nucleic acids, have been incorporated into biosynthetic nucleic acids or formed in natural nucleic acids by chemical means. These include hypoxanthine and 5-bromouracil.

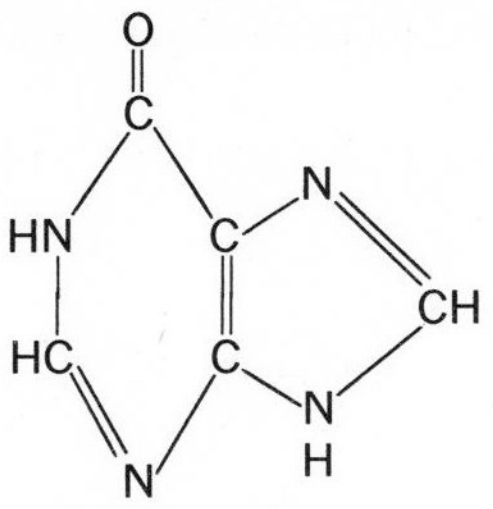

hypoxanthine 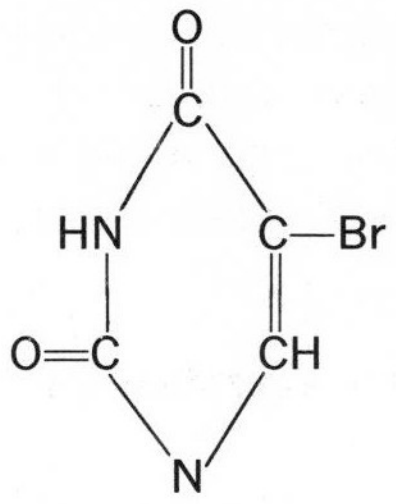   5-bromouracil

Figure 7

II. PHYSICAL PROPERTIES

The purine and pyrimidine bases which occur in nucleic acids are colorless solids at 25°, sparingly soluble in water. They decompose upon melting. The physical properties of the more common bases are cited in Table 1.

Table I

Base	Molecular weight	Solubility in water at 25° (1 part in x parts water)	Melting point
adenine	135.13	1086[14]	360–365° (dec.)[14]
cytosine	111.11	129[15]	320–325° (dec.)[15]
uracil	112.09	280[16]	338° (dec.)[16]
thymine	126.11	250[16]	326° (dec.)[16]
guanine	151.13	26,000 (40.1°)[17]	
xanthine	152.11	5,500 (40.1°)[17]	

III. IONIZATION

All of the bases occurring in nucleic acids are weak electrolytes whose degree of ionization depends upon the pH. One class of ionization is associated with the primary amino groups which occur in adenine, guanine, and cytosine,[18] although the actual site of attachment of the proton is the adjacent ring nitrogen (N_1 in adenine; N_3 in guanine and cytosine).

Another class of ionization is that associated with the $-NH-\overset{\overset{\text{O}}{\|}}{C}-$ groups[18] ($-N_1H-\overset{\overset{\text{O}}{\|}}{C}-$ in guanine and cytosine; $-N_3H-\overset{\overset{\text{O}}{\|}}{C}-$ in thymine and uracil). A third type of ionization has been attributed to the imidazole $-N_9H-$ group of adenine and guanine.[18] The first two classes of ionizable site persist in nucleotides and polynucleotides, while the third is lost in formation of the base-sugar bond.

The pK's corresponding to the above ionizable sites are listed below in Table 2. The pK is defined by

$$pK = -\log_{10} K$$

where K is the ionization constant.

Table II

Base	—NH$_2$ pK	—NHCO— pK	imidazole —NH— pK
adenine[19]	4.15		9.8
cytosine[20]	4.45	12.2	
guanine[19]	3.3	9.6	12.3
thymine[19]		9.82	
uracil[19]		9.45	

IV. ABSORPTION SPECTRA

All of the purine and pyrimidine bases possess intense absorption bands in the ultraviolet and account for virtually all of the absorption of nucleotides and nucleic acids in the 250–300 mμ range. The molar absorbancies depend upon the state of ionization and are listed for three pH's.

Table III

Base	pH	Maximum (mμ)	Molar absorbance (x10^{-3})
adenine[19]	1	262.5	13.1
	7	260.5	13.35
	13	269	12.3
cytosine[21]	1	276	10.0
	7	267	6.13
	13	281.5	7.06
5-methylcytosine[21]	1	283.5	9.79
	7	273.5	6.23
	13	288	6.95
5-hydroxymethylcytosine[20]	1	279	9.7
	7	269.5	—
	13	283.5	—
guanine[19]	1	248.5	11.4
		275.5	7.35
	7	246	10.7
		275.5	8.15
	11	246	6.3
		273.5	8.0
thymine[21]	2	264.5	7.89
	7	264.5	7.89
	13	291	5.44
uracil[21]	2	259.5	8.2
	7	259.5	8.2
	13	284	6.15

V. SYNTHESIS

Uracil is most readily synthesized, in 50% yield, by heating a mixture of malic acid and urea in fuming sulfuric acid.[22]

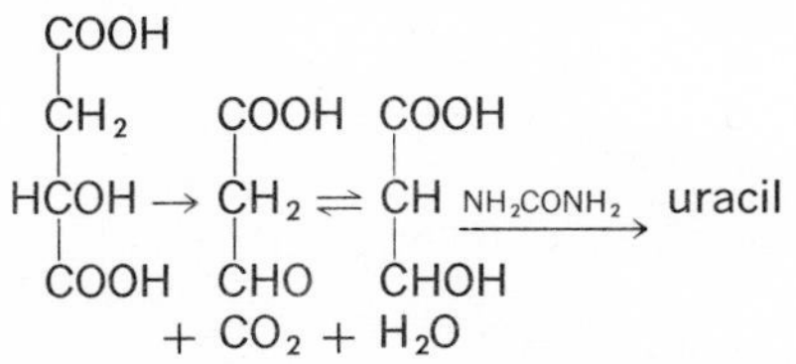

$$
\begin{array}{ccc}
\text{COOH} & & \\
| & & \\
\text{CH}_2 & \text{COOH} & \text{COOH} \\
| & | & | \\
\text{HCOH} \rightarrow & \text{CH}_2 \rightleftharpoons & \text{CH} \quad \xrightarrow{\text{NH}_2\text{CONH}_2} \quad \text{uracil} \\
| & | & | \\
\text{COOH} & \text{CHO} & \text{CHOH} \\
& + \text{CO}_2 + \text{H}_2\text{O} &
\end{array}
$$

Thymine is best synthesized by heating urea and methyl-cyanoacetic acid to form methyl cyanoacetylurea, which may be hydrogenated in the presence of platinum to yield thymine and ammonia.[23]

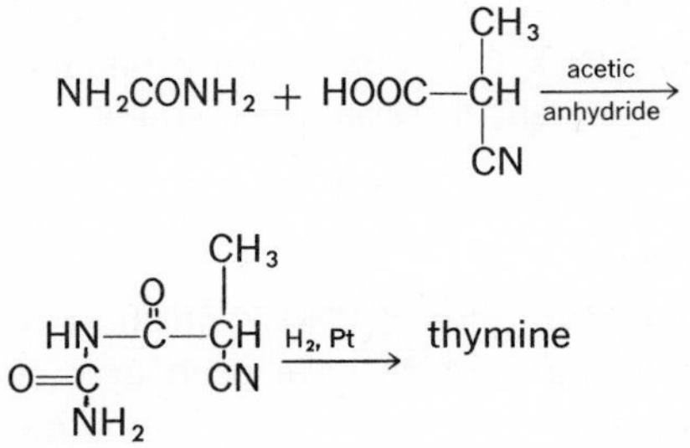

$$
\text{NH}_2\text{CONH}_2 + \text{HOOC}-\overset{\displaystyle \overset{\text{CH}_3}{|}}{\underset{\displaystyle \underset{\text{CN}}{|}}{\text{CH}}} \xrightarrow[\text{anhydride}]{\text{acetic}}
$$

$$
\underset{\displaystyle \underset{\text{NH}_2}{\overset{\displaystyle O=C}{}}}{\text{HN}}-\overset{O}{\overset{||}{C}}-\overset{\overset{\text{CH}_3}{|}}{\underset{\underset{\text{CN}}{|}}{\text{CH}}} \xrightarrow{\text{H}_2,\ \text{Pt}} \quad \text{thymine}
$$

Cytosine may be synthesized in reasonable yield by condensing malondi-aldehyde acetal with hydroxylamine hydrochloride to form isoxazole. The latter is converted to β-ethoxyacrylonitrile by treatment with diethyl sulfate and alkali. A final condensation with urea yields cytosine.[24]

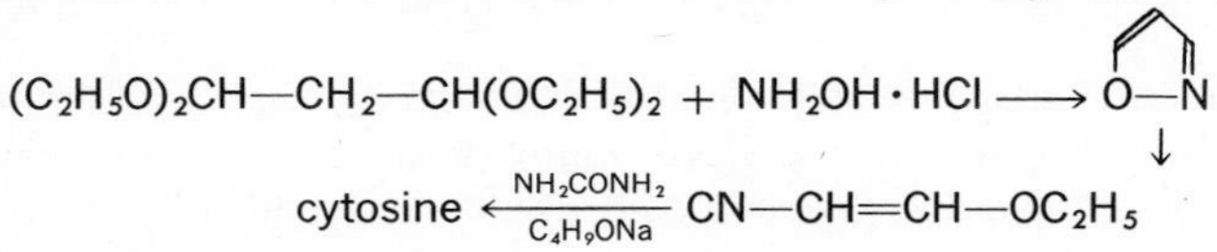

$$
(\text{C}_2\text{H}_5\text{O})_2\text{CH}-\text{CH}_2-\text{CH}(\text{OC}_2\text{H}_5)_2 + \text{NH}_2\text{OH}\cdot\text{HCl} \longrightarrow \text{O--N}
$$

$$
\text{cytosine} \xleftarrow[\text{C}_4\text{H}_9\text{ONa}]{\text{NH}_2\text{CONH}_2} \text{CN}-\text{CH}=\text{CH}-\text{OC}_2\text{H}_5
$$

Adenine may be prepared by treating 4,5,6-triaminopyrimidine with sodium dithioformate to form the 5-thioformyl derivative, which is converted to adenine with the elimination of hydrogen sulfide by boiling in water.[25]

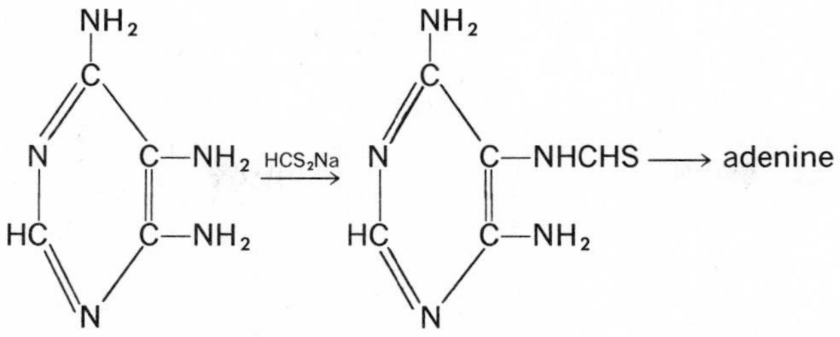

Figure 8

Similarly, guanine may be synthesized in excellent yield by refluxing 2,5,6-triamino-4-hydroxypyrimidine with formic acid-sodium formate.[28]

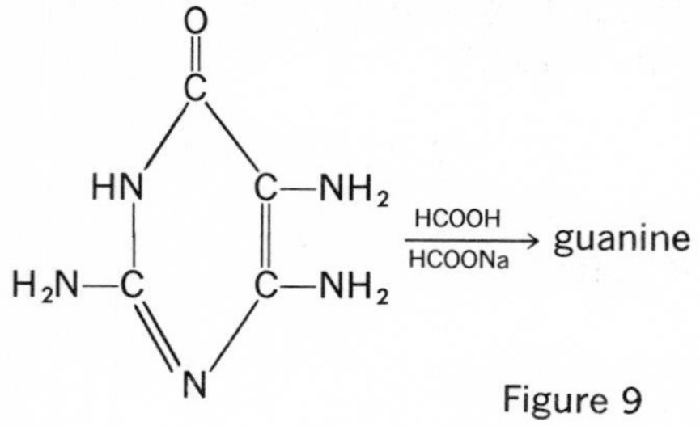

Figure 9

VI. PREPARATION

The purine bases of DNA may be quantitatively split off by rather mild acid treatment (24 hours at pH 1.6 and 37°).[27] Both purine and pyrimidine bases may be liberated quantitatively by any of several procedures, including:

70% perchloric acid for 1 hour at 100°[28]

98% formic acid for 2 hours at 175°[29]

The quantitative separation of the free bases of RNA is much more difficult to achieve. Among the procedures which have been used is hydrolysis with 70% perchloric acid at 100° for one hour.[28] The purine bases of RNA may be selectively split off by hydrolysis for one hour in 1 M HCl at 100°.[30]

VII. PHOTOCHEMISTRY[31]

The irradiation of aqueous solutions of uracil and cytosine with limited doses of ultraviolet light of the wave-length of the primary absorption band produces a rapid decrease in the ultraviolet absorption of uracil and cytosine, while almost no change occurs for thymine, adenine, and

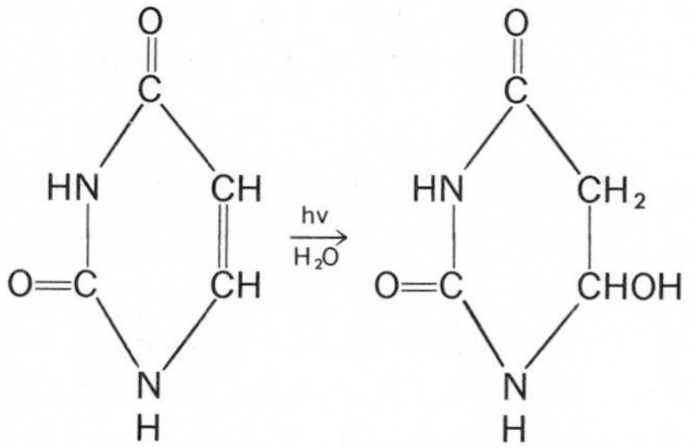

Figure 10

guanine.[32] In the case of uracil and several of its derivatives, the initial reaction is a hydration of the 5,6-double bond.[33]

The reaction is reversed by exposure to heat or acid. Prolonged exposure to ultraviolet radiation results in the irreversible formation of a complex mixture of degradation products.

Irradiation of frozen aqueous solutions of thymine results in the formation of a dimer with the probable structure shown in figure 11.[11]

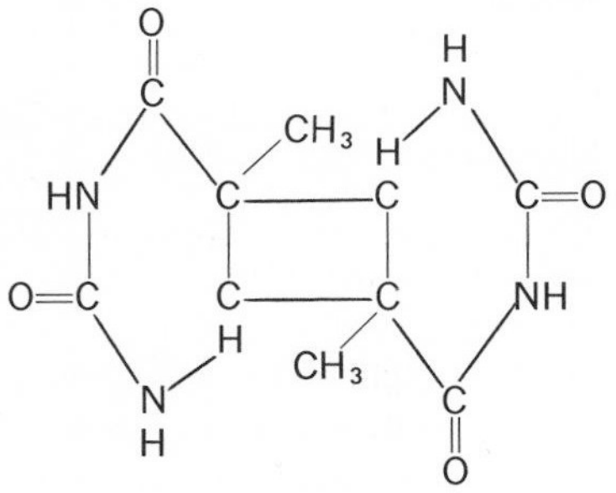

Figure 11

The dimerization is reversed by irradiation of the thawed solution.

VIII. ANALYSIS

The most generally useful techniques for analyzing mixtures of bases are chromatographic. Ion-exchange resins have been widely used. In acid solution, guanine, adenine, and cystonine are cationic, with pK values increasing in that order; they are retained by cation exchangers in an acid system. Uracil and thymine do not acquire a positive charge and are not adsorbed by cation-exchangers. Hypoxanthine and xanthine are also uncharged in acid medium, but are retained to an appreciable extent by cation-exchangers.

All of the bases occurring in nucleic acids have anionic pK's in the free state whose descending order is cytosine, adenine, thymine, guanine, and uracil. They are thus adsorbed by anion-exchangers under alkaline conditions.

Both cation- and anion-exchangers have been used to separate and analyze mixtures of bases. Two representative separations are summarized in Table IV.

Paper chromatography has also been extensively used for the analysis of base mixtures. Aqueous n-butanol, with or without added ammonia, is one of the most useful solvents. Table V cites the R_f values for the common bases in a number of solvents.

Table IV

Basis of separation:	cation-exchange
Exchanger:	Dowex-50-H$^+$, 300 mesh
Column dimensions:	8.1 cm × 0.74 cm^2
Solvent:	2 N HCl, 0.6 ml/min.
Order of appearance:	uracil, 50 ml; cytosine, 100 ml; guanine, 200 ml; adenine, 550 ml
Reference:	34

Basis of separation:	anion-exchange
Exchanger:	Dowex-1-Cl$^-$, 300 mesh
Column dimensions:	8.5 cm × 0.74 cm^2
Solvent:	0.2 M NH$_4$OH + 0.025 M NH$_4$ Cl, pH 10.6 for first 580 ml, then changed to 0.2 M NH$_4$OH + 0.10 M NH$_4$Cl, pH 10.0
Order of appearance:	cytosine, 20 ml; uracil, 160 ml; thymine, 260 ml; guanine, 440 ml; adenine, 680 ml
Reference:	34

Table V

R$_f$ Values of Purine and Pyrimidine Bases

Base	a	b	c	d	e	f	g	h	i	j
adenine	0.38	0.28	0.40	0.33	0.37	0.32	0.34	0.83	0.44	0.37
guanine	0.15	0.11	0.15	0.13	0.16	0.22	0.22	0.70	0.02	0.40
uracil	0.31	0.19	0.33	0.39	0.38	0.66	0.74	0.67	0.73	0.76
thymine	0.52	0.35	0.50	0.56	0.52	0.76	0.84	0.78	0.73	0.74
cytosine	0.22	0.24	0.28	0.26	0.32	0.44	0.21	0.80	0.73	0.70
hypoxanthine	0.26	0.12	0.19	0.30	0.16	0.29	0.44	0.69	0.57	0.63
5-hydroxymethyl cytosine	0.13	0.12	—	—	0.25	0.44	—	—	—	0.75

a. 86% aqueous n-butanol; Whatman No. 1 paper, descending.[35]

b. 86% aqueous n-butanol, plus 5% by volume of concentrated NH$_3$ (density 0.88); Whatman No. 1 paper, descending.[35]

c. 100 volumes n-butanol saturated with water at 23° plus one volume 15 N NH$_4$OH; Whatman No. 4, ascending.[36]

d. n-butanol 77%, water 13%, formic acid 10% by volume; Whatman No. 1, descending.[35]

e. 85 volumes isopropanol, 15 volumes water, 1.3 volumes concentrated (28%) NH$_3$; Whatman No. 1, descending.[37]

f. 170 volumes isopropanol, 41 volumes concentrated HCl (density 1.19), 39 volumes water; Whatman No. 1, descending.[38]

g. 1 volume collidine, 2 volumes quinoline, 1.5 volumes water; Schleicher and Shull No. 597 paper, descending.[39]

h. 400 volumes isobutyric acid, 208 volumes water, 0.4 volumes 25% NH$_3$, Whatman No. 4, descending.[40]

i. 5% aqueous Na$_2$HPO$_4$ saturated with isoamyl alcohol, Whatman No. 1, descending.[41]

j. Water adjusted to pH 10 with N NH$_4$OH, Whatman No. 1, ascending.[42]

BIBLIOGRAPHY

1. Chargaff, E., and J. N. Davidson, *The Nucleic Acids,* 1955.
2. Steiner, R. F., and R. F. Beers, *Polynucleotides,* 1961.
3. Florkin, M., and E. Stotz, *Comprehensive Biochemistry,* Vol. 8, 1963.
4. Michelson, A. M., *The Chemistry of Nucleosides and Nucleotides,* 1963.
5. Jordan, D., *The Chemistry of Nucleic Acids,* 1960.
6. Dunn, D. B., and J. D. Smith, "Occurrence of a New Base in the Deoxyribo-nucleic Acid of a Strain of Bacterium coli," *Nature,* 175:336, 1955.
7. Dunn, D. B., and J. D. Smith, "Methylaminopurine in Deoxyribonucleic Acids," *Biochem. J.,* 68:627, 1958.
8. Littlefield, J. W., and D. B. Dunn, "Natural Occurrence of Thymine and 3 Methylated Adenine Bases in Several Ribonucleic Acids," *Nature,* 181:254, 1958.
9. Amos, H., and M. Korn, "5-Methyl Cytosine in RNA of Escherichia coli," *Biochim. Biophys. Acta,* 29:444, 1958.
10. Dunn, D. B., "Additional Components in RNA of Rat-Liver Fractions," *Biochim. Biophys. Acta,* 34:286, 1959.
11. Ulbricht, T. L. V., *Comprehensive Biochemistry,* 8:158, 1963.
12. Adler, M., B. Weissmann, and A. B. Gutman, "Occurrence of Methylated Purine Bases in Yeast RNA," *J. Biol. Chem.,* 230:717, 1958.
13. Smith, J. D., and D. B. Dunn, "Occurrence of Methylated Guanines in Ribo-nucleic Acids from Several Sources," *Biochem. J.,* 72:294, 1959.
14. Bredereck, H., in Flaschentrager and Lehnartz, *Physiologische Chemie,* 1:796, 1951.
15. Wheeler, W. L., and T. B. Johnson, "Synthesis of Aminooxypyrimidines having the Composition of Cytosine: 2-Amino-6-Oxypyrimidine and 2-Oxy-6-Aminopyrimidine," *Am. Chem. J.,* 29:492, 1903.
16. Wheeler, H. L., and H. F. Merriam, "On some Condensation Products of the Pseudothioureas: Synthesis of Uracil, Thymine, and Similar Compounds," *Am. Chem. J.,* 29:478, 1903.
17. Wood, J. K., "The Affinities of some Feebly Basic Substances," *J. Chem. Soc.,* 83:568, 1903.
18. Jordan, D. O., *The Nucleic Acids,* 1:447, 1955.
19. Jordan, D., *The Chemistry of Nucleic Acids,* p. 134, 1960.
20. Baddiley, J., J. G. Buchanan, R. Hodges, and J. F. Prescott, "Chemical studies of the Biosynthesis of Purine Nucleotides II. The Synthesis of N-Glycyl-D-Ribofuranosylamines," *J. Chem. Soc.,* p. 4769, 1957.
21. Fox, J. J., J. F. Codington, N. Yung, L. Kaplan, and J. O. Lampen, "Pyrimi-dine Nucleosides, The Synthesis of 1-β-D-Lyxofuranosylthymine," *J. Am. Chem. Soc.,* 80:5155, 1958.
22. Shirley, D. A., *Preparation of Organic Intermediates,* p. 297, 1951.
23. Bergmann, W., and T. B. Johnson, "Researches on Pyrimidines, a Synthesis of Thymine," *J. Am. Chem. Soc.,* 55:1733, 1933.
24. Tarsio, P. J., and L. Nicholl, "Preparation of Cytosine," *J. Org. Chem.,* 22:192, 1957.
25. Baddiley, J., B. Lythgoe, and A. R. Todd, "Experiments on the Synthesis of Purine Nucleosides. II. a new and Convenient Synthesis of Adenine," *J. Chem. Soc.,* p. 386, 1943.
26. Traube, W., "Uber Eine Neue Synthese des Guanins and Xanthins," *Ber.,* 33:1371, 1900.

27. Tamm, C., M. E. Hodes, and E. Chargaff, "The Formation of Apurinic Acid from the Desoxyribonucleic Acid of Calf Thymus," *J. Biol. Chem.*, 195:49, 1952.

28. Marshak, A., and H. J. Vogel, "Microdetermination of Purines and Pyrimidines in Biological materials," *J. Biol. Chem.*, 189:597, 1951.

29. Vischer, E., and E. Chargaff, "The Composition of the Pentose Nucleic Acids of Yeast and Pancreas," *J. Biol. Chem.*, 176:715, 1948.

30. Hotchkiss, R. D., "The Quantitative Separation of Purines, Pyrimidines and Nucleosides by Paper Chromatography," *J. Biol. Chem.*, 175:315, 1948.

31. Shugar, D., *The Nucleic Acids*, 3:39, 1955.

32. Sinsheimer, R. L., and R. Hastings, "A Reversible Photochemical Alteration of Uracil and Uridine," *Science*, 110:525, 1949.

33. Moore, A. M., and C. H. Thomson, "Ultraviolet Irradiation of Pyrimidine Derivatives," *Science*, 122:594, 1955.

34. Cohn, W. E., "The Separation of Purine and Pyrimidine Bases and of Nucleotides by Ion Exchange," *Science*, 109:377, 1949.

35. Markham, R., and J. D. Smith, "A Technique for the Identification and Estimation of Purine and Pyrimidine Bases Nucleosides and Related Substances," *Biochem. J.*, 45:294, 1949.

36. Macnutt, W. S., "The Enzymically Catalysed Transfer of the Deoxyribosyl Group from one Purine or Pyrimidine to Another," *Biochem. J.*, 50:384, 1952.

37. Hershey, A. D., J. Dixon, and M. Chase, "Nucleic Acid Economy in Bacteria Infected with Bacteriophage T-2," *J. Gen. Physiol*, 36:777, 1953.

38. Wyatt, G. R., "The Purine and Pyrimidine Composition of Deoxypentose Nucleic Acids," *Biochem. J.*, 48:584, 1951.

39. Vischer, E., and E. Chargaff, "The Separation and Quantitative Estimation of Purines and Pyrimidines in Minute Amounts," *J. Biol. Chem.*, 176:703, 1948.

40. Lofgren, N., "The Qualitative Separation of Purines, Pyrimidines and Nucleosides by Paper Chromatography," *Acta Chem. Scand.*, 6:1030, 1952.

41. Carter, C. E., "Paper Chromatography of Purine and Pyrimidine Derivatives of Yeast RNA," *J. Am. Chem. Soc.*, 72:1466, 1950.

42. Wyatt, G. R., *The Nucleic Acids*, 1:243, 1955.

NUCLEOPROTEINS

I. INTRODUCTION

One of the most important classes of conjugated proteins is nucleoproteins, which consist structurally of a non-amino acid unit, nucleic acid, in the form of a prosthetic group, linked to simple proteins (protamine or histone), rather basic in character. Protein components of nucleoproteins vary from relatively simple polypeptide structures in sperm to complex protein molecules of very high particle weight in the virus nucleoproteins. Nucleoproteins make up a large part of the nuclear material of cells and are concerned with vital cellular organization and function. They are also present in the extracellular material of living cells. Nucleoproteins have attracted much interest because of their close association with the chromosomes of cell nuclei. It is widely believed that they play an important role in the process of cell division and reproduction and in the process of transmission of hereditary characteristics.

The combination of nucleic acid with proteins is either by primary (non-polar) or salt-like (polar) linkages. Nucleoprotein salts may be considered as arising largely from electrostatic forces of attraction between the positively-charged groups on the protein and the negatively-charged groups on the nucleic acid. The weight of present evidence favors the view that the nucleoproteins are probably salts of oppositely-charged components, profoundly modified by the presence of each other. The nucleoproteins have been isolated by one or a combination of the following precipitations: by dilute acids, by salts, and by centrifugation. Less important ways of precipitation include various hydrophilic colloids or calcium chloride. The hydrophilic colloids method has been applied to the crystallization of already-purified preparations of various plant viruses. The calcium chloride method has been applied to the nucleohistones.

II. PROTAMINES

Protamines, the simplest protein components of nucleoproteins, have been isolated from the sperm and ripe testes of fish, where they exist in the form of salts with the thymus type of nucleic acid. The properties of

Table I.   Amino Acid Composition of the Protamines*

Protamine	Species	Arginine	Lysine	Histi-dine	Glycine	Alanine
Clupeine	Clupeus harengus	65 (71)	—	—	—	7
		53 (71)	—	—	—	4
		60 (82)	—	—	—	5
Salmine	Salmo salar	51 (70)	—	—	—	4
		55 (74)	—	—	3	2
		41 (70)	—	—	3	1
		75 (70)	—	—	7	1
		34 (69)	—	—	3	1
		50 (70)	—	—	4	1
		78 (85)	—	—	4	1
Scombrine	Scombre scombrus	112 (81)	—	—	—	9
Spheroidine	Spheroides rubripes	71 (78)	—	—	—	9
Iridine	Salmo irideus	50 (73)	2	—	2	2
Truttine	Salmo trutta	50 (75)	—	—	2	2
Fontinine	Salmo fontinalis	50 (75)	—	—	2	2
Lacustrine	Salmo lacustris	50 (66)	—	5–15	2	2
Sturine	Acipenser sturio	35 (54)	9	7	2	5
	Gallus domesticus	75 (60)	—	2	10	2
Galline		44 (66)	—	—	1	5

*The values represent the number of residues of the amino acids in the protamines; the amino acid in lowest concentration was assigned the value of 1. The numbers in parentheses after the values for arginine are the percentages of the total moles of amino acids in the protamine accounted for by arginine.

protamines include (a) alkaline reaction in aqueous solution; (b) relatively low molecular weight ranging in the thousands (2,000–12,000); (c) high isoelectric pH values (12–12.4); (d) an extended structure in which the amino acids are united by peptide bonds; (e) ready hydrolysis by trypsin; (f) ability to form compounds with salts of heavy metals; (g) ready staining with fast green dye; (h) capacity to combine with some of the acedic proteins to form insoluble salt-type complexes; (i) basic amino acid yield upon hydrolysis, chiefly arginine and a few of the monoaminomonocarboxylic types in the ratio 2:1; and (j) for the most part, a lack of the aromatic amino acids, such as tryptophan, tyrosine and phenylaline.

The amino acid analysis of protamines by Felix, Fischer and Knobles (1956) has shown that they consist of about 70% basic residues. Of the basic residues, arginine forms the largest fraction. Smaller amounts are found of lysine and histidine. It has also been shown that non-basic residues occur in pairs in the amino acid sequence. Arginine, the main basic component, contains the guanidinium group

$$-NH \cdot C \cdot (NH_2)_2{}^+$$

Table I (cont.).   Amino Acid Composition of the Protamines*

Serine	Threo-nine	Pro-line	Valine	Iso-leucine	Aspar-tic acid	Glutamic acid	Tyro-sine	Total
4	2	9	4	1	—	—	—	92
6	2	5	4	1				75
1	1	4	1	1				73
6	—	7	4	1	—	—	—	73
5	—	5	4	—	—	—	—	74
7	—	4	2	1	—	—	—	59
8	—	6	5	2	—	—	—	104
4	—	4	3	?	—	—	—	49
7	—	6	3	1	—	—	—	72
4	—	3	1	1	—	—	—	92
4	2	7	3	1	—	—	—	138
7	1	1	1	1	—	—	—	91
3	—	5	4	1	—	—	—	69
3	—	5	5	—	—	—	—	67
3	—	5	5	—	—	—	—	67
2	—	5	2	1	1	1	—	76
3	1	—	—	2	—	1	—	65
14	3	7	2	1	1	2	6	125
5	2	5	3	1	—	1	—	67

Reference: Reproduced by permission from *Histone and Other Nuclear Proteins* by H. Busch, 1965, published by Academic Press, New York.

in its side chain while lysine and histidine contain

$(NH_3)^+$ and $(=NH_2)^+$

respectively. Kossel classified protamines into three groups based on the fact that the predominant basic amino acids are present in different amounts in different fishes: (1) simple protamines or monoprotamines, such as salmine and clupeine, which contain arginine as the only basic amino acid; (2) diprotamines (gridine), which contain arginine and either lysine or histidine; and (3) triprotamines, such as slurine, which contain all the basic amino acids.

That the findings by different researchers regarding the amino acid composition found in a single species (Table I) are at such variance indicates that individual samples differ in amino-acid composition or that there are differing amounts of individual protamines in the total pro-tamine fraction. Scanes and Tozer, who separated clupeine into three fractions, support the latter possibility because their first fraction contained only arginine, alanine, proline, serine and valine. The second contained threonine but no glycine, leucine or isoleucine. The third contained threonine, leucine or isoleucine, and glycine.

Felix and his co-workers isolated and characterized peptides present in clupeine and suggested a formula:

$$\text{pro—ala—arg}_4(\text{monoamino acid}_2 \cdot \text{arg}_4)_n\text{monoamino acid}_2\text{arg}_2$$

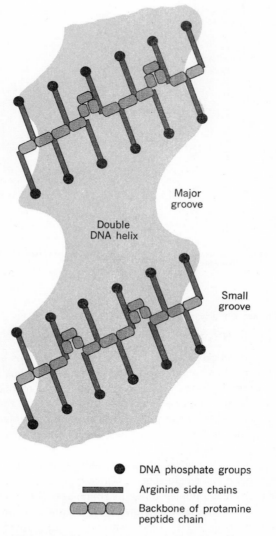

Major
groove

Double
DNA helix

Small
groove

● DNA phosphate groups

▬▬ Arginine side chains

◯◯◯◯ Backbone of protamine
peptide chain

Figure 1.   Schematic drawing showing nucleoprotamine structure, suggested on the basis of X-ray diffraction study.

Reproduced from Haggis, *Introduction to Molecular Biology*, 1964.

Later, without certainty, Busch put forward a formula for clupeine which has a molecular weight of 12,000:

pro—ala—arg$_4$—pro—val—arg$_4$ · ileu—ala—arg$_4$—val—ser—arg$_4$—
ser—prol—arg$_4$—ser—threo—arg$_4$—ser—ala—arg$_4$—prol—ser—
arg$_4$—ser—val—arg$_4$—threo—prol—arg$_4$—val—ala—arg$_2$

Feughelman, Wilkin and their co-workers suggested that the protamines lie in the shallow groove of the DNA helix. X-ray diffraction and polarized infrared light studies suggest that the protamines are not aggregated in the deoxyribonucleoprotamine and may be present as random coils rather than in the α-helical or β-sheet form. The protamine peptide chain in this structure is wrapped around the DNA double helix in the shallow groove, in such a way that the positively-charged basic side-chain groups lie close to the negatively-charged phosphate groups of the double helix (Figure 1).

The main and primary function of protamine is generally believed to be to maintain the DNA in a stable, compact and transportable form. It is commonly accepted that protamine is also a simple carrier of DNA. Addition of RNA to chick embryo fibroblasts decreases the initial lag in protein synthesis. Protamines block the breakdown of RNA. They also enhance the uptake of labelled RNA by a factor of 10. Addition of protamines increases the plague-forming capacity and infectivity of polio virus.

Protamines have been reported as having some inhibitory characteristic effects on biological systems. One such effect inhibits the excitability of cerebral cortex slices. This process is reversible with acid addition. Also, high doses of protamines inhibit the growth of some tumors.

Research as yet has not discovered substances of a protamine nature in sources other than fish sperm. In higher forms, the protamines may be completely coupled with amino acids. Thus their apparent absence so far must not be read as non-existence. Rather, they just may not have been isolated.

III. HISTONE

The histones, which in complexity stand between the simple protamines and higher proteins, are certainly associated with DNA in the somatic cells of animals and plant tissues, whereas their presence in some of the single cell specimens is under question. Even though histones contain a greater assortment of amino acids (Table II) than protamines, they resemble protamines in having a high proportion of the basic amino acids, especially arginine. Also, like protamines, histones have an alkaline isoelectric point.

According to the amino acid content and molar ratio of lysine to arginine, histones are divided into four groups: (1) arginine-rich histone;

Table II. Early Studies on the Amino Acid Composition[a] of Calf Thymus Histones Prior to Fractionation

Amino acid	Nucleohistone	Isolated nuclei	Nucleoprotein	Chromosomal material	Nucleoprotein
Starting material:	Nucleohistone	Isolated nuclei	Nucleoprotein	Chromosomal material	Nucleoprotein
References:	Kossel	Daly et al	Hamer	Morris and Harper	Crampton et al
Histone extraction:	dil. H_2SO_4	0.2 N HCl	0.1 N HCl	0.2 N HCl	2.6 M NaCl
Histone precipitation:	Ammonia	NaOH to pH 10.0	Ammonia	NaOH to pH 10.4	Ethanol
Alanine	5.4	11.2	9.8	14.2	13.5
Arginine	9.6	8.5	11.0	9.3	8.3
Aspartic acid	—	6.1	5.5	6.0	4.8
Cystine	—	0.4	0.03	—	0.0
Glutamic acid	0.8	9.2	9.8	9.4	8.2
Glycine	0.8	9.0	9.3	7.8	8.3
Histidine	0.9	1.7	2.0	2.5	2.0
Isoleucine	—	4.4	—	6.3	4.3
Leucine	18.0	8.5	14.8	7.3	7.7
Lysine	6.1	7.9	8.0	11.6	14.7
Methionine	—	0.8	0.9	0.6	0.9
Phenylalanine	3.4	2.4	3.0	1.9	2.2
Proline	2.3	4.5	3.8	4.4	4.9
Serine	—	5.1	4.3	4.8	5.9
Threonine	—	6.0	6.0	6.6	5.7
Tryptophan	—	—	0.21	0.0	0.0
Tyrosine	8.0	2.1	2.7	2.8	2.5
Valine	—	5.9	8.7	4.7	6.2

[a] The values are percentages of total moles of amino acids recovered in the particular amino acid. The data were recalculated from the original papers. The values reported by Crampton et al are now accepted as standard values since they have been confirmed by most later studies.

Reference: Reproduced by permission from Histone and other Nuclear Proteins by H. Busch, 1965, published by Academic Press, N. Y.

(2) moderately lysine-rich 2b or N-proline histone; (3) moderately lysine-rich 2a or N-acetylalanine; (4) high lysine-rich histone. None of these groups of proteins has been extracted in pure form up to this point. They are usually isolated in a more or less contaminated state from cell nuclei or from the isolated chromatin-like material (desoxyribonucleoprotein) by acids. Two major problems arise in the isolation and characterization of histones: the susceptibility of these proteins to enzymatic degradation, and their tendency to aggregate at pH values above 4.5.

The structure and position of the histones in the nucleohistones are not as well established as those of the protamines in the nucleoprotamines. Optical dispersions and infrared studies suggest that two-thirds of the histone polypeptide chain is in the α-helical form, wrapped around the DNA double helix in the major groove, the rest in the shallow groove (Figure 2).

In the gel state, histone bridges form between DNA molecules. These bridges lie parallel to the large groove at 120° angles to the short axis of the DNA coil (Figure 3). In the mitotic chromosome, DNA molecules form supercoils, dimensions unknown, in which the adjacent coils of the super-

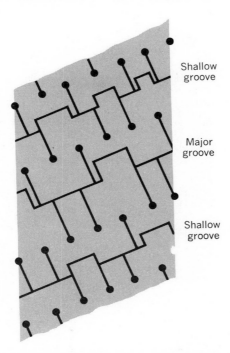

Shallow
groove

Major
groove

Shallow
groove

Figure 2.   Simplified diagram showing how histone might bind to DNA (compare with the scheme for Protamine in Figure 1).

Reproduced from *Biochemical Society Symposium*, No. 14, 1927.

coiled DNA are held together by histone bridges (Figure 4). Nucleohistones have been isolated from bird erythrocytes, from the ripe sperms of certain animals, and from the thymus gland. It has been pointed out with some certainty that calf thymus nucleohistones have a molecular weight of 2,000,000 and an acidic isoelectric pH of about 4.

As far as the function of histone is concerned, further investigation is still needed to confirm the knowledge we have now. It is possible to conclude, however, that (1) histone may act as a gene inhibitor and play a vital role in cell differentiation; (2) histone might block off one of the two strands of the DNA double helix, so that only a single strand would function in RNA synthesis; (3) histone may neutralize the charge on RNA that passes from the nucleus into the cytoplasm; (4) the loosely-bound histone fraction of the nucleus might play a role in the transport of ribosomal RNA; and (5) firmly-bound histone will serve to stabilize the DNA double helix.

Today there is not enough information to decide how many histones

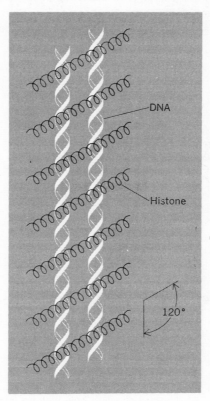

Figure 3. A model of oriented nucleohistone in the gel state.
Reproduced from *The Nucleohistones*, 1964.

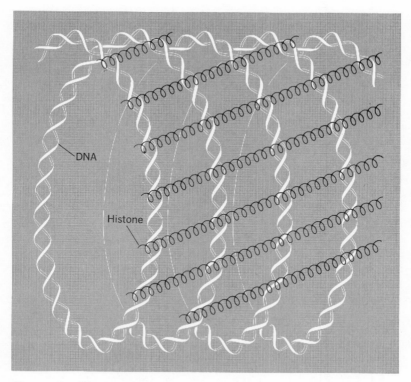

Figure 4.   Diagram suggesting the function of histone bridges in chromosomes.
Reproduced from Bonner, and Ts'o, *The Nucleohistones*, 1964.

there are, or where they are synthesized. Whether they are synthesized in the nucleus as Smetana thinks, or in the DNA, as others have suggested, it is currently believed that RNA has a role in the process. Since histone has not been found in cytoplasm but is present in the nucleus in small quantities, it is very likely synthesized in the nucleus. But so far, no one can rule out the possibility that histone might originate in the cytoplasm and later migrate into the nucleus.

IV. LIVER AND VIRUS NUCLEOPROTEINS

Besides the simple protamines and histones, complex proteins enter into the composition of many nucleoproteins. These nucleoproteins have much firmer combinations than nucleoprotamines and nucleohistones. Their structures are linked with the native configuration of the proteins. Many nucleoproteins of this kind have been isolated but only the proteins

Table III. Analytical Values for Fat-Free Liver Nucleoprotein Preparations

Source	N	Amide N	P	Total S	Free SH in native Protein as Cysteine	Free SH in denatured Protein as Cysteine	Cystine-Cysteine	Methionine	Tyrosine	Tryptophan
	%	%	%	%	%	%	%	%	%	%
Rabbit	15.6	1.0	0.8	1.0	1.3	1.3	1.3	3.0	3.8	1.3
"	15.6	1.0	0.8	1.2	1.4	1.4	1.3	3.1	3.9	1.3
"	15.6	0.9	0.8	1.2	1.4	1.4	1.4	2.9	4.0	1.5
"	15.7	1.0	0.8	1.1	1.2	1.2	1.5	3.1	4.0	1.5
Calf	15.6	1.0	0.8	1.1	0.7	0.7	1.4	3.2	3.9	1.4
"	15.7	1.0	0.8	1.1	0.7	0.7	1.4	3.1	3.9	1.4
Cow	15.8	1.0	0.9	1.2	0.6	0.6	1.5	3.1	3.7	1.7
Rat	15.6	0.9	0.9	1.2	0.2	0.2	1.3	3.0	3.8	1.5
"	15.7	1.0	0.8	1.2	0.2	0.2	1.4	3.1	3.8	1.5
Transplanted Rat Hepatoma	15.5	0.9	0.7	1.1	0.2	0.2	1.4	2.9	3.6	1.5

Reference: Reproduced by permission from *Advances in Protein Chemistry*, Vol. 1, 1940 by Anson and Edsall (eds.), published by Academic Press, N. Y.

Table IV. Plant Virus Nucleoproteins

Virus	Conc. in[1] Infected Sap (g. per liter)	Host	Isolation	Form	Nucleic[2] Acid Content (per cent)	Sedimentation Constant (Svedbergs)	Axial[3] Ratio	Average Particle Diameter	Approx. Mol. Wt.
Tobacco mosaic	2.	Tobacco	$(NH_4)_2SO_4$ Centrifugation	Paracrystalline needles	5	193	40	150	59×10^6
Ribgrass	0.4	Tobacco	Centrifugation	''	5	187	40	150	40×10^6
Cucumber	0.3	Cucumber	''	''	5	187	40	146	40×10^6
Cucumber	0.3	Cucumber	''	''	5	187	40	146	40×10^6
Alfalfa mosaic	0.2	Tobacco	''	Amorphous	15	74	(Spherical)[1]	165	2×10^6
Potato X	0.1	Tobacco	$(NH_4)_2SO_4$ Centrifugation	Amorphous	5	130	(43)[1]	(98)[1]	26×10^6
Tobacco necrosis	0.04	Tobacco	$(NH_4)_2SO_4$	Crystalline plates	15	112	(Spherical)[1]	200	6×10^6
Tobacco ringspot	0.012	Tobacco	Centrifugation	Amorphous	40	115	(Spherical)[1]	190	3×10^6
Tomato bushy stunt	0.05	Tomato	$(NH_4)_2SO_4$ Centrifugation	Isotropic dodecahedra	15	132	(Spherical)[1]	260	7×10^6

[1] Approximate.

[2] Based on phosphorus content.

[3] Ratio of long to short axes of extended particles; the average length of the particles may be estimated by multiplying this value by the average particle diameter.

Reference: Reproduced by permission from *Advances in Protein Chemistry*, Vol. 1, 1940 by Anson and Edsall (eds.), published by Academic Press, N. Y.

of liver and virus nucleoproteins have been characterized to any large extent.

Lipids make up 15 to 20% of the liver nucleoproteins. Of these lipids, nearly 35% is phospholipid. The nucleic acid of the liver nucleoproteins is of the deoxypentose type. The nucleoproteins of the livers of the various specimens are differentiated on the basis of their content of free sulfhydrl groups (Table III). Similar nucleoproteins having pentose type nucleic acid and lipoprotein have been isolated from a number of animal tissues.

As mentioned, a number of plant viruses have been isolated as crystalline nucleoproteins by differential centrifugation and salting out with ammonium sulphate. Data on the isolation procedures, elemental composition, and physical properties of the plant virus nucleoproteins are listed on Table IV.

Whenever growth occurs with a living medium, nucleoproteins are found in high concentration, whether in the metaphase chromosome, the normal gland cell, the embryonic cell, the ovian neoplasm or the plant or animal lesion. Many different functions are involved in any one tissue and, to our knowledge, the forms in which nucleic acid appears are too limited to explain the possible diversities of the functions of the nucleoproteins. Since the proteins possess a far greater capacity to exist in diverse form, they must be considered responsible for the specificity of each function.

BIBLIOGRAPHY

Allen, F. W., *Ribonucleoproteins and Ribonucleic Acids*, 1962.

Amos, H., and Katherine E. Kearns, "Influence of Bacterial Ribonucleic Acid or Animal Cell in Culture—Protamine Enhancement of RNA Uptake," *Exptl. Cell. Research*, 32:14, 1963.

Bonner, J., and R. C. Huang, "Properties of Chromosomal Nucleohistone," *J. Mol. Biol.*, 6:169, 1963.

Bonner, J., and P. Ts'o, *The Nucleohistones*, 1964.

Bradbury, E. M., W. C. Price, and G. R. Wilkinson, "Polarized Infrared Studies of Nucleoproteins—Nucleoprotamines," *J. Mol. Biol.*, 4:39, 1962.

Busch, H., *Histone and Other Nuclear Proteins*, 1965.

Cohen, S. S., "The Isolation and Crystallization of Plant Viruses and Other Protein Macro Molecules by Means of Hydrophilic Colloids," *J. Biol. Chem.*, 144:353, 1942.

Cruft, H. J., et al., "Amino-Acid Composition of the Six Histones of Calf Thymocytes," *Nature*, 180:1107, 1957.

Cruft, H. J., C. M. Mauritzen and E. Stedman, "The Nature and Physicochemical Properties of Histones," *Phil. Trans. Roy. Soc. London*, Series B, 241:93, 1957.

DeLoze, C., "Infrared Spectra and Structure of Deoxyribonucleoproteins and Their Components," *Ann. Chim.*, Paris, 3:145, 1958.

Dounce, A. L., "The State of DNA in the Nesting Cells Nucleus," *Ann. N. Y. Acad. Sci.*, 81:794, 1959.

Felix, K., et al., "Protamines and Nucleoprotamines," *Progr. Biophys. Biophys. Chem.*, 6:1, 1956.

Feughelman, M., et al., "Molecular Structure of Deoxyribosenucleic Acid and Nucleoprotein," *Nature*, 175:834, 1955.

Frearson, P. M., and K. S. Kirby, "Nucleoproteins," *Biochem. J.*, 90:578, 1964.

Greenstein, J. P., *Advan. in Protein Chem.*, 1:209, 1940.

Greenstein, J. P., and W. V. Jenrette, "Note on the Composition of the Nucleoprotein Fraction of Normal Liver of the Transplanted Hepatic Tumor in the Rat," *J. Natl. Cancer Inst.*, 2:305, 1941.

Haggis, G., *Introduction to Molecular Biology*, 1964.

Johns, E. W., and J. A. Butler, "Further Fractionations of Histones from Calf Thymus," *Biochem. J.*, 82:15, 1962.

Kossel, A., *Protamines and Histones*, New York, 1928.

Ludwig, E. H., and C. E. Smull, "Infectivity of Histone-Poliovirus Ribonucleic Acid Preparations," *J. Bacteriol.*, 85:1034, 1963.

Luzzati, V., "The Structure of Nucleohistones and Nucleoprotamines," *J. Mol. Biol.*, 7:758, 1963.

Luzzati, V., and A. Nicolaieff, "The Structure of Nucleohistones and Nucleoprotamines," *J. Mol. Biol.*, 7:142, 1963.

McIlwain, H., "Polybasic and Polyacidic Substances or Aggregates and the Excitability of Cerebral Tissues, Electrically Stimulated *In Vitro*," *Biochem. J.*, 90:442, 1964.

Mirsky, A. E., and H. Ris, "The Composition and Structure of Isolated Chromosomes," *J. Gen. Physiol.*, 34:475, 1951.

Muggleton, P. W., J. G. MacLaren and W. J. Dyke, "Effect of Protamine Sulphate on Experimental Tumors in Mice," *Lancet*, 1:409, 1964.

Murray, K., "Basic Proteins of Cell Nuclei," *Ann. Rev. of Biochem.*, 34:209, 1965.

Phillips, D. M. P., "The Histones," *Progr. Biophys. Biophys. Chem.*, 12:211, 1962.

Scanes, F. S., and B. T. Tozer, "Fractionation of Basic Proteins and Polypeptides," *Biochem. J.*, 63:565, 1956.

Smetana, K., M. Muramatsu and H. Busch, "Quantitative Aspects of Isolation of Nucleoli of the Walker Carcino-Sarcoma and Liver of the Rat," *Cancer Res.*, 23:510, 1963.

Smull, C. E., and E. H. Ludwig, "Enhancement of the Plague Forming Capacity of Poliovirus Ribonucleic Acid with Basic Proteins," *J. Bacteriol.*, 84:1035, 1962.

Stedman, E., and E. Stedman, "The Basic Proteins of Cell Nuclei," *Phil. Trans. Roy. Soc. London*, Series B, 235:565, 1951.

Stedman, E., and E. Stedman, "Cell Specificity of Histones," *Nature*, 166:780, 1950.

Stoops, R., *Nucleoproteins*, 1959.

Svedberg, T., "A Discussion on the Protein Molecule," *Proc. Roy. Soc. London*, Series B, 127:1, 1939.

Wilkins, M. H. F., *Biochem. Soc. Symp.*, 14:13, 1956.

Wilkins, M. H. F., and G. Zubay, "X-Ray Diffraction Study of the Structure of Nucleohistones and Nucleoprotamines," *J. Mol. Biol.*, 7:756, 1963.

Wilkins, M. H. F., G. Zubay, and H. R. Wilson, "X-Ray Diffraction Studies of the Molecular Structure of Nucleohistones and Chromosomes," *J. Mol. Biol.*, 1:179, 1963.

Zubay, G., and P. Doty, "The Isolation and Properties of Deoxyribonucleoprotein Particles Containing Single Nucleic Acid Molecules," *J. Mol. Biol.*, 1:1, 1959.

Zubay, G., and M. H. Wilkins, "An X-Ray Diffraction Study of Histone and Protamine in Isolation and in Combination with DNA," *J. Mol. Biol.*, 4:444, 1962.

THE GENETIC CODE AND PROTEIN SYNTHESIS

The primary biological role of nucleic acids is to specify the synthesis of proteins and to carry this information from generation to generation. The mechanism of protein synthesis has been extensively studied in extracts prepared from microorganisms (notably *E. coli*), mammalian liver, and reticulocytes. Sufficient work throughout the biological spectrum has been carried out, however, to suggest that the process may be similar in various species.

GENETIC INFORMATION

The genetic information of the *E. coli* cell is contained in a single large (approximately 3.7 billion daltons) double-stranded helical macromolecule of *deoxyribonucleic acid* (DNA) which forms a single *chromosome*. This chromosome forms a closed loop on itself as demonstrated by genetic evidence and electron microscope pictures. The linear sequence of nucleotide bases in DNA specifies the amino acid sequence of protein. Each amino acid corresponds to a sequence of three bases which is known as a *codeword* or *codon*. A sequence of codons which contains the information for the synthesis of a given protein is known as a *gene* or *cistron*. The circular *genetic map* for the known genes of *E. coli* is shown in Figure 1. The cell's nucleic acids contain, in addition, a variety of trace bases (see Figure 2). The role of these structures in the carrying and transfer of genetic information is not yet determined.

In higher organisms, many different DNA molecules are present per cell. These are combined with protein to form a variable number of chromosomes which are located within the cell's nucleus. In addition, some cytoplasmic organelles (namely, mitochondria and chloroplasts) may carry their own genetic information independent of the nucleus (perhaps in their own molecules of DNA).

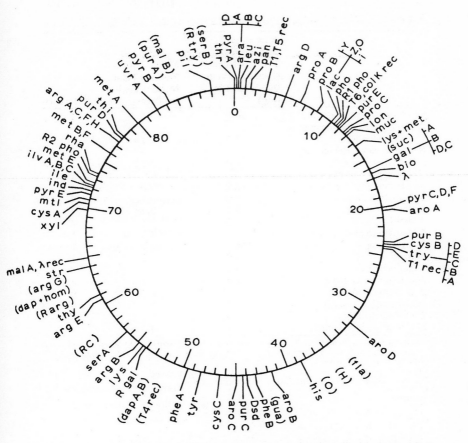

Figure 1. Genetic map of *E. coli*, drawn to scale. The map is graduated in one-minute intervals (89 minutes total) and numbered at 10-minute intervals to facilitate computation of interlocus distances. Markers enclosed in parentheses are only approximately mapped at the positions indicated. The exact sequence of markers in crowded regions is not always known.

Source: Taylor, A. L. and M. S. Thomas, *Genetics*, 50:659, 1964.

MECHANISM OF PROTEIN SYNTHESIS

The general outline of steps required for protein synthesis seems clear (see Figure 3). The genetic information corresponding to the amino acid sequence of a protein is transcribed from DNA into single-stranded molecules of RNA known as *messenger RNA* (mRNA; also known as *complementary RNA* or *informational RNA*). This process of transcription is initiated

Figure 2.   Minor Nucleosides Isolated From Yeasts s-RNA[a]

Nucleoside	Total amount obtained from 11.5 g of Mixed Nucleoside in the Digest of s-RNA (mg)	Moles/1000 Moles of Total Nucleosides in the Digest	Reference
N^6-Methyladenosine	48.7	3.9	1
2′ (3′)-O-Ribosyladenosine (adenosine-R)	2.4	0.13	
N^6-(Aminoacyl)adenosines	5.7	0.34	2
1-Methylguanosine	12.0	0.90	3
N^2-Methylguanosine	1.9	0.14	3
N^2, N^2-Dimethylguanosine	32.9	2.36	3
3-Methylcytidine	2.0	0.18	4
5-Methylcytidine	9.6	0.84	5
3-Methyluridine	1.1	0.1	4
5-Methyluridine	78	6.9	1
Pseudouridine	488	45.0	6
Inosine	26.0	2.2	7
1-Methylinosine	5.1	0.4	7
2′-O-Methyladenosine	3.4	0.28	8, 9
2′-O-Methyluridine	3.4	0.29	8
2′-O-Methylguanosine	40.2	3.1	8
2′-O-Methylcytidine	13.0	1.1	8
2′-O-Methylpseudouridine	0.1	0.009	8

[a] Five additional compounds not detected in the present work have been isolated from the hydrolysates of RNA of yeast and/or other tissues: N^6, N^6-dimethyladenine and 2-methyladenine (1), 1, 5-diribosyluracil (10) 7-methylguanine (11), and N^2-ribosylguanine (12, 13)

Source: Hall, Ross H., *Biochemistry*, 4:668, 1964.

References:

(1)   Littlefield, J. W., and D. B. Dunn, *Biochem. J.*, 70:642, 1958.

(2)   Hall, R. H., *Biochemistry*, 3:769, 1964.

(3)   Smith, J. D., and D. B. Dunn, *Biochem. J.*, 72:294, 1959.

(4)   Hall, R. H., *Biochem. Biophys. Res. Commun.*, 12:361, 1963.

(5)   Dunn, D. B., *Biochim. Biophys. Acta*, 38:176, 1960.

(6)   Cohn, W. E., *J. Biol. Chem.*, 235:1488, 1960.

(7)   Hall, R. H., *Biochem. Biophys. Res. Commun.*, 13:394, 1963.

(8)   Hall, R. H., *Biochemistry*, 3:876, 1964.

(9)   Smith, J. D., and D. B. Dunn, *Biochim. Biophys. Acta*, 31:573, 1959.

(10)   Lis, A. W., and E. W. Lis, *Biochim. Biophys. Acta*, 61:799, 1962.

(11)   Dunn, D. B., *Biochem. J.*, 86:14p, 1963.

(12)   Hemmens, W. F., *Biochim. Biophys. Acta*, 91:332, 1964.

(13)   Shapiro, R., and C. N. Gordon, *Biochem. Biophys. Res. Commun.*, 17:160, 1964.

at specific DNA sites and the synthesis is catalyzed by the enzyme *RNA polymerase*. Only one of the two antiparallel strands of the DNA is copied. Since the mRNA is formed directly on the DNA by means of complementary base-pairing (see Figure 4), its linear sequence of bases is exactly complementary to one parent DNA strand. Sometimes a series of adjacent cistrons are transcribed as a unit under the control of a single initiator site

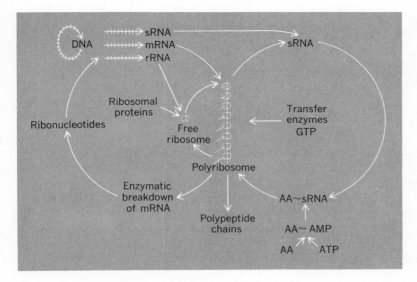

Figure 3.   A diagrammatic outline of protein synthesis.
Source: Watson, J. D., *Bull. Soc. Chim. Biol.*, 46:1399, 1964.

or *operator region;* the large mRNA formed is called a *polycistronic mes-senger.* The entire DNA region composed of operator and cistron(s) is known as an *operon.*

In order for a protein to be synthesized, the information in the mRNA must be translated into a linear sequence of amino acids. This process of *translation* takes place on the cell's *ribosomes.* Ribosomes are slightly flat-tened spherical structures of ribosomal RNA and protein and composed of two subunits. The latter are characterized by their behavior in a sedi-mentation field. In *E. coli,* they are called the *50s* and *30s* subunits. The intact ribosome is a *70s* particle.

Messenger RNA is read, in cases studied, 10 to 20 times before degra-dation. It becomes attached probably at its 5'-terminus to the 30s portion of the ribosome. Each amino acid is brought to this complex attached to its own adaptor: a molecule of *soluble RNA* (sRNA; also known as *transfer RNA* or *adaptor RNA*). There are one or more species of sRNA molecules (of approximately 78 nucleotides in length) for the transport of each of the twenty amino acids. Most molecules have a pG at the 5'-terminus and the base sequence CpCpA at the 3'-terminus. (See Figure 5). Enzymes termed *aminoacyl-sRNA-synthetases* catalyze with high specificity the attachment of amino acids to the terminal adenine of their corresponding sRNA mole-cules via an ester linkage. There is at least one type of synthetase in the cell for each amino acid. Each sRNA specifically recognizes, perhaps via complementary base-pairing, a codon in the mRNA; this hypothesized region in the sRNA is known as an *anticodon.*

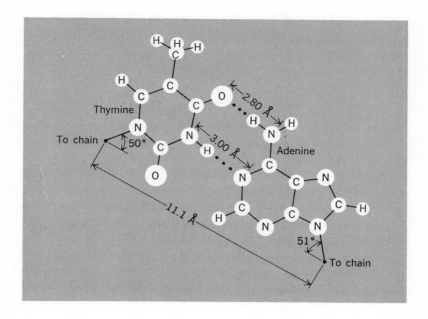

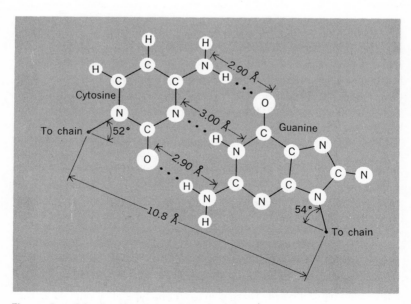

Figure 4.   Adenine-thymine pairing in DNA, and Guanine-cytosine pairing in DNA.

Source: Rich, Alexander, *Rev. Mod. Phys.*, 31:191, 1959.

The aminoacyl-sRNA molecules whose anticodons match the initial codons of the mRNA attach to the 50s subunit of the ribosome. The transfer of the carboxyl group of the first amino acid from its sRNA molecule to the amino group of the second to form a *peptide bond* is dependent upon two *transfer enzymes* and GTP.

The first sRNA, which is now deacylated, is released from the ribosome and is then acylated with another amino acid. The ribosome "moves" one codon unit along the mRNA in order to shift the second sRNA, with its attached dipeptide (representing the first two amino acids of the final protein) into the first position of the ribosome and to allow another sRNA to attach to the second position. The codon of the mRNA specifies sRNA attachment. As this process continues, the peptide chain increases in length one amino acid at a time (see Figure 6).

When a certain length of mRNA has been read, a second ribosome becomes attached to its starting end. In time, there is a whole series of ribosomes moving at intervals down the long mRNA strand. This total structure is known as a *polysome* (or *ergosome*).

Release of the completed *polypeptide chain* depends upon an unknown mechanism(s) probably specified by a codon. The sequence of amino acids in the polypeptide chain (*primary structure*) appears to determine the *secondary structure* (amount and type of helical content) and *tertiary structure* (folding and cross-linking) of the final protein molecule.

THE CELL-FREE PROTEIN SYNTHESIZING SYSTEM

The components usually required for cell-free protein synthesis are:

1   Messenger RNA—either natural (synthesized on either DNA or RNA templates) or synthetic (polyribonucleotides which are not synthesized on templates and hence contain randomly ordered base sequences).
2   Enzymes—obtained either by using the supernatant from a 30,000 g centrifugation of *E. coli* extract, known as the *S-30 fraction;* or from a 100,000 g centrifugation (which now has the ribosomes removed), known as the *S-100 fraction;* or by combining enzymes individually purified from the S-100 fraction.
3   Ribosomes—present in the S-30 fraction or else purified from the pellet of the 100,000 g centrifugation.
4   Amino acids—the one or ones being studied can be labelled with C^{14} or H^3.
5   GTP, ATP, and an ATP-generating system.
6   Buffer, Mg^{++} and salts (potassium or ammonium ions) and 2-mercaptoethanol or reduced glutathione.

Many modifications for special purposes have been employed. In addi-

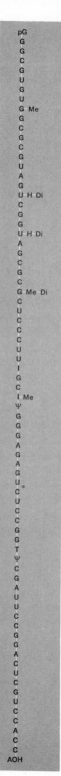

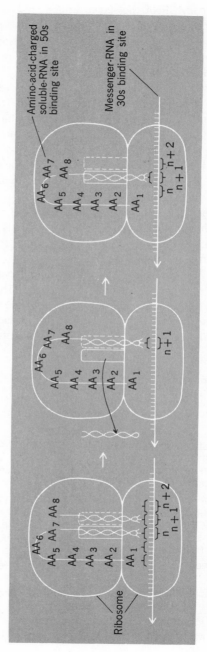

Figure 6. Diagrammatic hypothetical representation of the addition of an AA sRNA molecule to the COOH growing end of a growing polypeptide chain. The mRNA molecule moves from the right to the left.

Source: Watson, J. D., *Bull. Soc. Chim. Biol.*, 46:1399, 1964.

Figure 5. Structure of an Alanine RNA.

Source: Holley, R. W., J. Apgar, G. A. Everett, J. T. Madison, M. Marquisee, S. H. Merrill, J. R. Penwick, and A. Zamir, *Science*, 147:1462, 1965.

tion, cell-free systems have been developed using components isolated from a wide range of microorganisms, plants, and animals.

THE GENETIC CODE

The genetic code for one or more strains of *E. coli* is now known (see Figure 7). Several approaches have been utilized in these investigations.

Data were obtained initially by directing radioactive amino acids into protein with randomly ordered polyribonucleotides containing varying proportions of the four bases A, C, U, and G. These polynucleotides were synthesized using the enzyme *polynucleotide phosphorylase*. Base compositions of RNA codons and the nature of the RNA code were estimated from the specificity and amount of each amino acid incorporated into polypeptide chains. It is a *triplet code* (i.e., each codon is composed of three nucleotide bases in sequence); it is *non-overlapping* (i.e., adjacent codons *UUU UUU* are read, rather than overlapping codons U̲U̲U̲U̲U̲U̲U̲); it is heavily *degenerate* (i.e., there are several codons for each amino acid); codon specificity is usually high (however, ambiguities have been found); different species employ similar codes, although variations have been observed (i.e., the code is generally *universal*).

The exact base sequence of each codon was determined by studying the process of codon recognition prior to peptide bond synthesis. The assay depended upon the ability of trinucleoside diphosphates of known base sequence to direct the association of the corresponding aminoacyl-sRNA to ribosomes. By synthesizing each of the 64 triplet combinations of A, U, C, and G, and testing each one with the twenty-plus acylated sRNA's, it was possible to measure the affinity of each sRNA with each codon and thus to match codon base sequences with amino acids. The binding affinity of a trinucleoside for sRNA is called its *template activity*.

Further evidence can be obtained by enzymatically synthesizing polynucleotide chains composed of repeating sequences of doublets or triplets. These precisely ordered artificial messengers produce specific polypeptides in the cell-free system. Certain repeating doublet polymers produce polypeptides consisting of an alternating sequence of two amino acids; polymers containing repeating triplets can produce three types of homopolymer peptide chains, depending upon the phase of reading.

The vast majority of the data obtained from the approaches mentioned above are consistent with the codon assignments listed in Figure 7.

Several further generalizations can be made concerning the code and interrelationships among codons.

1 Most of the 64 possible triplet combinations correspond to amino acids. Codons which show little activity for amino acids (*nonsense*

Figure 7. Nucleotide Sequences of RNA Codons

UpUpU UpUpC } PHE	UpCpU UpCpC } SER	UpApU UpApC } TYR	UpGpU UpGpC } CYS
UpUpA UpUpG } PHE	UpCpA UpCpG } SER	UpApA UpApG } TERM	UpGpA UpGpG (?-CYS, TRYPT, TERM) TRYPT
CpUpU CpUpC } LEU	CpCpU CpCpC } PRO	CpApU CpApC } HIS	CpGpU CpGpC } ARG
CpUpA CpUpG } LEU	CpCpA CpCpG } PRO	CpApA CpApG } GLU-NH$_2$	CpGpA CpGpG } ARG
ApUpU ApUpC } ILEU	ApCpU ApCpC } THR	ApApU ApApC } ASP-NH$_2$	ApGpU ApGpC } SER
ApUpA ApUpG } ILEU	ApCpA ApCpG } THR	ApApA ApApG } LYS	ApGpA ApGpG } ARG
GpUpU GpUpC } VAL	GpCpU GpCpC } ALA	GpApU GpApC } ASP	GpGpU GpGpC } GLY
GpUpA GpUpG } VAL	GpCpA GpCpG } ALA	GpApA GpApG } GLU	GpGpA GpGpG } GLY

Figure 8. Nucleic Acid and Protein Content of Bacteria*

	RNA	DNA	Protein
Micromoles of nucleotides or amino acids per gram dry weight	650	120	5130
Average molecular weight of monomer†	325	309	109.5
Milligrams of nucleotides or amino acids per gram dry weight	211	37	560
Milligrams of nucleotides or amino acids per gram dry weight, data for S. *typhimurium*, generation time 50 minutes‡	220	35	740

* Data for *E. coli* from CIW Publication 607.
† Without water of hydrolysis.
‡ From p. 63 of Kjeldgaard.[6]

Source: Roberts, R. B. (ed.), *Studies in Macromolecular* Biosynthesis, Publ. 624, 1964. p. 629.

Figure 9. Single-amino-acid Mutations in Proteins

Amino Acid Change	Base Change	Protein and Location of Residue, if known	Reference
Ala/val	C/U	Lgb, AP	13, 14
Val/ala	U/C	TS	15
Arg/gly	A/G, C/G	TMV 46, 61, 122, 134	16
Gly/arg	G/A, G/C	TS	15
Arg/ilu	G/U	TS	47
Arg/lys	G/A	TMV 46	17
Arg/ser	A/C, U	TS	15
Arg/thr	G/C	TS	15
Arg/try	C/U	MD	52
AsN/arg	. . .	TMV 33	18
AsN/asp	A/G	TMV 126	18
Asp/asN	G/A	Hb β79	19
AsN/lys	C,U/A,G	Hb α68, TMV 140	18, 20
AsN/ser	A/G	TMV 25, 33, 73, 126	17, 18
Asp/ala	A/C	TMV 19 (?)	18
Asp/gly	A/G	TMV 66, Lgb	13, 18
Gly/asp	G/A	Hb α22, α57, β16, TS	15, 21, 22, 23
GIN/arg	A/G	Hb α54, TMV 99	17, 24
Glu/ala	A/C	TS	15, 37
Glu/glN	G/C	Hb α30, β121	25, 26
GIN/glu	C/G	Hb α54	54
Glu/gly	A/G	Hb β7 TMV 97	18, 27
Gly/glu	G/A	TS	15
Glu/lys	G/A	Hb α116, β6, β7, β26, β121, γ5 or 6	27–31, 51
Glu/val	A/U	Hb β6, TMV 22* (?), TS	15, 18, 32, 33
Val/glu	U/A	Hb β67	23
Gly/ala	G/C	TMV	34
Gly/cys	G/U	TS	15
Gly/val	G/U	TS	15
His/arg	A/G	Hb β63	35
His/glN	C,U/A,G	Lgb	36
His/tyr	C/U	Hb α58, 87, β63	38, 39, 40
Ilu/met	A,C,U/G	TMV	18
Ilu/thr	U/C	TMV 21, 129	16, 17, 18
Thr/ilu	C/U	TMV 5, 59, TS	15, 18
Ilu/val	A/G	TMV 21, 24, 125, 129	17, 18
Leu/arg	U/G	TS	15
Leu/phe	C/U	TMV	18
Met/leu	A/U	Cyt.c	42
Pro/leu	C/U	TMV 20, 156	18, 34
Pro/ser	C/U	TMV 63	18
Pro/thr	C/A	TMV 20	17
Ser/gly	A/G	TMV 65	17
Ser/leu	C/U	TMV 55, TS	15, 18
Ser/phe	C/U	TMV 138, 148	16, 17, 18
Thr/ala	A/G	TMV 81	17
Thr/met	C/U	TMV 107	18
Thr/lys	C/A	Hb β87	50
Tyr/cys	A/G	TS	15
Tyr/phe	A/U	TMV	33
Val/met	G/A	TMV 11	17

* formerly glN/val

AP, alkaline phosphatase, *E. coli;* Lgb, bovine β lactoglobulin; Cyt c; human cytochrome c; TS, tryptophan synthetase, *E. coli;* TMV, tobacco mosaic virus coat protein; Hb, hemoglobin; MD, malate dehydrogenase *(Neurospora).*

References:

13. Gordon, W. G., J. J. Basch, and E. B. Kalan, *J. Biol. Chem.*, 236:2900, 1961.
14. Garen, A., C. Levinthal, and F. Rothman, "Deoxyribonucleic Acid," 190, N.Y. Macmillan, 1961.
15. Yanofsky, C., *The Bacteria*, 5:373, 1964.
16. Tsugita, A., *J. Mol. Biol.*, 5:284, 1962.
17. Funatsu, G., and H. Fraenkel-Conrat, *Biochemistry*, 3:1356, 1964.
18. Wittman, H. G., and B. Wittman-Liebol, *Cold Spring Harbor Symp. Quant. Biol.*, 28:589, 1963.
19. Lehmann, H., D. Beale and F. D. Bio-Daku, *Nature*, 203:363, 1964.
20. Baglioni, C., and V. M. Ingram, *Biochim. et Biophys. Acta*, 48:253, 1961.
21. Baglioni, C., *J. Biol. Chem.*, 237:69, 1962.
22. Gottlieb, A. J., A. Restrepi and H. A. Itano, *Fed. Proc.*, 23:172, 1964.
23. Chernoff, A. I. and P. E. Perrillie, *Biochem. Biophys. Res. Comm.*, 16:368, 1964.
24. Hanadu, M. and D. Rucknagel, *Biochem. Biophys. Res. Comm.*, 11:229, 1963.
25. Swenson, R. T., R. L. Hill, H. Lehmann and R. T. S. Jim, *J. Biol. Chem.*, 237:1517, 1962.
26. Baglioni, C., *Biochim. et Biophys. Acta*, 59:437, 1962.
27. Baglioni, C., and H. Lehmann, *Nature*, 196:229, 1962.
28. Hunt, J. A. and V. M. Ingram, *Nature*, 184:640, 1959.
29. Hill, R. L. and H. C. Schwartz, *Nature*, 184:641, 1959.
30. Hunt, J. A. and V. M. Ingram, *Nature*, 184:870, 1959.
31. Pierre, L. E., C. E. Rath and K. McCoy, *New England J. Med.*, 268:862, 1963.
32. Ingram, V. M., *Nature*, 180:326, 1957.
33. Tsugita, A., cited by Speyer, et al., *Proc. Nat. Acad. Sci.*, 48:441, 1962.
34. Tsugita, A. and H. Graenkel-Conrat, *J. Mol. Biol.*, 4:73, 1962.
35. Muller, C. J. and S. Kingma, *Biochim. Biophys. Acta*, 50:595, 1961.
36. Kalan, E. B., R. Greenberg, M. Walter and W. C. Gordon, *Biochem. & Biophys. Res. Comm.*, 16:199, 1964.
37. Yanofsky, C., *Cold Spring Harbor Symp. Quant. Biol.*, 28:581, 1963.
38. Gerald, P. A. and M. L. Efron, *Proc. Nat. Acad. Sci.*, 47:1758, 1961.
39. Jones, R. T., R. D. Coleman and P. Heller, *Fed. Proc.*, 23:173, 1964.
40. Ingram, V. M., *The Molecular Control of Cellular Activity*, (McGraw-Hill, N.Y.), p. 179, 1962.
41. Murayama, N., *Fed. Proc.*, 19:78, 1960.
42. Smith, E. L., *Fed. Proc.*, (in press) 1964.
43. Harada, K., and S. W. Fox, *Nature*, 201:335, 1964.
47. Yanofsky, C. A., *Biochem. Biophys. Res. Comm.*, 18:898, 1965.
50. Watson-William, E. S., et al., *Nature*, 205:1273, 1965.
51. Schneider, R. G., and R. T. Jones, *Science*, 148:240, 1965.
52. Munkres, K. D., and F. M. Richard, *Biochem. Biophys.*, 109:457, 1965.
54. Lister, R. G., J. V. Ruiz-Reyes, and A. Loria, *Blood*, 22:342, 1963.

codons)* may serve special functions, such as specifying the attachment of mRNA to ribosomes, the initiation and termination of a peptide chain (the first codon to be read and the phase or reading frame to be used), the release of a chain from sRNA and ribosome, etc.

2 Amino acids which are structurally or metabolically related (such as being synthesized *in vivo* from a common precursor) often have similar codons.

3 Codons for some of the amino acids are arranged in strikingly symmetric patterns. The following *synonym codon* sets have been found: (1) XpYpU, XpYpC; (2) XpYpA, XpYpG; (3) XpYpU, XpYpC, XpYpA, XpYpG, and (4) in the case of Leu codons, UpYpZ, CpYpZ.

4 In most cases, the efficiency of template activity of one member of a synonym codon differs from that of another.

5 Each triplet can occur in any one of three positions within the chain; i.e., as a 5′-terminal-, 3′-terminal-, or internal codon. The template activity of a codon may differ from that of the same codon in a different geographic position.

In summary, the sequential reading of three nucleotide bases at a time in a mRNA molecule results in the synthesis of a protein, one amino acid at a time, starting from its N-terminal end. Since the *E. coli* cell (see Figure 8) contains one active DNA strand composed of 3×10^6 bases, or one million triplets, sufficient information is available (if each triplet were used only for the coding of amino acids) to specify the sequence of 4000 proteins each with 250 amino acids.

MUTATIONS

A mutation represents an alteration or deletion of one or more bases in DNA. Such alterations often result in the replacement of one amino acid by another if the mutation occurs in a structural gene. Mutations can occur spontaneously or be induced by chemical or physical agents. In Figure 9 are listed the various single amino acid substitutions which have been found in different proteins occurring as a result of natural or artificially induced mutations.

Since the substitution of one amino acid for another has apparently occurred in each case in Figure 9 as the result of a one-step mutation, this implies that the codons for the two amino acids must differ by only a single base. Codon assignments can be checked in this way. Because almost every amino acid is represented by two or more synonym codons,

---

* There is some confusion over the term "nonsense" codon. Previously, three classes of codons were defined: "sense" meaning readable, "nonsense" meaning not readable, and "missense" meaning read incorrectly. As more was learned about the code, sense and missense ceased to be meaningful terms, while nonsense has been used to designate a codon with a special function such as chain initiation or termination.

many mutations (so-called *silent mutations*) will have no effect on the amino acid incorporated.

CODON SPECIFICITY

Codon specificity usually is high. However, the codon recognition mechanism is capable of being modified, and it is clear that a codon sometimes is read differently, in different cells. In other words, the codon dictionary is not invariant.

Besides interspecies variations, codon recognition within a cell can be influenced under certain conditions. For example, it is known that a small molecule (namely, streptomycin) can produce misreadings in the code *in vivo*. Furthermore, *in vitro*, large changes in reading properties are observed with variations in ionic environment (level of magnesium or potassium), pH, temperature, or presence of organic solvents. The influence of such factors upon the specificity of protein synthesis *in vivo* has not yet been fully assessed.

BIBLIOGRAPHY

Reviews:

Annual Review of Biochemistry
Cold Spring Harbor Symposia on Quantitative Biology, 28, 29: 1963, 1964.
Taylor, J. H., (ed.), *Molecular Genetics*, I, II: 1962, 1965.
Davidson, J. N. and W. E. Cohn, (ed.), *Progress in Nucleic Acid Research*, 1, 3: 1963, 1964.

General:

(1)   Chargaff, E., *Essays on Nucleic Acids*, 1963.
(2)   Chargaff, E., and J. N. Davidson (ed.), *The Nucleic Acids*, I, II: 1955, III: 1960.
(3)   Jordan, D., *The Chemistry of Nucleic Acids*, 1960.
(4)   Michelson, A. M., *The Chemistry of Nucleosides and Nucleotides*, 1963.
(5)   Roberts, R. B. (ed.), *Studies in Macromolecular Biosynthesis*, Publ. 624, 1964.
(6)   Steiner, R. F. and R. F. Beers, *Polynucleotides*, 1961.

METABOLISM OF NUCLEIC ACIDS

I. INTRODUCTION

Nucleic acids were discovered by Miecher in 1869 in fish sperms and other biologic materials. Since then, many theories have been postulated concerning the mode of biosynthesis of nucleic acids. Still we cannot adequately describe the process by which nucleic acids are formed in the living cell. This is due partly to the complex nature of the nucleic acids, and partly to the incompletely-understood heterogeneity of the substance. As proteins are built up by stringing together large numbers of amino acids, nucleic acids are built up from building units called nucleotides. The chief difference lies in the fact that about twenty amino acids are combined in the makeup of protein, whereas only four nucleotides are common in the production of nucleic acids. Each individual nucleotide consists of a nitrogenous base, a pentose sugar and a phosphate radical.

Base—Pentose—Phosphate

Nucleotides can be linked together in varying numbers, forming chains called polynucleotides. The inter-unit link is formed by a secondary connection of the phosphate group of one nucleotide to Carbon 3′ of the pentose radical of the next chain.

$$
\begin{array}{l}
\quad\quad\quad\quad | \\
\quad\quad\quad\quad | \\
\text{Base—Pentose—Phosphate} \\
\quad\quad\quad\quad\quad\quad | \\
\quad\quad\quad\text{Base—Pentose—Phosphate} \\
\quad\quad\quad\quad\quad\quad\quad\quad | \\
\quad\quad\quad\quad\quad\text{Base—Pentose—Phosphate} \\
\quad\quad\quad\quad\quad\quad\quad\quad\quad\quad | \\
\quad\quad\quad\quad\quad\quad\quad\quad\quad\quad |
\end{array}
$$

Two classes of these substances exist, differing mainly by the presence of the carbohydrate which they contain, although there are also minor differences between the bases: in one class, Ribonucleic acid (RNA), the carbohydrate is ribose and in the other class, Deoxyribonucleic acid (DNA), the ribose is substituted by 2-deoxyribose. Besides the pure chemical difference, they differ in biological function. DNA rep-

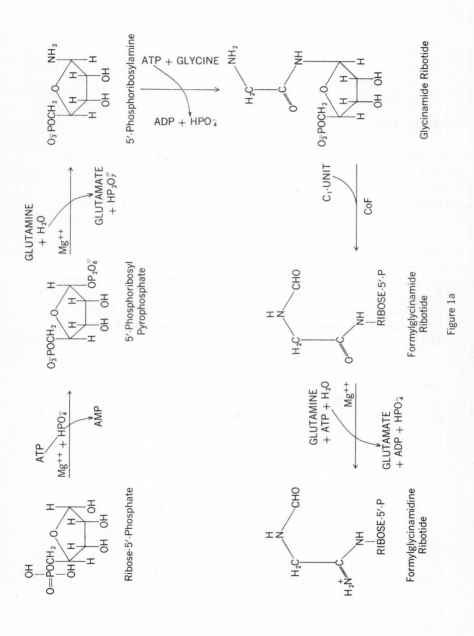

Figure 1a

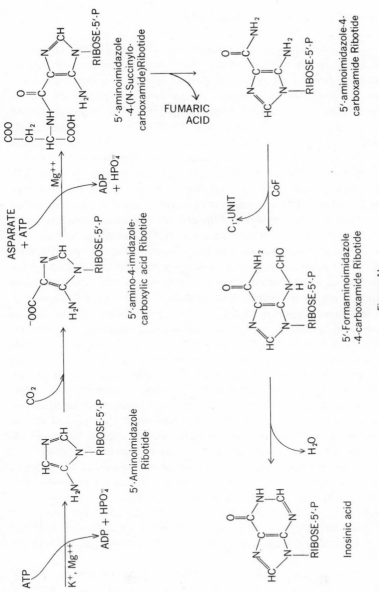

Figure 1b

SCHEME FOR THE SYNTHESIS OF INOSINIC ACID

resents the genetic material, whereas RNA participates in all phases of protein synthesis.

II. BIOSYNTHESIS OF PURINE NUCLEOTIDE

Formation of Inosinic Acid. The purines are synthesized in the body not as free purine, but as the nucleotide inosinic acid (hypoxanthine-ribose-5'-phosphate) which in turn is converted to adenine and guanine nucleotides. The formation of inosinic acid from ribose-5'-phosphate and its various intermediate forms is shown in Figure 1. The 5'-phosphoribosyl pyrophosphate reacts with glutamine, resulting in the formation of 5'-phosphoribocylamine by the replacement of the pyrophosphate group by an NH_2 group. In the next step, amide, the central piece of the purine ring, is formed by the condensation of 5'-phosphoribosylamine with glycine (the source of the carbon 4, 5 and nitrogen 7 of the purine ring). With the aid of ATP, the reaction is catalyzed by the glycinamide ribotide kinosynthase. In the presence of the enzyme glycinamide ribotide transformylase, glycinamide ribotide is converted to formylglycinamide ribotide, involving the participation of N^5, N^{10} anhydroformyl tetrahydrofolic acid. The formation of formylglycinamide ribotide is followed by the formation of formylglycinamidine ribotide; this in turn undergoes ring closure to give 5'-aminoimidazole ribotide. The 5'-aminoimidazole ribotide molecule is carboxylated by the enzyme aminoimidazole ribotide carboxylase, resulting in the formation of 5'-amino-4-imidazole-carboxylic acid ribotide; this is then converted to 5'-aminoimidazole-4-carboxamide ribotide in a process which requires ATP, and the participation of aspartic acid. During the above conversion, 5'-aminoimidazole-4- (N-Succinylocarboxamide) ribotide is formed as an intermediate compound and is cleaved by adenylosuccinase to 5'-aminoimidazole-4-carboxamide ribotide and fumaric acid. Finally, inosinic acid is formed by the action of the inosinicase enzyme upon 5'-formamido-4-imidazole carboxamide ribotide, with closure of hypoxanthine ring.

Synthesis of Adenylic Acid. The conversion of inosinic acid to adenylic acid is accomplished through the formation of an intermediate compound, adenylosuccinic acid, as shown in Figure 2.

Adenylosuccinic acid, formed by the participation of L-aspartic acid and guanosine triphosphate, causes the formation of fumaric acid and adenylic acid by its splitting in the presence of adenylosuccinase enzyme.

Formation of Guanylic Acid. Inosinic acid is first converted to xanthylic acid in the presence of diphosphopyridine nucleotide (DPN), which in turn undergoes amination in the 2 position due to the presence of glutamine and adenosine triphosphate (ATP). The scheme for synthesis is given in Figure 3.

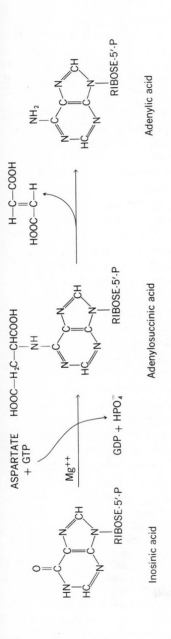

Figure 2

PROBABLE PATHWAY FOR THE CONVERSION OF INOSINIC ACID TO ADENYLIC ACID

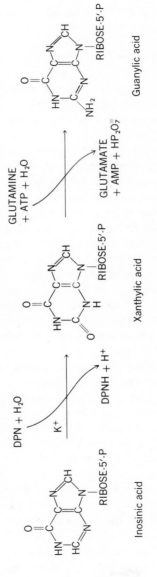

Figure 3

PROBABLE PATHWAY FOR THE CONVERSION OF INOSINIC ACID TO GUANYLIC ACID

III.   BIOSYNTHESIS OF PYRIMIDINE NUCLEOTIDE

The Pyridine. The pyrimidine ring is a six-membered ring with two nitrogen atoms; the pyrimidine bases of nucleotides bear an amino or hydroxy group in position 6, with an oxygen function in position 2. Besides the main pyrimidine base, cytosine, uracil, and thymine, several rare bases have been found recently. Viral nucleic acid contains 5'-hydroxymethyl cytosine and 5'-hydroxymethyluridine; in soluble RNA, pseudouridine, a "C-glycoside," was found.

The pathways of pyrimidine synthesis have been established, mainly through studies with microbial and liver enzymes acting upon labelled compounds. Like the purines, pyrimidines are synthesized as the nucleotides.

The biosynthesis of the pyrimidine ring begins with the reaction of the energy-rich compound, carbamyl phosphate, with aspartic acid; this forms carbamyl aspartate or ureidosuccinic acid. The reaction is catalyzed by the enzyme aspartate carbamyl transferase. Next the dihydro orotase enzyme acts upon carbamyl aspartic acid, forming dihydro orotic acid; this in turn is dehydrogenated to orotic acid by the enzyme dihydro orotic dehydrogenase, in the presence of diphosphopyridine nucleotide (DPN). Orotic acid, the key precursor of pyrimidine nucleotide, is then changed to orotidine-5'-phosphate, which in turn is decarboxylated to uridylic acid (uridine-5'-phosphate) by the action of orotidine-5'-phosphate pyrophosphorylase and orotidine-5'-phosphate decarboxylase respectively. Phosphorylation with ATP and kinase enzyme converts uridine-5'-phosphate to uridine monophosphate (UMP) or uridine triphosphate (UTP).

The cytidine nucleotide and thymidine nucleotide arise from the uridine derivatives. By enzymatic action in the presence of ammonia or glutamine, the C-6 hydroxyl group of uridine triphosphate is converted to an amino group, thus resulting in the formation of cytidine triphosphate. The transition to deoxyribose derivatives occurs at the level of the monophosphates by reduction of the sugar moiety followed by the methylation of the pyrimidine ring. The over-all scheme is given in Figure 4.

IV.   BIOSYNTHESIS OF DNA AND RNA

The mode of assembly of nucleotide units in the intracellular synthesis of RNA and DNA is not yet clear. But it can be said that the high molecular DNA is built up in the cell by the incorporation of triphosphate of the deoxynucleosides. The synthesis is accomplished by the addition of nucleotides to the free 3'-hydroxyl of deoxyribose, with loss of phos-

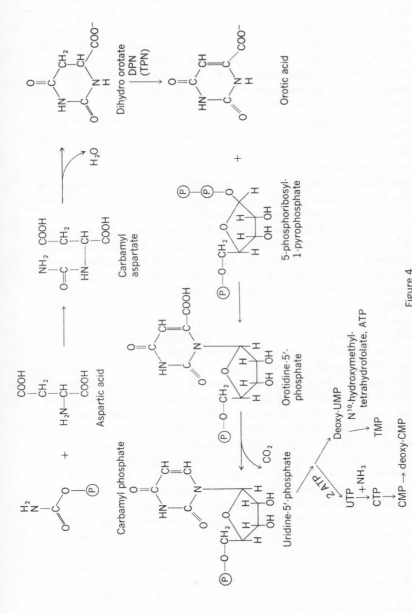

Figure 4

PROBABLE PATHWAY FOR THE BIOSYNTHESIS OF PYRIMIDINE NUCLEOTIDE

phate, thereby causing the elongation of the chain link by link as shown in Figure 5.

Incorporation of any one of the triphosphates of deoxyadenosine, deoxyguanosine, deoxycytidine or deoxythymidine requires the presence of all four deoxynucleoside triphosphates: deoxyadenosine triphosphate, deoxyguanosine triphosphate, deoxycytidine triphosphate and thymidine triphosphate, besides the presence of the highly polymerized primer DNA. The primer nucleic acid controls the nature of the nucleic acid formed; base composition, base sequence, and physical dimensions of the product correspond with the compound used as primer.

Inhibition of Nucleic Acid Synthesis. The synthesis of nucleic acids is inhibited by a number of substances which interfere with individual enzymic steps in the biosynthesis of purines and pyrimidines. Thus, structural analogs of pteroylglutamic acid interfere with the formation of cofactors required for formylation reactions involved in purine and pyrimidine synthesis. Azaserine and 6-diazo-5-keto-L-norleucine inhibit the utilization of glutamine in the formation of formylglycinamidine for purine synthesis. A number of purine derivatives such as 8-azaquanin and 6-mercaptopurine have been found to interfere with the nucleic acid synthesis through an unknown mechanism, probably through incorporation in the nucleic acids with the formation of abnormal nucleic acids. Structural analogs of pyrimidines such as 4-azathymine appear to act similarly.

Catabolism of Purines. The end products of purine metabolism vary widely with different animal species. In higher animals, pentose nucleic acids are degraded by various enzyme systems to yield mononucleotides, and the resulting purine compounds are converted stepwise to uric acid, which may be excreted unchanged, or may be further degraded to allantoin, or to glyoxylic acid and urea. On the other hand, in some microorganisms, purines are broken down to glyoxylic acid and urea via allantoin. Glyoxylic acid formed thus is converted to oxalic acid, whereas urea is hydrolyzed to carbon dioxide and ammonia.

Adenine and some guanine are deaminated to hypoxanthine, which is oxidized via xanthine and through the action of xanthine oxidase to uric acid. In most mammals, uric acid is further degraded to allantoin by the enzyme uricase. In man, however, and in other primates, and in some species of dogs, purine metabolism stops with uric acid, and is then excreted in the urine. (See Figure 6.) It has been postulated that hydroxyacetylene-diareine-carboxylic acid may be an intermediate in the conversion of uric acid to allantoin. Griffiths[1], after showing that uric acid can be oxidized at physiological pH in the presence of the cytochrome-cytochrome oxidase system, mentioned the possibility that uric acid is degraded in small quantities in organisms lacking uricase.

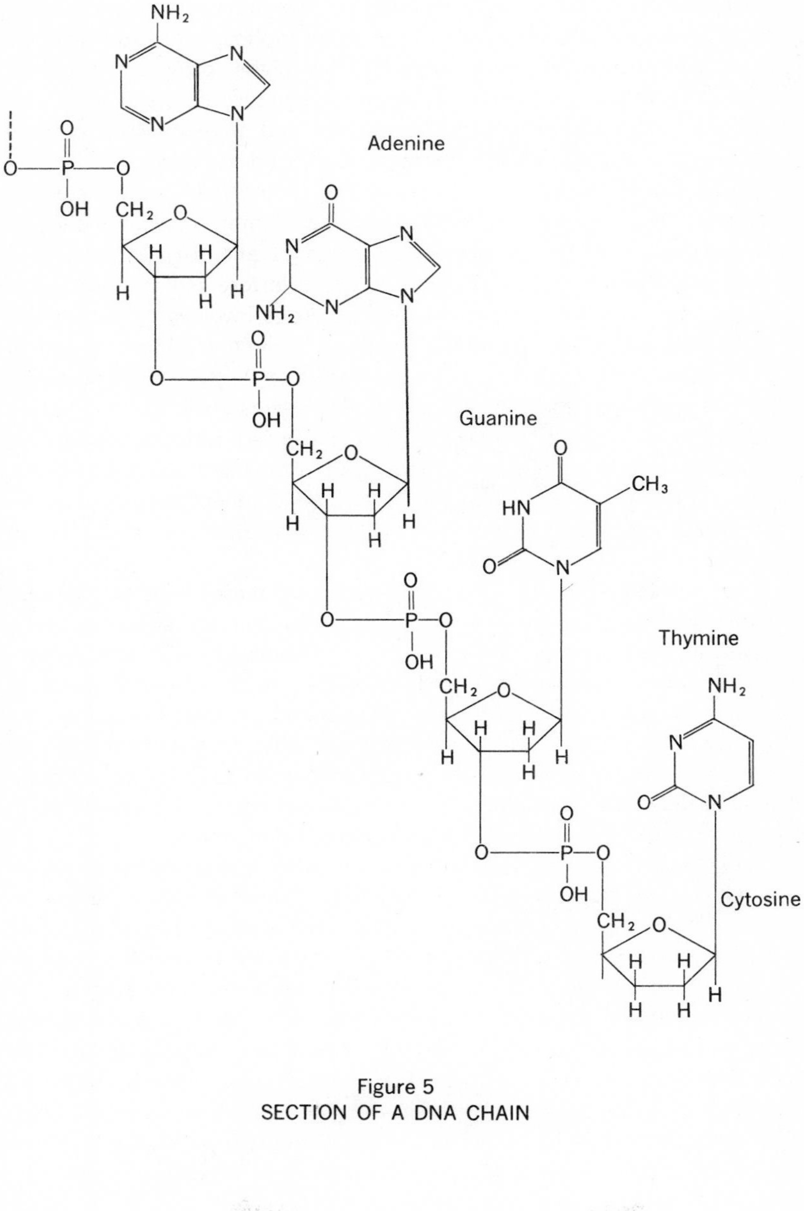

Figure 5
SECTION OF A DNA CHAIN

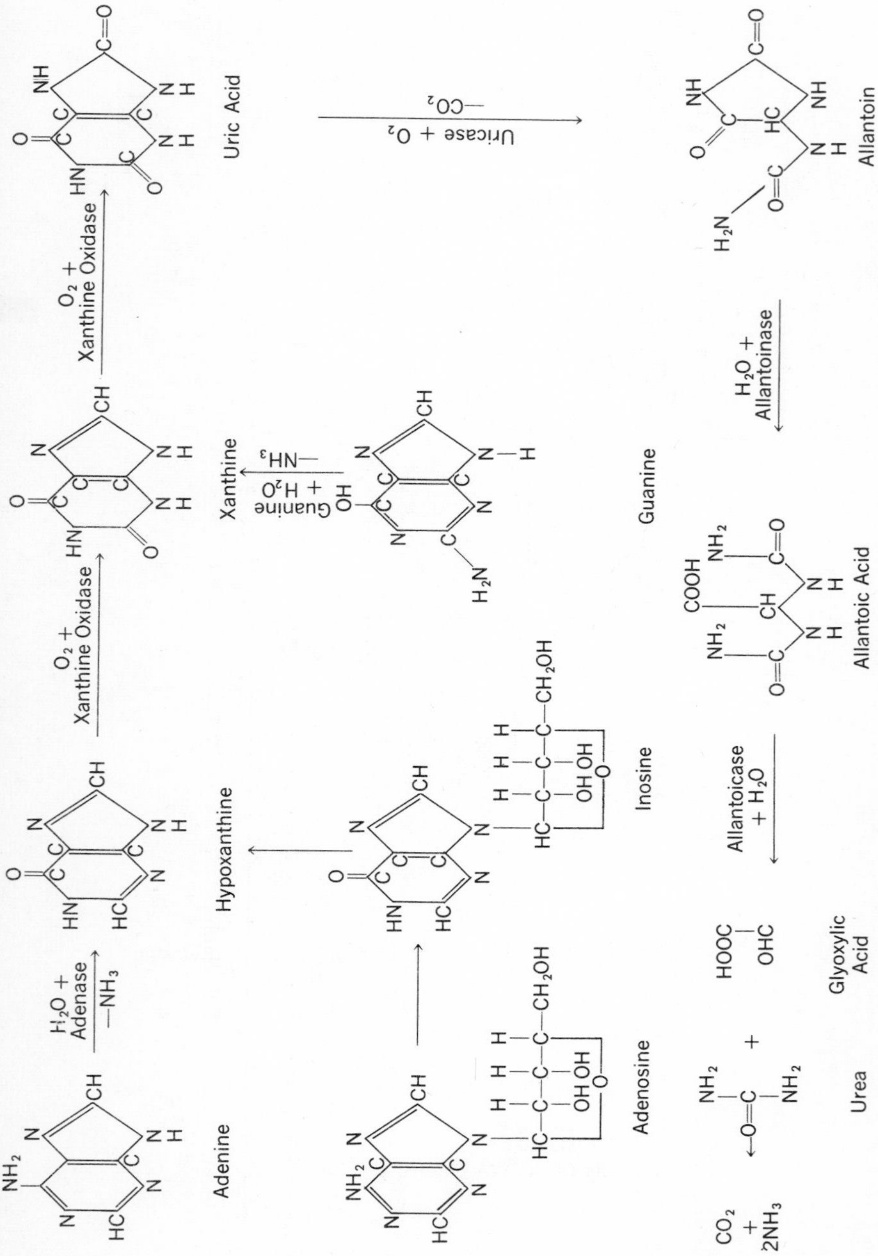

Figure 6

SCHEME OF PURINE CATABOLISM

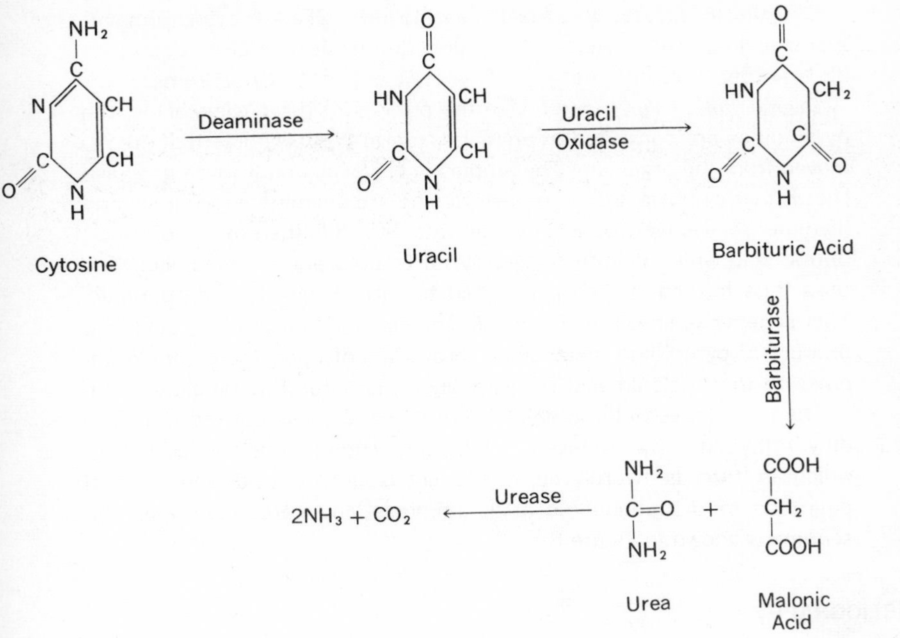

Figure 7
URACIL DEGRADATION

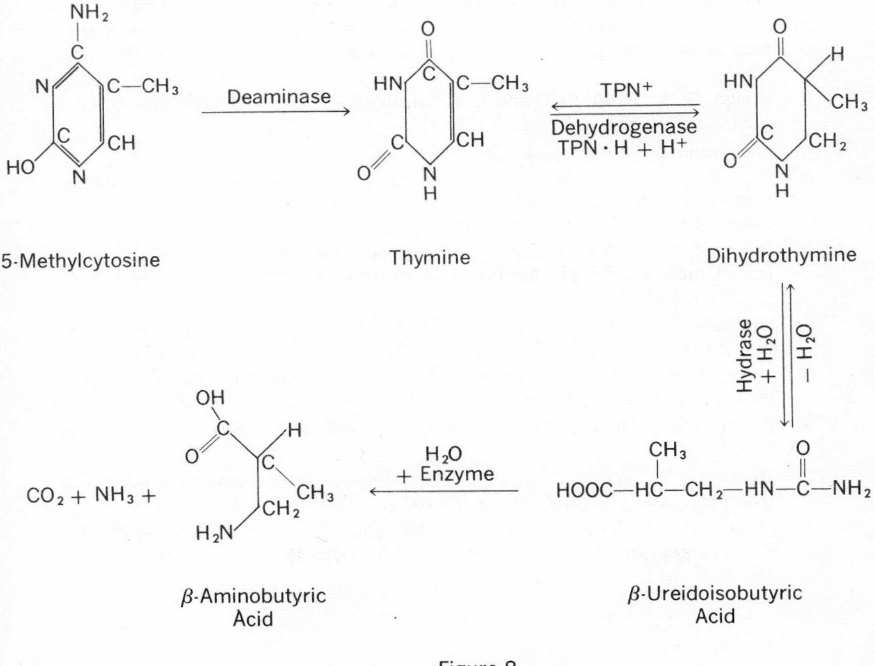

Figure 8
THYMINE DEGRADATION

Griffiths formulates the reaction as follows: $2Fe^{+++}$ cytochrome + 2 uric acid $\rightarrow$ $2Fe^{++}$ cytochrome + dehydrouric acid + $2H^+$; $2H^+ + 2Fe^{++}$ cytochrome + $\frac{1}{2} O_2 \rightarrow H_2O + 2Fe^{+++}$ cytochrome.

Degradation of Pyrimidines. Like the purines of the nucleic acids, the pyrimidines are converted in animal tissue to end products that are removed from the organism. The studies of Hayaishi and Kornberg[6,7] have shown that cytosine and 5'-methylcytosine are deaminated to uracil and thymine, respectively by a single enzyme. Uracil is then oxidized to barbituric acid which in turn is hydrolyzed to urea and malonic acid. The urea thus formed is then hydrolyzed to carbon dioxide and ammonia. This scheme is shown in Figure 7. The finding that malonic acid is a product of pyrimidine metabolism throws doubt upon the common impression that malonic acid is invariably an unnatural metabolic poison.

The first stages in the breakdown of thymine consist of reductions to dihydrothymine by reduced triphosphopyridine nucleotide(TPN.H), which in turn is hydrolyzed to β-ureidoisobutyric acid and is then degraded to β-aminobutyric acid, ammonia and carbon dioxide. The scheme is shown in Figure 8.

BIBLIOGRAPHY

References

1. Griffiths, M., "Oxidation of Uric Acid Catalyzed by Copper and by the Cytochrome-Cytochrome Oxidase System," *J. Biol. Chem.*, 197:399, 1952.

2. Cavalieri, L. F., and G. B. Brown, "The Mechanism of the Oxidation of Uric Acid Studied with Isotopic Nitrogen as a Tracer," *J. Am. Chem. Soc.*, 70:1242, 1948.

3. Brown, G. B., P. M. Roll, and L. F. Cavalieri, "The *in vivo* Oxidation of Uric Acid," *J. Biol. Chem.*, 171:835, 1947.

4. Laskowski, M., *Enzymes*, 1:956, 1951.

5. Franke W., and G. E. Hahn, "Untersuchungen zum Bakterillen Purinabbau. I. Über den Harnsäurenabbau durch Pseudomonas Aeruginosa (Bact. Pyocyaneum)," *Z. Physiol. Chem.*, 299:15, 1955.

6. Hayaishi, O., and A. Kornberg, "Enzymatic Formation of Barbituric Acid from Uracil and 5-Methylbarbituric Acid from Thymine," *J. Am. Chem. Soc.*, 73:2975, 1951.

7. Hayaishi, O., and A. Kornberg, "Metabolism of Cytosine, Thymine, Uracil, and Barbituric Acid by Bacterial Enzymes," *J. Biol. Chem.*, 197:717, 1952.

8. Wang, T. P., and J. O. Lampen, "Uracil Oxidase and the Isolation of Barbituric Acid from Uracil Oxidation," *J. Biol. Chem.*, 194:785, 1952.

9. Deuel, H. J., "The Metabolism of Some Pyrimidines," *J. Biol. Chem.*, 60:749, 1924.

10. Mendel, L. B., and V. L. Meyers, "The Metabolism of Some Pyrimidine Derivatives," *Am. J. Physiol.*, 26:77, 1910.

11. Elion, G. B., S. Singer, and G. H. Hitchings, "The Purine Metabolism of a 6-Mercaptopurine-Resistant Lactobacillus Casei," *J. Biol. Chem.*, 204:35, 1953.

12. Hitchings, G. H., and C. P. Rhoads, "6-Mercaptopurine," *Ann. N. Y. Acad. Sci.*, 60:183, 1954.
13. Reichard, P., et al., *The Nucleic Acids*, Vol. 1 and 2, 1955.
14. Schulman, M. P., et al., "Biosynthesis of the Purines. I. Hypoxanthine Formation in Pigeon Liver Homogenates and Extracts," *J. Biol. Chem.*, 196:499, 1952.
15. Greenberg, E., "De Novo Synthesis of Hypoxanthine Via Inosine-5-Phosphate and Inosine," *J. Biol. Chem.*, 190:611, 1951.
16. Schulman, M. P., and J. M. Buchanan, "Biosynthesis of the Purines. II. Metabolism of 4-Amino-5-Imidazolecarboxamide in Pigeon Liver," *J. Biol. Chem.*, 196:513, 1952.
17. Goldthwait, D. A., "5-Phosphoribosylamine, a Precursor of Glycinamide Ribotide," *J. Biol. Chem.*, 222:1051, 1956.
18. Carter, C. E., "Metabolism of Purines and Pyrimidines," *Ann. Rev. Biochem.*, 25:123, 1956.
19. Lukens, L. N., and J. M. Buchanan, "Further Intermediates in the Biosynthesis of Inosinic Acid," *J. Am. Chem. Soc.*, 79:1511, 1957.
20. Levenberg, B., and J. M. Buchanan, "Biosynthesis of the Purines. XII. Structure, Enzymatic Synthesis, and Metabolism of 5-Aminoimidazole Ribotide," *J. Biol. Chem.*, 224:1005, 1957.
21. Levenberg, B., and J. M. Buchanan, "Biosynthesis of the Purines. XII." *J. Biol. Chem.*, 224:1009, 1957.
22. Levenberg, B., J. M. Buchanan, and I. Melnick, "Biosynthesis of Purines. XV. The Effect of Aza-L-Serine and 6-Diazo-5-Oto-L-Norleucine on Inosinic Acid Biosynthesis De Novo," *J. Biol. Chem.*, 225:163, 1957.
23. Carter, C. E., and L. H. Cohen, "The Preparation and Properties of Adenylosuccinase and Adenylosuccinic Acid," *J. Biol. Chem.*, 222:17, 1956.
24. Liberman, I., "Enzymatic Synthesis of Adenosine-5' -Phosphate from Inosine-5'-Phosphate," *J. Biol. Chem.*, 223:327, 1956.
25. Franke, W., and L. E. Hahn, *Z. Physiol. Chem.*, 229:15, 1934.
26. Wright, L. D., et al., "Biological Precursors of the Pyrimidines," *J. Am. Chem. Soc.*, 73:1898, 1951.
27. Mitchell, H. K., M. B. Houlahan, and J. F. Nye, "The Accumulation of Orotic Acid by a Pyrimidineless Mutant of Neurospora," *J. Biol. Chem.*, 172:525, 1948.
28. Arvidson, H., et al., "Orotic Acid as a Precursor of Pyrimidines in the Rat," *J. Biol. Chem.*, 179:169, 1949.
29. Plentl, A. A., and R. Schoenheimer, "Studies in the Metabolism of Purines and Pyrimidines by Means of Isotopic Nitrogen," *J. Biol. Chem.*, 153:203, 1944.
30. Kalckar, H. M., and D. Rittenberg, "Rejuvenation of the Muscle Adenylic Acid Nitrogen *in vivo* Studied with Isotopic Nitrogen," *J. Biol. Chem.*, 170:455, 1947.
31. Hartman, S. C., and J. M. Buchanan, "Nucleic Acids, Purines, Pyrimidines (Nucleotide Synthesis)," *Ann. Rev. Biochem.*, 28:365, 1959.
32. Borell, U., "Influence of Ovarian Hormones on the Metabolism of Nucleic Acids and Phospholipids in the Rabbit Uterus," *Acta Endocrinol.*, 9:141, 1952.
33. Skipper, H. E., L. L. Bennett, Jr., and L. W. Law, "Effects of A-Methopterin on Formate Incorporation into the Nucleic Acids of Susceptible and Resistant Leukemic Cells," *Cancer Res.*, 12:677, 1952.
34. Shive, W., J. M. Ravel, and R. E. Eakin, "An Interrelationship of Thymidine and Vitamin B_{12}," *J. Am. Chem. Soc.*, 70:2614, 1948.

35. Kitay, E., W. S. McNutt, and E. E. Snell, "The Non-Specificity of Thymidine as a Growth Factor for Lactic Acid Bacteria," *J. Biol. Chem.*, 177:993, 1949.

36. Leslie, I., and J. N. Davidson, "The Effect of Insulin on Cellular Composition and Growth of Chick-Heart Explants," *Biochem. J.*, 49:Proc. xli, 1951.

37. Telfer, M. A., "Influence of Estradiol on Nucleic Acids, Respiratory Enzymes, and the Distribution of Nitrogen in the Rat Uterus," *Arch. Biochem. Biophys.*, 44:111, 1953.

38. Jeener, R., "Acides Nucléiques et Phosphatases au cours de Phénomènes de Croissance Provoqués par l'Oestradiol et la Prolactine," *Biochim. Biophys. Acta*, 2:439, 1948.

39. MacLeod, P. R., and H. A. Lardy, "Metabolic Functions of Biotin. II. The Fixation of Carbon Dioxide by Normal and Biotin-Deficient Rats," *J. Biol. Chem.*, 179:733, 1949.

40. Sahasrabudhe, M. R., and M. V. L. Rao, "Effect of Vitamin B_{12} on the Synthesis of Protein and Nucleic Acids in the Liver," *Nature*, 168:605, 1951.

41. Buchanan, J. M., and D. W. Wilson, "Biosynthesis of Purines and Pyrimidines," *Federation Proc.*, 12:646, 1953.

42. Greenberg, E., "Mechanisms Involved in the Biosynthesis of Purines," *Federation Proc.*, 12:651, 1953.

I. INTRODUCTION

Definitions[1] and General Properties.

a. aldoses and ketoses

Carbohydrates are polyhydroxy aldehydes (aldoses) or polyhydroxy ketones (ketoses), or substances that yield such compounds on hydrolysis. The simpler carbohydrates (sugars) have names which end in -ose. Carbohydrates that cannot be hydrolyzed to give simpler sugars are termed monosaccharides. Polysaccharides are condensation polymers of a large number of monosaccharide residues, linked by acetal bridges. Homopolysaccharides yield only one type of monosaccharide on hydrolysis, heteropolysaccharides yield more than one type of monosaccharide on hydrolysis. Oligosaccharides are carbohydrates that yield a few monosaccharide residues per molecule on hydrolysis: those that yield two such residues are termed disaccharides. Toward alkaline copper(II) reagents, all monosaccharides and some oligosaccharides behave as reducing substances. Non-reducing oligosaccharides have no free carbonyl or hemiacetal group.

Generic names for monosaccharides have a stem indicating the number of carbon atoms, and a suffix -ose (aldose) or -ulose (ketose): for example pentose, hexulose. The carbon chain is numbered starting from the aldehyde group (aldoses), or from the chain terminus nearest the carbonyl group (ketoses). The carbonyl function of ketoses is understood to be in the 2-position, unless it is specified by number, as, for example, 3-hexulose.

Monosaccharides are rarely encountered as the free aldehyde or ketone forms, and commonly exist as cyclic hemiacetals, formed by intramolecular addition to the carbonyl group by the hydroxyl group on the carbon atom in the γ or δ (rarely ε)-position to the carbonyl group. The resultant ring-form is indicated in the name of the monosaccharide by replacement of the final -se by the suffix -furanose, -pyranose (or -septanose), according to whether the resultant oxygen-containing heterocyclic ring contains five, six (or seven) atoms, respectively.

b. reduced, oxidized, and other modified forms

Reduction of the carbonyl group of an aldolase yields a polyhydric alcohol generically termed an alditol. Oxidation of C-1 of an aldose to a carboxyl group gives a product termed an aldonic acid. The product formed by oxidation of the ω-carbon of an aldose to a carboxyl group is known as a uronic acid. Oxidation of the ω-carbon of an aldose to an aldehyde group gives a product termed a dialdose. Oxidation of C-1 and the ω-carbon of an aldose to carboxyl groups yields a dicarboxylic acid known as an aldaric acid. A dicarbonyl monosaccharide, derived by oxidation of one of the secondary alcohol groups in an aldose to a carbonyl group, is termed an aldosulose; the ketone group is understood to be at the 2-position unless it is specified by number to be otherwise, for example, 3-hexosulose.

The term "deoxy" indicates replacement of a hydroxyl group by a hydrogen atom at a position denoted by a numerical prefix, for example 2-deoxypentose. Replacement of a hydroxyl function by another group normally requires two prefixes, for example 2-deoxy-2-fluoropentose, 2-amino-2-deoxyhexose. The prefixes "thio" (and "seleno"), which indicate replacement of oygen by sulfur (or selenium), do not require the use of deoxy, for example, 4-thiohexofuranose.

c. glycosides

Glycosides are mixed acetals formed by condensation of a reducing sugar and an alcohol (or phenol) in equimolar proportion, with elimination of one equivalent of water. They can be regarded as being formed from one of the intramolecularly cyclized hemiacetal forms of the sugar, by further condensation with a molecule of the alcohol to give a mixed full acetal. Simple glycosides are named from the radical of the alcohol, and the appropriate stem from the name of the sugar, with the suffix -ide, for example, methyl hexopyranoside. Complex glycosides may be named more conveniently as O-glycosyl derivatives of the appropriate alcohol. The term glycosyl is the name of the radical formed when the hemiacetal hydroxyl group is removed from a cyclic sugar. The non-sugar moiety of a glycoside is known as the aglycon. The so-called N-glycosides are N-glycosyl derivatives of amines.

d. osazones and osotriazoles

Aldoses and 2-ketoses react with excess arylhydrazines to give products termed arylosazones, which are chelated 1,2-bis(arylhydrazones) of the corresponding aldosuloses. Arylosazones are converted by acidified aqueous-alcoholic copper(II) sulfate solution into heterocyclic derivatives known as osotriazoles. The latter frequently serve as excellent characterizing derivatives for monosaccharides.

$$\begin{array}{ccc} \text{CHO} & \text{CH}_2\text{OH} \\ | & | \\ \text{CHOH} & \text{CO} \\ | & \text{or} & | \\ (\text{CHOH})_n & (\text{CHOH})_n \\ | & | \\ \text{CH}_2\text{OH} & \text{CH}_2\text{OH} \\ \text{aldose} & \text{ketose} \end{array} \xrightarrow{\text{ArNHNH}_2} \begin{array}{c} \text{HNAr} \\ \text{N} \\ \text{HC} \quad \text{H} \\ \text{C} \quad \text{NAr} \\ \text{N} \\ (\text{CHOH})_n \\ \text{CH}_2\text{OH} \\ \text{arylosazone} \end{array} \xrightarrow{\text{CuSO}_4} \begin{array}{c} \text{HC=N} \\ \quad \text{NAr} \\ \text{C=N} \\ (\text{CHOH})_n \\ \text{CH}_2\text{OH} \\ \text{arylosotriazole} \end{array}$$

Optical Activity and Stereochemistry.

a. basic relationships

A straight-chain monosaccharide having n asymmetrically-substituted carbon atoms can have 2^n stereoisomeric forms. Like-ended derivatives, such as alditols, aldaric acids, and dialdoses, have fewer stereoisomeric forms. Basic configurational relationships between the sugars may be indicated by formulas of the acyclic sugars in the Fischer projection.[2] Bonds on the vertical axis project below the plane of the paper, and those on the horizontal axis project above the plane. The (+)-enantiomorph of glyceraldehyde is used as the primary configurational standard[3] and is given the symbol[4] D-; its enantiomorph is given the symbol L-. The formulas as depicted are known to be

$$\begin{array}{cccc} \text{HC=O} & \text{HC=O} & \text{HC=O} & \text{HC=O} \\ \text{H} \diamondsuit \text{OH or} & \text{H——OH} & \text{HO} \diamondsuit \text{H or} & \text{HO——H} \\ \text{CH}^2\text{OH} & \text{CH}_2\text{OH} & \text{CH}_2\text{OH} & \text{CH}_2\text{OH} \\ \multicolumn{2}{c}{\text{D-(+)-Glyceraldehyde}} & \multicolumn{2}{c}{\text{L-(−)-Glyceraldehyde}} \end{array}$$

configurationally correct in the absolute sense, as are all structures which have been unambiguously correlated with this standard.[5] Those sugars having the hydroxyl group of the highest-number asymmetrically-substituted carbon atom on the right in the Fischer projection are termed D-sugars; those having it on the left are termed L-sugars. Configurational relationships between D-glyceraldehyde, and the tetroses, pentoses, and hexoses of the D series are shown in Chart 1. The mirror-image form of each structure is the corresponding L enantiomorph. The terms *glycero-*, *erythro-*, *threo-*, *ribo-*, *arabino-*, *xylo-*, *lyxo-*, *allo-*, *altro-*, *gluco-*, *manno-*, *gulo-*, *ido-*, *galacto-*, and *talo-*, are used, italicized, in conjunction with D- or L-, as configurational prefixes for groups of one, two, three, or four asymmetric centers on a carbon chain, whenever suitable trivial names are

Chart 1.

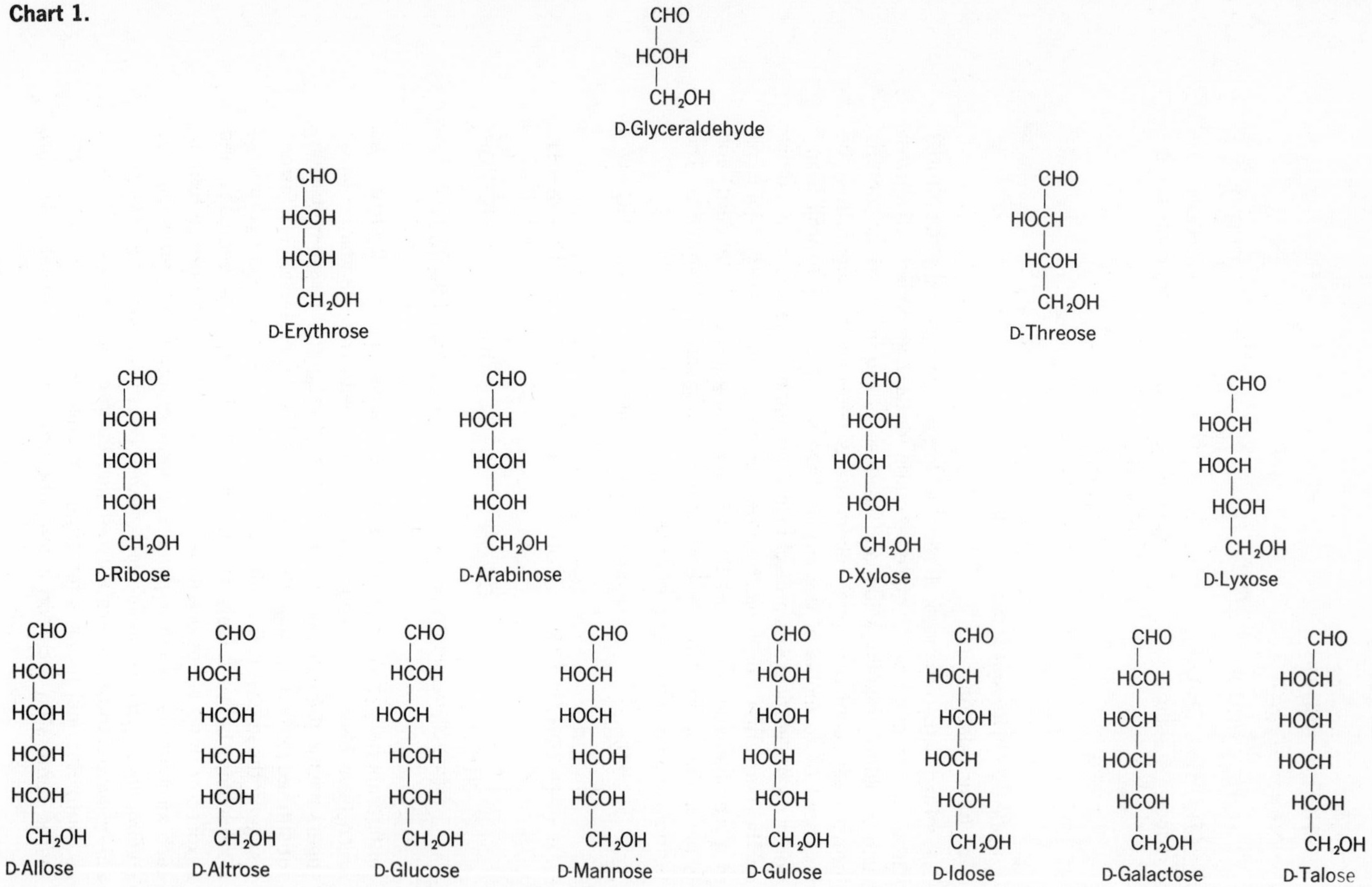

D-Glyceraldehyde

D-Erythrose

D-Threose

D-Ribose

D-Arabinose

D-Xylose

D-Lyxose

D-Allose

D-Altrose

D-Glucose

D-Mannose

D-Gulose

D-Idose

D-Galactose

D-Talose

not available. The hexuloses psicose, fructose, sorbose, and tagatose have the *ribo-, arabino-, xylo-,* and *lyxo-* configurations, respectively, and each can exist in D- and L-forms. Prefixes sufficient to describe the number of asymmetric centers are used, for example, 2-deoxy-D-*erythro*-pentose, D-*glycero*-tetrulose. Asymmetric centers need not be contiguous carbons, for example, D-*xylo*-3-hexulose. Sugars having more than four asymmetric centers are named with appropriate supplementary prefixes, for example, D-*glycero*-D-*gulo*-heptose, D-*erythro*-D-*manno*-nonulose.

b. cyclic forms

A new center of asymmetry is generated when a sugar undergoes intramolecular hemiacetal formation. Two diastereoisomers are possible for each ring form; they differ in configuration at the carbon atom where cyclization takes place. The two forms are termed anomers, and the new asymmetrically-substituted carbon is termed the anomeric (or lactolic) carbon atom. Anomers are differentiated by the prefixes α and β, defined by Hudson[4,6] as follows: in the D-series the more dextrorotatory member of an α,β-pair of anomers is to be named α-D-, the other being β-D-. In the L series the more levorotatory member of such a pair is given the name α-L- and the other β-L-. Although based on rotatory relationships, these definitions are consistent in the absolute sense for the free cyclic sugars and the vast majority of their derivatives. These anomeric configurations may be represented by formal Fischer projections of the cyclic sugars, drawn so that the ring bridge emerges vertically from the anomeric carbon atom. In this arrangement, α-anomers have the anomeric hydroxyl group, and the hydroxyl group on the highest-numbered asymmetrically-substituted carbon atom, in a formal *cis*-relation; β-anomers have the two groups in a formal *trans*-relation. The anomeric prefix *and* the configurational symbol are required to describe the total stereochemistry at the anomeric carbon atom.

Haworth-type formulas[7] are useful for expressing configurational relationships in cyclic sugars. The ring is to be considered in a horizontal plane perpendicular to the plane of the paper, with the shaded edge toward the observer. Substituent groups are represented as projected above or below a hypothetical planar ring. The Fischer formula for a cyclic compound may be related to the Haworth formula by rotating, through 120 degrees, the tetrahedron of the carbon atom bearing the ring oxygen atom, to bring all of the atoms of the ring into the vertical plane. In this representation, all groups on the left in the Fischer projection are "up" in the Haworth formula, and all groups on the right in the Fischer projection are "down" in the Haworth formula. These relationships are illustrated for α-D-glucopyranose and β-D-fructofuranose.

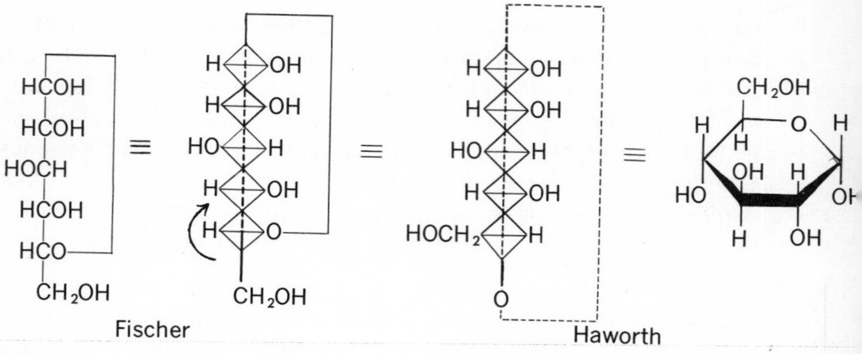

Fischer   Haworth

α-D-Glucopyranose

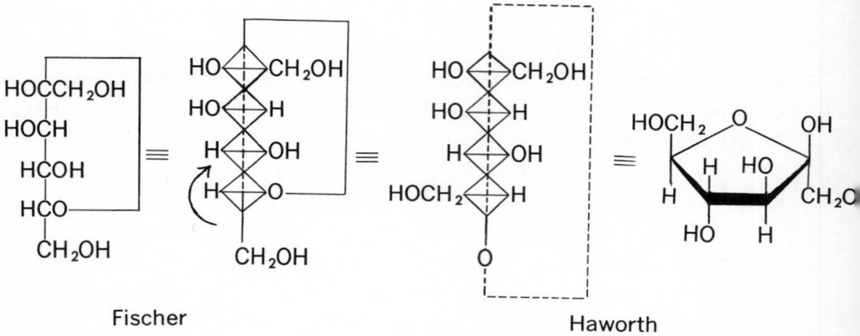

Fischer   Haworth

β-D-Fructofuranose

Haworth formulas are customarily drawn with the anomeric carbon atom on the extreme right, and with clockwise ring numbering. These formulas are formalized perspective drawings rather than projections, and if the formulas are rotated in the plane of the paper, simultaneous rotation of three planes takes place. Addenda on the plane of substituents above the ring, and those on the plane of substituents below the ring, must remain in the same relative positions above and below the ring. It is common practice to omit from Haworth formulas the hydrogen atoms attached to the ring carbons.

Conformations of monosaccharides.

The favored conformation of acyclic sugar derivatives is generally considered[8] to be that in which the chain of carbon atoms adopts a planar, zig-zag arrangement, by antiparallel disposition of the largest groups along each carbon-carbon bond, as illustrated for D-glucitol.

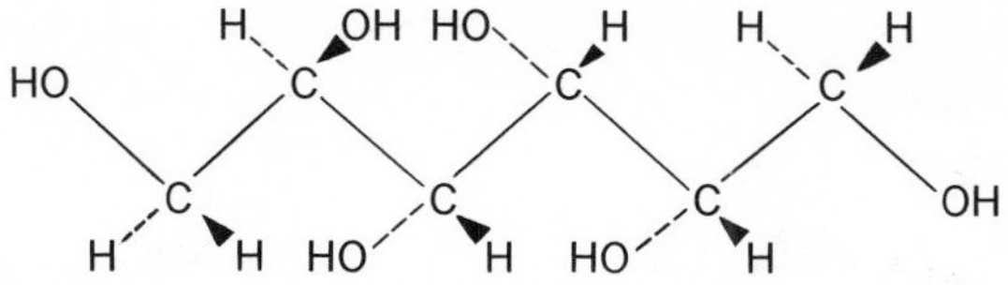

D-Glucitol
Planar Zig-zag Conformation

X-ray crystallographic analyses have verified, in a number of examples, the validity of this postulate for certain solid, crystalline derivatives.[9] In solution, rotation about carbon–carbon bonds undoubtedly occurs at room temperature, but the planar, zig-zag conformation appears to be the most highly-populated rotamer state. Fischer projections of acyclic sugar chains, while useful for indicating configurational relationships, represent very improbable conformations; a vicinal diol configurationally *cis* in the Fischer projection is *trans* (antiparallel) in the favored conformation.

Pyranoid sugars and their derivatives can be formulated in two chairlike conformations which are free from bond-angle strain.[10-13] In the representation given below, it is understood that ring-numbering runs

C1   *1C*
Pyranoid Ring Conformations

clockwise, and the symbols given are those of the Rèeves system.[10] Other systems of nomenclature have been proposed,[13,14] but have been less widely used. The formulas are readily related to the Haworth (and thus to Fischer) formulas; groups which are "up" or "down" in the Haworth formula are correspondingly "up" or "down" in any conformational representation, provided both types of formula are so oriented that the ring-numbering is in the same direction. The pyranoid chair conformations are geometrically similar to the chair conformation of cyclohexane, but are considered to be somewhat more easily distorted. The energy barrier for interconversion between the two pyranoid ring conformations is not considered high enough to permit isolation of individual conformers at room temperature.

One of the two conformers is usually much more stable than the other. For most sugars commonly encountered in nature, the *C1* conformation is the favored pyranoid ring conformation, as shown below for α-D-glucopyranose. Axial substituents are subject to steric crowding, and that

Cl
favored

1C
not favored

α-D-Glucopyranose

conformer having the more groups equatorial is usually the more stable. A polar group at the anomeric carbon atom may be more stable in the axial rather than the equatorial orientation, owing to dipole interactions with the unshared electron pairs on the ring oxygen atom (anomeric effect).[12, 13, 15, 16] Solvation and hydrogen-bonding effects may also be significant in determining the favored conformation. Interaction energies have been determined which permit calculation of approximate values for the conformational free energies of pyranoid sugars.[12, 13, 17] The predicted favored conformations of a number of pyranoid sugars and derivatives have been verified for the solid state by X-ray crystallography,[18] and supporting evidence for the sugars and their derivatives has been provided by infrared,[19] and especially (in solution) by nuclear magnetic resonance[20,21] and spectroscopy. Most pyranoid sugars and their derivatives appear to exhibit a high degree of conformational purity in solution at room temperature.

In addition to the chair conformations, the pyranoid ring may be formulated in the flexible cycle,[22] where it is also free of bond-angle strain. The cycle includes six boat forms and six skew (twist) forms; each boat form represents a maximum-energy transition state between a pair of skew forms. Non-bonded interactions render the skew, and more especially the boat, forms less stable than the favored chair form. The boat forms may be disregarded as significant contributors to the conformational population of pyranoid sugars at room temperature.[12] The energy required for conversion from the favored chair form into the flexible cycle is small compared with that required for most chemical reactions, and consequently the skew and boat forms may be significant intermediates in reactions of the sugars.

When four of the atoms of the pyranoid ring are constrained to coplanarity, as by a double bond, two half-chair forms are possible, one of which will usually be favored.[11]

$H1$ $1H$

Half-chair Conformations

The favored conformation of furanoid ring-systems is one that is distorted from planarity, so that some relief of the severe non-bonded interactions, present in the planar structure, is achieved. Two relatively strain-free conformations are possible for cyclopentane,[23] one in which four of the carbon atoms define a plane and the fifth is above or below this plane (C_s, or envelope, conformation), and another in which three carbon atoms lie in a plane, and the other two carbon atoms are displaced by equal amounts on either side of the plane (C_2, or twist, conformation).

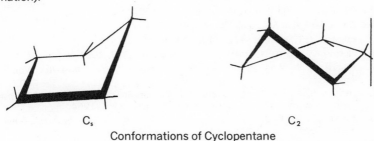

C_s C_2

Conformations of Cyclopentane

X-Ray crystallographic data show[18] that, in the solid state, the furanoid ring-system is non-planar, corresponding to the C_s conformation, and in solution the evidence of nuclear magnetic resonance spectroscopy indicates that the C_s, and sometimes the C_2, conformation of the furanoid ring is the favored form.[12, 24] For any furanoid ring there are ten possible C_s and ten C_2 modes.[21]

BIBLIOGRAPHY

1. "Rules of Carbohydrate Nomenclature," *J. Org. Chem.*, 28:281, 1963.
2. Fischer, E., "Uber die Configuration des Traubenzuckers und Seiner Isomeren," *Ber.*, 24:1836, 1891.
3. Rosanoff, M. A., "On Fischer's Classification of Stereo-Isomers," *J. Am. Chem. Soc.*, 28:114, 1906.
4. Hudson, C. S., "Historical Aspects of Emil Fischer's Fundamental Conventions for Writing Stereo-Formulas in a Plane," *Advan. Carbohydrate Chem.*, 3:1, 1948.
5. Bijvoet, J. M., A. F. Peerdeman, and A. J. van Bommel, "Determination of the Absolute Configuration of Optically Active Compounds by Means of X-Rays," *Nature*, 168:271, 1951.

6. Hudson, C. S., "The Significance of Certain Numerical Relations in the Sugar Group," *J. Am. Chem. Soc.,* 31:66, 1909.

7. Drew, H. D. K., and W. N. Haworth, "A Critical Study of Ring Structure in the Sugar Group," *J. Chem. Soc.,* p. 2303, 1926.

8.a. Barker, S. A., E. J. Bourne, and D. H. Whiffen, "An Explanation of the Preferential Formation of Certain Rings in Acetals of the Polyhydric Alcohols," *J. Chem. Soc.,* p. 3865, 1952.

8.b. Schwarz, J. C. P., "Steric Effects in the Oxidation of Hexitols with Periodate," *J. Chem. Soc.,* p. 276, 1957.

9. Littleton, C. D., *Acta Cryst.,* 6:775, 1953.

10. Reeves, R. E., "Cuprammonium-Glycoside Complexes," *Advan. Carbohydrate Chem.,* 6:107, 1951.

11. Capon, B., and W. G. Overend, "Constitution and Physico-chemical Properties of Carbohydrates," *Advan. Carbohydrate Chem.,* 15:11, 1960.

12. Lemieux, R. U., in de Mayo, P. (ed.), *Molecular Rearrangements,* p. 709, 1963.

13. Angyal, S. J., in Eliel, E. L., et al. (eds.), *Conformational Analysis,* p. 351, 1965.

14.a. Isbell, H. S., *J. Res. Natl. Bur. Std.,* 57:171, 1956.

14.b. Guthrie, R. D., *Chem. Ind.,* p. 1593, 1958.

14.c. Isbell, H. S., and R. S. Tipson, *Science,* 130:793, 1959.

14.d. *J. Res. Natl. Bur. Std.,* 64A:171, 1960.

15. Edward, J. T., *Chem. Ind.,* p. 1102, 1955.

16. Horton, D. and W. N. Turner, *J. Org. Chem.,* 30:3387, 1965.

17. Angyal, S. J., V. A. Pickles and R. Ahluwahlia, *Carbohydrate Res.,* Vol. 1, 1966.

18. Jeffrey, G. A., and R. D. Rosenstein, "Crystal-Structure Analysis in Carbohydrate Chemistry," *Advan. Carbohydrate Chem.,* 19:7, 1964.

19.a. Barker, S. A., E. J. Bourne, and D. H. Whiffen, *Methods Biochem., Anal.,* 3:213, 1956.

19.b. Isbell, H. S., et al., *J. Res. Natl. Bur. Std.,* 57:179, 1956.

19.c. Tipson, R. S., and H. S. Isbell, *J. Res. Natl. Bur. Std.,* 64A:239, 1960; 65A:249, 1961.

20.a. Lemieux, R. U., et al., "Configuration Effects on the Proton Magnetic Resonance Spectra of Six-Membered Ring Compounds," *J. Am. Chem. Soc.,* 80:6098, 1958.

20.b. Lemieux, R. U., and J. D. Stevens, *Can. J. Chem.,* 43:2059, 1965.

21. Hall, L. D., "Nuclear Magnetic Resonance," *Advan. Carbohydrate Chem.,* 19:51, 1964.

22. Bentley, R., "The Conformation of Methyl Idopyranosides," *J. Am. Chem. Soc.,* 82:2811, 1960.

23. Kilpatrick, J. E., K. S. Pitzer, and R. Spitzer, "The Thermodynamics and Molecular Structure of Cyclopentane," *J. Am. Chem. Soc.,* 69:2483, 1947.

24. Lemieux, R. U., *Can. J. Chem.,* 39:116, 1961.

II. NATURAL MONOSACCHARIDES

General.[1-4]

The monosaccharides are all soluble in water, in most cases highly so, and the solutions usually have a sweet taste. Most of the free sugars have been obtained in crystalline form, but crystallization may be difficult, especially if crystal nuclei are not available.[5] Crystalline sugars may undergo decomposition at or near their melting points, and identification by melting point data[6] alone is not always reliable. Infrared spectral comparison[7] gives a more reliable indication of the identity of two samples of a sugar, provided the spectra are measured under similar conditions. The identity of two crystalline samples is established unequivocally if they have the same sign of optical rotation and give identical X-ray powder diffraction patterns.[8] Enantiomorphs are not distinguished by the X-ray powder technique. Dimorphous forms of the same sugar give different X-ray diffraction patterns. The most reliable criteria of purity of a crystalline sugar are chromatographic homogeneity, and the equilibrium specific rotation,[9, 10] as determined on a concentrated solution.

In aqueous solution, a single anomeric form of a free sugar undergoes aldehyde-hemiacetal equilibration, giving rise to the observed phenomenon of mutarotation. Small proportions of added acid or base cause marked acceleration of mutarotation. Although the proportion of free aldehyde form of the sugar present during mutarotation is usually very small, several of the cyclic forms may be involved, and the final value of the specific rotation corresponds to an equilibrated mixture of the various tautomeric forms in solution.

Aldoses do not restore the color to Schiff reagent, since little or no free aldehyde form is present in solution, but are oxidized to aldonic acids by aqueous bromine, a reaction that can be used to distinguish aldoses from ketoses. Monosaccharide sugars are relatively stable in dilute aqueous acid. Hot concentrated mineral acids cause dehydration by a series of β-eliminations with concomitant cyclization, to give 2-furaldehyde (from pentoses) or derivatives thereof (from hexoses). These derivatives give characteristic color reactions with various polyhydric phenols, according to whether the precursor is a pentose, hexose, 6-deoxyhexose, and so on. These color reactions form the basis of many qualitative tests and analytical determinations used for sugars.[11]

In aqueous alkaline solution, sugars undergo numerous isomerizations, fragmentations, and intramolecular oxidation-reduction reactions, to give complex mixtures of products. For this reason, ketoses as well as aldoses reduce alkaline copper(II) reagents, and the reaction requires several equivalents of reagent per mole of sugar. Under rigidly-standardized conditions, and with empirically-determined standard values, cuprimetric methods can be used for accurate quantitative determination of sugars.[12, 13]

Definitive characterization of individual sugars in a mixture requires separation of the mixture on an isolative scale, to permit unambiguous identification of the components by standard methods. Fractional crystallization[5] is sometimes possible, and fermentative methods[14] have also been used. Paper[15] and thin-layer[16] chromatography permit rapid, micro-scale separation of sugar mixtures, and components indicated by these techniques may be characterized by preparative chromatographic techniques, as on cellulose columns[15, 17] or by preparative thin-layer chromatography.[18] Acetylated sugars may be separated by column chromatography on various silicate adsorbents.[19] Gas-liquid chromatography[20] of blocked sugars, especially through the trimethylsilyl derivatives[21] or the alditol acetates,[22] is very effective, and may supersede many of the older separation methods. The procedure can provide quantitative data on the composition of a mixture, and also furnish samples for definitive characterization.

Macro- and micro-scale analytical methods, based on cuprimetric and other oxidative procedures, are available for determination of isolated sugars.[23] Certain colorimetric methods,[11, 13] and methods based on specific enzymes,[24] may be applicable for determination of individual sugars in a mixture. Minute quantities of reducing sugars may be determined by treatment with sodium cyanide-^{14}C or lithium borohydride-t, to give radioactively-labeled products.[25] Individual sugars in mixtures may be reliably identified and determined by isotope-dilution methods.[25] Other analytical methods for sugar mixtures are based on micro-scale separation of the sugars by paper (or thin-layer) chromatography, followed by excision of the zones, elution, and determination by one of the standard oxidative or colorimetric methods.[13, 15, 18, 23, 26] Densitometric determination of relative paper chromatogram zone intensities may also be used.[15, 27]

Zone electrophoresis of sugars and their derivatives,[28] as charged complexes, on paper or other support, can be used to furnish structural information as well as to effect separation.

Oxidations with glycol-cleaving reagents, such as periodate[29] and lead tetraacetate,[30] are of wide utility, both analytically and preparatively, in structural studies on sugars and their derivatives. The classic methylation technique for structure analysis has found still wider application through development of improved procedures for methylation,[31] and by the use of thin-layer and gas-liquid chromatographic separation methods.

Polarimetry[9] at the sodium D line has been the most widely-used physical technique for structural studies on sugars and their derivatives, especially for determination of anomeric configuration. Unsubstituted sugars are normally transparent in the visible and near-ultraviolet spectral regions. Absorption bands in the vacuum ultraviolet give rise to the "anomalous" optical rotatory dispersion curves (Cotton effect) observed[32] with the free sugars in the spectral region 185–220 mμ; the sign of these curves has been correlated with the conformations of the sugars in solution. Cotton-effect curves may be observed at higher wavelengths when optically-active chromophores absorbing in the near-ultraviolet are present.[33] The infrared spectra of sugars and their derivatives[7] show the usual absorptions characteristic of functional groups, and correlation of conformation with absorptions in the "fingerprint" region is possible with certain pyranoid derivatives.

Nuclear magnetic resonance spectroscopy is the most valuable physical tool for structural studies with sugars and derivatives;[34, 35] it provides information on functional groups present, relative configuration of groups, and favored conformation in solution. Partial spectral analyses on a first-order basis are commonly employed, although it is frequently possible to make complete first-order spectral interpretations for simple sugar derivatives, by use of spin-decoupling techniques, solvent shifts, and measurements at different field strengths.

Sugar derivatives give characteristic fragmentation patterns under electron bombardment in a mass spectrometer, and these patterns can be correlated with structure.[36] The patterns are affected little by variations in configuration within a series, but are markedly affected by features such as position of substituent groups. Mass spectrometry provides a very effective technique for location of the position of the methylene group in a deoxy sugar, or the amino group in an amino sugar.

BIBLIOGRAPHY

References:

1. W. Pigman, ed., *The Carbohydrates*, 2nd edition, Academic Press, Inc., New York, 1957; W. Pigman and D. Horton, eds., *The Carbohydrates*, 3rd edition, Academic Press, Inc., New York, 1967, in press.
2. J. Staněk, M. Černý, J. Kocourek, and J. Pacák, *The Monosaccharides*, Academic Press, Inc., New York, 1963.
3. R. L. Whistler and M. L. Wolfrom, eds., *Methods in Carbohydrate Chemistry*, Vol. 1, *Analyses and Preparations of Sugars*, Academic Press, Inc., New York, 1962.
4. R. L. Whistler and M. L. Wolfrom, eds., *Methods in Carbohydrate Chemistry*, Vol. 2, *Reactions of Carbohydrates*, Academic Press, Inc., New York, 1963.
5. R. S. Tipson, in *Technique of Organic Chemistry*, A. Weissberger, ed., Interscience Publishers, Inc., New York, 1956, Vol. III, Part I, p. 395; A. Thompson and M. L. Wolfrom, ref. 3, p. 8.
6. A. Thompson and M. L. Wolfrom, ref. 3, p. 517.
7. H. Spedding, *Advan. Carbohydrate Chem.*, **19**, 23 (1964); ref. 3, p. 539.
8. F. R. Senti and H. F. Zobel, ref. 3, p. 535.

9. F. J. Bates and Associates, *Polarimetry, Saccharimetry, and The Sugars*, Circular of the National Bureau of Standards C 440, 1942.
10. C. F. Snyder, H. L. Frush, H. S. Isbell, A. Thompson, and M. L. Wolfrom, ref. 3, p. 524.
11. Z. Dische, *Methods Biochem. Anal.*, **2**, 313 (1955); ref. 3, section V.
12. M. Somogyi, *J. Biol. Chem.*, **195**, 19 (1952).
13. J. E. Hodge and B. T. Hofreiter, ref. 3, p. 380.
14. L. E. Wise, ref. 3, p. 404.
15. L. Hough, *Methods Biochem. Anal.*, **1**, 205 (1954); L. Hough and J. K. N. Jones, ref. 3, p. 21.
16. K. Randerath, *Thin-Layer Chromatography*, Academic Press, New York, 1963; J. M. Bobbitt, *Thin-Layer Chromatography*, Reinhold, New York, 1963.
17. R. L. Whistler and J. N. BeMiller, ref. 3, p. 47.
18. M. L. Wolfrom, D. L. Patin, and R. M. de Lederkremer, *J. Chromatog.*, **17**, 488 (1965); M. L. Wolfrom, R. M. de Lederkremer, and G. Schwab, *J. Chromatog.*, in press.
19. A. Thompson, ref. 3, p. 36.
20. C. T. Bishop, *Advan. Carbohydrate Chem.*, **19**, 95 (1964); H. W. Kircher, ref. 3, p. 13.
21. C. C. Sweeley, R. Bentley, M. Makita, and D. D. Wells, *J. Am. Chem. Soc.*, **85**, 2497 (1963).
22. J. S. Sawardeker, J. H. Sloneker, and A. Jeanes, *Anal. Chem.*, **37**, 1602 (1965).
23. K. Paech and M. V. Tracey, eds., *Modern Methods of Plant Analysis*, Springer-Verlag, Berlin, Vol. 2, 1965.
24. L. Hough and J. K. N. Jones, ref. 3, p. 400.
25. H. S. Isbell and H. L. Frush, ref. 3, p. 409.
26. R. L. Whistler and J. N. BeMiller, ref. 3, p. 395.
27. E. Lederer and M. Lederer, in *Comprehensive Biochemistry*, (M. Florkin and E. H. Stotz, eds.), Vol. 4, Elsevier Publishing Co., Amsterdam, 1962, p. 200.
28. A. B. Foster, ref. 3, p. 51; *Advan. Carbohydrate Chem.*, **12**, 81 (1957); H. Weigel, *Advan. Carbohydrate Chem.*, **18**, 61 (1963).
29. R. D. Guthrie, ref. 3, p. 432; J. M. Bobbitt, *Advan. Carbohydrate Chem.*, **11**, 1 (1956).
30. A. S. Perlin, ref. 3, p. 427; A. S. Perlin, *Advan. Carbohydrate Chem.*, **14**, 9 (1959).
31. R. Kuhn and H. Trischmann, *Ber.*, **96**, 284 (1963).
32. I. Litowsky, G. Avigad, and S. Englard, *J. Am. Chem. Soc.*, **87**, 1765 (1965).
33. H. Hudson, M. L. Wolfrom, and T. M. Lowry, *J. Chem. Soc.*, 1179 (1933).
34. L. D. Hall, *Advan. Carbohydrate Chem.*, **19**, 51 (1964).
35. D. Horton and D. R. Lineback, *Handbook of Carbohydrate N. M. R. Spectra*, Marcel Dekker, Inc., New York, 1966, *in press*.
36. N. K. Kochetkov and O. S. Chizhov, *Advan. Carbohydrate Chem.*, **21**, (1966), in press.

Tabulated data for monosaccharides.

A comprehensive tabulation of natural monosaccharides, including aldoses, ketoses, alditols, aldonic acids, and amino sugars, complete through 1962, has been published.[1] Extensive lists of sugars and their derivatives are given in recent[2-4] and older[5-8] monographs on the carbohydrates. Physical data (melting points and specific rotations) for the following selected groups of sugar derivatives have been tabulated: derivatives of ribose;[9] the altrose group of substances;[10] fructose derivatives;[11] derivatives of psicose, sorbose, and tagatose;[12] higher-carbon sugars;[13] sugars from antibiotics;[14] streptomycin derivatives;[15] 2-amino-2-deoxy sugars and their derivatives;[16] dicarbonyl carbohydrates;[17] anhydro sugars;[18] sulfate esters;[19] carbonate and thiocarbonate derivatives;[20] glycosyl halides;[21] glycosyl fluorides and azides;[22] cyclic acetals of aldoses and aldosides;[23] methyl and phenyl glycosides of common sugars;[24] mustard-oil glucosides;[25] methyl ethers of D-glucose,[26] D-galactose,[27] D-mannose,[28] aldopentoses, rhamnose, and fucose,[29] and hexuronic acids;[30] benzyl ethers of sugars;[31] trityl ethers of sugars;[32] sugar derivatives isolated from plant gums and mucilages;[33] methyl ethers of 2-amino-2-deoxy sugars;[34] hexitols and derivatives;[35] acetals of alditols;[36] anhydrides of pentitols and hexitols;[37] cyclitols and derivatives;[38, 39] unsaturated sugars;[40] 2-hydroxyglycals;[41] glycosylamines;[42] glycosyl ureides;[43] products of the Amadori rearrangement;[44] osotriazoles;[45] formazans;[46] 2-(polyhydroxyalkyl)benzimidazoles;[47] condensation products of sugars with β-ketonic esters,[48] and of amino sugars with β-dicarbonyl compounds;[49] acylated nitriles of aldonic acids;[50] saccharinic acids;[51] and four-carbon saccharinic acids.[52]

Lists have been compiled, for a number of sugars and derivatives, of paper-chromatographic mobilities,[53-55] gas-liquid chromatographic retention volumes,[56] electrophoretic mobilities,[57, 58] and X-ray powder diffraction data.[59] Specifications of purity for a number of sugars, based on criteria of equilibrium specific rotation and chromatographic homogeneity, have been made.[60] Synthetic procedures for many sugars[61] and their derivatives[62] have been published.[5]

The following tables give physical data for a selection of the more important natural monosaccharides. Names given are definitive, or are permissible trivial names;[63] in the latter case the definitive name is given subsequently. Other trivial names are given in quotation marks. Compounds are grouped according to number of carbons in the principal chain, and are alphabetized within groups. Unless otherwise noted, specific rotations refer to aqueous solutions.

Selected Natural Monosaccharides and Derivatives

Name	Abbreviation	Molecular formula	Formula weight	Melting point, °C	Specific rotation, degrees	Occurrence[a]	References Isolation	Preparation, Specifications
1,3-Dihydroxypropanone ("dihydroxyacetone")		$C_3H_6O_3$	90.08	77	inactive	intermediate in metabolism	64	65
D-Glyceraldehyde		$C_3H_6O_3$	90.08	syrup	+8.7 ± 0.5	intermediate in metabolism	66	67
D-Glyceric acid		$C_3H_6O_4$	106.08	syrup	b	intermediate in metabolism	68	68
Glycerol		$C_3H_8O_3$	92.09	18	inactive	lipids	69	69
Erythritol		$C_4H_{10}O_4$	122.12	120	inactive	algae and lichens	70	60, 71, 72
D-Erythrose	D-Ery	$C_4H_8O_4$	120.11	syrup	−41	intermediate in metabolism	72	73
L-*glycero*-Tetrulose ("L-erythrulose")		$C_4H_8O_4$	120.11	syrup	+11.4 ± 1	intermediate in metabolism	74	75
D-Arabinitol		$C_5H_{12}O_5$	152.15	103	+130 ± 1[c]	lichens, fungi	76	60, 77, 78
L-Arabinitol		$C_5H_{12}O_5$	152.15	102	−130 ± 1[c]	pentosuric urine	79	60, 78, 80
β-D-Arabinose	D-Ara	$C_5H_{10}O_5$	150.13	160	−175 → −104.5 ± 0.5	glycosides of *Aloe*, polysaccharides of tubercle bacilli	81	60, 81, 82
β-L-Arabinose	L-Ara	$C_5H_{10}O_5$	150.13	160	+191 → +104.5 ± 0.5	plant gums, hemicelluloses, pectic substances, bacterial polysaccharides	83	60, 82, 83

Name	Abbrev.	Formula	M.W.	M.p.	Specific rotation	Major sources[a]	Ref.	Ref.
2-Deoxy-β-D-*erythro*-pentose ("2-deoxy-D-arabinose," "2-deoxy-D-ribose," "thyminose")		$C_5H_{10}O_4$	134.13	95–97	$-91 \rightarrow$ -57.3 ± 0.3	deoxyribonucleic acid	84	60, 85
D-*erythro*-Pentulose ("D-arabinulose," "D-ribulose")		$C_5H_{10}O_5$	150.13	syrup	-16.3	intermediate in photosynthesis and in D-glucose metabolism	86	86, 87
D-*threo*-Pentulose ("D-lyxulose," "D-xylulose")		$C_5H_{10}O_5$	150.13	syrup	-33	intermediate in photosynthesis	88	89, 90
L-*threo*-Pentulose ("L-lyxulose," "L-xylulose")		$C_5H_{10}O_5$	150.13	syrup	$+34.8$	pentosuric urine	91	88, 90
Ribitol ("adonitol")		$C_5H_{12}O_5$	152.15	102	inactive	*Adonis vernalis*	92	60, 93
D-Ribose	D-Rib	$C_5H_{10}O_5$	150.13	87	-20.4 ± 0.4	ribonucleic acid	94	60, 95
α-D-Xylose	D-Xyl	$C_5H_{10}O_5$	150.13	153	$+96 \rightarrow$ $+18.8 \pm 0.6$	xylans and glucuronoxylans of woody tissues	96	60, 96
2-Amino-2-deoxy-α-D-galactose hydrochloride ("D-galactosamine," "chondrosamine" hydrochloride)	GalN	$C_6H_{14}ClNO_5$	215.64	178 (dec.)	$+124 \rightarrow$ $+96.2 \pm 1$	cartilage	97	60, 98
2-Amino-2-deoxy-α-D-glucose hydrochloride ("D-glucosamine," "chitosamine" hydrochloride)	GN	$C_6H_{14}ClNO_5$	215.64	190–210 (dec.)	$+100 \rightarrow$ $+72.5 \pm 0.7$	chitin	99	60, 100
2-Amino-2-deoxy-D-mannose hydrochloride ("D-mannosamine" hydrochloride)	ManN	$C_6H_{14}ClNO_5$	215.64	178–180	-3.2	component of N-acetyl-neuraminic acid	101	102

[a] Major sources, in free or combined form.   [b] Barium salt, partially racemized.   [c] In acidified molybdate solution.

Selected Natural Monosaccharides and Derivatives (continued)

Name	Abbreviation	Molecular formula	Formula weight	Melting point, °C	Specific rotation, degrees	Occurrence[a]	Isolation	Preparation,	Specifications
2-Deoxy-D-*arabino*-hexose ("2-deoxy-D-glucose")		$C_6H_{12}O_5$	164.16	148	+46.6 ± 0.2	glycosides	103	60	104
α-D-Fucose (6-deoxy-α-D-galactose, "rhodeose")	D-Fuc	$C_6H_{12}O_5$	164.16	140–145	+127 → +76	glycosides	105	106	
α-L-Fucose (6-deoxy-α-L-galactose, "L-galactomethylose")	L-Fuc	$C_6H_{12}O_5$	164.16	140–141	−75.9 ± 0.2	seaweed polysaccharides, blood group substances	107	60	108
β-D-Fructose (D-*arabino*-hexulose, "levulose")	D-Fru	$C_6H_{12}O_6$	180.16	102–104	−132 → −92.4 ± 0.5	fruits, honey, inulin	109	60	110
Galactitol ("dulcitol")		$C_6H_{14}O_6$	182.17	188–189	inactive	seaweeds, yeasts	111	60	112
α-D-Galactose ("cerebrose")	D-Gal	$C_6H_{12}O_6$	180.16	165–167	+80.2 ± 0.2	lactose, other oligosaccharides, plant gums	113	60	114
α-L-Galactose	L-Gal	$C_6H_{12}O_6$	180.16	165	−130 → −81	agar, flaxseed gum	115	60	116
D-Glucitol ("sorbitol")		$C_6H_{14}O_6$	182.17	97.5	+103 ± 1[c]	algae, fruits	117	60	118
α-D-Glucose ("dextrose," "grape sugar")	G	$C_6H_{12}O_6$	180.16	147 (dec.)	+113.4 → +52.2	widely distributed in living tissues	119	60	120
D-Mannitol		$C_6H_{14}O_6$	182.17	166–168	+141 ± 1[c]	mannas, algae, fruits	121	60	122

Name	Abbrev.	Formula	Mol. wt.	M.p. (°C)	Specific rotation	Major sources[a]	Ref.	Ref.
β-D-Mannose ("seminose," "carubinose")	D-Man	$C_6H_{12}O_6$	180.16	132 (dec.)	$-17.0 \rightarrow +14.2 \pm 0.4$	many polysaccharides	123	60, 124
Muramic acid [2-amino-3-O-(D-1-carboxyethyl)-2-deoxy-D-glucose]		$C_9H_{17}NO_9$	251.24	dec.	$+109 \pm 3$	bacterial cell walls	125	126
α-L-Rhamnose [6-deoxy-α-L-mannose (monohydrate)]	L-Rha	$C_6H_{12}O_5 \cdot H_2O$	182.17	93–94	$+8.2 \pm 0.4$	"lemon flavin" (quercitrin) and other glycosides	127	60, 128
L-Sorbose (L-xylo-hexulose)	L-Sor	$C_6H_{12}O_6$	180.16	159–161	-43.4 ± 0.2	biochemical oxidation of D-glucitol	129	60, 130
D-Tagatose (D-lyxo-hexulose)	D-Tag	$C_6H_{12}O_6$	180.16	134–135	-5	Sterculia gum	131	132
D-manno-Heptulose		$C_7H_{14}O_7$	210.19	151–152	$+29$	avocado	133	134
Sedoheptulosan (2,7-anhydro-β-D-altro-heptulopyranose)		$C_7H_{12}O_6$	192.17	155–156	-146	photosynthesis, Sedum spp.	135	136
Sedoheptulose (D-altro-heptulose, "volemulose")		$C_7H_{14}O_7$	210.19	syrup	$+8$	photosynthesis, Sedum spp.	135	136
N-Acetylneuraminic acid (5-acetamido-3,5-dideoxy-D-glycero-D-talo-nonulosonic acid, "lactaminic acid," "gynaminic acid")		$C_{11}H_{19}NO_9$	298.29	185–187	-32 ± 1	serum glycoproteins, glycolipids	137	138

[a] Major sources, in free or combined form. [b] Barium salt, partially racemized. [c] In acidified molybdate solution.

BIBLIOGRAPHY

References:

1. Wolfrom, M. L., and G. G. Maher, and R. Pagnucco, in Altman, P. L., and D. S. Dittmer (eds.), *Biology Data Book*, p. 351, 1964.
2. Staněk, J., et al., *The Monosaccharides*, 1963.
3. Pigman, W. (ed.), *The Carbohydrates*, 2nd ed., 1957.
4. Micheel, F., and A. Klemer, *Chemie der Zucker und Polysaccharide*, 1956.
5. Bates, F. J., and Associates, "Mutarotation and Sugars in Solution," *Polarimetry, Saccharimetry, and The Sugars*, p. 439, 1942.
6. *Beilsteins Handbuch der Organischen Chemie*, 4th ed., *Carbohydrates*, 31(1), *Monosaccharides and Oligosaccharides*, 1938.
7. Tollens, B., and H. Elsner, *Kurzes Handbuch der Kohlenhydrate*, 3rd ed., 1933.
8. Vogel, H., and A. Georg, *Tabellen der Zucker und Ihrer Derivate*, 1931.
9. Jeanloz, R. W., and H. G. Fletcher, Jr., "The Chemistry of Ribose," *Advan. Carbohydrate Chem.*, 6:135, 1951.
10. Richtmyer, N. K., "The Altrose Group of Substances," *Advan. Carbohydrate Chem.*, 1:37, 1946.
11. Barry, C. P., and J. Honeyman, "Fructose and its Derivatives," *Advan. Carbohydrate Chem.*, 7:53, 1952.
12. Karabinos, J. V., "Psicose, Sorbose and Tagatose," *Advan. Carbohydrate Chem.*, 7:99, 1952.
13. Webber, J. M., "Higher-Carbon Sugars," *Advan. Carbohydrate Chem.*, 17: 15, 1962.
14. Dutcher, J. D., "Chemistry of the Amino Sugars Derived from Antibiotic Substances," *Advan. Carbohydrate Chem.*, 18:259, 1963.
15. Lemieux, R. U., and M. L. Wolfrom, "The Chemistry of Streptomycin," *Advan. Carbohydrate Chem.*, 3:337, 1948.
16. Horton, D., "Tables of Properties of 2-Amino-2-deoxy Sugars and Their Derivatives," *Advan. Carbohydrate Chem.*, 15:159, 1960.
17. Theander, O., "Dicarbonyl Carbohydrates," *Advan. Carbohydrate Chem.*, 17:223, 1962.
18. Peat, S., "The Chemistry of Anhydro Sugars," *Advan. Carbohydrate Chem.*, 2:38, 1947.
19. Turvey, J. R., *Advan. Carbohydrate Chem.*, 20:183, 1965.
20. Hough, L., J. E. Priddle, and R. S. Theobald, "The Carbonates and Thiocarbonates of Carbohydrates," *Advan. Carbohydrate Chem.*, 15:91, 1960.
21. Haynes, L. J., and F. H. Newth, "The Glycosyl Halides and Their Derivatives," *Advan. Carbohydrate Chem.*, 10:207, 1955.
22. Micheel F., and A. Klemer, "Glycosyl Fluorides and Azides," *Advan. Carbohydrate Chem.*, 16:85, 1961.
23. de Belder, A. N., *Advan. Carbohydrate Chem.*, 20:219, 1965.
24. Conchie, J., G. A. Levvy, and C. A. Marsh, "Methyl and Phenyl Glycosides of the Common Sugars." *Advan. Carbohydrate Chem.*, 12:157, 1957.
25. Horton, D., and D. H. Hutson, "Developments in the Chemistry of Thio Sugars," *Advan. Carbohydrate Chem.*, 18:123, 1963.
26. Bourne, E. J., and S. Peat, "The Methyl Ethers of D-Glucose," *Advan. Carbohydrate Chem.*, 5:145, 1950.
27. Maher, G. G., "The Methyl Ethers of D-Galactose," *Advan. Carbohydrate Chem.*, 10:273, 1955.

28. Aspinall, G. O., "The Methyl Ethers of D-Mannose," *Advan. Carbohydrate Chem.*, 8:217, 1953.

29. Maher, G. G., "The Methyl Ethers of the Aldopentoses and of Rhamnose and Fucose," *Advan. Carbohydrate Chem.*, 10:257, 1955.

30. Aspinall, G. O., "The Methyl Ethers of Hexuronic Acids," *Advan. Carbohydrate Chem.*, 9:131, 1954.

31. McCloskey, C. M., "Benzyl Ethers of Sugars," *Advan. Carbohydrate Chem.*, 12:137, 1957.

32. Helferich, B., "Trityl Ethers of Carbohydrates," *Advan. Carbohydrate Chem.*, 3:79, 1948.

33. Jones, J. K. N., and F. Smith, "Plant Gums and Mucilages," *Advan. Carbohydrate Chem.*, 4:243, 1949.

34. Jeanloz, R. W., "The Methyl Ethers of 2-Amino-2-deoxy Sugars," *Advan. Carbohydrate Chem.*, 13:189, 1958.

35. Lohmar, R., and R. M. Goepp, Jr., "The Hexitols and Some of Their Derivatives," *Advan. Carbohydrate Chem.*, 4:211, 1949.

36. Barker, S. A., and E. J. Bourne, "Acetals and Ketals of the Tetritols, Pentitols and Hexitols," *Advan. Carbohydrate Chem.*, 7:137, 1952.

37. Wiggins, L. F., "Anhydrides of the Pentitols and Hexitols," *Advan. Carbohydrate Chem.*, 5:191, 1950.

38. Posternak, T., *The Cyclitols*, 1965.

39. Angyal, S. J., and L. Anderson, "The Cyclitols," *Advan. Carbohydrate Chem.*, 14:135, 1959.

40. Ferrier, R. J., *Advan. Carbohydrate Chem.*, 20:67, 1965.

41. Blair, Mary Grace, "The 2-Hydroxyglycals," *Advan. Carbohydrate Chem.*, 9:97, 1954.

42. Ellis, G. P., and J. Honeyman, "Glycosylamines," *Advan. Carbohydrate Chem.*, 10:95, 1955.

43. Goodman, I., "Glycosyl Ureides," *Advan. Carbohydrate Chem.*, 13:215, 1958.

44. Hodge, J. E., "The Amadori Rearrangement," *Advan. Carbohydrate Chem.*, 10:169, 1955.

45. El Khadem, H., "Chemistry of Osotriazoles," *Advan. Carbohydrate Chem.*, 18:99, 1963.

46. Mester, L., "The Formazan Reaction in Carbohydrate Research," *Advan. Carbohydrate Chem.*, 13:105, 1958.

47. Richtmyer, N. K., "The 2-(*aldo*-Polyhydroxyalkyl)benzimidazoles," *Advan. Carbohydrate Chem.*, 6:175, 1951.

48. García González, F., "Reactions of Monosaccharides with Beta-Ketonic Esters and Related Substances," *Advan. Carbohydrate Chem.*, 11:97, 1956.

49. García González, F., and A. Gómez Sánchez, *Advan. Carbohydrate Chem.*, 20:303, 1965.

50. Deulofeu, V., "The Acylated Nitriles of Aldonic Acids and Their Degradation," *Advan. Carbohydrate Chem.*, 4:119, 1949.

51. Sowden, J. C., "The Saccharinic Acids," *Advan. Carbohydrate Chem.*, 12:35, 1957.

52. Crum, J. D., "The Four-Carbon Saccharinic Acids," *Advan. Carbohydrate Chem.*, 13:169, 1958.

53.a. Hough, L., "Analysis of Mixtures of Sugars by Paper and Cellulose Column Chromatography," *Methods Biochem. Anal.*, 1:205, 1954.

53.b. Hough, L., and J. K. N. Jones, "Chromatography on Paper," *Methods Carbohydrate Chem.*, 1:21, 1962.

54. Kowkabany, G. N., "Paper Chromatography of Carbohydrates and Related Compounds," *Advan. Carbohydrate Chem.*, 9:303, 1954.

55. Lederer, E., and M. Lederer, *Chromatography*, 2nd ed., 1957.

56. Bishop, C. T., "Gas-Liquid Chromatography of Carbohydrate Derivatives," *Advan. Carbohydrate Chem.*, 19:95, 1964.

57. Weigel, H., "Paper Electrophoresis of Carbohydrates," *Advan. Carbohydrate Chem.*, 18:61, 1963.

58. Foster, A. B., "Zone Electrophoresis of Carbohydrates," *Advan. Carbohydrate Chem.*, 12:81, 1957.

59. "Index to the X-Ray Powder Data File," American Society for Testing and Materials, 1959.

60. *Specifications and Criteria for Biochemical Compounds*, National Academy of Sciences—National Research Council Publication 719, 1960.

61. Whistler, R. L., and M. L. Wolfrom (eds.), *Methods in Carbohydrate Chemistry*, Vol. 1, 1962.

62. Whistler, R. L., and M. L. Wolfrom (eds.), *Methods in Carbohydrate Chemistry*, Vol. 2, 1963.

63. "Rules of Carbohydrate Nomenclature," *J. Org. Chem.*, 28:281, 1963.

64. Bertrand, G., "Sur la Préparation Biochimique de la Dioxyacétone (Propanediolone)," *Bull. Soc. Chim.* France, 19:502, 1898.

65. Rutten, A. M. G., "Biochemical Production of Dihydroxyacetone from Glycerol," *Rec. Trav. Chim.*, 70:449, 1951.

66. Wohl, A., and F. Momber, "Die Sterische Beziehung Zwischen Glycerinaldehyd und Weinsaure," *Ber. Deut. Chem. Ges.*, 50:455, 1917.

67. Perlin, A. S., "D-,L-, and DL-Glyceraldehyde, Oxidative Degradation of Ketohexoses," *Methods in Carbohydrate Chemistry*, 1:61, 1962.

68. Wohl, A., and R. Schellenberg, "Die Überfuhrüng des Aktiven Glycerinaldehyds in die Aktive Glycerinsäure," *Ber. Deut. Chem. Ges.*, 55:1404, 1922.

69. Miner, C. S., and N. N. Dalton (eds.), *Glycerol*, 1953.

70. Bamberger, M., and A. Landsiedl, "Erythrit in Trentepholia Jolithus," *Monatsh. Chem.*, 21:571, 1900.

71. Raphael, R. A., "Synthesis of Carbohydrates by Use of Acetylenic Precursors. Part II. Addition Reactions of *cis*- and *trans*-But-2-ene-1: 4-Diol Diacetates. Synthesis of DL-Erythrulose," *J. Chem. Soc.*, p. 401, 1952.

72.a. Ruff, O., "*d*-Erythrose," *Ber.*, 32:3672, 1899.

72.b. cf. Wohl, A., "Abbau des Traubenzuckers. Arabinose; Abbau der Arabinose; Arabinosoxim," *Ber.*, 26:743, 1893.

73. Perlin, A. S., "D-Erythrose," *Methods in Carbohydrate Chemistry*, 1:64, 1962.

74. Bertrand, G., "Sur l'Oxydation de l'Érythrite par la Bactérie du Sorbose. Production de Deux Noveaux Sucres: le d-Érythrulose et la d-Érythrite," *Bull. Soc. Chim.*, (Ser. 3), 23:681, 1900.

75. Müller, H., C. Montigel, and T. Reichstein, "Reine 1-Erythrulose (*l*-2-Keto-Tetrose)," *Helv. Chim. Acta*, 20:1468, 1937.

76. Lindberg, B., A. Misiorny, and C. A. Wachtmeister, "Studies on the Chemistry of Lichens. IV. Investigation of the Low-molecular Carbohydrate Constituents of Different Lichens," *Acta Chem., Scand.*, 7:591, 1953.

77. Ruff, O., "d- und r-Arabinose," *Ber.*, 32:550, 1899.

78. Richtmyer, N. K., and C. S. Hudson, "The Rotation of Polyols in Ammonium Molybdate Solutions," *J. Am. Chem. Soc.*, 73:2249, 1951.

79. Touster, O., and S. O. Harwell, "The Isolation of L-Arabitol from Pentosuric Urine," *J. Biol. Chem.*, 230:1031, 1958.

80. Kiliani, H., "Ueber die Einwirkung von Natriumamalgam auf Arabinose," *Ber.*, 20:1233, 1887.

81. Whistler, R. L., and J. N. BeMiller, "β-D-Arabinose. Hypochlorite Oxidation of D-Glucose," *Methods in Carbohydrate Chemistry*, 1:71, 1962.

82. Isbell, H. S., and W. W. Pigman, "Bromine Oxidation and Mutarotation Measurements of the Alpha- and Beta-Aldoses," *J. Res. Natl. Bur. Std.*, 18: 141, 1937.

83. White, E. V., "β-L-Arabinose. Partial Hydrolysis of Mesquite Gum," *Method in Carbohydrate Chemistry*, 1:76, 1962.

84. Levene, P. A., and E. S. London, "The Structure of Thymonucleic Acid," *J. Biol. Chem.*, 83:793, 1929.

85.a. Hardegger, E., "2-Deoxy-β-D-*erythro*-pentose (2-Deoxy-D-Ribose) from 1,2:5,6-Di-*O*-isopropylidene-3-methylsulfonyl-α-D-Glucose," *Methods in Carbohydrate Chemistry*, 1:177, 1962.

85.b. Richards, G. N., "2-Deoxy-β-D-Erythro-pentose (2-Deoxy-β-D-Ribose) from D-Glucometasaccharinic Acid or D-Glucose," *Methods in Carbohydrate Chemistry*, 1:180, 1962.

86.a. Schmidt, O. T., and K. Heintz, "Über Zucker mit Verzweigter Kohlenstoffkette. V. Die Synthese der Hamamelonsäure," *Ann.*, 515:77, 1935.

86.b. Hall, A. N., D. Kulka, and T. K. Walker, "Formation of Arabinose, Ribulose and Tartronic Acid from 2-Keto-D-gluconic Acid," *Biochem. J.*, 60:271, 1955.

87. Glatthaar, C., and T. Reichstein, "d-Adonose (d-Erythro-2-keto-pentose)," *Helv. Chim. Acta*, 18:80, 1935.

88. Schmidt, O. T., and R. Treiber, "D-Xyloketose," *Ber.*, 66:1765, 1933.

89. Hough, L., and R. S. Theobald, "D-threo-Pentulose. From D-Xylose by Epimerization and from D-Arabinol *Acetobacter xylinum*," *Methods in Carbohydrate Chemistry*, 1:94, 1962.

90. Touster, O., "D- and L-*threo*-Pentulose (D and L-Xylulose) Pyridine-Catalyzed Epimerization of Xylose," *Methods in Carbohydrate Chemistry*, 1:98, 1962.

91. Greenwald, I., "The Nature of the Sugar in Four Cases of Pentosuria," *J. Biol. Chem.*, 88:1, 1930.

92. Podwykassozki, W. V., *Arch. Pharm.*, 227:141, 1889.

93. Fischer, E., "Ueber Adonit, Einen Neuen Pentit," *Ber.*, 26:633, 1893.

94. Levene, P. A., and E. P. Clark, "d-Ribohexosaminic Acids," *J. Biol. Chem.*, 46:19, 1921.

95. Bates, F. J., and Associates, "d-Ribose," *Polarimetry, Saccharimetry, and The Sugars*, p.476, 1942.

96. Whistler, R. L., and J. N. BeMiller, "α-D-Xylose. Isolation from Corn Cobs of Xylan," *Methods in Carbohydrate Chemistry*, 1:88, 1962.

97. Levene, P. A., and F. B. LaForge, "On Chondroitin Sulphuric Acid," *J. Biol. Chem.*, 18:123, 1914.

98.a. Brossmer, R., "2-Amino-2-deoxy-α-D-galactose Hydrochloride. Synthesis from D-Lyxose; Qualitative and Quantitative Determinations," *Methods in Carbohydrate Chemistry*, 1:216, 1962.

98.b. Jeanloz, R. W., and P. J. Stoffyn, "2-Amino-2-deoxy-α-D-galactose Hydrochloride. Addition of Ammonia to 2,3:1,6-Dianhydro-β-D-Talopyranose," *Methods in Carbohydrate Chemistry*, 1:221, 1962.

99. Ledderhose, G., "Ueber Salzsaures Glycosamin," *Ber.*, 9:1200, 1876.

100. Stacey, M., and J. M. Webber, "2-Amino-2-deoxy-α-D-glucose (α-D-Glucosamine). From Crustacean Shell," *Methods in Carbohydrate Chemistry*, 1: 228, 1962.

101. Comb, D. G., and S. Roseman, "Composition and Enzymatic Synthesis of N-Acetylneuraminic Acid (Sialic Acid)," *J. Am. Chem. Soc.*, 80:497, 1958.

102. Sowden, J. C., and M. Oftedahl, "2-Amino-2-deoxy-D-mannose Hydrochloride. From D-Arabinose Through D-arabino-Tetra-acetoxy-1-nitro-1-hexene," *Methods in Carbohydrate Chemistry*, 1:235, 1962.

103. Kowaleski, Z., et al., "Die Cardenolide von *Erysimum perofskianum* Fisch. et Mey.," *Helv. Chim. Acta*, 43:1280, 1960.

104. Bolliger, H. R., and D. M. Schmid, "2-Deoxy-D-arabino-hexose (2-Deoxy-D-Glucose) Reduction of the 2-Thioethyl Derivative," *Methods in Carbohydrate Chemistry*, 1:186, 1962.

105.a. Votoček, E., and F. Valentin, "Sur L'acide Rhamnoconvolvulique," *Collection Czech. Chem. Commun.*, 1:47, 1929.

105.b. Votoček, E., and F. Valentin, "Sur le Troisième Composant Sucré de la Scamonine," *Collection Czech. Chem. Commun.*, 1:606, 1929.

106. Schmidt, O. T., "6-Deoxy-α-D-galactose (α-D-Fucose) Hydrogenation of 6-Deoxy-6-iodo-D-galactose," *Methods in Carbohydrate Chemistry*, 1:191, 1962.

107. Gunther, A., and B. Tollens, "Ueber die Fucose, Einen der Rhamnose Isomeren Zucker aus Seetang," *Ber.*, 23:2585, 1890.

108. Percival, E., "6-Deoxy-α-L-galactose (α-L-Fucose) from the Phyeophyceae (Brown Seaweeds) Fucoidan," *Methods in Carbohydrate Chemistry*, 1:195, 1962.

109.a. Jungfleisch, E., and E. Lefranc, "Chimie Organique—Sur le Lévulose," *Compt. Rend.*, 93:547, 1881.

109.b. Hudson, C. S., and D. H. Brauns, "Crystalline β-Methyl Fructoside and its Tetracetate," *J. Am. Chem. Soc.*, 38:1216, 1916.

110. Bates, F. J., and Associates, "Preparation of Levulose," *Polarimetry, Saccharimetry, and The Sugars*, p. 399, 1942.

111.a. Bouchardt, G., "Recherches sur la Dulcite et les Sucres en Général," *Ann. Chim. Phys.*, (Ser. 4), 27:68, 1872.

111.b. Hunefeld, "Melampyrin," *Ann.*, 24:241, 1837.

112.a. Delépine, M., and A. Horeau, "Catalyse de la Réaction de Cannizzaro par le Nickel et le Platine Actifs. Application à Quelques Aldoses. Essai sur la Théorie du Phénomene," *Bull. Soc. Chim. France*, (Ser. 5), 4:1524, 1937.

112.b. Wolfrom, M. L., and A. Thompson, "Reduction with Sodium Borohydride. D-glycero-D-gulo-Heptose, Meso-glycero-gulo-Heptitol, and Galactitol," *Methods in Carbohydrate Chemistry*, 2:65, 1963.

113. Pasteur, L., "Note sur le Sucre de Lait," *Compt. Rend.*, 42:347, 1856.

114. Wolfrom, M. L., and A. Thompson, "D-Galactose. α-(and β-)D-Galactose from Lactose," *Methods in Carbohydrate Chemistry*, 1:120, 1962.

115. Anderson, E., "The Preparation of l-Galactose from Flaxseed Mucilage," *J. Biol. Chem.*, 100:249, 1933.

116. Araki, C., and K. Arai, "α-L-Galactose. From Agar or Flaxseed Gum," *Methods in Carbohydrate Chemistry*, 1:122, 1962.

117. Boussingault, J., "Sur la Sorbite, Matière Sucrée Analogue à la Mannite, Trouvée dans le jus de Baies du Sorbier des Oiseleurs," *Compt. Rend.*, 74: 939, 1872.

118. Creighton, H. J., "The Electrochemical Reduction of Sugars," *Trans. Electrochem. Soc.*, 75:289, 1939.

119. Newkirk, W. B., "Development and Production of Anhydrous Dextrose," *Ind. Eng. Chem.*, 28:760, 1936.

120. Hudson, C. S., and E. Yanovsky, "Indirect Measurements of the Rotatory Powers of Some Alpha and Beta Forms of the Sugars by Means of Solubility Experiments," *J. Am. Chem. Soc.*, 39:1013, 1917.

121. Proust, "Sur le Sucre de Raisin," *Ann. Chim.*, (Ser. 1), 57:131, 1806.

122.a. Fischer, E., and J. Hirschberger, "Ueber Mannose," *Ber.*, 21:1805, 1888.

122.b. Nanji, D. R., and F. J. Paton, *J. Chem. Soc.*, 125:2474, 1924.

123. Reiss, R., "Ueber die in den Samen als Reservestoff Abgelagerte Cellulose und Eine Daraus Erhaltene Neue Zuckerart," *Ber.*, 22:609, 1889.

124. Isbell, H. S., "Preparation of D-Mannose," *J. Res. Natl. Bur. Std.*, 26:47, 1941.

125. Park, J. T., "Uridine-5'-Pyrophosphate Derivatives. II. A. Structure Common to Three Derivatives," *J. Biol. Chem.*, 194:885, 1952.

126. Kent, L. H., and R. E. Strange, "Muramic Acid [2-amino-3-0-(1-Carboxyethyl)-2-deoxy-D-glucose] Isolation from Spores of *Bacillus megatherium*, Identification, and Chemical Synthesis," *Methods in Carbohydrate Chemistry*, 1:250, 1962.

127. Liebermann, C., and O. Hörmann, "Ueber die Farbstoffe und Glycosidzucker der Gelbbeeren," *Ann.*, 196:299, 1879.

128. Wolfrom, M. L., and A. Thompson, "6-Deoxy-α-L-mannose (α-L-Rhamnose) Monohydrate from Quercitrin," *Methods in Carbohydrate Chemistry*, 1:202, 1962.

129. Pelouze, J., "Sur une Nouvelle Matière Sucrée Extraite des Baies de Sorbier," *Ann. Chim. Phys.*, (Ser. 3), 35:222, 1852.

130. Wells, P. A., et al., "Sorbose from Sorbitol. Productions by Submerged growths of *Acetobacter suboxydans*," *Ind. Eng. Chem.*, 29:1385, 1937.

131. Bertrand, G., "Action de la Bactérie du Sorbose sur les Alcools Plurivalents," *Compt. Rend.*, 126:762, 1898.

132.a. Reichstein, T., and W. Bosshard, "D-Tagatose, Diaceton-D-Tagatose and D-Tadaturonisaure," *Helv. Chim. Acta*, 17:753, 1934.

132.b. Totton, E. L., and H. A. Lardy, "The Synthesis of D-Tagatose by Biochemical Oxidation and by an Improved Chemical Method," *J. Am. Chem. Soc.*, 71:3076, 1949.

133. LaForge, F. B., "D-Mannoketoheptose, a New Sugar from the Avocado," *J. Biol. Chem.*, 28:511, 1916.

134.a. Richtmyer, N. K., "D-manno-Heptulose Isolation from the Avocado," *Methods in Carbohydrate Chemistry*, 1:173, 1962.

134.b. Montgomery, E. M., "D-manno-Heptulose Epimerization of D-glycero-D-galacto-Heptose in Pyridine," *Methods in Carbohydrate Chemistry*, 1:175, 1962.

135. LaForge, F. B., and C. S. Hudson, "Sedoheptose, a New Sugar from Sedum spectabile. I.," *J. Biol. Chem.*, 30:61, 1917.

136. Richtmyer, N. K., "D-Altro-Heptulose (Sedoheptulose) from *Sedum spectabile* via Sedoheptulosan and Sedoheptulose Hexaacetate," *Methods in Carbohydrate Chemistry*, 1:167, 1962.

137.a. Klenk, E., and H. Faillard, "Zur Kenntnis der Kohlenhydratgruppen der Mucoproteide," *Z. Physiol. Chem.*, 298:230, 1954.

137.b. Zilliken, F., G. A. Braun, and P. György, "Gynaminic Acid. A Naturally Occurring Form of Neuraminic Acid in Human Milk," *Arch. Biochem. Biophys.*, 54:564, 1955.

137.c. Zilliken, F., G. A. Braun, and P. György, "Gynaminic Acid" and Other Naturally Occurring Forms of *N*-Acetylneuraminic Acid," *Arch. Biochem. Biophys.*, 63:394, 1956.

137.d. Kuhn, R., R. Brossmer, and W. Schulz, "Über die prosthetische Gruppe der Mucoproteine der Kuh-Colostrums," *Ber.*, 87:123, 1954.

138. Blix, G., "Sialic Acids," *Methods in Carbohydrate Chemistry*, 1:246, 1962.

CARBOHYDRATES ESTERS

The phosphate esters of carbohydrates occupy key positions as intermediates both in biochemical reactions and in the chemical syntheses of biologically important compounds. Much of the biochemical literature is concerned with their roles in the intermediary metabolism of polysaccharides, in glycolytic and oxidative processes and as constituents of nucleic acids. An example of their use in chemical synthesis is the employment of the sugar-1-phosphates in the preparation of sugar nucleotides. This section is an attempt to make some of the physical data of a number of these compounds (and several sulfate esters) readily accessible in tabular form (see also Ref. 238). In addition to the data for the various compounds presented in Table I, references to methods for their preparation and analysis are given. Together with the chemical and/or enzymatic methods that are suggested for their analysis, phosphate determinations can be utilized as a quantitative assay procedure and as criteria of identity by taking advantage of the differential lability of these compounds in acid. To this end the compilation of hydrolysis constants by Leloir and Cardini[239] has been included (Table IV) with the kind consent of their publishers.

Attention should be drawn to the separations of the sugar phosphates that can be achieved by gas chromatography of their trimethylsilyl di(tetra)methyl esters,[174] and by the technique of thin-layer chromatography,[240] in addition to the paper chromatographic systems presented in Table II.

While by no means exhaustive in their present form, tables of the sort presented here must of necessity be supplemented periodically as new data on the carbohydrate esters is obtained.

Table I

Compounds	Molecular weight	Empirical formula	Derivative	Specific Rotation		Conditions	pK_a	Prep. Ref.	Analysis	Miscellaneous
				$[\alpha]_D$	$[\alpha]_x$					
1. D-glyceraldehyde 3-phosphate	170.1	$C_3H_7O_6P$	Ca salt ($C_3H_5O_6PCa\ 2H_2O$) Free acid	$+14.5°[1]$ $+14°[3] +12°[4]$		25°, C = 1.2 0.1 N HCl Calc. as free acid H_2O	$pK_1 = 2.10[2]$ $pK_2 = 6.75$	1	Enzymatic[151]	
2. L-glyceraldehyde 3-phosphate	170.1	$C_3H_7O_6P$						149	Enzymatic[150]	Prepared from DL-DAP by removing D-isomer enzymatically
3. Dihydroxyacetone 1-phosphate	170.1	$C_3H_7O_6P$					$pK_1 = 1.77[2]$ $pK_2 = 6.85\ (\mu = 0)$ $6.52\ (\mu = .15)$ $6.31\ (0.15\ M\ NaCl)$ $pK_2 = 6.45$	6	Enzymatic[151]	Cyclohexyl ammonium dimethylketal[5]; Stable salt; Mwt 432; MP 183–185 (decomp)
4. Hydroxypyruvic acid 3-phosphate	184	$C_3H_5O_7P$								Dimethyl ketal[7]; Mwt 545; MP 183–185
5. Enolpyruvic acid 2-phosphate	168	$C_3H_5O_6P$					$pK_1 \approx 1$ $pK_2 = 3.5$ $pK_3 = 6.38$	8, 9 10, 11	Enzymatic[154] UV[152] Chemical[153, 197]	Silver barium salt;[12] stable at room temp., $C_3H_2O_6PBa\cdot Ag\cdot 2H_2O$ recommended form; $-\Delta H°$ of hydrolysis, pH 7 = 8500 cal;[13] $-\Delta F°$ of hydrolysis, pH 8.5, 25° = 15,950 cal;[14] Molar extinction coef. at 240 mμ pH 7 = 1.44×10^6 cm^2/mole; Tricyclohexyl ammonium salt; stable

Table I (cont.)

Compounds	Molecular weight	Empirical formula	Derivative	Specific Rotation $[\alpha]_D$	$[\alpha]_x$	Conditions	pK_a	Prep. Ref.	Analysis	Miscellaneous
6. L-glycerol α 1-phosphate	172	$C_3H_9O_6P$	Ba salt ($C_3H_7O_6PBa$)	none			$\begin{array}{ll}\alpha & \beta\\ pK_1 = 1.40 & 1.37^2\\ pK_2 = 6.44 & 6.34\end{array}$	15 16 17	Enzymatic[155]	$-\Delta H°$ of hydrolysis, pH 7.0 = 1,280 cal[20]
			Free acid	−1.45[15]		10% solution of Ba salt in 2 N HCl	$\begin{array}{l}\alpha + \beta\\ pK_2 = 6.65 \ (\mu = 0)^{18,19}\\ 6.32\\ 6.11 \ (\mu = .15)\ (.15\,M\,NaCl)\end{array}$			$-\Delta F°$ of hydrolysis, pH 8.5, 38° = 2200 cal[21] Phos. group migrates to β position in hot alkaline soln. and optical activity is lost.[24]
			Dimethyl ester	−4.78						
			Ag salt	+1.0[22,23]		C = 6.5				
7. D-glyceric acid 3-phosphate	186.1	$C_3H_7O_7P$	Ba salt	−13.8°[28]	$[\alpha]_{5461} -950^{29}$	20°	$pK_1 = 1.42^2$	25 26 27	Enzymatic[154] Rotation[156]	Tricyclohexylammonium salt
			molybdate complex	−745°[29]		20°	$\begin{array}{l}pK_2 = 3.42\\ pK_3 = 5.98\\ pK_3^2 = 6.74 \ (\mu = 0)\\ 6.20 \ (\mu = .15)\\ 5.69 \ (.15\,M\,NaCl)\end{array}$			3PG—$(C_3H_{13}N)_3$·$3H_2O$ sol. in H_2O. $-\Delta F°$ of hydrolysis pH 8.5, 30° = 3,000 cal[30] Trisodium salt soluble in water
8. D-glyceric acid 2-phosphate	186.1	$C_3H_7O_7P$	Ba salt	+24.3°[33]		N HCl	$pK_1^{36} = 1.42$	31 32	Enzymatic[154]	$-\Delta F°$ of hydrolysis pH 8.5,[30] 30° = 4,050 cal.
			molybdate complex	−68°[31]		1% neutral 25% ammonium molybdate calc. as free acid	$pK_2 = 3.42$			A negative rotation in molybdate indicates a contamination with D-glyceric acid 3-phosphate[35]
				+5°[35]			$pK_3 = 6.48$			
			Tri Na ($C_3H_4O_7PNa_3$·$5H_2O$)	+3.6°[35]		C = 2.0, H_2O	$pK_3 = 7.48 \ (\mu = 0)$			
			free acid	+12.9°[35]		C = 1.8, 1 N HCl cac. as free acid	$6.94 \ (\mu = .15)$			
			anhydrous	+13.0°[35]		C = 2.4 in 1 N HCl calc. as free acid	$6.43 \ (.15\,M\,NaCl)$			

No. & Name	M.W.	Formula	Form	$[\alpha]$	Conditions	pK	Ref.	Method	Properties
9. D-glyceric acid 1,3-diphosphate	186.1	$C_3H_9O_7P$	Molybdate complex Free acid	-675[34] -1.7 to -2.3[32]	8.3% ammonium molybdate C = 6.4 to 17 in H_2O or in $1\,N$ HNO_3	$pK_4{}^2 = 7.40$ $pK_5 = 7.99$	38 39	Enzymatic[39]	Strychnine salt $C_{97}H_{90}N_8P_4O_{18}$; unstable in dry state. More stable frozen and in weakly alkaline solution. A neutral aqueous solution has a characteristic U.V. band at 215 mμ sp. extinction = 2.11×10^5 cm^2 mole -1.
10. D-glyceric acid 2,3-diphosphate	266	$C_3H_8O_{10}P_2$	Free acid Pentasodium salt	-3.36[40] -2.3[41] -3.5[22] -4.9[22]	C = 27.7 C = 8.3 C = 8.3 C = 5.9 calc. as free acid		40 22	Enzymatic[157]	Also isolated as the tri barium salts $Ba_3(C_3H_5O_{10}P_2)_2 \cdot H_2O$ and 3 H_2O. Extremely resistant to hydrolysis
11. D-glycero-tetrulose 1-phosphate	200	$C_4H_9O_7P$	Dimethyl ketal dicyclohexyl-ammonium salt	$+13.3$[43]	H_2O		43	Enzymatic[43, 223]	MP = 160–165°
12. L-glycero-tetrulose 1-phosphate (L-erythrulose 1-phosphate)	200	$C_4H_9O_7P$	Dimethyl acetal biscyclohexyl-ammonium salt ($C_{16}H_{41}N_2O_8P \cdot H_2O$)	-13.0[42] -7.2	C = 2 Phos. buffer pH 8.0 C = 2, acetate buffer, pH 4.0	$pK_2 = 6.24$[42] L-glyceroletrulose-1 phosphate dimethyl acetal: $pK_1 = 1.8$[42], $pK_2 = 6.45$	42	Enzymatic[43]	MP = 165–167° Base labile, hydrolysis completed in 3 min. in $2\,N$ NaOH 100°
13. D-glycero-tetrulose 4-phosphate	200	$C_4H_9O_7P$	Dimethyl ketal ($C_{18}H_{41}O_8PN_2 \cdot 2H_2O$)	$+21.5°$	H_2O		43	phosphate assay[43] after acid hydrolysis ($1\,N$ HCl; 30 min)	
14. D-erythrose 4-phosphate	200	$C_4H_9O_7P$	Dimethyl acetal Free acid K salt	-2.6[46]	C = 5, H_2O or $1\,N$ HCl, 25° $[\alpha]_{589} = 0 + 0.2$[44] $[\alpha]_{420} - 0.9$[45] $[\alpha]_{500} + 0.3$ $[\alpha]_{589} + 0.5$ $[\alpha]_{700} + 0.6$ $[\alpha]_{420} - 14.8$[45] $[\alpha]_{500} - 7.8$ $[\alpha]_{589} - 4.7$ $[\alpha]_{700} - 3.8$		44 43	Enzymatic[158]	

Table I (cont.)

	Compounds	Molecular weight	Empirical formula	Derivative	Specific Rotation $[\alpha]_D$	Rotation $[\alpha]_x$	Conditions	pK_a	Prep. Ref.	Analysis	Miscellaneous
15.	D-glycero-tetrulose 1,4-diphosphate	280	$C_4H_{10}O_{10}P_2$	Tricyclohexyl-ammonium dimethyl acetal monohydrate	+13.5		$C = 2, H_2O, 27°$		161	phosphate assay after treatment with 1 N NaOH at room temp. of 1 N HCl, 100°	
				Free acid		$\alpha_{400} - 11.7$[161]	$C = 0.5, H_2O, 25°$ $C = 0.5, H_2O, 25°$				
16.	D-erythronic acid 3-phosphate	216	$C_4H_9O_8P$		-1.4[161]			pK = 3.9[47]	47	Enzymatic[47]	
17.	α-D-ribofuranose 5-phosphate 1-pyrophosphate	389	$C_5H_{11}O_{14}P_3$						48, 49	Orcinol determination[49,162] Enzymatic[198]	
18.	3-deoxy-D-erythro-pentose 5-(dihydrogen phosphate)	214	$C_5H_{11}O_7P$	Ba salt $C_5H_9BaO_7P \cdot H_2O$	-10.7[50]		$C = 0.122, H_2O, 25°$		50	Diphenylamine[159]	
19.	D-arabinose 1-phosphate	230	$C_5H_{11}O_8P$	Ba salt (monohydrate) Furanose Pyranose	$+6.4$[53] -44.3[53]		$C = 1.7, H_2O, 23°$ $C = 2.1, H_2O, 24°$		53	Orcinol[162]	
20.	D-arabinose 5-phosphate	230	$C_5H_{11}O_8P$	Ba salt Brucine salt	-18.8[51] -48.6[51]		H_2O 50% pyridine		51	Orcinol[162]	
21.	L-arabinose 1-phosphate	230	$C_5H_{11}O_8P$	Cyclohexylamine salt α anomer β anomer Free acid (furanose) Ba salt (pyranose) dicyclohexyl-ammonium salt	$+30.8$[52] $+91$[52] $+16.9$[53] $+48.2$[53] $+40.4$[53]		$C = 2.5\%, H_2O, pH\ 7.8$ $C = 0.98, H_2O$ $C = 2.09, H_2O$ $C = 2.11, H_2O$		52, 53	After dephosphorylation Enzymatic[160] assay Orcinol[162]	MP dicyclohexyl-ammonium salt β anomer 155–161° α anomer 144–150°
22.	D-ribose 1-phosphate	230	$C_5H_{11}O_8P$	Cyclohexylamine salt α anomer (D-ribofuranose-1-phosphate) β anomer Ba salt (D-ribofuranose-1-phosphate) β anomer	$+40.3$[54] -13.6[55] -47.1[56,53]		H_2O ethanol 5% HAC		164 57	Orcinol[162]	Separation of the various ribose phosphates can be effected by the use of ion exchange chromatography[58]

No.	Name	M.W.	Formula	Form / Salt	Rotation	Conditions	Ref.	Detection	Notes
23.	D-ribose 2-phosphate	230	$C_5H_{11}O_8P$	Ba salt	−6.8[58]	C = 5%, H₂O, pH 6.8	58	Orcinol[162]	
				Brucine salt	−27.5[58]	C = 5%, Pyridine: H₂O (1:1)			
				Na salt	−10.3[58]	C = 3.75, H₂O, pH 8.0			
					−14.3[58]	C = 1.87, pH 9, borax			
24.	D-ribose 3-phosphate	230	$C_5H_{11}O_8P$	Ba salt	−6.8[58]	C = 5%, H₂O, pH 7.2		Orcinol, Dische modification[165]	
				Na salt	−9.75[59, 60]	C = 3.75[58], H₂O, pH 6.9			
					−10.8[58]	C = 1.8%, borax, pH 9.0		cysteine-H_2SO_4[167]	
					+50[58]	C = 5% water-pyridine (1:1)			
				Dibrucine salt	−35.0[58]				
25.	D-ribose 5-phosphate	230	$C_5H_{11}O_8P$	Ba salt	+0.63[61]	C = 0.120 μ moles/ml 0.02 N HCl	61, 62, Enzymatic[166] 58	Orcinol[165]	
				Free acid	+22.8[61]	C = 0.120 μ moles/ml 0.02 N HCl			
					+18	0.02 N HCl N HCl[163] 0.2–1.0			
26.	α-D-ribose 1,5-diphosphate	322	$C_5H_{12}O_{11}P_2$	Tetracyclohexyl-amine salt	+20.8[64]		64	Orcinol[165]	
27.	2-deoxy-D-erythro-pentose 1-phosphate	214	$C_5H_{11}O_7P$	Cyclohexylamine salt $C_{17}H_{37}O_7N_2P$			65	Diphenylamine[159]	
28.	2-deoxy-D-erythro-pentose 5-phosphate	214	$C_5H_{11}O_7P$	Free acid	+19[67]	C = 0.47	66, 67	Enzymatic[225]	Ester link stable to 1N NaOH in 20 min. at room temperature
				Dicyclohexyl-ammonium dimethyl acetal	−10.3[67]	C = 2.0, H₂O, 20°		Diphenylamine reaction[159]	
								Reducing sugar[168]	
29.	D-erythro-pentulose 5-phosphate	230	$C_5H_{11}O_8P$		−40[68]	0.02 N HCl	171	Enzymatic[186] Orcinol[170]	
30.	L-erythro-pentulose 5-phosphate	230	$C_5H_{11}O_8P$	Free acid	+28[69]	C = 30 mg/ml		Orcinol[170]	
31.	D-erythro-pentulose 1,5-diphosphate	310	$C_5H_{12}O_{11}P_2$			0.2 N HBr	70, 71	Orcinol[170, 71]	

Table I (cont.)

Compounds	Molecular weight	Empirical formula	Derivative	Specific Rotation $[\alpha]_D$	$[\alpha]_x$	Conditions	pK_o	Prep. Ref.	Analysis	Miscellaneous
32. α-D-xylose 1-phosphate	230	$C_5H_{11}O_8P$	Ba salt ($C_5H_9O_8PBa$) 1½ H_2O	+65[72]		C = 2, H_2O	$pK_1 = 1.25$[72]	52	Orcinol[165]	
			Di K salt $C_5H_9O_8PK_2 \cdot 2H_2O$ Cyclohexylamine salt	+76[72]		C = 2, H_2O	$pK_2 = 6.15$		Cysteine-H_2SO_4[167]	
			α anomer	+58[52]		H_2O				
			β anomer	+0.85[52]		H_2O				
33. D-xylose 3-phosphate	230	$C_5H_{11}O_8P$	Cyclohexylamine salt	+14.1[73]		H_2O		73	Orcinol[165]	
			Ba salt	+1.27[73]		H_2O				
34. D-xylose 5-phosphate	230	$C_5H_{11}O_8P$	Na salt	+3.2[74]		C = 5%, H_2O		74	Orcinol[165]	
			Na salt	+4.8[74]		C = 2.5%, 0.5 saturated borax				
			Ba salt	+5.0[74]		C = 2%, H_2O				
35. D-glucose 1-phosphate α-anomer	260.1	$C_6H_{13}O_9P$	Cyclohexylamine salt	+60.8[75]		C = 2, H_2O, 26°	$pK_1 = 1.11$[78]	52, 75 76, 77 78	Enzymatic[172]	$-\Delta F°$ of hydrolysis 4,900[21]
			$C_{18}H_{39}N_2O_9P$½H_2O Brucine salt	+21[73]	$[\alpha]_{5461}$	C = 2, H_2O, 21°	$pK_2 = 6.13$		α anomer demonstrated by the UDPG-	
			di K salt $C_6H_{11}K_2O_9P \cdot 2H_2O$	+78.6[76,77]	+90[52,76,77]	C = 2, H_2O, 20°	pK_2[79] = 6.50 ($\mu = 0$)		pyrophosphory-	
			Ba salt			C = 4, H_2O, 20°	6.17 ($\mu = .15$)		lase reaction[177]	
			$C_6H_{11}O_5PO_4 \cdot 3H_2O$	+75[78]		C = 1.26, H_2O	5.96 (.15 M NaCl)			
			Free acid	+125[78]		C = 1, H_2O				
			Brucine salt	−20[77]		H_2O				
				−17[80]						
β-anomer	260.1	$C_6H_{13}O_9P$	Na₂ salt	+13[80]		C = 1.7, 29°		52, 80		
			$C_6H_{11}O_9PNa_2$ di cyclohexyl-amine salt	+7.3[52]		C = 3.81, 20° cal. as free acid				
36. α-L-glucose 1-phosphate	260.1	$C_6H_{13}O_9P$	Ba salt	−73.2[81]		C = 1.01, H_2O		81	Reducing sugar after hydrolysis not active as a substrate for potato phos-phorylase[81]	
			K₂ salt	−78.2[81]		C = 1.01, H_2O				

No.	Name	Formula	M.W.	Salt/form	$[\alpha]$	$[\alpha]_{5461}$	Conditions	pK	Ref.	Method	Notes
37.	D-glucose 2-phosphate	$C_6H_{13}O_9P$	260.1	K_2 salt	$+15$[82] $+35$		H_2O $0.1\,N\,H_2SO_4$		82	Phosphate liberation with phenylhydrazine[173]	
38.	D-glucose 3-phosphate	$C_6H_{13}O_9P$	260.1	Free acid	$+39.5$[84] -14.5[85]	$[\alpha]_{5461} +39$[83]	H_2O $C=0.62\%,\ H_2O$ pyridine, water (1:1) $C=5.0\%$	$pK_1 = 0.84$[86] $pK_2 = 5.67$	84 87 111	Reducing sugar[199] Hypoiodite titration[84]	
				di Brucine salt			$C=2.0$, pyridine $C=1.0$, H_2O				
				Ba salt	-41.8[84] $+26.5$[84]	$[\alpha]_{5461} +27$[83]					
				Na salt during lactone formation	$+1.3$[85] -1.24[85]		$C=5.0\%$, H_2O $C=5.0\%$, $2\,N\,HCl$ 31 min.				
39.	D-glucose 4-phosphate	$C_6H_{13}O_9P$	260.1	di Brucine salt	-45.3[88] -43.3[89] -16.1[89]		$C=1.7$, pyridine $C=2.1$, 20% ethanol	$pK_1 = 0.84$ $pK_2 = 5.67$	89	Reducing sugar[199]	$-\Delta F°$ of hydrolysis, pH 8.5, 38° = 3,000 cal
				di Na salt	$+51.5$[89]		$C=2.1$, H_2O, 20°				
40.	D-glucose 5-phosphate	$C_6H_{13}O_9P$	260.1	Ba salt	$+15$[90]				83	Reducing sugar[199]	
41.	D-glucose 6-phosphate	$C_6H_{13}O_9P$	260.1	Free acid	$+35.1$[91]	$[\alpha]_{5461} +41.4$	H_2O	$pK_1 = 0.94$[86]	94 95 96 97 98	Enzymatic[175]	$-\Delta F°$ of hydrolysis, pH 8.5, 38° = 3,000 cal[21]
				K salt ($C_6H_{11}O_9PK_2$) (336.32)	$+21.2$[92]		$C=1.3$, H_2O	$pK_2 = 6.11$			Ba heptahydrate ($C_6H_{11}O_9PBa·7H_2O$), unlike the amorphous product is highly insoluble in water (2×10^{-3} moles/l at 25°[9a])
				Ba salt ($C_6H_{11}O_9PBa$) (395.5)	$+17.9$[91]	$[\alpha]_{5461} +21.2$[91]	$C=1.0$, H_2O	$pK_2 = 6.51\ (\mu=0)$ $6.18\ (\mu=.15)$ 5.97 $(0.15\,M\,NaCl)$			
				CH_3 α-D-glucuronide dicyclohexylamine salt	$+61$[93]						
42.	D-glucose 1,6-diphosphate	$C_6H_{12}O_{12}P_2$	340	Brucine salt $C_6H_{14}O_{12}P_2$ $(C_{23}H_{26}O_2N_2)_4$					99	Enzymatic[176]	α form activates phosphoglucomutase, whereas the β form is enzymatically inactive.
				α anomer	-16.3[99]		$C=0.8$, H_2O, 26°				
				β anomer	-30.4[99]		$C=0.64$, H_2O, 25°				
				Na salt α anomer	$+83°$		$C=0.229\ H_2O$ (calc. as anhydrous free acid) 28°				
				β anomer	$-19°$		$C=0.373$, H_2O (calc. as anhydrous free acid)				

Table I (cont.)

	Compounds	Molecular weight	Empirical formula	Derivative	Specific Rotation $[\alpha]_D$	$[\alpha]_x$	Conditions	pK_a	Prep. Ref.	Analysis	Miscellaneous
43.	D-gluconic acid 6-phosphate	276	$C_6H_{13}O_{10}P$			$[\alpha]_{5461} + 0.2^{100}$			101	Enzymatic[178]	
44.	α-D-glucuronic acid 1-phosphate	274	$C_6H_{11}O_{10}P$	K salt $(C_6H_{10}O_{10}PK_3 \cdot 2H_2O)$	$+53.6^{102}$				103, 213	Carbazole assay for uronic acid[200]	
45.	D-galactose 1-phosphate	260.1	$C_6H_{13}O_9P$	α isomer Free acid	$+148.5^{104}$ $+143^{105}$ $+108^{106}$		$C = 1.67, H_2O, 18°$ $H_2O, 25°$ H_2O	$pK_1 = 1.00^{110}$ $pK_2 = 6.17$	52 α isomer 105, 107, 108	Reducing after acid hydrolysis	
				K salt $(C_6H_{11}O_9PK_2 \cdot 2H_2O)$	$+100^{107}$ $+97.3^{75}$		$C = 1.57, H_2O$ $C = 2, H_2O, 20°$				
				cyclohexylamine salt $(C_{18}H_{35}N_2O_9P \cdot \frac{1}{2}H_2O)$ Brucine salt	$+64^{75}$ $+78.5^{2,75}$ $+30^{75}$ $+92^{106}$		$C = 1.5, H_2O, pH\ 7.8$ $C = 2, H_2O, 20°$ $0.5\%, H_2O, 25°$				
				β isomer Ba salt $(C_6H_{11}O_9PBa)$ Ba salt	$+96^{108}$ $+31.3^{105}$ $+31.2^{109}$	$[\alpha]_{5461} + 112^{106}$	H_2O H_2O		β isomer 109, 52	Enzymatic[108]	
				Cyclohexylamine salt	$+21^{52}$		$C = 1.2, H_2O, 30°$ $pH\ 7.8$				
46.	D-galactose 6-phosphate	260.1	$C_6H_{13}O_9P$	Ba salt	$+25.2^{112}$		$16°$		112	Enzymatic[11,222] after hydrolysis with alkaline phosphatase	
47.	α-D-mannose 1-phosphate	260.1	$C_6H_{13}O_9P$	Ba salt $(C_6H_{11}O_9PBa)$ Free acid	$+36^{105}$ $+33.7^{113}$ $+58°^{105}$		$H_2O, 25°$ $C = 3.0, H_2O, 23°$		105	Enzymatic[206] (identification)	
48.	D-mannose 6-phosphate	260.1	$C_6H_{13}O_9P$	Free acid Ba salt		$[\alpha]_{5461} + 15.1^{114}$ $[\alpha]_{5461} + 3.5^{114}$	H_2O		207, 113	Enzymatic[207]	
49.	mannose 1,6-diphosphate	340	$C_6H_{14}O_{12}P_2$	K salt	-29.9^{113}						$-\Delta F°$ of hydrolysis[21] 2650 cal. at pH 8.5, 38°.
50.	D-mannonic acid 6-phosphate	276	$C_6H_{13}O_{10}P$	Delta lactone Gamma lactone Ba salt	$-.005$ (20 min.) $+.116$ (4 days)	$[\alpha]_{5461} + 60.6^{100}$ $[\alpha]_{5461} + 54.1^{100}$ $[\alpha]_{5461} - 1.0$ (20 min.) to $+23.7$ (4 days)	Aqueous solution		100	Phosphate assay[100] after acid hydrolysis Polarimetric[100] observation of lactone formation	M P Delta lactone 127.5–128.5°C gamma lactone M.P. 125–125.5°C

No. & Name	M.W.	Formula	Salt	$[\alpha]$	$[\alpha]_{5461}$	Conditions	pK	Ref.	Detection	Notes
51. D-fructose 1-phosphate	260.1	$C_6H_{13}O_9P$	Free acid Ba salt ($C_6H_{11}O_9PBa$)	-52.5[115]	-64.2[115] -39	11.3%, H_2O, 26° 11.3%, H_2O, 26° 11.3%, H_2O, 26°		116 117 118	Resorcinol[204,205]	$-\Delta F°$ of hydrolysis[21] 2790 cal at pH 8.5, 38°
52. D-fructose 6-phosphate	260.1	$C_6H_{13}O_9P$	Brucine salt Ba salt $C_6H_{11}O_9PBa \cdot H_2O$ Free acid	-30.4[116] +3.6[119] +2.5[86]	-36.4[116]	C=4.3, H_2O, 26° 11.3%, H_2O, 26° H_2O C=3, H_2O, 21°	pK_1 = 0.97[86] pK_2 = 6.11 pK_2[86] = 6.51 (μ = 0) 6.18 (μ = .15) 5.97 (0.15 M NaCl)	119 120	Enzymatic[203] Resorcinol[205]	Ca salt, sol in H_2O $-\Delta F°$ of hydrolysis[21] at pH 8.5, 38°C = 3000 cal
53. D-fructose 1,6-diphosphate	340.1	$C_6H_{14}O_{12}P_2$	Free acid	+4.1[119]	-52.1[115]	H_2O	pK_1 = 1.48[121] pK_2 = 6.1–6.5[86] pK_2[86] = 6.71 (μ = 0) 6.38 (μ = .15) 6.17 (0.15 M NaCl)	122 123 124	Resorcinol[205] Carbazole[208] Enzymatic[202]	Ca + Ba salts difficultly soluble in H_2O Mg salt readily soluble
54. L-sorbose 1-phosphate	260.1	$C_6H_{13}O_9P$	Ba salt ($C_6H_{11}O_9PBa \cdot H_2O$) K salt $C_6H_{12}O_9PK$	-7.2[125] -16.5[125]		C=2.5 in 0.104 N HCl C=2.0, H_2O		210	Enzymatic[209]	
55. L-sorbose 6-phosphate	260.1	$C_6H_{13}O_9P$	Ba salt $C_6H_{11}O_9PBa$	-12.0[125]		C=2.0, H_2O, 29°		210	Enzymatic[201]	
56. D-tagatose 6-phosphate	260.1	$C_6H_{13}O_9P$	Ba salt $C_6H_{11}O_9PBa$	+5.65[126]		C=1.06, H_2O, 25°		127	Enzymatic[127]	
57. 6-deoxy-L-*lyxo*-hexulose 1-phosphate		$C_6H_{13}O_8P$	Ba salt	-2.3[128]		C = 5.1% calc. as free acid pH 4.5 25°		128	Enzymatic[214]	
58. 2-amino-2-deoxy-D-glucose 1-phosphate	259.2	$C_6H_{14}O_8NP$	K salt ($C_6H_{13}O_8NPK$)	α_{isomer} +100[129] β_{isomer} -20[129]		C = 1.98, H_2O, 23°	pK_2 = 5.4 (0.15 M NaCl)[129] 5.5 (H_2O) pK_3 = 8.5 (0.15 M NaCl) 8.7 (H_2O)	129	Elson-Morgan reaction after hydrolysis[136,148,143]	

Table I (cont.)

Compounds	Molecular weight	Empirical formula	Derivative	Specific Rotation $[\alpha]_D$	Specific Rotation $[\alpha]_x$	Conditions	pK_0	Prep. Ref.	Analysis	Miscellaneous
59. 2-amino-2-deoxy-D-glucose 6-phosphate	259.2	$C_6H_{14}O_8NP$	Free acid	$+48.5$[130] $+54$[131] $+56 \rightarrow +58.8$[132] at equilib.[134]		$C = 0.51\%$, H_2O, pH 2.50, 24° 5%, H_2O, 25°	$pK_2 = 6.08$[130] $pK_2 = 8.10$	132 133 134	Reduction[135, 137] Elson-Morgan[148, 136] Enzymatic[212]	M.P. 166-167 (decomp) Solns have an absorption spectrum with a λ max. at 273 mu and a min. at 241 mu
60. 2-acetamido-2-deoxy-D-glucose 1-phosphate	301.2	$C_8H_{16}O_9NP$	K salt $(C_8H_{14}O_9PK_2 \cdot 2H_2O)$ α isomer β isomer Na salt β isomer	$+79$[129] $+76.1$[138] -40[129] -1.7[138] -1.6[139]		$C = 0.954$, H_2O, 23° $C = 3.44$, H_2O, 25° Calculated value[129] $C = 2.93$, H_2O, 25°	$pK_1 < 1.5$[129] < 1.4[138] pK_2 6.1[129] 6.0[138]	138	Morgan-Elson[143] determination after mild acid hydrolysis[138]	
61. 2-acetamido-2-deoxy-D-glucose 6-phosphate	301.2	$C_8H_{16}O_9NP$	Free acid	$+29.5$[134]		Equilibrium value[134] 8% soln. in 0.5 M NaAc, pH 3.0		212 134	Morgan-Elson reaction[143, 144]	
62. 2-deoxy-2-glycolylamido-D-glucose 6-phosphate	317.2	$C_8H_{16}O_{10}NP$	K salt	$+24.8$[140]		$C = 4.2-9.5\%$, H_2O, 25°		140	Modification of the Morgan-Elson reaction[143, 144, 140]	
63. 2-amino-2-deoxy-2-D-galactose 1-phosphate	259.2	$C_6H_{14}O_8NP$	Free acid	$+142.6$[141]		$C = 2.0$, H_2O, 25°		141	Morgan-Elson[141, 144] assay after N-acetylation and mild acid hydrolysis	Galn 1-phosphate is very resistant to acid hydrolysis,[142] while the N-acetyl derivative is quite labile.
64. 2-acetamido-2-deoxy-D-galactose 1-phosphate	301.2	$C_8H_{16}O_9NP$	Free acid K salt $(C_8H_{14}O_9NPK_2)$ Li salt	$+178$[145] 112[141]	$[\alpha]_{578} +118$[141] $[\alpha]_{578} +189$[146]	$C = 2.9$, H_2O		141	Morgan-Elson reaction after mild acid hydrolysis[141, 144]	
65. 2-acetamido-2-deoxy-D-galactose 6-phosphate	301.2	$C_8H_{16}O_9NP$		$+48.4$[134]		1% solution in 0.05 M Na Acetate, pH 4.5 Equilibrium value			Modification of the Morgan-Elson reaction[143, 144]	
66. 2-deoxy-2-glycolylamido-D-galactose 6-phosphate	317.2	$C_8H_{16}O_{10}NP$	K salt	$+19.5$[140]		H_2O, $C = 4.2-9.5\%$		140	Modification of the Morgan-Elson reaction[143, 144, 140]	

No.	Name	MW	Formula	Form	$[\alpha]$	Conditions	Detection method	Ref.	M.P.
67.	2-amino-2-deoxy-D-mannose 6-phosphate	259.2	$C_6H_{14}O_8NP$	Free acid	$-2.3 \rightarrow +0.23$ (equilib. value)[132]	C = 1.29, H_2O	Modification of the Morgan-Elson reaction[148]	140	M.P. 120–127° (decomp.)
68.	2-acetamido-2-deoxy-D-mannose 6-phosphate	301.2	$C_8H_{16}O_9NP$	K salt	$+14.6$[140]; $+11.2$[147]	C = 1.4%, H_2O, 25°; C = 1%, H_2O, Calc. as free acid	Modification of the Morgan-Elson reaction[143, 144, 140]	140	
69.	2-deoxy-2-glycolylamido-D-mannose 6-phosphate	317.2	$C_8H_{16}O_{10}NP$	K salt	$+15.0$[140]	C = 4.2–9.5%, H_2O	Modification of the Morgan-Elson reaction[143, 144, 140]	180	
70.	myo-inositol 1-phosphate	260.1	$C_6H_{13}O_9P$	Dicyclohexylamine salt $C_6H_{13}O_9P\cdot2(C_6H_{11}NH_2)$; Free acid	$+3.1$[179]; $+3.4$[180]; -9.8[180]	C = 2.0, H_2O; C = 3.0, pH 9; C = 3, H_2O, pH 2	After hydrolysis in boiling in 6 N HCl for 14 hrs., micro-biological or Enzymatic analysis[184]	183	MP 195–197 (decomp.)
71.	L-myo-inositol 1-phosphate	260.1	$C_6H_{13}O_9P$	Dicyclohexylamine salt	-3.2[183]; $+9.3$[183]	pH 9, H_2O[183]; pH 2, H_2O		182; 180	MP 195–197 (decomp.)
72.	myo-inositol 2-phosphate (meso)	260.1	$C_6H_{13}O_9P$		0[183] (inactive)				
73.	inositol 3-phosphate	260.1	$C_6H_{13}O_9P$	Dicyclohexylamine salt	-9.8[180, 183]	pH 2			
74.	3-deoxy-D-arabino-heptulosonic acid 7-phosphate	288	$C_7H_{13}O_{10}P$	Tricyclohexyl-ammonium salt $C_{25}H_{54}N_3O_{10}P$; K salt; Free acid	$+9.4$[185]; $+15.7$; $+42$	C = 4.9%, H_2O; C = 3.8, H_2O, 25°; C = 1.5, H_2O, 25°	Thiobarbituric acid assay[216]	185	MP 155–158°
75.	sedoheptulose 7-phosphate	290	$C_7H_{15}O_{10}P$				Orcinol[170] (absorption max. at 580 mµ); Enzymatic[187]	186	
76.	sedoheptulose 1,7-diphosphate	370	$C_7H_{16}O_{13}P_2$				Enzymatic[188] phosphate determination after treatment with sedoheptulose diphosphatase[189]	188	
77.	shikimic acid 5-phosphate	254	$C_7H_{11}O_8P$	K salt	-107.6°[190]	C = 1.02, H_2O, 29°	Bioassay[215]	190	

Table I (cont.)

Compounds	Molecular weight	Empirical formula	Derivative	Specific Rotation $[\alpha]_D$	Rotation $[\alpha]_x$	Conditions	pK$_a$	Prep. Ref.	Analysis	Miscellaneous
78. trehalose 6-phosphate	422	$C_{12}H_{23}O_{14}P$	Free acid	+185[192]	$[\alpha]_{5461}$ + 185[191]	C = 0.044 M, 0.1 N HCl		191 192	Reducing power after acid hydrolysis[191]	
			Ba salt	+99[193]	$[\alpha]_{5461}$ + 132[191]	C = 3.2%, H$_2$O, 20°			Anthrone[224]	
			Brucine salt			C = 0.6, H$_2$O, 22°				
			Cyclohexylamine salt	+62[193]	$[\alpha]_{5461}$ + 31[191]	C = 0.77%, H$_2$O, 20°				
						C = 0.7, H$_2$O, 22°				
79. lactose 1-phosphate	422	$C_{12}H_{23}O_{14}P$	Ba salt	+73.3[194]				194	Reducing power after heating with 0.01 N HCl for 10 minutes. Phenol H$_2$SO$_4$ assay.[217]	
			α anomer	+24.8[194]						
			β anomer							
80. maltose 1-phosphate	422	$C_{12}H_{23}O_{14}P$	Ba salt	+107[72]		C = 2.0, H$_2$O	pK$_1$ = 1.52[72] pK$_2$ = 5.89	72	Arsenomolybdate assay[199] after acid hydrolysis	
81. glucose sulfate	260	$C_6H_{12}O_9S$	Ba salt $(C_6H_{11}O_9S)_2$ Ba	+33.4[195]		C = 2.4, H$_2$O, 14°		195	As BaSO$_4$.[195] Benzidine[219] Turbidimetric[220] Enzymatic[220, 221]	
			Brucine salt	−4[195] (5 min)		C = 0.25, H$_2$O, 16°				
			$C_6H_{12}O_9S$–$C_{23}H_{26}O_4N_2$	−6 (24 hrs)		C = 0.25, H$_2$O, 16°				
			Ba methyl glucoside sulfate							
			α anomer	+90		C = 0.4, H$_2$O, 15° 18°				
				+72[196]		C = 1.0, H$_2$O, 20°				
			β anomer	−12°[196]						
82. galactose 6-sulfate	260	$C_6H_{12}O_9S$	Ba salt	+46[195]		C = 1.7, H$_2$O, 18°		195	[195, 219, 220, 221]	
			Brucine salt	−5[195] (5 min) −11° (24 hrs)		C = 0.35, H$_2$O, 17°				
			Ba diacetyl gal-6-sulfate	−35.7[195] −42.4		C = 7.3, H$_2$O C = 8.2, CHCl$_3$				
			Brucine-gal-6-sulfate	+5[195] (30 min) +1° (24 hrs)		C = 0.5, H$_2$O, 18°				
			Ba methyl galactoside sulfate							
			α anomer	+142[195]		C = 0.5, H$_2$O, 17°				
			β anomer	−12		C = 3.4, H$_2$O				
83. mannose sulfate	260	$C_6H_{12}O_9S$	Ba α methyl	+38[195]		C = 1.0, H$_2$O, 18°		195	[195, 219, 220, 221]	

Table II. Paper Chromatographic Data (Rf values)

Compound	Solvents					
	1^{226}	2^{226}	3^{227}	4^{227}	5^{228}	6^{229}
D-glucose 1-P	—	0	.27	.68	.22	.14
D-glucose 6-P	.35	0	.38	.48	—	.12
D-fructose 6-P	.38	0	.34	.44	.31	.17
D-fructose 1,6-diP	—	—	.40	.24	.39	.08
Ribose 5-P	.50	0	—	—	—	—
Ribose 1-P	—	—	—	—	—	.15
D-arabinose 5-P	.50	.25	—	—	—	—
D-xylose 5-P	.55	.25	—	—	—	—
2-Phosphoglycerate	—	—	.46	.18	—	.27
3-Phosphoglycerate	—	—	.50	.35	—	.23
2-3 diphosphoglycerate	—	—	—	—	—	.11
D-glyceraldehyde 3-P	—	—	—	—	—	.07
Glycerol 1-P	—	—	—	—	—	.26
Enolpyruvic acid 2-P	—	—	.52	.46	—	—
D-gluconic acid 6-P	.89	—	—	—	—	—
D-ribose 3-P	.50	.019	—	—	—	—
D-xylose 3-P	.53	.023	—	—	—	—

1. 80% ETOH: 0.8% acetic acid
2. 80% ETOH: 0.64% boric acid
3. Methanol: 88% formic acid—water—(80:15:5)
4. Methanol: 28% Ammonia—water—(60:10:30)
5. Acetone: 25% TCA in water—(75:25)
6. Ethyl acetate: acetic acid: water (3:3:1 at 4°)

Table II. (cont'd) Paper Chromatographic Data (Rf values)

Compound	Solvents					
	7^{229}	8^{230}	9^{230}	10^{228}	11^{229}	12^{229}
D-glucose 1-P	.44	1.28*	.51*	.31	.36	.44
D-glucose 6-P	.50	1.05*	.46*	—	.29	.50
D-fructose 6-P	.54	1.19*	.64*	.37	.36	.54
D-fructose 1,6-diP	.13	.40*	.68*	.37	.08	.13
Ribose 5-P	—	—	—	.46	—	—
Ribose 1-P	.50	1.0*	1.0*	—	.40	.50
2-Phosphoglycerate	.23	—	—	—	.41	.23
3-Phosphoglycerate	.28	1.05*	.87*	—	.22	.28
2-3 diphosphoglycerate	—	—	—	—	.07	.15
D-glyceraldehyde 3-P	—	—	—	—	.19	—
Glycerol 1-P	—	—	—	—	.39	.54

*R_{pi}

7. Ethyl acetate: formamide: pyridine—(1:2:1), 26°
8. n-propanol: ammonia: water—(60:30:10)
9. Picric acid: 2-methyl-2 propanol: water—(4:80:20)
10. Acetone: 35% chloroacetic acid—(60:40 v/v)
11. Methyl Cellosolve: methylethyl ketone: $3N$ NH_4OH—(7:2:3)
12. Ethyl acetate: formamide: pyridine—(6:4:1)

Table II.   (cont'd) Paper Chromatographic Data (Rf values)   162

Compound	13^{231}	$14^{53, 75,}_{180**}$	$15^{232,}_{235}$	16^{103}	17^{103}	18^{103}
D-glucose 1-P	.03	1.60*	—	0.30	.10	.29
D-glucose 6-P	—	—	.40*	—	—	—
D-fructose 6-P	—	—	.61*	—	—	—
Fructose 1-P	—	—	.40*	—	—	—
Galactose 1-P	—	—	—	.35	.13	.31
Mannose-1-P	—	—	—	.36	.10	.34
2-Acetamido-2-deoxy-D-glucose 1-P	—	—	—	.42	.22	.33
Glycerol-1-P	—	—	—	.52	.22	.38
Mannose-6-P	—	—	0.52*	—	—	—
Sedoheptulose-7-P	—	—	.52*	—	—	—
Phosphoglycolic acid	—	—	1.06*	—	—	—
Enolpyruvic acid 2-P	—	—	1.20*	—	—	—
Ribulose-1-5 diP	—	—	.58*	—	—	—
2-Deoxyribose-5-P	—	0.13	—	—	—	—
D-arabinose 1-P	—	0.10	—	—	—	—
Myo-inositol 1-P	—	0.55	—	—	—	—
Myo-inositol 2-P	—	0.75	—	—	—	—
Myo-inositol 5-P	—	0.65	—	—	—	—
(−) Inositol 3-P	—	0.95	—	—	—	—
Myo-inositol 1,2-di-phosphate	—	2.30	—	—	—	—

*R_{pi} **$R_{Glycerol-1-Phosphate}$

13. Butanol: acetic acid: water—(4:1:5)
14. Isopropanol: ammonia: water—(7:1:2)
15. Tert—butanol: water: picric acid—(7:1:2)
16. Ethyl alcohol—0.5 *M* ammonium acetate buffer, pH 3.8—(5:2)
17. Ethyl alcohol—1.0 *M* ammonium acetate, pH 7.5—(5:2)
18. Isopropanol: 1% aqueous ammonium sulfate—(2:1)

Compound	19^{233}	20^{234}	21^{232}	22^{235}	23^{235}
D-glucose 1-P	—	.23	.18	—	—
D-glucose 6-P	—	.20	.18	1.13	.40
D-fructose 6-P	—	.24	.28	1.25	.46
D-fructose 1,6-diP	—	.12	.15	0.26	.22
Fructose 1-P	—	—	—	1.35	.46
Ribose 5-P	—	.27	—	1.39	.49
2-Phosphoglycerate	—	.38	.59	—	—
3-Phosphoglycerate	—	.26	—	1.00	.65
2-3 diphosphoglycerate	.32	.15	—	—	—
D-glyceraldehyde 3-P	—	.13	—	—	—
Mannose-6-P	—	.19	—	1.25	.46
D-galactose 6-P	—	.19	—	—	—
Sedoheptulose 7-P	—	.20	—	1.13	.40
3-Phosphoglyceraldehyde	—	—	—	1.70	—
Phosphoglycolic acid	—	—	—	1.02	.75
Dihydroxyacetone 1-P	—	—	—	1.70	.59
Enolpyruvic acid 2-P	—	—	—	1.10	.92
Ribulose-5-P	—	—	—	1.47	.53
Ribulose-1-5 diP	—	—	—	.26	.22
Sedoheptulose diP	—	—	—	.26	.22
D-glucose-1, 6 diP	—	—	—	.26	.22

19. n-propanol: NH_4OH: water—(50:40:10)
20. 69% v/v butyric acid—0.85% w/v NaOH, 20°, for 3 days following electrophoresis in 9.2% butyric acid: 0.1% NaOH, 400 V, 4.5 has Whatman 3 MM paper
21. Isopropyl ether: 90% Formic acid—(90:60), 20°
22. Phenol: water—78 g: 28 ml
23. Butanol: propionic acid, water—(100:50:70), 22°

Table III. Chromatography of Sulfate Esters

Chromatography Systems	1[236] $R_{glucose}$	2[237] R_f	3[237] R_1
2-acetamido-2-deoxy-D-galactose disulfate	0.54	—	—
2-acetamido-2-deoxy-D-galactose sulfate	0.72	—	—
2-acetamido-2-deoxy-D-glucose disulfate	0.54	—	—
2-acetamido-2-deoxy-D-glucose sulfate	0.76	—	—
D-fucose disulfate	0.59	—	—
L-fucose disulfate	0.59	—	—
D-fucose sulfate	0.92	—	—
L-fucose sulfate	0.98	—	—
D-galactose disulfate	0.43	—	—
D-galactose 6-sulfate	0.58	0.40	—
D-glucose	1.0	0.21	0.18
D-glucose disulfate	0.42	—	—
D-glucose 3-sulfate	—	0.67	.85
D-glucose 6-sulfate	0.66	0.44	0.77

1. 1-Butanol: acetic acid: water (50:12:25)
   (48 hrs., 20°, Whatman #1, descending)
2. 1-Butanol: ethanol: water, containing 3% w/v cetylpyridinium chloride—
   (3:1:1)
   (Whatman #1, 20 hrs.)
3. Water-saturated butanone: cetylpyridinium chloride—(100 ml: 3 gm)

Table IV. Observed Hydrolysis Constants of Some Phosphates*

Compound	Normality of acid	Temperature C	tl/2, min.	K x 10³	Reference
Aldose 1-phosphates					
2-Deoxy D-erithro-pento-pyranose 1-phosphate (pH 4)		25	12	25	1
α-D-Galactopyranose 1-phosphate	0.25	25	333	0.90	8
-D-Galactopyranose 1-phosphate	0.25	37	50	5.9	8
-D-Galactopyranose 1-phosphate	0.1	100	2.1	140	9
-D-Galactopyranose 1-phosphate	0.25	37	53	5.6	9
2-Amino-2-deoxy-D-galactopyranose 1-phosphate	1	100	4.1	73.7	9
α-D-Glucopyranose 1-phosphate	0.1	36	158	1.9	3
α-D-Glucopyranose 1-phosphate	0.25	37	230	1.30	4
α-D-Glucopyranose 1-phosphate	1	33	60	5.00	5
α-D-Glucopyranose 1-phosphate	0.95	30	200	1.15	6

*Reproduced by permission from *Methods in Enzymology*, by Colowick and Kaplan, Vol. III, Academic Press Inc.

Table IV. (cont'd) Observed Hydrolysis Constants of Some Phosphates*

Compound	Normality of acid	Temperature C	tl/2, min.	K x 10³	Reference
Aldose 1-phosphates (continued)					
α-D-Glucopyranose 1-phosphate	1	100	1.05	200	7
α-D-Glucopyranose 1-phosphate	1	33	20	15	6
2-Amino-2-deoxy-D-glucopyranose 1-phosphate	1	100	4	75.0	11
Maltose 1-phosphate	0.1	36	214	1.4	3
α-D-Mannopyranose 1-phosphate	0.95	30	360	0.82	6
D-Ribopyranose 1-phosphate	0.5	25	2.5	120	2
D-Xylopyranose 1-phosphate	0.1	36	111	2.7	3
Other Sugar Phosphates					
2-Deoxy-D-erythro-pentose 5-phosphate	1	100	6.2	56	14
D-erythro-pentulose 5-phosphate	1	100	60	5	18
D-Fructose 1-phosphate	1	100	2.8	70	23
D-Fructose 1-phosphate	0.1	100	33	9	23
D-Fructose 6-phosphate	1	100	70	4.36	21
D-Fructose 1,6-diphosphate	1	100	5.7	a.52 b.4.2	27
D-Glucose 2-phosphate	0.1	100	136	2.18	19
D-Glucose 6-phosphate	0.1	100	2300	0.13	20
D-Glucose 6-phosphate	1	100	1300	0.22	21
-D-Glucose 1,6-diphosphate	0.25	37	967	0.31	25
-D-Glucose 1,6-diphosphate	1	30	900	0.33	26
-D-Glucose 1,6-diphosphate	1	30	220	1.37	26
D-gluconic acid 6-phosphate	1	100		0.26-0.15	22
D-glycero-pentulose 1-phosphate	1	100	30	9.7	13
D-Mannose 6-phosphate	0.1	100	2300	0.13	21
D-Mannose 6-phosphate	1	100	1034	0.29	21
-D-Mannose 1,6-diphosphate	0.95	30	1420	0.21	6
D-mannonic acid 6-phosphate	1	100		0.199-0.131	22
D-Mannono-1, 4-lactone 6-phosphate	1	100	2500	0.12	22
D-Ribose 3-phosphate	0.01	100	180	1.7	15

Table IV. (cont'd) Observed Hydrolysis Constants of Some Phosphates*

	Normality of acid	Temperature C	tl/2, min.	K x 10³	Reference
Other Sugar Phosphates					
D-Ribose 3-phosphate	0.25	100	66	4.5	16
D-Ribose 5-phosphate	0.01	100	1000	0.3	15
D-Ribose 5-phosphate	0.25	100	600	0.5	16
L-Sorbose 6-phosphate	1	100	62	4.8	24
Triose phosphates	1	100	8.1	37	12
D-Xylose 5-phosphate	1	100	90	3.3	17
Other Phosphate Esters					
Glycerol 1-phosphate	1	100	3300	0.09	7
Glycerol 1-phosphate	2.14	127	300	0.98	28
Glycerol 2-phosphate	2.035	124	300	0.97	28
glyceric acid 3-phosphate	1	100	2140	0.14	7
Phosphorylcholine	1	100	2300	0.13	28
Phosphorylcholine	2	124	1870	0.16	28
Aminoethyl phosphoric acid	1	100	940	0.32	29
Aminoethyl phosphoric acid	4.5	100	300	1.0	29
Acid Anhydrides					
Acetyl phosphate	0.5	40	11	27.8	31
Acetyl phosphate molybdate	0.5	25	0.86	350	31
glyceric acid 1,3-diphosphate	neuter	38	27	11	32
Pyrophosphoric acid	1	100	1.2	250	7

*The constants are calculated with the formula $K = \frac{1}{t} \log_{10} \frac{a}{a - K'}$ or more usually $K = \frac{1}{t_2 - t_1} \log_{10} \frac{a - x_1}{a - x_2}$. The time is in minutes, and a is the initial concentration of the substance. The time for 50% hydrolysis, $t\frac{1}{2} = 0.30/K$; the time for 98% hydrolysis, $t = 1.7/K$.

References to Table IV:

1. Friedkin, M., H. M. Kalckar, and E. Hoff-Jorgensen, *J. Biol. Chem.*, 178:527, 1949.
2. Kalckar, H. M., *J. Biol. Chem.*, 167:477, 1947.
3. Meagher, W. R., and W. Z. Hassid, *J. Am. Chem. Soc.*, 68:2135, 1946.
4. Cori, C. F., S. P. Colowick, and G. T. Cori, *J. Biol. Chem.*, 121:465, 1937.
5. Wolfrom, M. L., C. S. Smith, D. E. Pletcher, and A. E. Brown, *J. Am. Chem. Soc.*, 64:23, 1942.
6. Posternak, T., and J. P. Rosselet, *Helv. Chim. Acta.*, 36:1641, 1953.
7. Robison, R., and M. G. MacFarlane (Bamann and Myrbäck, eds.), in *Methoden der Fermenforschung*, 1:296, 1941.
8. Kosterlitz, H. W., *Biochem. J.*, 33:1087, 1939.
9. Cardini, C. E., and L. F. Leloir, *Arch. Biochem. and Biophys.*, 45:55, 1953.
10. Reithel, F. J., *J. Am. Chem. Soc.*, 67:1056, 1945.
11. Brown, D. H., *J. Biol. Chem.*, 204:877, 1953.

12. Meyerhof, O., and K. Lohmann, *Biochem. Z.*, 271:79, 1934.
13. Charalampous, F. C., and G. C. Mueller, *J. Biol. Chem.*, 201:161, 1953.
14. Racker, E., *J. Biol. Chem.*, 196:347, 1952.
15. Levene, P. A., and E. T. Stiller, *J. Biol. Chem.*, 104:299, 1934.
16. Albaum, H. G., and W. W. Umbreit, *J. Biol. Chem.*, 167:369, 1947.
17. Levene, P. A., and A. L. Raymond, *J. Biol. Chem.*, 102:347, 1933.
18. Horecker, B. L., P. Z. Smyrniotis, and J. E. Seegmiller, *J. Biol. Chem.*, 193:383, 1951.
19. Farrar, K. R., *J. Chem. Soc.*, p. 3131, 1949.
20. Robison, R., and E. J. King, *Biochem. J.*, 25:323, 1931.
21. Robinson, R., *Biochem. J.*, 26:2191, 1932.
22. Patwardhan, V. R., *Biochem. J.*, 29:961, 1935.
23. Tanko, B., and R. Robison, *Biochem. J.*, 29:961, 1935.
24. Mann, K. M., and H. A. Lardy, *J. Biol. Chem.*, 187:339, 1950.
25. Cardini, C. E., A. C. Paladin, R. Caputto, L. F. Leloir, and R. E. Trucco, *Arch. Biochem.*, 22:87, 1949.
26. Posternak, T., *J. Biol. Chem.*, 180:1269, 1949.
27. MacLeod, M., and R. Robison, *Biochem. J.*, 27:286, 1933.
28. Meyerhof, O., and W. Kiessling, *Biochem. Z.*, 264:40, 1933.
29. Cherbuliez, E., and M. Bouvier, *Helv. Chim. Acta*, 36:1200, 1953.
30. Miller, O. N., C. G. Huggins, and K. Arai, *J. Biol. Chem.*, 202:263, 1953.
31. Lipmann, F., and L. C. Tuddle, *J. Biol. Chem.*, 153:571, 1944.
32. Negelein, E., and H. Bromel, *Biochem. Z.*, 303:132, 1939.

BIBLIOGRAPHY

References:

1. Ballou, C. E., and H. O. L. Fisher, "The Synthesis of D-Glyceraldehyde-3-Phosphate," *J. Am. Chem. Soc.*, 77:3329, 1955.
2. Kiessling, W., "Über die Titrationskuruen Einiger 3-Kohlenstoff-Phosphorsaureester und der Inosinpyro Phosphorsaure," *Biochem. Z.*, 273:103, 1934.
3. Meyerhof, O., and Junowicz-Kocholaty, "The Equilibria of Isomerase and Aldolase and the Problem of the Phorylation of Glyceraldehyde Phosphate," *J. Biol. Chem.*, 149:71, 1943.
4. Fisher, H. O. L., and E. Baer, "Über die 3-Glycerinaldehyd-Phosphorsaure," "3-Glycerinaldehyd-Phosphorsaure, II. Mitteil: Calciumsalz," *Ber. Deut. Chem. Ges.*, 65:337, 1040, 1932.
5. Ballou, C. E., "Dihydroxyacetone Phosphate," *Biochem. Preps.*, 7:45, 1960.
6. Ballou, C. E., and H. O. L. Fisher, "The Synthesis of Dehydroxyacetone Phosphate," *J. Am. Chem. Soc.*, 78:1659, 1955.
7. Ballou, C. E., and R. Hesse, "The Synthesis and Properties of Hydroxypyruvic Acid Phosphate," *J. Am. Chem. Soc.*, 78:3718, 1956.
8. Kiessling, W., "Die Synthese der (Enol-) Brenztraubensaure-Phosphorsaure," *Ber. Deut. Chem. Ges.*, 68:597, 1935.
9. Kiessling, W., "Verbesserungen in der Darstellung der (Enol-) Brenztraubensaure-Phosphorsaure," *Ber. Deut. Chem. Ges.*, 69:2331, 1936.
10. Schmidt, G., and S. J. Tannhouser, "Intestinal Phosphatase," *J. Biol. Chem.*, 149:369, 1943.
11. Ohlmeyer, P., "A New Coenzyme of Alcoholic Fermentation," *J. Biol. Chem.*, 190:21, 1951.

12. Utter, M. F., and K. Kurahashi, "Mechanism of Action of Oxalacetic Carboxylase," *J. Biol. Chem.*, 207:821, 1954.

13. Meyerhof, O., and W. Schulz, *Biochem. Z.*, 179:1371, 1949.

14. Lohman, F., "Metabolic Generation and Utilization of Phosphate Bond Energy," *Advan. Enzymol.*, 1:99, 1941.

15. Baer, E., and H. O. L. Fisher, "Studies on Acetone-Glyceraldehyde," *J. Biol. Chem.*, 128:491, 1939.

16. Karrer, P., and P. Benz, "Die Spaltung der Glycerin-α-Phosphorsaure in optisch aktive Formen," "Über die Zerlegung der Glycerin-α-Phosphorsaure in optische Isomere II," *Helv. Chim. Acta*, 9:23, 598, 1926.

17. Meyerhof, O., and W. Kiessling, "Über das Auftreten und den Umsatz der α-Glycerinphosphorsaure bei der enzymatischen Kohlenhydratspaltung," *Biochem. Z.*, 264:62, 1933.

18. Datta, S. P. and A. K. Grzybowski, "Thermodynamic Quantities for the Dissociation Equilibria of Biologically Important Compounds, 7-The Second Acid Dissociation of Glycerol-1-Phosphate," *Biochem. J.*, 69:218, 1958.

19. Ashby, J. H., E. M. Crook, and S. P. Datta, "Thermodynamic Quantities of Biologically Important Compounds, 2-The Acid Dissociations of Glycerol 2-Phosphoric Acid," *Biochem. J.*, 56:198, 1954.

20. Oesper, P., in W. D. McElroy and B. Glass (eds.), *Phosphorus Metabolism*, 1:523, 1951.

21. Meyerhof, O. and H. Green, "Synthetic Action of Phosphatase. I. Equilibria of Biological Esters," *J. Biol. Chem.*, 178:655, 1949.

22. Baer, E., "A Synthesis of 2,3-Dyphospho-D-Glyceric Acid," *J. Biol. Chem.*, 185:763, 1950.

23. Weil-Malherbe, H. and R. H. Green, "The Catalytic Effect of Molybdate on the Hydrolysis of Organic Phosphate Bonds," *Biochem. J.*, 49:286, 1951.

24. Baer, E., "L-α-Glycerophosphoric Acid (Barium Salt)," *Biochem. Preps.*, 2:31, 1952.

25. Neuberg, C., and M. Kobel, "Über das Nerhalten der Glycerinsaure-Mono-Phosphorsaure gegen Hefe," *Biochem. Z.*, 263:219, 1933.

26. Neuberg, C., and M. Kobel, "Über Glycerinsaure-Mono-Phosphorsaure," *Biochem. Z.*, 264:456, 1933.

27. Neuberg, C., and M. Kobel, "Über Darstellung und Bedeutung der Glycerinsaure-Mono Phosphorsaure," *Angew. Chem.*, 46:711, 1933.

28. Forrest, I. S., and C. Neuberg, "Preparation and Analytical Data of Pure D(−)3-Phosphoglyceric Acid," *Biochim. Biophys. Acta*, 11:588, 1953.

29. Meyerhof, O. and W. Schulz, "Eine neue Bestinmungsmethode der Phosphoglycerinsaure," *Biochem. Z.*, 297:60, 1938.

30. Meyerhof, O. and P. Oesper, "The Enzymatic Equilibria of Phospho (Enol) Pyruvate," *J. Biol. Chem.*, 179:1371, 1949.

31. Meyerhof, O. and W. Kiessling, "Über die Isolierung der Isomeren Phosphoglycerinsauren aus Garanslazen und ihr enzymatisches Gleichgewicht," *Biochem. Z.*, 276:239, 1935.

32. Neuberg, C., "Synthesis of d(−)3-Phosphoglyceric Acid and d(+)2-Phosphoglyceric Acid," *Arch. Biochem.*, 3:105, 1943.

33. Neuberg, C., and M. Kobel, "Kristallisierte und Gelatinose Salze der Glycerinsaure Mono-Phosphorsaure," *Biochem. Z.*, 272:461, 1934.

34. Martland, M., and R. Robinson, "Possible Significance of Hexosephospheric Esters in Ossification-VI-Phosphoric Esters in Blood Plasma," *Biochem. J.*, 20:847, 1926.

35. Ballou, C. E., and H. O. L. Fisher, "A New Synthesis of 2-Phosphoryl-D-Glyceric Acid," *J. Am. Chem. Soc.*, 76:3188, 1954.

36. Kiessling, W., "Die Synthese der Isomeren Glycerinsaure-Phosphorsauren ("Phosphoglycerinsaure")," *Ber. Deut. Chem. Ges.*, 68:243, 1935.

37. Wold, F., and C. E. Ballou, "Studies on the Enzyme Enolase. I. Equilibrium Studies," *J. Biol. Chem.*, 227:301, 1957.

38. Negelein, E., and H. Bromel, "Isolierung Eines Reversibeln Zwischenprodukts der Garung," *Biochem. Z.*, 301:135, 1939.

39. Negelein, E., and H. Bromel, "R-Diphosphoglycerinsaure, ihre Isolierung und Eigenschaften," *Biochem. Z.*, 303:132, 1939.

40. Greenwald, I., "A New Type of Phosphoric Acid Compound Isolated from Blood, with Some Remarks on the Effect of Substitution on the Rotation of L-Glyceric Acid," *J. Biol. Chem.*, 63:339, 1925.

41. Jost, H., "Über die Biologishe Bedeutung Des saureloslishen Organishen Blutphosphors," *Z. Physiol. Chem.*, 165:171, 1927.

42. Gillet, J. W., and C. E. Ballou, "The Synthesis of L-Glycero-Tetrulose-1-Phosphate (L-Erythrulose 1-Phosphate)," *Biochem.*, 2:547, 1963.

43. Chii, N. J., and C. E. Ballou, "The Syntheses and Properties of D-Glycero-Tetrulose 1-Phosphate and 4-Phosphate (D-Erythrulose 1-Phosphate and 4-Phosphate)," *J. Am. Chem. Soc.*, 83:1711, 1961.

44. Ballou, C. E., H. O. L. Fisher, and D. L. MacDonald, "The Synthesis and Properties of D-Erythrose 4-Phosphate," *J. Am. Chem. Soc.*, 77:5967, 1955.

45. Ballou, C. E., in S. P. Colowick and N. O. Kaplan (eds.), *Methods in Enzymology*, 6:484, 1963.

46. Shetter, J. K., "Formation of D-Erythrutol 4-Phosphate by Propionibacterium Pentosaceum," *J. Am. Chem. Soc.*, 78:3722, 1956.

47. Wold, F., and R. Barker, "D-Erythronic Acid-3-Phosphate a Substrate for Enolase," *Biochim. Biophys. Acta*, 85:475, 1964.

48. Kornberg, A., and H. G. Khorana, "5-Phosphoryl 2-D-Ribofuranose 1-Pyrophosphate, (Lithium Salt)," *Biochem. Preps.*, 8:110, 1961.

49. Remy, C. N., W. T. Remy, and J. M. Buchanan, "Biosyntheses of the Purines: VIII Enzymatic Syntheses and Utilization of α-5-Phosphoribosylpyrohosphate," *J. Biol. Chem.*, 217:885, 1955.

50. Szabo, P., and L. Szabo, "Phosphorylated Sugars. Part X. A Simple Synthesis of 3-Deoxy-D-Erythro-Pentose 15-(Dihydrogen Phosphate)," *J. Chem. Soc.*, p. 2944, 1965.

51. Levene, P. A., and C. C. Christman, "Synthesis of 5-Phospho-d-Arabinose," *J. Biol. Chem.*, 123:607, 1938.

52. Putman, E. W., and W. Z. Hassid, "Anomeric-1-Dicyclohexylammonium Phosphate Esters of D-Glucopyranose, D-Galactopyranose, D-Xylopyranose and 1-Arabinopyranose," *J. Am. Chem. Soc.*, 79:5057, 1957.

53. Wright, R. S., and H. G. Khorana, "Phosphorylated Sugars. V. Synthesis of Arabinopyranose and Arabinopyranose 1-Phosphates," *J. Am. Chem. Soc.*, 80:1994, 1958.

54. Tenner, G. M., R. S. Wright, and H. G. Khorana, "A Synthesis of α-D-Ribofuranose 1-Phosphate," *J. Am. Chem. Soc.*, 78:506, 1956.

55. Tenner, G. M., R. S. Wright, and H. G. Khorana, "Phosphorylated Sugars III. Synthesis of α-D-Ribofuranose 1-Phosphate," *J. Am. Chem. Soc.*, 79:441, 1957.

56. Wright, R. S., and H. G. Khorana, "Phosphorylated Sugars I. A Synthesis of β-D-Ribofuranose 1-Phosphate," *J. Am. Chem. Soc.*, 78:811, 1956.

57. Plesner, P. E., and H. Klenow, in S. P. Colowick, and N. O. Kaplan (eds.), "Preparation of Ribose-1-Phosphate," *Methods in Enzymology*, 3:181, 1957.

58. Khym, J. X., D. G. Doherty, and W. E. Cohn, "Ribose Phosphates! Production from Nucleotides, Ion-Exchange Separation and Characterization," *J. Am. Chem. Soc.*, 76:5523, 1954.

59. Levene, P. A., and S. A. Harris, "The Ribosephosphoric Acid from Yeast Adenylic Acid," *J. Biol. Chem.*, 101:419, 1933.

60. Albaum, H. G. and W. W. Umbreit, "Differentiation Between Ribose-3-Phosphate and Ribose-5-Phosphate by Means of the Orcinol-Pentose Reaction," *J. Biol. Chem.*, 167:369, 1947.

61. Le Page, G. A., and W. W. Umbreit, "The Occurrence of Adenosine-3-Triphosphate in Autotrophic Bacteria," *J. Biol. Chem.*, 148:255, 1943.

62. Levene, P. A., and E. T. Stiller, "The Synthesis of Ribose-5-Phosphoric Acid," *J. Biol. Chem.*, 104:299, 1934.

63. Horecker, B. L., and P. Z. Smyrniotis, "The Enzymatic Production of Ribose-5-Phosphate from 6-Phosphogluconate," *Arch. Biochem.*, 29:232, 1950.

64. Tenner, G. M., and H. G. Khorana, "Phosphorylated Sugars VI. Syntheses of α-D-Ribofuranose 1,5-Diphosphate and α-D-Ribofuranose 1-Pyrophosphate 5-Phosphate," *J. Am. Chem. Soc.*, 80:1999, 1958.

65. Friedkin, M. and H. M. Kalckar, in S. P. Colowick and N. O. Kaplan (eds.), "Preparation of Deoxyribose-1-Phosphate," *Methods in Enzymology*, 3:183, 1957.

66. Pricer, W. E., and B. L. Horecker, "Deoxyribose Aldolase from Lactobacillus Plantarum," *J. Biol. Chem.*, 235:1292, 1960.

67. MacDonald, D. L., and H. G. Fletcher, "2-Deoxy-D-Ribose. II. The Synthesis of 2-Deoxy-D-Ribose 5-Phosphate," *J. Am. Chem. Soc.*, 81:3719, 1959.

68. Horecker, B. L., P. Z. Smyrniotis, and J. E. Seegmiller, "The Enzymatic Conversion of 6-Phosphogluconate to Ribulose-5-Phosphate and Ribose-5-Phosphate," *J. Biol. Chem.*, 193:383, 1951.

69. Simpson, F. J. and W. A. Wood, "L-Ribulose-5-Phosphate: Formation by Purified Kinase from Aerobacter Aerogenes," *J. Am. Chem. Soc.*, 78:5452, 1956.

70. Horecker, B. L., J. Hurwitz, and A. Weissback, "Ribulose Diphosphate," *Biochem. Preps.*, 6:83, 1958.

71. Horecker, B. L., J. Hurwitz, and P. K. Stumpf, in S. P. Colowick, and N. O. Kaplan (eds.), "The Enzymatic Synthesis of Ribulose-1,5-Diphosphate and Xylulose-5-Phosphate," *Methods in Enzymology*, 3:193, 1957.

72. Meagher, W. R. and W. Z. Hassid, "Synthesis of Maltose-1-Phosphate and D-Xylose-1-Phosphate," *J. Am. Chem. Soc.*, 68:2135, 1946.

73. Moffatt, J. G. and H. G. Khorana, "D-Xylose-3-Phosphate," *J. Am. Chem. Soc.*, 78:883, 1958.

74. Levene, P. A., and A. L. Raymond, "Phosphoric Esters of Xylose and of 5-Methyl Monoacetone Xylose. Their Bearing on the Nature of the Pentose of Yeast Nucleic Acid," *J. Biol. Chem.*, 102:347, 1933.

75. MacDonald, D. L., "A New Route to Glycosyl Phosphates," *J. Org. Chem.*, 27:1107, 1962.

76. Krahl, M. E., and C. F. Cori, "The α-Glucose-1-Phosphates," *Biochem. Preps.*, 1:33, 1949.

77. Wolfrom, M. L., and D. E. Pletcher, "The Structure of the Cori Ester," *J. Am. Chem. Soc.*, 63:1050, 1941.

78. Cori, C. F., S. P. Colowick, and G. T. Cori, "The Isolation and Synthesis of Glucose-1-Phosphoric Acid," *J. Biol. Chem.*, 121:465, 1937.

79. Ashby, J. H., et al., "Thermodynamic Quantities for the Dissociation Equilibria of Biologically Important Compounds," *Biochem. J.*, 59:203, 1955.

80. Wolfrom, M. L., et al., "The β-Form of the Cori Ester (d-Glucopyranose 1-Phosphate)" *J. Am. Chem. Soc.*, 64:23, 1942.

81. Potter, A. L., et al., "α-L-Glucose-1-Phosphate," *J. Am. Chem. Soc.*, 70:1751, 1948.

82. Farrar, K. R., "Glucose-2-Phosphate: Its Preparation and Characterization by Hydrolysis Studies," *J. Chem. Soc. (London)*, p. 3131, 1949.

83. Josephson, K. and S. Proffe, "Über Umlagerungsreaktionen in der Kohlenhydratgruppe. III. Zur Kenntnis Synthetischer Hexose-Phosphorsaure-Ester," *Ann. Chem.*, 481:91, 1930.

84. Levene, P. A., and A. L. Raymond, "Herosemonophosphates: Glucose-3-Phosphate, Glucose-6-Phosphate and their Bearing on the Structure of Robeson's Ester," *J. Biol. Chem.*, 89:479, 1930.

85. Levene, P. A., and A. L. Raymond, "Hexosemonophosphate (Robeson) Natural and Synthetic," *J. Biol. Chem.*, 91:751, 1931.

86. Meyerhof, O. and K. Lohmann, "Über die Enzymatische Milchsaurebildung in Muskelextrakt," *Biochem. Z.*, 185:113, 1927.

87. Nodzu, R., "On the Synthesis of Phosphoric Acid Esters, III," *J. Biochem.*, 6:31, 1926.

88. Raymond, A. L., "Hexosemonophosphates: Glucose-4-Phosphate," *J. Biol. Chem.*, 113:375, 1936.

89. Reithel, F. J., and C. K. Claycomb, "The Synthesis of Derivative of Glucose-4-Phosphoric Acid," *J. Am. Chem. Soc.*, 71:3669, 1949.

90. Josephson, K. and S. Proffe, "Zur Kenntnis Synthetischer Hexosephosphorsaureester," *Biochem. Z.*, 258:147, 1933.

91. Robison, R. and E. J. King, "Hexosemonophosphoric Esters," *Biochem. J.*, 25:323, 1931.

92. Lardy, H. A. and H. O. L. Fisher, "Phosphoric Esters of Biological Importance: The Synthesis of Glucose-6-Phosphate," *J. Biol. Chem.*, 164:513, 1946.

93. Szabo, P. and L. Szabo, "Phosphorylated Sugars. II. The Synthesis of Some Methyl Glycoside Phosphates," *J. Chem. Soc.*, p. 3762, 1960.

94. Wood, W. A., and B. L. Horecker, "D-Glucose-6-Phosphoric Acid," *Biochem. Preps.*, 3:71, 1953.

95. Fisher, H. O. L., and H. A. Lardy, "Phosphoric Esters of Biological Importance I. The Synthesis of Glucose-6-Phosphate," *J. Biol. Chem.*, 164:513, 1946.

96. Colowick, S. P. and E. W. Sutherland, "Polysaccharide Synthesis from Glucose by Means of Purified Enzymes," *J. Biol. Chem.*, 144:423, 1942.

97. Lardy, H. A., and H. O. L. Fisher, "Glucose-6-Phosphate," *Biochem. Preps.*, 2:39, 1952.

98. Saito, T., J. Noguchi, and Komatsu, *J. Chem. Soc. (Japan)*, 82:469, 1961.

99. Posternak, T., "Synthesis of α- and β-Glucose-1,6 Diphosphate," *J. Biol. Chem.*, 180:1269, 1949.

100. Patwardhan, V. R., "CCXLIV. Mannosemonophosphate. III-Phosphomannonic Acid and its Lactones," *Biochem. J.*, 28:1854, 1934.

101. Horecker, B. L., in S. P. Colowick, and N. O. Kaplan (eds.), "Preparation and Analysis of 6-Phosphogluconate," *Methods in Enzymology*, 3:172, 1957.

102. Barker, S. A., et al., "Catalytic Oxidation of Carbohydrates. Some Properties of Potassium α-D-Glucopyranuronate 1-(Dipotassium Phosphate)," *J. Chem. Soc.*, p. 4128, 1958.

103. Roseman, S., et al., "Nucleoside Polyphosphate-XI. An Improved General Method for the Synthesis of Nucleotide Coenzymes. Synthesis of Uridine-5′ and Guanosine-5′ Diphosphate Derivatives," *J. Am. Chem. Soc.*, 83:659, 1961.

104. Kosterlitz, H. W., CXXXII—Synthetic Galactose-1-Phosphoric Acid," *Biochem. J.*, 33:1087, 1939.

105. Colowick, S. P., "Synthetic Mannose-1-Phosphoric Acid and Galactose-1-Phosphoric Acid," *J. Biol. Chem.*, 124:557, 1938.

106. Kosterlitz, H. W., "The Presence of a Galactose-Phosphate in the Livers of Rabbits Assimilating Galactose," *Biochem. J.*, 31:2217, 1937.

107. Posternak, T., "Syntheses of α-D-Glucose-1-Phosphate and α-D-Galactose-1-Phosphate," *J. Am. Chem. Soc.*, 72:4824, 1950.

108. Hansen, R. G., W. J. Utter, and P. Kritchevski, *Biochem. Preps.*, 4:1, 1955.

109. Reithel, F. J., β-D-Galactose-1-(Barium Phosphate)," *J. Am. Chem. Soc.*, 67:1056, 1945.

110. Kosterlitz, H. W., "The Apparent Dissociation Constants of Galactose-1-Phosphoric Acid," *Biochem. J.*, 37:321, 1943.

111. Inouye, T., M. Tannenbaum, and D. Y. Hsia, "Identification of Galactose-6-Phosphate in Galactosaemic Erythrocytes," *Nature*, 193:67, 1962.

112. Tanaka, T., "Phosphorylation VI. Preparation of D-Glucose 6-Phosphate and D-Galactose 6-Phosphate by the Use of Bis(2,4-Dichlorophenyl) Phosphorochloridite," *Chem. Anal.*, 55:27064, 1961.

113. Posternak, T. and J. P. Rosselet, "Syntheses D'esters Phosphoriques d'interest Biologique. (III). Synthese des Acides α-D-Mannose-1-Phosphorique, D-Mannose-6-Phosphorique et α-D-Mannose-1,6-Diphosphorique Action de la Phosphoglucomtase," *Helv. Chim. Acta*, 36:1614, 1953.

114. Robinson, R., "Hexosemonophosphoric Esters: Mannosemonophosphate," *Biochem. J.*, 26:2191, 1932.

115. Tanko, B. and R. Robison, "The Hydrolysis of Hexosediphosphoric Ester by Bone Phosphatase," *Biochem. J.*, 29:961, 1935.

116. Pogel, B. M., "D-Fructose 1-Phosphate (Barium Salt)," *Biochem. Preps.*, 7:58, 1960.

117. Raymond, A. L., and P. A. Levene, "Synthetic Hexosephosphates and their Phenylhydrazine Derivatives," *J. Biol. Chem.*, 83:619, 1929.

118. McLeod, M. and R. Robison, "The Hydrolysis of Hexosediphosphoric Ester by Bone Phosphatase—A New Fructosemonophosphate," *Biochem. J.*, 27:286, 1933.

119. Neuberg, C., H. Lustig, and M. A. Rothenberg, "Fructose-1,6-Diphosphoric Acid and Fructose-6-Monophosphoric Acid," *Arch. Biochem.*, 3:33, 1944.

120. Neuberg, C., "Überfuhrung der Fructose-Diphosphorsaure in Fructose-Monophosphorsaure," *Biochem. Z.*, 88:432, 1917.

121. Meyerhof, O. and J. Suranyi, "Über die Dissoziationskonstanten der Hexosediphosphorsaure und Glycerinphosphorsaure," *Biochem. Z.*, 178:427, 1926.

122. Neuberg, C. and O. Delmer, "Krystallisierte Salze Einiger Physiologisch wichtiger Zuckerphosphorsaure-Verbindungen," *Biochem. Z.*, 131:188, 1922.

123. Neuberg, C., and H. Lustig, "Preparation of d-Fructose-1,6-Diphosphate by Means of Baker's Yeast," *J. Am. Chem. Soc.*, 64:2722, 1942.

124. Sable, H. Z., "Fructose-1,6-Diphosphate Purification," *Biochem. Preps.*, 2:52, 1952.

125. Mann, K. M., and H. A. Lardy, "Phosphoric Esters Biological Importance: V. The Synthesis of L-Sorbose-1-Phosphate and L-Sorbose-6-Phosphate," *J. Biol. Chem.*, 187:339, 1950.

126. Totton, E. L., and H. A. Lardy, "Phosphoric Esters of Biological Importance: IV. Synthesis and Biological Activity of D-Tagatose-6-Phosphate," *J. Biol. Chem.*, 181:701, 1949.

127. Totton, E. L., and H. A. Lardy, in S. P. Colowick, and N. O. Kaplan (eds.), "Synthetic Ketohexose Phosphates," *Methods of Enzymology*, 3:174, 1957.

128. Heath, E. C., and M. A. Ghalambor, "The Metabolism of L-Fucose I—The Purification and Properties of L-Fuculose Kinase," *J. Biol. Chem.*, 237:2423, 1962.

129. Maley, F., G. F. Maley, and H. A. Lardy, "The Synthesis of α-D-Glucosamine-1-Phosphate and N-Acetyl-α-D-Glucosamine-1-Phosphate-Enzymatic Formation of Uridine Diphosphoglucosamine," *J. Am. Chem. Soc.*, 78:5303, 1956.

130. Brown, D. H., "Action of Phosphogluconutose on D-Glucosamine-G-Phosphate," *J. Biol. Chem.*, 204:877, 1953.

131. Anderson, J. M., and E. Percival, "The Synthesis of Glucosamine 6-(Dihydrogen Phosphate)," *J. Chem. Soc.*, p. 814, 1956.

132. Jourdian, G. W., and S. Roseman, "D-Glucosamine 6-Phosphoric Acid and D-Mannosamine 6-Phosphoric Acid," *Biochem. Preps.*, 9:44, 1962.

133. Brown, D. H., in S. P. Colowick and N. O. Kaplan (eds.), "Preparation and Analysis of D-Glucosamine-6-Phosphate," *Methods in Enzymology*, 3:158, 1957.

134. Distler, J. J., J. M. Merrick, and S. Roseman, "Glucosamine Metabolism: III. Preparation and N-Acetylation of Crystalline D-Glucosamine-6-Phosphoric Acids," *J. Biol. Chem.*, 230:497, 1958.

135. Shaffer, P. A., and M. Somogyi, "Copper-Iodometric Reagents for Sugar Determination," *J. Biol. Chem.*, 100:695, 1933.

136. Elson, L. A., and W. T. J. Morgan, "A Colorimetric Method for the Determination of Glucosamine and Chondrosamine," *Biochem. J.*, 27:1824, 1933.

137. Park, J. T., and M. J. Johnson, "A Submicrodetermination of Glucose," *J. Biol. Chem.*, 181:149, 1949.

138. O'Brien, P. J., "The Synthesis of N-Acetyl-a-and N-Acetyl-α-D-Glucosamine 1-Phosphates (2-Acetamido-2-Deoxy-a-and α-D-Glucose-1-Phosphates)," *Biochim. Biophys. Acta*, 86:628, 1964.

139. Baluja, G., et al., "Nucleotides—XLV.—Derivatives of β-2-Amino-2-Deoxy D-Glucose (β-D-Glucosamine) 1-Phosphate," *J. Chem. Soc.*, p. 4678, 1960.

140. Jourdian, G. W., and S. Roseman, "The Sialic Acids—II. Preparation of N-Glycolylherosamines, N-Glycolylhexosamine 6-Phosphates, Glycolyl Coenzyme A, and Glycolyl Glutathione," *J. Biol. Chem.*, 237:2442, 1962.

141. Carlson, D. M., A. L. Swanson, and S. Roseman, "Preparation of Crystalline α-D-Galactosamine-1-Phosphoric Acid and its Conversion to UDP-N-Acetylgalactosamine," *Biochem.*, 3:402, 1964.

142. Cardine, C. E., and L. F. Leloir, "Enzymatic Phosphorylation of Galactosamine and Galactose," *Arch. Biochem. Biophys.*, 45:55, 1953.

143. Reissig, J. L., J. L. Strominger, and L. F. Leloir, "A Modified Colorimetric Method for the Estimation of N-Acetylamino Sugars," *J. Biol. Chem.*, 217:959, 1956.

144. Spivak, C. T. and S. Roseman, "Preparation of N-Acetyl-D-Mannosamine (2-Acetamido-2-Deoxy-D-Mannose) and D-Mannosamine Hydrochloride (2-Amino-2-Deoxy-D-Mannose)," *J. Am. Chem. Soc.*, 81:2403, 1959.

145. Cardini, C. E. and L. F. Leloir, "Enzymatic Formation of Acetylgalactosamine," *J. Biol. Chem.*, 225:317, 1957.

146. Davidson, E. A., and R. W. Wheat, "N-Acetyl-Galactosamine α-1-Phosphate and Uridine-Diphospho-N-Acetyl Galactosamine," *Biochem. Biophys. Acta*, 72:112, 1963.

147. Ghosh, S., and S. Roseman, "Enzymatic Phosphorylation of N-Acetyl-D-Mannosamine," *Proc. Nat. Acad. Sci.*, 47:955, 1961.

148. Blix, G., "The Determination of Hexosamines According to Elson and Morgan," *Acta Chem. Scand.*, 2:467, 1948.

149. Venkataraman, R., and E. Racker, "Mechanism of Action of Transaldolase I—Crystallization and Properties of Yeast Enzyme," *J. Biol. Chem.*, 236:1876, 1961.

150. Racker, E., in H. U. Bergmeyer (ed.), "L-Glyceraldehyde-3-Phosphate," *Methods of Enzymatic Analysis*, p. 241, 1963.

151. Bücher, T. and H. J. Hohorst, "Dihydroxyacetone Phosphate, Fructose 1,6-Diphosphate and D-Glyceraldehyde-3-Phosphate. Determination with Glycerol-1-Phosphate Dehydrogenase, Aldose and Triosephosphate Isomerase," *ibid.*, p. 246.

152. Warburg, O. and W. Christian, "Isolierung und Kristallisation des Garungsfermonts Enolase," *Biochem. Z.*, 310:384, 1941.

153. Schmidt, G., in S. P. Colowick, and N. O. Kaplan (eds.), "Preparation of Phosphopyruvic Acid," *Methods in Enzymology*, 3:223, 1957.

154. Czok, R. and L. Eckert, in H. U. Bergmeyer (ed.), "D-3-Phosphoglycerate, D-2-Phosphoglycerate, Phosphoenolpyruvate," *Methods of Enzymatic Analysis*, p. 224, 1963.

155. Hohorst, H. J., "L-(−)-Glycerol-1-Phosphate. Determination with Glycerol-1-Phosphate Deydrogenase," *ibid*, p. 215.

156. Mandl, I., and C. Neuberg, in S. P. Colowick and N. O. Kaplan (eds.), "Preparation of D(−)-3-Phosphoglyceric Acid," *Methods in Enzymology*, 3:208, 1957.

157. Krinsky, I., in H. U. Bergmeyer (ed.), "D-2,3-Diphosphoglycerate," *Methods of Enzymatic Analysis*, p. 238, 1963.

158. Racker, E., "D-Erythrose-4-Phosphate," *ibid*, p. 205.

159. Dische, Z., "Über Einige Neue Charakteristische Farbreaktionen der Thymonukleinsaure und Eine Mikro Methode Zur Bestimmung Derselbew in Tierischen Organen Mit Hilfe Dieser Reaktionen," *Mikrochem.*, 8:4, 1930.

160. Horecker, B. L., in H. U. Bergmeyer (ed.), "L-Ribulose and L-Arabinose," *Methods of Enzymatic Analysis*, p. 178, 1963.

161. Taylor, G. A., C. E. Ballou, "D-Glycero-Tetrulose 1,4-Diphosphate (D-Erythrulose 1,4-Diphosphate)," *Biochem.*, 2:553, 1963.

162. Mejbaum, W., "Über die Bestimmung Kleiner Pentosemengen, Insbesondere in Derivaten der Adenylsaure," *Z. Physiol. Chem.*, 258:117, 1939.

163. Khorana, H. G., et al., "Cyclic Phosphates III—Some General Observations on the Formation and Properties of Five, -Six- and 5 Even Numbered Cyclic Phosphate Esters," *J. Am. Chem. Soc.*, 79:430, 1957.

164. Kalckar, H. M., "The Enzymatic Synthesis of Purine Ribosides," *J. Biol. Chem.*, 167:477, 1947.

165. Dische, Z., "Qualitative and Quantitative Colorimetric Determination of Heptoses," *J. Biol. Chem.*, 204:983, 1953.

166. Racker, E., in H. U. Bergmeyer (ed.), "D-Ribose-5-Phosphate," *Methods of Enzymatic Analysis*, p. 175, 1963.

167. Dische, Z., "Spectrophotometric Method for the Determination of Free Pentose and Pentose in Nucleotides," *J. Biol. Chem.*, 181:379, 1949.

168. Manson, L. A., and J. O. Lampen, "Some Chemical Properties of Desoxyribose Nucleosides," *J. Biol. Chem.*, 191:87, 1951.

169. Racker, E., in H. U. Bergmeyer (ed.), *Methods of Enzymatic Analysis*, p. 186, 1963.

170. Horecker, B. L., in S. P. Colowick and N. O. Kaplan (eds.), *Methods in Enzymology*, 3:105, 1957.

171. Horecker, B. L., *ibid.*, p. 190.

172. Bergmeyer, H. U. and H. Klotzsch, in H. U. Bergmeyer (ed.), *Methods of Enzymatic Analysis*, p. 131, 1963.

173. Paladini, A. C. and L. F. Leloir, "Studies on Uridine-Diphosphate Glucose," *Biochem. J.*, 51:426, 1952.

174. Wells, W. W., et al., "Gas Chromatography of Sugar Phosphates," *Biochim. Biophys. Acta*, 82:408, 1964.

175. Hohorst, H. J., in H. U. Bergmeyer (ed.), *Methods of Enzymatic Analysis*, p. 134, 1963.

176. Leloir, L. F. and A. C. Paladini, in S. P. Colowick, and N. O. Kaplan (eds.), *Methods in Enzymology*, 3:143, 1957.

177. Munch-Peterseh, A., et al., "Uridyl Transferases and the Formation of Uridine Triphosphate, Enzymic Production of Uridine Triphosphate: Uridine Diphosphoglucose Pyrophosphorolysis," *Nature*, 172:1036, 1953.

178. DeMoss, R. D. in S. P. Colowick and N. O. Kaplan (eds.), *Methods in Enzymology*, 3:232, 1957.

179. Hawthorne, J. W., P. Kemp, and R. B. Ellis, "Phosphornositides 2. The Inositol 1-Phosphate Structure in Liver Phosphatidylinositol," *Biochem. J.*, 75:501, 1960.

180. Pizer, F. L., and C. E. Ballou, "Studies on Myo-Inositol Phosphates of Natural Origin," *J. Am. Chem. Soc.*, 81:915, 1959.

181. Norris, F. W., and A. Darbre, "The Microbiological Assay of Inositol with a Strain of Schizosaccharo Myces Pombe," *Analyst*, 81:394, 1956.

182. McCormic, M. H., and H. Carter, "Inositol Monophosphate," *Biochem. Preps.*, 2:65, 1952.

183. Ballou, C. E., and L. I. Pizer, "Synthesis of an Optically Active Myo-Mositol-1-Phosphate," *J. Am. Chem. Soc.*, 81:4745, 1959.

184. Kean, E. L., and F. C. Charalampous, "New Methods for the Quantitative Estimation of Myo-Inositol," *Biochem. Biophys. Acta*, 36:1, 1959.

185. Sprinson, D. B., Rothschild, and M. Sprecher, in S. P. Colowick, and N. O. Kaplan (eds.), *Methods in Enzymology*, 6:493, 1963.

186. Horecker, B. L., P. Z. Smyrniotis, and H. Klenow, "The Formation of Sedoheptulose Phosphate from Pentose Phosphate," *J. Biol. Chem.*, 205:661, 1953.

187. Cooper, J., et al., "The Oxidative Pentose Phosphate Cycle: II. Quantitative Determination of Intermediates and Enzymes," *Arch. Biochem. Biophys.*, 74:306, 1958.

188. Horecker, B. L., et al., "Tetrose Phosphate and the Formation of Sedoheptulose Diphosphate," *J. Biol. Chem.*, 212:827, 1955.

189. Racker, E., in H. U. Bergmeyer (ed.), *Methods of Enzymatic Analysis*, p. 113, 1963.

190. Weiss, U., and E. S. Mingioli, "Aromatic Biosynthesis. XV—The Isolation and Identification of Shikemic Acid 5-Phosphate," *J. Am. Chem. Soc.*, 78:2894, 1956.

191. Robinson, R., and W. T. J. Morgan, "Trehalosemonophosphoric Ester Isolated from the Products of Fermentation of Sugars with Dried Yeast," *Biochem. J.*, 22:1277, 1928.

192. Cabib, E., and L. F. Leloir, "The Biosynthesis of Trehalose Phosphate," *J. Biol. Chem.*, 231:259, 1958.

193. MacDonald, D. L., and R. Y. K. Wong, "A Chemical Syntheses of Trehalose 6-Phosphate," *Biochem. Biophys. Acta*, 86:390, 1964.

194. Gander, J. E., W. E. Petersen, and P. D. Boyer, "On the Enzyme Synthesis of Lactose-1-PO$_4$," *Arch. Biochem. Biophys.*, 69:85, 1957.

195. Percival, E. G. V., and T. A. Soutar, "Carbohydrate Sulphuric Esters. Part I—Glucose and Galactose Sulphates," *J. Chem. Soc. (London)*, p. 1475, 1940.

196. Duff, R. B., and E. G. V. Percival, "Carbohydrate Sulphuric Esters. Part II—The Isolation of 3:6 Anhydromethylhexosides from Methylhexopyranoside Sulphates," *J. Chem. Soc. (London),* p. 830, 1941.

197. Lohman, K., and O. Meyerhof, "Über die Enzymatische Umwandlung Von Phosphoglycerinsaure und Phosphorsaure," *Biochem. Z.,* 273:60, 1934.

198. Kornberg, A., I. Lieberman, and E. S. Simms, "Enzymatic Synthesis and Properties of 5-Phosphoribosylpyrophosphate," *J. Biol. Chem.,* 215:389, 1955.

199. Nelson, N., "A Photometric Adaptation of the Somogyi Method for the Determination of Glucose," *J. Biol. Chem.,* 153:375, 1944.

200. Dische, Z., "A New Specific Color Reaction of Hexuronic Acids," *J. Biol. Chem.,* 167:189, 1947.

201. Racker, E., in H. U. Bergmeyer (ed.), "L-Sorbose 6-Phosphate," *Methods of Enzymatic Analysis,* p. 164, 1963.

202. Racker, E., in H. U. Bergmeyer (ed.), "L-Sorbose 6-Phosphate," *Methods of Enzymatic Analysis,* p. 160, 1963.

203. Klotzsch, H. and H. U. Bergmeyer, in Bergmeyer, H. U. (ed.), "D-Fructose," *Methods of Enzymatic Analysis,* p. 156, 1963.

204. Roe, J. H., "A Colorimetric Method for the Determination of Fructose in Blood and Urine," *J. Biol. Chem.,* 107:15, 1934.

205. Ashwell, G., in S. P. Colowick, N. O. Kaplan (eds.), "P(73) Colorimetric Analysis of Sugars, P(75) Subtitle → Resorcinol Method of Roe," *Methods of Enzymology,* 3:75, 1957.

206. Munch-Petersen, A., "Enzymatic Syntheses and Pyrophosphorolysis of Guanosine Diphosphate Mannose," *Arch. Biochem. Biophys.,* 55:592, 1955.

207. Slein, M. W., in S. P. Colowick and N. O. Kaplan (eds.), "Synthesis of Mannose-6-Phosphate by Hexokinase," *Methods in Enzymology,* 3:154, 1957.

208. Dische, Z., and E. Borenfreund, "A New Spectrophotometric Method for the Detection and Determination of Keto-Sugars and Trioses," *J. Biol. Chem.,* 192:583, 1951.

209. Tung, T., et al., "Substrate Specificity of Muscle Aldolase," *Biochim. Biophys. Acta,* 14:488, 1954.

210. Mann, K. M., and H. A. Lardy, in S. P. Colowick and N. O. Kaplan (eds.), "L-Sorbose-1-Phosphate," *Methods in Enzymology,* 3:177, 1957.

211. Mann, K. M., and H. A. Lardy, in S. P. Colowick and N. O. Kaplan (eds.), "L-Sorbose-6-Phosphate," *Methods in Enzymology,* 3:179, 1957.

212. Brown, D. H., in H. U. Bergmeyer (ed.), "D-Glucosamine-6-Phosphate," *Methods of Enzymatic Analysis,* p. 151, 1963.

213. Barker, S. A., E. J. Bourne, and M. Stacey, "Communications to the Editor. The Synthesis of Uronic Acids," *Chem. and Ind.,* p. 970, 1951.

214. Ghalambor, M. A., and E. C. Heath, "The Metabolism of L-Fucose II—The Enzymatic Cleavage of L-Fuculose 1-Phosphate," *J. Biol. Chem.,* 237:2427, 1962.

215. Davis, B. D., and E. S. Mingioli, "Aromatic Biosynthesis VII. Accumulation of two Derivatives of Shikimic Acid by Bacterial Mutants," *J. Bact.,* 66:129, 1953.

216. Warren, L., "The Thiobarbituric Acid Assay of Sialic Acids," *J. Biol. Chem.,* 234:1971, 1959.

217. Dubois, M., et al., "Colorimetric Method for Determination of Sugars and Related Substances," *Ann. Chem.,* 28:350, 1956.

218. Holzer, H., and H. W. Goedde, in Bergmeyer, H. U. (ed.), "L-Erythrulose," *Methods of Enzymatic Analysis,* p. 208, 1963.

219. Dodgson, K. S. and B. Spencer, "Studies on Sulphatases: The Determination of Inorganic Sulphate in the Study of Sulphatases," *Biochem. J.*, 55:436, 1953.

220. Dodgson, K. S., "Determination of Inorganic Sulphate in Studies on the Enzymic and Non-Enzymic Hydrolysis of Carbohydrate and Other Sulphate Esters," *Biochem. J.*, 78:312, 1961.

221. Dodgson, K. S., and B. Spencer, "Assay of Sulfatases," *Methods of Biochem. Anal.*, 4:211, 1957.

222. Cooper, J. A. D., et al., "Galactose Oxidase from Polyporus—Circinatus, Fr.," *J. Biol. Chem.*, 234:445, 1959.

223. Beisenherz, G., T. Bücher, and K. H. Garbade, in Colowick, S. P., N. O. Kaplan (eds.), "α-Glycerophosphate Dehydrogenase from Rabbit Muscle. Dihydroxyacetone Phosphate DPNH H—L-α-Glycerophosphate DPN," *Methods in Enzymology*, 1:391, 1955.

224. Trevelyan, W. E., and J. S. Harrison, "Studies on Yeast Metabolism: Fractionation and Micro-Determination of Cell Carbohydrates," *Biochem. J.*, 50:298, 1952.

225. Domayk, G. F., and B. L. Horecker, "Pentose Fermentation by *Lactobacillus plantarum*," *J. Biol. Chem.*, 233:283, 1958.

226. Cohen, S. S., and D. B. M. Scott, "Formation of Pentose Phosphate from 6-Phosphogluconate," *Science*, 111:543, 1950.

227. Bandurski, R. S., and B. Axelrod, "The Chromotagraphic Identification of Some Biologically Important Phosphate Esters," *J. Biol. Chem.*, 193:405, 1951.

228. Burrows, S., F. S. M. Grylls, and J. S. Harrison, "Paper Chromatography of Phosphoric Esters," *Nature*, 170:800, 1952.

229. Mortimer, D. C., "Paper Chromatographic Separation of Some Biologically Important Phosphate Esters," *Can. J. Chem.*, 30:653, 1952.

230. Brooks, S. A., J. C. Lawrence, and C. R. Ricketts, "The Phosphate Esters of Mammalian Skin Maintained on Glucose and various Deoxyglucoses," *Biochem. J.*, 73:566, 1959.

231. Buchanan, J. G., C. A. Decker, and A. G. Long, "The Detection of Glycosides and Non-Reducing Carbohydrate Derivatives in Paper Partition Chromatography," *J. Chem. Soc. (London)*, p. 3162, 1950.

232. Hanes, C. S., and F. A. Isherwood, "Separation of the Phosphoric Esters on the Filter Paper Chromatogram," *Nature*, 164:1107, 1949.

233. Towne, J. C., V. W. Rodwell, and S. Grisolia, "2,3-Diphosphoglyceric Acid," *Biochem. Preps.*, 6:12, 1958.

234. Wade, H. E., and D. M. Morgan, "Fractionation of Phosphates by Paper Ionophoresis and Chromatography," *Biochem. J.*, 60:264, 1955.

235. Benson, A. A., in Colowick, S. P., and N. O. Kaplan (eds.), "Sugar Phosphates, Paper and Column Chromatography," *Methods in Enzymology*, 3:110, 1957.

236. Lloyd, A. G., "Fractionation of the Products of the Direct Sulphonation of Monosaccharides on Anion-Exchange Resin," *Biochem. J.*, 83:455, 1962.

237. Rees, D. A., "Paper Chromatography of Acidic Carbohydrates," *Nature*, 185:309, 1960.

IV. THE NATURAL OLIGOSACCHARIDES

Compounds formed by the glycosidic linking of a small number of monosaccharide molecules or their simple derivatives are called oligosaccharides. They are hydrolyzed by acids to the monosaccharides of
which they are composed. The number of monosaccharide units that
make up an oligosaccharide molecule distinguishes it as a disaccharide,
trisaccharide, or higher saccharide. This number is at least two and its
upper limit, though not defined, may be considered to lie in the range 10
to 20. Oligosaccharides are dialyzable through cellophane. In a single
oligosaccharide molecule the monosaccharide units may be the same or
different. They may be pentoses, hexoses, or higher sugars; aldoses or
ketoses; in pyranose or furanose form; or they may be simple modifications of monosaccharides such as deoxyglycoses, glycosamines, or
glycuronic acids.[1]

In disaccharides the glycosidic linkage between the two monosaccharide units may involve the anomeric carbon of only one of the units
and a non-anomeric carbon of the second unit. α-Lactose is a familiar
example:

Figure 1

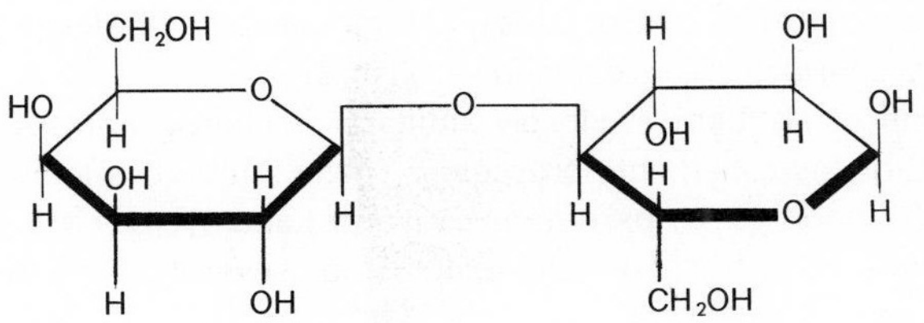

4-O-β-D-Galactopyranosyl-α-D-glycopyranose
O-β-D-Gal$p$-(1→4)-α-D-Gp

Lactose is thus a reducing sugar. In a few disaccharides the glycosidic
link occurs between the anomeric carbons of both monosaccharide units,
as in sucrose:

Figure 2

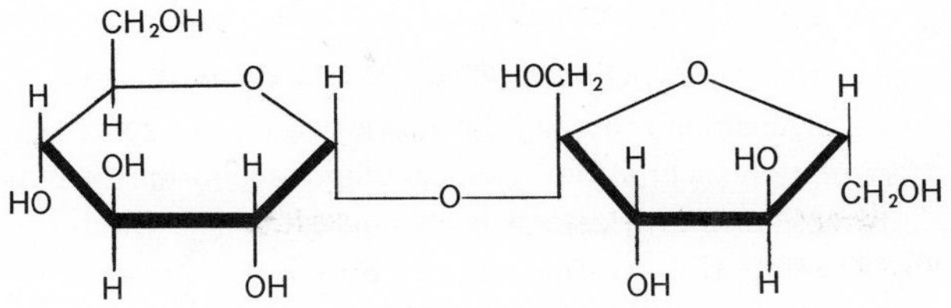

α-D-Glucopyranosyl-β-D-fructofuranoside
α-D-Gp-(1↔2)-β-D-Fru$f$

Sucrose is thus a non-reducing sugar. Higher oligosaccharides may likewise have reducing properties or not, depending on whether or not one anomeric is free of glycosidic linkage.

Under the structures of lactose and sucrose shown above are given two different ways of indicating each structure without having to write out the whole structural formula. The first has been in use longer but is awkward for describing many higher oligosaccharides; the second is shorter and is particularly useful to indicate structures of higher oligosaccharides and even polysaccharides. It uses abbreviations for each monosaccharide unit, as Gal, Fru, Xyl, Rha, Fuc, or GN or GalN for the corresponding 2-amino 2-deoxyhexoses, or GA or GalA for the corresponding uronic acids, with p or f to indicate its pyranoid or furanoid structure, and the usual prefixes D or L, and α or β. The numbers in parenthesis indicate the carbons of the first and second monosaccharide units linked by the glycosidic oxygen. The arrow points from the anomeric carbon to the non-anomeric carbon. In case both are anomeric the arrow points in two directions and indicates a non-reducing sugar.

Natural oligosaccharides may occur free or they may occur bound to another molecule, either carbohydrate or non-carbohydrate. They occur most commonly and in largest amounts in plant tissues. Sucrose occurs free and glycosidically linked to other monosaccharide units in the trisaccharides raffinose, melezetiose, gentianose, and planteose, and in the higher saccharides stachyose and verbascose.[2]

A group of antibiotics, closely similar to oligosaccharides, occurs in microorganisms called actinomycetes. These antibiotics include streptomycin, the neomycins, paromomycin, and kanamycin. Each contains a 1,3-diamino-1,2,3-trideoxycyclohexitol and several hitherto unknown amino sugars.[3]

Besides oligosaccharides known to occur in the free state, a large number occur as glycosides of noncarbohydrate molecules called aglycons.[4] Cardiac glycosides and saponins contain oligosaccharides consisting of deoxyhexoses and glucose attached to steroid aglycons.[5] Gangliosides contain complex oligosaccharides composed of N-acetylneuraminic acid, 2-acetamiacetamido-2-deoxy-D-galactosamine, D-glucose and D-galactose.[6] Among the glycolipids of Mycobacteria are a phosphatidylinositol-D-mannobioside, and the cord factor containing trehalose.[7]

The wide distribution of glycosidases suggests that oligosaccharides that occur as glycosides may also be found free.[8, 9] Enzymes that cause degradation of polysaccharides release oligosaccharides as intermediates. Cellulases[10] and amylases[11] form oligoglucoses. Bacteria produce hyaluronidases that split hyaluronate by an elimination reaction to give the unsaturated disaccharide, Δ4,5-GAp-(1$\rightarrow$3)-GNAc,[12] while testicular hyaluronidase produces a series of oligomers of N-acetyl-hyalobiouronic acid.[13]

Oligosaccharides also occur combined with protein in the glycoproteins. Submaxillary mucin, with a molecular weight about 10^6, contains 42% carbohydrate attached as over 1000 side chains of the disaccharide, α-N-Ac-Neuraminyl-(2→6) D-GalNAc.[14] Orosomucoid, a glycoprotein of human plasma, contains about 40% carbohydrate as several oligosaccharides, one of which is β-D-Galp-(1→4)-D-GNAc.[15]

Functions of oligosaccharides may include a reserve deposit of sugar in mobile form that can serve as a source of either energy or of material for structural purposes; a means of converting insoluble aglycones to soluble forms to facilitate their transport or metabolism; a means of controlling osmotic pressure; a means of modifying properties of proteins or of lipids; a natural anti-metabolite as a defense against invaders.

Where oligosaccharides occur in the free state they can usually be extracted from the natural material (plant tissue, honey, manna) with water, methanol, or ethanol.[16] A whole family of oligosaccharides related to lactose can be isolated from mammalian milk.[17]

Structure determination among oligosaccharides involves tests for reducing properties (a free anomeric hydroxyl), the number, identity, and sequence of the component monosaccharide units, the positions at which glycosidic bonds are attached, the configuration of each glycosidic bond, the ring structure of each monosaccharide unit (pyranose or furanose), and the presence of any substituent groups. Detailed analysis of all these points, as well as the use of periodate oxidation, methylation analysis, specific enzymes, and some special techniques has been recently reviewed.[18]

In the past only a small number of oligosaccharides have been recognized to occur free in nature. A far larger number must occur as intermediates of enzymatic transformations in normal and pathological metabolism and in the action of parasites on hosts. The following Table can include few of the many examples that must occur.

	Allolactose	β-Cellobiose	Chondrosine	
Structure	O-β-D-Galp-(1→6)-D-Gp	O-β-D-Gp-(1→4)-β-D-Gp	O-β-D-GAp-(1→3)-D-GalN	Δ4,5-GAp-(1→3)-D-GNAc
Formula	$C_{12}H_{22}O_{11}$	$C_{12}H_{22}O_{11}$	$C_{12}H_{21}O_{11}N$	$C_{14}H_{21}O_{11}N$
M W	342.3	342.3	355.3	379.3
M P	165	225	Decomp	
$[\alpha]_D$	+25	+14.2 → +34.6	+40 (.15M HCl)	−20°
Occurrence	fr. lactose by yeast transgalactosylase	Digestion of cellulose or lichenin by herbivores or molds	Unsubstituted repeating unit of chondroitin sulfate	Digestion of hyaluronate by bacteria
Isolation	16, 303	23	30	12
Structure	24	1	29	12

	Fucosyllactose	Gentianose	β-Gentiobiose	Hyalobiouronic acid
Structure	O-α-L-Fucp-(1→2)-O-β-D-Galp-(1→4)-D-G	O-β-D-Gp-(1→6)-O-α-D-Gp-(1↔2)-β-D-Fruf	O-β-D-Gp-(1→6)-β-D-Gp	O-β-D-GAp-(1→3)-D-GN
Formula	$C_{18}H_{32}O_{15}$	$C_{18}H_{32}O_{16}$	$C_{12}H_{22}O_{11}$	$C_{12}H_{21}O_{11}N$
M W	488.4	504.4	342.3	355.3
M P	230–231 dec.	209–211	190–195	Decomp
$[\alpha]_D$	−57.5°	+31.5	−5→+10.5	+30.5 (.1 M HCl)
Occurrence	In mammalian milk with related oligosacs	Gentian root	Gentian root	Repeating unit of hyaluronate
Isolation	17	2	16, 313	25
Structure	17	1	1	26, 27

	Isomaltose	Inulobiose	6-Kestose, fructosylsucrose	Lactose, milk sugar
Structure	O-α-D-Gp-(1→6)-D-G	O-β-D-Fruf-(2↔1)-D-Fru	O-β-D-Fruf-(2→6)-O-β-D-Fruf-(2↔1)-α-D-Gp	O-β-D-Galp-(1→4)-D-Gp
Formula	$C_{12}H_{22}O_{11}$	$C_{12}H_{22}O_{11}$	$C_{18}H_{32}O_{16}$	$C_{12}H_{22}O_{11}$
M W	342.3	342.3	504.4	342.3
M P			144–145	(α) 223 (β) 252
$[\alpha]_D$	+120	−32.6	+27	(α) 90→55.3 (β) 34.9→55.3
Occurrence	In digestion of maltose with amylases	Component of inulin	From sucrose by invertase action	In mammalian milk
Isolation	16, 319	28	16, 360	17
Structure	1	1	1	17, 1

	α-Laminaribiose	β-Maltose	Maltotriose	Melezitose
Structure	O-β-D-Gp-(1→3)-α-D-Gp	O-α-D-Gp-(1→4)-D-Gp	O-α-D-Gp-(1→4)-O-α-D-Gp-(1→4)-D-G	O-α-D-Gp-(1↔2)-β-D-Fruf-(3←1)-α-D-Gp
Formula	$C_{12}H_{22}O_{11}$	$C_{12}H_{22}O_{11}$	$C_{18}H_{32}O_{16}$	$C_{18}H_{32}O_{16}\cdot2\cdot H_2O$
M W	342.3	342.3	504.4	504.4
M P	204–206	100–103		153–154
$[\alpha]_D$	24.9→18.6	117.3→130.4	158	88
Occurrence	In laminarin and pachyman	From starch with β-amylase	From amylose with salivary amylase	Manna on Douglas fir and many other plants
Isolation	16, 328	16, 335	16, 337	19
Structure	1	1	1	20, 1

	α-Melibiose	α-Panose	Planteobiose, melibulose	Planteose
Structure	O-α-D-Gal$p$-(1→6)-D-Gp	O-α-D-Gp-(1→6)-O-α-D-Gp-(1→4)-D-G	O-α-D-Gal$p$-(1→6)-D-Fru	O-α-D-Gal$p$-(1→6)-O-β-D-Fru$f$-(2↔1)-D-Glu$p$
Formula	$C_{12}H_{22}O_{11}$	$C_{18}H_{32}O_{16}$	$C_{12}H_{22}O_{11}$	$C_{18}H_{32}O_{16} \cdot 2H_2O$
M W	342.3	504.4	342.3	504.4
M P	183–184	220		123–124
$[\alpha]_D$	166→142	160→151	125	130
Occurrence	From raffinose by transglycosylation	From maltose by transglycosylation	From planteose	In *Plantago*
Isolation	16, 366	16, 341	2	2
Structure	1	1	1	1

	Primeverose	Raffinose, gossypose	Rutinose	α-Schardinger dextrin
Structure	O-β-D-Xyl-(1→6)-D-G	O-α-D-Gal$p$-(1→6)-O-α-D-Gp-(1↔2)-β-D-Fru$f$	O-β-L-Rha-(1→6)-D-G	Cyclo-[O-α-D-Gp-(1→4)]$_6$
Formula	$C_{11}H_{20}O_{10}$	$C_{18}H_{32}O_{16} \cdot 5 \cdot H_2O$	$C_{12}H_{22}O_{10}$	$C_{36}H_{60}O_{30}$
M W	312.3	504.4	326.3	972.6
M P	209–210	118–119	189–192	242–243
$[\alpha]_D$	23→ − 3.2	105.2	3.2→ − .8	151
Occurrence	From gaultherin by enzyme action	By-product from sugar beet molasses	From rutin by enzyme action	From starch by *Bacillus macerans* enzyme
Isolation	1	16, 366	1	22
Structure	1	1, 2	1	22

	Sophorose	Stachyose	Sucrose, cane sugar, beet sugar	Trehalose
Structure	O-β-D-Gp-(1→2)-D-G	O-α-D-Gal$p$-(1→6)-O-α-D-Gal$p$-(1→6)-O-α-D-Gp-(1↔2)-β-D-Fru$f$	O-β-D-Fru$f$-(2↔1)-α-D-Gp	O-α-D-Gp-(1↔1)-α-D-Gp
Formula	$C_{12}H_{22}O_{11}$	$C_{24}H_{42}O_{21}$	$C_{12}H_{22}O_{11}$	$C_{12}H_{22}O_{11}$
M W	342.3	666.6	342.3	342.3
M P	196–198 monohydrate	101–105	188, 170	203
$[\alpha]_D$	34→19	131	66.5	178
Occurrence	In glycoside of *Sophora japonica*	In tubers of *Stachys tubifera*	In many parts of many plants	In trehala manna and in some fungi
Isolation	16, 345	16, 368 2	1	21 16, 370
Structure	1	1	1	21

	β-Turanose	Vicianose
Structure	O-α-D-Glup- (1→3)-D-Fru	O-β-L-Ara- (1→6)-D-G
Formula	$C_{12}H_{22}O_{11}$	$C_{12}H_{20}O_{10}$
M W	342.3	312.3
M P	157	210
$[\alpha]_D$	27→75.8	63→40
Occurrence	In melezitose	In vicianin and gein
Isolation	19 MI, 353	1
Structure	1	1

BIBLIOGRAPHY

1. Hassid, W. Z., and E. C. Ballou, in Pigman, W. (ed.), *The Carbohydrates*, p. 478, 1957.
2. French, D., "The Raffinose Family of Oligosaccharides," *Advan. Carbohydrate Chem.*, 9:149, 1954.
3. Dutcher, J. D., "Chemistry of Amino Sugars Derived from Antibiotic Substances," *Advan. Carbohydrate Chem.*, 18:259, 1963.
4. Baumann, H., and W. Pigman, in Pigman, W. (ed.), *The Carbohydrates*, p. 526, 1957.
5. Reichstein, T., and E. Weiss, "The Sugars of the Cardiac Glycosides," *Advan. Carbohydrate Chem.*, 17:65, 1962.
6. Svennerholm, L., "The Gangliosides," *J. Lipid Res.*, 5:145, 1964.
7. Lederer, E., "Glycolipids of Acid-Fast Bacteria," *Advan. Carbohydrate Chem.*, 16:207, 1961.
8. Pigman, W., *Advan. Enzymol.*, 4:41, 1944.
9. Wallenfels, K., and O. P. Malhotra, "Galactosidases," *Advan. Carbohydrate Chem.*, 16:239, 1961.
10. Nord, F. F., and J. C. Vitucci, "Certain Aspects of the Microbiological Degradation of Cellulose," *Advan. Enzymol.*, 8:253, 1948.
11. Bernfeld, P., "Enzymes of Starch Degradation and Synthesis," *Advan. Enzymol.*, 12:379, 1951.
12. Linker, A., K. Meyer and P. Hoffman, "The Production of Unsaturated Uronides by Bacterial Hyaluronidases," *J. Biol. Chem.*, 219:13, 1956.
13. Weissmann, B. K. Meyer, P. Sampson, et al., "Isolation of Oligosaccharides Enzymatically Produced from Hyaluronic Acid," *J. Biol. Chem.*, 208:417, 1954.
14. Gottschalk, A., and H. A. McKenzie, "Studies on Mucoproteins. VIII. On the Molecular Size and Shape of Ovine Submaxillary Gland Mucoprotein," *Biochim. Biophys. Acta*, 54:226, 1961.
15. Eylar, E. H., and R. W. Jeanloz, "Oligosaccharides from the α Acid Glycoprotein of Human Plasma," *J. Biol. Chem.*, 237:622, 1962.
16. Whistler, R. L., and M. L. Wolfrom (eds.), *Methods in Carbohydrate Chemistry*, 1:368, 1962.
17. Clamp, J. R., L. Hough, J. L. Hickson, et al., "Lactose," *Advan. Carbohydrate Chem.*, 16:159, 1961.

18. Bailey, R. W., and J. B. Pridham, "Oligosaccharides," *Advan. Carbohydrate Chem.*, 17:121, 1962.
19. Hudson, C. S., "Melezitose and Turanose," *Advan. Carbohydrate Chem.*, 2:1, 1946.
20. Hehre, E. J., "The Substituted-Sucrose Structure of Melezitose," *Advan. Carbohydrate Chem.*, 8:277, 1953.
21. Birch, G. G., "Trehaloses," *Advan. Carbohydrate Chem.*, 18:201, 1963.
22. French, D., "The Schardinger Dextrins," *Advan. Carbohydrate Chem.*, 12:189, 1957.
23. Braun, G., "Preparation of Cellobiose from Octaacetate," *Org. Syn.*, 17:34, 1937.
24. Pazur, J. H., C. L. Tipton, T. Budovich, et al., "Structural Characterization of Products of Enzymatic Disproportionation of Lactose," *J. Am. Chem. Soc.*, 80:119, 1958.
25. Weissman, B., M. M. Rapport, A. Linker, et al., "Isolation of the Aldobionic Acid of Umbilical Cord Hyaluronic Acid," *J. Biol. Chem.*, 205:205, 1953.
26. Weissman, B., and K. Meyer, "The Structure of Hyalobiuronic Acid and of Hyaluronic Acid from Umbilical Cord," *J. Am. Chem. Soc.*, 76:1753, 1954.
27. Hirano, S., and P. Hoffman, "The Hexosaminidic Linkage of Hyaluronic Acid," *J. Org. Chem.*, 27:395, 1962.
28. Pazur, J. H., and A. L. Gordon, "Studies on Insulin: The Preparation and Properties of Inuloliose," *J. Am. Chem. Soc.*, 75:3458, 1953.
29. Davidson, E. A., and K. Meyer, "Structural Studies on Chondroitin Sulfuric Acid. II The Glucuronidic Linkage," *J. Am. Chem. Soc.*, 77:4796, 1955.
30. Davidson, E. A., and K. Meyer, "Structural Studies on Chondroitin Sulfuric Acid. I The Nature of Chondrosine," *J. Am. Chem. Soc.*, 76:5686, 1954.

V. THE POLYSACCHARIDES

Compounds formed by the glycosidic linking of large numbers of mono-saccharide units or their simple derivatives are called polysaccha-rides.[1, 2, 3] Like oligosaccharides, they can be hydrolyzed by acids and yield the monosaccharide units of which they are composed. With sharper methods for detection, separation, and characterization of nat-urally occurring products and their transitory intermediates, the distinc-tion between oligosaccharides and polysaccharides will disappear.

There is a superficial resemblance between proteins and poly-saccharides. Both are high molecular weight chains of their respective units: in each the residues are linked in a polarized manner so the pro-tein chain has an amino end and a carboxylate end, while the poly-saccharide has a non-reducing and a reducing end. A sharp difference between protein and polysaccharide chains is that in most individual proteins there are about 18 different amino acid units and there are almost no proteins with only one or two different units, while among polysaccharides none are clearly known to have more than a half dozen different monosaccharide units and many have only one or two. Many polysaccharides have highly branched chains with many nonreducing ends and only one reducing end. In polysaccharides there may occur a repeating unit that can be regarded as an oligosaccharide, and the poly-saccharide itself as a polymer of this repeating unit. Repeating units are sometimes found by a high yield of disaccharide after partial hydrolysis of a polysaccharide. For example, by acid hydrolysis, hyalobiouronic acid can be made from hyaluronate;[4] $4\text{-}O\text{-Me-}\alpha\text{-}D\text{-GA}p$ (1→2)-D-Xyl from birch wood meal;[17] and cellobiouronic acid from pneumococcal Type III capsular polysaccharide.[6] More complicated repeating units have been inferred on the basis of the isolation of products that accumulate during the early stages of hydrolysis. Yet few polysaccharides consist only of repeating units.

One of the greatest difficulties in the study of polysaccharides is the practical problem of isolating a product that can be proved to be a single molecular species. The first to have their structures worked out were those that occur naturally in a nearly pure condition. Cotton fiber is an outstanding and lonely example. Starch granules proved more trouble-some and the clear separation of amylose and amylopectin was not achieved until 1942 by Schoch.[8] In cases such as plant gums it is not yet possible to decide to what extent they are mixtures.[9, 10] Problems of purification and fractionation among polysaccharides are formidable due to several interrelated factors: (a) they may be variable in composition, (b) they cannot generally be crystallized, (c) they are often highly polydisperse, (d) they sometimes constitute the structural elements of living organisms and so are either insoluble in water or so intimately mingled with other insoluble materials (lignin of plants, collagen of mammals, calcified structures of molluscs) as to be scarcely extractable without degradation, (e) they sometimes occur as mixtures of protein compounds difficult to recognize and to separate. Isolation methods are varied to suit the polysaccharide sought and the biological material in which it exists.[1, 2, 3]

Physicochemical methods of separating polysaccharide mixtures, judging their homogeneity, and measuring molecular weights and dimensions in solution are being increasingly used and critically studied.[7]

	Agarose Agar	Alginate	Amylopectin	Amylose
Repeat Unit	-β-D-Galp-(1→4)- 3,6-anhydro-α-L- Galp-(1→3)-	-β-D-ManAp- (1→4)-with D- GulA-	-α-D-Gp-(1→4)- with 5% branching at (1→6)	-α-D-Gp-(1→4)-
Solution	Sol. in hot H_2O	Sol. in H_2O as Na or K salt	Sol. in hot H_2O	Sol. in hot H_2O
$[\alpha]_D$			150	220
AV. MW		about 150,000	→50 × 10^6	→1 × 10^6
% Comp.	40% D-Gal 40% 3,6- anhydro-L-Gal 3% ester SO$_4$ 2% pyruvate	Variable depending on source. 70% D-ManA 30% D-GulA	100% D-G	100% D-G
Occurrence	*Rhodophyceae*	*Phaeophyceae*	Main component of many starches	Minor component of many starches
Isolation	MV,* 65	MV,* 69	19	19
Structure	23	23	11	11

*Whistler and Wolfrom, *Methods in Carbohydrate Chemistry*, vol. 5, 1965.

	Arabinan	Kappa-Carrageenan	Cellulose	Chitin
Repeat Unit	-α-L-Araf-(1→5)- with (1→3)	-3,6-anhydro-α-D-Galp-(1→3)- -β-D-Galp-(1→4)-with ester sulfate	-β-D-Gp-(1→4)-	-β-D-GpNAc-(1→4)-
Solution	Sol. H₂O	Sol. H₂O as Na salt	Insol.	Insol. H₂O Sol. in HCl
[α]ᴅ	−114 −129			−14.7 (HCl)
AV. MW			Probably →1 × 10⁶	
% Comp.	95% L-Ara	45% D-Gal 31% 3,6-anhydro-D-Gal 19% ester SO₄	100% D-G	100% D-GNAc
Occurrence	In pectic substances	*Rhodophyceae*	All plants	Skeletal subst. in many invertebrates, in some fungi
Isolation	MV,* 74	MV,* 98	1, 2	MV, 103
Structure	12	23	1, 2	13

	Chondroitin 4-Sulfate	Colominic Acid	Dermatan 4-Sulfate	Dextran
Repeat Unit	-β-D-GpA-(1→3)- β-D-GalpNAc-4-SO₄-(1→4)-	-N-Acetyl-neuraminic acid-(2→8)-	-α-L-IdopA-(1→3)- -β-D-GalpNAc-4-SO₄-(1→4)-	-α-D-Gp-(1→6)- with about 8% -(1→3)-and-(1→4)-
Solution	Sol. in H₂O as Na, K, salts	Sol. in H₂O	Sol. in H₂O as Na, K, salt	Sol. in H₂O
[α]ᴅ	−25		−85	210
AV. MW	40,000	4,000	27,000	1–10 × 10⁶
% Comp.	32% D-GA 30% D-GalN	Mainly N-Acetyl-neuraminic acid	32% L-IdoA 30% D-GalN	100% D-G
Occurrence	In cartilage, intervertebral discs of mammals	Produced by *Escherichia coli*	In derma of mammals	From sucrose by *leuconostoc* species
Isolation	MV,* 110	16	MV, 114	MV, 118
Structure	15	16	18	14

*Whistler and Wolfrom, *Methods in Carbohydrate Chemistry*, vol. 5, 1965.

	Galactan	Glucomannans	Glycogen	Heparin
Repeat Unit	-β-D-Gal$p$-(1→4)-	-β-D-Man$p$-(1→4)-β-D-Gp-(1→4)-	-α-D-Gp-(1→4)- with 12 or 18% branching at (1→6)	GpA-(1→4)-α-D-GNSO$_4$-(1→4) backbone
Solution	Sol. in H$_2$O	Sol. in alk.	Sol. in hot H$_2$O	Sol. in H$_2$O
$\alpha]_D$	38	−30 in alk.	196	53
AV. MW	20,000	10,000	1–100 × 10^6	16,000
% Comp.	100% D-Gal	60% D-Man 30% D-G	100% D-G	30% D-GA 26% D-GN 35% SO$_4$
Occurrence	In pectic substances	In wood of angiosperms	In animal cells	In liver, lung, mast cells
Isolation	12	17	20	MV, 150
Structure	12	17	21	24

	Hyaluronate	Inulin	Nigeran	Pectins
Repeat Unit	-β-D-GpA-(1→3)-β-D-GpNAc-(1→4)-	-β-D-Fru$f$-(2→1)- also (2→6)	-α-D-Gp-(1→4)-α-D-Gp-(1→3)-	-β-D-Gal$p$A-(1→4)-
Solution	Sol. in water as Na or K salt	Sol. in H$_2$O	Sol. in hot H$_2$O	Sol. in hot H$_2$O
$\alpha]_D$	−67	−38	254	230
AV. MW	→ 2 × 10^6	7,000		50,000
% Comp.	44% D-GA 40% D-GN	95% D-Fru 3% D-G	100% D-G	85% D-GalA 9% OCH$_3$
Occurrence	In vitreous body, umbilical cord and synovial fluid	Food reserve in plant roots	In some molds	In fruits and vegetables
Isolation	MV, 154	MV, 157	MV, 165	MV, 167
Structure	5	22		12

	Pneumococcal Capsular Polysaccharide (Type III)	Xylans
Repeat Unit	-β-D-GpA-(1→4)-β-D-G-(1→3)-	-β-D-Xyl$p$-(1→4)-
Solution	Sol. in H$_2$O as Na salt	Sol. in NaOH
$\alpha]_D$	−32	−106 (.5N NaOH)
AV. MW	140,000	25,000
% Comp.	45% D-G 50% D-GA	95% D-Xyl 3% D-GA
Occurrence	In Type III *Pneumococcus* capsules	In all woods and straw
Isolation	6	MV, 170
Structure	6	17

BIBLIOGRAPHY

1. Whistler, R. L., and C. L. Smart, *Polysaccharide Chemistry*, 1953.
2. Whistler, R. L., and W. M. Corbett, in Pigman, W. (ed.), *The Carbohydrates*, p. 641, 1957.
3. Pigman, W., and D. Platt, in Pigman, W. (ed.), *The Carbohydrates*, p. 709, 1957.
4. Weissmann, B., M. M. Rapport, A. Linker and K. Meyer, "Isolation of the Aldobionic Acid of Umbilical Cord Hyaluronic Acid," *J. Biol. Chem.*, 205:205, 1953.
5. Whistler, R. L., and E. J. Olson, "The Biosynthesis of Hyaluronic Acid," *Advan. Carbohydrate Chem.*, 12:299, 1957.
6. How, M. J., J. S. Brimacombe and M. Stacey, "The Pneumococcal Polysaccharides," *Advan. Carbohydrate Chem.*, 19:303, 1964.
7. Banks, W., and C. T. Greenwood, "Physical Properties of Solutions of Polysaccharides," *Advan. Carbohydrate Chem.*, 18:357, 1963.
8. Schoch, T. J., "Fractionation of Starch," *Advan. Carbohydrate Chem.*, 1:247, 1945.
9. Anderson, E., and L. Sands, "A Discussion of Methods of Value in Research on Plant Polyuronides," *Advan. Carbohydrate Chem.*, 1:329, 1945.
10. Jones, J. K. N., and F. Smith, "Plant Gums and Mucilages," *Advan. Carbohydrate Chem.*, 4:243, 1949.
11. Meyer, K. H., and G. C. Gibbons, "The Present Status of Starch Chemistry," *Advan. Enzymol.*, 12:341, 1951.
12. Hirst, E. L., and J. K. N. Jones, "Chemistry of Peptic Materials," *Advan. Carbohydrate Chem.*, 2:235, 1946.
13. Foster, A. B., and J. M. Webber, "Chitin," *Advan. Carbohydrate Chem.*, 15:371, 1960.
14. Neely, W. B., "Dextran: Structure and Synthesis," *Advan. Carbohydrate Chem.*, 15:341, 1960.
15. Davidson, E., and K. Meyer, "Structural Studies on Chondroitin Sulfuric Acid. II The Glucuronidic Linkage," *J. Am. Chem. Soc.*, 77:4796, 1955.
16. McGuire, E. J., and S. B. Binkley, "The Structure and Chemistry of Colominic Acid," *Biochemistry*, 3:247, 1964.
17. Timell, T. E., "Wood Hemecelluloses," *Advan. Carbohydrate Chem.*, 19:247, 1964.
18. Stoffyn, P. J., and R. W. Jeanloz, "The Identification of the Uronic Acid Component of Dermatan Sulfate (β-Heparin, Chondroitin Sulfate B)," *J. Biol. Chem.*, 235:2507, 1960.
19. Muetgeert, J., "The Fractionation of Starch," *Advan. Carbohydrate Chem.*, 16:299, 1961.
20. Bueding, E., and S. A. Orrell, "A Mild Procedure for the Isolation of Polydisperse Glycogen from Animal Tissues," *J. Biol. Chem.*, 239:4018, 1964.
21. Manners, D. J., "The Molecular Structure of Glycogens," *Advan. Carbohydrate Chem.*, 12:261, 1957.
22. McDonald, E., "The Polyfructosans and Difructose Anhydrides," *Advan. Carbohydrate Chem.*, 2:253, 1946.
23. Mori, T., "Seaweed Polysaccharides," *Advan. Carbohydrate Chem.*, 8:315, 1953.
24. Wolfrom, M. L., J. R. Vercellotti, and D. Horton, "Two Disaccharides from Carboxyl-Reduced Heparin. The Linkage Sequence in Heparin," *J. Org. Chem.*, 29:540, 1964.

VI. PATHWAYS OF CARBOHYDRATE METABOLISM

Introduction. Carbohydrates are components of important structural and regulatory substances in cells, as well as a major source of metabolites leading to the formation of ATP. Moreover, carbohydrate oxidation often provides the NADPH required for biosynthetic processes. The most common carbohydrate available to animals is glucose, which is a constituent of dietary disaccharides and polysaccharides. Smaller amounts of galactose and fructose are supplied in the form of lactose and sucrose, respectively. In microbial metabolism, a variety of nutritionally useful sugars may be supplied.

The initial step in the utilization of monosaccharides is usually the phosphorylation of the sugar, although oxidative or reductive reactions occasionally precede phosphorylation reactions. Subsequent transformations involve a variety of metabolic pathways which vary in importance in different tissues and species and vary in cellular function. The most common metabolic pathways for carbohydrates will be discussed separately, but their interrelationships within cells should not be overlooked.

Embden-Meyerhof Pathway. Also referred to as the glycolytic pathway, this sequence of reactions effects the conversion of hexose phosphates to pyruvate and lactate (see Figure 1). The glycolytic breakdown of glucose and glycogen is quantitatively the major degradative pathway for hexoses in animals, and it occurs in plants and microorganisms as well. As shown in Fig. 1, this pathway is an anaerobic process capable of producing directly only limited quantities of ATP. The pyruvate produced is ultimately used for ATP production via the citric acid cycle and electron transport system. The several irreversible enzymatic steps in the catabolism of hexoses are effected in the direction of synthesis by other enzymes; differential effects of cellular components on the enzymes at these points serve to regulate the direction of flow of metabolism. Thus, various physiological factors may determine whether glycolysis or gluconeogenesis predominates at a given time. In addition to the direct production of small amounts of ATP (2 ATP per glucose) and the production of pyruvate, the Embden-Meyerhof pathway serves in the production of carbohydrate from non-carbohydrate precursors (gluconeogenesis), in supplying precursors of important carbohydrates such as hexosamines, pentoses, and uronic acids, and in providing points of entry of dietary sugars (such as fructose and galactose) into the mainstream of carbohydrate metabolism.

Pyruvate Oxidation and the Krebs Tricarboxylic Acid Cycle. The conversion of pyruvate to acetyl coenzyme A is followed by the oxidation of the acetyl moiety through the tricarboxylic acid cycle (Fig. 2). This cycle pro-

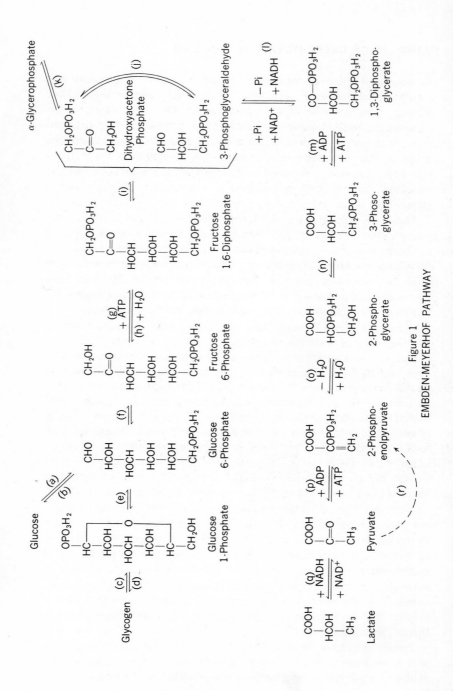

Figure 1
EMBDEN-MEYERHOF PATHWAY

Figure 1.

ENZYMES

a. Hexokinase or glucokinase
b. Glucose 6-phosphatase
c. Phosphorylase
d. UDGP pyrophosphorylase and glycogen synthetase
e. Phosphoglucomutase
f. Phosphohexoisomerase
g. Phosphofructokinase
h. Fructose diphosphatase
i. Aldolase
j. Triose phosphate isomerase
k. α-Glycerophosphate dehydrogenase
l. Triosephosphate dehydrogenase
m. Phosphokinase
n. Phosphoglyceromutase
o. Enolase
p. Pyruvate kinase
q. Lactic dehydrogenase
r. Pyruvate carboxylase and phosphoenolpyruvate carboxykinase

duces reduced coenzymes and high energy phosphate, ultimately yielding 12 ATP per acetyl-CoA. The net production of 2 ATP in the conversion of glucose to pyruvate, 3 ATP (via DPNH) in the conversion of each pyruvate molecule to acetyl-CoA, and 12 ATP in the conversion of each acetyl-CoA to CO_2 and water, amounts to a yield of 38 ATP per mole of glucose. The complete oxidation of a mole of glucose to CO_2 and H_2O in a bomb calorimeter yields 685,500 cal. The 38 moles of ATP are equivalent to $38 \times 7,000$ cal or 266,000 cal of utilizable energy. Accordingly, the overall efficiency of the complete oxidation is 39 per cent.

In animal cells, the Embden-Meyerhof pathway is located in the nonparticulate portion of cells, while the tricarboxylic acid cycle is in the mitochondria. The performance of the tricarboxylic acid cycle is dependent upon the continuous regeneration of oxidized coenzymes by the mitochondrial electron transport system that produces ATP in an aerobic process.

Pentose Phosphate Cycle. This pathway (Fig. 3), which begins and terminates with intermediates of the Embden-Meyerhof pathway, has crucial roles in most cells, although it usually makes a relatively minor contribution to the net oxidation of carbohydrate. As is evident from Fig. 3, CO_2 can be continually produced from Carbon 1 of hexose phosphate by repeated turns of the cycle. More specific functions of widespread impor-

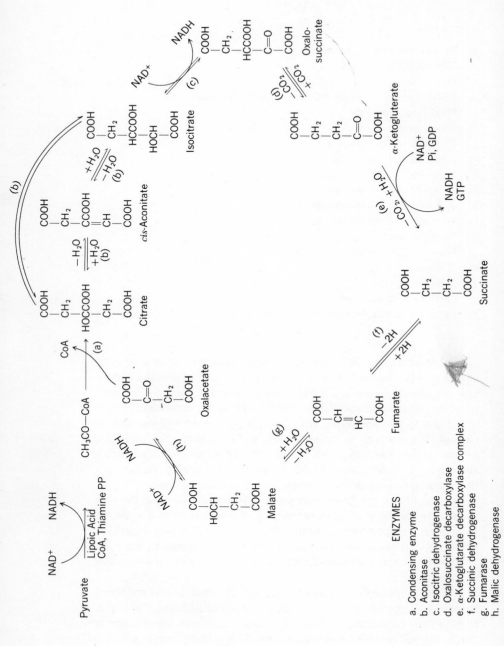

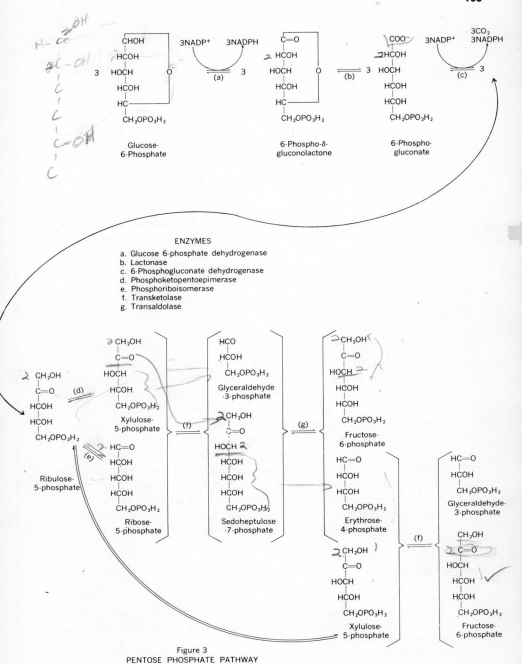

Figure 3
PENTOSE PHOSPHATE PATHWAY

ENZYMES

a. Glucose 6-phosphate dehydrogenase
b. Lactonase
c. 6-Phosphogluconate dehydrogenase
d. Phosphoketopentoepimerase
e. Phosphoriboisomerase
f. Transketolase
g. Transaldolase

tance are the production of NADPH for reductive biosynthetic reactions, pentose phosphate for nucleotide synthesis, and ribulose phosphate for ribulose diphosphate synthesis in photosynthetic organisms. The extent of glucose oxidation via the pentose phosphate cycle usually depends upon the need for intermediates of the cycle and on the availability of NADP (*e.g.*, on the rate of utilization of NADPH).

Glucuronic Acid Pathways. A glucuronate-xylulose cycle (Fig. 4) occurs in mammals, but its physiological role has not been determined. Early steps in the process do, however, permit most animals to produce L-ascorbic acid, a vitamin in primates and in a few lower animals. UDP-glucuronic acid, an intermediate in the cycle, is an important precursor of components of mucopolysaccharides. There is as yet little evidence that the cycle plays an appreciable role in the net oxidation of hexose or in the regulation of the oxidation state of pyridine nucleotide coenzymes.

Entner-Doudoroff Pathway. This sequence of reactions (Fig. 5) is limited to microorganisms. In some species it is the sole catabolic pathway for carbohydrates.

Other pathways. Since a very large number of sugars occur naturally, it is apparent that many other biosynthetic processes exist in addition to those implicit in the sequences discussed above. In many of these transformations, alterations in the structure of sugars take place while they are linked to nucleotides. Representative of these reactions are the interconversion of uridine diphosphate glucose and uridine diphosphate galactose and the decarboxylation oi uridine diphosphate glucuronic acid to uridine diphosphate xylose. 6-Deoxyhexoses are produced by more complicated sequences involving oxidation-reduction and dehydration reactions, linked to particular nucleoside diphosphates (Fig. 6). The production of L as well as D sugars is accomplished by these processes. Since the biosynthesis of complex carbohydrates such as mucopolysaccharides generally utilizes nucleoside diphosphate sugars as donors of the monomeric units, the biosynthetic processes leading to the formation of special sugars may simultaneously produce the actual donors of the sugars to be incorporated into larger carbohydrates.

BIBLIOGRAPHY

References:

1. White, A., P. Handler, and E. Smith, *Textbook of Biochemistry*, 3rd ed., 1964.
2. Hollmann, S., *Non-glycolytic Pathways of Metabolism of Glucose*, transl. and rev. by O. Touster, 1964.
3. Neufield, E. F., and V. Ginsberg, in *Ann. Rev. Biochem.*, p. 297, 1965.

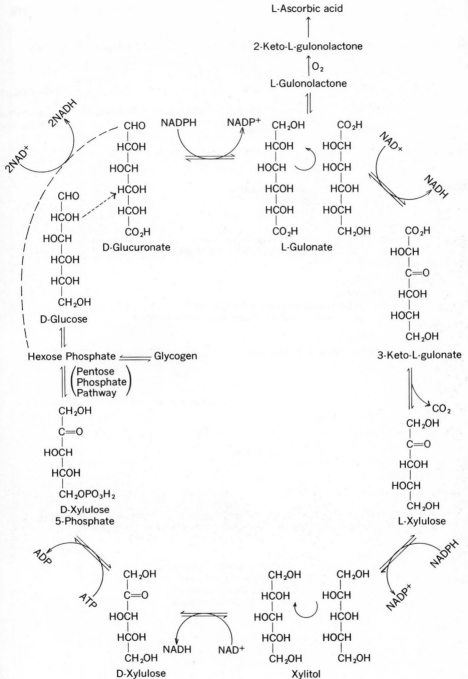

Figure 4
GLUCURONATE-XYLULOSE CYCLE
Dashed arrows leading to glucuronate, indicate uncertainty regarding inter-
mediates (UDPG and UDP-glucuronic acid are probably involved)

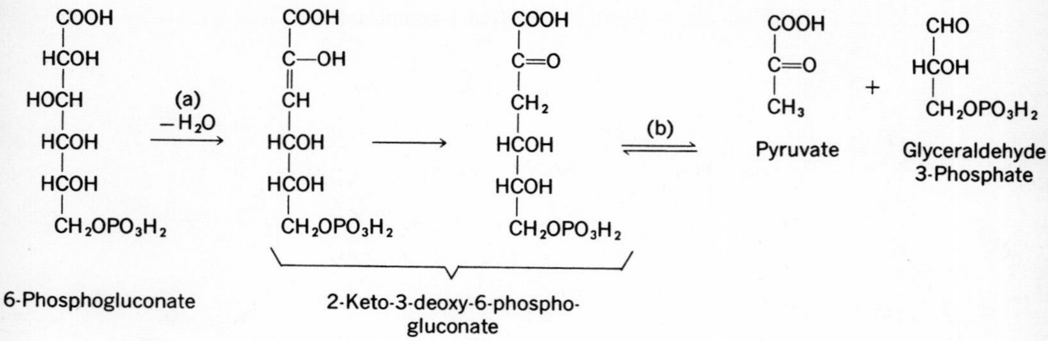

Figure 5
ENTNER-DOUDOROFF PATHWAY

Enzymes
    (a) 6-Phosphogluconate Dehydrase
    (b) 2-Keto-3-deoxy-6-phosphogluconate Aldolase

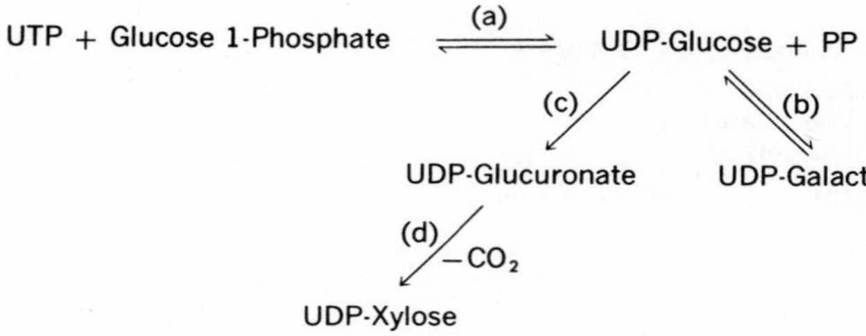

Figure 6
EXAMPLES OF THE ROLE OF NUCLEOSIDE DIPHOSPHATE GLYCOSYL
DERIVATIVES IN THE INTERCONVERSION OF SUGARS

Enzymes
    (a) UDPG Pyrophosphorylase
    (b) UDPGal 4-Epimerase
    (c) UDPG Dehydrogenase
    (d) UDPGA Decarboxylase

I. ISOLATION AND ANALYSIS OF FATTY ACIDS

Fatty acids exist in nature primarily as esters of glycerol or long chain alcohols and as amides of sphingosine. The problem of fatty acid analysis can therefore be considered a two-step process. The lipids must first be quantitatively isolated, free of non-lipid material.[1,2] Secondly, the fatty acids must be converted to derivatives, usually methyl esters, which are then analyzed by gas liquid chromatography (GLC). Methyl ester formation is carried out either by saponifying the lipid and then methylating, or alternatively by direct interesterification. Diazomethane,[3] 2,2-dimethoxypropane,[4] boron trifluoride,[5] boron trichloride,[6] anhydrous methanolic-HCl,[7] sulfuric acid in methanol[8] and sodium methoxide in methanol[9] are all reagents which have been used for methyl ester formation. Various quantitative aspects of fatty acid methylation are discussed by Vorbeck et al.[10] The conditions and methodology routinely used for the GLC analysis of lipids are compiled in excellent reviews by James[11] and more recently by Horning et al.[12] Horning et al[13] have also discussed pertinent data concerning the quantitative analysis of fatty acids by GLC.

Since most lipids contain a broad spectrum of both saturated and unsaturated acids, it is frequently difficult to establish the structure of every fatty acid in an unambiguous manner. Fortunately, considerable information concerning the identity of the various fatty acids can be obtained directly from GLC analysis. Saturated fatty acids can be distinguished from unsaturated acids simply by hydrogenating an aliquot of the methyl esters and noting which components have an altered retention time upon GLC analysis. Tentative and frequently reliable identification of saturated as well as unsaturated acids can be made by comparing the relative retention times of unknown components with suitable standards. Several systematic studies have been reported in the literature in which double bond positions are correlated with relative retention time.[14-21] In Table I, the relative retention times of 79 methyl esters and 7 ethyl esters, as determined on four different liquid phases, are reproduced from a recent paper by Hofstetter et al.[21] The relative retention times are expressed as equivalent chain lengths (ECL).[20] The authors point out that the increment, $ECL_{EGS} - ECL_{Apiezon\ L}$ is approximately 0.84 for each double bond in the

Table 1. Equivalent Chain Lengths of Unsaturated Acids on Four Different Phases Used for Gas Chromatography

Acid in Form of Methyl Ester		β-cyclo-dextrin acetate (β-CDX-AC)	Diethylene Glycol Succinate (DEGS)	Ethylene Glycol Succinate (EGS)	Apiezon L (ApL)	$ECL_{EGS} - ECL_{ApL}$
2-6:1	6:1w4	7.52	7.43	7.60	6.50	1.10
3-6:1	6:1w3	6.77	7.08	7.06	6.00	1.06
2-8:1	8:1w6	9.57	9.62	9.60	8.55	1.05
2-9:1	9:1w7	10.53	10.42	10.52	9.63	0.89
2-10:1	10:1w8	11.53	11.43	11.55	10.63	0.92
n-Decadiene-2,8-diyne-4,6-oic		19.35	19.15	19.10	9.93	9.17
9-14:1	14:1w5	}14.71	14.80	14.75	13.83	0.92
7-14:1	14:1w7					
6,9-15:2	15:2w6	16.30	16.43	16.42	14.60	1.82
9,12-15:2	15:2w3	16.50	16.77	16.70	14.77	1.93
9-16:1	16:1w7	16.55	16.55	16.56	15.70	0.86
6,9-16:2	16:2w7	}17.25	17.50	17.32	15.47	1.85
7,10-16:2	16:2w6					
6,9,12-16:3	16:3w4	}18.10	18.52	18.33	15.47	2.86
7,10,13-16:3	16:3w3					
9-17:1	17:1w8	17.56	17.60	17.55	16.73	0.82
9,12-17:2	17:2w5	18.32	18.50	18.40	16.62	1.78
6,9,12-17:3	17:3w5	18.93	19.23	19.00	16.40	2.60
6c-18:1	18:1w12	18.52	18.57	18.54	17.71	0.83
6t-18:1	18:1w12	18.45	18.47	18.47	17.75	0.72
8t-18:1	18:1w10	18.49	18.50	18.52	17.73	0.84
9c-18:1	18:1w9	18.55	18.51	18.50	17.71	0.79
9t-18:1	18:1w9	18.47	18.47	18.43	17.76	0.67
10t-18:1	18:1w8	18.50	18.51	18.50	17.78	0.72
11t-18:1	18:1w7	18.60	18.58	18.53	17.80	0.73
12c-18:1	18:1w6	18.60	18.75	18.64	17.75	0.82
12t-18:1	18:1w6	18.54	18.65	18.58	17.80	0.78
17-18:1	18:1w1	18.75	19.00	18.82	17.90	0.92
Octadeca-6-ynoic		20.03	20.33	20.40	17.84	2.56
Octadeca-7-ynoic		20.04	20.35	20.45	17.82	2.63
Octadeca-8-ynoic		20.04	20.40	20.45	17.80	2.65
Octadeca-9-ynoic		20.12	20.44	20.48	17.70	2.78
Octadeca-11-ynoic		20.17	20.53	20.60	17.87	2.73
5,11-18:2	_____	18.93	19.03	18.90	17.40	1.50
8,11-18:2	18:2w7	19.40	19.46	19.43	17.48	1.95
9,12-18:2	18:2w6	19.23	19.30	19.22	17.53	1.69
9,15-18:2	_____	19.33	19.46	19.43	17.60	1.83
10,13-18:2	18:2w5	19.37	19.55	19.55	17.57	1.98
11,14-18:2	18:2w4	19.47	19.60	19.73	17.62	2.11
12,15-18:2	18:2w3	19.50	19.63	19.63	17.75	1.88
9t,11t-18:2	_____	20.60	20.70	21.00	18.68	2.32
Octadeca-9-ene-12-ynoic		20.97	21.48	21.23	17.90	3.33
Octadeca-9,12-diynoic		23.75	24.10	23.74	18.30	5.44
3,9,12-18:3	_____	20.00	20.33	20.32	17.42	2.90
3,11,14-18:3	_____	19.60	19.86	19.63	17.24	2.39
6,9,12-18:3	18:3w6	19.70	20.00	19.78	17.30	2.48
9,12,15-18:3	18:3w3	20.10	20.40	20.13	17.51	2.62
Octadeca-6,9,12-triynoic		27.33	27.80	27.90	18.70	9.20
6,9,12,15-18:4	18:4w3	20.73	21.00	21.15	17.30	3.85
11-19:1	19:1w8	19.53	19.60	19.50	18.60	0.90
8,11-19:2	19:2w8	20.10	20.28	20.10	18.25	1.85
9,12-19:2	19:2w7					
11,14-19:2	19:2w5		20.43	20.27	18.32	1.85
8,11,14-19:3	19:3w5	20.80	21.05	20.85	18.25	2.60
5,8,11,14-19:4	19:4w5	21.27	21.54	21.30	18.02	3.28
11-20:1	20:1w9	20.32	20.44	20.38	19.78	0.60
5,11-20:2	_____	20.77	21.00	20.80	19.32	1.48

Table 1. (cont'd) Equivalent Chain Lengths of Unsaturated Acids on Four Different Phases Used for Gas Chromatography

Acid in Form of Methyl Ester		β-cyclo-dextrin acetate (β-CDX-AC)	Diethylene Glycol Succinate (DEGS)	Ethylene Glycol Succinate (EGS)	Apiezon L (ApL)	ECL$_{EGS}$-ECL$_{ApL}$
11,14-20:2	20:2w6	21.13	21.36	21.13	19.48	1.65
7,13-20:2	_____	21.00	21.17	20.93	19.30	1.63
Eicosa-7-ene-13-ynoic	}22.63	23.10	22.75	19.50	3.25
Eicosa-13-ene-7-ynoic						
Eicosa-7,13-diynoic		24.20	24.92	24.47	19.77	4.70
5,8,11-20:3	20:3w9	21.53	21.65	21.57	19.15	2.42
8,11,14-20:3	20:3w6	21.72	22.13	21.65	19.23	2.42
5,11,14-20:3	_____	21.50	21.75	21.60	19.15	2.45
7,10,13-20:3	20:3w7	—	—	21.63	19.23	2.40
5,8,11,14-20:4	20:4w6	22.15	22.43	22.25	19.00	3.25
5,8,11,14,17-20:5	20:5w3	22.88	23.45	22.92	19.00	3.92
7,10,13,16-21:4	21:4w5	23.27	23.50	23.45	20.00	3.45
4,7,10,13,16-21:5	21:5w5	23.70	24.05	23.97	19.78	4.19
13-22:1	22:1w9	22.27	22.28	22.30	21.57	0.73
7,10,13-22:3	22:3w9	23.30	23.73	23.17	21.15	2.02
10,13,16-22:3	22:3w6	23.36	23.94	23.38	21.23	2.15
7,10,13,16-22:4	22:4w6	24.03	24.58	23.85	20.93	2.92
4,7,10,13,16-22:5	22:5w6	24.43	24.97	24.37	20.87	3.50
7,10,13,16,19-22:5	22:5w3	24.87	25.38	24.93	21.00	3.93
4,7,10,13,16,19-22:6	22:6w3	25.35	26.03	25.40	20.73	4.67
15-24:1	24:1w9	24.20	24.27	24.40	23.67	0.73
9,12,15,18-24:4	24:4w6	25.87	26.50	25.73	22.87	2.86
Acid in Form of Ethyl Ester						
18:0	_____	18.30	18.23	18.36	18.62	—
9-18:1	18:1w9	18.75	18.62	18.75	18.30	0.45
Octadeca-9-ynoic		20.53	20.57	20.60	18.33	2.27
9,12-18:2	18:2w6	19.60	19.65	19.70	18.13	1.57
9,12,15-18:3	18:3w3	20.46	20.63	20.75	18.17	2.58
5,8,11,14-20:4	20:4w6	22.43	22.63	22.60	19.60	3.00
4,7,10,13,16-22:5	22:5w6	24.97	25.04	25.18	21.24	3.94

long chain unsaturated methyl esters. The experimentally determined increments, as depicted in Table I, thus provide an additional parameter for determining the structure of unsaturated fatty acids.

To establish the structure of a fatty acid in an unequivocal manner, the component must be isolated, degraded, and the resulting fragments characterized. Although a variety of different approaches can be used to fractionate complex mixtures of fatty acids, frequently the first step is removal of the high-melting saturated fatty acids by low-temperature fractional crystallization.[22] The unsaturated acids may then be further sub-fractionated as their mercuric acetate adducts,[23, 24] or alternatively, by one of several other chromatographic methods.[25] Frequently the final step in purification is carried out by preparative GLC.[26] Finally, characterization is accomplished by determining the location of the double bonds. Although several different methods have been used to cleave fatty acids at the site of unsaturation,[27] ozonolysis followed by reduction,[28] ozonolysis followed by oxidation,[29] and permanganate-periodate oxidation[30] are three of the most commonly used techniques. The fragments obtained are then analyzed by GLC.

II. STRUCTURE AND PROPERTIES OF FATTY ACIDS

Recent rapid advances in lipid chemistry have resulted in the isolation and characterization of numerous fatty acids. Space limitations make it impossible to consider in detail the properties of all the known acids. An attempt has been made to list in Table II only the properties of those acids encountered in relatively large amounts in several different fats. The reader is referred to several reviews on fatty acid metabolism for bibliographies describing the isolation and characterizaton of the more highly unsaturated acids of importance in metabolic and nutritional studies.[31-33] The data summarized in Table II were abstracted from Markley,[34] Duel[35] and the *Biology Data Book*.[36] The reader is referred to these sources, as well as to the review on hydroxy fatty acids by Downing[37] for chemical and physical properties of fatty acids not included in this treatise.

III. FATTY ACID COMPOSITION OF NATURAL FATS

The physical and chemical characteristics of fats and oils, presented in Table III, were reproduced from the *Biology Data Book*.[36]

IV. ANALYSIS OF GLYCERIDE STRUCTURE

Glycerides are by definition esters of glycerol. Since triglycerides are the major class of glycerides in virtually every mixed lipid sample, the ensuing discussion will be concerned primarily with the analysis of these compounds. The complexity of the triglycerides isolated from any natural source is dictated by the variety of fatty acids present. Triglyceride analysis is therefore concerned with resolving this complex class of compounds into homogeneous molecular species and the subsequent analysis of the fractions obtained.

Although enormous progress has been made in the analysis of triglycerides, techniques have not yet been developed for resolving complex mixtures of triglycerides into homogeneous molecular entities. In pioneering work, Hilditch[38] made extensive use of low-temperature fractional crystallization for triglyceride fractionation. Since that time, structural studies of these compounds have been revolutionized by the finding that pancreatic lipase specifically cleaves only the fatty acids esterified to positions 1 and 3 of glycerol.[39, 40] Lipase treatment thus provides a method for

Table II. Properties of Some Fatty Acids Most Commonly Found in Natural Fats

					A	B	C	D
Systematic Name	Common Name	Chemical Formula	Molecular Weight	Melting Point °C	Boiling Point °C	Specific Gravity	Refractive Index	Iodine Value Calculated
Saturated Fatty Acids								
Butanoic	Butyric	$C_4H_8O_2$	88.10	−7.9	163.5	0.9587[20]	1.33906[20]	
Hexanoic	Caproic	$C_6H_{12}O_2$	116.15	−3.4	205.8	0.929[20]	1.41635[20]	
Octanoic	Caprylic	$C_8H_{16}O_2$	144.21	16.7	239.7	0.90884[20]	1.4285[20]	
Decanoic	Capric	$C_{10}H_{20}O_2$	172.26	31.6	149[11]	0.8858[40]	1.42855[40]	
Dodecanoic	Lauric	$C_{12}H_{24}O_2$	200.31	44.2	176[15]	0.8690[50]	1.4225[70]	
Tetradecanoic	Myristic	$C_{14}H_{28}O_2$	228.36	54.4	199[16]	0.8622[54]	1.4273[70]	
Hexadecanoic	Palmitic	$C_{16}H_{32}O_2$	256.42	62.85	219[20]	0.8487[70]	1.4303[70]	
Octadecanoic	Stearic	$C_{18}H_{36}O_2$	284.47	69.6	158–160[0.25]	0.8386[80]	1.4300[80]	
Eicosanoic	Arachidic	$C_{20}H_{40}O_2$	312.52	75.3	203–205[1]	0.8240[100]	1.4250[100]	
Docosanoic	Behenic	$C_{22}H_{44}O_2$	340.57	79.9	306[60]	0.8221[100]	1.4270[100]	
Tetracosanoic	Lignoceric	$C_{24}H_{48}O_2$	368.62	84.2	–	0.8207[100]	1.4287[100]	
Monoethenoic Acids								
9-Tetradecenoic	Myristoleic	$C_{14}H_{26}O_2$	226.35	–	–	0.9018[20]	1.4549[20]	112.2
9-Hexadecenoic	Palmitoleic	$C_{16}H_{30}O_2$	254.40	−0.5−+0.5	–	–	–	99.8
6-Octadecenoic	Petroselinic	$C_{18}H_{34}O_2$	282.45	32–33	208–210[10]	0.8795[40]	1.4533[40]	89.9
9-Octadecenoic	Oleic	$C_{18}H_{34}O_2$	282.45	13	200–201[1.2]	0.8905[20]	1.45823[20]	89.9
trans-9-Octadecenoic	Elaidic	$C_{18}H_{34}O_2$	282.45	46.5	234[15]	0.8568[70]	1.4405[70]	89.9
trans-11-Octadecenoic	Vaccenic	$C_{18}H_{34}O_2$	282.45	44	–	0.8563[70]	1.4406[70]	89.9
11-Docosenoic	Cetoleic	$C_{22}H_{42}O_2$	338.56	–	–	–	–	75.0
13-Docosenoic	Erucic	$C_{22}H_{42}O_2$	338.56	34.7	241–243[5]	–	–	75.0
15-Tetracosenoic	Nervonic	$C_{24}H_{46}O_2$	366.61	42.5–43	–	–	–	69.2
Di- and Polyethenoic Acids								
9,12-Octadecadienoic	Linoleic	$C_{18}H_{32}O_2$	280.42	−5.0	202[1.4]	0.9038[18]	1.4715[11.5]	181.0
9,12,15-Octadecatrienoic	Linolenic	$C_{18}H_{30}O_2$	278.42	−14.4 to −14.5	157–158[0.001]	0.9046[20]	1.4595[20]	273.5
6,9,12-Octadecatrienoic	γ-Linolenic	$C_{18}H_{30}O_2$	278.42	–	–	–	–	273.5
5,8,11,14-Eicosatetraenoic	Arachidonic	$C_{20}H_{32}O_2$	304.5	−49.5	163[1.0]	0.9082[20]	1.4824[20]	333.4
7,10,13,16,19-Docosapentaenoic	–	$C_{22}H_{34}O_2$	330.5	–	–	–	–	384.0
4,7,10,13,16,19-Docosahexaenoic	–	$C_{22}H_{32}O_2$	328.5	−44.5 to −44.1	–	–	1.5017[26]	463.6

A—At atmospheric pressure, unless indicated.
B—At temperature referred to in superscript, referred to water at 4°C.
C—Refractive Index at Sodium D-line at the temperature indicated in superscript.
D—Iodine values are calculated.

Table III. Physical and Chemical Characteristics of Fats and Oils

Fat or Oil	Source	Melting (or Solidification) Point, °C	Specific Gravity (or Density)	Refractive Index $n\frac{40°C}{D}$	Iodine Value	Saponification Value
(A)	(B)	(C)	(D)	(E)	(F)	(G)
Land Animals						
1 Butterfat	Bos taurus	32.2	0.911 40°/15°	1.4548	36.1	277
2 Depot fat	Homo sapiens	(15)	0.918 15°	1.4602	67.6	196.2
3 Lard oil	Sus scrofa	(30.5)	0.919 15°	1.4615	58.6	194.6
4 Neat's-foot oil	B. taurus	–	0.910 15°	1.464 25°	69–76	190–199
5 Tallow, beef	B. taurus	–	–	–	49.5	197
6 Tallow, mutton	Ovin aries	(42.0)	0.945 15°	1.4565	40	194
Marine Animals						
7 Cod-liver oil	Gadus morhua	–	0.925 15°	1.481 25°	165	186
8 Herring oil	Clupea harengus	–	0.900 60°	1.4610 40°	140	192
9 Menhaden oil	Brevoortia tyrannus	–	0.903 60°	1.4645 40°	170	191
10 Sardine oil	Sardinops caerulea	–	0.905 60°	1.4660 40°	185	191
11 Sperm oil, body	Physeter macrocephalus	–	–	–	76–88	122–130
12 Sperm oil, head	P. macrocephalus	–	–	–	70	140–144
13 Whale oil	Balaena mysticetus	–	0.892 60°	1.460 40°	120	195

Plants						
14	Babassu oil	Attalea funifera	22–26	$(0.893^{60°})$	$1.443^{60°}$	15.5	247
15	Castor oil	Ricinus communis	(−18.0)	$0.961^{15°}$	1.4770	85.5	180.3
16	Cocoa butter	Theobroma cacao	34.1	$0.964^{15°}$	1.4568	36.5	193.8
17	Coconut oil	Cocos mucifera	25.1	$0.924^{15°}$	1.4493	10.4	268
18	Corn oil	Zea mays	(−20.0)	$0.922^{15°}$	1.4734	122.6	192.0
19	Cottonseed oil	Gossypium hirsutum	(−1.0)	$0.917^{25°}$	1.4735	105.7	194.3
20	Linseed oil	Linum usitatissimum	(−24.0)	$0.938^{15°}$	$1.4782^{25°}$	178.7	190.3
21	Mustard oil	Brassica hirta	–	$0.9145^{15°}$	1.475	102	174
22	Neem oil	Melia azadirachta	−3	$0.917^{15°}$	1.4615	71	194.5
23	Niger-seed oil	Guizotia abyssinica	–	$0.925^{15°}$	1.471	128.5	190
24	Oiticica oil	Licania rigida	–	$0.974^{25°}$	–	140–180	–
25	Olive oil	Olea europaea sativa	(−6.0)	$0.918^{15°}$	1.4679	81.1	189.7
26	Palm oil	Elaeis guineensis	35.0	$0.915^{13°}$	1.4578	54.2	199.9
27	Palm-kernel oil	E. guineensis	24.1	$0.923^{15°}$	1.4569	37.0	192.1
28	Peanut oil	Arachis hypogaea	(3.0)	$0.914^{15°}$	1.4691	93.4	192
29	Perilla oil	Perilla frutescens	–	$(0.935^{15°})$	$1.481^{25°}$	195	194
30	Poppy-seed oil	Papaver somniferum	(−15)	$0.925^{15°}$	1.4685	135	174.7
31	Rapeseed oil	Brassica campestris	(−10)	$0.915^{15°}$	1.4706	98.6	192
32	Safflower oil	Carthamus tinctorius	–	$(0.900^{60°})$	$1.462^{60°}$	145	187.9
33	Sesame oil	Sesamum indicum	(−6.0)	$0.919^{25°}$	1.4646	106.6	190.6
34	Soybean oil	Glycine soja	(−16.0)	$0.927^{15°}$	1.4729	130.0	188.7
35	Sunflower-seed oil	Helianthus annuus	(−17.0)	$0.923^{15°}$	1.4694	125.5	193.1
36	Tung oil	Aleurites fordi	(−2.5)	$0.934^{15°}$	$1.5174^{25°}$	168.2	–
37	Wheat-germ oil	Triticum aestivum	–	–	–	125	

Table III.   Physical and Chemical Characteristics of Fats and Oils (continued)

	Constituent Fatty acids, g/100 g total fatty acids										
	Saturated						Unsaturated				
Lauric	Myristic	Palmitic	Stearic	Arachidic	Other	Palmitoleic	Oleic	Linoleic	Linolenic	Other	
(H)	(I)	(J)	(K)	(L)	(M)	(N)	(O)	(P)	(Q)	(R)	
2.5	11.1	29.0	9.2	2.4	2.0[1];0.5[2];2.3[3]	4.6	26.7	3.6	—	3.6[4];0.1[5];0.1[6];0.9[7];1.4[8];	1
—	2.7	24.0	8.4	—	—	5	46.9	10.2	—	1.0[9];1.0[10];0.4[11]	2
—	1.3	28.3	11.9	—	—	2.7	47.5	6	—	2.5[8]	3
—	—	17–18	2–3	—	—	—	74–76	—	—	0.2[7];2.1[8]	4
—	6.3	27.4	14.1	—	—	—	49.6	2.5	—	—	5
—	4.6	24.6	30.5	—	—	—	36.0	4.3	—	—	6
—	5.8	8.4	0.6	—	—	20.0	←——— 29.1 ———→		—	25.4[12];9.6[13]	7
—	7.3	13.0	Trace	0.6	—	4.9	—	—	20.7	30.1[12];23.2[13]	8
—	5.9	16.3	0.6	0.6	—	15.5	—	—	29.6	19.0[12];11.7[13];0.8[14]	9
—	5.1	14.6	3.2	—	—	11.8	←——— 17.8 ———→		—	18.1[12];14.0[13];trace[7];15.4[15]	10
1	5	6.5	—	—	—	26.5	37	19	—	1[13];4[7];19[16]	11
16	14	8	2	—	3.5[3]	15	17	6.5	—	4[6];14[7];6.5[16]	12
0.2	9.3	15.6	2.8	—	—	14.4	35.2	—	—	13.6[12];5.9[13];2.5[7];0.2[17]	13

											Row
44.1	15.4	8.5	2.7	0.2	0.2[1];4.8[2];6.6[3]	–	16.1	1.4	–	–	14
↓	2.4		↑	–	–	–	7.4	3.1	–	87[18]	15
45.4	–	24.4	35.4	0.4[19]	0.8[1];5.4[2];8.4[3]	0.4	38.1	2.1	–	–	16
–	18.0	10.5	2.3	–	–	1.5	7.5	Trace	–	–	17
–	1.4	10.2	3.0	1.3	–	2.0	49.6	34.3	–	–	18
–	1.4	23.4	1.1	0.5	–	–	22.9	47.8	–	0.2[14]	19
–	–	6.3	2.5	0.8[20]	–	–	19.0	24.1	47.4	1.1[14];1.0[21];51.0[22]	20
–	1.3[20]	–	–	0.5[20]	–	–	27.2[20]	16.6[20]	1.8[20]	–	21
–	2.6[20]	14.1[20]	24.0[20]	↑	–	–	58.5[20]	–	–	–	22
–	3.3[20]	8.2[20]	4.8[20]	–	–	–	30.3[20]	57.3[20]	–	–	23
–	–	11.3[23]	↑	–	–	–	6.2	–	–	82.5[24]	24
–	Trace	6.9	2.3	0.1	–	–	84.4	4.6	–	–	25
–	1.4	40.1	5.5	–	–	–	42.7	10.3	–	–	26
–	14.1	8.8	1.3	–	2.7[2];7.0[3]	–	18.5	0.7	–	–	27
46.9	–	8.3	3.1	2.4	–	–	56.0	26.0	–	3.1[14];1.1[21]	28
↓	–	9.6[23]	2.9[20]	–	–	–	17.8	–	17.5	–	29
–	–	4.8[20]	–	–	–	–	30.1[20]	62.2[20]	–	–	30
–	–	1	↑	↑	–	–	32	15	1	50[22]	31
–	–	6.8[23]	–	–	–	–	18.6	70.1	3.4	–	32
–	–	9.1	4.3	0.8	–	–	45.4	40.4	–	–	33
0.2	–	9.8	2.4	0.9	–	0.4	28.9	50.7	6.5	0.1[7]	34
–	0.1	5.6	2.2	0.9	–	–	25.1	66.2	–	–	35
–	–	4.6[23]	↑	↑	–	–	4.1	0.6	–	90.7[25]	36
↓	–	16.0[23]	↑	↑	–	–	28.1	52.3	3.6	–	37

1) Caproic
2) Caprylic
3) Caprio
4) Butyric
5) Decenoic
6) C_{12} Monoethenoic
7) C_{14} Monoethenoic
8) Gadoleic plus erucic
9) C_{12}-pentadecanoic acid
10) C_{17} Margaric
11) 12-methyl tetradecanoic
12) C_{20} polyethenoic
13) C_{22} polyethenoic
14) Behenic
15) C_{14} polyethenoic
16) Gadoleic
17) C_{24} Polyethenoic
18) Ricinoleic
19) Includes behenic and lignoceric
20) percent by weight
21) lignoceric
22) Erucic
23) Includes behenic
24) Licanic
25) Eleostearic

determining the fatty acid composition of the 1 and 3 position, independently of the 2 position. Triglycerides may be considered to consist of the six different types of molecular species shown below. Youngs[41] has developed a method of triglyceride analysis based on the permanganate periodate oxidation of the entire triglyceride fraction. The six glycerol acid cores 1a to 6a, were obtained from the respective glyceride types 1–6. Following fractionation, lipase treatment and GLC analysis of the mono- and dicarboxylic acids the amounts of the glyceride types, 1–6, could be computed.

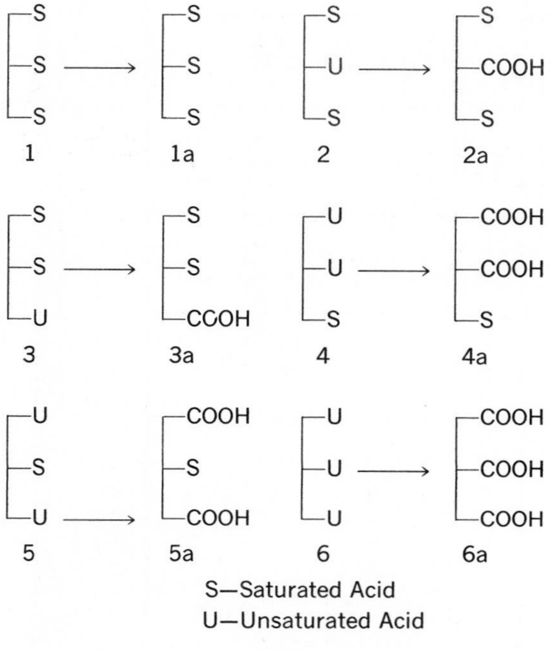

```
 ⎡–S           ⎡–S           ⎡–S           ⎡–S
 ⎢–S    ⟶      ⎢–S           ⎢–U    ⟶      ⎢–COOH
 ⎣–S           ⎣–S           ⎣–S           ⎣–S
    1            1a            2             2a

 ⎡–S           ⎡–S           ⎡–U           ⎡–COOH
 ⎢–S    ⟶      ⎢–S           ⎢–U    ⟶      ⎢–COOH
 ⎣–U           ⎣–CCOH        ⎣–S           ⎣–S
    3            3a            4             4a

 ⎡–U           ⎡–COOH        ⎡–U           ⎡–COOH
 ⎢–S           ⎢–S           ⎢–U    ⟶      ⎢–COOH
 ⎣–U    ⟶      ⎣–COOH        ⎣–U           ⎣–COOH
    5            5a            6             6a
```

S—Saturated Acid
U—Unsaturated Acid

Figure I

Privett and co-workers[42–44] have utilized two different procedures for triglyceride structural studies. Triglycerides were fractionated according to the number of double bonds in the molecule by $AgNO_3$—silicic acid thin-layer chromatography (TLC).[45–46] The various fractions were then treated with pancreatic lipase and subsequently the liberated fatty acids quantitated by GLC. Alternatively, the triglycerides sample was ozonized and the ozonides fractionated on TLC. The ozonide bands were scraped from the plate, reduced to the aldehyde-glycerol core, and rechromatographed. From densitometry measurements of both the intact ozonides and the aldehyde-glycerol cores, useful information was obtained about triglyceride structure.

In recent years, gas chromatographic techniques have progressed to the extent where it is now possible to fractionate triglycerides directly.[47, 48]

Table IV. Triglyceride Composition of Fats (Mole %) (55)

						Cocoa butter					
O Double bond	A*	B+	1 Double bond	A*	B+	2 Double bonds	A*	B+	3 and more double bonds	A*	B+
PMSt		0.1	MOP	0.9	0.6	POO	3.7	5.4	OOO	0.5	0.6
StMSt		0.1	MOSt	1.3	0.8	StOO	4.9	7.7	POL	0.4	1.1
PPP	0.1	0.3	POP	12.0	11.9	PLP	1.2	0.8	StOL	0.4	1.5
PPSt	0.5	0.9	POSt	34.8	34.2	PLSt	3.1	2.5	PLO	0.3	0.4
StPSt	0.8	0.7	StOSt	25.2	24.5	StLSt	2.0	1.8	StLO	0.3	0.6
PStP		0.2	PMO	0.2					SLeS		0.2
PStSt	0.3	0.6	StMO	0.3					Remaining ones	0.7	0.1
StStSt	0.4	0.4	PPO	0.6	0.1						
			StPO	0.9	0.2				4 Double bonds	0.9	0.8
			PStO	0.8	0.1						
			StStO	1.1	0.1						
Remaining ones	0.1	0.2	Remaining ones	0.2	0.2	Remaining ones	1.1	0.3			
	2.2	3.5		78.3	72.7		16.0	18.5		3.5	5.3

P = Palmitic Acid
M = Myristic Acid
St = Stearic Acid
O = Oleic Acid
L = Linoleic Acid

Le = Linolenic Acid
S = Saturated Acids
*A = Calculated from the Fatty Acid Composition Fractions
+B = Calculated according to Coleman (54)

Table IV. (cont'd) Triglyceride Composition of Fats (Mole %) (55)

Groundnut oil

1 Double bond	A*	B+	2 Double bonds	A*	B+	3 Double bonds	A*	B+	4 Double bonds	A*	B+	5 Double bonds	A*	B+	6 Double bonds	A*	B+
SOS	2.3	2.4	SOO	8.7	7.5	OOO	7.8	7.9	OOL	6.2	5.9	OLL	17.8	16.4	LLL	3.9	5.5
SSO	0.7	0.4	OSO	0.8	0.5	SOL	8.7	12.3	OLO	5.0	5.0	LOL	2.2	2.6	OLLe	0.4	0.4
			SSL	0.6	0.3	SLO	10.7	10.3	SLL	15.7	15.5	SLeL			LOLe		
			SLS	5.3	4.9	OSL	1.2	0.6	LSL	1.0	1.0	LSLe	0.7	0.3	OLeL		
								0.1	SLeO			SLLe			Remaining ones	0.1	—
												OLeO	0.2	0.2			
												OOLe					
	3.0	2.8		15.4	13.2		28.4	31.2		27.9	27.4		20.9	19.5		4.4	5.9

Sumatra palm oil

0 Double bond	A*	B+	1 Double bond	A*	B+	2 Double bonds	A*	B+	3 Double bonds	A*	B+	4 Double bonds	A*	B+
PMP	0.3	0.3	MOP	1.3	1.1	POO	18.9	19.1	OOO	3.2	4.2	OOL	1.5	2.2
MPP	0.6	0.3	POP	25.9	21.8	StOO	2.6	1.7	POL	2.6	4.8	OLO	1.3	1.5
PPP	6.1	6.6	POSt	3.1	3.9	OPO	1.2	1.3	PLO	4.3	6.2	PLL	2.6	1.5
PPSt	0.9	1.2	PPO	6.0	5.8	PPL	1.7	1.5	StLO	0.5	0.6	StLL	0.5	0.1
PStP	0.3	0.5	StPO	0.3	0.5	PLP	6.8	7.1	OPL	0.5	0.6	SOLe		
			PStO	0.5	0.4	PLSt	1.9	1.2				SLeO	0.8	
Remaining ones	0.3	0.1	Remaining ones	0.8	0.7	Remaining ones	1.9	1.2	Remaining ones	0.6	0.7	OSLe		
												Remaining ones	0.2	1.3
	8.5	9.0		37.9	34.2		35.0	33.1		11.7	17.1		6.9	6.6

Lard

0 Double bond	A*	B+	1 Double bond	A*	B+	2 Double bonds	A*	B+	3 Double bonds	A*	B+	4 and more double bonds	A*	B+
PMP	0.1	0.1	POP	0.6	0.6	POO	5.2	5.0	OOO	11.7	10.2	OOL	1.4	4.2
PMSt	0.4	0.3	POSt	1.9	1.6	StOO	6.1	6.4	PLO	0.2	0.6	OLO	1.5	1.2
StMSt	0.4	0.2	StOSt	1.5	1.0	OMO	1.6	1.9	StLO	0.6	0.7	LPL	0.5	0.7
PPP	0.5	0.1	PMO	0.4	0.9	OPO	18.4	16.8	OML	0.6	0.8	LStL	0.1	0.1
PPSt	2.0	2.6	StMO	0.7	1.2	OStO	1.2	1.8	OPL	7.2	7.0	OPLe	0.3	0.2
StPSt	2.0	1.7	MPO	0.8		PPL	1.8	1.7	OStL	1.2	0.7	OLL	......	0.5
PStP	0.1	.....	PPO	7.9	8.2	StPL	2.1	2.2						
PStSt	0.4	0.3	StPO	12.8	10.6									
StStSt	0.4	0.2	PStO	0.9	0.9									
			StStO	1.6	1.1									
Remaining ones	0.3	0.1	Remaining ones	0.6	0.4	Remaining ones	1.5	1.4	Remaining ones	0.3	2.6	Remaining ones	0.2	1.2
	6.6	5.6		29.7	26.5		37.9	37.2		21.8	22.6		4.0	8.1

*A = Calculated from experimentally determined Fatty Acid Composition
+B = Calculated according to Coleman (54)

P = Palmitic Acid
M = Myristic Acid
St = Stearic Acid
O = Oleic Acid
L = Linoleic Acid
Le = Linolenic Acid
S = Saturated Acids

Table IV. (cont'd) Triglyceride Composition of Fats (Mole %) (55)

Soybean oil

1 Double bond

	A*	B+
SOS	1.1	1.0
SSO	0.3	0.2
	1.4	1.2

2 Double bonds

	A*	B+
SOO	2.9	2.3
OSO	0.4	0.1
SSL	0.6	0.3
SLS	2.8	2.7
	6.7	5.4

3 Double bonds

	A*	B+
OOO	1.5	1.2
SOL	4.1	4.9
SLO	5.0	6.0
OSL	0.4	0.4
SSLe	0.1	0.1
SLeS	—	0.2
	11.1	12.8

4 Double bonds

	A*	B+
OOL	6.7	5.4
OLO	2.5	3.3
SLL	13.9	13.0
LSL	0.9	0.4
SOLe	0.2	1.0
SLeO	0.2	0.5
OSLe		0.1
	24.4	23.7

5 Double bonds

	A*	B+
OLL	13.5	14.4
LOL	5.1	5.8
OOLe	0.2	1.0
OLeO	0.6	0.3
SLLe	0.3	2.6
SLeL	0.4	1.1
LSLe	0.5	0.2
	20.6	25.4

6 and more double bonds

	A*	B+
LLL		15.7
OLLe		2.9
OLeL		1.2
LOLe		2.3
SLeLe		0.2
OLeLe		0.3
LeOLe		0.2
LLeL		6.2
LLeL		1.3
LLeLe		0.6
LeLeL		0.5
LeLeLe		0.1
	35.8	31.5

Cottonseed oil

0 and 1 Double bond

	A*	B+
SSS	0.5	0.6
SOS	4.5	6.3
SSO	0.8	0.4
	5.8	7.3

2 Double bonds

	A*	B+
SOO	4.8	3.5
OSO	0.3	0.1
SSL	0.6	1.2
SLS	12.4	12.5
	18.1	17.3

3 Double bonds

	A*	B+
OOO	0.8	0.5
SOL	9.4	12.5
SLO	8.4	7.0
OSL	0.6	0.3
	19.2	20.3

4 Double bonds

	A*	B+
OOL	4.1	3.5
OLO	1.6	1.0
SLL	22.5	24.7
LSL	1.1	0.6
	29.3	29.8

5 Double bonds

	A*	B+
OLL	6.4	6.9
LOL	6.5	6.2
Remaining ones	0.4	
	13.3	13.1

6 Double bonds

	A*	B+
LLL	13.0	12.2
Remaining ones	1.3	
	14.3	12.2

P = Palmitic Acid
M = Myristic Acid
St = Stearic Acid
O = Oleic Acid
L = Linoleic Acid
Le = Linolenic Acid
S = Saturated Acids
*A = Calculated from the Fatty Acid Composition of the Fractions
+B = Calculated according to Coleman (54)

For example, butterfat has been separated into 16 different triglyceride fractions by this method. Of equal importance is the analysis of 1- and 2-mono glycerides as their trimethylsilyl ether derivatives by GLC.[49]

Other techniques which have been used for triglyceride fractionation include counter current distribution,[50] thermal gradient fractionation,[51] and mass spectral analysis.[52]

Several mathematical derivations have been proposed whereby the fatty acid composition of the various triglyceride fractions can be calculated. Of these proposals the 1, 3 random, 2 random distribution hypothesis has been shown to describe experimental findings most accurately. The use and validity of these formulations are discussed in detail by Vander Wal[53] and Coleman.[54]

V. GLYCERIDE COMPOSITION OF SOME NATURAL FATS

The triglyceride composition of some other fats and oils is discussed in the following references: Congo palm oil,[56] butterfat,[57, 58] sunflower oil,[59] rat adipose and liver triglycerides,[44, 60] human adipose tissue,[61] and the seed oil of *Cuphea ilaria*.[62]

BIBLIOGRAPHY

1. Entenman, C., in Colowick, S., and N. Kaplan (eds.), *Methods in Enzymology*, 3:299, 1957.
2. Hanahan, D., *Lipide Chemistry*, p. 11, 1960.
3. Schlenk, H., and J. L. Gellerman, "Esterification of Fatty Acids with Diazomethane on a Small Scale," *Anal. Chem.*, 32:1412, 1960.
4. Radin, N., A. K. Hajra, and Y. Akahori, "Preparation of Methyl Esters," *J. Lipid Res.*, 1:250, 1960.
5. Metcalfe, L. D., and A. A. Schmitz, "Rapid Preparation of Fatty Acid Esters for Gas Chromatographic Analysis," *Anal. Chem.*, 33:363, 1961.
6. Peterson, J. I. H. Schmertzing, and K. Abel, "Transesterification of Lipids with Boron Trichloride," *J. Gas Chro.*, 3:126, 1965.
7. Stoffel, W., F. Chu, and E. H. Ahrens, "Analysis of Long-Chain Fatty Acids by Gas-Liquid Chromatography," *Anal. Chem.*, 31:307, 1959.
8. Rogozinski, M., "A Rapid Quantitative Esterification Technique for Carboxylic Acids," *J. Gas Chro.*, 2:136, 1964.
9. Luddy, F. R., R. A. Bradford, and R. W. Riemenschneider, "Direct Conversion of Lipid Components to Their Fatty Acid Methyl Ester," *J. Am. Oil Chemists' Soc.*, 37:447, 1960.
10. Vorbeck, M. L., L. R. Mattick, F. A. Lee, and C. S. Pederson, "Preparation of Methyl Esters of Fatty Acids for Gas-Liquid Chromatography. Quantitative Comparison of Methylation Techniques," *Anal. Chem.*, 33:1512, 1961.
11. James, A. T., in Glick, D. (ed.), *Methods of Biochemical Analysis*, 8:1, 1960.
12. Horning, E. C., A. Kavmen and C. C. Sweeley, in Holman, R. T. (ed.), *Progress in the Chemistry of Fats and Other Lipids*, 8(2):167, 1964.

13. Horning, E. C., E. H. Ahrens, S. R. Lipsky, F. H. Mattson, J. F. Mead, D. A. Turner, and W. H. Goldwater, "Quantitative Analysis of Fatty Acids by Gas-Liquid Chromatography," *J. Lipid Res.*, 5:20, 1964.

14. Woodford, F. P., and C. M. Van Gent, "Gas-Liquid Chromatography of Fatty Acid Methyl Esters; the "Carbon-Number" as a Parameter for Comparison of Columns," *J. Lipid Res.*, 1:188, 1960.

15. Farquhar, J. W., W. Insull, P. Rosen, W. Stoffel, and E. H. Ahrens, *Nutr. Rev. Suppl.*, 17:1, 1959.

16. Ackman, R. G., "Structural Correlation of Unsaturated Fatty Acid Ester Through Graphical Comparison of Gas-Liquid Chromatographic Retention Time on a Polyester Substance," *J. Am. Oil Chemists' Soc.*, 40:558, 1963.

17. Ackman, R. G., "Structure and Retention Time in the Gas-Liquid Chromatography of Unsaturated Fatty Acids on Polyester Substrates," *Nature*, 194:970, 1962.

18. Ackman, R. G., "An Analysis of Separation Factors Applicable in the Gas-Liquid Chromatography of Unsaturated Fatty Acid Methyl Esters on a Polyester Substrate," *J. Am. Oil Chemists' Soc.*, 40:564, 1963.

19. Ackman, R. G., and R. D. Burgher, "A Proposed Basis for the Systematic Identification of Unsaturated Fatty Acid Esters Through Gas-Liquid Chromatography on Polyester Substrates," *J. Chromatog.*, 11:185, 1963.

20. Miwa, T. K., K. L. Mikolajczak, E. R. Fontaine and I. A. Wolff, "Gas Chromatographic Characterization of Fatty Acids Identification Constants for Mono- and Dicarboxylic Methyl Esters," *Anal. Chem.*, 32:1739, 1960.

21. Hofstetter, H. H., N. Sen, and R. T. Holman, "Characterization of Unsaturated Fatty Acids by Gas-Liquid Chromatography," *J. Am. Oil Chemists' Soc.*, 42:537, 1965.

22. Brown, J. B., and D. K. Kolb, in Holman, R. T., W. O. Lundberg, and T. Malkin (eds.), *Progress in the Chemistry of Fats and Other Lipids*, 3:57, 1955.

23. Jantzen, E., and H. Andreas, "Reaktion Ungesättigter Fettsäuren mit Quecksilber (II)-Acetat; Anwendung für Präparative Trennugen," *Chem. Ber.*, 92:1427, 1959.

24. Mangold, H. K., "Thin-Layer Chromatography of Lipids," *J. Am. Oil Chemists' Soc.*, 38:708, 1961.

25. Schlenk, H., in Markley, K. S. (ed.), *Fatty Acids*, part 3, p. 2125, 1964.

26. Henley, R. S., "Preparative Gas-Liquid Chromatography of Lipids," *J. Am. Oil Chemists' Soc.*, 42:673, 1965.

27. Stein, R. A., "Determination of Structure of Unsaturated Fatty Acid Positional Isomers," *J. Am. Oil Chemists' Soc.*, 42:326, 1965.

28. Privett, O. S., and C. Nickell, "Determination of Structure of Unsaturated Fatty Acids via Reductive Ozonolysis," *J. Am. Oil Chemists' Soc.*, 39:414, 1962.

29. Stoffel, W., and E. H. Ahrens, "Isolation and Structure of the C_{16} Unsaturated Fatty Acids in Menhaden Body Oil," *J. Am. Chem. Soc.*, 80:6604, 1958.

30. Von Rudloff, E., "Periodate-Permanganate Oxidations. V. Oxidation of Lipids in Media Containing Organic Solvents," *Can. J. Chem.*, 34:1413, 1956.

31. Mead, J. F., "Synthesis and Metabolism of Polyunsaturated Acids," *Federation Proc.*, 20:952, 1961.

32. Carroll, K. K., "Dietary Fat and the Fatty Acids Composition of Tissue Lipids," *J. Am. Oil Chemists' Soc.*, 42:516, 1965.

33. Klenk, E., "The Metabolism of Polyenoic Fatty Acids," *J. Am. Oil Chemists' Soc.*, 42:580, 1965.

34. Markley, K. S., in Markley, K. S. (ed.), *Fatty Acids*, part 1, p. 23, 1960.

35. Duel, H. J., *The Lipids*, 1:44, 1951.

36. Altman, P. L., and D. S. Dittmer (eds.), *Biology Data Book*, 1964.

37. Downing, D. T., "Naturally Occurring Aliphatic Hydroxyacids," *Rev. Pure Appl. Chem.*, 11:196, 1961.

38. Hilditch, T. P., *The Chemical Constitution of Natural Fats*, 1956.
39. Desnuelle, P., and P. Savary, "Specificities of Lipases," *J. Lipid Res.*, 4:369, 1963.
40. Mattson, F. H., and R. A. Volpenhein, "The Use of Pancreatic Lipase for Determining the Distribution of Fatty Acids in Partial and Complete Glycerides," *J. Lipid Res.*, 2:58, 1961.
41. Youngs, C. G., "Determination of the Glyceride Structure of Fats," *J. Am. Oil Chemists' Soc.*, 38:62, 1961.
42. Privett, O. S., and M. L. Blank, "A New Method for the Analysis of Component Mono-, Di-, and Triglycerides," *J. Lipid Res.*, 2:37, 1961.
43. Privett, O. S., and M. L. Blank, "A Method for the Structural Analysis of Triglycerides and Lecithins," *J. Am. Oil Chemists' Soc.*, 40:70, 1963.
44. Blank, M. L., B. Verdino, and O. S. Privett, "Determination of Triglyceride Structure via Silver Nitrate-TLC," *J. Am. Oil Chemists' Soc.*, 42:87, 1965.
45. de Vries, B., "Quantitative Separations of Lipid Materials by Column Chromatography on Silica Impregnated with Silver Nitrate," *Chem. & Ind.*, 81:1049, 1962.
46. Kaufmann, H. P., and H. Wessels, *Fette, Seifen, Anstrichmittel*, 66:13, 1964.
47. Huebner, V. R., "The Analysis of Glycerides by High Temperature Gas-Liquid Partition Chromatography," *J. Am. Oil Chemists' Soc.*, 38:628, 1961.
48. Kuksis, A., "Gas-Liquid Chromatography of Glycerides," *J. Am. Oil Chemists' Soc.*, 42:269, 1965.
49. Wood, R. D., P. K. Raju, and R. J. Reiser, "Gas-Liquid Chromatographic Analysis of Monoglycerides as Their Trimethylsilyl Ether Derivatives," *J. Am. Oil Chemists' Soc.*, 42:161, 1965.
50. Scholfield, C. R., J. Nowakowska, and H. J. Dutton, "Glyceride Structure of Vegetable Oils by Countercurrent Distribution. VI. Corn Oil," *J. Am. Oil Chemists' Soc.*, 38:175, 1961.
51. Jones, G. V., and E. G. Hammond, "Analysis of the Glyceride Structure of Cocoa Butter by Thermal Gradient Crystallization," *J. Am. Oil Chemists' Soc.*, 38:69, 1961.
52. Barber, M., T. O. Merren, and W. Kelley, "The Mass Spectrometry of Large Molecules. I. The Triglycerides of Straight Chain Fatty Acids," *Tetrahedron Letters*, 18:1063, 1964.
53. Vander Wal, R. J., in Paoletti, R., and D. Kritchevsky (eds.), *Advan. in Lipid Res.*, 2:1, 1964.
54. Coleman, M. H., in Paoletti, R., and D. Kritchevsky (eds.), *Advan. in Lipid Res.*, 1:2, 1963.
55. Jurriens, G., and A. C. J. Kroesen, "Determination of Glyceride Components of Several Solid and Liquid Fats," *J. Am. Oil Chemists' Soc.*, 42:9, 1965.
56. Jurriens, G., B. de Vries, and L. Schouten, "Quantitative Semimicro Analysis of Triglyceride Fatty Acid Distribution in Congo Palm Oil," *J. Lipid Res.*, 5:366, 1964.
57. Ast, H. J., and R. J. Vander Wal, "The Structural Components of Milk Triglycerides," *J. Am. Oil Chemists' Soc.*, 38:67, 1961.
58. Blank, M. L., and O. S. Privett, *J. Dairy Sci.*, 47:481, 1964.
59. Kaufmann, H. P., and H. Wessels, *Fette, Seifen, Anstrichmittel*, 66:81, 1964.
60. Barford, R. A., *et al.*, "Glyceride Distribution in Adipose and Liver Glyceride of Animals," *J Am. Oil Chemists' Soc.*, 42:446, 1965.
61. Brockerhoff, H., "Stereospecific Analysis of Triglycerides: an Analysis of Human Depot Fat," *Arch. Biochem. Biophys.*, 110:586, 1965.
62. Litchfield, C., M. Farquhar, and R. Reiser, "Analysis of Triglycerides by Consecutive Chromatographic Techniques. I. *Cuphea ilaria* Seed Fat," *J. Am. Oil Chemists' Soc.*, 41:588, 1964.

PHOSPHOLIPIDS AND GLYCOLIPIDS

I. INTRODUCTION

The phospholipids may be defined as those lipids which contain phosphate esters of glycerol or sphingosine. The glycolipids are those lipids which contain carbohydrate. This section will contain a brief discussion of nomenclature, typical structures, and notes on the isolation, fractionation, analysis and occurrence of these complex lipids. Reviews of the subject are available.[1, 3]

There is currently no unanimity in the nomenclature of glycerophosphatides, but it is hoped that the Commission on Biochemical Nomenclature of the International Union of Biochemistry will agree on this subject in the near future. Terms such as phosphatidyl choline are sometimes used to denote all mixed choline glycerophosphatides. The specific term, "phosphatidyl choline," as well as "phosphatidyl ethanolamine," "phosphatidyl serine," etc., should probably be reserved for *known diacyl* glycerophosphatides. Aldehydogenic choline glycerophosphatides should be referred to as plasmalogens. The terms "phosphatidal choline" and "acetal phosphatidyl choline" are sometimes used in the literature, but these terms appear less satisfactory. "Phosphatidal choline" suffers from the fact that it differs from "phosphatidyl choline" by only one letter. The term "acetal phosphatidyl choline" is misleading, since it suggests the presence of an acetal linkage in the molecule. When the complete structure is known, a more specific nomenclature such as monoalkenyl or dialkenyl choline glycerophosphatide should be employed.

Most plasmalogens appear to be of the 1-O-alkenyl glycerol type, or more specifically 1-O-alk-1'-enyl type, but evidence is available for 2-O-alkenyl and/or 1,2-O, O-dialkenyl compounds.

The glycerophosphatides containing alkyl ethers may be named in the same way. Thus a lipid mixture may be described as containing alkyl glycerophosphatides. Most alkyl glycerophosphatides are of the 1-O-alkyl type but evidence is available for 1,2-O, O-dialkyl compounds.

Naturally-occurring glycerophosphatides are derivatives of L-3-glycerophosphate. The formulae shown below indicate this L-configuration.

II. STRUCTURE

A. Phospholipids.

1. Phosphatidyl choline (lecithin)

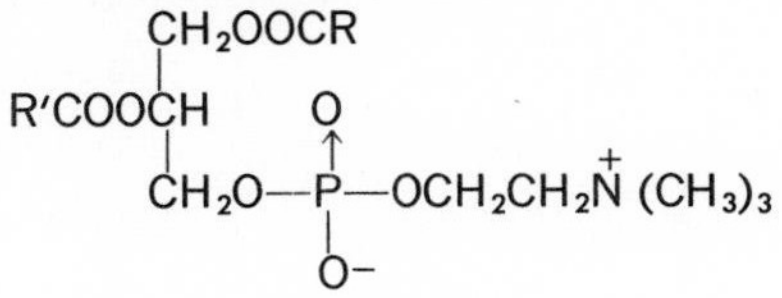

$$CH_2OOCR$$

R'COOCH   O

CH₂O—P—OCH₂CH₂$\overset{+}{N}$(CH₃)₃

O⁻

2. Phosphatidyl ethanolamine

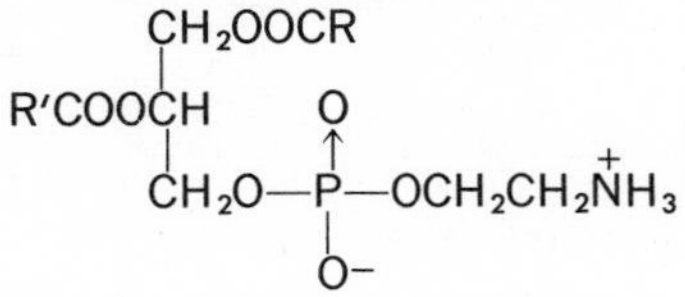

$$CH_2OOCR$$

R'COOCH   O

CH₂O—P—OCH₂CH₂$\overset{+}{N}$H₃

O⁻

3. Phosphatidyl serine

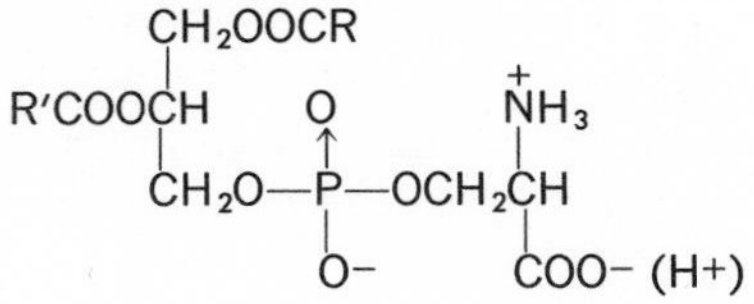

$$CH_2OOCR$$

R'COOCH   O $\overset{+}{N}$H₃

CH₂O—P—OCH₂CH

O⁻   COO⁻ (H⁺)

4. Phosphatidic acid

$$CH_2OOCR$$

R'COOCH   O

CH₂—O—P—O⁻ (H⁺)

O⁻ (H⁺)

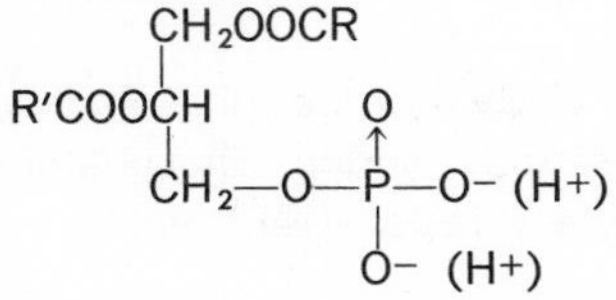

5. Phosphatidyl inositol

$$CH_2OOCR$$

R'COOCH   O

CH₂—O—P—O   OH   (H⁺)

O⁻   OH   OH

OH   OH

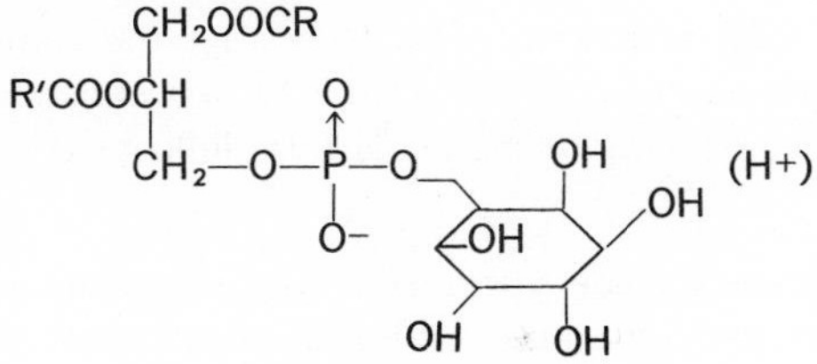

6. Polyphosphoinositides

Diphosphoinositides and triphosphoinositides have been reported in mammalian brain. Diphosphoinositide may be represented as phosphatidyl inositol with an additional phosphate esterified to the 4-hydroxyl position of inositol. Ox brain triphosphoinositides contain phosphate esterified at the 4- and 5-hydroxyl.[4, 5] Even more complex inositol phospholipids have been reported in plants.[6]

7. **Phosphatidyl glycerol**[7]

$$
\begin{array}{l}
CH_2OOCR \\
R'COOCH \qquad\quad O \qquad\quad OH \\
\quad\ CH_2—O—\overset{\uparrow}{P}—O—CH_2CHCH_2OH \\
\qquad\qquad\quad O^- \quad (H+)
\end{array}
$$

8. **Diphosphatidylglycerol (cardiolipin)**[8, 9]

$$
\begin{array}{l}
\qquad\qquad\qquad\qquad\qquad\qquad\qquad\quad CH_2OOCR''' \\
\quad CH_2OOCR \qquad\qquad\qquad R''COOCH \\
R'COOCH \qquad O \qquad\quad OH \qquad O \\
\quad\ CH_2—O—\overset{\uparrow}{P}—O—CH_2CHCH_2O—\overset{\uparrow}{P}—O—CH_2 \\
\qquad\qquad\quad O^- \quad (H+) \qquad\qquad\ O^- \quad (H+)
\end{array}
$$

9. **Sphingomyelin**

$$
\begin{array}{l}
\qquad\qquad\qquad\qquad\qquad\qquad\qquad\quad O \\
H_3C(CH_2)_{12}CH=CHCH—CH—CH_2—O—\overset{\uparrow}{P}—OCH_2CH_2\overset{+}{N}(CH_3)_3 \\
\qquad\qquad\qquad\quad OH \quad\ NH \qquad\qquad O^- \\
\qquad\qquad\qquad\qquad\qquad\quad C=O \\
\qquad\qquad\qquad\qquad\qquad\quad R
\end{array}
$$

10. **Lysophosphatides**

These have the structure of the parent phosphatide (i.e. phosphatidyl choline, phosphatidyl ethanolamine, phosphatidyl serine, phosphatidyl inositol, or phosphatidic acid) with one fatty acyl residue removed.

11. **Alkyl ethers**

Phospholipids containing a true ether linkage between a fatty alcohol and glycerol have been isolated from animal sources. They have the same structure as various other glycerophosphatides except for the substitution of an ether linkage for one or more of the usual ester linkages.[10, 11]

12. **Alkenyl ethers (plasmalogens)**

A similar group of lipids contains an aldehydogenic linkage. These compounds may be envisioned as alkyl ethers except for an unsaturation of the alkyl sidechain α, β to the ether linkage.[12]

B. Glycolipids. Many unusual glycolipids have been reported to occur in various tissues. Because of space limitations these will not be discussed in detail here. The reader is referred to the recent excellent review of the field by Carter et al[2] for amplification.

1. Glycosyl ceramides

Glycosyl ceramides are those glycolipids in which a mono- or oligosaccharide is attached by a glycosidic linkage to the primary hydroxyl of a ceramide. In the particular case where a monosaccharide is attached (glucose or galactose), the compounds are called cerebrosides.[2] Cerebrosides containing a sulfate ester on the carbohydrate moiety are referred to as cerebroside sulfates or as sulfatides.

Ceramide-oligosaccharides have been reported in which the oligosaccharide has up to four units[13, 14]including amino sugars. Glycosyl ceramides containing sialic acid (N-acyl neuraminic acid) are referred to as gangliosides. It should be noted that their occurrence is not limited to nervous tissue.[15] Within the brain gangliosides there is a large amount of a C_{20}-sphingosine in addition to the usual C_{18} base.[16]

Glycosyl ceramides containing an aldehydogenic moiety have been reported to occur in brain. An alkoxysphingolipid has also been suggested.[17]

2. Glycosyl glycerides

Monogalactosyl and digalactosyl diglycerides have been reported in various plants and algae. In each case the mono- or disaccharide is attached by a glycosidic linkage to an α-position of glycerol.[18] The presence of tri- and tetragalactosyl glycerides in spinach chloroplasts has been suggested.[19]

3. Glyceryl sulfolipid

Closely related to the glycosyl glycerides are the sulfolipids of plants, algae, and bacteria. Rather than a sulfate ester, however, the sulfur occurs in the form of a sulfonic acid functional group on the 6-deoxy position of glucopyranosyl diglyceride.[20]

III.   ISOLATION

Isolation of the various lipids from tissues involves the following basic steps: extraction of total lipids, removal of non-lipid contaminants from the extract, and fractionation of the lipid mixture. In some cases, specific methods allow the partial elimination of one or more of the usual steps in the isolation of a reasonably pure concentrate.

Extraction.   Although accuracy and the lability of the lipids under study will ultimately determine the care required, the following considerations should probably govern most extraction procedures.[21]
  1. All operations should be performed with purified solvents in an inert atmosphere.

2. Tissues should be excised, subdivided, and extracted as soon as possible after sacrifice.
3. The extraction solvent and ratio of solvent to tissue should be chosen with care. Heat should be used only if necessary.
4. Storage conditions should be chosen to minimize structural alterations.

Purified solvents and inert atmosphere are both helpful in protecting against possible oxidative decomposition during extraction and later manipulations. The use of chemical antioxidants[22, 23] or low temperature[24] is also helpful in minimizing this type of degradation.

The requirement for quick excision, subdivision, and extraction of tissues probably needs no justification. In regard to subdivision, however, it should be pointed out that mortar and pestle, blender, tissue disintegrator, homogenizing tube, or tissue crusher may be used depending upon the amount and identity of the tissue and the degree of subdivision required.[21]

The two most popular solvents for lipid extraction are ethanol-ether (3:1) and chloroform-methanol (2:1). The former (Bloor's solvent) is less satisfactory because heat is required in the extraction of some tissues and because extraction is not always quantitative. Extraction with 20 volumes of chloroform-methanol (2:1) will remove most lipids at ambient or sub-ambient temperatures.[21] Extraction of diphosphoinositides and triphosphoinositides requires acidic or basic solvent.[24] Ultimate storage of lipids will usually be in neutral solution (in purified solvents) in an inert atmosphere at low temperature. Antioxidants may also be added to retard decomposition during storage.

Removal of Non-lipid Contaminants. Non-lipid contaminants may be removed from a lipid extract by partitioning against an aqueous solvent[25] or by evaporating and drying the lipid extract and re-extracting the lipids into fresh solvent.[24] Another method[26] which is used in the extraction of lipids from very wet tissues employs slightly different amounts of chloroform in methanol, two filtrations, and separation of chloroform and aqueous phases (leaving virtually no non-lipid contaminants in the chloroform phase). Other methods include chromatography on silicic acid-impregnated paper[27] or Sephadex.[28]

Fractionation of the Lipid Mixture. Various methods have been used to fractionate lipid mixtures. These include methods for crude separation of lipids into broad groups and those for isolation of various pure lipids. Crude separations include selective precipitation of phospholipids and cerebrosides from a lipid mixture in solution,[29] dialysis of neutral fats through a rubber membrane,[30] and adsorption of phospholipids and cerebrosides on silicic acid.[31] A recent report indicates the usefulness of gel filtration in this preliminary separation.[32]

Preparation of pure lipids may involve isolation from a crude fraction or it may proceed directly from a total lipid extract. This is accomplished almost exclusively by chromatography on columns, impregnated paper or glass fiber paper, or thin layers of material on glass plates (TLC).

1. Column chromatography is most popular for preparative separations. The column packing is usually silicic acid[33] or alumina,[34] but recently columns of diethylaminoethyl cellulose and silicates[24] are finding increasing favor.

    It should be recognized that in practice one will often precede column fractionation with one of the other techniques mentioned above. If this is not done, the preparation of pure lipids from a complex mixture may require two or even three columns. In multiple-column chromatography, a fraction from one column is introduced into the next column for further separation. These subsequent columns may be of the same or different material depending upon the separation required.

2. TLC or chromatography on impregnated paper or glass fiber paper may be used for preparative separations, but these are used primarily for analytical purposes. By use of the quick separations produced by these methods it is possible to estimate the amounts of various lipid classes, approximate a column for purposes of experimenting with chromatographic materials and solvents, or to monitor the separations given in various fractions by other methods such as column chromatography.[35] Probably the most popular method at this time is thin-layer chromatography on silicic acid.

IV. ANALYSIS AND CRITERIA OF PURITY

Analysis without Degradation. We have discussed the use of chromatography in the separation of lipids. This is also one of the best methods available for the analysis of lipids. As noted above, column chromatography will more often be used preparatively, but chromatography on impregnated paper or thin layers of silicic acid on glass is quite useful in estimating the purity of the isolated lipid fraction. In many cases, it is possible to obtain very good separation of lipids which were eluted in the same fraction by column chromatography.

Thin-layer chromatography has also been used alone to fractionate naturally-occurring lipid mixtures.[36] If separate fractions are scraped from the plate, it is possible to estimate the proportions of various lipids.[35] In addition, the plate may be sprayed with suitable agents to develop color, and then later scanned with a densitometer for estimation of the various constituents.[37]

Techniques such as infrared spectrophotometry and counter-current distribution may also be used to establish purity of a lipid sample. The latter (in common with chromatographic methods) is a technique based on separation. Infrared spectrophotometry, however, makes use of absorbance of specific functional groups at various wave lengths of the infrared portion of the spectrum. In this way (without separation) it is sometimes possible to demonstrate the presence or absence of small amounts of impurities in a sample.

Degradative Analysis. In addition to the above methods for estimation of purity, degradative procedures may be used. The following functional groups or constituents of lipids may be determined. Comparison of ratios obtained with the isolated lipid for two or more of these with theoretical ratios for the "pure" lipid gives a good approximation of the purity.

1. Phosphorus[38]
2. Ester[39]
3. Nitrogen[40]
4. Aldehydogenic moiety[41, 42]
5. Glycerol[43, 44]
6. Alkyl ether moiety[45]
7. Ethanolamine and serine[46]
8. Choline[47]
9. Inositol[48, 49]
10. Sphingosine[50]
11. Hexose[51]
12. Hexosamine[52]
13. Sialic acid[53, 54]

In addition to the previous degradative methods, various selective hydrolytic methods have been used. These depend on varying degrees of susceptibility of different lipids to certain reagents. (For example, the aldehydogenic moiety of plasmalogens is stable to mild base but not mild acid; however the ether moiety of the glyceryl ether phospholipids is completely stable to both.[55])

V. COMPOSITION AND TISSUE DISTRIBUTION

Many analyses of tissue lipids are available in the literature, but because of changes in terminology and improvements in the accuracy of analytical methods, earlier reported values should be critically examined.

The following tables are recent examples of published analyses of various tissues and sub-cellular particles. The tables are presented largely as they appeared in the references, but additional footnotes have been added in an attempt to reconcile the tables with the nomenclature given here.

Table I. Distribution of Individual Phospholipids in Various Tissues[55]

Compound	Phosphorus as percent of total phospholipid-phosphorus			
	Human erythrocyte stroma	Ox heart	Ox Liver	Ox Brain
Phosphatidylcholine	33.5	24.2	54.2	29.2
Phosphatidylethanolamine	17.6	16.5	9.4	12.1
Phosphatidylserine	14.3	2.4	4.2	16.6
Phosphatidylinositol	0	4.1	7.9	3.2
Phosphatidic acid	2.2	0	2.2	0.5
Cardiolipin	0	8.9	4.1	0.7
Choline plasmalogen	1.2	17.5	1.5	0
Ethanolamine plasmalogen	10.4	11.0	3.6	21.1
Serine plasmalogen	0	0	0	Trace
Sphingomyelin	20.1	11.5	5.8	12.5
Alkyl ether phospholipid	1.5	11.5	0.5	2.1
Recovery (% of total lipid P analysed)	100.8	96.1	93.4	98.0

Table II. Phospholipid Composition of the Rat-Liver Nucleus and Whole Liver[56]

Compound	Phosphorus as percent of total phospholipid-phosphorus	
	Nucleus	Whole liver
Phosphatidylcholine	52.2	57.9
Phosphatidylethanolamine	25.1	23.7
Phosphatidylserine	5.6	4.1
Phosphatidylinositol	4.1	6.9
Cardiolipin	—	2.6
Phosphatidic acid	Trace?	Trace
Plasmalogen*	1.1	0.5
Sphingomyelin	6.3	5.5
Unidentified	1.2	—

* Type of plasmalogen is not specified, but other glycerophosphatides represent known diacyl glycero-phosphatides.

Table III. Fatty Acid and Aldehyde Composition of Rabbit Kidney Phospholipids[57]

Kidney portion	Chain length															Total	
	14:0	14:1	15:0	15:1	16:0	16:1	17:0	18:0	18:1	18:2	18:3	20:0	20:4	20: unsat.[a]	b	Sat-urates	Unsat-urates
Cortex																	
PA/PG*	3	2	1	3	2	3	—	3	9	61	4	—	—	—	9c	9	91
PE—total	6	7	2	5	5	—	3	15	20	21	2	—	29	5a	—	24	76
—aldehyde	—	—	—	—	33	7	7	19	12	3	—	—	—	—	—	66	34
PI	1	—	1	—	12	1	2	33	10	11	2	2	18	4	5d	55	45
PS	1	—	2	—	12	1	—	31	13	32	2	—	9	—	—	46	54
PC—total	—	—	3	—	20	1	2	16	15	34	3	—	8	—	1	40	60
—alpha'	—	—	—	—	21	1	2	29	4	20	1	—	14	—	3	58	42
—beta	2	2	2	—	16	2	1	—	25	45	1	—	1	2	4e	22	72
Sph.	—	—	—	—	35	—	2	32	2	1	—	5	7	3	12	86	14
Medulla																	
PA/PG	—	—	1	—	2	2	1	5	9	65	3	—	7	—	6	14	86
PE—total	7	—	—	—	5	2	—	7	10	5	2	—	28	24	11	19	81
—alpha'	5	—	—	—	1	4	—	6	16	3	3	—	42	20	1	14	86
—beta	8	—	2	—	9	—	1	7	2	7	1	2	9	30	22f	28	72
PI	5	—	—	—	6	1	—	31	9	9	1	1	33	8	—	39	61
PS	5	—	1	—	2	1	—	16	15	10	1	—	17	24	7	24	76
PC—total	—	—	3	—	26	3	—	9	24	22	1	—	10	2	—	39	61
—alpha'	—	—	5	—	40	2	—	16	18	14	1	—	2	3	—	61	39
—beta	2	—	1	—	10	3	—	1	30	30	2	—	19	1	1	16	84
Sph.	5	5	1	—	16	4	—	7	5	5	2	7	6	17	18g	43	57

All figures are mole %. Fatty acids less than 1 mole % are omitted. Alpha' acids calculated by difference.
a Exact degree of unsaturation undetermined.
b Chain length greater than 20 carbons.
c Includes 3 mole % 16:2.2 mole % 17:1.
d Includes 2 mole % 17:1.
e Includes 2 mole % 16:2.
f Includes 10 mole % 20:2.
g Includes 11 mole % 20:2.
* PA/PG, a mixture of phosphatidic acid and polyglycerophosphatides; PE, ethanolamine glycerophosphatides; PI, phosphatidyl inositol; PS, phosphatidyl serine; PC, phosphatidyl choline; Sph, Sphingomyelin

BIBLIOGRAPHY

References

1. Ansell, G. B., and J. N. Hawthorne, *Phospholipids—Chemistry, Metabolism, and Function*, 1964.
2. Carter, H. E., P. Johnson, and E. J. Weber, "Glycolipids," *Ann. Rev. Biochem.*, 34:109, 1965.
3. Hanahan, D. J., *Lipide Chemistry*, 1960.
4. Dittmer, J. C., and R. M. C. Dawson, "The Isolation of a New Lipid, Triphosphoinositide, and Monophosphoinositide from Ox Brain," *Biochem. J.*, 81: 535, 1961.
5. Dawson, R. M. C., and J. C. Dittmer, "Evidence for the Structure of Brain Triphosphoinositide from Hydrolytic Degradation Studies," *Biochem. J.*, 81: 540, 1961.
6. Hawthorne, J. N., "The Inositol Phospholipids," *J. Lipid Res.*, 1:255, 1960.
7. Benson, A. A., and B. Maruo, "Plant Phospholipids. I. Identification of the Phosphatidyl Glycerols," *Biochim. Biophys. Acta*, 27:189, 1958.
8. Gray, G. M., and M. G. Macfarlane, "Separation and Composition of the Phospholipids of Ox Heart," *Biochem. J.*, 70:409, 1958.
9. Benson, A. A., and E. H. Strickland, "Plant Phospholipids. III. Identification of Diphosphatidyl Glycerol," *Biochim. Biophys. Acta*, 41:328, 1960.
10. Carter, H. E., D. B. Smith, and D. N. Jones, "A New Ethanolamine-Containing Lipide from Egg Yolk," *J. Biol. Chem.*, 232:681, 1958.
11. Popovic, M., "Über die Glycerinäther des Menschlichen Herzmuskels," *Z. Physiol. Chem.*, 340:18, 1965.
12. Marinetti, G. V., J. Erbland, and E. Stotz, "The Structure of Beef Heart Plasmalogens," *J. Am. Chem. Soc.*, 81:861, 1959.
13. Rapport, M. M., L. Graf, and H. Schneider, "Immunochemical Studies of Organ and Tumor Lipids. XII. Isolation of Cytolipin K_1 A Glycosphingolipid Hapten Present in Human Kidney," *Arch. Biochem. Biophys.*, 105:431, 1964.
14. Makita, A., "Biochemistry of Organ Glycolipids. II. Isolation of Human Kidney Glycolipids," *J. Biochem.* (Tokyo), 55:269, 1964.
15. Svennerholm, L., "The Gangliosides," *J. Lipid Res.*, 5:145, 1964.
16. Sambasivarao, K., and R. H. McCluer, "Lipid Components of Gangliosides," *J. Lipid Res.*, 5:103, 1964.
17. Kochetkov, N. K., I. G. Zhukova, and I. S. Glukhoded, "Sphingoplasmalogens. A New Type of Sphingolipids," *Biochim. Biophys. Acta*, 70:716, 1963.
18. Allen, C. F., and P. Good, "Plant Lipids," *J. Am. Oil Chemists' Soc.*, 42:610, 1965.
19. Neufeld, E. F., and C. W. Hall, "Formation of Galactolipids by Chloroplasts," *Biochem. Biophys. Res. Commun.*, 14:503, 1964.
20. Benson, A. A., "The Plant Sulfolipid," *Advan. Lipid Res.*, 1:387, 1963.
21. Entenman, C., *J. Am. Oil Chemists' Soc.*, 38:534, 1961.
22. Mattson, F. H., and R. A. Volpenhein, "Synthesis and Properties of Glycerides," *J. Lipid Res.*, 3:281, 1962.
23. Wren, J. J., and A. D. Szczepanowska, *J. Chromatog.*, 14:405, 1964.
24. Rouser, G., et al., "Lipid Composition of Beef Brain, Beef Liver, and the Sea Anemone: Two Approaches to Quantitative Fractionation of Complex Lipid Mixtures," *J. Am. Oil Chemists' Soc.*, 40:425, 1963.
25. Folch, J., M. Lees, and G. H. Sloane-Stanley, "A Simple Method for the Isolation and Purification of Total Lipids from Animal Tissues," *J. Biol. Chem.*, 226:497, 1957.

26. Bligh, E. G., and W. J. Dyer, "A Rapid Method of Total Lipid Extraction and Purification," *Can. J. Biochem. Physiol.*, 37:911, 1959.

27. Biezinski, J. J., "A Simple Chromatographic Technique for Removal of Non-Lipid Contaminants from Lipid Extracts," *J. Lipid Res.*, 3:120, 1962.

28. Wells, M. A., and J. C. Dittmer, "The Use of Sephadex for the Removal of Non-Lipid Contaminants from Lipid Extracts," *Biochemistry*, 2:1259, 1963.

29. Ansell, G. B., and J. N. Hawthorne, *op. cit*, p. 43.

30. van Beers, G. A., H. de Iongh, and J. Boldingh, "Isolation of Phospholipids by Dialysis Through a Rubber Membrane," in Sinclair, H. M. (ed.), *Essential Fatty Acids*, p. 43, 1958.

31. Borgstrom, B., "Investigation on Lipid Separation Methods. Separation of Phospholipids from Neutral Fat and Fatty Acids," *Acta Physiol. Scand.*, 25:101, 1952.

32. Tipton, C. L., J. W. Paulis, and M. D. Pierson, *J. Chromatog.*, 14:486, 1964.

33. Hanahan, D. J., J. C. Dittmer, and E. Warashina, "A Column Chromatographic Separation of Classes of Phospholipides," *J. Biol. Chem.*, 228:685, 1957.

34. Long, C., and D. A. Staples, "Chromatographic Separation of Brain Lipids. 2. Ethanolamine—Containing Phospholipids," *Biochem. J.*, 80:557, 1961.

35. Mangold, H. K., *J. Am. Oil Chemists' Soc.*, 38:708, 1961.

36. LePage, M., "The Separation and Identification of Plant Phospholipids and Glycolipids by Two-Dimensional Thin-Layer Chromatography," *J. Chromatog.*, 13:99, 1964.

37. Privett, O. S., M. L. Blank, and W. O. Lundberg, *J. Am. Oil Chemists' Soc.*, 38:312, 1961.

38. Marinetti, G. V., "Chromatographic Separation, Identification, and Analysis of Phosphatides," *J. Lipid Res.*, 3:1, 1962.

39. Rapport, M. M., and N. Alonzo, "Photometric Determination of Fatty Acid Ester Groups in Phospholipids," *J. Biol. Chem.*, 217:193, 1955.

40. Long, C., and D. A. Staples, "Chromatographic Separation of Brain Lipids. Cerebroside and Sulphatide," *Biochem. J.*, 78:179, 1961.

41. Wittenberg, J. B., S. R. Korey, and F. H. Swenson, "The Determination of Higher Fatty Aldehydes in Tissues," *J. Biol. Chem.*, 219:39, 1956.

42. Gottfried, E. L., and M. M. Rapport, "The Biochemistry of Plasmalogens. I. Isolation and Characterization of Phosphatidal Choline, a Pure Native Plasmalogen," *J. Biol. Chem.*, 237:329, 1962.

43. Mendelsohn, D., and A. Antonis, "A Fluorimetric Micro Glycerol Method and its Application to the Determination of Serum Triglycerides," *J. Lipid Res.*, 2:45, 1961.

44. Holla, K. S., L. A. Horrocks, and D. G. Cornwell, "Improved Determination of Glycerol and Fatty Acids in Glycerides and Ethanolamine Phosphatides by Gas-Liquid Chromatography," *J. Lipid Res.*, 5:263, 1964.

45. Guyer, K. E., T. E. Beardmore, and D. G. Cornwell, "Isolation, Composition, and Quantitative Estimation of Glyceryl Ethers," *Federation Proc.*, suppl. 13, 22:414, 1963.

46. Collins, F. D., and L. W. Wheeldon, "Studies on Phospholipids. 4. Determination of Ethanolamine and Serine," *Biochem. J.*, 70:46, 1958.

47. Wheeldon, L. W., and F. D. Collins, "Studies on Phospholipids. 3. Determination of Choline," *Biochem. J.*, 70:43, 1958.

48. Agranoff, B. W., R. M. Bradley, and R. O. Brady, "The Enzymatic Synthesis of Inositol Phosphatide," *J. Biol. Chem.*, 233:1077, 1958.

49. Wells, W. W., T. A. Pittman, and H. J. Wells, "Quantitative Analysis of Myo-inositol in Rat Tissue by Gas-Liquid Chromatography," *Anal. Biochem.*, 10:450, 1965.

50. Lauter, C. J., and E. G. Trams, "A Spectrophotometric Determination of Sphingosine," *J. Lipid Res.*, 3:136, 1962.

51. Hodge, J. E., and B. T. Hofreiter, in Whistler, R. L., and M. L. Wolfrom (eds.), *Methods in Carbohydrate Chemistry*, vol. 1, p. 388, 1962.

52. Svennerholm, L., *Acta Soc. Med. Upsal.*, 61:287, 1956.

53. Svennerholm, L., "Quantitative Estimation of Sialic Acids. II. A Colorimetric Resorcinol-Hydrochloric Acid Method," *Biochim. Biophys. Acta*, 24:604, 1957.

54. Miettinen, T., and I. T. Takki-Luukkainen, "Use of Butyl Acetate in Determination of Sialic Acid," *Acta Chem. Scand.*, 13:856, 1959.

55. Dawson, R. M. C., N. Hemington, and J. B. Davenport, "Improvements in the Method of Determining Individual Phospholipids in a Complex Mixture by Successive Chemical Hydrolyses," *Biochem. J.*, 84:497, 1962.

56. Gurr, M. I., J. B. Finean, and J. N. Hawthorne, "The Phospholipids of Liver-Cell Fractions. I. The Phospholipid Composition of the Liver-Cell Nucleus," *Biochim. Biophys. Acta*, 70:406, 1963.

57. Morgan, T. E., D. O. Tinker, and D. J. Hanahan, "Phospholipid Metabolism in Kidney. I. Isolation and Identification of Lipids of Rabbit Kidney," *Arch. Biochem. Biophys.*, 103:54, 1963.

I. PIGMENTS

Carotenoids. Representatives of this class of non-saponifiable lipids are found in small amounts in all higher plants, in many microorganisms, and probably in all animals. These pigments, composed basically of eight isoprenoid units linked symmetrically about the center of the molecule, contain a chromophoric system of conjugated carbon-carbon double bonds. Although *de novo* synthesis of carotenoids occurs only in plants, both plants and animals effect molecular interconversions among carotenoids. Carotenoid biosynthesis closely parallels steroid synthesis to the formation of geranylgeranyl pyrophosphate, but the C-40 analogue of squalene, lycopersene, has not been demonstrated. Instead, the first detectable C-40 compound is phytoene, which undergoes subsequent stepwise dehydrogenation to lycopene.[1-5]

Most carotenoids may be considered derivatives of the red pigment lycopene, which undergoes structural modification by terminal ring closure to an analogue of either α-ionone (α-carotene) or β-ionone (β-carotene), by introduction of oxygen (epoxy, hydroxy, or carbonyl) into the molecule (xanthophylls), or by oxidative cleavage of the carbon-carbon chain (apo-carotenoids, such as azafrin). Cis isomers of carotenoids are designated by the prefix *neo-* and a letter indicating the specific isomer.[6] The numbering system, shown in Figure 1 for lycopene, and the nomenclature regarding carotenoids have been assigned with general agreement in the U. S.[7] and in Europe.[8]

Extraction and saponification of carotenoids are generally performed in dim light and under an inert atmosphere to prevent light-catalyzed reactions and oxidation of the pigments. Complete extraction of carotenoids is facilitated if the tissue is dried initially by grinding with anhydrous sodium sulfate,[9-11] or by repetitive extraction with anyhdrous acetone, ethanol or methanol.[12-15] Pigments are usually transferred to petroleum ether and the solution is dried if necessary before further study.

Hydrocarbon carotenoids and xanthophylls containing one hydroxyl or two carbonyl groups are generally soluble in a wide range of solvents, including carbon disulfide, benzene, chloroform, acetone, ether and petroleum ether, and are also slightly soluble in ethanol and methanol. As the degree of oxygenation increases, the solubility in petroleum ether, ether, etc., diminishes with corresponding increases in solubility in the alcohols. Acidic carotenoids, such as astaxanthin, bixin and crocetin, are very soluble in pyridine and slightly soluble in dilute alkaline solutions. All other carotenoids are insoluble in water. The technique of separating complex mixtures of carotenoids by partitioning them between two immiscible solvents has been extensively used.[16, 17] When partitioned in a petroleum ether-95% methanol system, hydrocarbon carotenoids distribute exclusively in the epiphase, and diol carotenoids distribute largely in the hypophase. Only recently, however, have quantitative partition coefficients been reported for use in the analytical characterization of carotenoids.[9, 18-29]

Chromatography of carotenoids is most frequently performed on columns of alumina, calcium hydroxide, calcium carbonate or zinc carbonate.[16] Petroleum ether, alone or mixed with benzene, ether or acetone, is commonly used as an eluant for carotenes. For more polar carotenoids, benzene-ether, ether, or acetone is used. Methods for the isolation and analysis of β-carotene are thoroughly described by Bickoff.[245] Absorption of visible and ultra-violet light is most extensively used in the characterization of carotenoids,[30] but this has been supplemented by infra-red absorption[31-35] and nuclear magnetic resonance and proton resonance studies.[31, 32, 36] Ketocarotenoids have been examined spectrophotometrically before and after reduction by sodium borohydride.[9] Carotenoid 5-6 epoxides can be identified by a spectral shift toward shorter wavelengths when treated in ethanolic solution with a trace of HCl.[9, 16] Finally, thin-layer chromatography has been applied to carotenoid studies.[37-42] The following table draws heavily from the review of Karrer and Jucker.[16] For a more comprehensive coverage of the chemistry and biochemistry of carotenoids, see this and other reviews. [5, 43, 44]

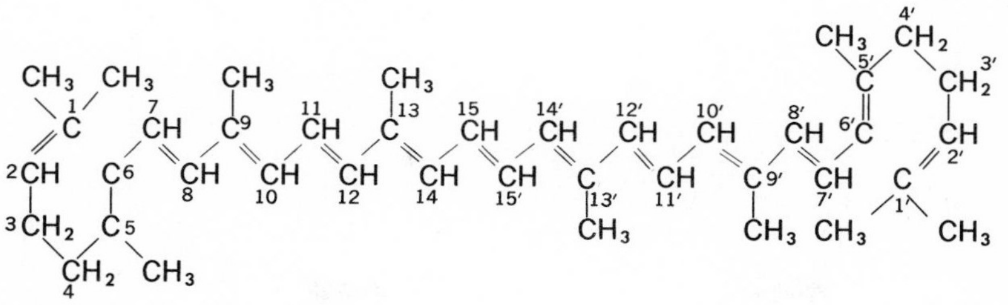

Figure 1.   Structure and numbering of Lycopene.

Table I. Properties of Carotenoids (References are shown in brackets)

No.	Carotenoid	Formula	M. wt.	Crystallization	M.P.	Absorption Maxima		Part Coeff.	Occurrence
1	Antheraxanthin	5:6 epoxy-zeaxanthin $C_{40}H_{56}O_3$	584.85	needles or thin platelets from MeOH or benz.-MeOH	205 [45]	CS_2 510 478	$CHCl_3$ 490.5 460.5	4/96 (p.e./85) [9] 39/61(p.e./70)	anthers of Lilium trigrinum [45, 46] berries of Euonymus europaeus [47] flower of Delonix regia [28] Euglena gracilis [9]
2	Aphanin	see Echinenone [43, 48, 49]	–	–	–	–		–	–
3	Aphanizophyll	see Myxoxanthophyll ? [43, 50, 51]	–	–	–	–		–	–
4	Astacene	3,3' di-hydroxy, 4,4' tetra-keto β-carotene $C_{40}H_{48}O_4$	592.78	violet needles from pyr.-H_2O	228 [52]	CS_2 500	hexane 470	–	not naturally occurring, but readily formed from astaxanthin [52, 53]
5	Astaxanthin	3,3' di-hydroxy, 4,4' di-keto β-carotene $C_{40}H_{52}O_4$	596.82	platelets from pyr.	215–216d [16]	CS_2 502	hexane 466–467	–	protein complexes in Crustacea [53–56]; Crustacea [43, 57]; Echinoderms [58–60]; Fish [61, 62]; Birds [52, 63, 64]; green algae [65]
6	Auroxanthin	5:8,5':8'-diepoxy-zeaxanthin $C_{40}H_{56}O_4$	600.85	yellow needles from MeOH	203	CS_2 454 423	EtOH 428 402 382	50/50 (p.e./66.7) [29]	flowers of Viola tricolor [66]
7	Azafrin	5,6-di-hydroxy-β-apo-10'-carotenoic acid $C_{27}H_{38}O_4$	426.85	red-orange needles from benz; prisms from toluene	212–214	$CHCl_3$ 458 428 pyr. 458 428 aq. NaOH 447 422		–	Escobedia scabrifolia; Escobedia linearis [67]
8	Bixin	$C_{23}H_{30}O_4$	394.99	violet dichroic prisms from acetic acid	191.5	CS_2 523.5 489 457	$CHCl_3$ 503 469.5 439	–	Bixa orellana [68]

No.	Name / Formula	Structure	M.W.	Crystal form	m.p. [ref]	Solvent	Absorption maxima	(hex/95)	Occurrence
9	Canthaxanthin, 4,4'-diketo-β-carotene, $C_{40}H_{52}O_2$		564.82	platelets from benz.:MeOH	204 [69]	benz. hexane pet. eth.	480 / 466 / 462–3	50/50 (hex/95)	Mushroom, Cantharellus cinnabarinus [70]; birds [69, 71–74]; Crustacea [75, 76]; insects [77]
10	Capsanthin, $C_{40}H_{58}O_3$		586.86	red needles from pet. eth.; prisms from MeOH	175–176 [46, 78]	CS_2 benz. pet. eth.	542 503 / 520 486 / 505 475	4/96 (hex/95)	Lillium tigrinum [46]; Capsicum annuum [79]
11	Capsorubin, $C_{40}H_{60}O_4$		604.88	violet-red needles from benz.:pet. eth.; rhombic plates from CS_2	201	CS_2 benz. pet. eth.	541.5 503 468 / 520 486 455 / 506 474 444	1/99 (hex/95)	Capsicum annuum [80, 81]
12	α-Carotene, $C_{40}H_{56}$		536.85	violet prisms from benz.:MeOH	187–188 [82]	CS_2 $CHCl_3$ hexane pet. eth.	509 477 / 485 454 / 475 445 420 [395] / 478 447.5	100/0 (hex/95)	Plant tissues generally [16]
13	β-Carotene, $C_{40}H_{56}$		536.85	violet hexagonal prisms from benz.:MeOH; red plates from pet. eth.	183 [83]	CS_2 $CHCl_2$ hexane pet. eth.	520 485 450 / 497 466 / 477 450 425 / 483.5 452 426	100/0 (hex/95)	Plant and animal tissues generally [16]
14	γ-Carotene, $C_{40}H_{56}$		536.85	red prisms from benz.:MeOH	178 [84] 176.5 [85]	CS_2 benz. $CHCl_3$ hexane pet. eth.	533.5 496 463 / 510 477 447 / 508.5 475 446 / 494 462 431 / 495 462 431	100/0 (hex/95)	Traces in many plant tissues [16, 84]

Table I. Properties of Carotenoids (References are shown in brackets) (cont'd)

No.	Carotenoid	Formula	M. wt.	Crystallization	M.P.	Absorption Maxima	Part Coeff.	Occurrence
15	δ-Carotene	$C_{40}H_{56}$ [89]	536.85	yellow-orange crystals from benz.-MeOH	140.5 [199]	hexane 485 456 430	—	Traces in many plant tissues Tomatoes [86] Bacteria [87, 88]
16	ε-Carotene	$C_{40}H_{56}$	536.85	yellow-red leaflets from benz.-MeOH	190 [90]	hexane 469 439 415 benz. 482 451 425	—	Marine diatoms and algae: Bryopsis, Navicula, Cryptomonas [91, 92]
17	ζ-Carotene	$C_{40}H_{60}$	540.88	—	—	hexane 424 399 377	100/0 (hex./95)	Traces in many plant tissues; Carica papaya [93]
18	Celaxanthin	$C_{40}H_{54-56}O$?	550.83 552.85?	long needles from pet. eth.–EtOH	209–210	CS_2 562 521 487 455 EtOH 520.5 488 455 pet. eth. 520 486.5 456 [429]	—	Celastrus scandens [94]
19	Chloroxanthin	$C_{40}H_{60}O$	556.88	needles from pet. eth.	139 [23]	pet. eth. 468 437.5 413	90/10 (p.e./95)	Rhodopseudomonas spheroides [23] [96]
20	Chrysanthemaxanthin	Cis-trans isomer of flavoxanthin [43]	—	—	—	—	—	

No.	Name	Structure / formula	M.W.	Crystal form	M.p.	Solvent	Absorption maxima	Ratio	Source
21	β-Citraurin	(aldehyde structure)	432.62	yellow plates from benz.:petrol	147	CS_2 / benz. / hexane	525 490 457 / 497 467 / 487 458	–	orange peels (Citrus aurantium) [97, 98]
22	Citroxanthin	$C_{30}H_{40}O_2$ see Mutatochrome							
23	Crocetin	(structure, OH) $C_{20}H_{24}O_4$	328.39	red rhombs from acetic anhydride	285	CS_2 / pyr. / $CHCl_3$ / pet. eth. / hexane	482 453 426 / 464 436 411 / 463 434.5 / 450.5 424.5 / 445 420 400	4/96 (hex/95)	Crocus species and other flowers and fruits [99]
24	Cryptoxanthin	3-hydroxy-β-carotene $C_{40}H_{56}O$	552.85	prisms from benz.:MeOH	169	CS_2 / $CHCl_3$ / EtOH / hexane	519 483 452 / 497 463 433 / 486 452 424 / 484 451 423	82/18 (hex/95) [18]; 77/23 (p.e./95) [9]	several plants, incl. Physalis species [100]; Crustacea [101, 102]; chicken eyes [103]; egg yolks [104]; butter [105]
25	Echinenone	4-keto-β-carotene $C_{40}H_{54}O$	550.83	violet needles from benz.:MeOH or pet. eth.	178–179	CS_2 / pet. eth.	488 / 458	93/7 (hex/95)	echinoderms [106, 107]; Crustacea [75]; Euglena gracilis [9]
26	Eloxanthin	5:6-epoxy-lutein $C_{40}H_{56}O_3$	584.85	red-yellow crystals from benz.:MeOH	192 [108]	CS_2 / benz. / EtOH / pet. eth.	501.5 472 / 482 453 / 473 445 / 471 442	–	leaves and flowers of various plants [16], incl. Elodea canadensis [109]
27	Eschscholtzxanthin	– $C_{40}H_{54}O_2$? [110, 111]	566.83	from acetone or ether	185–186	CS_2 / benz. / EtOH / $CHCl_3$ / pyr.	536 502 475 / 516 485 458 / 503 472 446 / 513 484 456 / 521 489 463	–	Eschscholtzia californica [112]
28	Euglenanone	3,4-diketo-β-carotene? $C_{40}H_{52}O_2$?	564.82	–	–	$CHCl_3$ / EtOH / pet. eth.	478–482 / 473 / 458	44/56 (p.e./95)	Euglena gracilis [9]
29	Flavacin	?see ζ-carotene [43]	–				–	–	
30	Flavochrome	5:8-epoxy-α-carotene $C_{40}H_{56}O$	552.85	yellow plates from benz.:MeOH	189	CS_2 / benz. / $CHCl_3$ / pet. eth.	482 451 / 462 434 / 461 433 / 450 422	–	Ranunculus acer [113]; Tragopogon pratensis [113]
31	Flavorhodin	?see ε-carotene [43]	–				–	–	

Table I. Properties of Carotenoids (References are shown in brackets) (cont'd)

No.	Carotenoid	Formula	M. wt.	Crystallization	M.P.	Absorption Maxima			Part Coeff.	Occurrence
32	Flavoxanthin	5:8-epoxy-lutein $C_{40}H_{56}O_3$	584.85	yellow prisms from MeOH	184	CS_2 $CHCl_3$ EtOH pet. eth.	479 459 448 450	449 430 421 421	–	many plant tissues [16]; incl. dandelion [114], Ranunculus acer [115]
33	Fucoxanthin	? $C_{40}H_{56-60}O_6$	–	red needles from eth.-pet., eth.	159.5–160.5 [116]; 166–168 [117]	CS_2 $CHCl_3$ hexane	510 477 492 457 469 451	445 438	2/98 (p.e./85) [21] 72/28 (p.e./60)	brown algae, incl. Fucus, Dictyota, -Cystosira, and Laminaria [118]
34	Galloxanthin	–	–	–	–	CS_2 $CHCl_3$ EtOH hexane	446 424 427 407 421 400 422 401	– [387] 378 [380]	hypophasic (p.e./90)	chicken retina [119]
35	Gazaniaxanthin	? $C_{40}H_{54-58}O$	–	red plates from benz.-MeOH	133–134	CS_2 benz. EtOH pet. eth.	531 496.5 509 476 494.5 462 494.5 462.5	461 447.5 434.5 434.5	80/20 (hex/95)	Gazania rigens [120]
36	Leprotene	 $C_{40}H_{48}$ [329]	528.78	–	198–200 [328] 189–192 [329]	pet. eth. acetone benz. CS_2	(428) 452 (435) 458 (440) 465 (460) 484	480 485 494 515	–	Mycobacterium species [329]
37	Lutein	3,3'-dihydroxy-α-carotene $C_{40}H_{56}O_2$	584.85	violet prisms from MeOH	193 [120]	CS_2 $CHCl_3$ EtOH hexane	508 475 487 456 476 446.5 477 447	445 428 420 420	12/88 (hex/95) 43/57 (hex/85) 50/50 (hex/82.3)	Widely distributed in green plants; leaves, flowers, fruits, and seeds; also from many animal tissues [16]
38	Lycopene	 $C_{40}H_{56}$	536.85	red needles from CS_2-EtOH	174 [121] 175 [122]	CS_2 $CHCl_3$ benz. EtOH hexane	548 507.5 517 480 522 487 503 472 504 472	477 453 455 443 443	100/0 (hex/95)	fruits and seeds, e.g., tomatoes; green plants; some animal tissues [16]

No.	Name / Structure	M.W.	Crystal form	M.p.	Solvent	Absorption maxima	Ratio	Occurrence
39	Lycopersene $C_{40}H_{66}$	546.93	colorless oil	octa-HCl: 126 [336]	—	—	—	not occurring naturally in carotenoid-biosynthetic organisms [2]
40	Lycophyll 3,3'-dihydroxy-lycopene $C_{40}H_{56}O_2$	568.85	violet leaflets from benz.-MeOH; red needles from benz.-pet. eth.	179	CS_2 benz. EtOH pet. eth.	546 506 472 / 521 487 456 / 505 474 444 / 504 473 444	—	Solanum dulcamara, Solanum esculentum [123]
41	Lycoxanthin 3-hydroxy-lycopene $C_{40}H_{58}O$	552.85	red-brown plates from benz.-pet. eth.; violet needles from CS_2	168	CS_2 benz. EtOH pet. eth.	546 506 472 / 521 487 456 / 505 474 444 / 504 473 444	—	S. dulcamara; S. esculentum [123]
42	Mutatochrome 5:8-epoxy-β-carotene $C_{40}H_{56}O$	552.85	yellow-orange leaflets from benz.-MeOH	163–164 [124]	CS_2 benz. $CHCl_3$ pet. eth.	489.5 459 / 470 440 / 469 438 / 456 427	98/2 (hex./95) [28]	orange peels [125]
43	Myxoxanthin see Echinenone [43, 48, 49]	—	—	—	—	—	—	—
44	Myxoxantho-phyll ?[126] $C_{40}H_{56}O_7$	648.85	violet needles from acetone	182 [126]	pyr. $CHCl_3$ EtOH	526 489 458 / 518 484 454 / 503 471 445	—	Oscillatoria rubescens [126, 127]
45	Neoxanthin ?[128, 133] $C_{40}H_{58}O_4$	602.86	—	—	$CHCl_3$ EtOH	475 445 421 / 466 437–8 (390) / 413–4 (390)	0/100 (p.e./70) 8/92 (p.e./60) 37/63 (p.e./50)	leaves of green plants [129] Euglena gracilis [9, 128][130]

Table I. Properties of Carotenoids (References are shown in brackets) (cont'd)

No.	Carotenoid	Formula	M. wt.	Crystallization	M.P.	Absorption Maxima	Part Coeff.	Occurrence
46	Neurosporene	$C_{40}H_{58}$	538.87	crystals from EtOH	117 [23]	pet. eth. 468 437.5 413	100/0 (p.e./95)	Neurospora crassa and other fungi [43, 131] Rhodopseudomonas spheroides [23] [96]
47	Neurosporoxanthin	(acidic carotenoid)?	–	purple leaflets from hexane	192 [132]	hexane 472 benzene 486	–	Neurospora crassa [132, 133] Fusarium aquaeductuum
48	Petaloxanthin	?cis-trans isomer of antheraxanthin [16, 43]	–	–	–	–	–	–
49	Phytoene	$C_{40}H_{64}$	544.91	colorless oil	–	hexane 298 286 275	100/0 (hex./95)	trace amounts widely distributed in plants [134, 135]
50	Phytofluene	$C_{40}H_{62}$	542.89	colorless oil	–	pet. eth. 367–8 348 332	100/0 (hex./95)	trace amounts widely distributed in plants [136, 137]
51	Rhodopin	$C_{40}H_{58}O$	554.86	from acetone-pet. ether	172–174 [31]	pet. eth. 504 472 445 acetone 504 472 445	76/24 (p.e./95)	photosynthetic green bacteria, incl. Chloropseudomonas ethylicus, Chlorobium thiosulfatophilum, Chlorobium limicola, Rhodomicrobium vannielii [31, 32]

No.	Name	Structure / Formula	M.W.	Crystal form	M.p. [ref]	Solvent	Absorption maxima	Partition ratio	Occurrence
52	Rhodovibrin	OCH₃ / OH, $C_{41}H_{60}O_2$	584.89	red crystals from CS₂-pet. ether	168 [138]	CS₂ acetone	556 517 521 488 460	66/34 (p.e./95) [24] 95/5 (p.e./85)	Rhodovibrio bacteria [138] Rhodomicrobium vannielii [31]
53	Rhodoviolascin	see spirilloxanthin	—	—	—	—	—	—	—
54	Rhodoxanthin	3,3'-diketo-dehydro-β-carotene $C_{40}H_{50}O_2$	562.80	violet needles from benz.:MeOH	219	CS₂ CHCl₃ benz. EtOH hexane	564 525 491 546 510 482 474 542 503.5 474 538 496 524 489 458	— —	widely distributed in plants, incl. Taxus baccata [139]
55	Rubixanthin	3-hydroxy-γ-carotene $C_{40}H_{56}O$	552.85	orange-red needles from benz.-pet. ether	160	CS₂ CHCl₃ EtOH hexane	533 494 461 509 474 439 496 463 433 494 462 432	82/18 (hex/95) [28]	Cuscuta salina, Cuscuta subinclusa [140]; Rosa species [141, 142]
56	Sarcinaxanthin	?	—	red spheroids from benz.:petrol	149–150	CS₂ CHCl₃ benz. EtOH	499 466.5 436 480 451 423 481 451 424 469.5 441 [415]	—	Sarcina lutea [143]
57	Spheroidene	OCH₃, $C_{41}H_{60}O$ [96]	568.89	yellow needles from pet. eth.	145 [23]	CS₂ CHCl₃ benz. pet. eth.	518 485 458 497 465 437.5 498 466 438 484 452 426.5	—	Rhodopseudomonas spheroides [23, 330]
58	Spheroidenone	2-keto-spheroidene $C_{41}H_{58}O_2$ [96]	582.87	red platelets from pet. eth.	163 [23]	CS₂ CHCl₃ benz. pet. eth.	553 519.5 495 499 530 499 475 513 482 460	—	Rhodopseudomonas spheroides [23, 330]
59	Spirilloxanthin	OCH₃ / CH₃O, $C_{42}H_{60}O_2$	596.90	red spindles from benz.	218	CS₂ benz. CHCl₃ EtOH	573.5 534 496 548 511 482 544 507 476 526 491 [465]	88/14 (p.e./95) [26]	rhodovibrio and thiocystis bacteria [144, 145]

Table I. Properties of Carotenoids (References are shown in brackets) (cont'd)

No.	Carotenoid	Formula	M. wt.	Crystallization	M.P.	Absorption Maxima		Part Coeff.	Occurrence
60	Taraxanthin	? $C_{40}H_{56}O_4$	600.85	prisms or plates from MeOH	184–185 [146]	CS_2 petrol	501 469 441 472 443	–	dandelion (Taraxacum officinale) [147–149]
61	Torularhodin	$C_{37}H_{48}O_2$	474.75	red needles from MeOH-eth.	201–203d	CS_2 benz. pyr. $CHCl_3$ EtOH	582 541 502 557 519 485 558 518 485 554 515 [483] 532 495 463	–	Torula rubra [150, 151] [152]
62	Torulin	?	–	from benz.-MeOH	185	CS_2 pyr. benz. $CHCl_3$ EtOH	565 525 491 545 508 475 541 503 470 539 501 469 520 486 456	–	Torula rubra, Sporobolomyces species Lycogala epidendron [152, 153]
63	Trollixanthin	(mono-epoxy-tri-hydroxy) ? $C_{40}H_{56}O_4$	600.85	yellow leaflets from benz.	199	CS_2 benz. $CHCl_3$ EtOH	501 473 483 457 482 455 474 447	–	Trollius europaeus [154, 155]
64	Violaxanthin	5:6,5':6'-diepoxy-zeaxanthin $C_{40}H_{56}O_4$	600.85	yellow-orange prisms from MeOH	200	CS_2 $CHCl_3$ EtOH MeOH	501 470 440 482 451.5 424 471.5 442.5 417.5 469 440 415	50/50 (p.e./66.2) [29]	widely distributed in flowers and fruits [16]; incl. Viola tricolor (pansy) [156–168]
65	Zeaxanthin	3,3'-dihydroxy-β-carotene $C_{40}H_{56}O_2$	568.85	yellow plates from MeOH	215.5 [159]	CS_2 $CHCl_3$ EtOH MeOH	517 482 450 495 462 429 483 451 423.5 480.5 449.5 421.5	11/89 (hex/95) 40/60 (hex/85)	widely distributed in plants [16], incl. Zea mays [160]; egg yolk [161]; human fat [162]

[a]Additional spectral data are presented in references [30, 327].
[b]Partition coefficients are presented as the ratio of the epiphasic to hypophasic carotenoid, with the phasic system described in parentheses. (p. e. = petroleum ether; hex = hexane; 95 = 95% methanol; 90 = 90% methanol, etc.) Additional data are available from references [18, 29].

Chromolipids. This class of pigments, which gives rise to the yellow to brown coloration frequently observed in the adipose tissues of animals, is very poorly defined chemically. In addition, confusion exists in the literature because the term lipochrome is variously used as a synonym for both chromolipid and carotenoid. Chromolipids are generally regarded as complex mixtures of oxidation products of fatty acids or phospholipids, but, although they are probably produced metabolically, the function and fate of these pigments are not known.[163] Histochemical staining methods are frequently used in the study of chromolipids,[164-166] and, *in vitro*, autoxidation products of unsaturated lipids give the same reactions as cellular chromolipids.[165] Chromolipids exhibit absorption in both the ultraviolet and visible regions of the spectrum,[167] but can be differentiated from carotenoids by the absence of absorption bands in the blue-green region.[163]

II. FAT-SOLUBLE VITAMINS

Vitamin A. Carotenoids containing an unsubstituted β-ionine ring are converted in certain animal tissues to vitamn A or retinol. The conversion to $retinol_1$ occurs in terrestrial and marine vertebrates, including man, and in several invertebrate groups, particularly molluscs, crustaceans, and insects.[168] $Retinol_2$, or dehydroretinol, is found only in amphibia and freshwater fish and turtles.[169, 170] Fish which migrate from fresh to salt water, or vice-versa, during their life cycle, and amphibians which metamorphose from freshwater tadpoles to semiterrestrial adults, undergo transitions from one form of the vitamin to the other.[169, 171]

In mammals, the conversion of β-carotene to retinol occurs mainly in the mucosa of the small intestine.[172-174] The mechanism of this conversion, whether by terminal or central cleavage of the conjugated chain, is not yet settled,[175-177] although experiments with labeled β-carotene favor the central cleavage hypothesis.[178, 179, 242] Retinol is probably absorbed from the intestinal lumen in the free form, then re-esterified in the intestinal mucosa.[180, 181] In mammals, retinol appears to be preferentially esterified with palmitic acid,[181-183] although this specificity is not so pronounced in marine fish.[184] Retinol is enzymatically oxidized to the corresponding aldehyde, retinal,[185, 186] and carboxylic acid, retinoic acid.[187,-189] Recently, these relations have been thoroughly reviewed.[177]

Retinol and retinal undergo isomerization in the liver[190, 191] and in the retina,[192] where 11-cis retinal is bound to the protein opsin to form photosensitive visual pigments.[193] Retinoic acid will not function in the visual cycle, but does stimulate normal growth in vitamin A-deficient rats.[194] Retinoic acid appears to be involved in the activation of sulfate in sulfurylation reactions[195, 196] required for mucopolysaccharide synthesis.

Retinoic acid is excreted in rat bile as the retinoyl-β-glucuronide.[197] The possible metabolic functions of vitamin A are discussed in a recent review.[269]

Problems encountered in the isolation of vitamin A are similar to those for carotenoids. Various methods for extraction and saponification of vitamin A from animal tissues have recently been compared,[243] and losses of the vitamin are best avoided by acetone extraction in the presence of anhydrous Na_2SO_4, followed by a brief saponification in the presence of an antioxidant.[244] Vitamin A is frequently assayed directly in the non-saponifiable mixture, but purification is necessary to eliminate carotenoids if a biological assay is used, or to eliminate spectral interference if either a spectrophotometric or colorimetric method is used. Purification is usually by chromatography, including thin-layer chromatography[265, 266] and paper chromatography.[267, 268] Losses on column chromatography can be reduced by the addition of soy bean oil.[246] Recently gas-liquid chromatography has been used for separation of retinol derivatives.[253]

Estimation of vitamin A by bioassay and spectrophotometric and colorimetric procedures is thoroughly discussed by Embree *et al.*[247] and by Moore.[248] Other colorimetric procedures have been devised[249, 250] and 9-cis isomers of vitamin A have been estimated by reaction with opsin.[251] Spectrophotometric corrections are further discussed by Wilkie.[252]

Vitamin D.   Compounds of the vitamin D group are formed by the action of ultraviolet light on 3-hydroxy,Δ5,7-dienoic sterols. In man, sunlight promotes the formation of vitamin D from 7-dehydrocholesterol in the outer layers of the skin. The same reaction occurs in the fur and feathers of mammals and birds, which then obtain the vitamin orally, by grooming and preening, or by direct absorption. Several pro-vitamins D, including ergosterol and 22-dihydro-ergosterol, are found only in plants. The active vitamins can be produced artificially by ultraviolet irradiation of these sterols. Vitamins D of unknown origin and structure occur in fish liver oils. These are likely produced enzymatically instead of by irradiation.[200] 7-Dehydrocholesterol is produced from cholesterol in the animal intestine,[201, 202] while ergosterol is synthesized by yeast and other plants from squalene with lanosterol as an intermediate.[203–205] The overall biosynthesis of the vitamins D is discussed by Goodwin.[206]

Vitamin D causes an increased calcium and phosphorous absorption from the intestine,[207, 208] and also affects phosphatase reactions.[209] In addition, vitamin D promotes phosphate reabsorption from the kidney tubules. The relationships of these reactions with normal bone formation are not yet firmly established. The actions of vitamin D and parathyroid hormone on calcium and phosphate metabolism have been discussed by Albright and Reifenstein.[210]

Table II. Properties of Some Vitamin A-Active Compounds

Name	Synonyms	Formula	Mol. wt.	Crystallization	m.p.	Absorption maximum [30] mμ	Absorption maximum [30] $E_{1cm}^{1\%}$	Carr-Price absorption maximum [30] mμ	Carr-Price absorption maximum [30] $E_{1cm}^{1\%}$	Vitamin A activity relative to retinol₁
Retinol₁	Vitamin A Axerophthol	[structure] $C_{20}H_{30}O$	286.44	needles from MeOH	63–64	EtOH 325, EtOH 324–5 [254] retinyl acetate:	1830, 1800 [254]	618, 620	4400, 4420 [254]	100%, 87.4% [258]
Retinal₁	Vitamin A₁ aldehyde retinene₁ axerophthal	[structure] $C_{20}H_{28}O$	284.42	orange-red needles from light petrol	61–62 [257]	EtOH 385, C_6H_{12} 373, CHCl₃ 389	1400, 1548, 1303	664	3400	84%
Retinoic acid	Vitamin A₁ acid	[structure] $C_{20}H_{28}O_2$	300.42	bright yellow needles from MeOH [255]	179–180 [198] 181–182 [255]	EtOH 353, EtOH 351, C_6H_{12} 357 [255]	1510, 1540 [198]	—	—	42.8% (oral) [198] 123% (intra-peritoneal)
Retinol₂	Vitamin A₂	[structure] $C_{20}H_{28}O$	284.42	—	—	EtOH 287, 351, CHCl₃ 406	820, 1460	693	4100	39% [259]
Retinal₂	Vitamin A₂ aldehyde retinene₂	[structure] $C_{20}H_{26}O$	282.41	orange-red prisms from pentane [256]	77–78 [256]	C_6H_{12} 386, CHCl₃ 405	1440	735–705	3270	see [260]
Kitol	dimer of vitamin A,? occurs in mammalian liver oils	$C_{40}H_{60}O_2$ [334]	572.88	elongated prisms	88–90	EtOH 290	—	—	—	—

The vitamins D and their precursors are not readily isolated from natural sources because of their low concentrations. The procedure may involve saponification, partition, digitonide precipitation, and preparation and purification of a 3,5-dinitrobenzoate derivative which is then hydrolyzed before crystallization of the vitamin.[261-264] Instead, vitamins D are usually synthesized from cholesterol or other readily obtained sterols.

The determination of vitamin D is most frequently by bioassay, although in high concentrations, it can be assayed by spectrophotometric and colorimetric means.[270] Vitamins D_2 and D_3 can be separated and determined by gas-liquid chromatography.[332] Provitamins D are assayed by colorimetry, spectrophotometry, or digitonide precipitation.[271] These various methods have been compared and discussed by reviewers.[272, 273] Conditions for extraction and saponification of vitamin D with minimal degradation are described by Chen *et al.*[274]

Vitamin E, Tocopherol. Tocopherols are widely distributed in plant tissues with small amounts occurring in animal tissues such as muscle and blood. It was established in the early 1920's that this lipid-soluble factor was required for normal reproduction in rats,[211, 212] and since then eight naturally-occurring tocopherols have been demonstrated in cereal grains.[213-215] Very little is known about the biosynthesis and metabolism of tocopherols. The variety of tocopherols found in barley, wheat, and pea seeds and seedlings diminishes as the plants grow,[216] while the contents of α-tocopherol and total tocopherol increase.[216-218] Tocopherol metabolites of unknown structure have been noted in animals.[220, 221] In mammals, tocopherol is transported by the serum lipoproteins.[219]

In vitamin E deficiency, sterility and muscular dystrophy result. A number of other effects may also be related to deficiency of the vitamin.[222] The mechanism for vitamin E activity most probably involves the antioxidant capacity of the tocopherols. α-Tocopherol protects various lipids, including vitamin A, from oxidation in air.[223-225] In addition, tocopherols may activate muscle cytochrome C reductase.[226, 227]

The tocopherols from the unsaponifiable portions of natural oils can be purified by chromatography,[283] fractional crystallization,[284] or molecular distillation.[285] Tocopherol can be separated from other fat-soluble vitamins and identified by paper chromatography.[294] Because they exhibit very low melting points, the tocopherols are usually crystallized as allophanate or phenylazobenzoate derivatives, although α- and γ-tocopherols have been obtained in crystalline form.[284, 286]

The most commonly used method of estimation of tocopherols is based on the reduction of ferric to ferrous ions in the presence of α, α-dipyridyl.[287, 288] The red color produced is measured spectrophotometrically. Ferricyanide[289] and phosphomolybdic acid[290] have also been used for color reactions with tocopherol. A thorough review of the colorimetric methods and of bioassay is presented by Gyorgy.[273]

Table III. Properties of Some Vitamins D and Precursors

Name	Synonyms	Formula	Mol. wt.	Crystallization	m.p.	Absorption Maxima	$[\alpha]_D$
7-dehydro-cholesterol	provitamin D_3	$C_{27}H_{44}O$	384.62 402.64 (hydrate)	platelets from ether-MeOH	149–150 [279]	EtOH 262.5 271 281.5 293 [280]	-124^{20} (CHCl$_3$) [279]
Ergosterol	provitamin D_2 ergosterin	$C_{28}H_{44}O$	396.63 414.65 (hydrate)	white needles from ether, CHCl$_3$ or acetone	165 [277]	EtOH 262 271 282 293.5	-135^{20} (CHCl$_3$) -174^{20} (CHCl$_3$) [278]
Vitamin D_3	cholecalciferol	$C_{27}H_{44}O$	384.62	needles from MeOH	84–85 [281]	EtOH 265 [278]	$+84.8^{20}$ (acetone) [281]
Vitamin D_4	irradiated 22-dihydro-ergosterol	$C_{28}H_{46}O$	398.65	long needles from acetone	96–98 [282]	EtOH 265	$+85.7^{21}$ (acetone)
Vitamin D_2	calciferol	$C_{28}H_{44}O$	396.63	colorless needles from MeOH	121 [275]	EtOH 265, $E_{1cm}^{1\%} = 490$ [275]	$+106^{20}$ (EtOH) [276] $+125^{20}$ (EtOH) 5461

Table IV. Properties of Tocopherols

Name	Synonyms	Formula	Mol. wt.	m.p.	Absorption maxima* mμ [286]	$[\alpha]^{25}_{546.1}$ [286]
α-tocopherol	5,7,8-trimethyltocol**	$C_{29}H_{50}O_2$	430.69	2.5–3.5 [284] Allophanate 157–8	EtOH 292	+0.32 (EtOH) −3.0 (benz)
β-tocopherol	5,8-dimethyltocol	$C_{28}H_{48}O_2$	416.66	Allophanate 138–9	EtOH 297	+2.9 (EtOH)
γ-tocopherol	7,8-dimethyltocol	$C_{28}H_{48}O_2$	416.66	−3 to −2 [284] Allophanate 136–7	EtOH 298	+2.2 (EtOH) −2.4 (benz)
δ-tocopherol	8-methyltocol	$C_{27}H_{46}O_2$	402.64	phenylazobenzoate 41–42 [291]	EtOH 298 [291]	+3.4 (EtOH) [291] +1.1 (benz)

*IR spectra have also been obtained [292, 293].

**Tocol is an accepted name for 2-methyl-2-(4′,8′,12′-trimethyldecyl)-6-chromanol.

Vitamin K. Vitamin K, or antihemorrhagic factor, occurs naturally in both plant and animal sources.[228-231] Vitamin K_1 occurs throughout the leaves of alfalfa, including the chloroplasts,[232] and also occurs with other vitamins K in many bacteria.[233,295] Egger[335] has studied the distribution of vitamins K in various plants. Two different vitamins K, designated $K_{2(35)}$ and $K_{2(30)}$, occur in putrefied fish meal.[234,235] The more abundant form has a 35-carbon side chain, whereas a second form occurring only in small amounts has a 30-carbon side chain. The characteristics of the K-vitamins are discussed by Isler and Wiss.[236]

Vitamin K is synthesized by green leaves in the light.[237] Animals degrade administered vitamins K to menadione (vitamin K_3), then resynthesize an unsaturated side chain (of the K_2 type) of 20 carbon atoms.[238,239] Vitamin K may act as an electron carrier in biological oxidations,[240,241] and also is involved in the activation of proconvertin (factor VII) in the production of prothrombin.[238] The metabolic relationships of the various K vitamins have been recently discussed.[299]

The K vitamins are isolated by chromatography of an unsaponified ether extract of a dried biological sample. Various adsorbents have been used,[296] although some, like Decalso and alumina,[297] promote decomposition of the vitamin during chromatography. The different forms of vitamin K can be separated from each other by reversed phase partition chromatography on paper impregnated with silicone.[295,298]

Vitamin K is most frequently estimated by bioassay using young chicks. In most other animals, synthesis of the vitamin by intestinal microorganisms is sufficient to supply the requirements for this vitamin. Bioassay of the vitamin is thoroughly discussed by Gyorgy[273] and by Almquist.[300] Vitamin K can be estimated from its ultraviolet spectrum,[236,295] although the absorption decreases rapidly upon exposure to ultraviolet light.[300] The vitamins K exhibit absorption maxima at 243, 248, 260, 269 and 325 mμ; the 248 mμ peak is frequently used for estimation. Colorimetric assays of the vitamins K have used reactions with sodium ethylate,[301] sodium diethyl dithiocarbamate,[302] and xanthene hydride.[319] The synthetic vitamin K_3, menadione, can be estimated colorimetrically using 2,4-dinitrophenylhydrazine.[303]

III. PROSTAGLANDINS

The term prostaglandin was first applied in 1935 to a lipid-soluble acidic fraction of human seminal plasma which stimulated smooth muscle contraction and caused blood pressure to fall.[304-306] Six different structurally related prostaglandins (PGE$_1$, PGE$_2$, PGE$_3$, PGF$_{1\alpha}$, PGF$_{2\alpha}$, PGF$_{3\alpha}$) were isolated in pure form between 1957 and 1964 from vesicular glands or lung tissue.[307-309] Although present in highest concentrations in vesicular

Table V. Properties of the Vitamins K

Name	Synonyms	Formula	Mol. wt.	Crystallization	m.p.	$E_{1\ cm}^{1\%}$, 248 mμ^a	$[\alpha]_D$
Vitamin K$_1$	2-methyl-3-phytyl-1,4-naphthoquinone phylloquinone	$C_{31}H_{46}O_2$	450.71	yellow oil	−20	420	−0.71[21] [236]
Vitamin K$_{2(30)}$	2-methyl-3-farnesyl-farnesyl-1,4-naphthoquinone	$C_{41}H_{56}O_2$	580.90	yellow crystals from EtOH	50 [235]	319 [235]	—
Vitamin K$_{2(35)}$	2-methyl-3-farnesyl-geranylgeranyl-1,4-naphthoquinone	$C_{46}H_{64}O_2$	649.02	yellow crystals from pet. eth.	54 [235]	295 [235]	—
Vitamin K$_3$	2-methyl-1,4-naphthoquinone menadione	$C_{11}H_8O_2$	172.19	yellow crystals	106	1100	—

^{a}The molar extinction coefficient for the 1,4-naphthoquinone system at 248 mμ is about 1900 [236].

Table VI. Structural Relationships of Prostaglandins

Fatty acid precursor	PGE series	PGF series
8,11,14-eicosa-trienoid acid (homo-γ-linolenic)	PGE₁	PGF₁α
5,8,11,14-eicosa-tetraenoic acid (arachidonic)	PGE₂	PGF₂α
5,8,11,14,17-eicosa-pentaenoic acid	PGE₃	PGF₃α

Table VII. Physiological Properties of the Prostaglandins

Prostaglandin tested	Tissue or Organism	Effect	Reference
PGE₁	man	tachycardia; reddening of face; headache; fall of arterial blood pressure and cardiac output	320, 323
PGE₁	cat	reduces duration of contraction of nictitating membrane after sympathetic nervous stimulation	326
PGE₁, PGE₂, PGE₃	rabbit guinea pig	stimulates contraction of jejunum and ileum; reduces blood pressure and heart rate	321
PGE₁	toad bladder	diminishes the increase in permeability to water induced by vasopressin and theophylline	331
PGE₁	rat epididymal fat pad	reduces basal fat mobilization; inhibits stimulation of same by epinephrine, norepinephrine, ACTH, glucagon, and TSH	322
PGE series PGF series	dog	blocks norepinephrine-stimulated increase of plasma FFA concentration (PGF series only 1/10 as active)	324, 325

glands and seminal plasma, the prostaglandins are widely distributed in mammalian organs.[310] The relationship between prostaglandins and the essential fatty acids was established by the demonstrated conversions of homo-γ-linolenic, arachidonic, and eicosa-8,11,14-trienoic acids into prostaglandins (PGE_1, PGE_2 and PGE_3, respectively).[311, 312] The structural relationships of various prostaglandins and fatty acids are shown in Table VI. After subcutaneous or intravenous administration of tritium-labeled PGE_1 to rats, labeled products occur in kidney, liver, lungs, pituitary, adrenals, ovaries, uterus, heart and other organs. Labeled metabolites were found mainly in the urine, with some excretion also via the bile.[313] Conversion of PGE_1 into two metabolites by a soluble enzymatic system of guinea pig lung has been demonstrated.[314] The chemistry and physiology of the prostaglandins have been recently reviewed.[315]

For the isolation[309] of prostaglandins, a tissue homogenate is suspended in ethanol and stirred. The supernatant is then concentrated and extracted once with ethyl acetate to remove neutral lipids. The solution is then acidified (pH 3) and re-extracted with ethyl acetate. The extract is washed with buffer (pH 8) and the buffer is then acidified and extracted with ethyl acetate. After partition of this extract between petroleum ether and 66% ethanol, the aqueous phase is acidified and extracted with ether. The ether extract, washed with water until neutral, contains prostaglandin, which is then purified chromatographically.[316]

The prostaglandins have been separated and characterized by thin-layer chromatography on silver nitrate-impregnated silica gel.[317] Quantitative spectrophotometric estimation of PGE_1, PGE_2, and PGE_3 is possible after alkali isomerization.[318] Gas-liquid chromatography of trimethylsilyl ether derivatives of PGF_{1a}, PGF_{2a}, and PGF_{3a} methyl esters also permits quantitative estimation.[309, 318] The biological activity of the prostaglandins is determined by the relative stimulation of isolated duodenal strips from rabbits compared to a standard preparation of prostaglandin.[307] The physiological properties, recently reviewed by Bergstrom and Samuelsson,[315] are briefly summarized in Table VII.

BIBLIOGRAPHY

1. Porter, J. W., and D. G. Anderson, "The Biosynthesis of Carotenes," *Arch. Biochem. Biophys.*, 97:520, 1962.
2. Goodwin, T. W., (ed.), *The Biosynthesis of Vitamins and Related Compounds*, p. 270, 1963.
3. Chichester, C. O., and T. O. M. Nakayama, P. Bernfeld, (ed.), in *The Biogenesis of Natural Compounds*, p. 475, 1963.
4. Olson, J. A., "The Biosynthesis and Metabolism of Carotenoids, and Retinol (Vitamin A)," *J. Lipid Res.*, 5:281, 1964.
5. Goodwin, T. W., (ed.), *Chemistry and Biochemistry of Plant Pigments*, p. 143, 1965.

6. Zechmeister, L., *Cis-Trans Isomeric Carotenoids, Vitamins A and Arylpolyenes*, p. 251, 1962.

7. Anonymous, "Nomenclature of Carotenoid Pigments," *Chem. Eng. News*, 24:1235, 1946.

8. Karrer, P., "Sur la Nomenclature des Carotenoides," *Bull. Soc. Chim. Biol.*, 30:150, 1948.

9. Krinsky, N. I., and T. H. Goldsmith, "The Carotenoids of the Flagellated Alga, *Euglena gracilis*," *Arch. Biochem. Biophys.*, 91:271, 1960.

10. Briggs, M. H., "The Presence of Vitamin A Alcohol and Aldehyde," *Life Sci.*, 5:223, 1962.

11. Wolken, J. J., J. M. Bowness, and I. J. Scheer, "The Visual Complex of the Insect: Retinene in the Housefly," *Biochim. Biophys. Acta*, 43:531, 1960.

12. Iwata, I., H. Nakata and Y. Sakurai, "The Carotenoids of the Flagellated Alga, *Euglena gracilis*," *Agri. Biol. Chem.*, 25:377, 1961.

13. Valadon, L. R. G., "Carotenoid Pigments of some Lower Asomycetes," *J. Exp. Bot.*, 15:219, 1964.

14. Krinsky, N. I., A. Gordon, and A. I. Stern, "The Appearance of Neoxanthin during the Regreening of Dark-Grown Euglena," *Plant. Physiol.*, 39:441, 1964.

15. Green, J., "Occurrence of Astaxanthin in the Euglenoid *Trachelomonas volvocina*," *Comp. Biochem. Physiol.*, 9:313, 1963.

16. Karrer, P. and E. Jucker, *Carotinoide*, 1948.

17. Fox, D. L., "Metabolic Fractionation, Storage and Display of Carotenoid Pigments by Flamingos," *Comp. Biochem. Physiol.*, 6:1, 1962.

18. Petracek, F. J. and L. Zechmeister, "Determination of Partition Coefficients of Carotenoids as a Tool in Pigment Analysis," *Anal. Chem.*, 28:1484, 1956.

19. Bush, W. V. and L. Zechmeister, "On Some Cleavage Products of the Boron Tri-Fluoride Complexes of α-Carotene, Lycopene and γ-Carotene," *J. Am. Chem. Soc.*, 80:2991, 1958.

20. Goldsmith, T. H. and N. I. Krinsky, "The Epoxide Nature of the Carotenoid, Neoxanthin," *Nature*, 188:491, 1960.

21. Jensen, A., "Alga Carotenoids—Fucoxanthin Monoacetate," *Acta Chem. Scand.*, 15:1604, 1961.

22. Jensen, A., "Alga Carotenoids—The Fucoxanthols—and Fucoxanthin," *Acta Chem. Scand.*, 15:1605, 1961.

23. Nakayama, T. O. M., *Arch. Biochem. Biophys.*, 75:352, 1958.

24. Liaaen Jensen, S., "A Note on the Constitution of Rhodovibrin," *Acta Chem. Scand.*, 13:2143, 1959.

25. Liaaen Jensen, S., "A Note on the Constitution of Bacterioruberine," *Acta Chem. Scand.*, 14:950, 1960.

26. Liaaen Jensen, S., "A Partial Synthesis of Spirilloxanthin and OH-Spirilloxanthin," *Acta Chem. Scand.*, 14:953, 1960.

27. Liaaen Jensen, S., Kgl. Norske Videnskab. Selskabs, Skritter No. 8, 1962.

28. Jungalwala, F. B., and H. A. Cama, "Carotenoids in *Delonix regia* (Gul Mohr) Flower," *Biochem. J.*, 85:1, 1962.

29. Krinsky, N. I., "A Relationship between Partition Coefficients of Carotenoids and their Functional Groups," *Anal. Biochem.*, 6:293, 1963.

30. Morton, R. A., M. Florkin and E. Stotz (eds.), in *Comprehensive Biochemistry*, 3:66, 1962.

31. Ryvarden, L., and S. Liaaen Jensen, "The Carotenoids of *Rhodomicrobium vannielii*," *Acta Chem. Scand.*, 18:643, 1964.

32. Liaaen Jensen, S., E. Hegge and L. M. Jackman, "The Carotenoids of Photosynthetic Green Bacteria," *Acta Chem. Scand.*, 18:1703, 1964.

33. Schmidt, K., S. Liaaen Jensen and J. G. Schlegel, "Die Carotinoide der Thiorhodaceae Okenon als Hauptcarotinoid von Chromatium okenii," *Arch. Mikrobiol.*, 46:117, 1963.

34. Bodea, C., E. Nicoarà, V. Tamas and H. Mantsch, "Zur Kenntnis der IR-Spektran Sauerstoff-Haltiger Carotinoide," *Ann.*, 666:189, 1963.

35. Lunde, K. and L. Zechmeister, "Infrared Spectra and Cis-Trans Configurations of some Carotenoid Pigments," *J. Am. Chem. Soc.*, 77:1647, 1955.

36. Jackman, L. M., and S. Liaaen Jensen, "On the Constitution of the Minor Carotenoids of Rhodopseudomonas," *Acta Chem. Scand.*, 18:1403, 1964.

37. Bolliger, H. R., A. König, and U. Schweiter, "Beitrag zur Dünnschicht-Chromatographieder Carotene," *Chimia*, 18:136, 1964.

38. Colman, B., and W. Vishniac, "Separation of Chloroplast Pigments on Thin Layers of Sucrose," *Biochim. Biophys. Acta*, 82:616, 1964.

39. Davies, B. H., T. W. Goodwin and E. I. Mercer, "Attempts to Detect Lycopersene in Carotenogenic Systems," *Biochem. J.*, 81:40P, 1961.

40. Hager, A., and T. Bertenrath, "Verteilungschromatographische Trennung von Chlorophyllen und Carotinoiden Gruner Pflanzen an Dunnschichen," *Planta*, 58:564, 1962.

41. Rollins, C., "Thin Layer Chromatographic Separation of Leaf Pigments," *J. Chem. Educ.*, 40:32, 1963.

42. Rai, H. and G. F. Lee, "Separation of Planktonic Algal Pigments by Thin Layer Chromatography," *Anal. Chem.*, 36:2208, 1964.

43. Goodwin, T. W., *Comparative Biochemistry of the Carotenoids*, 1952.

44. Goodwin, T. W., Paech and Tracey (eds.), in *Moderne Methoden der Pflanzenanalyse*, 3:272, 1955.

45. Karrer, P., and E. Jucker, "Partial Synthesen des Flavozanthins, Chrysanthemaxanthins, Antheraxanthins, Violaxanthins, Mutatoxanthins and Auroxanthins," *Helv. Chim. Acta*, 28:300, 1945.

46. Karrer, P., and A. Oswald, "Carotinoide aus den Staubbeuteln von Lilium Tigrinum. Ein Neues Carotinoid: Antheraxanthin," *Helv. Chim. Acta*, 18:1303, 1935.

47. Karrer, P., and E. Jucker, "Die Konstitution des Citroxanthins," *Helv. Chim. Acta*, 30:536, 1947.

48. Goodwin, T. W., and M. M. Taha, "The Carotenoids of the Gonads of the Limpets *Patella vulgata* and *Patella depressa*," *Biochem. J.*, 47:244, 1950.

49. Goodwin, T. W., and M. M. Taha, "A Study of the Carotenoids Echinenone and Moxoxanthin with Special Reference to their Probable Identity," *Biochem. J.*, 48:513, 1951.

50. Tischer, J., "Uber die Polyenpigmente der Blaualge Aphanisomenon Flos-Aquae. I. (Carotinoide der Sübwasseralgen, IV. Teil)," *Z. physiol. Chem.*, 251:109, 1938.

51. Heilbron, I. M., "Some Aspects of Algal Chemistry," *J. Chem. Soc.*, 79, 1942.

52. Kuhn, R., J. Stene and N. A. Sörensen, "Über die Verbreitung des Astaxanthins im Tier—und Pflanzenreich," *Ber.*, 72:1688, 1939.

53. Kuhn, R., and N. A. Sörensen, "Uber Astaxanthin und Ovoverdin," *Ber.*, 71:1879, 1938.

54. Stern, K. G., and K. Salomon, "On Ovoverdin, The Carotenoid-Protein Pigment of the Egg of the Lobster," *J. Biol. Chem.*, 122:461, 1938.

55. Ball, E. G., "A Blue Chromoprotein Found in the Eggs of the Goose-Barnacle," *J. Biol. Chem.*, 152:627, 1944.

56. Wald, G., N. Nathanson, W. P. Jencks, and E. Tarr, "Crustacyanin, the Blue Carotenoid-Protein of the Lobster Shell," *Biol. Bull.*, 95:249, 1948.

57. Wolfe, D. A., *Dissert. Abstracts* 25 (8) 4395, 1965.

58. Karrer, P., and F. Benz, "Pflanzenfarbstoffe LVIII. Über ein Neues Vorkommen des Astacins. Ein Beitrag zu Dessen Konstitution," *Helv. Chim. Acta*, 17:412, 1934.

59. deNicola, M., "The Carotenoids of the Carapace of the *Echinoderm ophidiaster ophidianus*," *Biochem. J.*, 56:555, 1954.

60. Vevers, H. G., and N. Millot, *Proc. Zool. Soc. Lond.*, 129:75, 1957.

61. Lederer, E., "Sur Le Pigment Rouge De La Peau De Deux Poissons: Dorade (*Beryx decadactylus*) Et Poisson Rouge (*Carassius auratus*)," *Compt. Rend. Soc. Biol.*, 118:542, 1935.

62. Steven, D. M., "Carotenoid Pigmentation of Trout," *Nature*, 160:540, 1947.

63. Völker, O., *J. Ornithol.*, 102:430, 1961.

64. Fox, D. L., "Metabolic Fractionation, Storage and Display of Carotenoid Pigments by Flamingos," *Comp. Biochem. Physiol.*, 6:1, 1962.

65. Tischer, J., "Über Die Carotinoide Von *Haematococcus pluialis*. I. (Carotinoide Der Sübwasseralgen, III. Teil)," *Z. Physiol. Chem.*, 250:147, 1937.

66. Karrer, P. and J. Rutschmann, "Auroxanthin, Ein Kurzwellig Absorbierender Carotinefarbstoff," *Helv. Chim. Acta*, 25:1624, 1942.

67. Takeda, Y., and T. Ohta, "Über Leprotin, Ein Carotinoid Der Formel $C_{40}H_{54}$," *Z. Physiol. Chem.*, 258:6, 1939.

68. Kuhn, R. and L. Ehmann, "Über Konjugierte Doppelbindungen. XI. Über Das Bixin Und Seinen Abbau Zum Bixan," *Helv. Chim. Acta*, 12:904, 1929.

69. Völker, O., *Carotine und Carotinoide*, 9:282, 1963.

70. Haxo, F., "Carotenoids of the Mushroom *Cantharellus Cinnabarinus*," *Botan. Gaz.*, 112:228, 1950–51.

71. Völker, O., "Canthaxanthin in Vogelfedern," *Naturwiss.*, 48:581, 1961.

72. Fox, D. L., "Carotenoids of the Scarlet Ibis," *Comp. Biochem. Physiol.*, 5:31, 1962.

73. Thommen, H., and H. Wackernagel, "Isolierung und Nachweis von Canthaxanthin im Kleinen Flamingo," *Biochim. Biophys. Acta*, 69:387, 1963.

74. Fox, D. L., "Carotenoids of the Roseate Spoonbill," *Comp. Biochem. Physiol.*, 6:305, 1962.

75. Thommen, H., and H. Wackernagel, "Zum Vorkommen von Keto-Carotinoiden in Crustaceen," *Naturwiss.*, 51:87, 1964.

76. Krinsky, N., "Canthaxanthin, the Major Carotenoid of the Crustacean *Artemia salina*," *Abstracts, VI Int. Cong. Biochem.*, IUB 32:582, 1964.

77. Merlini, L., and G. Cardillo, "Sui Carotenoids di Leptinotarsa Decemlineata Say," *Gazz. Chim. Ital.*, 93:949, 1963.

78. Zechmeister, L., and L. v. Cholnoky, "Untersuchungen Über den Paprika-Farbstoff. I.," *Ann.*, 454:54, 1927.

79. Zechmeister, L., and L. v. Cholnoky, "Untersuchungen Über den Paprika-Farbstoff. VI. Das Pigment des Japanischen Paprikas," *Ann.*, 489:1, 1931.

80. Zechmeister, L., and L. v. Cholnoky, "Untersuchungen Über den Paprika-Farbstoff. VII. (Adsorptionsanalyse des Pigments)," *Ann.*, 509:269, 1934.

81. Garcia, F. M., *Farmacognosia* (Madrid), 12:169, 1952.

82. Karrer, P., and O. Walker, "Pflanzenfarbstoffe LI. Reines α-Carotin," *Helv. Chim. Acta*, 16:642, 1933.

83. Kuhn, R., and H. Brockman, "γ-Carotin (Über das Vitamin des Wachstume, IV. Mitteil)," *Ber.*, 66:408, 1933.

84. Kuhn, R., and H. Brockman, "γ-Carotin (Über das Vitamin des Wachstume, IV. Mitteil)," *Ber.*, 66:407, 1933.

85. Willstaedt, H., "Über Die Farbstoffe Der Früchte von Rosa *Rugosa thune,*" *Chem. Centr.*, 2:707, 1935.

86. Kargl, T. E., F. W. Quackenbush and M. L. Tomes, *Proc. Am. Soc., Hort. Sci.,* 75:574, 1960.

87. Suzue, G., "Enzymatic Conversion of Bacterial Phitoene into δ-Carotene," *Biochim. Biophys. Acta,* 50:593, 1961.

88. Prebble, J. N., "Carotenoid Production in *Cornebacterium fascians* (Telford Dowson)," *Biochem. J.*, 85:13P, 1962.

89. Kargl, T. E., and F. W. Quackenbush, "The Structure of δ-Carotene," *Arch. Biochem. Biophys.*, 88:59, 1960.

90. Karrer, P., and C. H. Eugster, "Synthese von Carotinoiden IV. Synthese Eines ε_1-Carotins," *Helv. Chim. Acta*, 33:1433, 1950.

91. Strain, H. H. and W. M. Manning, "A Unique Polyene Pigment of the Marine Diatom Navicula Torquatum," *J. Am. Chem. Soc.*, 65:2258, 1943.

92. Chapman, D. J. and F. T. Haxo, "Identity of ε-Carotene and ε_1-Carotene," *Plant. Cell Physiol.*, 4:57, 1963.

93. Yamamoto, H. Y., "Comparison of the Carotenoids in Yellow and Red-fleshed *Carica papaya,*" *Nature*, 201:1049, 1964.

94. LeRosen, A. L., and L. Zechmeister, "The Carotenoid Pigments of the Fruit of *Celastrus scandens,*" *Arch. Biochem.*, 1:17, 1943.

95. Nakayama, T. O. M., "The Carotenoids of Rhodopseudomonas I. Carotenoids of the Green Mutant," *Arch. Biochem. Biophys.*, 75:352, 1958.

96. Davis, J. B., L. M. Jackman, P. T. Siddons, and B. C. L. Weedon, "The Structures of Phytoene, Phytofluene, ζ-Carotene, and Neurosporene," *Proc. Chem. Soc.*, July, 261, 1961.

97. Zechmeister, L., and P. Tuzson, "Über das Polyen-Pigment der Orange (I. Mitteil)," *Ber.*, 69:1878, 1936.

98. Zechmeister, L., and P. Tuzson, "Über das Polyen-Pigment der Orange (II. Mitteil): Citraurin," *Ber.*, 70:1966, 1937.

99. Kuhn, R., A. Winterstein and W. Wiegand, "Über Konjugierte Doppelbindungen VI.) Der Farbstoff der Chinesischen Gelbschoten. Uber das Vorkommen von Polyen-Farbstoffen im Pflanzenreiche," *Helv. Chim. Acta*, 11:718, 1928.

100. Kuhn, R., and C. Grundmann, "Über Krypto-xanthin, ein Xanthophyll der Formel $C_{40}H_{56}O$ (Uber das Vitamin des Wachstume, V. Mitteil)," *Ber.*, 66: 1746, 1933.

101. Lenel, R., Thesis, University of Nancy, France, 1961.

102. Wolfe, D. A., and D. G. Cornwell, "Composition and Tissue Distribution of Carotenoids in Crayfish," *Comp. Biochem. Physiol.*, 16:205, 1965.

103. Busch, L., and H. J. Neumann, "Kryptoxanthin in der Hühner-Iris," *Naturwiss.*, 29:782, 1941.

104. Gillam, A. E., and I. M. Heilbron, "Vitamin A-Active Substances in Egg-Yolk," *Biochem. J.*, 29:1064, 1935.

105. Gillam, A. E., and I. M. Heilbron, "The Carotenoids of Butter," *Biochem. J.*, 29:834, 1935.

106. Lederer, E., "Sur la Constitution de la Pectenoxanthine," *Compt. Rend. Soc. Biol.*, 117:411, 1934.

107. Goodwin, T. W., and M. M. Taha, "The Carotenoids of the Gonads of the Limpets *Patella vulgata* and *Patella depressa,*" *Biochem. J.*, 47:244, 1950.

108. Karrer, P., and E. Jucker, "Partial Synthesen des Flavoxanthins, Chrysanthemaxanthins, Antheraxanthins, Violaxanthins, Mutatoxanthins und Auroxanthins," *Helv. Chim. Acta*, 28:300, 1945.

109. Karrer, P., and J. Rutschmann, "Uber die Carotinoide aus Elodea Canadensis," *Helv. Chim. Acta,* 28:1526, 1945.

110. Zechmeister, L., and L. Wallcave, "Action of N-Bromosuccinimide on β-Carotene," *J. Am. Chem. Soc.,* 75:4493, 1953.

111. Strain, H. H., M. R. Thomas and J. J. Katz, "Spectra of Eschscholtzxanthin and other Carotenoid Pigments," *J. Org. Chem.,* 26:5061, 1961.

112. Strain, H. H., "Eschscholtzxanthin: A New Xanthophyll from the Petals of the California Poppy, *Eschscholtzia Californica," J. Biol. Chem.,* 123:425, 1938.

113. Karrer, P., E. Jucker, J. Rutschmann and K. Steinlin, "Zur Kenntnis der Carotinoid-Epoxyde. Naturliches Vorkommen von Xanthophyll-Epoxyd und α-Carotin-Epoxyd," *Helv. Chim. Acta,* 28:1146, 1945.

114. Karrer, P. and J. Rutschmann, "Über die Phytoxanthine der Löwenzahnbluten Flavoxanthin," *Helv. Chim. Acta,* 25:1144, 1942.

115. Kuhn, R., and H. Brockmann, "Flavoxanthin," *Z. physiol. Chem.,* 213:192, 1932.

116. Willstätter, R., and H. J. Page, "Uber Fucoxanthin, $C_{40}H_{54}O_6$," *Ann.,* 404:253, 1914.

117. Heilbron, I. M., and R. F. Phipers, "The Lipochromes of *Fucus vesiculosis," Biochem. J.,* 29:1369, 1935.

118. Willstätter, R., and H. J. Page, "Uber die Pigmente der Braunalgen," *Ann.,* 404:237, 1914.

119. Wald, G., "Galloxanthin, a Carotenoid from the Chicken Retina," *J. Gen. Physiol.,* 31:377, 1948.

120. Schön, K., "Studies on Carotenoids. Gazaniaxanthin," *Biochem. J.,* 32:1566, 1938.

121. Brockmann, H., "Die Carotinoide der Aprikose (*Prunus armeniaca*)," *Z. physiol. Chem.,* 216:47, 1933.

122. Zechmeister, L., and P. Tuzson, "Der Farbstoff der Wasser-Melone," *Ber.,* 63:2881, 1930.

123. Zechmeister, L., and L. v. Cholnoky, "Lycoxanthin und Lycophyll, Zwei Naturliche Derivate des Lycopins," *Ber.,* 69:422, 1936.

124. Karrer, P., and E. Jucker, "Die Konstitution des Citroxanthins," *Helv. Chim. Acta,* 30:536, 1947.

125. Karrer, P., and E. Jucker, "Vorlaüfige Mitteilung Über ein Neues Carotinoid aus Orangenschalen: Citroxanthin," *Helv. Chim. Acta,* 27:1695, 1944.

126. Karrer, P., and J. Rutschmann, "Beitrag zur Kenntnis der Carotinoide aus Oscillatoria Rubrescens," *Helv. Chim. Acta,* 27:1691, 1944.

127. Heilbron, I. M., and B. Lythgoe, "The Chemistry of Algae. Part II. The Carotenoid Pigments of Oscillatoria Rubrescens," *J. Chem. Soc.,* 1376, 1936.

128. Goldsmith, T. H., and N. I. Krinsky, "The Epoxide Nature of the Carotenoid, Neoxanthin," *Nature,* 188:491, 1960.

129. Goodwin, T. W., "Studies in Carotenogenesis. 24. The Changes in Carotenoid and Chlorophyll Pigments in the Leaves of Deciduous Trees during Autumn Necrosis," *Biochem. J.,* 68:503, 1958.

130. Krinsky, N. I., A. Gordon and A. I. Stern, "The Appearance of Neoxanthin During the Regreening of Dark-Grown Euglena," *Plant Physiol.,* 39:441, 1964.

131. Haxo, F., "Studies on the Carotenoid Pigments of Neurospora I. Composition of the Pigment," *Arch. Biochem.,* 20:400, 1949.

132. Zalokar, M., "Isolation of an Acidic Pigment in "Neurospora"," *Arch. Biochem. Biophys.,* 70:568, 1957.

133. Rau, W., and C. Zehender, "Die Carotinoide von Fusarium Aquaeductuum Lagh," *Arch. Mikrobiol.*, 32:423, 1959.

134. Goodwin, T. W., "Identification of the Minor Polyene Components of the Fungus *Phycomyces blakesleeanus* and a Study of Their Synthesis under Various Cultural Conditions," *Biochem. J.*, 50:550, 1952.

135. Rabourn, W. J., F. W. Quackenbush and J. W. Porter, "Isolation and Properties of Phytoene," *Arch. Biochem. Biophys.*, 48:267, 1954.

136. Wallace, V., and J. W. Porter, "Phytofluene," *Arch. Biochem. Biophys.*, 36:468, 1952.

137. Koe, B. K., and L. Zechmeister, "Preparation and Spectral Characteristics of all trans- and a cis-Phytofluene," *Arch. Biochem. Biophys.*, 46:100, 1953.

138. Karrer, P., and U. Solmssen, "Carotinoide aus Purpurbakterien III." *Helv. Chim. Acta*, 19:1019, 1936.

139. Kuhn, R., and H. Brockmann, "Über Rhodo-xanthin, den Arillus-Farbstoff der Eibe (*Taxus baccata*)," *Ber.*, 66:828, 1933.

140. Mackinney, G., "On the Plastid Pigments of Marsh Dodder," *J. Biol. Chem.*, 112:421, 1935.

141. Kuhn, R., and C. Grundmann, *Ber.*, 67:341, 1934.

142. Willstaedt, H., *Svensk. Kemisk. Tidskr.*, 47:113, 1935.

143. Takeda, Y. and T. Ohta, "Ein Neues Bakterien-Carotinoid, Sacinaxanthin." *Z. Physiol. Chem.*, 268:I–II, 1941.

144. Karrer, P. and U. Solmssen, "Die Carotinoide Der Purpurbakterien I." *Helv. Chim. Acta*, 18:1306, 1935.

145. Karrer, P. and H. Koenig, "Carotinoide Der Purpurbakterien V. Uber Rhodoviolascin." *Helv. Chim. Acta*, 23:460, 1940.

146. Kuhn, R. and H. Brockmann, "Bestimmung Von Carotinoiden." *Z. Physiol. Chem.*, 206:41, 1932.

147. Kuhn, R. and E. Lederer, "Taraxanthin, Ein Neues Xanthophyll Mit 4 Sauerstoffatomen." *Z. Physiol. Chem.*, 200:108, 1931.

148. Strain, H. H., "Leaf Xanthophylls: The Action of Acids on Violaranthin, Violeoxanthin, Taraxanthin and Tareoxanthin." *Arch. Biochem. Biophys.*, 48:458, 1954.

149. Booth, V. H., "Taraxien, The Carotenoid Ester in Dandelion Flowers." *Phytochem.*, 3:229, 1964.

150. Lederer, E., "Sur Les Carotenoides D'Une Levure Rouge (*Torula rubra*)." *Compt. Rend.*, 197:1694, 1933.

151. Karrer, P. and J. Rutschmann, "Uber Torularhodin II." *Helv. Chim. Acta*, 28:795, 1945.

152. Karrer, P. and J. Rutschmann, "Uber Torularhodin III." *Helv. Chim. Acta*, 29:355, 1946.

153. Lederer, E., "Sur Les Carotenoides Des Vertebres Inferieurs." *Bull. Soc. Chim. Biol.*, 20:554, 1938.

154. Karrer, P. and E. Jucker, "Uber Weitere Vorkommen Von Carotinoid-Epoxyden. Trollixanthin Und Trollichrom." *Helv. Chim. Acta*, 29:1539, 1946.

155. Karrer, P. and A. Notthafft, "Pflanzenfarbstoffe XLIII. Zur Kenntnis Der Carotinoide Der Bluten." *Helv. Chim. Acta*, 15:1195, 1932.

156. Kuhn, R. and A. Winterstein, "Viola-Xanthin, Das Xanthophyll Des Gelben Stiefmutterchens (Viola Tricolor) (Uber Konjugierta Doppelbundungen, XVI.)." *Ber.*, 64:326, 1931.

157. Karrer, P. and J. Rutschmann, "Auroxanthin, Ein Kurzwellig Absorbierender Carotinfarbstoff." *Helv. Chim. Acta*, 25:1624, 1942.

158. Karrer, P. and J. Rutschmann, "Uber Violaxanthin, Auroxanthin Und Andere Pigmente Der Bluten Von Viola Tricolor." *Helv. Chim. Acta*, 27:1684, 1944.

159. Karrer, P. and U. Solmssen, "B-Citraurin, Ein Abbauprodukt Des Zeaxanthins." *Helv. Chim. Acta,* 21:448, 1938.

160. Karrer, P., H. Salomon, and H. Wehrli, "Pflanzenfarbstoffe XIV. Uber Einen Carotinoidfarbstoff Aus Mais: Zeaxanthin." *Helv. Chim. Acta,* 12:790, 1929.

161. Kuhn, R., A. Winterstein and E. Lederer, "Zur Kenntnis Der Xanthophylle." *Z. Physiol. Chem.,* 197:141, 1931.

162. Zechmeister, L. and P. Tuzson, 'Isolierung Von Komponenten Des Menschlichen Lipochroms." *Z. Physiol. Chem.,* 231:259, 1935.

163. Fox, D. L., *Animal Biochromes and Structural Colours,* p. 191, 1953.

164. Wolman, M. and S. Shoshan, "The Chromolipoids: Dependance of Histochemical Characteristics on the Degree of Polymerification and their Differentiation from DNA," *Histochemie,* 2:69, 1960.

165. Ciaccio, C., *Boll. Soc. Ital. Biol. Sper.,* 27:874, 1951.

166. Zorzoli, G., *Monit. Zool. Ital.,* 61 (Suppl.):381, 1953.

167. Bottino, D., *Riv. Istochim. Norm. e Patol.,* 4:137, 1958.

168. Fisher, L. R. and S. K. Kon, "Vitamin A in the Invertebrates," *Biol. Rev.,* 34:1, 1959.

169. Wald, G., M. Florkin, and H. S. Mason (Eds.), in *Comparative Biochemistry,* 1:311, 1960.

170. Naito, K. and F. H. Wilt, "The Conversion of Vitamin A to Retinene in a Fresh-Water Fish," *J. Biol. Chem.,* 237:3060, 1962.

171. Wilt, F. H., "The Differentiation of Visual Pigments in Metamorphosing Larvae of Rana Catesbeiana," *Devel. Biol.,* 1:199, 1959.

172. Thompson, S. Y., J. Ganguly, and S. K. Kon, "The Conversion of β-Carotene to Vitamin A in the Intestine," *Brit. J. Nutr.,* 3:50, 1949.

173. Bieri, J. G. and C. J. Pollard, "Studies of the Site of Conversion of β-Carotene Injected Intravenously into Rats," *Brit. J. Nutr.,* 8:32, 1954.

174. Zachman, R. D. and J. A. Olson, "The Uptake of C^{14} B Carotene and its Conversion to Retinol Ester (Vitamin A Ester) by the Isolated-Perfused Rat Liver," *J. Biol. Chem.,* 238:541, 1963.

175. Moore, T., *Vitamin A,* p. 180, 1957.

176. Glover, J., "The Conversion of β-Carotene into Vitamin A," *Vitamins Hormones,* 18:371, 1960.

177. Olson, J. A., "The Biosynthesis and Metabolism of Carotenoids and Retiol (Vitamin A)," *J. Lipid Research,* 5:281, 1964.

178. Olson, J. A., "Studies of Patients with Hyperglyceridemia," *Am. J. Clin. Nutr.,* 9:1, 1961.

179. Suzuki, T., I. Koisumi, and Y. Sahashi, *J. Vitaminol.* (Kyoto), 5:102, 1959.

180. Mahadevan, S., P. Seshadri Sastry, and J. Ganguly, "Studies on Metabolism of Vitamin A," *Biochem. J.,* 88:531, 1963.

181. Mahadevan, S., D. S. Deshmuth and J. Ganguly, "The Fate of Intracardially Administered Retinyl Esters in the Rat," *Biochem. J.,* 93:499, 1964.

182. Mahadevan, S., and J. Ganguly, "Further Studies on the Absorption of Vitamin A," *Biochem. J.,* 81:53, 1961.

183 Futterman, S., and J. S. Andrews, "Metabolism of the Retina," *J. Biol. Chem.,* 239:81, 1964.

184. Kinumaki, T., H. Taguchi and K. Iwasaki, *J. Vitaminol.* (Kyoto), 9:160, 1963.

185. Glover, J., T. W. Goodwin and R. A. Morton, "Conversion in Vivo of Vitamin A Aldehyde (Retinene), to Vitamin A," *Biochem. J.,* 43:109, 1948.

186. Zachman, R. D. and J. A. Olson, "A Comparison of Retinene Reductase and Alcohol Dehydrogenase of Rat Liver," *J. Biol. Chem.*, 236:2309, 1961.

187. Elder, T. D. and Y. J. Topper, "The Oxidation of Retinene (Vitamin A Aldehyde) to Vitamin A Acid by Mammalian Steroid-Sensitive Aldehyde Dehydrogenase," *Biochim. Biophys. Acta*, 64:430, 1962.

188. Futterman, S., "Enzymatic Oxidation a-Aldehyde to Vitamin A Acid," *J. Biol. Chem.*, 237:677, 1962.

189. Mahadevan, S., S. K. Murthy and J. Ganguly, "Enzymatic Oxidation of Vitamin A. Aldehyde to Vitamin A Acid by Rat Liver," *Biochem. J.*, 85:326, 1962.

190. Stainer, D. W., T. K. Murray, and J. A. Campbell, "Isomerization of 11-*cis* Vitamin A in Vivo," *Can. J. Biochem. Physiol.*, 38:1219, 1960.

191. Stainer, D. W. and T. K. Murray, "Isomerization of Vitamin A by Tissue Homogenates," *Can. J. Biochem. Physiol.*, 38:1467, 1960.

192. Hubbard, R., "Retinene Isomerase," *J. Gen. Physiol.*, 39:935, 1956.

193. Yoshizawa, T. and G. Wald, "Pre-Lumirhodopsin and the Bleaching of Visual Pigments," *Nature*, 197:1279, 1963.

194. Dowling, J. E. and G. Wald, "The Role of Vitamin A Acid," *Vitamins Hormones*, 18:515, 1960.

195. Wolf, G., J. G. Bergan, and P. R. Sundaresan, "Vitamin A and Mucopolysaccharide, Biosynthesis by Cell-Free Particle Suspension," *Biochim. Biophys. Acta*, 69:524, 1963.

196. Subba Rao, K. P. Seshadri Sastry and J. Ganguly, "Studies on Metabolism of Vitamin A; Enzymatic Synthesis and Hydrolysis of Phenolic Sulphates in Vitamin-A-Deficient Rats," *Biochem. J.*, 87:312, 1963.

197. Dunagin, P. E., E. H. Meadows and J. A. Olson, "Retinayl Beta-Glucuronic Acid: A Major Metabolite of Vitamin A in Rat Bile," *Science*, 148:86, 1965.

198. Malathi, P., K. Subba Rao, P. Seshadri Sastry and J. Ganguly, "Studies on Metabolism of Vitamin A-The Biological Activity of Vitamin A Acid in Rats," *Biochem. J.*, 87:305, 1963.

199. Petzold, E. N., F. W. Quackenbush and Marylin McQuistan, "Zeacarotenes, New Provitamins A from Corn," *Arch. Biochem. Biophys.*, 82:117, 1959.

200. Goodwin, T. W., *The Biosynthesis of Vitamins and Related Compounds*, p. 264, 1963.

201. Glover, M., J. Glover, and R. A. Morton, "Provitamin D_3 in Tissues and the Conversion of Cholesterol to 7-Dehydrocholesterol in Vivo," *Biochem. J.*, 51:1, 1952.

202. Dempsy, M. E., "Properties of a Soluble 7-Dehydrocholesterol Reductase," *Fed. Proc.*, 21:299, 1962.

203. Alexander, G. J., A. M. Gold, and E. Schwenk, "Biogenesis of Yeast Sterols III. The Origin of Carbon 28 of Ergosterol," *J. Biol. Chem.*, 232:599, 1958.

204. Alexander, G. J. and E. Schwenk, "Biogenesis of Yeast Sterols IV. Transmethylation in Ergosterol Synthesis," *J. Biol. Chem.*, 232:611, 1958.

205. Parks, L. W., "S-Adenosylmethionine and Ergosterol Synthesis," *J. Am. Chem. Soc.*, 80:2023, 1958.

206. Goodwin, T. W., *The Biosynthesis of Vitamins and Related Compounds*, p. 240, 1963.

207. Harrison, H. E. and H. C. Harrison, "The Uptake of Radiocalcium by the Skeleton: The Effect of Vitamin D and Calcium Intake," *J. Biol. Chem.*, 185:857, 1950.

208. Harrison, H. E. and H. C. Harrison, "Studies with Radiocalcium: The intestinal Absorption of Calcium," *J. Biol. Chem.*, 188:83, 1951.

209. Zetterström, R., "Phosphorylation of Vitamin D_2, and the Action of the Phosphorylated Compound on Alkaline Kidney Phosphatase," *Nature*, 167: 409, 1951.

210. Albright, F. and E. C. Reifenstein, *The Parathyroid Glands and Metabolic Bone Disease*, p. 134, 1948.

211. Mattill, H. A. and R. E. Conklin, "The Nutritive Properties of Milk, with Special Reference to Reproduction in the Albino Rat," *J. Biol. Chem.*, 44: 137, 1920.

212. Evans, H. M. and K. S. Bishop, "On the Existence of a Hitherto Unrecognized Dietary Factor Essential for Reproduction," *Science*, 55:650, 1922.

213. Evans, H. M., O. H. Emerson, and G. A. Emerson, "The Isolation from Wheat Germ Oil of an Alcohol, α-Tocopherol, having the Properties of Vitamin E," *J. Biol. Chem.*, 113:319, 1936.

214. Green, J., S. A. Price, and L. Gare, "Tocopherols in Microorganisms," *Nature*, 184:1339, 1959.

215. Green, J., P. Mamalis, S. Marcinkiewicz, and D. McHale, "Structure of E-Tocopherol," *Chem. Ind. London*, 79:73, 1960.

216. Green, J., "The Distribution of Tocopherols during the Lifecycle of some Plants," *J. Sci. Food Agri.*, 9:801, 1958.

217. Giovannini, E. and G. Condorelli, *Ric. Sci.*, 78:1863, 1958.

218. Booth, V. H. and A. Hobson-Frohock, "The α-Tocopherol Content of Leaves as Affected by Growth Rate," *J. Sci. Food Agri.*, 12:251, 1961.

219. McCormick, E. C., D. G. Cornwell, and J. B. Brown, "Studies on the Distribution of Tocopherol in Human Serum Lipoproteins," *J. Lipid Res.*, 1:221, 1960.

220. Martius, C. and J. Costelli, "Uber Die Bildung Von Trimethyl-Phytylbenzochinon Aus α-Tokopherol in Mitochondrien," *Biochem. Z.*, 329:449, 1957.

221. Simon, E. J., A. Eisengart, L. Sundheim, and A. T. Milhorat, "The Metabolism of Vitamin E II. Purification and Characterization of Urinary Metabolites of α-Tocopherol," *J. Biol. Chem.*, 221:807, 1956.

222. Harris, R. S. et al., in W. H. Sebrell, Jr., and R. S. Harris, *The Vitamins*, Vol. III, Chapt. 17, 1954.

223. Barnes, R. H., W. O. Lundberg, H. T. Hanson and G. O. Burr, "The Effect of Certain Dietary Ingredients on the Keeping Quality of Body Fat," *J. Biol. Chem.*, 149:313, 1943.

224. Harrison, W. H., et al., "Interconvertions of α-Tocopherol and its Oxidation Poducts," *Biochem. Biophys. Acta*, 21:150, 1956.

225. Miles, S. M. C., et al., "Tocopherol vs. Tocopherol Acetate as a 'Sparer' of Vitamin A," *Proc. Soc. Exptl. Biol. Med.*, 70:162, 1949.

226. Nason, A. and I. R. Lehman, "Tocopherol as an Activator of Cytochrome C Reductase," *Science*, 122:19, 1955.

227. Donaldson, K. O. and A. Nason, "Interrelationship Between Vitamin E and Lipide Cofactor in the Cytochrome C Reductase System," *Proc. Natl. Acad. Sci.*, 43:364, 1951.

228. McKee, R. W., S. B. Binkley, D. W. MacCorqudale, et al., "The Isolation of Vitamins K, and K_2," *J. Am. Chem. Soc.*, 61:1295, 1939.

229. Binkley, S. B., L. C. Cheney, W. F. Holcomb, et al., "The Constitution and Synthesis of Vitamin K," *J. Am. Chem. Soc.*, 61:2558, 1939.

230. Dam, H., A. Geiger, J. Glavind, et al., "Isolierung Des Vitamins K in Hochgereinigter Form," *Helv. Chim. Acta*, 22:310, 1939.

231. Karrer, P. and A. Geiger, "Vitamin K Aus Alfalfa," *Helv. Chim. Acta*, 22: 945, 1939.

232. Kegel, L. P., M. D. Henninger, and F. L. Crane, "Two New Quinones from Chloroplasts," *Biochem. Biophys. Res. Commun.*, 8:294, 1962.

233. Bishop, D. H. L., K. P. Pandya, and W. K. King, "Ubiquinone and Vitamin K in Bacteria," *Biochem. J.*, 83:606, 1962.

234. Isler, O., R. Rüegg, L. H. Chopard-dit-Jean, et al., *Chimia*, 12:69, 1958.

235. Ibid, "Synthese Und Isolierung Von Vitamin K_2 und Isoprenoolgen Verbindungen," *Helv. Chim. Acta*, 41:786, 1958.

236. Isler, O. and O. Wiss, "Chemistry and Biochemistry of the K Vitamins," *Vitamin Hormones*, 17:53, 1959.

237. Lichtenthaler, H. K., *Planta*, 54:431, 1962.

238. Martius, C. and H. O. Esser, "Uber die Konstitution des im Tierkorper aus Methylnaphthochinon gebildeten K-Vitamines," *Biochem. Z.*, 331:1, 1958.

239. Billeter, M. and C. Martius, "Uber die Umwandlung von Phyllochinon (Vitamin K_1) in Vitamin K_2(20) im Tierkorper," *Biochem. Z.*, 333:430, 1960.

240. Martius, C. and D. Nitz-Litzow, "Zum Wirkungsmechanismus des Vitamin K," *Biochem. Z.*, 327:i, 1955.

241. Colpa-Boonstra, J. P. and E. C. Slater, "The Enzymic Oxidation of Reduced Vitamin K_3 (Menadione)," *Biochem. Biophys. Acta*, 23:222, 1957.

242. Goodman, D. S. and H. S. Huang, "Biosynthesis of Vitamin A with Rat Intestinal Enzymes," *Science*, 149:879, 1965.

243. Diplock, A. T., J. Green, and J. Bunyan, "The Determination of Vitamin A in Animal Tissues and its Presence in the Liver of the Vitamin A-Deficient Rat," *Brit. J. Nutr.*, 17:199, 1963.

244. Diplock, A. T., et al., "Studies on Vitamin E-The Simultaneous Determination of Tocopherols, Ubiquinones and Ubichromenols (Substance SC) in Animal Tissue: A," *Biochem. J.*, 76:563, 1960.

245. Bickoff, E. M., in *Methods of Biochemical Analysis*, IV:1, 1957.

246. Lambertsen, G. and O. R. Braekkan, "The Classes of Vitamin A during Chromatography," *Acta Chem. Scand.*, 12:360, 1958.

247. Embree, N. D., S. R. Ames, R. W. Lehman and P. L. Harris, *Methods of Biochemical Analysis*, IV:43, 1957.

248. Moore, T., *Vitamin A*, 1957.

249. Dugan, R. E., N. A. Friegerio, and J. M. Siebert, "Colorimetric Determination of Vitamin A and its Derivatives with Trifluoroacetic Acid," *Anal. Chem.*, 36:114, 1964.

250. Futterman, S. and L. D. Saslaw, "The Estimation of Vitamin A Aldehyde with Thiobarbituric Acid," *J. Biol. Chem.*, 236:1652, 1961.

251. Herting, D. C., E. J. E. Dury, and P. L. Harris, "Determination of 9-cis Isomers of Vitamin A by Reaction with Opsin," *Anal. Biochem.*, 4:459, 1962.

252. Wilkie, J. B., "Corrections for Background in Spectrophotometry Using Different-in-Absorbance Value-Application to Vitamin A," *Anal. Chem.*, 36:896, 1964.

253. Dunagin, P. E., Jr., and J. A. Olson, "Gas Liquid Chromatography of Retinol (Vitamin A) Derivatives," *Anal. Chem.*, 36:756, 1964.

254. Cama, H. R., F. D. Collins, and R. A. Morton, "Spectroscopic Properties of All-Trans-Vitamin A and Vitamin A Acetate Analysis of Liver Oils," *Biochem. J.*, 50:48, 1951.

255. Huisman, H. O., A. Smit, P. H. Van Leeuwen, and J. H. VanRij, "Rearrangement of the Retro-System to the Normal System of Conjugated Double Bonds in the Vitamin A Series," *Rec. Trav. Chem. Pays-bas*, 75:977, 1956.

256. Farrar, K. R., J. C. Hamlet, and H. B. Henbest, et al., "Studies in the Polyene Series. Part XLIII. The Structure and Synthesis of Vitamin A_2 and Related Compounds," *J. Chem. Soc.*, p.2657, 1952.

257. Ball, S., T. W. Goodwin, R. A. Morton, "The Preparation of Retinene,-Vitamin A Aldehyde," *Biochem. J.*, 42:516, 1948.

258. Sebrell, W. H., Jr., and R. S. Harris (Eds.), *The Vitamins*, 1:29, 1954.

259. Sebrell, W. H., Jr., and R. S. Harris (Eds.), *The Vitamins*, 1:63, 1954.

260. Cama, H. R., P. D. Dalvi, and R. A. Morton, "Retinene$_2$ and Vitamin A$_2$," *Biochem. J.*, 52:542, 1952.

261. Brockmann, H. and A. Busse, "Kristallisiertes Vitamin D aus Thunfischleberol," *Naturwissenschaften*, 26:122, 1938.

262. Brockmann, H. and A. Busse, "Die Konstitution des antirachitischen Vitamins der Tunfischleber," *Z. Physiol. Chem.*, 256:252, 1938.

263. Sebrell, W. H., Jr., and R. S. Harris (Eds.) *The Vitamins*, II:131, 1954.

264. Shaw, W. H. C. and J. P. Jefferies, "The Determination of Ergosterol in Yeast," *Analyst*, 78:509, 1953.

265. Davidek, J. and J. Blattna, "Chromatography of Fat-Soluble Vitamins on thin Layers of Alumina," *J. Chromatog.*, 7:204, 1962.

266. Blattna, J. and J. Davidek, "A Simple Detection of Fat-Soluble Vitamins on Alumina thin Layer-Chromatograms," *Experientia*, 17:474, 1961.

267. Jungalwala, F. B. and H. R. Cama, "Separation of Vitamins A$_1$, A$_2$ and Allied Substances by Reverse Phase Paper Chromatography," *J. Chromatog.*, 8:535, 1962.

268. Jensen, A., "Chromatographie Separation of Carotenes and other Chloroplast Pigments on Aluminum Oxide-Containing Paper," *Acta Chem. Scand.*, 14:2051, 1960.

269. Dingle, J. T. and J. A. Lucy, "Vitamin A, Carotenoids and Cell Function," *Biol. Rev.*, 40:422, 1965.

270. Green, J., "Studies on the Irradiation of Ergosterol and 7-Dehydrocholesterol and the Analysis of the Products for Calciferol, Vitamin D$_3$, and Component Sterols," *Biochem. J.*, 49:36, ?32, 1951.

271. Shaw, W. H. C. and J. P. Jefferies, 'The Determination of Ergosterol in Yeast," *Analyst*, 78:509, 1953.

272. Bills, C. E., W. H. Sebrell, Jr., and R. S. Harris (eds.), in *The Vitamins*, II: 215, 1954.

273. Gyorgy, P., *Vitamin Methods*, 1950.

274. Chen, P. S., Jr., A. R. Terepka, K. Lane, and A. Marsh, "Studies of the Stability and Extractibility of Vitamin D," *Anal. Biochem.*, 10:421, 1965.

275. Pénau, H. and G. Hagemann, "Vitamine D$_2$. Etude De La Purification Et Du Dosag De La Vitamine D$_2$ Dans Les Preparations Pharmaceutiques Et De Quelques Esters De Calciferol," *Helv. Chim. Acta*, 29:1366, 1946.

276. Bacharach, A. L., E. L. Smith, and S. G. Stevenson, "Some Properties of Ergosterol and Calciferol," *Analyst*, 58:128, 1933.

277. Bills, E. C., W. H. Sebrell, Jr., and R. S. Harris (eds.), in *The Vitamins*, II: 132, 1954.

278. Huber, W., G. W. Ewing, and J. Kriger, "The Absorption Spectra of the Vitamins and Provitamins D[1]," *J. Am. Chem. Soc.*, 67:609, 1945.

279. Windaus, A. and F. Schenck, U. S. Patent 2,098,984, 1937.

280. Hogness, T. R., A. E. Sidwell, Jr., and F. P. Zscheile, Jr., "The Absorption Spectra of Compounds Related to the Sterols," *J. Biol. Chem.*, 120:239, 1937.

281. Huber, W. and O. W. Barlow, "Chemical and Biological Stability of Crystalline Vitamins D$_2$ and D$_3$ and their Derivatives," *J. Biol. Chem.*, 149:125, 1943.

282. Windaus, A. and B. Güntzel, "Uber einige Bestrahlungsprodukte des 22-Dihydro-Ergosterins," *Ann.*, 538:120, 1939.

283. Moss, A. R., and J. C. Drummond, "A New Method for the Isolation of α- and β-Tocopherols," *Biochem. J.,* 32:1953, 1938.

284. Robeson, C. D., "Crystalling Natural α- and γ-Tocopherols," *J. Am. Chem. Soc.,* 65:1660, 1943.

285. Wall, M. E., "Concentrates of Fat-Soluble Constituents of Leaf Meal Extracts. Preparation by Molecular Distillation," *Ind. Eng. Chem.,* 41:1465, 1949.

286. Baxter, J. G., C. D. Robeson, J. D. Taylor, and R. W. Lehman, "Natural α-, β- and γ-Tocopherols and Certain of Physiological Interest," *J. Am. Chem. Soc.,* 65:918, 1943.

287. Emmerie, A. and C. Engel, "Colorimetric Determination of α-Tocopherol (Vitamin E)," *Rec. Trav. Chim,* 57:1351, 1938.

288. Farber, M., A. T. Milhorat, and H. Rosenkrantz, "Rapid Determination of Plasma Tocopherols," *Proc. Soc. Exptl. Biol. Med.,* 79:225, 1952.

289. Meunier, P. and A. Vinet, "Un Reactif D'oxydation Quantitative Du Tocopherol. Principe D'une Methode De Dosage De La Vitamine E," *Compt. Rend.,* 211:611, 1940.

290. Rosenkrantz, H., "Studies in Vitamin E Deficiency III. The Estimation of Tissue Tocopherol with Phosphomolybdic Acid," *J. Biol. Chem.,* 224:165, 1957.

291. Stern, M. H., C. D. Robeson, and L. Weisler," δ-Tocopherol. I. Isolation from Soybean Oil and Properties," *J. Am. Chem. Soc.,* 69:869, 1947.

292. Rosenkrantz, H., and A. T. Milhorat, "Infra-Red Absorption Spectra of Tocopherols and Some of Their Chemical Products," *J. Biol. Chem.,* 187:83, 1950.

293. Rosenkrantz, H. and A. T. Milhorat, "Some Physical Constants of α-Tocopheryl-Hydroquinone," *J. Am. Chem. Soc.,* 72:3304, 1950.

294. Lichtenthaler, H. K., "A Rapid Method for the Identification of Small Quantities of Lipid-Soluble Vitamins and Quinones in Biological Material," *J. Chromatog.,* 13:166, 1964.

295. Jacobsen, B. K., and H. Dam, "Vitamin K in Bacteria," *Biochim. Biophys. Acta,* 40:211, 1960.

296. Losito, R. and G. J. Millar, *J. Chromatog.,* 14:496, 1964.

297. Green, J. P. and H. Dam, "Adsorptionchromism of 1,4-Naphthoquinones," *Acta Chem. Scand.,* 8:1093, 1954.

298. Green, J. P. and H. Dam, "Paper Chromatography of Vitamin K$_1$ and Related Compounds with some Observations in Products of Ultro-Violet Irradiation," *Acta. Chem. Scand.,* 8:1341, 1954.

299. Martius, C., *Am. J. Clin. Nutr.,* 9:97, 1961.

300. Almquist, H. J., W. H. Sebrell, Jr., and R. S. Harris (eds.), in *The Vitamins,* II:389, 1954.

301. Almquist, H. J. and A. A. Klose, "Color Reactions in Vitamin K Concentrates," *J. Am. Chem. Soc.,* 61:1610, 1939.

302. Irreverre, F. and M. X. Sullivan, "A Colorimetric Test for Vitamin K," *Science,* 94:497, 1941.

303. Cañady, W. J. and J. H. Roe, "The Determination of Menadione and Methods for the Identification of Quinones," *J. Biol. Chem.,* 220:563, 1956.

304. v. Euler, U. S., "On the Specific Vaso-Dilatine and Plain Muscle Stimulating Substances from Accessory Genital Glands in Man and Certain Animals (Prostaglandin and Vesiglandin)," *J. Physiol.,* 88:213, 1936.

305. v. Euler, U. S., "Weitere Untersuchungen uber Prostaglandin, Die physiologisch Aktive Sobstanz Gewisser Genitaldrusen," *Skand. Arch. Physiol.,* 81:65, 1939.

306. Goldblatt, M. W., "Properties of Human Seminal Plasma," *J. Physiol.*, 84: 208, 1935.

307. Bergstrom, S. and J. Sjovall, "The Isolation of Prostaglandin F from Sheep Prostate Glands," *Acta Chem. Scand.*, 14:1693, 1701, 1960.

308. Bergstrom, S., F. Dressler, R. Ryhage, B. Samuelsson, and J. Sjovall, "The Isolation of Two Further Prostaglandins From Sheep Prostate Glands, Prostaglandin and Related Factors 8," *Arkiv. Kemi.*, 19:563, 1962.

309. Samuelsson, B., "Identification of Prostaglandin F in Bovine Lung Prostaglandin and Related Factors 26," *Biochim. Biophys. Acta*, 84:707, 1964.

310. Bergstrom, S., *J. Am. Oil Chem. Soc.*, 42:608, 1965.

311. Bergstrom, S., H. Danielsson, D. Klenberg, and B. Samuelsson, "The Enzymatic Conversion of Essential Fatty Acids into Prostaglandins," *J. Biol. Chem.*, 239:PC4006, 1964.

312. Van Dorp, D. A., R. K. Beerthuis, D. H. Nugteren, and H. Vonkeman, "Enzymatic Conversion of all-cis-Polyunsaturated Fatty Acids into Prostaglandins," *Nature*, 203:839, 1964.

313. Samuelsson, B., "Prostaglandins and Related Factors," *J. Biol. Chem.*, 239:4091, 1964.

314. Anggard, E. and B. Samuelsson, "Prostaglandins and Related Factors," *J. Biol. Chem.*, 239:4097, 1964.

315. Bergstrom, S. and B. Samuelsson, "Prostaglandins" *Ann. Rev. Biochem.*, 34:101, 1965.

316. Samuelsson, B., "Isolation Identification of Prostaglandins for Human Seminal Plasma," *J. Biol. Chem.*, 238:3229, 1963.

317. Green, K. and B. Samuelsson, "Prostaglandins and Related Factors: XIX. Thin-Layer Chromatography of Prostaglandins," *J. Lipid Research*, 5:117, 1964.

318. Bygdeman, M. and B. Samuelsson, *Clin. Chim. Acta*, 10:566, 1964.

319. Schilling, K. and H. Dam, "A Sensitive and Stable Color Reaction for Quantitative Determination of Vitamin K_1," *Acta Chem. Scand.*, 12:347, 1958.

320. Bergstrom, S., H. Duner, U. S. v.Euler, B. Pernow, and J. Sjovall, "Observations on the Effects of Infusion of Prostaglandin E in Man," *Acta Physiol. Scand.*, 45:145, 1959.

321. Bergstrom, S. and U. S. v.Euler, "The Biological Activity of Prostaglandin E_1, E_2 and E_3," *Acta Physiol. Scand.*, 59:493, 1963.

322. Steinberg, D., M. Vaughan, P. Nestel, O. Strand, and S. Bergstrom, "Effect of Prostaglandins E_1 on the Metabolism of the Free Fatty Acids of Plasma in Man," *J. Clin. Invest.*, 43:1533, 1964.

323. Bergstrom, S., L. A. Carlson, L. G. Ekelund, and L. Oro, "Effect of Prostaglandin E_1 on the Metabolism of the Free Fatty Acids of Plasma in Man," *Biochem. J.*, 92:42P, 1964.

324. Bergstrom, S., L. A. Carlson, and L. Oro, "Effect of Prostaglandins on Catecholamine Induced Changes in Free Fatty Acids of Plasma and in Blood Pressure in the Dog," *Acta Physiol. Scand.*, 60:170, 1964.

325. Bergstrom, S., L. A. Carlson, L. G. Ekelund, and L. Oro, "Effect of Prostaglandin E_1 on Blood Pressure, Heart Rate and Concentration of Free Fatty Acids of Plasma in Man," *Proc. Soc. Exptl. Biol. Med.*, 118:110, 1965.

326. Holmes, S. W., E. W. Horton, and I. H. M. Main, "The Effect of Prostaglandin E_1 on Responses of Smooth Muscle to Catechol Amines, Angiotensin and Vasopressin," *Brit. J. Pharmacol.*, 21:538, 1963.

327. Savinov, B. G., "Spectrophotometric Testing in a Series of Carotene Dyes," *Chem. Abstracts*, 54:626d, 1960.

328. Grundmann, C. and Y. Takeda, "Ein neues Bakterien-Carotenoid, Leprotin," *Naturwiss.*, 25:27, 1937.

329. Liaaen Jensen, S., "Bacterial Carotenoids XVI. a Comparative Study of Leprotene and Isorenieratene," *Acta Chem. Scand.*, 18:1562, 1964.

330. Goodwin, T. W., D. G. Land, and M. E. Sissins, "Studies in Carotenogenesis: the Nature of the Carotenoids in the Photosynthetic Bacterium *Rhodopseudomonas spheroides* (Athiorhodaceae)," *Biochem J.*, 64:486, 1956.

331. Orloff, J., J. S. Handler, and S. Bergstrom, "Effect of Prostaglandin (PGE,) on the Permeability Response of Toad Bladder to Vasopressin, Theophylline and Adenosine 3', 5'-Monophosphate," *Nature*, 205:397, 1965.

332. Nair, P. P., C. Bucana, S. de Leon, and D. A. Turner, "Gas Chromatographic Studies of Vitamins D_2 and D_3," *Anal. Chem.*, 37:631, 1965.

333. Curl, A. L., "Structure of the Carotenoid Neoxanthin," *J. Food Sci.*, 30:426, 1965.

334. Embree, N. D. and E. M. Shantz, "Kitol, a New Provitamin A'," *J. Am. Chem. Soc.*, 65:910, 1943.

335. Egger, K., "Die Verbreitung von Vitamin K_1 und Plastochinon in Pflanzen," *Planta*, 64:41, 1965.

336. Karrer, P. and H. Kramer, "Lycopersen, ein Isoprenhomologer Kohlenwasserstoff des Squalens mit 40 C-Atomen," *Helv. Chim. Acta*, 27:1301, 1944.

I. INTRODUCTION

Enzymes are catalysts present in all living organisms. Their function is to catalyze individual biochemical reactions and to direct essentially all the dynamic events of the life process. Enzymes are usually present in minute amounts in the cells. One molecule of enzyme reacts over and over again in acting on thousands or millions of molecules of substrates in a very short period of time. A particular enzyme is usually specific, in that it catalyzes only one kind of reaction and acts only on one type of substrate. Each enzyme discriminates between closely similar chemical compounds.

The presence of an enzyme is detected by the occurrence of the specific reaction which it catalyzes, and the amount of enzyme present is estimated from the reaction velocity. The measurement of this reaction velocity is an essential part of the technique of investigations on enzymes.

Most enzymes can be extracted and isolated from the cell and their catalytic action duplicated in the test tube under controlled conditions. So far, approximately 900 different enzymes have been isolated and characterized.

Enzymes are found to be proteins with molecular weight from about 10,000 to a million; they cannot pass through semi-permeable membranes that allow the passage of water, salt, and other substances of small molecular size. Many enzymes are sensitive to heat and can be inactivated by heating to about 130° F for a few minutes.

II. ENZYME UNITS AND DEFINITIONS

Substrate is a substance on which an enzyme acts and which is activated by the enzyme. The enzyme lowers the necessary *activation energy* (Ea) for the conversion of the substrate to the reactive state.

Enzyme assays should be based upon measurement of initial rates of reaction, and the substrate concentration should be sufficient for saturation of the enzyme. It is essential to establish that the rate of the reaction is proportional to the enzyme concentration under specified assay conditions.

One *unit* (U) of any enzyme should be defined wherever possible as that amount which will catalyze the transformation of one micromole of substrate per minute, or, where more than one bond of each substrate molecule is attacked, one micro-equivalent of the group concerned per minute, under defined conditions.

The *concentration* of an enzyme solution (as distinct from its purity) is usually given as units per ml.

The *specific activity* of an enzyme preparation is defined as units per mg of protein. It is directly related to the purity of the preparation.

The *purity* of an enzyme is increased if the enzyme protein shows homogeneity in sedimentation pattern and in electrophoretic mobility (on paper, starch gel or acrylamide gel). Maximal enzyme specific activity and freedom from other enzyme activities are added criteria. The purity of an enzyme cannot be ascertained on crystallization alone.

The *molecular activity* is defined as the number of molecules of substrate transformed per minute by one molecule of enzyme at optimal substrate concentration, or as units per μmole of enzyme. This is one of the senses in which the term *turnover number* has been used in the past.

When the enzyme has a distinguishing prosthetic group or catalytic center whose concentration can be measured, the catalytic power can be expressed as the *catalytic center activity*, which is defined as the number of molecules of substrate transformed per minute per catalytic center. This is another sense in which the term *turnover number* has been used.

The presence of a non-amino acid component of many enzymes is found to be essential for the enzymatic activity of these conjugated enzyme proteins. The nonprotein component is termed the *coenzyme* (or the prosthetic group); the protein portion, the *apoenzyme;* and the conjugated protein, the *holoenzyme.*

Coenzymes have been known by various names: Nicotinamide-adenine dinucleotide (NAD) = diphosphopyridine nucleotide (DPN) = coenzyme I (Co I) = codehydrogenase I = cozymase. The reduced form of NAD may be written as "reduced NAD," $NADH_2$, or $DPNH_2$.

Nicotinamide-adenine dinucleotide phosphate (NADP) = triphosphopyridine nucleotide (TPN) = coenzyme II (Co II) = codehydrogenase II = phosphocozymase. The reduced form of NADP may be written as "reduced NADP," $NADPH_2$, or $TPNH_2$.

III. ENZYME KINETICS—SYMBOLS AND FORMULAE

Symbols.
  v = observed velocity of enzyme-catalyzed reaction.
  V = maximum velocity, attainable at saturation level of substrates.
  k = rate constant (reaction velocity constant).

K_s = substrate constant, it is the dissociation constant of ES, where

    ES = the enzyme substrate compound (complex),

     E = concentration of the enzyme, and

     S = concentration of the substrate,

K_m = Michaelis constant.

Combination of enzyme with substrate. The mechanism of an enzyme-catalyzed reaction conforms to equilibrium as follows (first described by Michaelis and Menten):

$$E + S \underset{k_{-1}}{\overset{k_{+1}}{\rightleftharpoons}} ES \overset{k_{+2}}{\longrightarrow} E + P$$

where K_{+1} is the rate constant for the formation of ES, k_{-1} is the rate constant for the dissociation of ES to E and S, and K_{+2} is the rate constant for the breakdown of ES to give the product (P).

$$K_m = \frac{k_{-1} + k_{+2}}{k_{+1}}$$

From the mechanism just described, the Michaelis-Menten equation can be derived

$$v = \frac{V(S)}{K_s + (S)} \text{ or } K_s = (S) \left[\frac{V}{v} - 1 \right]$$

when (S) = K_s, v will be equal to $V/2$, the value of (S) which is experimentally to give half maximum velocity is equal to Km. Under such conditions $K_m = K_s$. This equality depends on the truth of the assumption that equilibrium is maintained between ES, E, and S (k_{+2} is small compared with K_{-1}), which may not always be true.

Combination of enzyme with inhibitor. In a reaction E + I → EI (where I is the inhibitor), K_i is the dissociation constant of EI (the inhibitor constant).

In *competitive inhibition*, the extent of inhibition depends on the relative concentrations of substrate and inhibitor. In *noncompetitive inhibition*, the inhibition (inactivation) of the enzyme depends solely on the concentration of the inhibitor.

IV. CLASSIFICATION AND NUMBERING OF ENZYMES*

The International Union of Biochemistry (in 1961 and 1964) recommended a scheme for numbering enzymes, which was closely linked with the classification. The enzymes are divided into groups on the basis of the type of reaction catalyzed, and this, together with the name(s) of the

*See Reference (3)

substrate(s), provides a basis for naming individual enzymes. Each enzyme number contains four elements, separated by points; the first figure shows to which of the six main divisions of the enzyme list the particular enzyme belongs; the second and third figure show the sub-class and sub-sub-class respectively, thus defining the type of reaction, and the fourth is the number of the enzyme within its sub-sub-class.

Enzymes can be divided into six main groups, as follows:

1. **Oxidoreductases.** Enzymes which are concerned with biological oxidation and reduction, and therefore with respiration and fermentation processes. The class includes not only the dehydrogenases and oxidases, but also the peroxidases, which use H_2O_2 as the oxidant, the hydroxylases, which introduce hydroxyl groups, and the oxygenases, which introduce molecular O_2 in place of a double bond in the substrate.

2. **Transferases.** Enzymes which catalyze the transfer of one-carbon groups (methyl-, formyl-, carboxyl-groups), aldehydic or ketonic residues, alkyl groups, nitrogenous groups, and phosphorus- and sulfur-containing groups.

3. **Hydrolases.** Esterases, phosphatases, glycosidases, peptidases, etc.

4. **Lyases.** Enzymes which remove groups from their substrates (not by hydrolysis), leaving double bonds, or which conversely add groups to double bonds. The class also includes decarboxylases, aldolases, dehydratases, etc.

5. **Isomerases.** Racemases, epimerases, cis-trans isomerases, intramolecular oxidoreductases, and intramolecular transferases.

6. **Ligases.** Enzymes which catalyze the joining together of two molecules coupled with the breakdown of a pyrophosphate bond in ATP or a similar triphosphate (also known as synthetases).

BIBLIOGRAPHY

General information; listing of enzymes and reactions:

(1) Boyer, P. D., H. Lardy, and K. Myrback (eds.), *The Enzymes*, 2nd ed., 8 vols., 1958–1963.

(2) Dixon, M. and E. C. Webb, *Enzymes*, 2nd ed., 1964.

(3) "Recommendations (1964) of the International Union of Biochemistry on the Nomenclature and Classification of Enzymes," *Enzyme Nomenclature*, 1965.

For detailed information on procedures for the assay of enzymes:

(4) Bergmeyer, H. U. (ed.), *Methods of Enzymatic Analysis*, 1963.

(5) Colowick, S. P. and N. O. Kaplan (eds.), *Methods in Enzymology*, 7 vols., 1954–1964.

(6) Hoppe-Seyler, Thierfelder, "Handbuch der Physiologisch und Pathologisch-Chemischen Analyse," *Enzyme*, Vol. 6, Part B, 1965.

Table 1. Distribution of Some Enzymes in Animal Tissues

For each enzyme all the activities are expressed with reference to the most active tissue, taken as 100. The figures are not to be taken as accurate values, but merely as showing the general pattern of distribution.

Enzyme	Species	Liver	Kidney	Spleen	Heart	Skeletal muscle	Lung	Gastric mucosa	Small intestine	Large intestine	Pancreas	Brain	Adrenal	Thymus	Thyroid	Testis	Blood
3-hydroxypropionate dehydrogenase (1.1.1.59)	Pig	89	100		100							0					
	Chicken					20											
Lactate dehydrogenase (1.1.1.27) . . .	Rabbit	1	8		14	27	3					29					
	Rat		71		100	25						66					
	Pigeon	2	3		4	6	1					0.4					
Lactate dehydrogenase (1.1.1.27) . . .	Rat	43	20		62		9	20	75		16	23		20		20	
	Mouse		38	15	30	100											
3-hydroxybutyrate de-hydrogenase (1.1.1.30)	Monkey	27															
	Dog	22															
	Cat	28															
	Rabbit	18															
	Guinea pig	6															
	Rat	100	12	2	8	2					2.5	5	8		0	2	
	Mouse	70															
	Frog	14															
Malate dehydrogenase (1.1.1.37) . . .	Rabbit	13	10		26	2						25					
	Rat	19	5		100	38						28					
	Pigeon	28	57		86	80						33					
Isocitrate dehydrogenase (1.1.1.41) . . .	Rat	17	100		85	24	38										
Glycerolphosphate de-hydrogenase (1.1.99.5)	Mouse	70	63		21	71											
	Rabbit					38			23			100					

Enzyme	Species														
D-aminoacid oxidase (1.4.3.3)	Horse	0.5	0.5												
	Sheep	26	100												
	Pig	6	24												
	Dog	12	22												
	Jackal	5	15												
	Cat	2	13												
	Guinea pig	0.5	1	0											
	Rat	0.2	2												
	Hedgehog		0.2											3		
Monoamine oxidase (1.4.3.4)	Man	100	40	0	53	0	24	0							
	Sheep	59	53	9	0.5	15		30	16	2	5				
	Pig	24	43	1	3			8	9	7					
Diamine oxidase (1.4.3.6)	Man	22	27	17		5	3	10							
	Horse	20	70												
	Ox	18	100												
	Sheep	23	54												
	Pig	17	100					8							
	Guinea pig	17	17					100							
	Rat	18	±					3							
	Pigeon	33	15	4	12	7									
Pyrroline-2-carboxylate reductase (1.5.1.1)	Rat	25	100							60					
NAD(P) transhydrogenase (1.6.1.1)	Ox	0	19	0	100			0							
	Pig	54	41	0	54	5		0							
	Rabbit	15	10		10	33		4							
	Pigeon				2.5										
Cytochrome oxidase (1.9.3.1)	Man	7	9	1	20	6	10	10							
	Rabbit	7	12	2	24	5	10	12							
	Guinea pig	10	13	2	24	4	10	15							
	Rat	30	35	11	100	16	10	32							
	Mouse	20	27	5	46	7	14	24							
Cytochrome oxidase (1.9.3.1)	Rat	65	69	15	100	67	14	36	5	10	2.5	2	52	13	
Catalase (1.11.1.6)	Rat	25	12	5	0.1	1	3	1	1			0		0	
	Mouse	100	40	0.1	0.1	0.1		0.1	0						0

Table 1. Distribution of Some Enzymes in Animal Tissues (continued)

For each enzyme all the activities are expressed with reference to the most active tissue, taken as 100. The figures are not to be taken as accurate values, but merely as showing the general pattern of distribution.

Enzyme	Species	Liver	Kidney	Spleen	Heart	Skeletal muscle	Lung	Gastric mucosa	Small intestine	Large intestine	Pancreas	Brain	Adrenal	Thymus	Thyroid	Testis	Blood
Peroxidases (1.11.1.7)	Rat	0	2.5	48	1.5	2	40	37	100	75		1					0
Homogentisate oxygenase (1.13.1.5)	Rat	100	50	0	0	0	0	0	0			0					
Catechol methyltransferase (2.1.1.6)	Rat	100	30	7	3	0	4		4		89	3					
Histamine methyltransferase (2.1.1.8)	Cat	56	<5	56	49	15	64	65	<5			72	52				
	Guinea pig	21	63	78	50	46	85	92	74			100	17				
	Rabbit	62	55	29	32	25	40	60	13			52	27				
	Rat	0	46	0	<5	<5	0	0	29			22	0				
	Mouse	47	73	50	36	25	69	44				62					
Dimethylthetin homo-cysteine methyltransferase (2.1.3)	Dog	52															
	Rabbit	60	9	0		0						0					
	Guinea pig	33	16	0		0						0					
	Rat	48	3	0		0						0					
	Mouse	100															
	Pigeon	29															
	Eel	92															
	Tortoise	10															
Thiaminase I (2.5.1.2)	Carp	10	5	100		0						0.8					
Aspartate aminotransferase (2.6.1.1)	Rat	66	53		100	85						85					
Glutamine-fructose-6-phosphate aminotransferase (2.6.1.16)	Ox	4	35				38		2								
	Rabbit	0							32								
	Rat	100					10		10								
	Pigeon	0															

Enzyme	Species	1	2	3	4	5	6	7	8	9	10	11	12	13	14	Plasma or serum
Phosphoglyceromutase (2.7.5.3)	Ox	11	18		55	55	6		87			43				0.5
	Sheep	7	25		93	100	8		53			38				0.75
Ribonuclease (2.7.7.16)	Rabbit	2	7.5	30	2	2					14					
	Rat	15	10	23	5	9	4				100					
Ribonuclease (2.7.7.16)	Mouse			36							100	23	15		9	0.2
Carboxylesterase (3.1.1.1)	Rat	17	4	4	0.7	0.2		35			87	0.4	0.2			
	Mouse	23	6	6		0.7		3			100	2.5				
Phospholipase B (3.1.1.5)	Rat	43	10	70	3	7	75		100		38					
Acetylcholinesterase (3.1.1.7)	Man		3					9								1.3†(80)
	Horse	7														2.5†(12)
	Ox	0.05		7	2	4			21							1†(18)
	Sheep		2.5				1.5									2†(15)
	Dog	6														2†(11)
	Cat								14							3†(2)
	Guinea pig	4	6						19			13				12†(19)
	Rabbit	35	1				4		11							3†(5)
	Rat	6		25	15	10				23		100		24		6†(10)
	Fowl	55										43				11†(0.7)
	Labrus	23										7				1†(0)
	Scyllium	2					10									2†(0)
	Helix															75
Cholinesterases (3.1.1.8 + 9), using benzoylcholine	Man	9	25													94†(1.6)
	Horse	4	36													100†(1.6)
	Ox			3	12											0.5†(0.5)
	Sheep					24	0.5									2.5†(1)
	Dog							19	5	5		15				68†
	Cat															14†(0)
	Guinea pig	28	24						30							57†(1)
	Rabbit	43	5						9							34†(0)
	Rat	16	2	20	100				100	62		17				7†
	Fowl	50														2†(0.5)
	Labrus	10				7								1.5		1†(1)
	Scyllium	4	2									9				1†(0)
	Helix											4				16

† Plasma or serum (values for erythrocytes in parentheses).

Table 1. Distribution of Some Enzymes in Animal Tissues (continued)

For each enzyme all the activities are expressed with reference to the most active tissue, taken as 100. The figures are not to be taken as accurate values, but merely as showing the general pattern of distribution.

Enzyme	Species	Liver	Kidney	Spleen	Heart	Skeletal muscle	Lung	Gastric mucosa	Small intestine	Large intestine	Pancreas	Brain	Adrenal	Thymus	Thyroid	Testis	Blood
Tropinesterase (3.1.1.10), using atropine	Horse	0	22	10	27	6			55			0	11				0†
	Guinea pig	100															0†
	Rabbit (+)																100† (0)
	Rabbit (−)																0
	Frog	60															
Alkaline phosphatase (3.1.3.1), using glycerol phosphate	Man	0.7	4	0.8			0.8	0.4	10	3			1				
	Dog	2	10	3	0.2	0.1	2		100		3	0.5	1	4	0.3		
	Cat	0.6	12	0.8	0.3	0.1	2	1	65	8	0.3	0.7	2	0.6	0.6		
	Rabbit	1	2	2	0.2	0.2	2		10	4	0.5	1	0.4		0.4		
	Guinea pig	0.3	7		0.4		2	0.2	20				6		1		
	Rat	0.4	5				5						2		3		
	Mouse	0.5	23	1	0.8	1	1		57		0.3		0.4	1	3		
Alkaline phosphatase (3.1.3.1), using phenyl phosphate	Rabbit	0.1	54	1													
	Rat	0.1	39	0.6	0.5	0.1	1				0.1	0.5					
	Mouse	0.1				0.05		0.6	100		0.04	0.4		0.1			
Acid phosphatase (3.1.3.2), using phenyl phosphate	Rat	39	35	100	9	4	23		16			10				17	0.3†
Acid phosphatase (3.1.3.2), using phenyl phosphate	Rabbit	15	100	45		17					19	17					
	Rat	26	16	77		20	35	28	36		10	16					0.4†
	Mouse	13															
Phosphatidate phosphatase (3.1.3.4)	Rat	71	100		32	34						60					

5′-nucleotidase (3.1.3.5)	Horse		4		2	0	1					0.1					
	Ox	2	0		0	0.5	3		1			6				100	
	Dog	0	0		0.1	0.1	2		1			1.5					
	Rabbit	0.1	0		0.1	0.1	1		0.7			0.6				19	
	Rat	2.5	3		6	1	5		3			1.5					
	Pigeon		0		0	0	3					0.1					
Glucose-6-phosphatase	Man																0.1† (0.1)
(3.1.3.9)	Rat	100	31	1	0.8	0.8	0.4	0.4	18			0.8					
Deoxyribonucleotidase	Rabbit	65															
(3.1.4.5)	Rat	41															
	Mouse	89	63	100	55	75	50	38	94		31	25		19			
β-galactosidase (3.2.1.23)	Man		17														
	Rat	42	100	72							10					17	
	Mouse	13	32	45								5				26	
α-mannosidase (3.2.1.24)	Man		32														
	Rat	54	100	22	2	0	13		29		77	5	15			18	0.5
	Mouse	68	99	36	4	3	10		32			8	0			50	
β-acetylaminodeoxy-	Man		100														
glucosidase (3.2.1.30)	Rat	32	60	17	3	0.7	10		10		4	9	8			16	
	Mouse	25	34													10	
β-glucuronidase (3.2.1.31)	Man		11														
	Rat	100	21								5					2	
	Mouse	16	10									0.6				3	
β-glucuronidase (3.2.1.31)	Rat	63	21	100		0.4	20						18		26	0.4	
Leucine aminopeptidase	Man	2	3	2.5		3		1.5	3	2.5	1.5	3		0.8		2.5	0.1†
(3.4.1.1)	Rat	13	100	12	10	10	14		59		11	8					
Arginase (3.5.3.1) . .	Dog	65	0.4	0					0		0				0	0.5	0
	Cat	48	0.4	0	0				0		0				0	0.2	0
	Rabbit	46	2	0	0				0		0				0	0.02	0
	Guinea pig	72	0.4	0	0				0		0				0	0.02	0
	Rat	70	10	4	0	3			0		2	1			0	0.02	0
	Mouse	100	10	1	3	1	14	2	32		3	1		1			
	Fowl	0.01	0.6	0	0	.0					0					0.3	0

† Plasma or serum (values for erythrocytes in parentheses).

Table 1. Distribution of Some Enzymes in Animal Tissues (continued)

For each enzyme all the activities are expressed with reference to the most active tissue, taken as 100. The figures are not to be taken as accurate values, but merely as showing the general pattern of distribution.

Enzyme	Species	Liver	Kidney	Spleen	Heart	Skeletal muscle	Lung	Gastric mucosa	Small intestine	Large intestine	Pancreas	Brain	Adrenal	Thymus	Thyroid	Testis	Blood
Guanine deaminase (3.5.4.3)	Rat	80	76	92	11	0					57	100					
	Mouse	82	86	96					92			76					
Adenosine deaminase (3.5.4.4)	Rabbit	9	19	100		2	20	7	60	25	32	21	38	96	21	65	15
AMP deaminase (3.5.4.6)	Rabbit	0.2	0.5	1	0.5	100	0.5	0.2	1		0.3	1	1			1.5	1
AMP deaminase (3.5.4.6)	Rat	80	96	100	100	0					72	0					
	Mouse	80	84	100		0	80		100			70		80			
ATPase (3.6.1.3) (Ca-activated)	Rat	47	75	48	100	82					42	25					
Histidine decarboxylase (4.1.1.22)	Man	0	0						0								
	Horse		0														
	Ox		0														
	Sheep		0														
	Pig	17	0														
	Dog		0														
	Cat		0														
	Rabbit	15	90	0				0	0								
	Guinea pig	18	100	0			0	0	75								
Aldolases (4.1.2.7 + 8)	Rabbit				0	100						0					
	Rat	6	5	2	6	100						7					
Citrate synthase (4.1.3.7)	Pig	8	22		73	34											
	Dog	6	21		67	2											
	Rabbit	2	13		47	6											
	Rat	6	13		80											4	0.3
	Pigeon	2			63	100											0.3

Enzyme	Species	1	2	3	4	5	6	7	8	9	10	11	12	13	14	15
Carbonic anhydrase (4.2.1.1)	Man	0.6‡	1‡	1‡			0.5‡		0			0.8	0			10
	Whale															25
	Horse											0.7				11
	Ox															20
	Goat															24
	Dog		12									1				30
	Cat	0.6‡	21									1				21
	Rabbit															21
	Guinea pig	0‡	0.2‡	4							16				4	100
	Rat	16	3									1				30
	Rat	0.2‡	2‡									5				
	Mouse	13	37									0.6				
	Fowl				±	±		76								
Fumarate hydratase (4.2.1.2)	Rat	50	47		73											100
	Mouse	100														45
Aconitate hydratase (4.2.1.3)	Rat	35	70			17										
	Mouse	46			100							6				
Glutamine synthetase (6.3.1.2)	Rat	51	2	6		2.5	0.2				1	61			80	
	Mouse	53	1	0.2		0.7	0.4					100			23	
Cytochrome c	Man	3	3	2	30	5	2	2	2	1.5	2		2			
	Horse	2	6		36	14		1						2		0.2
	Ox	3	6	1	43	14						3				
	Pig		14			21						2				
	Dog		14		55	11										
	Rabbit	7	16							4					2	
	Rat	50	80	10	100	22						10				
	Mouse											18				
	Pigeon		67			100						23				0.3 (0.6)

‡ Corrected for blood in tissue.

Reference: Reproduced from Dixon and Webb, *Enzymes*, 2nd ed., 1964.

Table 2. Intracellular Localization of Enzymes in Rodent Liver

The fractions are designated as follows: N, nuclei; Mt, mitochondria; Ms, microsomes; S, supernatant

	N	Mt	Ms	S
A. Enzymes present mainly in the nucleus				
NMN adenylyltransferase (2.7.7.1)	+++	–		+
B. Enzymes present mainly in the mitochondria				
D-3-hydroxybutyrate dehydrogenase (1.1.1.30)	+	++++	–	–
Isocitrate dehydrogenase (1.1.1.41)	–	++++	–	–
Succinate dehydrogenase (1.3.99.1)	–	+++++		
Glutamate dehydrogenase (1.4.1.3)	±	++++	±	–
Urate oxidase (1.7.3.3)	–	+++++	–	–
Cytochrome oxidase (1.9.3.1)		+++++		
Acetyl-CoA acyltransferase (2.3.1.16)	±	+++++	–	
Adenylate kinase (2.7.4.3)	–	++++	–	+
Ribonuclease (2.7.7.16)	–	++++	+	+
Thiosulphate sulphurtransferase (2.8.1.1)	±	++++	–	±
Acid phosphatase (3.1.3.2)	+	++++	+	+
Deoxyribonuclease II (3.1.4.6)	±	++++	±	+
Arylsulphatases A and B (3.1.6.1)	+	+++	+++	+
β-galactosidase (3.2.1.23)	±	++	+++	±
β-acetylaminodeoxyglucosidase (3.2.1.30)	+	+++	++	
C. Enzymes present mainly in the microsomes				
Aryl 4-hydroxylase (1.14.1.1)	–	–	+++	–
Carboxylesterase (3.1.1.1)	–	+	+++	+
Acetylcholinesterase (3.1.1.7)	±	+	+++	–
Cholinesterase (3.1.1.8)	±	±	+++	–
Vitamin A esterase (3.1.1.12)	–	–	+++	–
Cholesterol esterase (3.1.1.13)	+	–	+++	±
Alkaline phosphatase (3.1.3.1)	±	±	+	±
Glucose-6-phosphatase (3.1.3.9)	–	+	+++	–
Arylsulphatase C (3.1.6.1)	±	±	+++	–
Choloyl-CoA synthetase (6.2.1.7)		–	+++	–

Table 2. Intracellular Localization of Enzymes in Rodent Liver (continued)

The fractions are designated as follows: N, nuclei; Mt, mitochondria; Ms, microsomes; S, supernatant

	N	Mt	Ms	S
D. Soluble enzymes, present mainly in the supernatant				
Lactate dehydrogenase (1.1.1.27)	−	−	−	+ + + +
Isocitrate dehydrogenase (1.1.1.42)	−	±	−	+ + +
Glucose-6-phosphate dehydrogenase (1.1.1.49)	−	−	−	+ + + +
Xanthine oxidase (1.2.3.2)	−	−	−	+ + + +
Glutathione reductase (1.6.4.2)	±	−	−	+ + + +
α-glucan phosphorylase (2.4.1.1)	±	−	−	+ + +
Purine nucleoside phosphorylase (2.4.2.1)	−	−	−	+ + + +
Aspartate aminotransferase (2.6.1.1)	−	+	−	+ + +
Glucokinase (2.7.1.2)	−	−	−	+ + + +
Ketohexokinase (2.7.1.3)	−	−	−	+ + + +
Phosphoglucomutase (2.7.5.1)	−	−	−	+ + + +
FMN adenylyltransferase (2.7.7.2)	−	−	−	+ + + +
Hexosediphosphatase (3.1.3.11)	−	−	−	+ + + +
Leucine aminopeptidase (3.4.1.1)	−	±	±	+ + + +
Adenosine deaminase (3.5.4.4)	−	−	−	+ + + +
Aldolase (4.1.2.7)	+	+	−	+ + + +
Aconitate hydratase (4.2.1.3)	±	+	−	+ + + +
E. Enzymes not present mainly in one fraction				
Malate dehydrogenase (1.1.1.37)	−	+ + +	+	+ + +
NADPH$_2$ cytochrome c reductase (1.6.2.3)	±	+ + +	+	+ + +
Catalase (1.11.1.6)	+ +	+	−	+ +
5'-nucleotidase (3.1.3.5)	+	+	+ + +	±
β-glucuronidase (3.2.1.31)	−	+	+ + +	−
NAD(P) nucleosidase (3.2.2.6)	+ +	+	+ + +	+ +
Arginase (3.5.3.1)	+ +	+ + +	+ + +	−
ATPase (3.6.1.3)	+ +	+ + +	+ + +	−
ATPase (3.6.1.4)	−	+	+ +	−
Fumarate hydratase (4.2.1.2)	±	±	+	±

Reference: Reproduced from Dixon and Webb, *Enzymes*, 2nd ed., 1964.

Table 3. Amino Acid Sequences in the Active Centers* of di-isopropylphosphorofluoridate-Sensitive Enzymes

Carboxylesterase (3.1.1.1)
    (Horse liver)

$\overset{\text{P}}{\text{Gly-Glu-Ser-Ala-Gly-Gly-(Ser, Glu)}}$

Cholinesterase (3.1.1.8)
    (horse serum)

$\overset{\text{P}}{\text{Phe-Gly-Glu-Ser-Ala-Gly-(Ala, Ser, Ala)}}$

Trypsin (3.4.4.4) (Ox)
    (pancreas)

$\overset{\text{NH}_2}{\text{Asp-Ser}}$-Cys-Glu-Gly-Gly-Asp-$\overset{\text{P}}{\text{Ser}}$-Gly-Pro-Val-Cys-Ser-Gly-Lys

Chymotrypsin (3.4.4.5)
    (ox pancreas)

$\overset{\text{P}}{\text{Gly-Asp-Ser-Gly-Glu-Ala}}$

Chymotrypsin (3.4.4.5)
    (ox pancreas)

$\overset{\text{P}}{\text{Gly-Asp-Ser-Gly-Gly-Pro-Leu}}$

Pancreatopeptidase E (3.4.4.7)
    (ox pancreas)

$\overset{\text{P}}{\text{Asp-Ser-Gly}}$

Thrombin (3.4.4.13)
    (ox blood)

$\overset{\text{P}}{\text{Asp-Ser-Gly}}$

Subtilopeptidase A
    (3.4.4.16) (B. subtilis)

$\overset{\text{P}}{\text{Thr-Ser-Met-Ala}}$

P denotes the phosphoryl group derived from the organophosphorus reagent used to label the active centre.

*Active center of an enzyme in the active catalytic portion of the enzyme molecule to which substrate molecule(s) is combined and through such interaction enzyme catalysis is accomplished.

Reference: Reproduced from Dixon and Webb, *Enzymes*, 2nd ed., 1964.

Table 4. Enzymes: Classification and Reactions

Systematic name	Recommended trivial name	Reaction
1. OXIDOREDUCTASES		
1.1 Acting on the CH—OH groups of donors		
1.1.1 With NAD or NADP as Acceptor		
1.1.1.1		
Alcohol:NAD oxidoreductase	Alcohol dehydrogenase NRN—Aldehyde reductase	Alcohol + NAD = aldehyde or ketone + reduced NAD

[*Note: Acts on primary or secondary alcohols or hemiacetals; the animal, but not the yeast, enzyme acts also on cyclic secondary alcohols*]

1.1.1.2		
Alcohol:NADP oxidoreductase	Alcohol dehydrogenase (NADP)	Alcohol + NADP = aldehyde + reduced NADP

[*Note: Acts on primary alcohols only*]

1.1.1.3		
L-Homoserine:NAD oxidoreductase	Homoserine dehydrogenase	L-Homoserine + NAD = L-aspartate β-semialdehyde + reduced NAD

[*Note: NADP also acts, more slowly*]

1.1.1.4		
2,3-Butanediol:NAD oxidoreductase	Butanediol dehydrogenase NRN—Butyleneglycol dehydrogenase	2,3-Butanediol + NAD = acetoin + reduced NAD
1.1.1.5		
Acetoin:NAD oxidoreductase	Acetoin dehydrogenase	Acetoin + NAD = diacetyl + reduced NAD
1.1.1.6		
Glycerol:NAD oxidoreductase	Glycerol dehydrogenase	Glycerol + NAD = dihydroxyacetone + reduced NAD

[*Note: Also acts on 1,2-propanediol*]

1.1.1.7		
1,2-Propanediol-1-phosphate: NAD oxidoreductase	Propanediol-phosphate dehydrogenase	1,2-Propanediol 1-Phosphate + NAD = hydroxyacetone phosphate + reduced NAD
1.1.1.8		
L-Glycerol-3-phosphate: NAD oxidoreductase	Glycerol-3-phosphate dehydrogenase	L-Glycerol 3-phosphate + NAD = dihydroxyacetone phosphate + reduced NAD

[*Note: Also acts on 1,2-propanediol phosphate*]

1.1.1.9		
Xylitol:NAD oxidoreductase (D-xylulose-forming)	D-Xylulose reductase	Xylitol + NAD = d-xylulose + reduced NAD

[*Note: Also acts as an L-erythrulose reductase*]

NRN—*non recommended name*

Table 4. Enzymes: Classification and Reactions (continued)

Systematic name	Recommended trivial name	Reaction
1.1.1.10		
Xylitol:NADP oxidoreductase (L-xylulose-forming)	L-Xylulose reductase	Xylitol + NADP = L-xylulose + reduced NAD
1.1.1.11		
D-Arabinitol:NAD oxidoreductase	D-Arabinitol dehydrogenase	D-Arabinitol + NAD = D-xylulose + reduced NAD
1.1.1.12		
L-Arabinitol:NAD oxidoreductase (L-xylulose-forming)	L-Arabinitol dehydrogenase	L-Arabinitol + NAD = L-xylulose + reduced NAD
1.1.1.13		
L-Arabinitol:NAD oxidoreductase (L-ribulose-forming)	L-Arabinitol dehydrogenase (ribulose-forming)	L-Arabinitol + NAD = L-ribulose + reduced NAD
1.1.1.14		
L-Iditol:NAD oxidoreductase	L-Iditol dehydrogenase	L-Iditol + NAD = L-sorbose + reduced NAD
[*Note: Also acts on D-glucitol (giving D-fructose) and other closely related sugar alcohols*]		
1.1.1.15		
D-Iditol:NAD oxidoreductase	D-Iditol dehydrogenase	D-Iditol + NAD = D-sorbose + reduced NAD
[*Note: Also converts xylitol to L-xylulose and L-glucitol to L-fructose*]		
1.1.1.16		
Galactitol:NAD oxidoreductase	Galactitol dehydrogenase	Galactitol + NAD = D-tagatose + reduced NAD
[*Note: Also converts other alditols containing an L-threo configuration adjacent to a primary alcohol group to the corresponding sugars*]		
1.1.1.17		
D-Mannitol-1-phosphate: NAD oxidoreductase	Mannitol-1-phosphate dehydrogenase	D-Mannitol 1-phosphate + NAD = D-fructose 6-phosphate + reduced NAD
1.1.1.18		
meso-Inositol:NAD oxidoreductase	Inositol dehydrogenase	*meso*-Inositol + NAD = *meso*-inosose-2 + reduced NAD
1.1.1.19		
L-Gulonate:NADP oxidoreductase	Glucuronate reductase	L-Gulonate + NADP = D-glucuronate + reduced NADP
[*Note: Also reduces D-galacturonate*]		
1.1.1.20		
L-Gulono-γ-lactone:NADP oxidoreductase	Glucuronolactone reductase	L-Gulono-γ-lactone + NADP = D-glucurono-γ-lactone + reduced NADP
1.1.1.21		
Alditol:NADP oxidoreductase	Aldose reductase	Alditol + NADP = aldose + reduced NADP
[*Note: Wide specificity*]		
1.1.1.22		
UDPglucose:NAD oxidoreductase	UDPG dehydrogenase	UDPglucose + 2 NAD + H_2O = UDPglucuronate + 2 reduced NAD

Table 4. Enzymes: Classification and Reactions (continued)

Systematic name	Recommended trivial name	Reaction
1.1.1.23		
L-Histidinol:NAD oxidoreductase	Histidinol dehydrogenase	L-Histidinol + 2 NAD = L-histidine + 2 reduced NAD
[*Note: Also oxidizes L-histidinal*]		
1.1.1.24		
Quinate:NAD oxidoreductase	Quinate dehydrogenase	Quinate + NAD = 5-dehydroquinate + reduced NAD
1.1.1.25		
Shikimate:NADP oxidoreductase	Shikimate dehydrogenase	Shikimate + NADP = 5-dehydroshikimate + reduced NADP
1.1.1.26		
Glycollate:NAD oxidoreductase	Glyoxylate reductase	Glycollate + NAD = glyoxylate + reduced NAD
[*Note: Reduces glyoxylate to glycollate or hydroxypyruvate to D-glycerate*]		
1.1.1.27		
L-Lactate:NAD oxidoreductase	Lactate dehydrogenase	L-Lactate + NAD = pyruvate + reduced NAD
[*Note: Also oxidizes other L-2-hydroxymonocarboxylic acids. NADP also acts, more slowly*]		
1.1.1.28		
D-Lactate:NAD oxidoreductase	D-Lactate dehydrogenase	D-Lactate + NAD = pyruvate + reduced NAD
1.1.1.29		
D-Glycerate:NAD oxidoreductase	Glycerate dehydrogenase	D-Glycerate + NAD = hydroxypyruvate + reduced NAD
1.1.1.30		
D-3-Hydroxybutyrate:NAD oxidoreductase	3-Hydroxybutyrate dehydrogenase	D-3-Hydroxybutyrate + NAD = acetoacetate + reduced NAD
[*Note: Also oxidizes other 3-hydroxymonocarboxylic acids*]		
1.1.1.31		
3-Hydroxyisobutyrate:NAD oxidoreductase	3-Hydroxy-isobutyrate dehydrogenase	3-Hydroxyisobutyrate + NAD = methylmalonate semialdehyde + reduced NAD
1.1.1.32		
Mevalonate:NAD oxidoreductase	Mevaldate reductase	Mevalonate + NAD = mevaldate + reduced NAD
1.1.1.33		
Mevalonate:NADP oxidoreductase	Mevaldate reductase (NADP)	Mevalonate + NADP = mevaldate + reduced NADP
1.1.1.34		
Mevalonate:NADP oxidoreductase (acylating CoA)	Hydroxymethyl-glutaryl-CoA reductase	Mevalonate + CoA + 2 NADP = 3-hydroxy-3-methylglutaryl-CoA + 2 reduced NADP
1.1.1.35		
L-3-Hydroxyacyl-CoA:NAD oxidoreductase	3-Hydroxyacyl-CoA dehydrogenase NRN— β-hydroxyacyl dehydrogenase, β-ketoreductase	L-3-Hydroxyacyl-CoA + NAD = 3-oxo-acyl-CoA + reduced NAD
[*Note: Also oxidizes S-3-hydroxyacyl-N-acylthioethanolamine and S-3-hydroxyacyl-hydrolipoate*]		

Table 4. Enzymes: Classification and Reactions (continued)

Systematic name	Recommended trivial name	Reaction
1.1.1.36		
D-3-Hydroxyacyl-CoA:NADP oxidoreductase	Acetoacetyl-CoA reductase	D-3-Hydroxyacyl-CoA + NADP = 3-oxo-acyl-CoA + reduced NADP
1.1.1.37		
L-Malate:NAD oxidoreductase	Malate dehydrogenase	L-Malate + NAD = oxalacetate + reduced NAD
[Note: Also oxidizes some other 2-hydroxy-dicarboxylic acids]		
1.1.1.38		
L-Malate:NAD oxidoreductase (decarboxylating)	Malate dehydrogenase (decarboxylating) NRN— "Malic" enzyme	L-Malate + NAD = pyruvate + CO_2 + reduced NAD
[Note: Also decarboxylates added oxaloacetate]		
1.1.1.39		
L-Malate:NAD oxidoreductase (decarboxylating)	Malate dehydrogenase (decarboxylating) NRN— "Malic" enzyme	L-Malate + NAD = pyruvate + CO_2 + reduced NAD
[Note: Does not decarboxylate added oxaloacetate]		
1.1.1.40		
L-Malate:NADP oxidoreductase (decarboxylating)	Malate dehydrogenase (decarboxylating) (NADP) NRN— "Malic" enzyme	L-Malate + NADP = pyruvate + CO_2 + reduced NADP
[Note: Also decarboxylates added oxaloacetate]		
1.1.1.41		
threo-D_s-Isocitrate:NAD oxidoreductase (decarboxylating)	Isocitrate dehydrogenase	threo-D_s-Isocitrate + NAD = 2-oxoglutarate + CO_2 + reduced NAD
[Note: Does not decarboxylate added oxalosuccinate]		
1.1.1.42		
threo-D_s-Isocitrate:NADP oxidoreductase (decarboxylating)	Isocitrate dehydrogenase (NADP)	threo-D_s-Isocitrate + NADP = 2-oxoglutarate + CO_2 + reduced NADP
[Note: Also decarboxylates added oxalosuccinate]		
1.1.1.43		
6-Phospho-D-gluconate:NAD(P) oxidoreductase	Phosphogluconate dehydrogenase NRN— 6-Phosphogluconic dehydrogenase	6-Phospho-D-gluconate + NAD(P) = 6-phospho-2-keto-D-gluconate + reduced NAD(P)
1.1.1.44		
6-Phospho-D-gluconate:NADP oxidoreductase (decarboxylating)	Phosphogluconate dehydrogenase (decarboxylating)	6-Phospho-D-gluconate + NADP = D-ribulose 5-phosphate + CO_2 + reduced NADP

NRN—*non recommended name*

Table 4. Enzymes: Classification and Reactions (continued)

Systematic name	Recommended trivial name	Reaction
1.1.1.45 L-Gulonate:NAD oxidoreductase	L-Gulonate dehydrogenase	L-Gulonate + NAD = 3-keto-L-gulonate + reduced NAD
[Note: Also oxidizes other L-3-hydroxyacids]		
1.1.1.46 L-Arabinose:NAD oxidoreductase	L-Arabinose dehydrogenase	L-Arabinose + NAD = L-arabinono-γ-lactone + reduced NAD
1.1.1.47 β-D-Glucose:NAD(P) oxidoreductase	Glucose dehydrogenase	β-D-Glucose + NAD(P) = D-glucono-δ-lactone + reduced NAD(P)
[Note: Also oxidizes D-xylose]		
1.1.1.48 D-Galactose:NAD oxidoreductase	Galactose dehydrogenase	D-Galactose + NAD = D-galactono-γ-lactone + reduced NAD
1.1.1.49 D-Glucose-6-phosphate:NADP oxidoreductase	Glucose-6-phosphate dehydrogenase NRN— "Zwischenferment"	D-Glucose-6-phosphate + NADP = D-glucono-δ-lactone 6-phosphate + reduced NADP
[Note: Also acts slowly on β-D-glucose and other sugars. Certain bacterial preparations also reduce NAD as well as NADP]		
1.1.1.50 3-α-Hydroxysteroid:NAD(P) oxidoreductase	3-α-Hydroxysteroid dehydrogenase	Androsterone + NAD(P) = androstane-3, 17-dione + reduced NAD(P)
[Note: Also acts on other 3-α-hydroxysteroids]		
1.1.1.51 3 (or 17)-β-Hydroxysteroid: NAD(P) oxidoreductase	β-Hydroxysteroid dehydrogenase	Testosterone + NAD(P) = Δ^5-androstene-3, 17-dione + reduced NAD(P)
[Note: Also acts on other 3-β-or 17-β-hydroxysteroids]		
1.1.1.52 3-α-Hydroxycholanate:NAD oxidoreductase	α-Hydroxycholanate dehydrogenase	3-α-Hydroxycholanate + NAD = 3-oxocholanate + reduced NAD
[Note: Also acts on other 3-α-hydroxysteroids with an acidic side-chain]		
1.1.1.53 20-Dihydrocortisone:NAD oxidoreductase	Cortisone reductase	20-Dihydrocortisone + NAD = cortisone + reduced NAD
[Note: Also acts on other 17, 20, 21-trihydroxysteroids]		
1.1.1.54 Allyl-alcohol:NADP oxidoreductase	Allyl alcohol dehydrogenase	Allyl alcohol + NADP = acrolein + reduced NADP
[Note: Acts slowly on saturated primary alcohols]		
1.1.1.55 1,2-Propanediol:NADP oxidoreductase	Lactaldehyde reductase	1,2-Propanediol + NADP = L-lactaldehyde + reduced NADP

Table 4. Enzymes: Classification and Reactions (continued)

Systematic name	Recommended trivial name	Reaction
1.1.1.56 Ribitol:NAD oxidoreductase	Ribitol dehydrogenase	Ribitol + NAD = D-ribulose + reduced NAD
1.1.1.57 D-Mannonate:NAD oxidoreductase [*Note: Also reduces D-tagaturonate*]	Fructuronate reductase	D-Mannonate + NAD = D-fructuronate + reduced NAD
1.1.1.58 D-Altronate:NAD oxidoreductase	Tagaturonate reductase	D-Altronate + NAD = D-tagaturonate + reduced NAD
1.1.1.59 3-Hydroxypropionate:NAD oxidoreductase	3-Hydroxy-propionate dehydrogenase	3-Hydroxypropionate + NAD = malonate semialdehyde + reduced NAD
1.1.1.60 D-Glycerate:NAD(P) oxidoreductase	Tartronate semialdehyde reductase	D-Glycerate + NAD(P) = tartronate semialdehyde + reduced NAD(P)
1.1.1.61 4-Hydroxybutyrate:NAD oxidoreductase	4-Hydroxybutyrate dehydrogenase	4-Hydroxybutyrate + NAD = succinate semialdehyde + reduced NAD
1.1.1.62 Oestradiol:NAD 17-β-oxidoreductase	Oestradiol 17-β-dehydrogenase	Oestradiol + NAD = oestrone + reduced NAD
1.1.1.63 17-β-Hydroxysteroid:NAD 17-β-oxidoreductase	Testosterone 17-β-dehydrogenase	Testosterone + NAD = Δ^5-androstene-3,17-dione + reduced NAD
1.1.1.64 17-β-Hydroxysteroid:NADP 17-β-oxidoreductase	Testosterone 17-β-dehydrogenase (NADP)	Testosterone + NADP = Δ^5-androstene-3,17-dione + reduced NADP
1.1.1.65 Pyridoxin:NADP oxidoreductase [*Note: Also oxidizes pyridoxin phosphate*]	Pyridoxin dehydrogenase	Pyridoxin + NADP = pyridoxal + reduced NADP
1.1.1.66 10-Hydroxydecanoate:NAD oxidoreductase [*Note: Also acts, more slowly, on 9-hydroxynonanoate and 11-hydroxyundecanoate*]	ω-Hydroxydecanoate dehydrogenase	10-Hydroxydecanoate + NAD = 10-oxodecanoate + reduced NAD
1.1.1.67 Mannitol:NAD oxidoreductase	Mannitol dehydrogenase	Mannitol + NAD = fructose + reduced NAD
1.1.1.68 5-Methyltetrahydrofolate:NAD oxidoreductase	5,10-Methylene-tetrahydrofolate reductase	5-Methyltetrahydrofolate + NAD = 5,10-methylenetetrahydro-folate + reduced NAD

Table 4. Enzymes: Classification and Reactions (continued)

Systematic name	Recommended trivial name	Reaction
1.1.1.69		
D-Gluconate:NAD(P) oxidoreductase	5-Ketogluconate reductase	D-Gluconate + NAD(P) = 5-keto-D-gluconate + reduced NAD(P)
1.1.1.70		
D-Glucurono-γ-lactone:NAD oxidoreductase	D-Glucuronolactone dehydrogenase	D-Glucurono-γ-lactone + NAD + 2 H_2O = D-glucarate + reduced NAD
1.1.2 With a Cytochrome as an Acceptor		
1.1.2.2		
D-Mannitol:ferricytochrome oxidoreductase	Mannitol dehydrogenase	D-Mannitol + ferricytochrome = D-fructose + ferrocytochrome
[*Note: Also oxidizes erythritol, D-glucitol, D-arabinitol and ribitol*]		
1.1.2.3		
L-Lactate:ferricytochrome c oxidoreductase	Lactate dehydrogenase	L-Lactate + 2 ferricytochrome c = pyruvate + 2 ferrocytochrome c
[*Note: Identical with cytochrome* b_2: *a flavohaemoprotein*]		
1.1.2.4		
D-Lactate:ferricytochrome c oxidoreductase	D-Lactate dehydrogenase	D-Lactate + 2 ferricytochrome c = pyruvate + 2 ferrocytochrome c
[*Note: A flavoprotein*]		
1.1.3 With Oxygen as Acceptor		
1.1.3.1		
Glycollate:oxygen oxidoreductase	Glycollate oxidase	Glycollate + O_2 = glyoxylate + H_2O_2
[*Note: A flavoprotein. Also oxidizes L-lactate and glyoxylate, more slowly*]		
1.1.3.2		
L-Lactate:oxygen oxidoreductase	Lactate oxidase	L-Lactate + O_2 = acetate + CO_2 + H_2O_2
[*Note: A flavoprotein*]		
1.1.3.3		
L-Malate:oxygen oxidoreductase	Malate oxidase	L-Malate + O_2 = oxaloacetate + (?)
1.1.3.4		
β-D-Glucose:oxygen oxidoreductase	Glucose oxidase NRN-Glucose aerodehydrogenase, notatin	β-D-Glucose + O_2 = D-glucono-δ-lactone + H_2O_2
[*Note: A flavoprotein*]		
1.1.3.5		
D-Hexose:oxygen oxidoreductase	Hexose oxidase	β-D-Glucose + O_2 = D-glucono-δ-lactone + H_2O_2
[*Note: A flavoprotein. Also oxidizes D-galactose, D-mannose, maltose, lactose and cellobiose*]		
1.1.3.6		
Cholesterol:oxygen oxidoreductase	Cholesterol oxidase	Cholesterol + O_2 = Δ^4-cholestene-3-one + (?)

Table 4.   Enzymes: Classification and Reactions (continued)

Systematic name	Recommended trivial name	Reaction
1.1.3.7		
Aryl-alcohol:oxygen oxidoreductase	Aryl-alcohol oxidase	An aromatic primary alcohol $+ O_2$ = an aromatic aldehyde $+ H_2O_2$

[*Note: Oxidizes many primary alcohols containing an aromatic ring; best substrates were β-naphthyl carbinol and 3-methoxybenzyl alcohol*]

1.1.3.8		
L-Gulono-γ-lactone:oxygen oxidoreductase	L-Gulonolactone oxidase	L-Gulono-γ-lactone $+ O_2$ = L-*xylo*hexulonolactone $+ H_2O_2$

[*Note: The product spontaneously isomerizes to L-ascorbate*]

NRN—*non recommended name*

1.1.3.9		
D-Galactose:oxygen oxidoreductase	Galactose oxidase	D-Galactose $+ O_2$ = D-*galacto*hexodialdose $+ H_2O_2$

[*Note: A cuproprotein. Oxidizes at the 6-position of D-galactose*]

1.1.99 With other Acceptors

1.1.99.1		
Choline: (acceptor) oxidoreductase	Choline dehydrogenase	Choline $+$ acceptor = betaine aldehyde $+$ reduced acceptor
1.1.99.2		
L-2-Hydroxyglutarate: (acceptor) oxidoreductase	2-Hydroxyglutarate dehydrogenase	L-2-Hydoxyglutarate $+$ acceptor = 2-oxoglutarate $+$ reduced acceptor
1.1.99.3		
D-Gluconate: (acceptor) oxidoreductase	Gluconate dehydrogenase	D-Gluconate $+$ acceptor = 2-keto-D-gluconate $+$ reduced acceptor
1.1.99.4		
2-Keto-D-gluconate: (acceptor) oxidoreductase	Ketogluconate dehydrogenase	2-Keto-D-gluconate $+$ acceptor = 2,5-diketo-D-gluconate $+$ reduced acceptor
1.1.99.5		
L-Glycerol-3-phosphate: (acceptor) oxidoreductase	Glycerolphosphate dehydrogenase	L-Glycerol 3-phosphate $+$ acceptor = dihydroxyacetone phosphate $+$ reduced acceptor

[*Note: Formerly EC 1.1.2.1*]

1.1.99.6		
D-2-Hydroxyacid: (acceptor) oxidoreductase	D-2-Hydroxyacid dehydrogenase	D-Lactate $+$ acceptor = pyruvate $+$ reduced acceptor

[*Note: A flavoprotein. Acts on a variety of D-2-hydroxy-acids*]

1.2 Acting on the aldehyde or keto-group of donors

    1.2.1 With NAD or NADP as Acceptor

1.2.1.1		
Formaldehyde:NAD oxidoreductase	Formaldehyde dehydrogenase	Formaldehyde $+$ NAD $+ H_2O$ = formate $+$ reduced NAD

[*Note: Needs reduced glutathione*]

1.2.1.2		
Formate:NAD oxidoreductase	Formate dehydrogenase	Formate $+$ NAD = $CO_2 +$ reduced NAD

Table 4. Enzymes: Classification and Reactions (continued)

Systematic name	Recommended trivial name	Reaction
1.2.1.3 Aldehyde:NAD oxidoreductase	Aldehyde dehydrogenase	Aldehyde + NAD + H_2O = acid + reduced NAD
[*Note: Wide specificity*]		
1.2.1.4 Aldehyde:NADP oxidoreductase	Aldehyde dehydrogenase (NADP)	Aldehyde + NADP + H_2O = acid + reduced NADP
1.2.1.5 Aldehyde:NAD(P) oxidoreductase	Aldehyde dehydrogenase (NAD(P))	Aldehyde + NAD(P) + H_2O = acid + reduced NAD(P)
1.2.1.7 Benzaldehyde:NADP oxidoreductase	Benzaldehyde dehydrogenase	Benzaldehyde + NADP + H_2O = benzoate + reduced NADP
1.2.1.8 Betaine-aldehyde:NAD oxidoreductase	Betaine aldehyde dehydrogenase	Betaine aldehyde + NAD + H_2O = betaine + reduced NAD
1.2.1.9 D-Glyceraldehyde-3-phosphate: NADP oxidoreductase	Glyceraldehyde-phosphate dehydrogenase, triosephosphate dehydrogenase	D-Glyceraldehyde 3-phosphate + NADP + H_2O = 3-phospho-D-glycerate + reduced NADP
1.2.1.10 Aldehyde:NAD oxidoreductase (acylating CoA)	Aldehyde dehydrogenase (acylating)	Aldehyde + CoA + NAD = acyl-CoA + reduced NAD
1.2.1.11 L-Aspartate-β-semialdehyde: NADP oxidoreductase (phosphorylating)	Aspartate semialdehyde dehydrogenase	L-Aspartate β-semialdehyde + phosphate + NADP = L-β-aspartylphosphate + reduced NADP
1.2.1.12 D-Glyceraldehyde-3-phosphate: NAD oxidoreductase (phosphorylating)	Glyceraldehyde-phosphate dehydrogenase, triosephosphate dehydrogenase	D-Glyceraldehyde 3-phosphate + phosphate + NAD = 1,3-diphospho-D-glyceric acid + reduced NAD

[*Note: Also acts very slowly on D-glyceraldehyde and some other aldehydes; thiols can replace phosphate*]

1.2.1.13 D-Glyceraldehyde-3-phosphate: NADP oxidoreductase (phosphorylating)	Glyceraldehyde-phosphate dehydrogenase (NADP), triosephosphate dehydrogenase (NADP)	D-Glyceraldehyde 3-phosphate + phosphate + NADP = 1,3-diphospho-D-glyceric acid + reduced NADP

Table 4.   Enzymes: Classification and Reactions (continued)

Systematic name	Recommended trivial name	Reaction
1.2.1.14		
IMP:NAD oxidoreductase	IMP dehydrogenase	IMP + NAD + H_2O = xanthosine 5′-phosphate + reduced NAD
1.2.1.15		
Malonate-semialdehyde: NAD(P) oxidoreductase	Malonate semialdehyde dehydrogenase	Malonate semialdehyde + NAD(P) = malonate + reduced NAD(P)
1.2.1.16		
Succinate-semialdehyde: NAD(P) oxidoreductase	Succinate semialdehyde dehydrogenase	Succinate semialdehyde + NAD(P) = succinate + reduced NAD(P)
1.2.1.17		
Glyoxylate:NADP oxidoreductase (acylating CoA)	Glyoxylate dehydrogenase	Glyoxylate + CoA + NADP = oxalyl-CoA + reduced NADP
1.2.1.18		
Malonate-semialdehyde: NAD(P) oxidoreductase (acylating CoA)	Malonate semialdehyde dehydrogenase (acylating)	Malonate semialdehyde + CoA + NAD(P) = acetyl-CoA + CO_2 + reduced NAD(P)
1.2.1.19		
4-Aminobutyraldehyde:NAD oxidoreductase	Aminobutyraldehyde dehydrogenase	4-Aminobutyraldehyde + NAD = 4-aminobutyrate + reduced NAD
[Note: Δ^1-*Pyrroline was used as source of substrate*]		
1.2.1.20		
Glutarate-semialdehyde:NAD oxidoreductase	Glutarate semialdehyde dehydrogenase	Glutarate semialdehyde + NAD = glutarate + reduced NAD

1.2.2 With a Cytochrome as an Acceptor

1.2.2.1		
Formate:ferricytochrome b_1 oxidoreductase	Formate dehydrogenase	Formate + ferricytochrome b_1 = CO_2 + ferrocytochrome b_1
1.2.2.2		
Pyruvate:ferricytochrome b_1 oxidoreductase	Pyruvate dehydrogenase	Pyruvate + ferricytochrome b_1 = acetate + CO_2 + ferrocytochrome b_1
[Note: A flavoprotein requiring thiamine pyrophosphate]		

1.2.3 With Oxygen as Acceptor

1.2.3.1		
Aldehyde:oxygen oxidoreductase	Aldehyde oxidase	Aldehyde + H_2O + O_2 = acid + H_2O_2
[Note: A flavohaemoprotein containing Mo. Also oxidizes quinoline and pyridine derivatives]		
1.2.3.2		
Xanthine:oxygen oxidoreductase	Xanthine oxidase NRN— Hypoxanthine oxidase	Xanthine + H_2O + O_2 = urate + H_2O_2

[Note: A flavoprotein containing Mo. Also oxidizes hypoxanthine, some other purines and pterins, and aldehydes]

NRN—*non recommended name*

Table 4. Enzymes: Classification and Reactions (continued)

Systematic name	Recommended trivial name	Reaction
1.2.3.3		
Pyruvate:oxygen oxidoreductase (phosphorylating)	Pyruvate oxidase	Pyruvate + phosphate + O_2 = acetylphosphate + CO_2 + H_2O_2
[*Note: A flavoprotein requiring thiamine phosphate*]		
1.2.3.4		
Oxalate:oxygen oxidoreductase	Oxalate oxidase NRN— Aero-oxalo dehydrogenase	Oxalate + O_2 = 2 CO_2 + H_2O_2
[*Note: A flavoprotein*]		
1.2.4 With Lipoate as Acceptor		
1.2.4.1		
Pyruvate:lipoate oxidoreductase (acceptor-acetylating)	Pyruvate dehydrogenase	Pyruvate + oxidized lipoate = 6-S-acetylhydrolipoate + CO_2
[*Note: Requires thiamine pyrophosphate; possibly a system*]		
1.2.4.2		
2-Oxoglutarate:lipoate oxidoreductase (acceptor-acylating)	Oxoglutarate dehydrogenase	2-Oxoglutarate + oxidized lipoate = 6-S-succinylhydrolipoate + CO_2
[*Note: Requires thiamine pyrophosphate; possibly a system*]		
1.2.99 With other Acceptor		
1.2.99.1		
Uracil: (acceptor) oxidoreductase	Uracil dehydrogenase	Uracil + acceptor = barbiturate + reduced acceptor
[*Note: Also oxidizes thymine*]		
1.3 Acting on the CH—CH group of donors		
1.3.1 With NAD or NADP as Acceptor		
1.3.1.1		
4,5-Dihydro-uracil:NAD oxidoreductase	Dihydro-uracil dehydrogenase	4,5-Dihydro-uracil + NAD = uracil + reduced NAD
1.3.1.2		
4,5-Dihydro-uracil:NADP oxidoreductase	Dihydro-uracil dehydrogenase (NADP)	4.5-Dihydro-uracil + NADP = uracil + reduced NADP
[*Note: Also acts on dihydrothymine*]		
1.3.1.3		
4,5-β-Dihydrocortisone:NADP Δ^4-oxidoreductase	Cortisone β-reductase	4,5-β-Dihydrocortisone + NADP = cortisone + reduced NADP
1.3.1.4		
4,5-α-Dihydrocortisone:NADP Δ^4-oxidoreductase	Cortisone α-reductase	4,5-α-Dihydrocortisone + NADP = cortisone + reduced NADP
1.3.1.5		
3,5-Cyclohexadiene-1,2-diol: NADP oxidoreductase	Catechol reductase	3,5-Cyclohexadiene-1,2-diol + NADP = catechol + reduced NADP

NRN—*non recommended name*

Table 4.   Enzymes: Classification and Reactions (continued)

Systematic name	Recommended trivial name	Reaction
1.3.2 With a Cytochrome as an Acceptor		
1.3.2.3		
L-Galactono-γ-lactone: ferricytochrome c oxidoreductase	Galactonolactone dehydrogenase	L-Galactono-γ-lactone $+$ 2 ferricytochrome $c =$ L-ascorbate $+$ 2 ferrocytochrome c
1.3.3 With Oxygen as Acceptor		
1.3.3.1		
L-4,5-Dihydro-orotate:oxygen oxidoreductase	Dihydro-orotate dehydrogenase	L-4,5-Dihydro-orotate $+$ $O_2 =$ orotate $+$ H_2O_2 (?)

[Note: A flavoprotein containing 1 FAD and 1 FMN group per molecule. NAD can replace O_2; reduced NAD can replace dihydro-orotate]

Systematic name	Recommended trivial name	Reaction
1.3.99 With other Acceptors		
1.3.99.1		
Succinate: (acceptor) oxidoreductase	Succinate dehydrogenase	Succinate $+$ acceptor $=$ fumarate $+$ reduced acceptor

[Note: A flavoprotein]

Systematic name	Recommended trivial name	Reaction
1.3.99.2		
Butyryl-CoA: (acceptor) oxidoreductase	Butyryl-CoA dehydrogenase NRN—Butyryl dehydrogenase, ethylene reductase	Butyryl-CoA $+$ acceptor $=$ crotonoyl-CoA $+$ reduced acceptor

[Note: A flavoprotein; forms with another flavoprotein ("electron-transferring flavo-protein") a system reducing cytochrome c and other acceptors. Formerly EC 1.3.2.1]

Systematic name	Recommended trivial name	Reaction
1.3.99.3		
Acyl-CoA: (acceptor) oxidoreductase	Acyl-CoA dehydrogenase NRN— Acyl dehydrogenase	Acyl-CoA $+$ acceptor $=$ 2,3-dehydroacyl-CoA $+$ reduced acceptor

[Note: A flavoprotein; forms with another flavoprotein ("electron-transferring flavo-protein") a system reducing cytochrome c and other acceptors. Formerly EC 1.3.2.2]

Systematic name	Recommended trivial name	Reaction
1.3.99.4		
3-Ketosteroid:(acceptor) Δ^1-oxidoreductase	3-Ketosteroid Δ^1-dehydrogenase	A 3-ketosteroid $+$ acceptor $=$ a Δ^1-3-ketosteroid $+$ reduced acceptor
1.3.99.5		
3-Ketosteroid:(acceptor) Δ^4-oxidoreductase	3-Ketosteroid Δ^4-dehydrogenase	A 3-ketosteroid $+$ acceptor $=$ a Δ^4-3-ketosteroid $+$ reduced acceptor
1.4 Acting on the CH—NH$_2$ group of donors		
1.4.1 With NAD or NADP as Acceptor		
1.4.1.1		
L-Alanine:NAD oxidoreductase (deaminating)	Alanine dehydrogenase	L-Alanine $+$ H_2O $+$ NAD $=$ pyruvate $+$ NH_3 $+$ reduced NAD

NRN—non recommended name

Table 4. Enzymes: Classification and Reactions (continued)

Systematic name	Recommended trivial name	Reaction
1.4.1.2 L-Glutamate:NAD oxidoreductase (deaminating)	Glutamate dehydrogenase	L-Glutamate + H_2O + NAD = 2-oxoglutarate + NH_3 + reduced NAD
1.4.1.3 L-Glutamate:NAD(P) oxidoreductase (deaminating) [*Note: A zinc-protein*]	Glutamate dehydrogenase (NAD(P))	L-Glutamate + H_2O + NAD(P) = 2-oxoglutarate + NH_3 + reduced NAD(P)
1.4.1.4 L-Glutamate:NADP oxidoreductase (deaminating)	Glutamate dehydrogenase (NADP)	L-Glutamate + H_2O + NADP = 2-oxoglutarate + NH_3 + reduced NADP
1.4.1.5 L-Amino-acid:NAD oxidoreductase (deaminating) [*Note: Acts on aliphatic amino acids*]	L-Amino-acid dehydrogenase	An L-amino acid + H_2O + NAD = a 2-oxo-acid + NH_3 + reduced NAD
1.4.1.6 5-Aminovalerate:NAD oxidoreductase (cyclizing)	D-Proline reductase	5-Aminovalerate + NAD = D-proline + reduced NAD

1.4.3 With Oxygen as Acceptor

Systematic name	Recommended trivial name	Reaction
1.4.3.1 D-Aspartate:oxygen oxidoreductase (deaminating) [*Note: A flavoprotein*]	D-Aspartate oxidase	D-Aspartate + H_2O + O_2 = oxaloacetate + NH_3 + H_2O_2
1.4.3.2 L-Amino-acid:oxygen oxidoreductase (deaminating)	L-Amino-acid oxidase NRN— Ophio-amino-acid oxidase (for the snake enzyme only)	An L-amino acid + H_2O + O_2 = a 2-oxo-acid + NH_3 + H_2O_2

[*Note: A flavoprotein. The enzyme from liver and kidney also oxidizes 2-hydroxy acids; that from snake venom does not*]

Systematic name	Recommended trivial name	Reaction
1.4.3.3 D-Amino-acid:oxygen oxidoreductase (deaminating) [*Note: A flavoprotein. Wide specificity for D-amino acids*]	D-Amino-acid oxidase	A D-amino acid + H_2O + O_2 = a 2-oxo-acid + NH_3 + H_2O_2
1.4.3.4 Monoamine:oxygen oxidoreductase (deaminating)	Monoamine oxidase NRN—Tyraminase, amine oxidase	A monoamine + H_2O + O_2 = an aldehyde + NH_3 + H_2O_2

[*Note: A cuproprotein. Acts on primary, secondary and tertiary amines*]

NRN—*non recommended name*

Table 4. Enzymes: Classification and Reactions (continued)

Systematic name	Recommended trivial name	Reaction
1.4.3.5		
Pyridoxaminephosphate:oxygen oxidoreductase (deaminating)	Pyridoxamine-phosphate oxidase	Pyridoxamine phosphate + $H_2O + O_2 =$ pyridoxal phosphate + NH_3 + H_2O_2

[*Note: A flavoprotein. Also oxidizes pyridoxin 5-phosphate and pyridoxin*]

1.4.3.6		
Diamine:oxygen oxidoreductase (deaminating)	Diamine oxidase, histaminase	A diamine + $H_2O + O_2 =$ an aminoaldehyde + NH_3 + H_2O_2

[*Note: A pyridoxal-phosphate protein. Also oxidizes histamine*]

1.5 Acting on the C—NH group of donors

1.5.1 With NAD or NADP as Acceptor

1.5.1.1		
L-Proline:NAD(P) 2-oxidoreductase	Pyrroline-2-carboxylate reductase	L-Proline + NAD(P) = Δ^1-pyrroline-2-carboxylate + reduced NAD(P)

[*Note: Reduces Δ^1-pyrroline-2-carboxylate to L-proline or Δ^1-piperidine-2-carboxylate to L-pipecolate*]

1.5.1.2		
L-Proline:NAD(P) 5-oxidoreductase	Pyrroline-5-carboxylate reductase	L-Proline + NAD(P) = Δ^1-pyrroline-5-carboxylate + reduced NAD(P)

[*Note: Also reduces Δ^1-pyrroline-3-hydroxy-5-carboxylate to L-hydroxyproline*]

1.5.1.3		
5,6,7,8-Tetrahydrofolate:NADP oxidoreductase	Tetrahydrofolate dehydrogenase NRN—Folic acid reductase	5,6,7,8-Tetrahydrofolate + NADP = 7,8-dihydrofolate + reduced NADP

[*Note: Also slowly oxidizes 7,8-dihydrofolate to folate*]

1.5.1.4		
7,8-Dihydrofolate:NADP oxidoreductase	Dihydrofolate dehydrogenase	7,8-Dihydrofolate + NADP = folate + reduced NADP
1.5.1.5		
5,10-Methylenetetra-hydrofolate:NADP oxidoreductase	Methylenetetra-hydrofolate dehydrogenase	5,10-Methylenetetrahydrofolate + H^+ + NADP = 5,10-methenyltetrahydrofolate + H_2O + reduced NADP

1.5.3 With Oxygen as Acceptor

1.5.3.1		
Sarcosine:oxygen oxidoreductase (demethylating)	Sarcosine oxidase	Sarcosine + $H_2O + O_2 =$ glycine + HCHO + H_2O_2
1.5.3.2		
N-Methyl-L-amino-acid:oxygen oxidoreductase (demethylating)	N-Methyl-amino-acid oxidase	An N-Methyl-L-amino acid + $H_2O + O_2 =$ an L-amino acid + HCHO + H_2O_2

[*Note: A flavoprotein*]

Table 4. Enzymes: Classification and Reactions (continued)

Systematic name	Recommended trivial name	Reaction
1.5.3.3 Spermine:oxygen oxido-reductase (donor-cleaving)	Spermine oxidase	Spermine + H_2O + O_2 = $H_2N \cdot (CH_2)_3 \cdot NH \cdot (CH_2)_3 \cdot CHO$ + $H_2N \cdot (CH_2)_3 \cdot NH_2$ + H_2O_2
[*Note: Also oxidizes spermidine*]		

1.6 Acting on reduced NAD or NADP

1.6.1 With NAD or NADP as Acceptor

1.6.1.1 Reduced-NADP:NAD oxidoreductase	NAD(P) transhydro-genase NRN—Pyridine nucleotide transhydrogenase, transhydrogenase	Reduced NADP + NAD = NADP + reduced NAD

[*Note: Also acts with deaminocoenzymes*]

1.6.2 With a Cytochrome as Acceptor

1.6.2.2 Reduced-NAD:ferricyto-chrome b_5 oxidoreductase	Cytochrome b_5 reductase	Reduced NAD + 2 ferricyto-chrome b_5 = NAD + 2 ferrocytochrome b_5

[*Note: A flavoprotein*]

1.6.4 With a Disulphide Compound as Acceptor

1.6.4.1 Reduced-NAD:L-cystine oxidoreductase	Cystine reductase	Reduced NAD + L-cystine = NAD + 2 L-cysteine
1.6.4.2 Reduced-NAD(P):oxidized-glutathione oxidoreductase	Glutathione reductase	Reduced NAD(P) + oxidized glutathione = NAD(P) + 2 glutathione

[*Note: A flavoprotein*]

1.6.4.3 Reduced-NAD:lipoamide oxidoreductase	Lipoamide dehydro-genase NRN—Diaphorase, lipoyl dehydro-genase	Reduced NAD + lipoamide = NAD + dihydro-lipoamide

[*Note: A flavoprotein*]

1.6.4.4 Reduced-NAD(P):protein-disulphide oxidoreductase	Protein disulphide reductase	Reduced NAD(P) + protein-disulphide = NAD(P) + protein-dithiol

1.6.5 With a Quinone or Related Compound as Acceptor

1.6.5.4 Reduced-NAD(P): oxidized-ascorbate oxidoreductase	Oxidized ascorbate reductase	Reduced NAD(P) + oxidized ascorbate = NAD(P) + ascorbate

1.6.6 With a Nitrogenous Group as Acceptor

NRN—*non recommended name*

Table 4. Enzymes: Classification and Reactions (continued)

Systematic name	Recommended trivial name	Reaction
1.6.6.1		
Reduced-NAD: nitrate oxidoreductase	Nitrate reductase	Reduced NAD + nitrate = NAD + nitrite + H_2O
[*Note: A flavoprotein containing a metal*]		
1.6.6.2		
Reduced-NAD(P): nitrate oxido-reductase	Nitrate reductase (NAD(P))	Reduced NAD(P) + nitrate = NAD(P) + nitrite + H_2O
[*Note: A flavoprotein*]		
1.6.6.3		
Reduced-NADP: nitrate oxidoreductase	Nitrate reductase (NADP)	Reduced NADP + nitrate = NADP + nitrite + H_2O
[*Note: A flavoprotein containing Mo*]		
1.6.6.4		
Reduced-NAD(P): nitrite oxidoreductase	Nitrite reductase	3 Reduced NAD(P) + nitrite = 3 NAD(P) + NH_4OH + H_2O
[*Note: A flavoprotein containing a metal*]		
1.6.6.6		
Reduced-NAD:hyponitrite oxidoreductase	Hyponitrite reductase	2 Reduced NAD + hyponitrite = 2 NAD + 2 NH_2OH
1.6.6.7		
Reduced-NADP: dimethylaminoazobenzene oxidoreductase	Azobenzene reductase	Reduced NADP + dimethylaminoazobenzene = NADP + dimethyl-*p*-phenylene-diamine + aniline
1.6.6.8		
Reduced-NADP: GMP oxidoreductase (deaminating)	GMP reductase	Reduced NADP + GMP = NADP + IMP + NH_3
1.6.99 With other Acceptors		
1.6.99.1		
Reduced-NADP: (acceptor) oxidoreductase	Reduced NADP dehydrogenase NRN—"Old yellow enzyme"	Reduced NADP + acceptor = NADP + reduced acceptor
[*Note: A flavoprotein*]		
1.6.99.2		
Reduced-NAD(P): (acceptor) oxidoreductase	Reduced NAD(P) dehydrogenase NRN—Menadione reductase, phylloquinone reductase, DT-diaphorase	Reduced NAD(P) + acceptor = NAD(P) + reduced acceptor
[*Note: A flavoprotein. Inhibited by dicoumarol. Formerly EC 1.6.5.2*]		
1.6.99.3		
Reduced-NAD: (acceptor) oxidoreductase	Reduced NAD dehydrogenase NRN—Cytochrome c reductase	Reduced NAD + acceptor = NAD + reduced acceptor
[*Note: A flavoprotein. After preparations have been subjected to certain treatments cytochrome c may act as acceptor. Formerly EC 1.6.2.1*]		

NRN—*non recommended name*

Table 4. Enzymes: Classification and Reactions (continued)

Systematic name	Recommended trivial name	Reaction
1.6.99.4		
Reduced-NADP: ferredoxin oxidoreductase	Ferredoxin-NADP reductase	Reduced NAD + oxidized ferredoxin = NAD + reduced ferredoxin

1.7 Acting on other nitrogenous compounds as donors

1.7.3 With Oxygen as Acceptor

1.7.3.1		
Nitroethane:oxygen oxidoreductase	Nitroethane oxidase	$C_2H_5NO_2 + H_2O + O_2 =$ $CH_3CHO + HNO_2 + H_2O_2$

[*Note: Acts on some other aliphatic nitro-compounds*]

1.7.3.2		
N-Acetylindoxyl:oxygen oxidoreductase	Acetylindoxyl oxidase	N-Acetylindoxyl + $O_2 =$ N-acetylisatin + (?)
1.7.3.3		
Urate: oxygen oxidoreductase	Urate oxidase NRN—Uricase	Urate + $O_2 =$ unidentified products

[*Note: a copper-protein*]

1.7.99 With other Acceptors

1.7.99.1		
Ammonia: (acceptor) oxidoreductase	Hydroxylamine reductase	Ammonia + acceptor = hydroxylamine + reduced acceptor

[*Note: A flavoprotein. Reduced pyocyanine, methylene blue or flavins act as donor for the reduction of hydroxylamine*]

1.7.99.2		
Nitrogen: (acceptor) oxidoreductase	Nitric oxide reductase	N_2 + acceptor = 2 NO + reduced acceptor

[*Note: A flavoprotein. Reduced pyocyanine acts as donor for the reduction of NO*]

1.7.99.3		
Nitric oxide: (acceptor) oxidoreductase	Nitrite reductase	2 NO + 2 H_2O + acceptor = 2 nitrite + reduced acceptor

[*Note: A flavoprotein. Reduced pyocyanine, flavins, etc. act as donor for the reduction of nitrite. Formerly EC 1.6.6.5*]

1.8 Acting on sulphur groups of donors

1.8.1 With NAD or NADP as Acceptor

1.8.1.2		
Hydrogen-sulphide:NADP oxidoreductase See also 1.6.4.1–4	Sulphite reductase	H_2S + 3 NADP + 3 $H_2O =$ sulphite + 3 reduced NADP

1.8.3 With Oxygen as Acceptor

1.8.3.1		
Sulphite:oxygen oxidoreductase	Sulphite oxidase	Sulphite + O_2 + $H_2O =$ sulphate + H_2O_2

[*Note: A haemoprotein*]

1.8.3.2		
Thiol:oxygen oxidoreductase	Thiol oxidase	$4 \, R{:}CR' \cdot SH + O_2 =$ $2 \, R{:}CR' \cdot S \cdot S \cdot CR'{:}R + 2 \, H_2O$

[*Note: R may be =S or =O, or a variety of other groups. The enzyme is not specific for R′*]

NRN—*non recommended name*

Table 4. Enzymes: Classification and Reactions (continued)

Systematic name	Recommended trivial name	Reaction

1.8.4 With a Disulphide Compound as Acceptor

1.8.4.1

Glutathione:homocystine oxidoreductase	Glutathione-homocystine transhydrogenase	2 Glutathione + homocystine = oxidized glutathione + 2 homocysteine

1.8.4.2

Glutathione: protein-disulphide oxidoreductase	Protein disulphide reductase	2 Glutathione + protein-disulphide = oxidized glutathione + protein-dithiol

[*Note: Reduces insulin and some other proteins*]

1.8.5 With a Quinone or Related Compound as Acceptor

1.8.5.1

Glutathione:dehydroascorbate oxidoreductase	Glutathione dehydrogenase	2 Glutathione + dehydroascorbate = oxidized glutathione + ascorbate

1.8.6 With a Nitrogenous Group as Acceptor

1.8.6.1

Glutathione:polyolnitrate oxidoreductase	Nitrate ester reductase	2 Glutathione + polyol nitrate = oxidized glutathione + nitrite + unidentified product

1.9 Acting on haem groups of donors

1.9.3 With Oxygen as Acceptor

1.9.3.1

Ferrocytochrome c:oxygen oxidoreductase	Cytochrome oxidase NRN— Cytochrome a_3	4 Ferrocytochrome c + O_2 = 4 ferricytochrome c + 2 H_2O

[*Note: A cytochrome of the* a *type containing Cu*]

1.9.3.2

Ferrocytochrome c_2:oxygen oxidoreductase	*Pseudomonas* cytochrome oxidase NRN— Cytochrome cd	4 Ferrocytochrome c_2 + O_2 = 4 ferricytochrome + 2 H_2O

[*Note: A cytochrome* cd]

1.9.6 With a Nitrogenous Group as Acceptor

1.9.6.1

Ferrocytochrome:nitrate oxidoreductase	Nitrate reductase (cytochrome)	Ferrocytochrome + nitrate = ferricytochrome + nitrite

1.10 Acting on diphenols and related substances as donors

1.10.3 With Oxygen as Acceptor

1.10.3.1

o-Diphenol:oxygen oxidoreductase	o-Diphenol oxidase NRN— Catechol oxidase, polyphenol oxidase, phenolase, tyrosinase	2 o-Diphenol + O_2 = 2 o-quinone + 2 H_2O

[*Note: Contains Cu. Acts on various o-quinols; monophenols also undergo oxidation in the system*]

NRN—*non recommended name*

Table 4. Enzymes: Classification and Reactions (continued)

Systematic name	Recommended trivial name	Reaction
1.13 Acting an single donors with incorporation of oxygen (oxygenases)		
1.13.1.1 Catechol:oxygen 1,2-oxidoreductase	Catechol 1,2-oxygenase NRN— Pyrocatechase, catechase	Catechol + O_2 = cis-cis-muconate
[Note: Needs ferrous ions. Formerly EC 1.99.2.2]		
1.13.1.2 Catechol:oxygen 2,3-oxidoreductase	Catechol 2,3-oxygenase NRN— Metapyrocatechase	Catechol + O_2 = 2-hydroxymuconate semialdehyde
[Note: Needs ferrous ions]		
1.13.1.3 Protocatechuate:oxygen 3,4-oxidoreductase	Protocatechuate oxygenase	Protocatechuate + O_2 = 3-carboxy-cis-cis-muconate
[Note: Needs ferrous ions. Formerly EC 1.99.2.3]		
1.13.1.4 Gentisate:oxygen oxidoreductase	Gentisate oxygenase	Gentisate + O_2 = maleylpyruvate
[Note: Needs ferrous ions. Formerly EC 1.99.2.4]		
1.13.1.5 Homogentisate:oxygen oxidoreductase	Homogentisate oxygenase NRN— Homogentisiscase	Homogentisate + O_2 = 4-maleylacetoacetate
[Note: Needs ferrous ions. Formerly EC 1.99.2.5]		
1.13.1.6 3-Hydroxyanthranilate: oxygen oxidoreductase	3-Hydroxy-anthranilate oxygenase	3-Hydroxyanthranilate + O_2 = 2-amino-3-carboxymuconate semialdehyde
[Note: Needs ferrous ions]		
1.13.1.7 Homoprotocatechuate: oxygen oxidoreductase	Homoproto-catechuate oxygenase	Homoprotocatechuate + O_2 = 3-carboxymethylmuconate
[Note: Needs ferrous ions]		
1.13.1.8 Protocatechuate: oxygen 4,5-oxidoreductase	Protocatechuate 4,5-oxygenase	Protocatechuate + O_2 = 2-hydroxy-4-carboxymuconate semialdehyde
[Note: Needs ferrous ions]		
1.13.1.9 2,5-Dihydroxypyridine: oxygen oxidoreductase	2,5-Dihydroxy-pyridine oxygenase	2,5-Dihydroxypyridine + O_2 = N-formylmaleamate
[Note: Needs ferrous ions]		

NRN—non recommended name

Table 4. Enzymes: Classification and Reactions (continued)

Systematic name	Recommended trivial name	Reaction
1.10.3.2 p-Diphenol:oxygen oxidoreductase	p-Diphenol oxidase NRN— Laccase, urushiol oxidase	2 p-Diphenol + O_2 = 2 p-quinone + 2 H_2O

[*Note: Contains Cu. Acts on various* p-*quinols and* p-*phenylenediamines*]

1.10.3.3 L-Ascorbate:oxygen oxidoreductase	Ascorbate oxidase	2 L-Ascorbate + O_2 = 2 dehydroascorbate + 2 H_2O

[*Note: Contains Cu*]

1.11 Acting on hydrogen peroxide as acceptor

1.11.1.1 Reduced-NAD:hydrogen-peroxide oxidoreductase	NAD peroxidase	Reduced NAD + H_2O_2 = NAD + 2 H_2O

[*Note: A flavoprotein. Ferricyanide, quinones, etc., can replace H_2O_2*]

1.11.1.2 Reduced-NADP:hydrogen-peroxide oxidoreductase	NADP peroxidase	Reduced NADP + H_2O_2 = NADP + 2 H_2O
1.11.1.3 Palmitate:hydrogen-peroxide oxidoreductase	Fatty acid peroxidase	Palmitic acid + 2 H_2O_2 = 1-pentadecanal + CO_2 + 3 H_2O

[*Note: Acts on long-chain fatty acids from lauric to stearic acid*]

1.11.1.5 Ferrocytochrome c : hydrogen-peroxide oxidoreductase	Cytochrome peroxidase	2 Ferrocytochrome c + H_2O_2 = 2 ferricytochrome c + 2 H_2O

[*Note: A haemoprotein*]

1.11.1.6 Hydrogen-peroxide:hydrogen-peroxide oxidoreductase	Catalase	H_2O_2 + H_2O_2 = O_2 + 2 H_2O

[*Note: A haemoprotein. Several organic substances, especially ethanol, can act as hydrogen donor*]

1.11.1.7 Donor:hydrogen-peroxide oxidoreductase	Peroxidase	Donor + H_2O_2 = oxidized donor + 2 H_2O

[*Note: A haemoprotein*]

1.11.1.8 Iodide:hydrogen-peroxide oxidoreductase	Iodinase	Iodide + H_2O_2 = iodine + 2 H_2O
1.11.1.9 Glutathione:hydrogen-peroxide oxidoreductase	Glutathione peroxidase	2 Glutathione + H_2O_2 = oxidized glutathione + 2 H_2O

1.12 Acting on hydrogen as donor

1.12.1.1 Hydrogen:ferredoxin oxidoreductase	Hydrogenase	H_2 + 2 ferredoxin = 2 reduced ferredoxin

[*Note: Contains Fe. Uses Molecular hydrogen for the reduction of a variety of substances. Formerly EC 1.98.1.1*]

NRN—*non recommended name*

Table 4. Enzymes: Classification and Reactions (continued)

Systematic name	Recommended trivial name	Reaction
1.6.99.4		
Reduced-NADP: ferredoxin oxidoreductase	Ferredoxin-NADP reductase	Reduced NAD + oxidized ferredoxin = NAD + reduced ferredoxin

1.7 Acting on other nitrogenous compounds as donors

1.7.3 With Oxygen as Acceptor

1.7.3.1		
Nitroethane:oxygen oxidoreductase	Nitroethane oxidase	$C_2H_5NO_2 + H_2O + O_2 =$ $CH_3CHO + HNO_2 + H_2O_2$

[*Note: Acts on some other aliphatic nitro-compounds*]

1.7.3.2		
N-Acetylindoxyl:oxygen oxidoreductase	Acetylindoxyl oxidase	N-Acetylindoxyl + O_2 = N-acetylisatin + (?)
1.7.3.3		
Urate: oxygen oxidoreductase	Urate oxidase NRN—Uricase	Urate + O_2 = unidentified products

[*Note: a copper-protein*]

1.7.99 With other Acceptors

1.7.99.1		
Ammonia: (acceptor) oxidoreductase	Hydroxylamine reductase	Ammonia + acceptor = hydroxylamine + reduced acceptor

[*Note: A flavoprotein. Reduced pyocyanine, methylene blue or flavins act as donor for the reduction of hydroxylamine*]

1.7.99.2		
Nitrogen: (acceptor) oxidoreductase	Nitric oxide reductase	N_2 + acceptor = 2 NO + reduced acceptor

[*Note: A flavoprotein. Reduced pyocyanine acts as donor for the reduction of NO*]

1.7.99.3		
Nitric oxide: (acceptor) oxidoreductase	Nitrite reductase	$2 NO + 2 H_2O$ + acceptor = 2 nitrite + reduced acceptor

[*Note: A flavoprotein. Reduced pyocyanine, flavins, etc. act as donor for the reduction of nitrite. Formerly EC 1.6.6.5*]

1.8 Acting on sulphur groups of donors

1.8.1 With NAD or NADP as Acceptor

1.8.1.2		
Hydrogen-sulphide:NADP oxidoreductase	Sulphite reductase	$H_2S + 3 NADP + 3 H_2O =$ sulphite + 3 reduced NADP
See also 1.6.4.1–4		

1.8.3 With Oxygen as Acceptor

1.8.3.1		
Sulphite:oxygen oxidoreductase	Sulphite oxidase	Sulphite + $O_2 + H_2O =$ sulphate + H_2O_2

[*Note: A haemoprotein*]

1.8.3.2		
Thiol:oxygen oxidoreductase	Thiol oxidase	$4 R:CR' \cdot SH + O_2 =$ $2 R:CR' \cdot S \cdot S \cdot CR':R + 2 H_2O$

[*Note: R may be =S or =O, or a variety of other groups. The enzyme is not specific for R'*]

NRN—*non recommended name*

Table 4. Enzymes: Classification and Reactions (continued)

Systematic name	Recommended trivial name	Reaction
1.8.4 With a Disulphide Compound as Acceptor		
1.8.4.1		
Glutathione:homocystine oxidoreductase	Glutathione-homocystine transhydrogenase	2 Glutathione + homocystine = oxidized glutathione + 2 homocysteine
1.8.4.2		
Glutathione: protein-disulphide oxidoreductase	Protein disulphide reductase	2 Glutathione + protein-disulphide = oxidized glutathione + protein-dithiol
[*Note: Reduces insulin and some other proteins*]		
1.8.5 With a Quinone or Related Compound as Acceptor		
1.8.5.1		
Glutathione:dehydroascorbate oxidoreductase	Glutathione dehydrogenase	2 Glutathione + dehydroascorbate = oxidized glutathione + ascorbate
1.8.6 With a Nitrogenous Group as Acceptor		
1.8.6.1		
Glutathione:polyolnitrate oxidoreductase	Nitrate ester reductase	2 Glutathione + polyol nitrate = oxidized glutathione + nitrite + unidentified product

1.9 Acting on haem groups of donors

Systematic name	Recommended trivial name	Reaction
1.9.3 With Oxygen as Acceptor		
1.9.3.1		
Ferrocytochrome c:oxygen oxidoreductase	Cytochrome oxidase NRN— Cytochrome a_3	4 Ferrocytochrome c + O_2 = 4 ferricytochrome c + 2 H_2O
[*Note: A cytochrome of the a type containing Cu*]		
1.9.3.2		
Ferrocytochrome c_2:oxygen oxidoreductase	*Pseudomonas* cytochrome oxidase NRN— Cytochrome cd	4 Ferrocytochrome c_2 + O_2 = 4 ferricytochrome + 2 H_2O
[*Note: A cytochrome cd*]		
1.9.6 With a Nitrogenous Group as Acceptor		
1.9.6.1		
Ferrocytochrome:nitrate oxidoreductase	Nitrate reductase (cytochrome)	Ferrocytochrome + nitrate = ferricytochrome + nitrite

1.10 Acting on diphenols and related substances as donors

Systematic name	Recommended trivial name	Reaction
1.10.3 With Oxygen as Acceptor		
1.10.3.1		
o-Diphenol:oxygen oxidoreductase	o-Diphenol oxidase NRN— Catechol oxidase, polyphenol oxidase, phenolase, tyrosinase	2 o-Diphenol + O_2 = 2 o-quinone + 2 H_2O
[*Note: Contains Cu. Acts on various o-quinols; monophenols also undergo oxidation in the system*]		

NRN—*non recommended name*

Table 4.   Enzymes: Classification and Reactions (continued)

Systematic name	Recommended trivial name	Reaction
1.13.1.10 7,8-Dihydroxykynurenate: oxygen oxidoreductase [*Note: Needs ferrous ions*]	7,8-Dihydroxy-kynurenate oxygenase	7,8,-Dihydroxykynurenate + O_2 = 5-(γ-carboxy-γ-oxo-)-propenyl-4,6-dihydroxypicolinate
1.13.1.11 meso-Inositol:oxygen oxidoreductase [*Note: Formerly EC 1.99.2.6*]	*meso*-Inositol oxygenase	*meso*-Inositol + O_2 = D-glucuronate
1.13.1.12 L-Tryptophan:oxygen oxidoreductase [*Note: A haemoprotein*]	Tryptophan oxygenase NRN— Tryptophan pyrrolase	L-Tryptophan + O_2 = L-formylkynurenine
1.13.1.13 Linoleate:oxygen oxidoreductase [*Note: Formerly EC 1.99.2.1*]	Lipoxygenase NRN—Lipoxidase	Unsaturated fat + O_2 = a peroxide of the unsaturated fat

1.14 Acting on paired donors with incorporation of oxygen into one donor (hydroxylases)

1.14.1 With Reduced NAD or NADP as One Donor

Systematic name	Recommended trivial name	Reaction
1.14.1.1 Aniline, reduced-NADP: oxygen oxidoreductase (4-hydroxylating) [*Note: Acts on many aromatic compounds. Formerly EC 1.99.1.1*]	Aryl 4-hydroxylase	Aniline + reduced NADP + O_2 = 4-hydroxyaniline + NADP + H_2O
1.14.1.2 L-Kynurenine, reduced-NADP: oxygen oxidoreductase (3-hydroxylating) [*Note: Formerly EC 1.99.1.5*]	Kynurenine 3-hydroxylase	L-Kynurenine + reduced NADP + O_2 = 3-hydroxy-L-kynurenine + NADP + H_2O
1.14.1.3 Squalene, reduced-NADP: oxygen oxidoreductase (hydroxylating) [*Note: Formerly EC 1.99.1.13*]	Squalene hydroxylase NRN—Squalene oxydocyclase	Squalene + reduced NADP + O_2 = lanosterol + NADP + H_2O
1.14.1.4 Kynurenate, reduced-NAD(P): oxygen oxidoreductase (hydroxylating)	Kynurenate hydroxylase	Kynurenate + reduced NAD(P) + O_2 = kynurenate 7,8-dihydrodiol + NAD(P) + H_2O
1.14.1.5 Imidazoleacetate, reduced-NAD:oxygen oxidoreductase (hydroxylating)	Imidazoleacetate hydroxylase	Imidazoleacetate + reduced NAD + O_2 = imidazoloneacetate + NAD + H_2O
1.14.1.6 Steroid, reduced-NADP: oxygen oxidoreductase (11-β-hydroxylating) [*Note: Formerly EC 1.99.1.7*]	Steroid 11-β-hydroxylase	A steroid + reduced NADP + O_2 = an 11-β-hydroxysteroid + NADP + H_2O

NRN—*non recommended name*

Table 4.   Enzymes: Classification and Reactions (continued)

Systematic name	Recommended trivial name	Reaction
1.14.1.7		
Steroid, reduced-NADP: oxygen oxidoreductase (17-α-hydroxylating) [*Note: Formerly EC 1.99.1.9*]	Steroid 17-α-hydroxylase	A steroid + reduced NADP + O_2 = a 17-α-hydroxysteroid + NADP + H_2O
1.14.1.8		
Steroid, reduced-NADP: oxygen oxidoreductase (21-hydroxylating) [*Note: Formerly EC 1.99.1.11*]	Steroid 21-hydroxylase	A steroid + reduced NADP + O_2 = a 21-hydroxysteroid + NADP + H_2O
1.14.1.9		
Cholesterol, reduced-NADP: oxygen oxidoreductase (20-β-hydroxylating)	Cholesterol 20-hydroxylase	Cholesterol + reduced NADP + O_2 = 20-β-hydroxycholesterol + NADP + H_2O
1.14.1.10		
Oestradiol, reduced-NADP: oxygen oxidoreductase (6-β-hydroxylating)	Oestradiol 6-β-hydroxylase	Oestradiol + reduced NADP + O_2 = 6-β-hydroxy-oestradiol + NADP + H_2O
1.14.1.11		
Oestriol, reduced -NAD(P): oxygen oxidoreductase (2-hydroxylating)	Oestriol 2-hydroxylase	Oestriol + reduced NAD(P) + O_2 = 2-hydroxy-oestriol + NAD(P) + H_2O

1.14.2 With Ascorbate as One Donor

1.14.2.1		
3,4-Dihydroxyphenyl-ethylamine, ascorbate: oxygen oxidoreductase (hydroxylating)	Dopamine hydroxylase	3,4-Dihydroxyphenylethylamine + ascorbate + O_2 = norepinephrine + dehydroascorbate + H_2O
1.14.2.2		
p-Hydroxyphenylpyruvate, ascorbate:oxygen oxidoreductase (hydroxylating) [*Note: Formerly EC 1.99.1.14*]	p-Hydroxyphenyl-pyruvate hydroxylase	p-Hydroxyphenylpyruvate + ascorbate + O_2 = homogentisate + dehydroascorbate + H_2O

1.14.3 With Reduced Pteridine as One Donor

1.14.3.1		
L-Phenylalanine, tetrahydropteridine: oxygen oxidoreductase (4-hydroxylating)	Phenylalanine 4-hydroxylase NRN— Phenylalaninase	L-Phenylalanine + tetrahydropteridine + O_2 = L-tyrosine + dihydropteridine + H_2O

[*Note: Formerly EC 1.99.1.2. A number of reduced pteridine derivatives can act as donor*]

2. TRANSFERASES

2:1 Transferring one-carbon groups

2.1.1 Methyltransferases
(For the trivial name, "methyltransferase" may be replaced by "transmethylase")

2.1.1.1		
S-Adenosylmethionine: nicotinamide N^1-methyltransferase	Nicotinamide methyltrans-ferase	S-Adenosylmethionine + nicotinamide = S-adenosylhomocysteine + N^1-methylnicotinamide

NRN—*non recommended name*

Table 4. Enzymes: Classification and Reactions (continued)

Systematic name	Recommended trivial name	Reaction
2.1.1.2 S-Adenosylmethionine: guanidinoacetate N-methyltransferase	Guanidinoacetate methyltrans-ferase	S-Adenosylmethionine + guanidinoacetate = S-adenosylhomocysteine + creatine
2.1.1.3 Dimethylthetin:L-homocysteine S-methyltransferase	Dimethylthetin-homocysteine methyl-transferase	Dimethylthetin + L-homocysteine = S-methylthioglycollate + L-methionine
2.1.1.4 S-Adenosylmethionine: N-acetylserotonin O-methyltransferase	Acetylserotonin methyltransferase	S-Adenosylmethionine + N-acetylserotonin = S-adenosylhomocysteine + N-acetyl-5-methoxytryptamine
[*Note Some other hydroxyindoles also act as acceptor, more slowly*]		
2.1.1.5 Betaine:L-homocysteine S-methyltransferase	Betaine-homocysteine methyltransferase	Betaine + L-homocysteine = dimethylglycine + L-methionine
2.1.1.6 S-Adenosylmethionine: catechol O-methyltransferase	Catechol methyltransferase	S-Adenosylmethionine + catechol = S-adenosylhomocysteine + guiacol
2.1.1.7 S-Adenosylmethionine: nicotinate N-methyltransferase	Nicotinate methyltransferase	S-Adenosylmethionine + nicotinate = S-adenosylhomocysteine + N-methylnicotinate
2.1.1.8 S-Adenosylmethionine: histamine N-methyltransferase	Histamine methyltransferase	S-Adenosylmethionine + histamine = S-adenosylhomocysteine + 1-methylhistamine
2.1.1.9 S-Adenosylmethionine:thiol S-methyltransferase	Thiol methyl-transferase	S-Adenosylmethionine + a thiol = S-adenosylhomocysteine + a thioether
[*Note: A variety of thiols and hydroxythiols can act as acceptor*]		
2.1.1.10 S-Adenosylmethionine: L-homocysteine S-methyltransferase	Homocysteine methyltransferase	S-Adenosylmethionine + L-homocysteine = S-adenosylhomocysteine + L-methionine
2.1.1.11 S-Adenosylmethionine: magnesium-protoporphyrin O-methyltransferase	Magnesium protoporphyrin methyltransferase	S-Adenosylmethionine + magnesium protoporphyrin = S-adenosylhomocysteine + magnesium protoporphyrin monomethyl ester

Table 4. Enzymes: Classification and Reactions (continued)

Systematic name	Recommended trivial name	Reaction

2.1.2 Hydroxymethyl-, Formyl- and Related Transferases
(For the trivial name, "hydroxymethyltransferase," "formyltransferase," "formiminotransferase" may be replaced by "transhydroxymethylase," "transformylase," and "transformiminase" respectively)

2.1.2.1

| L-Serine:tetrahydrofolate 5,10-hydroxymethyltransferase | Serine hydroxymethyltransferase NRN— Serine aldolase, serine hydroxymethylase | L-Serine + tetrahydrofolate = glycine + 5,10-methylenetetrahydrofolate |

[*Note: A pyridoxal-phosphate protein*]

2.1.2.2

| 5'-Phosphoribosyl-N-formylglycineamide:tetrahydrofolate 5,10-formyltransferase | Phosphoribosylglycineamide formyltransferase | 5'-Phosphoribosyl-N-formylglycineamide + tetrahydrofolate = 5'-Phosphoribosyl-glycineamide + 5,10-methenyltetrahydrofolate + H_2O |

2.1.2.3

| 5'-Phosphoribosyl-5-formamido-4-imidazolecarboxamide: tetrahydrofolate 10-formyltransferase | Phosphoribosylaminoimidazolecarboxamide formyltransferase | 5'-Phosphoribosyl-5-formamido-4-imidazolecarboxamide + tetrahydrofolate = 5'-Phosphoribosyl-5-amino-4-imidazolecarboxamide + 10-formyltetrahydrofolate |

2.1.2.4

| N-Formiminoglycine: tetrahydrofolate 5-formiminotransferase | Glycine formiminotransferase | N-Formiminoglycine + tetrahydrofolate = glycine + 5-formiminotetrahydrofolate |

2.1.2.5

| N-Formimino-L-glutamate: tetrahydrofolate 5-formiminotransferase | Glutamate formiminotransferase | N-Formimino-L-glutamate + tetrahydrofolate = L-glutamate + 5-formiminotetrahydrofolate |

2.1.2.6

| N-Formyl-L-glutamate: tetrahydrofolate 5-formyltransferase | Formylglutamate formyltransferase | N-Formyl-L-glutamate + tetrahydrofolate = L-glutamate + 5-formyltetrahydrofolate |

2.1.3 Carboxyl- and Carbamoyltransferases
(For the trivial name, "carboxyltransferase" and "carbamoyltransferase" may be replaced by "transcarboxylase" and "transcarbamoylase" respectively)

2.1.3.1

| Methylmalonyl-CoA:pyruvate carboxyltransferase | Methylmalonyl-CoA carboxyltransferase | Methylmalonyl-CoA + pyruvate = propionyl-CoA + oxaloacetate |

[*Note: Contains biotin*]

NRN—*non recommended name*

Table 4. Enzymes: Classification and Reactions (continued)

Systematic name	Recommended trivial name	Reaction
2.1.3.2 Carbamoylphosphate: L-aspartate carbamoyltransferase	Aspartate carba- moyltransferase NRN— Carbamylasparto- transkinase	Carbamoylphosphate + L-aspartate = orthophosphate + N-carbamoyl-L-aspartate
2.1.3.3 Carbamoylphosphate: L-ornithine carbamoyltransferase	Ornithine carbamoyl- transferase	Carbamoylphosphate + L-ornithine = orthophosphate + L-citrulline
2.1.3.4 Malonyl-CoA:pyruvate carboxyltransferase	Malonyl-CoA carboxyl- transferase	Malonyl-CoA + pyruvate = acetyl-CoA + oxaloacetate

2.1.4 Amidinotransferases
(For the trivial name, "amidinotransferase" may be replaced by "transamidinase")

2.1.4.1 L-Arginine:glycine amidinotransferase	Glycine amidino- transferase	L-Arginine + glycine = L-ornithine + guanidinoacetate

[*Note: Canavanine can act instead of arginine*]

2.2 Transferring aldehydic or ketonic residues

2.2.1.1 Sedoheptulose-7-phosphate: D-glyceraldehyde-3- phosphate glycolaldehydetransferase	Transketolase, glycolaldehyde- transferase	Sedoheptulose 7-phosphate + D-glyceraldehyde 3-phosphate = D-ribose 5-phosphate + D-xylulose 5-phosphate

[*Note: Needs thiamine pyrophosphate. Wide specificity for both reactants, e.g. converts hydroxypyruvate and $R \cdot CHO$ into CO_2 and $R \cdot CHOH \cdot CO \cdot CH_2OH$*]

2.2.1.2 Sedoheptulose-7-phosphate: D-glyceraldehyde-3- phosphate dihydroxyacetonetransferase	Transaldolase, dihydroxyacetone- transferase	Sedoheptulose 7-phosphate + D-glyceraldehyde 3-phosphate = D-erythrose 4-phosphate + D-fructose 6-phosphate

2.3 Acyltransferases

2.3.1 Acyltransferases
(For the trivial name, "acetyltransferase," etc., may be replaced by "transacetylase," etc.)

2.3.1.1 Acetyl-CoA:L-glutamate N-acetyltransferase	Amino acid acetyltransferase	Acetyl-CoA + L-glutamate = CoA + N-acetyl-L-glutamate

[*Note: Also acts with L-aspartate and, more slowly with some other amino acids*]

2.3.1.2 Acetyl-CoA:imidazole N-acetyltransferase	Imidazole acetyltransferase NRN—Imidazole acetylase	Acetyl-CoA + Imidazole = CoA + N-acetylimidazole

[*Note: Also acts with propionyl-CoA*]

NRN—*non recommended name*

Table 4. Enzymes: Classification and Reactions (continued)

Systematic name	Recommended trivial name	Reaction
2.3.1.3 Acetyl-CoA:2-amino-2-deoxy-D-glucose N-acetyltransferase	Glucosamine acetyltransferase NRN— Glucosamine acetylase	Acetyl-CoA + 2-amino-2-deoxy-D-glucose = CoA + 2-acetamido-2-deoxy-D-glucose
2.3.1.4 Acetyl-CoA:2-amino-2-deoxy-D-glucose-6-phosphate N-acetyltransferase	Glucosamine-phosphate acetyltransferase NRN—Phospho-glucosamine transacetylase	Acetyl-CoA + 2-amino-2-deoxy-D-glucose 6-phosphate = CoA + 2-acetamido-2-deoxy-D-glucose 6-phosphate
2.3.1.5 Acetyl-CoA:arylamine N-acetyltransferase	Arylamine acetyltransferase NRN—Arylamine acetylase	Acetyl-CoA + arylamine = CoA + N-acetylarylamine

[Note: Wide specificity for aromatic amines, including serotonin; also catalyses acetyl-transfer between arylamines without CoA]

Systematic name	Recommended trivial name	Reaction
2.3.1.6 Acetyl-CoA:choline O-acetyltransferase	Choline acetyltransferase NRN—Choline acetylase	Acetyl-CoA + choline = CoA + O-acetylcholine

[Note: Propionyl-CoA can act, more slowly, in place of acetyl-CoA]

Systematic name	Recommended trivial name	Reaction
2.3.1.7 Acetyl-CoA:carnitine O-acetyltransferase	Carnitine acetyltransferase	Acetyl-CoA + carnitine = CoA + O-acetylcarnitine
2.3.1.8 Acetyl-CoA:orthophosphate acetyltransferase	Phosphate acetyltransferase NRN—Phosphotrans-acetylase	Acetyl-CoA + orthophosphate = CoA + acetylphosphate
2.3.1.9 Acetyl-CoA:acetyl-CoA C-acetyltransferase	Acetyl-CoA acetyltransferase acetoacetyl-CoA thiolase NRN—Thiolase	Acetyl-CoA + acetyl-CoA = CoA + acetoacetyl-CoA
2.3.1.10 Acetyl-CoA:hydrogen-sulphide S-acetyltransferase	Hydrogen-sulphide acetyltransferase	Acetyl-CoA + H_2S = CoA + thioacetate
2.3.1.11 Acetyl-CoA:thioethanolamine S-acetyltransferase	Thioethanolamine acetyltransferase NRN—Thioltrans-acetylase B	Acetyl-CoA + thioethanolamine = CoA + S-acetylthioethanolamine

NRN—*non recommended name*

Table 4.   Enzymes: Classification and Reactions (continued)

Systematic name	Recommended trivial name	Reaction
2.3.1.12 Acetyl-CoA:dihydrolipoate S-acetyltransferase	Lipoate acetyltransferase NRN—Thioltrans- acetylase A	Acetyl-CoA + dihydrolipoate = CoA + 6-S-acetylhydrolipoate

[Note: Also acetylates monothioglycol]

2.3.1.13 Acyl-CoA:glycine N-acyltransferase	Glycine acyltransferase	Acyl-CoA + glycine = CoA + N-acylglycine

[Note: Acts with the CoA derivatives of a number of aliphatic and aromatic acids]

2.3.1.14 Phenylacetyl-CoA:L-glutamine α-N-phenylacetyltransferase	Glutamine phenylacetyl- transferase	Phenylacetyl-CoA + L-glutamine = CoA + α-N-phenylacetyl-L- glutamine
2.3.1.15 Acyl-CoA:L-glycerol- 3-phosphate O-acyltransferase	Glycerolphosphate acyltransferase	Acyl-CoA + L-glycerol 3-phosphate = CoA + monoglyceride phosphate

[Note: Acts only with CoA derivatives of fatty acids of chain length above C_{10}. Also forms diglyceride phosphates]

2.3.1.16 Acyl-CoA:acetyl-CoA C-acyltransferase	Acetyl-CoA acyltransferase 3-ketoacyl-CoA thiolase NRN— β-Ketothiolase	Acyl-CoA + acetyl-CoA = CoA + 3-oxoacyl-CoA
2.3.1.17 Acetyl-CoA:L-aspartate N-acetyltransferase	Aspartate acetyltransferase	Acetyl-CoA + L-aspartate = CoA + N-acetyl-L-aspartate
2.3.1.18 Acetyl-CoA:galactoside 6-O-acetyltransferase	Galactoside acetyltransferase NRN— Thiogalactoside acetyltransferase	Acetyl-CoA + a β-D-galactoside = CoA + a 6-acetyl-β-D-galactoside

[Note: Acts on thiogalactosides and phenylgalactoside]

2.3.1.19 Butyryl-CoA:orthophosphate butyryltransferase	Phosphate butyryl- transferase	Butyryl-CoA + orthophosphate = CoA + butyrylphosphate
2.3.1.20 Acyl-CoA:1,2-diglyceride O-acyltransferase	Diglyceride acyltransferase	Acyl-CoA + a 1,2-diglyceride = CoA + a triglyceride

2.3.2 Aminoacyltransferases

2.3.2.1 Glutamine:D-glutamyl glutamyltransferase	D-Glutamyl- transferase	L(or D)-Glutamine + D-glutamyl-R = NH_3 + 5-glutamyl-D- glutamyl-R

[Note: H—R represents a peptide]

NRN—non recommended name

Table 4. Enzymes: Classification and Reactions (continued)

Systematic name	Recommended trivial name	Reaction

2.4 Glycosyltransferases
(For the trivial name, "glucosyltransferase," "fructosyltransferase," etc., may be replaced by "transglucosylase," "transfructosylase," etc.)

2.4.1 Hexosyltransferases

2.4.1.1

α-1,4-Glucan:orthophosphate glucosyltransferase	α-Glucan phosphorylase, glycogen phosphorylase NRN— P-enzyme (only for the plant enzyme), muscle phosphorylase a	$(\alpha\text{-1,4-Glucosyl})_n +$ orthophosphate $=$ $(\alpha\text{-1,4-glucosyl})_{n-1} + \alpha\text{-D-glucose}$ 1-phosphate

[*Note: The mammalian enzyme contains pyridoxal phosphate*]

2.4.1.2

Dextrin:α-1,6-glucan 6-glucosyltransferase	Dextrin 6-glucosyltransferase NRN—Dextran dextrinase	$(\alpha\text{-1,4-Glucosyl})_n +$ $(\alpha\text{-1,6-glucosyl})_m =$ $(\alpha\text{-1,4-glucosyl})_{n-1} +$ $(\alpha\text{-1,6-glucosyl})_{m+1}$

2.4.1.3

α-1,4-Glucan:D-glucose 4-glucosyltransferase	Maltose 4-glucosyltransferase, amylomaltase	$(\alpha\text{-1,4-Glucosyl})_n + \text{D-glucose} =$ $(\alpha\text{-1,4-glucosyl})_{n-1} + \text{maltose}$

2.4.1.4

α-1,4-Glucan:D-fructose 2-glucosyltransferase	Sucrose glucosyltransferase, amylosucrase	$(\alpha\text{-1,4-Glucosyl})_n + \text{D-fructose} =$ $(\alpha\text{-1,4 glucosyl})_{n-1} + \text{sucrose}$

2.4.1.5

α-1,6-Glucan:D-fructose 2-glucosyltransferase	Sucrose 6-glucosyltransferase, dextransucrase	$(\alpha\text{-1,6-Glucosyl})_n + \text{D-fructose} =$ $(\alpha\text{-1,6-glucosyl})_{n-1} + \text{sucrose}$

2.4.1.6

Maltose:D-glucose 3-glucosyltransferase	Maltose 3-glucosyltransferase	Maltose $+$ D-glucose $=$ D-glucose $+$ α-1,3-glucosyl-glucose

2.4.1.7

Disaccharide glucosyltransferase (non-specific)	Sucrose glucosyltransferase NRN—Sucrose phosphorylase	α-D-Glucosyl-1-R $+$ R$'$ $=$ α-D-glucosyl-1-R$'$ $+$ R

[*Note: R and R$'$ may represent various ketoses, L-arabinose, phosphate or arsenate*]

2.4.1.8

Maltose:orthophosphate glucosyltransferase	Maltose phosphorylase	Maltose $+$ orthophosphate $=$ β-D-glucose-1-phosphate $+$ D-glucose

2.4.1.9

β-1,2-Fructan:D-glucose 1-fructosyltransferase	Sucrose 1-fructosyltransferase, inulosucrase	$(\beta\text{-1,2-Fructosyl})_n + \text{D-glucose} =$ $(\beta\text{-1,2-fructosyl})_{n-1} + \text{sucrose}$

[*Note: Converts sucrose into inulin and glucose*]

NRN—*non recommended name*

Table 4. Enzymes: Classification and Reactions (continued)

Systematic name	Recommended trivial name	Reaction
2.4.1.10		
β-2,6-Fructan: D-glucose 6-fructosyltransferase	Sucrose 6-fructosyl-transferase, levansucrase	$(\beta\text{-}2,6\text{-Fructosyl})_n$ + D-glucose = $(\beta\text{-}2,6\text{-fructosyl})_{n-1}$ + sucrose
[*Note: Some other sugars can act as fructosyl acceptors*]		
2.4.1.11		
UDPglucose: glycogen α-4-glucosyltransferase	UDPglucose-glycogen gluco-syltransferase, glycogen-UDP glucosyltransferase	UDPglucose + $(\text{glycogen})_n$ = UDP + $(\text{glycogen})_{n+1}$
[*Note: Activated by D-glucose 6-phosphate and other hexose phosphates*]		
2.4.1.12		
UDPglucose: β-1,4-glucan β-4-glucosyltransferase	UDPglucose-β-glucan glycosyl-transferase, UDPglucose-cellulose glucosyl-transferase, β-glucan-UDP glucosyltransferase	UDPglucose + $(\beta\text{-}1,4\text{-glucosyl})_n$ = UDP + $(\beta\text{-}1,4\text{-glucosyl})_{n+1}$
[*Note: Converts UDPglucose into cellulose and UDP*]		
2.4.1.13		
UDPglucose: D-fructose 2-glucosyltransferase	UDPglucose-fructose glucosyl-transferase, sucrose-UDP glucosyltransferase	UDPglucose + D-fructose = UDP + sucrose
2.4.1.14		
UDPglucose: D-fructose-6-phosphate 2-glucosyl-transferase	UDPglucose-fructose-phosphate gluco-syltransferase, sucrosephosphate-UDP glucosyl-transferase	UDPglucose + D-fructose 6-phosphate = UDP + sucrose 6-phosphate
2.4.1.15		
UDPglucose: D-glucose-6-phosphate 1-glucosyl-transferase	UDPglucose-glucose-phosphate glucosyltransferase, trehalosephosphate-UDP glucosyl-transferase	UDPglucose + D-glucose 6-phosphate = UDP + trehalose 6-phosphate
2.4.1.16		
UDP-2-acetamido-2-deoxy-D-glucose: chitin acetylamino-deoxyglucosyltransferase	Chitin-UDP acetylglucos-aminyltransferase NRN—Trans-N-acetylglucos-aminosylase	UDP-2-acetamido-2-deoxy-D-glucose + $[\beta\text{-}1,4\text{-}(2\text{-acetamido-2-deoxy-D-glucosyl})]_n$ = UDP + $[\beta\text{-}1,4\text{-}(2\text{-acetamido-2-deoxy-D-glucosyl})]_{n+1}$
[*Note: Converts UDP-2-acetamido-2-deoxy-D-glucose into chitin and UDP*]		

NRN—*non recommended name*

Table 4. Enzymes: Classification and Reactions (continued)

Systematic name	Recommended trivial name	Reaction
2.4.1.17 UDPglucuronate glucuronyl transferase (acceptor-unspecific)	UDPglucuronyl-transferase	UDPglucuronate + acceptor = UDP + acceptor-glucuronide
[*Note: A wide range of phenols, alcohols, amines and fatty acids can act as acceptor*]		
2.4.1.18 α-1,4-Glucan:α-1,4-glucan 6-glycosyltransferase	α-Glucan-branching glycosyl-transferase NRN—Q-enzyme, branching factor	Transfers part of a 1,4-glucan chain from a 4- to a 6-position
[*Note: Converts amylose into amylopectin*]		
2.4.1.19 α-1,4,-Glucan 4-glycosyl-transferase (cyclizing)	Cyclodextrin glycosyl-transferase	Transfers part of a 1,4-glucan chain to its own non-reducing end
[*Note: Forms cyclic dextrins*]		
2.4.1.20 Cellobiose:orthophosphate glucosyltransferase	Cellobiose phosphorylase	Cellobiose + orthophosphate = α-D-glucose 1-phosphate + D-glucose
2.4.1.21 UDPglucose:α-1,4-glucan α-4-glucosyltransferase	UDPglucose-starch glucosyl-transferase	UDPglucose + (α-1,4-glucosyl)$_n$ = UDP + (α-1,4-glucosyl)$_{n+1}$
[*Note: Starch, 1,4-linked oligosaccharides or maltose can act as acceptor; ADP-glucose can also act as donor*]		
2.4.1.22 UDPgalactose:D-glucose 1-galactosyltransferase	UDPgalactose-glucose galacto-syltransferase	UDPgalactose + D-glucose = UDP + lactose
2.4.1.23 UDPgalactose:sphingosine O-galactosyltransferase	UDPgalactose-sphingosine galactosyl-transferase, psychosine-UDP galactosyl-transferase	UDPgalactose + sphingosine = UDP + psychosine
2.4.1.24 α-1,4-Glucan:α-1,4-oligoglucan 6-glycosyltransferase	Oligoglucan-branching glyco-syltransferase NRN—T-enzyme	Transfers part of a 1,4-glucan chain from a 4- to a 6-position
[*Note: Acts on short-chain α-1,4-glucans*]		
2.4.1.25 α-1,4-Glucan:α-1,4-glucan 4-glycosyltransferase	Dextrin trans-glycosylase NRN—D-enzyme, disproportionating enzyme	Transfers part of 1,4-glucan chain to a new 4-position
[*Note: Can convert maltodextrins into amylose and glucose*]		

NRN—*non-recommended name*

Table 4. Enzymes: Classification and Reactions (continued)

Systematic name	Recommended trivial name	Reaction
2.4.1.26 UDPglucose:DNA α-glucosyltransferase	UDPglucose-DNA α-glucosyl-transferase	Transfers an α-glucosyl residue from UDP-glucose to a hydroxy-methylcytosine residue in DNA
2.4.1.27 UDPglucose:DNA β-glucosyltransferase	UDPglucose-DNA β-glucosyl-transferase	Transfers a β-glucosyl residue from UDP-glucose to a hydroxy-methylcytosine residue in DNA
2.4.1.28 UDPglucose:glycosyl-DNA β-glucosyltransferase	UDPglucose-glycosyl-DNA β-glucosyl-transferase	Transfers a β-glucosyl residue from UDP-glucose to a glucosyl-hydroxymethylcytosine residue in DNA
2.4.1.29 GDPglucose:β-1,4-glucan β-4-glucosyltransferase	GDPglucose-β-glucan glucosyl-transferase	GDPglucose + (β-1,4-glucosyl)$_n$ = GDP + (β-1,4-glucosyl)$_{n+1}$
2.4.2 Pentosyltransferases		
2.4.2.1 Purine-nucleoside: orthophosphate ribosyltransferase	Purine nucleoside phosphorylase	Purine nucleoside + ortho-phosphate = α-D-ribose 1-phosphate + purine
[*Note: Specificity not completely determined*]		
2.4.2.3 Uridine:orthophosphate ribosyltransferase	Uridine phosphorylase	Uridine + orthophosphate = uracil + D-ribose 1-phosphate
2.4.2.4 Thymidine:orthophosphate deoxyribosyltransferase	Thymidine phosphorylase	Thymidine + orthophosphate = thymine + 2-deoxy-D-ribose 1-phosphate
2.4.2.5 Nucleoside:purine (pyrimidine) ribosyltransferase	Nucleoside ribosyl-transferase	D-Ribose-R + R' = D-ribosyl-R' + R
[*Note: R and R' represent various purines and pyrimidines*]		
2.4.2.6 Nucleoside:purine (pyrimidine) deoxyribosyltransferase	Nucleoside deoxyribosyl-transferase NRN—Trans-N-glycosidase	2-Deoxy-D-ribosyl-R + R' = 2-deoxy-D-ribosyl-R' + R
[*Note: R and R' represent various purines and pyrimidines*]		
2.4.2.7 AMP:pyrophosphate phosphoribosyltransferase	Adenine phosphoribosyl-transferase, AMP pyrophos-phorylase	AMP + pyrophosphate = adenine + 5-phospho-α-D-ribosyl-pyrophosphate
[*Note: 5-Amino-4-imidazolecarboxamide can replace adenine*]		

NRN—*non recommended name*

Table 4.   Enzymes: Classification and Reactions (continued)

Systematic name	Recommended trivial name	Reaction
2.4.2.8		
IMP:pyrophosphate phosphoribosyltransferase	Hypoxanthine phosphoribosyl-transferase, IMP pyrophosphorylase	IMP + pyrophosphate = hypoxanthine + 5-phospho-α-D-ribosyl-pyrophosphate
[*Note: Guanine and 6-mercaptopurine can replace hypoxanthine*]		
2.4.2.9		
UMP:pyrophosphate phosphoribosyltransferase	Uracil phosphoribo-syltransferase, UMP pyrophos-phorylase	UMP + pyrophosphate = uracil + 5-phospho-α-D-ribosyl-pyrophosphate
2.4.2.10		
Orotidine-5′-phosphate: pyrophosphate phosphoribosyltransferase	Orotate phosphori-bosyltransferase, orotidine-5′-phosphate pyrophosphorylase NRN— Orotidylic acid phosphorylase	Orotidine 5′-phosphate + pyrophosphate = orotate + 5-phospho-α-D-ribosyl-pyrophosphate
2.4.2.11		
Nicotinatenucleotide: pyrophosphate phosphoribosyltransferase	Nicotinate phosphoribosyl-transferase	Nicotinate ribonucleotide + pyrophosphate = nicotinate + 5-phospho-α-D-ribosyl-pyrophosphate
2.4.2.12		
Nicotinamidenucleotide: pyrophosphate phosphoribosyltransferase	Nicotinamide phosphoribosyl-transferase, NMN pyrophos-phorylase	Nicotinamide ribonucleotide + pyrophosphate = nicotinamide + 5-phospho-α-D-ribosyl-pyrophosphate
2.4.2.14		
Ribosylamine-5-phosphate: pyrophosphate phosphoribosyltransferase (glutamate-amidating)	Amidophospho-ribosyl-transferase, phosphoribosyl-pyrophosphate amidotransferase	β-D-Ribosylamine 5-phosphate + pyrophosphate + L-glutamate = L-glutamine + 5-phospho-α-D-ribosyl-pyrophosphate + H_2O
2.4.2.15		
Guanosine:orthophosphate ribosyltransferase	Guanosine phosphorylase	Guanosine + orthophosphate = guanine + D-ribose 1-phosphate
[*Note: Also acts on deoxyguanosine*]		
2.4.2.16		
Urateribonucleotide: orthophosphate ribosyltransferase	Urateribonucleotide phosphorylase	Urate ribonucleotide + orthophosphate = urate + D-ribose 1-phosphate

NRN—*non recommended name*

Table 4. Enzymes: Classification and Reactions (continued)

Systematic name	Recommended trivial name	Reaction
2.5 Transferring alkyl or related groups		
2.5.1.1		
Dimethylallylpyrophosphate: isopentenylpyrophosphate dimethylallyltransferase	Dimethylallyl- transferase, prenyltransferase NRN—Farnesyl- pyrophosphate synthetase	Dimethylallyl pyrophosphate + isopentenyl pyrophosphate = pyrophosphate + geranyl pyrophosphate
[*Note: Also transfers geranyl and farnesyl residues*]		
2.5.1.2		
Thiamine:base 2-methyl- 4-aminopyrimidine- 5-methenyltransferase	Thiaminase 1	Thiamine + pyridine = heteropyrithiamine + 4-methyl-5-(2'-phospho-ethyl)- thiazole
[*Note: Various bases and thiol compounds can act instead of pyridine*]		
2.5.1.3		
2-Methyl-4-amino- 5-hydroxymethyl-pyrimidine- pyrophosphate:4-methyl- 5-(2'-phospho-ethyl)-thiazole 2-methyl-4-aminopyrimidine- 5-methenyltransferase	Thiaminephosphate pyrophos- phorylase	2-Methyl-4-amino-5-hydroxy- methyl-pyrimidine pyrophosphate + 4-methyl-5-(2'-phospho-ethyl)- thiazole = pyrophosphate + thiamine monophosphate
2.5.1.4		
S-Adenosylmethionine alkyl- transferase (cyclizing)	Adenosylmethionine cyclotransferase	S-Adenosylmethionine = 5'-(methylthio)-adenosine + 2-amino-γ-butyrolactone
2.5.1.5		
Galactose-6-sulphate alkyl- transferase (cyclizing)	Galactose-6- sulphatase, porphyran sulphatase	Eliminates sulphate from the galactose 6-sulphate residues of porphyran, producing 3,6- anhydrogalactose residues
2.5.1.6		
ATP:L-methionine S-adenosyltransferase	Methionine adenosyl- transferase	ATP + L-methionine + H_2O = orthophosphate + pyrophosphate + S-adenosylmethionine
[*Note: Formerly EC 2.4.2.13*]		
2.6 Transferring nitrogenous groups		
2.6.1 Aminotransferases **(For the trivial name, "aminotransferase" may be replaced by "transaminase")**		
2.6.1.1		
L-Aspartate:2-oxoglutarate aminotransferase	Aspartate amino- transferase NRN—Glutamicox- aloacetic transaminase, glutamicaspartic transaminase	L-Aspartate + 2-oxoglutarate = oxaloacetate + L-glutamate
[*Note: A pyridoxal-phosphate protein*]		

NRN—*non recommended name*

Table 4. Enzymes: Classification and Reactions (continued)

Systematic name	Recommended trivial name	Reaction
2.6.1.2		
L-Alanine:2-oxoglutarate aminotransferase	Alanine amino-transferase NRN—Glutamic-pyruvic transaminase, glutamicalanine transaminase	L-Alanine + 2-oxoglutarate = pyruvate + L-glutamate

[*Note: A pyridoxal-phosphate protein. 2-Aminobutyrate acts slowly instead of alanine*]

2.6.1.3		
L-Cysteine:2-oxoglutarate aminotransferase	Cysteine amino-transferase	L-Cysteine + 2-oxoglutarate = mercaptopyruvate + L-glutamate

[*Note: A pyridoxal-phosphate protein*]

2.6.1.4		
Glycine:2-oxoglutarate aminotransferase	Glycine amino-transferase	Glycine + 2-oxoglutarate = glyoxylate + L-glutamate

[*Note: A pyridoxal-phosphate protein*]

2.6.1.5		
L-Tyrosine:2-oxoglutarate aminotransferase	Tyrosine amino-transferase	L-Tyrosine + 2-oxoglutarate = p-hydroxyphenylpyruvate + L-glutamate

[*Note: A pyridoxal-phosphate protein. Phenylalanine can act instead of tyrosine*]

2.6.1.6		
L-Leucine:2-oxoglutarate aminotransferase	Leucine amino-transferase	L-Leucine + 2-oxoglutarate = 2-oxoisocaproate + L-glutamate

[*Note: A pyridoxal-phosphate protein*]

2.6.1.7		
L-Kynurenine:2-oxoglutarate aminotransferase	Kynurenine amino-transferase	L-Kynurenine + 2-oxoglutarate = o-aminobenzolypyruvate + L-glutamate

[*Note: A pyridoxal-phosphate protein*]

2.6.1.8		
2,5-Diaminovalerate:2-oxo glutarate aminotransferase	Diamino-acid aminotransferase	2,5-Diaminovalerate + 2-oxoglutarate = 5-amino-2-oxovalerate + L-glutamate

[*Note: A pyridoxal-phosphate protein. 2,5-Diaminoglutarate can act instead of di-aminovalerate*]

2.6.1.9		
L-Histidinolphosphate:2-oxo-glutarate aminotransferase	Histidinolphosphate aminotransferase	L-Histidinol phosphate + 2-oxoglutarate = imidazolacetol phosphate + L-glutamate

[*Note: A pyridoxal-phosphate protein*]

2.6.1.10		
D-Aspartate:2-oxoglutarate aminotransferase	D-Aspartate amino-transferase	D-Aspartate + 2-oxoglutarate = oxaloacetate + D-glutamate

[*Note: A pyridoxal-phosphate protein. Pyruvate can replace either ketoacid*]

NRN—*non recommended name*

Table 4. Enzymes: Classification and Reactions (continued)

Systematic name	Recommended trivial name	Reaction
2.6.1.11 α-N-Acetyl-L-ornithine:2-oxo-glutarate aminotransferase	Acetylornithine aminotransferase	α-N-Acetyl-L-ornithine + 2-oxoglutarate = N-acetyl-L-glutamate γ-semialdehyde + L-glutamate
[*Note: A pyridoxal-phosphate protein*]		
2.6.1.12 L-Alanine:2-oxoacid amino-transferase	Alanine-ketoacid aminotransferase	L-Alanine + a 2-oxoacid = pyruvate + an L-amino acid
[*Note: A pyridoxal-phosphate protein*]		
2.6.1.13 L-Ornithine:2-oxoacid amino-transferase	Ornithine-ketoacid aminotransferase	L-Ornithine + a 2-oxoacid = L-glutamate γ-semialdehyde + an L-amino acid
[*Note: A pyridoxal-phosphate protein*]		
2.6.1.14 L-Asparagine:2-oxoacid amino-transferase	Asparagine-ketoacid aminotransferase	L-Asparagine + a 2-oxoacid = 2-oxosuccinamate + an amino acid
[*Note: A pyridoxal-phosphate protein*]		
2.6.1.15 L-Glutamine:2-oxoacid amino-transferase	Glutamine-ketoacid aminotransferase	L-Glutamine + a 2-oxoacid = 2-oxoglutarate + an amino acid
[*Note: A pyridoxal-phosphate protein. L-Glutamine can be replaced by a few closely related compounds*]		
2.6.1.16 L-Glutamine:D-fructose-6-phosphate aminotransferase	Glutamine-fructose-6-phosphate amino-transferase, hexosephosphate aminotransferase	L-Glutamine + D-fructose 6-phosphate = 2-amino-2-deoxy-D-glucose 6-phosphate + L-glutamate
2.6.1.17 N-Succinyl-L-2,6-diamino-pimelate:2-oxoglutarate aminotransferase	Succinyl-diaminopimelate aminotransferase	N-Succinyl-L-diaminopimelate + 2-oxoglutarate = N-succinyl-2-amino-6-oxo-L-pimelate + L-glutamate
[*Note: A pyridoxal-phosphate protein*]		
2.6.1.18 L-Alanine:malonate-semialdehyde aminotransferase	β-Alanine aminotransferase	L-Alanine + malonate semialdehyde = pyruvate + β-alanine
2.6.1.19 4-Aminobutyrate:2-oxoglutarate aminotransferase	Aminobutyrate aminotransferase	4-Aminobutyrate + 2-oxoglutarate = succinate semialdehyde + L-glutamate
2.6.1.20 L-Tyrosine:pyruvate aminotransferase	Tyrosine-pyruvate aminotransferase	L-Tyrosine + pyruvate = p-hydroxyphenylpyruvate + L-alanine

Table 4. Enzymes: Classification and Reactions (continued)

Systematic name	Recommended trivial name	Reaction
2.6.3 Oximinotransferases		
2.6.3.1		
Pyruvateoxime:acetone oximinotransferase	Oximinotransferase, transoximinase	Pyruvateoxime + acetone = pyruvate + acetoxime

[*Note: Acetaldehyde can act instead of acetone; D-glucoseoxime can act instead of pyruvateoxime*]

2.7 Transferring phosphorus-containing groups

2.7.1 Phosphotransferases With an Alcohol Group as Acceptor

2.7.1.1		
ATP:D-hexose 6-phospho-transferase	Hexokinase	ATP + D-hexose = ADP + D-hexose 6-phosphate

[*Note: D-Glucose, D-mannose, D-fructose and D-glucosamine can act as acceptor; ITP and deoxy-ATP can act as donor*]

2.7.1.2		
ATP:D-glucose 6-phospho-transferase	Glucokinase	ATP + D-glucose = ADP + D-glucose 6-phosphate

[*Note: The enzyme from liver also acts on D-mannose*]

2.7.1.3		
ATP:D-fructose 1-phospho-transferase	Ketohexokinase	ATP + D-fructose = ADP + D-fructose 1-phosphate

[*Note: D-Sorbose and D-tagatose can also act as acceptor*]

2.7.1.4		
ATP:D-fructose 6-phospho-transferase	Fructokinase	ATP + D-fructose = ADP + D-fructose 6-phosphate
2.7.1.5		
ATP:L-rhamnulose 1-phosphotransferase	Rhamnulokinase	ATP + L-rhamnulose = ADP + L-rhamnulose 1-phosphate
2.7.1.6		
ATP:D-galactose 1-phosphotransferase	Galactokinase	ATP + D-galactose = ADP + α-D-galactose 1-phosphate

[*Note: D-galactosamine can also act as acceptor*]

2.7.1.7		
ATP:D-mannose 6-phosphotransferase	Mannokinase	ATP + D-mannose = ADP + D-mannose 6-phosphate
2.7.1.8		
ATP:2-amino-2-deoxy-D-glucose phospho-transferase	Glucosamine kinase	ATP + 2-amino-2-deoxy-D-glucose = ADP + 2-amino-2-deoxy-D-glucose phosphate
2.7.1.10		
ATP:D-glucose-1-phosphate 6-phosphotransferase	Phospho-glucokinase	ATP + D-glucose 1-phosphate = ADP + D-glucose 1,6-diphosphate
2.7.1.11		
ATP:D-fructose-6-phosphate 1-phosphotransferase	Phosphofructo-kinase NRN—Phospho-hexokinase	ATP + D-fructose 6-phosphate = ADP + D-fructose 1,6-diphosphate

[*Note: D-Tagatose 6-phosphate can act as acceptor; UTP, CTP and ITP can act as donor*]

NRN—*non recommended name*

Table 4.   Enzymes: Classification and Reactions (continued)

Systematic name	Recommended trivial name	Reaction
2.7.1.12 ATP:D-gluconate 6-phosphotransferase	Gluconokinase	ATP + D-gluconate = ADP + 6-phospho-D-gluconate
2.7.1.13 ATP:2-keto-D-gluconate 6-phosphotransferase	Ketogluconokinase	ATP + 2-keto-D-gluconate = ADP + 2-keto-6-phospho-D- gluconate
2.7.1.14 ATP:sedoheptulose 7-phosphotransferase	Sedoheptulokinase NRN— Heptulokinase	ATP + sedoheptulose = ADP + sedoheptulose 7-phosphate
2.7.1.15 ATP:D-ribose 5-phospho- transferase [*Note: 2-Deoxy-D-ribose can also act as acceptor*]	Ribokinase	ATP + D-ribose = ADP + D-ribose 5-phosphate
2.7.1.16 ATP:L(or D)-ribulose 5-phosphotransferase [*Note: Ribitol and L-arabinitol can also act as acceptor*]	Ribulokinase	ATP + L(or D)-ribulose = ADP + L(or D)-ribulose 5-phos- phate
2.7.1.17 ATP:D-xylulose 5-phosphotransferase	Xylulokinase	ATP + D-xylulose = ADP + D-xylulose 5-phosphate
2.7.1.18 ATP:D-ribose-5-phosphate 1-phosphotransferase	Phosphoribokinase	ATP + D-ribose 5-phosphate = ADP + D-ribose 1,5-diphosphate
2.7.1.19 ATP:D-ribulose-5-phosphate 1-phosphotransferase	Phosphoribulo- kinase NRN—Phospho- pentokinase	ATP + D-ribulose 5-phosphate = ADP + D-ribulose 1,5-diphosphate
2.7.1.20 ATP:adenosine 5'-phosphotransferase [*Note: 2-Aminoadenosine can also act as acceptor*]	Adenosine kinase	ATP + adenosine = ADP + AMP
2.7.1.21 ATP:thymidine 5'-phosphotransferase	Thymidine kinase	ATP + Thymidine = ADP + thymidine 5'-phosphate
2.7.1.22 ATP:N-ribosylnicotinamide 5'-phosphotransferase	Ribosylnico- tinamide kinase	ATP + N-ribosylnicotinamide = ADP + nicotinamide ribonucleotide
2.7.1.23 ATP:NAD 2'-phospho- transferase	NAD kinase	ATP + NAD = ADP + NADP
2.7.1.24 ATP:dephospho-CoA 3'-phosphotransferase	Dephospho-CoA kinase	ATP + dephospho-CoA = ADP + CoA
2.7.1.25 ATP:adenylylsulphate 3'-phosphotransferase	Adenylylsulphate kinase NRN—APS-kinase	ATP + adenylylsulphate = ADP + 3'-phospho- adenylylsulphate

NRN—*non recommended name*

Table 4. Enzymes: Classification and Reactions (continued)

Systematic name	Recommended trivial name	Reaction
2.7.1.26 ATP:riboflavin 5'-phosphotransferase	Riboflavin kinase NRN—Flavokinase	ATP + riboflavin = ADP + FMN
2.7.1.27 ATP:erythritol phospho- transferase	Erythritol kinase	ATP + erythritol = ADP + D-erythritol 4-phosphate
2.7.1.28 ATP:D-glyceraldehyde 3-phosphotransferase	Triokinase	ATP + D-glyceraldehyde = ADP + D-glyceraldehyde 3-phosphate
2.7.1.29 ATP:hydroxyacetone phosphotransferase	Acetol kinase	ATP + hydroxyacetone = ADP + hydroxyacetone phosphate
2.7.1.30 ATP:glycerol phosphotransferase	Glycerol kinase	ATP + glycerol = ADP + L-glycerol 3-phosphate

[Note: Dihydroxyacetone and L-glyceraldehyde can act as acceptor: UTP (and, in the case of the yeast enzyme, ITP and GTP) can act as donor]

2.7.1.31 ATP:D-glycerate 3-phosphotransferase	Glycerate kinase	ATP + D-glycerate = ADP + 3-phospho-D-glycerate
2.7.1.32 ATP:choline phosphotransferase	Choline kinase	ATP + choline = ADP + phosphocholine

[Note: Ethanolamine and its methyl and ethyl derivatives can also act as acceptor]

2.7.1.33 ATP:pantothenate 4'-phosphotransferase	Pantothenate kinase	ATP + pantothenate = ADP + 4'-phosphopantothenate
2.7.1.34 ATP:pantetheine 4'-phosphotransferase	Pantetheine kinase	ATP + pantetheine = ADP + pantetheine 4'-phosphate
2.7.1.35 ATP:pyridoxal 5-phosphotransferase	Pyridoxal kinase	ATP + pyridoxal = ADP + pyridoxal 5-phosphate

[Note: Pyridoxin, pyridoxamine and various derivatives can also act as acceptor]

2.7.1.36 ATP:mevalonate 5-phosphotransferase	Mevalonate kinase	ATP + mevalonate = ADP + 5-phospho-mevalonate

[Note: GTP, CTP, or UTP can also act as donor]

2.7.1.37 ATP:protein phosphotransferase	Protein kinase	ATP + a protein = ADP + a phosphoprotein
2.7.1.38 ATP:phosphorylase phosphotransferase	Phosphorylase kinase	4 ATP + 2 phosphorylase b = 4 ADP + phosphorylase a
2.7.1.39 ATP:L-homoserine O-phosphotransferase	Homoserine kinase	ATP + L-homoserine = ADP + O-phospho-L-homoserine

NRN—non recommended name

Table 4. Enzymes: Classification and Reactions (continued)

Systematic name	Recommended trivial name	Reaction
2.7.1.40 ATP:pyruvate 　phosphotransferase	Pyruvate kinase NRN— 　Phosphoenol- 　　pyruvate 　kinase	ATP + pyruvate = ADP + phosphoenolpyruvate

$$\left[\begin{array}{l}\textit{Note: UTP, GTP, CTP, ITP and deoxy-ATP can also act as donor. Also phosphorylates}\\ \textit{hydroxylamine and fluoride in the presence of } CO_2\end{array}\right]$$

Systematic name	Recommended trivial name	Reaction
2.7.1.41 D-Glucose-1-phosphate: 　D-glucose-1-phosphate 　6-phosphotransferase	Glucose-1- 　phosphate phos- 　phodismutase	D-Glucose 1-phosphate + D-glucose 1-phosphate = D-glucose 1,6-diphosphate + D-glucose
2.7.1.42 D-Glucose-1-phosphate: 　riboflavin 　5'-phosphotransferase	Riboflavin phospho- 　transferase	D-Glucose 1-phosphate + riboflavin = D-glucose + FMN
2.7.1.43 ATP:D-glucuronate 　1-phosphotransferase	Glucuronokinase	ATP + D-glucuronate = ADP + α-D-glucuronate 1-phosphate
2.7.1.44 ATP:D-galacturonate 　1-phosphotransferase	Galacturonokinase	ATP + D-galacturonate = ADP + α-D-galacturonate 1-phosphate
2.7.1.45 ATP:2-keto-3-deoxy- 　D-gluconate 　6-phosphotransferase	Ketodeoxyglucono- 　kinase	ATP + 2-keto-3-deoxy-D- gluconate = ADP + 2-keto-3- deoxy-6-phospho-D-gluconate
2.7.1.46 ATP:L-arabinose 　1-phosphotransferase	Arabinokinase	ATP + L-arabinose = ADP + β-L-arabinose 1-phosphate
2.7.1.47 ATP:D-ribulose 　5-phosphotransferase	D-Ribulokinase	ATP + D-ribulose = ADP + D-ribulose 5-phosphate
2.7.1.48 ATP:uridine 　5'-phosphotransferase	Uridine kinase	ATP + uridine = ADP + UMP

[*Note: Cytidine can act as acceptor; GTP or ITP can act as donor*]

Systematic name	Recommended trivial name	Reaction
2.7.1.49 ATP:2-methyl-4-amino- 　5-hydroxymethyl-pyrimidine 　5-phosphotransferase	Hydroxymethyl- 　pyrimidine 　kinase	ATP + 2-methyl-4-amino- 5-hydroxymethyl-pyrimidine = ADP + 2-methyl-4-amino- 5-phosphomethyl-pyrimidine

[*Note: CTP, UTP and GTP can act as donor*]

Systematic name	Recommended trivial name	Reaction
2.7.1.50 ATP:4-methyl- 　5-(2'-hydroxyethyl)-thiazole 　2'-phosphotransferase	Hydroxyethyl- 　thiazole kinase	ATP + 4-methyl- 5-(2'-hydroxyethyl)-thiazole = ADP + 4-methyl-5- (2'-phosphoethyl)-thiazole

NRN—*non recommended name*

Table 4. Enzymes: Classification and Reactions (continued)

Systematic name	Recommended trivial name	Reaction
2.7.1.51		
ATP:L-fuculose 1-phosphotransferase	L-Fuculokinase	ATP + L-fuculose = ADP + L-fuculose 1-phosphate

2.7.2 Phosphotransferases With a Carboxyl Group as Acceptor

2.7.2.1		
ATP:acetate phosphotransferase	Acetate kinase NRN—Acetokinase	ATP + acetate = ADP + acetylphosphate
[Note: Propionate also acts as acceptor, but more slowly]		
2.7.2.2		
ATP:carbamate phosphotransferase	Carbamate kinase	ATP + NH_3 + CO_2 = ADP + carbamoylphosphate
2.7.2.3		
ATP:3-phospho-D-glycerate 1-phosphotransferase	Phosphoglycerate kinase	ATP + 3-phospho-D-glycerate = ADP + 1,3-diphospho-D-glyceric acid
2.7.2.4		
ATP:L-aspartate 4-phosphotransferase	Aspartate kinase	ATP + L-aspartate = ADP + 4-phospho-L-aspartate
2.7.2.5		
ATP:carbamate phosphotransferase (dephosphorylating)	Carbamoylphosphate synthase	2 ATP + NH_3 + CO_2 + H_2O = 2 ADP + phosphate + carbamoylphosphate
[Note: May be a system]		
2.7.2.6		
ATP:formate phosphotransferase	Formate kinase	ATP + formate = ADP + formylphosphate

2.7.3 Phosphotransferases With a Nitrogenous Group as Acceptor

2.7.3.1		
ATP:guanidinoacetate phosphotransferase	Guanidinoacetate kinase	ATP + guanidinoacetate = ADP + phosphoguanidinoacetate
2.7.3.2		
ATP:creatine phosphotransferase	Creatine kinase	ATP + creatine = ADP + phosphocreatine
[Note: Negmine can also act as acceptor]		
2.7.3.3		
ATP:L-arginine phosphotransferase	Arginine kinase	ATP + L-arginine = ADP + L-phosphoarginine
2.7.3.4		
ATP:taurocyamine phosphotransferase	Taurocyamine kinase	ATP + taurocyamine = ADP + phosphotaurocyamine
2.7.3.5		
ATP:lombricine phosphotransferase	Lombricine kinase	ATP + lombricine = ADP + phospholombricine
2.7.3.6		
ATP:hypotaurocyamine phosphotransferase	Hypotaurocyamine kinase	ATP + hypotaurocyamine = ADP + phosphohypotaurocyamine
[Note: Also acts, more slowly, on taurocyamine]		

NRN—non recommended name

Table 4. Enzymes: Classification and Reactions (continued)

Systematic name	Recommended trivial name	Reaction
2.7.4 Phosphotransferases With a Phospho-Group as Acceptor		
2.7.4.1		
ATP:polyphosphate phosphotransferase	Polyphosphate kinase	$ATP + (phosphate)_n = ADP + (phosphate)_{n+1}$
2.7.4.2		
ATP:5-phosphomevalonate phosphotransferase	Phosphomeva-lonate kinase	$ATP + 5\text{-phosphomevalonate} = ADP + 5\text{-pyrophosphomevalonate}$
2.7.4.3		
ATP:AMP phosphotransferase	Adenylate kinase NRN—Myokinase	$ATP + AMP = ADP + ADP$
[Note: Inorganic triphosphate can also act as donor]		
2.7.4.4		
ATP:nucleosidemono-phosphate phosphotransferase	Nucleosidemono-phosphate kinase	$ATP + a$ nucleoside monophosphate $= ADP + a$ nucleoside diphosphate
[Note: Many nucleotides can act as acceptor; other nucleoside triphosphates can act instead of ATP]		
2.7.4.5		
ATP:deCMP phosphotransferase	Deoxycytidylate kinase	$ATP + deCMP = ADP + deCDP$
[Note: CMP can also act as acceptor]		
2.7.4.6		
ATP:nucleosidediphosphate phosphotransferase	Nucleosidediphos-phate kinase	$ATP + a$ nucleoside diphosphate $= ADP + a$ nucleoside triphosphate
[Note: Many nucleoside diphosphates can act as acceptor]		
2.7.4.7		
ATP:2-methyl-4-amino-5-phosphomethyl-pyrimidine phosphotransferase	Phosphomethyl-pyrimidine kinase	$ATP + 2\text{-methyl-4-amino-5-phosphomethyl-pyrimidine} = ADP + 2\text{-methyl-4-amino-5-pyrophosphomethyl-pyrimidine}$
2.7.4.8		
ATP:GMP phosphotransferase	Guanylate kinase	$ATP + GMP = ADP + GDP$
2.7.4.9		
ATP:thymidinemonophosphate phosphotransferase	Thymidinemono-phosphate kinase	$ATP + $ thymidine monophosphate $= ADP + $ thymidine diphosphate
2.7.4.10		
GTP:AMP phosphotransferase	GTP-adenylate kinase	$GTP + AMP = GDP + ADP$
[Note: ITP can act instead of GTP]		
2.7.5 Phosphotransferases With Regeneration of Donors (Apparently Catalysing Intramolecular Transfers)		
2.7.5.1		
α-D-Glucose-1,6-diphosphate: α-D-glucose-1-phosphate phosphotransferase	Phospho-glucomutase, glucose phosphomutase	α-D-glucose 1,6-diphosphate + α-D-glucose 1-phosphate = α-D-glucose 6-phosphate + α-D-glucose 1,6-diphosphate

NRN—*non recommended name*

Table 4. Enzymes: Classification and Reactions (continued)

Systematic name	Recommended trivial name	Reaction
2.7.5.2 2-Acetamido-2-deoxy-D-glucose-1,6-diphosphate: 2-acetamido-2-deoxy-D-glucose-1-phosphate phosphotransferase	Acetylglucosamine phosphomutase NRN— Phosphoacetyl-glucosamine mutase	2-Acetamido-2-deoxy-D-glucose 1,6-diphosphate + 2-acetamido-2-deoxy-D-glucose 1-phosphate = 2-acetamido-2-deoxy-D-glucose 6-phosphate + 2-acetamido-2-deoxy-D-glucose 1,6-diphosphate
2.7.5.3 2,3-Diphospho-D-glycerate: 2-phospho-D-glycerate phosphotransferase	Phospho-glyceromutase, glycerate phosphomutase	2,3-Diphospho-D-glycerate + 2-phospho-D-glycerate = 3-phospho-D-glycerate + 2,3-diphospho-D-glycerate
[*Note: See also 5.4.2.1*] **2.7.5.4** 1,3-Diphospho-D-glyceric acid: 3-phospho-D-glycerate phosphotransferase	Diphospho-glyceromutase, glycerate phosphomutase	1,3-Diphospho-D-glyceric acid + 3-phospho-D-glycerate = 3-phospho-D-glycerate + 2,3-diphospho-D-glycerate
2.7.6 Pyrophosphotransferases **2.7.6.1** ATP:D-ribose-5-phosphate pyrophosphotransferase	Ribosephosphate pyrophospho-kinase	ATP + D-ribose 5-phosphate = AMP + 5-phospho-α-D-ribosyl-pyrophosphate
2.7.6.2 ATP:thiamine pyrophosphotransferase	Thiamine pyro-phosphokinase NRN—Thiamine kinase	ATP + thiamine = AMP + thiamine pyrophosphate
2.7.7 Nucleotidyltransferases **2.7.7.1** ATP:NMN adenylyltransferase	NMN adenylyl-transferase, NAD pyrophos-phorylase	ATP + nicotinamide ribonucleotide = pyrophosphate + NAD
[*Note: Nicotinate nucleotide can also act as acceptor; see also 2.7.7.18*]		
2.7.7.2 ATP:FMN adenylyltransferase	FMN adenylyl-transferase, FAD pyrophos-phorylase	ATP + FMN = pyrophosphate + FAD

NRN—*non recommended name*

Table 4. Enzymes: Classification and Reactions (continued)

Systematic name	Recommended trivial name	Reaction
2.7.7.3 ATP:pantetheine-4′-phosphate adenylyltransferase	Pantetheine-phosphate adenylyl-transferase, dephospho-CoA pyrophosphorylase	ATP + pantetheine 4′-phosphate = pyrophosphate + dephospho-CoA
2.7.7.4 ATP:sulphate adenylyl-transferase	Sulphate adenylyl-transferase NRN— ATP-sulfurylase, sulfurylase	ATP + sulphate = pyrophosphate + adenylylsulphate
2.7.7.5 ADP:sulphate adenylyl-transferase	Sulphate adenylyl-transferase (ADP) NRN—ADP-sulfurylase	ADP + sulphate = orthophosphate + adenylylsulphate
2.7.7.6 Nucleosidetriphosphate: RNA nucleotidyltransferase	RNA nucleotidyl-transferase NRN— RNA polymerase	m Nucleoside triphosphate + RNA_n = m pyrophosphate + RNA_{n+m}
[*Note: Needs DNA as primer*]		
2.7.7.7 Deoxynucleosidetriphosphate: DNA deoxynucleotidyl-transferase	DNA nucleotidyl-transferase NRN— DNA polymerase	n Deoxynucleoside triphosphate + DNA_n = n pyrophosphate + 2 DNA_n
[*Note: A DNA chain acts as a primer, and the enzyme forms a complimentary chain*]		
2.7.7.8 Polyribonucleotide: orthophosphate nucleotidyltransferase	Polyribonucleotide nucleotidyltrans-ferase, polynucleotide phosphorylase	RNA_{n+1} + orthophosphate = RNA_n + a nucleoside diphosphate
[*Note: ADP, IDP, GDP, UDP and CDP can act as donor*]		
2.7.7.9 UTP:α-D-glucose-1-phosphate uridylyltransferase	Glucose-1-phos-phate uridylyl-transferase, UDPG pyrophos-phorylase	UTP + α-D-glucose-1-phos-phate = pyrophosphate + UDPglucose
2.7.7.10 UTP:α-D-galactose-1-phosphate uridylyltransferase	Galactose-1-phos-phate uridylyl-transferase	UTP + α-D-galactose 1-phosphate = pyrophosphate + UDPgalactose
2.7.7.11 UTP:α-D-xylose-1-phosphate uridylyltransferase	Xylose-1-phosphate uridylyl-transferase	UTP + α-D-xylose 1-phosphate = pyrophosphate + UDPxylose

NRN—*non recommended name*

Table 4. Enzymes: Classification and Reactions (continued)

Systematic name	Recommended trivial name	Reaction
2.7.7.12 UDPglucose:α-D-galactose-1-phosphate uridylyl-transferase	Hexose-1-phosphate uridylyl-transferase NRN—uridyl transferase	UDPglucose + α-D-galactose 1-phosphate = α-D-glucose 1-phosphate + UDPgalactose
2.7.7.13 GTP:α-D-mannose-1-phosphate guanylyltransferase	Mannose-1-phosphate guanylyltransferase	GTP + α-D-mannose 1-phosphate = pyrophosphate + GDPmannose
2.7.7.14 CTP:ethanolaminephosphate cytidylyltransferase	Ethanolaminephosphate cytidylyltransferase NRN—Phosphorylethanolamine transferase	CTP + ethanolamine phosphate = pyrophosphate + CDPethanolamine
2.7.7.15 CTP:cholinephosphate cytidylyltransferase	Cholinephosphate cytidylyltransferase NRN—Phosphorylcholine transferase	CTP + choline phosphate = pyrophosphate + CDPcholine
2.7.7.16 Ribonucleate pyrimidine-nucleotido-2'-transferase (cyclizing)	Ribonuclease NRN—RNAase I, RNase	Transfers the 3'-phosphate of a pyrimidine nucleotide residue of a polynucleotide from the 5'-position of the adjoining nucleotide to the 2'-position of the pyrimidine nucleotide itself, forming a cyclic nucleotide

[*Note: Also catalyses the transfer of the phosphate group from the 2'-position in the cyclic phosphate to water; the overall reaction brings about the depolymerization of RNA*]

2.7.7.17 Ribonucleate nucleotido-2'-transferase (cyclizing)	Ribonuclease	Acts on polyribonucleotides similarly to 2.7.7.16, but transfers purine nucleotide residues as well as pyrimidine nucleotide residues

[*Note: Also catalyses the transfer of the phosphate group from the 2'-position in the cyclic phosphate to water; the overall reaction brings about the depolymerization of RNA*]

NRN—*non recommended name*

Table 4. Enzymes: Classification and Reactions (continued)

Systematic name	Recommended trivial name	Reaction
2.7.7.18 ATP:nicotinatemononucleotide adenylyltransferase	Nicotinatemono-nucleotide adenylyltrans-ferase, deamido-NAD pyrophos-phorylase	ATP + nicotinate ribonucleo-tide = pyrophosphate + deamido-NAD
2.7.7.19 ATP:polynucleotide adenylyltransferase	Polyadenylate nucleotidyl-transferase transferase	ATP + (adenylate)$_n$ = pyrophosphate + (adenylate)$_{n+1}$
[Note: Also acts slowly with CTP]		
2.7.7.20 ATP:sRNA adenylyltransferase	sRNA adenylyl-transferase	ATP + sRNA$_n$ = pyrophosphate + sRNA$_{n+1}$ (sRNA$_n$ denotes an sRNA chain of n nucleotide units)
[Note: Also incorporates a CMP residue from CTP]		
2.7.7.21 CTP:sRNA cytidylyltransferase	sRNA cytidylyl-transferase	CTP + sRNA$_n$ = pyrophosphate + sRNA$_{n+1}$
2.7.7.22 GDP:D-mannose-1-phosphate guanylyltransferase	Mannose-1-phos-phate guanylyl-transferase, GDPmannose phosphorylase	GDP + D-mannose 1-phos-phate = orthophosphate + GDPmannose
2.7.7.23 UTP:2-acetamido-2-deoxy-α-D-glucose-1-phosphate uridylyltransferase	UDPglucosamine pyrophosphor-ylase	UTP + 2-acetamido-2-deoxy-D-glucose 1-phosphate = pyrophosphate + UDP-2-acetamido-2-deoxy-D-glucose
2.7.7.24 deTTP:α-D-glucose-1-phosphate thymidylyltransferase	Glucose-1-phosphate thymidylyl-transferase	deTTP + α-D-glucose 1-phos-phate = pyrophosphate + deTDPglucose
2.7.7.25 Nucleosidetriphosphate:sRNA nucleotidyltransferase	sRNA nucleotidyl-transferase	ATP + sRNA$_n$ = pyrophosphate + sRNA$_{n+1}$
[Note: Incorporates AMP, CMP and UMP, but not GMP]		
2.7.7.26 Ribonucleate guaninenucleo-tide-2'-transferase(cyclizing)	Guanyloribo-nuclease NRN—Aspergillus oryzae ribonuclease	Acts on polyribonucleotides similarly to 2.7.7.16, but trans-fers only at the 3'-position of a guanylate residue

[Note: Also catalyses the transfer of the phosphate from the 2'-position in the cyclic phosphate to water; the overall reaction brings about the depolymerization of RNA. Formerly EC 3.1.4.8]

NRN—*non recommended name*

Table 4. Enzymes: Classification and Reactions (continued)

Systematic name	Recommended trivial name	Reaction
2.7.8 Transferases for other Substituted Phospho-Groups		
2.7.8.1		
CDPethanolamine: 1,2-diglyceride ethanolaminephospho-transferase	Ethanolaminephos-photransferase	CDPethanolamine + 1,2-diglyceride = CMP + a phosphatidyl-ethanolamine
2.7.8.2		
CDPcholine:1,2-diglyceride cholinephosphotransferase	Cholinephospho-transferase NRN—Phosphoryl-choline-glyceride transferase	CDPcholine + 1,2-diglyceride = CMP + a phosphatidylcholine
2.7.8.3		
CDPchloine:ceramide cholinephosphotransferase	Ceramide cholinephospho-transferase	CDPcholine + ceramide = CMP + sphingomyelin
2.8 Transferring sulphur-containing groups		
2.8.1 Sulphurtransferases		
2.8.1.1		
Thiosulphate: cyanide sulphurtransferase	Thiosulphate sulphurtrans-ferase NRN—Rhodanese	Thiosulphate + cyanide = sulphite + thiocyanate
[*Note: A few other sulphur compounds can act as donor*]		
2.8.1.2		
3-Mercaptopyruvate:cyanide sulphurtransferase	3-Mercaptopyruvate sulphurtrans-ferase	3-Mercaptopyruvate + cyanide = pyruvate + thiocyanate
$\left[\begin{array}{l}\textit{Note: Sulphite, sulphinates, mercaptoethanol and mercaptopyruvate can also act}\\ \textit{as acceptor}\end{array}\right]$		
2.8.2 Sulphotransferases		
2.8.2.1		
3'-Phosphoadenylylsulphate: phenol sulphotransferase	Aryl sulphotrans-ferase NRN—Phenol sulphotransferase, sulfokinase	3'-Phosphoadenylylsulphate + a phenol = adenosine 3',5'-diphosphate + an aryl sulphate
2.8.2.2		
3'-Phosphoadenylylsulphate: 3-β-hydroxysteroid sulphotransferase	3-β-Hydroxysteroid sulphotransferase	3'-Phosphoadenylylsulphate + a 3-β-hydroxysteroid = adenosine 3',5'-diphosphate + a steroid 3-β-sulphate
2.8.2.3		
3'-Phosphoadenylylsulphate: arylamine sulphotransferase	Arylamine sulpho-transferase	3'-Phosphoadenylylsulphate + an arylamine = adenosine 3',5'-diphosphate + an aryl-sulphamate

NRN—*non recommended name*

Table 4. Enzymes: Classification and Reactions (continued)

Systematic name	Recommended trivial name	Reaction
2.8.2.4		
3'-Phosphoadenylylsulphate: oestrone sulphotransferase	Oestrone sulpho-transferase	3'-Phosphoadenylylsulphate + oestrone = adenosine 3',5'-diphosphate + oestrone 3-sulphate
2.8.2.5		
3'-Phosphoadenylylsulphate: chondroitin sulphotransferase	Chondroitin sulpho-transferase	3'-Phosphoadenylylsulphate + chondroitin = adenosine 3',5'-diphosphate + chondroitin 4-sulphate

[Note: Oligo- and polysaccharides containing 2-acetyl-D-galactosamine can act as acceptor]

2.8.3 CoA-Transferases

2.8.3.1		
Acetyl-CoA:propionate CoA-transferase	Propionate CoA-transferase	Acetyl-CoA + propionate = acetate + propionyl-CoA

[Note: Butyrate and lactate can also act as acceptor]

2.8.3.2		
Succinyl-CoA:oxalate CoA-transferase	Oxalate CoA-transferase NRN—Succinyl-β-ketoacyl-CoA transferase	Succinyl-CoA + oxalate = succinate + oxalyl-CoA
2.8.3.3		
Acetyl-CoA:malonate CoA-transferase	Malonate CoA-transferase	Acetyl-CoA + malonate = acetate + malonyl-CoA
2.8.3.5		
Succinyl-CoA:3-oxoacid CoA-transferase	3-Ketoacid CoA-transferase	Succinyl-CoA + a 3-oxoacid = succinate + a 3-oxoacyl-CoA

[Note: Acetoacetate or, more slowly, malonate semialdehyde, 3-oxovalerate, 3-oxo-isocaproate or 3-oxocaproate, can act as acceptor; malonyl-CoA can act instead of succinyl-CoA]

2.8.3.6		
Succinyl-CoA:3-oxoadipate CoA-transferase	3-Oxoadipate CoA-transferase	Succinyl-CoA + 3-oxoadipate = succinate + 3-oxoadipyl-CoA

3. HYDROLASES

3.1 Acting on ester bonds

3.1.1. Carboxylic Ester Hydrolases

3.1.1.1		
Carboxylic-ester hydrolase	Carboxylesterase NRN—Ali-esterase, B-esterase	A carboxylic ester + H_2O = an alcohol + a carboxylate

[Note: Wide specificity]

3.1.1.2		
Aryl-ester hydrolase	Arylesterase NRN—A-esterase, paraoxonase	A phenyl acetate + H_2O = a phenol + acetate

[Note: Acts on many phenolic esters; the enzyme from sheep serum also hydrolyses paraoxon]

NRN—non recommended name

Table 4. Enzymes: Classification and Reactions (continued)

Systematic name	Recommended trivial name	Reaction
3.1.1.3		
Glycerol-ester hydrolase	Lipase	A triglyceride + H_2O = a diglyceride + a fatty acid ion

[*Note: The pancreatic enzyme acts only at an ester-water interface; the outer ester links are preferentially hydrolysed*]

3.1.1.4		
Phosphatide acyl-hydrolase	Phospholipase A NRN— Lecithinase A	A lecithin + H_2O = a lysolecithin + an unsaturated fatty acid ion

[*Note: Also acts on phosphatidylethanolamine, choline plasmalogen and phosphatidates removing the fatty acid attached to the 2-position*]

3.1.1.5		
Lysolecithin acyl-hydrolase	Lysophospholipase, phospholipase B NRN— Lecithinase B, lysolecithinase	A lysolecithin + H_2O = glycerolphosphocholine + a fatty acid ion
3.1.1.6		
Acetic-ester hydrolase	Acetylesterase NRN— C-esterase (in animal tissues)	An acetic ester + H_2O = an alcohol + acetate
3.1.1.7		
Acetylcholine hydrolase	Acetylcholin-esterase NRN—True cholinesterase	Acetylcholine + H_2O = choline + acetate

[*Note: Acts on a variety of acetic esters; also catalyses transacetylations*]

3.1.1.8		
Acylcholine acyl-hydrolase	Cholinesterase NRN—Pseudo-cholinesterase	An aceylcholine + H_2O = choline + an anion

[*Note: Acts on a variety of choline esters and a few other compounds*]

3.1.1.9		
Benzoylcholine hydrolase	Benzoylcholin-esterase	Benzoylcholine + H_2O = choline + benzoate
3.1.1.11		
Pectin pectyl-hydrolase	Pectinesterase	Pectin + $n\,H_2O$ = n methanol + pectate
3.1.1.12		
Vitamin-A-acetate hydrolase	Vitamin A esterase	Vitamin A acetate + H_2O = vitamin A + acetate
3.1.1.13		
Sterol-ester hydrolase	Cholesterol esterase	A cholesterol ester + H_2O = cholesterol + an anion

[*Note: Also acts on esters of cholesterol and some other sterols*]

3.1.1.14		
Chlorophyll chlorophyllido-hydrolase	Chlorophyllase	Chlorophyll + H_2O = phytol + chlorophyllide

[*Note: Also catalyses chlorophyllide transfer, e.g. converts chlorophyll in methanol into methylchlorophyllide*]

NRN—*non recommended name*

Table 4.   Enzymes: Classification and Reactions (continued)

Systematic name	Recommended trivial name	Reaction
3.1.1.15 L-Arabinono-γ-lactone hydrolase	Arabinonolactonase	L-Arabinono-γ-lactone + H_2O = L-arabinoate
3.1.1.16 4-Carboxymethyl-4-hydroxyisocrotonolactone hydrolase	4-Carboxymethyl-4-hydroxyiso-crotonolactonase	4-Carboxymethyl-4-hydroxy-isocrotonolactone + H_2O = 3-oxoadipate
3.1.1.17 D-Glucono-δ-lactone hydrolase	Gluconolactonase NRN—Lactonase	D-Glucono-δ-lactone + H_2O = D-gluconate
[Note: Also acts on D-glucono-δ-lactone 6-phosphate]		
3.1.1.18 D(or L)-Gulono-γ-lactone hydrolase	Aldonolactonase	D(or L)-Gulono-γ-lactone + H_2O = gulonate
3.1.1.19 D-Glucurono-δ-lactone hydrolase	Uronolactonase	D-Glucurono-δ-lactone + H_2O = D-glucuronate
3.1.1.20 Tannin acyl-hydrolase	Tannase	Digallate + H_2O = 2 gallate
[Note: Also hydrolyses ester links in other tannins]		
3.1.2 Thiolester Hydrolases		
3.1.2.1 Acetyl-CoA hydrolase	Acetyl-CoA hydrolase NRN—Acetyl-CoA deacylase	Acetyl-CoA + H_2O = CoA + acetate
3.1.2.2 Palmitoyl-CoA hydrolase	Palmitoyl-CoA hydrolase	Palmitoyl-CoA + H_2O = CoA + palmitate
3.1.2.3 Succinyl-CoA hydrolase	Succinyl-CoA hydrolase	Succinyl-CoA + H_2O = CoA + succinate
3.1.2.4 3-Hydroxyisobutyryl-CoA hydrolase	3-Hydroxyiso-butyryl-CoA hydrolase	3-Hydroxyisobutyryl-CoA + H_2O = CoA + 3-hydroxyisobutyrate
[Note: Also hydrolyses 3-hydroxypropionyl-CoA]		
3.1.2.5 3-Hydroxy-3-methylglutaryl-CoA hydrolase	Hydroxymethyl-glutaryl-CoA hydrolase	3-Hydroxy-3-methylglutaryl-CoA + H_2O = CoA + 3-hydroxy-3-methylglutarate
3.1.2.6 S-2-Hydroxyacylglutathione hydrolase	Hydroxyacyl-glutathione hydrolase NRN—Glyoxalase II	S-2-Hydroxyacylglutathione + H_2O = glutathione + a 2-hydroxyacid anion

NRN—*non recommended name*

Table 4. Enzymes: Classification and Reactions (continued)

Systematic name	Recommended trivial name	Reaction
3.1.2.7 S-Acylglutathione hydrolase	Glutathione thiolesterase	S-Acylglutathione + H_2O = glutathione + an anion
3.1.2.8 S-Acetoacetylglutathione hydrolase	Acetoacetyl-glutathione hydrolase	S-Acetoacetylglutathione + H_2O = glutathione + acetoacetate
3.1.2.10 Formyl-CoA hydrolase	Formyl-CoA hydrolase	Formyl-CoA + H_2O = CoA + formate
3.1.3 Phosphoric Monoester Hydrolases		
3.1.3.1 Orthophosphoricmonoester phosphohydrolase	Alkaline phosphatase NRN—Alakine phosphomono-esterase	An orthophosphoric monoester + H_2O = an alcohol + orthophosphate

[*Note: Wide specificity. Also catalyses transphosphorylations*]

3.1.3.2 Orthophosphoric monoester phosphohydrolase	Acid phosphatase NRN—Acid phosphomonoesterase	An orthophosphoric monoester + H_2O = an alcohol + orthophosphate

[*Note: Wide specificity. Also catalyses transphosphorylations*]

3.1.3.3 Phosphoserine phosphohydrolase	Phosphoserine phosphatase	L-(or D-)Phosphoserine + H_2O = L-(or D-)serine + orthophosphate
3.1.3.4 L-α-Phosphatidate phosphohydrolase	Phosphatidate phosphatase	An L-α-phosphatidate + H_2O = a D-2,3(or L-1,2)-diglyceride + orthophosphate
3.1.3.5 5'-Ribonucleotide phosphohydrolase	5'-Nucleotidase	A 5'-ribonucleotide + H_2O = a ribonucleoside + orthophosphate

[*Note: Wide specificity for 5'-nucleotides*]

3.1.3.6 3'-Ribonucleotide phosphohydrolase	3'-Nucleotidase	A 3'-ribonucleotide + H_2O = a ribonucleoside + orthophosphate

[*Note: Wide specificity for 3'-nucleotides*]

3.1.3.7 Adenosine-3',5'-diphosphate 3'-phosphohydrolase	Phosphoadenylate 3-nucleotidase	Adenosine 3',5'-diphosphate + H_2O = AMP + orthophosphate

[*Note: Also acts on 3'-phosphoadenylylsulphate*]

3.1.3.8 meso-Inositol-hexaphosphate phosphohydrolase	Phytase	meso-Inositol hexaphosphate + $6 H_2O$ = meso-inositol + 6 orthophosphate

NRN—*non recommended name*

Table 4. Enzymes: Classification and Reactions (continued)

Systematic name	Recommended trivial name	Reaction
3.1.3.9		
D-Glucose-6-phosphate phosphohydrolase	Glucose-6-phosphatase	D-Glucose 6-phosphate + H_2O = D-glucose + orthophosphate
[Note: Also acts on D-glucosamine 6-phosphate]		
3.1.3.10		
D-Glucose-1-phosphate phosphohydrolase	Glucose-1-phosphatase	D-Glucose 1-phosphate + H_2O = D-glucose + orthophosphate
[Note: Also acts, more slowly, on D-galactose 1-phosphate]		
3.1.3.11		
D-Fructose-1,6-diphosphate 1-phosphohydrolase	Hexosediphosphatase	D-Fructose 1,6-diphosphate + H_2O = D-fructose 6-phosphate + orthophosphate
[Note: Also acts on sedoheptulose 1,7-diphosphate]		
3.1.3.12		
Trehalose-6-phosphate phosphohydrolase	Trehalosephosphatase	Trehalose 6-phosphate + H_2O = trehalose + orthophosphate
3.1.3.13		
2,3-Diphospho-D-glycerate 2-phosphohydrolase	Diphosphoglycerate phosphatase	2,3-Diphospho-D-glycerate + H_2O = 3-phospho-D-glycerate + orthophosphate
3.1.3.14		
1-Methylthio-3-phospho-D-glycerate phosphohydrolase	Methylthiophosphoglycerate phosphatase	1-Methylthio-3-phospho-D-glycerate + H_2O = methylthio-D-glycerate + orthophosphate
3.1.3.15		
L-Histidinolphosphate phosphohydrolase	Histidinol-phosphatase	L-Histidinol phosphate + H_2O = L-histidinol + orthophosphate
3.1.3.16		
Phosphoprotein phosphohydrolase	Phosphoprotein phosphatase	A phosphoprotein + $n\,H_2O$ = a protein + n orthophosphate
[Note: Acts on casein and other phosphoproteins; the spleen enzyme also acts on phenolic phosphates and phosphoamides]		
3.1.3.17		
Phosphorylase phosphohydrolase	Phosphorylase phosphatase NRN—PR-enzyme	Phosphorylase a + $4\,H_2O$ = 2 phosphorylase b + 4 orthophosphate
3.1.3.18		
Phosphoglycollate phosphohydrolase	Phosphoglycollate phosphatase	Phosphoglycollate + H_2O = glycollate + orthophosphate
3.1.3.19		
2-Phosphoglycerol phosphohydrolase	Glycerol-2-phosphatase	2-Phosphoglycerol + H_2O = glycerol + orthophosphate
3.1.4 Phosphoric Diester Hydrolases		
3.1.4.1		
Orthophosphoric diester phosphohydrolase	Phosphodiesterase	A phosphoric diester + H_2O = a phosphoric monoester + an alcohol
[Note: Wide specificity, varying with source; the spleen enzyme forms 3'-nucleotides, and the venom enzyme 5'-nucleotides, from polynucleotides]		

NRN—non recommended name

Table 4. Enzymes: Classification and Reactions (continued)

Systematic name	Recommended trivial name	Reaction
3.1.4.2		
L-3-Glycerylphosphorylcholine glycerophosphohydrolase	Glycerophosphorylcholine diesterase	L-3-Glycerylphosphorylcholine + H_2O = choline + glycerol 1-phosphate
[Note: Also acts on L-3-glycerylphosphorylethanolamine]		
3.1.4.3		
Phosphatidylcholine cholinephosphohydrolase	Phospholipase C NRN— Lipophosphodiesterase I, lecithinase C, *Clostridium welchii* α-toxin, *Clostridium oedematiens* β- and γ-toxins	A phosphatidylcholine + H_2O = a 1,2-diglyceride + choline phosphate
[Note: Also acts on sphingomyelin]		
3.1.4.4		
Phosphatidylcholine phosphatidohydrolase	Phospholipase D NRN— Lipophosphodiesterase II, lecithinase D	A phosphatidylcholine + H_2O = choline + a phosphatidate
[Note: Also acts on other phosphatides]		
3.1.4.5		
Deoxyribonucleate oligonucleotidyhydrolase	Deoxyribonuclease NRN— DNAase, DNase, streptodornase	DNA + $(n-1)H_2O$ = n oligodeoxyribonucleotides
3.1.4.6		
Deoxyribonucleate 3'-nucleotidohydrolase	Deoxyribonuclease II	Forms 3'-nucleotides from DNA
3.1.4.7		
Ribonucleate (deoxyribonucleate) 3'-nucleotidohydrolase	Micrococcal nuclease	Attacks RNA and DNA, forming 3'-nucleotides; DNA is attacked with preference for the adenine-thymine nucleotide pair
3.1.4.9		
Ribonucleate (deoxyribonucleate) 5'-nucleotidohydrolase	*Azotobacter* nuclease	Attacks RNA and DNA, forming 5'-nucleotides
3.1.5 Triphosphoric Monoester Hydrolases		
3.1.5.1		
deGTP triphosphohydrolase	deGTPase	deGTP + H_2O = deoxyguanosine + triphosphate
[Note: Also acts on GTP]		
3.1.6 Sulphuric Ester Hydrolases		
3.1.6.1		
Aryl-sulphate sulphohydrolase	Arylsulphatase	A phenol sulphate + H_2O = a phenol + sulphate
[Note: A group of enzymes with rather similar specificities]		

NRN—*non recommended name*

Table 4. Enzymes: Classification and Reactions (continued)

Systematic name	Recommended trivial name	Reaction
3.1.6.2 Sterol-sulphate sulphohydrolase	Sterol sulphatase	Dehydroepiandrosterone 3-sulphate + H_2O = dehydroepiandrosterone + sulphate

[*Note: Also acts on some related sterol sulphates*]

Systematic name	Recommended trivial name	Reaction
3.1.6.3 Sugar-sulphate sulphohydrolase	Glycosulphatase	D-Glucose 6-sulphate + H_2O = D-glucose + sulphate

[*Note: Also acts on other sulphates of mono- and disaccharides and on adenosine 5'-sulphate*]

Systematic name	Recommended trivial name	Reaction
3.1.6.4 Chondroitin-sulphate sulphohydrolase	Chondrosulphatase	Hydrolytically removes the 6-sulphate groups of the 2-acetamido-2-deoxy-D-galactose 6-sulphate units of chondroitin sulphate
3.1.6.6 Choline-sulphate sulphohydrolase	Cholinesulphatase	Choline sulphate + H_2O = choline + sulphate
3.1.6.7 Cellulose-sulphate sulphohydrolase	Cellulose polysulphatase	Hydrolytically removes the 2- and 3-sulphate groups of the poly-sulphates of cellulose and charonin

3.2 Acting on glycosyl compounds

3.2.1 Glycoside Hydrolases

Systematic name	Recommended trivial name	Reaction
3.2.1.1 α-1,4-Glucan 4-glucanohydrolase	α-Amylase	Hydrolyses α-1,4-glucan links in polysaccharides containing three or more α-1,4-linked D-glucose units

[*Note: Acts on starch, glycogen and related polysaccharides and oligosaccharides in a random manner*]

Systematic name	Recommended trivial name	Reaction
3.2.1.2 α-1,4-Glucan maltohydrolase	β-Amylase	Hydrolyses α-1,4-glucan links in polysaccharides so as to remove successive maltose units from the non-reducing ends of the chains

[*Note: Acts on starch, glycogen and related polysaccharides and oligosaccharides, producing β-maltose by an inversion*]

Systematic name	Recommended trivial name	Reaction
3.2.1.3 α-1,4-Glucan glucohydrolase	Glucoamylase	Hydrolyses α-1,4-glucan links in polysaccharides so as to remove successive glucose units from the non-reducing ends of the chains

[*Note: Acts on starch, glycogen and related polysaccharides and oligosaccharides*]

Systematic name	Recommended trivial name	Reaction
3.2.1.4 β-1,4-Glucan glucanohydrolase	Cellulase	Hydrolyses β-1,4-glucan links in cellulose

[*Note: A fungal enzyme also catalyses transcellobiosylation*]

NRN—*non recommended name*

Table 4. Enzymes: Classification and Reactions (continued)

Systematic name	Recommended trivial name	Reaction
3.2.1.6 β-1,3(4)-Glucan glucanohydrolase	Laminaranase NRN—Lichenase	Hydrolyses either β-1,3- or β-1,4-glucan links adjacent to a β-1,3-link

[*Note: Hydrolyses laminaran; also hydrolyses lichenan to β-1,3-cellobiosyl-D-glucose*]

Systematic name	Recommended trivial name	Reaction
3.2.1.7 β-2,1-Fructan fructano-hydrolase	Inulase	Hydrolyses β-1,2-fructan links in inulin
3.2.1.8 β-1,4-Xylan xylanohydrolase	Xylanase	Hydrolyses β-1,4-xylan links
3.2.1.9 Amylopectin 6-glucano-hydrolase	Amylopectin-1,6-glucosidase NRN—R-enzyme	Hydrolyses α-1,6-glucan links in amylopectin
3.2.1.10 Oligodextrin 6-glucanohydrolase	Oligo-1,6-glucosi-dase NRN—Limit dex-trinase	Hydrolyses α-1,6-glucan links in isomaltose, panose and dextrins produced from starch and glycogen by α-amylase
3.2.1.11 α-1,6-Glucan 6-glucanohydrolase	Dextranase	Hydrolyses α-1,6-glucan links
3.2.1.12 Cycloheptaglucan 4-glucanohydrolase	Cyclohepta-glucanase	Hydrolyses one α-1,4-glucan link in cycloheptaglucan, producing the linear heptaglucan
3.2.1.13 Cyclohexaglucan 4-glucanohydrolase	Cyclohexa-glucanase	Hydrolyses one α-1,4-glucan link in cyclohexaglucan, producing the linear hexaglucan

[*Note: Produces an inversion, giving a terminal β-configuration*]

Systematic name	Recommended trivial name	Reaction
3.2.1.14 Poly-β-1,4-(2-acetamido-2-deoxy)-D-glucoside glycanohydrolase	Chitinase NRN— β-1,4-Poly-N-acetyl gluco-samidinase	Hydrolyses α-1,4-acetamido-2-deoxy-D-glucoside links in chitin and chitodextrin
3.2.1.15 Poly-α-1,4-galacturonide glycanohydrolase	Polygalacturonase NRN— Pectin depolymerase, pectinase	Hydrolyses α-1,4-D-galacturonide links in pectate and other polygalacturonides
3.2.1.16 Poly-β-1,4-mannuronide glycanohydrolase	Alginase	Hydrolyses β-1,4-mannuronide links in alginate
3.2.1.17 Mucopeptide N-acetylmuramylhydrolase	Mucopeptide glucohydrolase, lysozyme NRN—Muramidase	Probably hydrolyses β-1,4-links between N-acetylmuramic acid and 2-acetamido-2-deoxy-D-glucose residues in a mucopoly-saccharide or mucopeptide

[*Note: Dissolves the cell-wall substance of certain bacteria; also acts slowly on chitin*]

NRN—*non recommended name*

Table 4.   Enzymes: Classification and Reactions (continued)

Systematic name	Recommended trivial name	Reaction
3.2.1.18 Mucopolysaccharide N-acetylneuraminylhydrolase	Neuraminidase	Probably hydrolyses terminal α-2,6-links between N-acetyl-neuraminic acid and 2-acetamido-2-deoxy-D-galactose residues in various mucopolysaccharides
3.2.1.19 Heparin glycanohydrolase	Heparinase	Hydrolyses α-1,4-links between 2-amino-2-deoxy-D-glucose and D-glucuronic acid residues in heparin
3.2.1.20 α-D-Glucoside glucohydrolase	α-Glucosidase NRN—Maltase	An α-D-glucoside + H_2O = an alcohol + D-glucose

[*Note: Wide specificity for α-D-glucopyranosides, varying with source; also catalyses glucotransferase reactions*]

Systematic name	Recommended trivial name	Reaction
3.2.1.21 β-D-Glucoside glucohydrolase	β-Glucosidase NRN—Gentiobiase, cellobiase	A β-D-glucoside + H_2O = an alcohol + D-glucose

[*Note: Wide specificity for β-D-glucopyranosides; possibly acts also on β-D-galactosides. Also catalyses glucotransferase reactions*]

Systematic name	Recommended trivial name	Reaction
3.2.1.22 α-D-Galactoside galactohydrolase	α-Galactosidase NRN—Melibiase	An α-D-galactoside + H_2O = an alcohol + D-galactose
3.2.1.23 β-D-Galactoside galactohydrolase	β-Galactosidase NRN—Lactase	A β-D-galactoside + H_2O = an alcohol + D-galactose

[*Note: Also catalyses galactotransferase reactions*]

Systematic name	Recommended trivial name	Reaction
3.2.1.24 α-D-Mannoside mannohydrolase	α-Mannosidase	An α-D-mannoside + H_2O = an alcohol + D-mannose
3.2.1.25 β-D-Mannoside mannohydrolase	β-Mannosidase	A β-D-mannoside + H_2O = an alcohol + D-mannose

[*Note: Substrates include mannan gums*]

Systematic name	Recommended trivial name	Reaction
3.2.1.26 β-D-Fructofuranoside fructohydrolase	β-Fructofuranosidase NRN—Sucrase, invertase, invertin, saccharase, β-h-fructosidase	A β-D-fructofuranoside + H_2O = an alcohol + D-fructose

[*Note: Substrates include sucrose; also catalyses fructotransferase reactions*]

Systematic name	Recommended trivial name	Reaction
3.2.1.27 α-1,3-Glucoside 3-glucohydrolase	α-1,3-Glucosidase	Nigerose + H_2O = 2 D-glucose

[*Note: Acts also on other α-1,3-D-glucosides*]

Systematic name	Recommended trivial name	Reaction
3.2.1.28 α,α'-Glucoside 1-glucohydrolase	Trehalase	Trehalose + H_2O = 2 D-glucose

[*Note: Acts also on 6-substituted trehalose derivatives*]

NRN—*non recommended name*

Table 4. Enzymes: Classification and Reactions (continued)

Systematic name	Recommended trivial name	Reaction
3.2.1.29		
Chitobiose acetamidodeoxygluco-hydrolase	Chitobiase NRN—N-Acetyl-β-glucosaminidase	Chitobiose + H_2O = 2 2-acetamido-2-deoxy-D-glucose
3.2.1.30		
β-2-Acetamido-2-deoxy-D-glucoside acetamidodeoxygluco-hydrolase	β-Acetylglucosaminase	β-Phenyl-2-acetamido-2-deoxy-D-glucoside + H_2O = phenol + 2-acetamido-2-deoxy-D-glucose
3.2.1.31		
β-D-Glucuronide glucuronohydrolase	β-Glucuronidase	A β-D-glucuronide + H_2O = an alcohol + D-glucuronate
[*Note: Also catalyses glucuronotransferase reactions*]		
3.2.1.32		
β-1,3-Xylan 3-xylanohydrolase	1,3-Xylanase	Hydrolyses β-1,3-xylan links
3.2.1.33		
Dextrin 6-glucanohydrolase	Dextrin-1,6-glucosidase NRN—Amylo-1,6-glucosidase	Hydrolyses α-1,6-glucan links in dextrins containing short 1,6-linked side-chains
3.2.1.34		
Chondroitinsulphate glycanohydrolase	Chondroitinase	Hydrolyses β-1,4-links between 2-acetamido-2-deoxy-D-galactose sulphate and D-glucuronate residues in chondroitin sulphate
[*Note: Also hydrolyses hyaluronate*]		
3.2.1.35		
Hyaluronate glycanohydrolase	Hyaluronidase	Hydrolyses links between 2-acetamido-2-deoxy-D-glucose and D-glucuronate residues in hyaluronate
[*Note: Also acts on chondroitin and mucoitin sulphates; can catalyse transglycosylation*]		
3.2.1.36		
Hyaluronate glycanohydrolase	Hyaluronidase	Hydrolyses β-1,3-links between D-glucuronate and 2-acetamido-2-deoxy-D-glucose
3.2.1.37		
β-D-Xyloside xylohydrolase	β-Xylosidase, xylobiase	A β-D-xyloside + H_2O = an alcohol + D-xylose
[*Note: Removes single xylose residues from a β-1,4-xylan; also hydrolyses xylobiose*]		
3.2.1.38		
β-D-Fucoside fucohydrolase	β-D-Fucosidase	A β-D-fucoside + H_2O = an alcohol + D-fucose
3.2.1.39		
β-1,3-Glucan glucanohydrolase	Oligo-1,3-glucosidase	Hydrolyses β-1,3-links in β-1,3-glucans
3.2.2. Hydrolysing N-Glycosyl Compounds		
3.2.2.1		
N-Ribosyl-purine ribohydrolase	Nucleosidase	An N-ribosyl-purine + H_2O = a purine + D-ribose

NRN—*non recommended name*

Table 4. Enzymes: Classification and Reactions (continued)

Systematic name	Recommended trivial name	Reaction
3.2.2.2 Inosine ribohydrolase	Inosinase	Inosine + H_2O = hypoxanthine + D-ribose
3.2.2.3 Uridine ribohydrolase	Uridine nucleo-sidase	Uridine + H_2O = uracil + D-ribose
3.2.2.4 AMP phosphoribohydrolase	AMP nucleosidase	AMP + H_2O = adenine + D-ribose 5-phosphate
3.2.2.5 NAD glycohydrolase	NAD nucleosidase NRN—NADase, DPNase	NAD + H_2O = nicotinamide + R
[Note: R-nicotinamide represents NAD]		
3.2.2.6 NAD(P) glycohydrolase	NAD(P) nucleosidase	NAD(P) + H_2O = nicotinamide + P(R)
[Note: R-nicotinamide represents NAD. Also catalyses R-transferase reactions]		

3.2.3 Hydrolysing S-Glycosyl Compounds

3.2.3.1 Thioglucoside glucohydrolase	Thioglucosidase NRN—Myrosinase, sinigrinase	A thioglycoside + H_2O = a thiol + a sugar
[Note: Has a wide specificity for thioglycosides]		

3.3 Acting on ether bonds

3.3.1 Thioether Hydrolases

3.3.1.1 S-adenosyl-L-homocysteine hydrolase	Adenosylhomocys-teinase	S-Adenosyl-L-homocysteine + H_2O = adenosine + L-homocysteine

3.4 Acting on peptide bonds (peptide hydrolases)

3.4.1 α-Amino-Acyl-Peptide Hydrolases

3.4.1.1 L-Leucyl-peptide hydrolase	Leucine aminopep-tidase	An L-leucyl-peptide + H_2O = L-leucine + a peptide
[Note: Hydrolyses many L-peptides, splitting off an N-terminal residue with a free amino-group (not necessarily leucine)]		
3.4.1.2 Amino-acyl-oligopeptide hydrolase	Aminopeptidase	An amino-acyl-oligopeptide + H_2O = an amino acid + an oligopeptide
[Note: Acts on dipeptides and tripeptides]		
3.4.1.3 Amino-acyl-dipeptide hydrolase	Aminopeptidase	An amino-acyl-dipeptide + H_2O = an amino acid + a dipeptide
[Note: Acts only on tripeptides]		
3.4.1.4 L-Prolyl-peptide hydrolase	Proline imino-peptidase	An L-prolyl-peptide + H_2O = L-proline + a peptide

NRN—*non recommended name*

Table 4. Enzymes: Classification and Reactions (continued)

Systematic name	Recommended trivial name	Reaction

3.4.2 Peptidyl-Amino-Acid Hydrolases

3.4.2.1

| Peptidyl-L-amino-acid hydrolase | Carboxypeptidase A | A peptidyl-L-amino acid + H_2O = a peptide + an L-amino acid |

[*Note: Acts on many peptides, unless the C-terminal residue is a basic amino acid or*
proline. A zinc-protein, formed from pro-carboxypeptidase A]

3.4.2.2

| Peptidyl-L-lysine hydrolase | Carboxypeptidase B NRN—Protaminase | A peptidyl-L-lysine + H_2O = a peptide + L-lysine |

[*Note: Acts also on peptides having a C-terminal L-arginine residue. A zinc-protein*]

3.4.2.3

| Peptidyl-glycine hydrolase | Yeast carboxy-peptidase | A peptidyl-glycine + H_2O = a peptide + glycine |

[*Note: Acts also on peptides having a C-terminal L-leucine residue*]

3.4.3 Dipeptide Hydrolases

3.4.3.1

| Glycyl-glycine hydrolase | Glycyl-glycine dipeptidase | Glycyl-glycine + H_2O = 2 glycine |

[*Note: Also acts on sarcosyl-glycine*]

3.4.3.2

| Glycyl-L-leucine hydrolase | Glycyl-leucine dipeptidase | Glycyl-L-leucine + H_2O = glycine + L-leucine |

3.4.3.3

| Amino-acyl-L-histidine | Amino-acyl-histidine dipeptidase, carnosinase | Amino-acyl-L-histidine + H_2O = an amino acid + L-histidine |

[*Note: Acts on many dipeptides containing L-histidine, and their amides*]

3.4.3.4

| Amino-acyl-1-methyl-L-histidine hydrolase | Amino-acyl-methyl-histidine dipeptidase, anserinase | Anserine + H_2O = β-alanine + 1-methyl-L-histidine |

3.4.3.5

| L-Cysteinyl-glycine hydrolase | Cysteinyl-glycine dipeptidase | L-Cysteinyl-glycine + H_2O = L-cysteine + glycine |

3.4.3.6

| L-Prolyl-amino-acid hydrolase | Iminodipeptidase NRN—Prolinase | An L-prolyl-amino acid + H_2O = L-proline + an amino acid |

[*Note: Also acts on amides of appropriate dipeptides*]

3.4.3.7

| Amino-acyl-L-proline hydrolase | Imidodipeptidase, prolidase | Amino-acyl-L-proline + H_2O = an amino acid + L-proline |

3.4.4 Peptidyl Peptide Hydrolases

(*No systematic names are yet possible in this sub-group*)

3.4.4.1

| | Pepsin | Hydrolyses peptides, including those with bonds adjacent to aromatic or dicarboxylic L-amino acid residues |

[*Note: Formed from pepsinogen*]

NRN—*non recommended name*

Table 4. Enzymes: Classification and Reactions (continued)

Systematic name	Recommended trivial name	Reaction
3.4.4.2		
	Pepsin B NRN—Parapepsin	Hydrolyses peptides; the specificity is similar to that of 3.4.4.1
[Note: Formed from pepsinogen B]		
3.4.4.3		
	Rennin NRN—Chymosin	Hydrolyses peptides; specificity may be similar to that of 3.4.4.1
[Note: Formed from prorennin]		
3.4.4.4		
	Trypsin	Hydrolyses peptides, amides, esters, etc., at bonds involving the carboxyl groups of L-arginine or L-lysine
[Note: Formed from trypsinogen]		
3.4.4.5		
	Chymotrypsin A	Hydrolyses peptides, amides, esters, etc., especially at bonds involving the carboxyl groups of aromatic L-amino acids
[Note: Formed from chymotrypsinogen; a number of chymotrypsins are formed, according to the number of bonds hydrolysed in the precursor]		
3.4.4.6		
	Chymotrypsin B	Specificity similar to that of 3.4.4.5
[Note: Formed from chymotrypsinogen B]		
3.4.4.7		
	Pancreatopepti- dase E NRN—Elastase	Hydrolyses peptides, especially at bonds adjacent to neutral amino acid residues
3.4.4.8		
	Enteropeptidase NRN—Enterokinase	Hydrolyses peptides; converts trypsinogen into trypsin
3.4.4.9		
	Cathepsin C	Hydrolyses peptides, especially at bonds involving an aromatic amino acid adjacent to a free α-amino group
3.4.4.10		
	Papain	Hydrolyses peptides, amides and esters, especially at bonds involving basic amino acids, or leucine or glycine
3.4.4.11		
	Chymopapain	Hydrolyses peptides, etc.; its specificity is similar to that of 3.4.4.10
3.4.4.12		
	Ficin	Hydrolyses peptides, amides and esters; its specificity is similar to that of 3.4.4.10

NRN—*non recommended name*

Table 4.   Enzymes: Classification and Reactions (continued)

Systematic name	Recommended trivial name	Reaction
3.4.4.13		
	Thrombin	Hydrolyses peptides, amides and esters of L-arginine; converts fibrinogen into fibrin
[Note: Formed from prothrombin]		
3.4.4.14		
	Plasmin NRN—Fibrinolysin	Hydrolyses peptides and esters of L-arginine and L-lysine; converts fibrin into soluble products
[Note: Formed from plasminogen]		
3.4.4.15		
	Renin	Converts hypertensinogen into hypertensin
3.4.4.16		
	Subtilopeptidase A NRN—Subtilisin	Hydrolyses peptides; converts ovalbumin into plakalbumin
[Note: Also hydrolyses some simple aliphatic esters]		
3.4.4.17		
	Aspergillo-peptidase A	Hydrolyses peptides, especially at bonds involving the carboxyl groups of arginine or leucine; converts trypsinogen into trypsin
3.4.4.18		
	Streptococcus peptidase A	Hydrolyses peptides and amides; shows wide specificity, but does not attack bonds close to a glycine residue
3.4.4.19		
	Clostridiopeptidase A NRN—Collagenase	Hydrolyses peptides containing proline, including collagen and gelatin
3.4.4.20		
	Clostridiopeptidase B	Hydrolyses peptides at bonds involving arginine residues
3.4.4.21		
	Kallikrein	Converts kallidinogen into kallidin
3.4.4.22		
	Gastricsin	Hydrolyses peptides
[Note: Optimum pH when acting on hemoglobin is 3, higher than that for 3.4.4.1]		
3.4.4.23		
	Cathepsin D	Hydrolyses peptides; its specificity is somewhat similar to 3.4.4.1, but more restricted
3.4.4.24		
	Bromelain	Hydrolyses peptides, amides and esters; its specificity is somewhat similar to that of 3.4.4.10

NRN—*non recommended name*

Table 4. Enzymes: Classification and Reactions (continued)

Systematic name	Recommended trivial name	Reaction
3.4.4.25	Keratinase	Hydrolyses some peptide bonds in keratin and poly-L-lysine

Many peptidases other than those listed above undoubtedly exist. Many of these have been described under such names as cathepsins, asclepain, pinguinain, mexicanain, tabermontanain, euphorbain, solanain, bacterial proteinase, yeast polypeptidase, etc.

3.5 Acting on C—N bonds, other than peptide bonds

3.5.1 In Linear Amides

Systematic name	Recommended trivial name	Reaction
3.5.1.1 L-Asparagine amidohydrolase	Asparaginase	L-Asparagine + H_2O = L-aspartate + NH_3
3.5.1.2 L-Glutamine amidohydrolase	Glutaminase	L-Glutamine + H_2O = L-glutamate + NH_3
3.5.1.3 ω-Amidodicarboxylate amidohydrolase	ω-Amidase	An ω-amido-dicarboxylic acid + H_2O = a dicarboxylate + NH_3

[*Note: Acts on glutaramate, succinamate, and the corresponding α-keto-ω-amidoacids*]

Systematic name	Recommended trivial name	Reaction
3.5.1.4 Acylamide amidohydrolase	Amidase	A monocarboxylic acid amide + H_2O = a monocarboxylate + NH_3
3.5.1.5 Urea amidohydrolase	Urease	Urea + H_2O = CO_2 + $2\,NH_3$
3.5.1.6 N-Carbamoyl-β-alanine amidohydrolase	β-Ureidopropionase	N-carbamoyl-β-alanine + H_2O = β-alanine + CO_2 + NH_3

[*Note: The animal enzyme also acts on β-ureidoisobutyrate*]

Systematic name	Recommended trivial name	Reaction
3.5.1.7 N-Carbamoyl-L-aspartate amidohydrolase	Ureidosuccinase	N-Carbamoyl-L-aspartate + H_2O = L-aspartate + CO_2 + NH_3
3.5.1.8 N-Formyl-L-aspartate amidohydrolase	Formylaspartate deformylase	N-Formyl-L-aspartate + H_2O = formate + L-aspartate
3.5.1.9. Aryl-formylamine amidohydrolase	Formamidase NRN—Kynurenine formamidase, formylase	N-Formyl-L-kynurenine + H_2O = formate + L-kynurenine

[*Note: Also acts on other aromatic formylamines*]

Systematic name	Recommended trivial name	Reaction
3.5.1.10 10-Formyltetrahydrofolate amidohydrolase	Formyltetrahydro-folate deformylase	10-Formyl-tetrahydrofolate + H_2O = formate + tetrahydrofolate
3.5.1.11 Penicillin amidohydrolase	Penicillin amidase	Penicillin + H_2O = an anion + penicin

NRN—*non recommended name*

Table 4. Enzymes: Classification and Reactions (continued)

Systematic name	Recommended trivial name	Reaction
3.5.1.12		
Biotin-amide amidohydrolase	Biotinidase	Biotin amide + H_2O = biotin + NH_3
[Note: Also acts on other biotinides]		
3.5.1.13		
Aryl-acylamide amidohydrolase	Aryl acylamidase	An N-acyl-anilide + H_2O = a fatty acid ion + aniline
[Note: Also acts on para-substituted acylanilides]		
3.5.1.14		
N-Acylamino-acid amidohydrolase	Aminoacylase NRN— Dehydro- peptidase II, hippuricase	An N-acyl-amino acid + H_2O = a fatty acid ion + an amino acid
[Note: Wide specificity; also hydrolyses dehydro-peptides]		
3.5.1.15		
N-Acylaspartate amidohydrolase	Aspartoacylase NRN— Aminoacylase II	N-Acyl-aspartate + H_2O = a fatty acid ion + aspartate
3.5.1.16		
α-N-Acetyl-L-ornithine amidohydrolase	Acetylornithine deacetylase	α-N-Acetyl-L-ornithine + H_2O = acetate + L-ornithine
[Note: Also hydrolyses N-acetylmethionine]		
3.5.1.17		
ε-N-Acyl-L-lysine amidohydrolase	Acyl-lysine deacylase	ε-N-Acyl-L-lysine + H_2O = a fatty acid ion + L-lysine
3.5.1.18		
N-Succinyl- LL-2,6-diaminopimelate amidohydrolase	Succinyl- diaminopimelate desuccinylase	N-Succinyl-L-2,6-diaminopimelate + H_2O = succinate + L-2,6-diaminopimelate
3.5.2 In Cyclic Amides		
3.5.2.1		
Barbiturate amidohydrolase	Barbiturase	Barbiturate + $2 H_2O$ = malonate + urea
3.5.2.2		
4,5-Dihydropyrimidine amidohydrolase	Dihydro- pyrimidinase NRN—Hydantoinase	4,5-Dihydrouracil + H_2O = 3-ureidopropionate
[Note: Also acts on dihydrothymine and hydantoin]		
3.5.2.3		
L-4,5-Dihydro-orotate amidohydrolase	Dihyro-orotase NRN— Carbamylaspartic dehydrase	L-4,5-Dihydro-orotate + H_2O = N-carbamoyl-L-aspartate
3.5.2.4		
L-5-Carboxymethylhydantoin amidohydrolase	Carboxymethyl- hydantoinase	L-5-Carboxymethylhydantoin + H_2O = N-carbamoyl-L-aspartate
3.5.2.5		
Allantoin amidohydrolase	Allantoinase	Allantoin + H_2O = allantoate

NRN—non recommended name

Table 4. Enzymes: Classification and Reactions (continued)

Systematic name	Recommended trivial name	Reaction
3.5.2.6		
Penicillin amido-β-lactam-hydrolase	Penicillinase	Penicillin + H_2O = penicilloate
3.5.2.7		
4-Imidazolone-5-propionate amidohydrolase	Imidazolone-propionase	4-Imidazolone-5-propionate + H_2O = N-formimino-L-glutamate
3.5.3 In Linear Amides		
3.5.3.1		
L-Arginine amidinohydrolase	Arginase	L-Arginine + H_2O = L-ornithine + urea
[*Note: Also hydrolyses α-N-substituted L-arginines and canavanine*]		
3.5.3.2		
Guanidinoacetate amidinohydrolase	Glycocyaminase	Guanidinoacetate + H_2O = glycine + urea
3.5.3.3		
Creatinine amidinohydrolase	Creatininase	Creatinine + H_2O = sarcosine + urea
3.5.3.4		
Allantoate amidinohydrolase	Allantoicase	Allantoate + H_2O = glyoxylate + 2 urea
3.5.3.5		
N-Formimino-L-aspartate iminohydrolase	Formiminoaspartate deiminase	N-Formimino-L-aspartate + H_2O = N-formyl-L-aspartate + NH_3
3.5.3.6		
L-Arginine iminohydrolase	Arginine deiminase	L-Arginine + H_2O = L-citrulline + NH_3
[*Note: Also acts on canavanine*]		
3.5.4 In Cyclic Amidines		
3.5.4.1		
Cytosine aminohydrolase	Cytosine deaminase	Cytosine + H_2O = uracil + NH_3
[*Note: Also acts on 5-methylcytosine*]		
3.5.4.2		
Adenine aminohydrolase	Adenine deaminase NRN—Adenase	Adenine + H_2O = hypoxanthine + NH_3
3.5.4.3		
Guanine aminohydrolase	Guanine deaminase NRN—Guanase	Guanine + H_2O = xanthine + NH_3
3.5.4.4		
Adenosine aminohydrolase	Adenosine deaminase	Adenosine + H_2O = inosine + NH_3
3.5.4.5		
Cytidine aminohydrolase	Cytidine deaminase	Cytidine + H_2O = uridine + NH_3
3.5.4.6		
AMP aminohydrolase	AMP deaminase	AMP + H_2O = IMP + NH_3
3.5.4.7		
ADP aminohydrolase	ADP deaminase	ADP + H_2O = IDP + NH_3

NRN—*non recommended name*

Table 4. Enzymes: Classification and Reactions (continued)

Systematic name	Recommended trivial name	Reaction
3.5.4.8 4-Aminoimidazole aminohydrolase	Aminoimidazolase	4-Aminoimidazole + H_2O = unidentified product + NH_3
3.5.4.9 5,10-methenyltetrahydrofolate 5-hydrolase (decyclizing)	Methenyltetra-hydrofolate cyclohydrolase	5,10-Methenyltetrahydrofolate + H_2O = 10-formyltetrahydrofolate
3.5.4.10 IMP 1,2-hydrolase (decyclizing)	IMP cyclohydrolase	IMP + H_2O = 5'-phosphoribosyl-5-formamido-4-imidazolecarboxamide
3.5.4.11 Pterin aminohydrolase	Pterin deaminase	A pterin + H_2O = a lumazine + NH_3
3.5.4.12 deCMP aminohydrolase	deCMP deaminase	deCMP + H_2O = deUMP + NH_3

[Note: Also acts on some 5-substituted deCMPs]

3.5.5 In Cyanides

3.5.5.1

Nitrile aminohydrolase	Nitrilase	A nitrile + H_2O = a carboxylate + NH_3

[Note: Acts on a wide range of aromatic nitriles including 3-indoleacetonitrile, and also on some aliphatic nitriles]

3.5.99 In other Compounds

3.5.99.1

Riboflavin hydrolase	Riboflavinase	Riboflavin + H_2O = ribitol + lumichrome

3.5.99.2

Thiamine hydrolase	Thiaminase II	Thiamine + H_2O = 2-methyl-4-amino-5-hydroxy-methyl-pyrimidine + 4-methyl-5-(2'-hydroxyethyl)-thiazole

3.6 Acting on acid anhydride bonds

3.6.1 In Phosphoryl-Containing Anhydrides

3.6.1.1

Pyrophosphate phosphohydrolase	Inorganic pyrophosphatase	Pyrophosphate + H_2O = 2 orthophosphate

[Note: Specificity varies with the source and with the activating metal ion]

3.6.1.2

Trimetaphosphate hydrolase	Trimeta-phosphatase	Trimetaphosphate + H_2O = triphosphate

3.6.1.3

ATP phosphohydrolase	ATPase	ATP + H_2O = ADP + orthophosphate

[Note: This activity occurs in myosin and actomyosin, mitochondria, microsomes, and cell membranes. In some cases the ATPase activity is activated by Mg^{2+}, in some by Ca^{2+}, and in other cases by both Ca^{2+} and Mg^{2+}. Another form of ATPase is stimulated by Na^+ + K^+ and is inhibited by ouabain. Some ATPases also hydrolyse ITP and other nucleoside 5'-triphosphates, as well as triphosphate. The substrate specificity may depend on the activating divalent cation and on the presence of monovalent cations]

Table 4. Enzymes: Classification and Reactions (continued)

Systematic name	Recommended trivial name	Reaction
3.6.1.5 ATP diphosphohydrolase	Apyrase NRN—ATP-diphosphotase	ATP + H_2O = ADP + orthophosphate
[*Note: Activated by Ca. Also acts on ADP*]		
3.6.1.6 Nucleosidediphosphate phosphohydrolase	Nucleosidedi-phosphatase	A nucleoside diphosphate + H_2O = a nucleotide + orthophosphate
[*Note: Activated by Mg. Acts on IDP, GDP, UDP and also D-ribose 5-pyrophosphate*]		
3.6.1.7 Acylphosphate phosphohydrolase	Acylphosphatase	An acylphosphate + H_2O = an anion + orthophosphate
3.6.1.8 ATP pyrophosphohydrolase	ATPase NRN—ATP-pyrophosphatase	ATP + H_2O = AMP + pyrophosphate
[*Note: Also acts on ITP, GTP, CTP, and UTP*]		
3.6.1.9 Dinucleotide nucleotidohydrolase	Nucleotide pyrophosphatase	A dinucleotide + H_2O = 2 mononucleotides
[*Note: Substrates include NAD, ATP, FAD, CoA, and also ATP and ADP*]		
3.6.1.10 Polyphosphate polyphosphohydrolase	Endopoly-phosphatase NRN—Polyphosphate depolymerase	Polyphosphate + $n\,H_2O$ = n pentaphosphate
3.6.1.11 Polyphosphate phosphohydrolase	Exopoly-phosphatase	$(\text{Polyphosphate})_n + H_2O$ = $(\text{polyphosphate})_{n-1}$ + orthophosphate
3.6.1.12 deCTP nucleotidohydrolase	deCTPase	deCTP + H_2O = deCMP + pyrophosphate
[*Note: Also hydrolyses deCDP to deCMP and orthophosphate*]		
3.6.1.13 ADPribose ribophosphohydrolase	ADPribose pyrophosphatase	ADPribose + H_2O = AMP + ribose 5-phosphate

3.7 Acting on C—C bonds

   3.7.1 In Ketonic Substances

3.7.1.1 Oxaloacetate acetylhydrolase	Oxaloacetase	Oxaloacetate + H_2O = oxalate + acetate
3.7.1.2 4-Fumarylacetoacetate fumarylhydrolase	Fumarylaceto-acetase NRN—β-Diketonase	4-Fumarylacetoacetate + H_2O = acetoacetate + fumarate
[*Note: Also acts on other 3,5- and 2,4-diketoacids*]		

NRN—*non recommended name*

Table 4.   Enzymes: Classification and Reactions (continued)

Systematic name	Recommended trivial name	Reaction
3.7.1.3		
L-Kynurenine hydrolase	Kynureninase	L-Kynurenine + H_2O = anthranilate + L-alanine
[Note: A pyridoxal-phosphate protein]		
3.8 Acting on halide bonds		
3.8.1 In C-Halide compounds		
3.8.1.1		
Alkyl-halide halidohydrolase	Alkylhalidase	$CH_2BrCl + H_2O$ = $H \cdot CHO$ + bromide + chloride
3.8.2 In P-halide compounds		
3.8.2.1		
Di-isopropylphosphoro-fluoridate fluorohydrolase	DFPase	Di-isopropyl phosphorofluoridate + H_2O = di-isopropyl phosphate + fluoride
[Note: Acts on other organophosphorus compounds and 'nerve gases']		
3.9 Acting on P—N bonds		
3.9.1.1		
Phosphoamide hydrolase	Phosphoamidase	Phosphocreatin + H_2O = creatine + orthophosphate
[Note: Also acts on phospho-arginine and other phosphoamides. Possibly identical with 3.1.3.16]		
4. LYASES		
4.1 Carbon-carbon Lyases		
4.1.1 Carboxy-Lyases		
4.1.1.1		
2-Oxoacid carboxy-lyase	Pyruvate decarboxylase NRN—α-Carboxylase	A 2-oxoacid = an aldehyde + CO_2
[Note: A thiamine-pyrophosphate protein. Also catalyses acyloin formation]		
4.1.1.2		
Oxalate carboxy-lyase	Oxalate decarboxylase	Oxalate = formate + CO_2
4.1.1.3		
Oxaloacetate carboxy-lyase	Oxaloacetate decarboxylase	Oxaloacetate = pyruvate + CO_2
4.1.1.4		
Acetoacetate carboxy-lyase	Acetoacetate decarboxylase	Acetoacetate = acetone + CO_2
4.1.1.5		
2-Hydroxy-3-oxomethyl-butyrate carboxy-lyase	Acetolactate decarboxylase	(+)-2-Hydroxy-3-oxomethylbutyrate = (−)-2-acetoin + CO_2
4.1.1.6		
cis-Aconitate carboxy-lyase	Aconitate decarboxylase	cis-Aconitate = itaconate + CO_2
4.1.1.7		
Benzoylformate carboxy-lyase	Benzoylformate decarboxylase	Benzoylformate = benzaldehyde + CO_2
[Note: A thiamine-pyrophosphate protein]		

NRN—non recommended name

Table 4. Enzymes: Classification and Reactions (continued)

Systematic name	Recommended trivial name	Reaction
4.1.1.8		
Oxalyl-CoA carboxy-lyase	Oxalyl-CoA decarboxylase	Oxalyl-CoA = formyl-CoA + CO_2
[*Note: A thiamine-pyrophosphate protein*]		
4.1.1.9		
Malonyl-CoA carboxy-lyase	Malonyl-CoA decarboxylase	Malonyl-CoA = acetyl-CoA + CO_2
4.1.1.10		
Aminomalonate carboxy-lyase	Aminomalonate decarboxylase	Aminomalonate = glycine + CO_2
4.1.1.11		
L-Aspartate 1-carboxy-lyase	Aspartate 1-decarboxylase	L-Aspartate = β-alanine + CO_2
[*Note: A pyridoxal-phosphate protein*]		
4.1.1.12		
L-Aspartate 4-carboxy-lyase	Aspartate 4-decarboxylase	L-Aspartate = L-alanine + CO_2
[*Note: A pyridoxal-phosphate protein*]		
4.1.1.13		
N-Carbamoyl-L-aspartate 1-carboxy-lyase	Carbamoyl-aspartate decarboxylase	N-Carbamoyl-L-aspartate = carbamoyl-β-alanine + CO_2
4.1.1.14		
L-Valine carboxy-lyase	Valine decarboxylase	L-Valine = isobutylamine + CO_2
[*Note: A pyridoxal-phosphate protein. Also acts on L-leucine*]		
4.1.1.15		
L-Glutamate 1-carboxy-lyase	Glutamate decarboxylase	L-Glutamate = 4-aminobutyrate + CO_2
[*Note: A pyridoxal-phosphate protein. The brain enzyme also acts on L-cysteate and L-cysteine sulphinate*]		
4.1.1.16		
3-Hydroxy-L-glutamate 1-carboxy-lyase	Hydroxyglutamate decarboxylase	3-Hydroxy-L-glutamate = 4-amino-3-hydroxybutyrate + CO_2
[*Note: A pyridoxal-phosphate protein*]		
4.1.1.17		
L-Ornithine carboxy-lyase	Ornithine decarboxylase	L-Ornithine = putrescine + CO_2
[*Note: A pyridoxal-phosphate protein*]		
4.1.1.18		
L-Lysine carboxy-lyase	Lysine decarboxylase	L-Lysine = cadaverine + CO_2
[*Note: A pyridoxal-phosphate protein. Also acts on 5-hydroxy-L-lysine*]		
4.1.1.19		
L-Arginine carboxy-lyase	Arginine decarboxylase	L-Arginine = agmatine + CO_2
[*Note: A pyridoxal-phosphate protein*]		

Table 4. Enzymes: Classification and Reactions (continued)

Systematic name	Recommended trivial name	Reaction
4.1.1.20		
meso-2,6-Diaminopimelate carboxy-lyase	Diaminopimelate decarboxylase	meso-2,6-Diaminopimelate = L-lysine + CO_2
[Note: A pyridoxal-phosphate protein]		
4.1.1.21		
5'-Phosphoribosyl-5-amino-4-imidazolecarboxylate carboxy-lyase	Phosphoribosyl-aminoimidazole carboxylase	5'-Phosphoribosyl-5-amino-4-imidazole-carboxylate = 5'-phosphoribosyl-5-aminoimidazole + CO_2
4.1.1.22		
L-Histidine carboxy-lyase	Histidine decarboxylase	L-Histidine = histamine + CO_2
[Note: A pyridoxal-phosphate protein]		
4.1.1.23		
Orotidine-5'-phosphate carboxy-lyase	Orotidine-5'-phosphate decarboxylase	Orotidine 5'-phosphate = UMP + CO_2
4.1.1.24		
Aminobenzoate carboxy-lyase	Aminobenzoate decarboxylase	p-(or o-)Aminobenzoate = aniline + CO_2
[Note: A pyridoxal-phosphate protein]		
4.1.1.25		
L-Tyrosine carboxy-lyase	Tyrosine decarboxylase	L-Tyrosine = tyramine + CO_2
[Note: A pyridoxal-phosphate protein. The bacterial enzyme also acts on 3-hydroxytyrosine and, more slowly, on 3-hydroxyphenylalanine]		
4.1.1.26		
3,4-Dihydroxy-L-phenylalanine carboxy-lyase	DOPA decarboxylase	3,4-Dihydroxy-L-phenylalanine = dihydroxyphenylethylamine + CO_2
[Note: A pyridoxal-phosphate protein. Also acts on 2-(or 3-)hydroxyphenylalanine and 3-hydroxyphenylserine]		
4.1.1.27		
L-Tryptophan carboxy-lyase	Tryptophan decarboxylase	L-Tryptophan = tryptamine + CO_2
4.1.1.28		
5-Hydroxy-L-tryptophan carboxy-lyase	Hydroxytryptophan decarboxylase	5-Hydroxy-L-tryptophan = 5-hydroxytryptamine + CO_2
[Note: A pyridoxal-phosphate protein]		
4.1.1.29		
L-Cysteinesulphinate carboxy-lyase	Cysteinesulphinate decarboxylase	L-Cysteine sulphinate = hypotaurine + CO_2
[Note: A pyridoxal-phosphate protein]		
4.1.1.30		
N-(L-Pantothenoyl)-L-cysteine carboxy-lyase	Pantothenoyl-cysteine decarboxylase	N-(L-Pantothenoyl)-L-cysteine = pantetheine + CO_2
4.1.1.31		
Orthophosphate:oxaloacetate carboxy-lyase (phosphorylating)	Phosphopyruvate carboxylase	Orthophosphate + oxaloacetate = H_2O + phosphoenolpyruvate + CO_2

Table 4. Enzymes: Classification and Reactions (continued)

Systematic name	Recommended trivial name	Reaction
4.1.1.32		
GTP:oxaloacetate carboxy-lyase (transphosphorylating)	Phosphopyruvate carboxylase	GTP + oxaloacetate = GDP + phospho-enolpyruvate + CO_2
[*Note: ITP can also act as phosphate donor*]		
4.1.1.33		
ATP:5-pyrophospho-mevalonate carboxy-lyase (dehydrating)	Pyrophospho-mevalonate decarboxylase	ATP + 5-pyrophospho-mevalonate = ADP + orthophosphate + isopentenyl pyrophosphate + CO_2
4.1.1.34		
3-Keto-L-gulonate carboxy-lyase	Keto-L-gulonate decarboxylase	3-Keto-L-gulonate = L-xylulose + CO_2
4.1.1.35		
UDPglucuronate carboxy-lyase	UDPglucuronate decarboxylase	UDPglucuronate = UDPxylose + CO_2
4.1.1.36		
4'-Phospho-N-(L-pantothenoyl)-L-cysteine carboxy-lyase	Phosphopanto-thenoylcysteine decarboxylase	4'-Phospho-N-(L-pantothenoyl)-L-cysteine = pantetheine 4'-phosphate + CO_2
4.1.1.37		
Uroporphyrinogen-III carboxy-lyase	Uroporphyrinogen decarboxylase	Uroporphyrinogen-III = coproporphyrinogen + $4 CO_2$
4.1.1.38		
Pyrophosphate:oxaloacetate carboxy-lyase (phosphorylating)	Phosphopyruvate carboxylase	Pyrophosphate + oxaloacetate = orthophosphate + phospho-enolpyruvate + CO_2
4.1.1.39		
3-Phospho-D-glycerate carboxy-lyase (dimerizing)	Ribulosedi-phosphate carboxylase NRN—Carboxydismutase	3-Phospho-D-glycerate = D-ribulose 1,5-diphosphate + CO_2
4.1.2 Aldehyde-Lyases		
4.1.2.1		
4-Hydroxy-2-oxobutyrate formaldehyde-lyase	Hydroxyoxo-butyrate aldolase	4-Hydroxy-2-oxobutyrate = pyruvate + formaldehyde
[*Note: Also acts on phenylpyruvate*]		
4.1.2.2		
Erythrulose-1-phosphate formaldehyde-lyase	Ketotetrose aldolase	Erythrulose 1-phosphate = dihydroxyacetone phosphate + formaldehyde
4.1.2.3		
Ribose-5-phosphate formaldehyde-lyase	Pentosealdolase	Ribose 5-phosphate = erythrulose 1-phosphate + formaldehyde
4.1.2.4		
2-Deoxy-D-ribose-5-phosphate acetaldehyde-lyase	Deoxyriboaldolase NRN—Deoxyribose-5-phosphate aldolase	2-Deoxy-D-ribose 5-phosphate = D-glyceraldehyde 3-phosphate + acetaldehyde

NRN—*non recommended name*

Table 4. Enzymes: Classification and Reactions (continued)

Systematic name	Recommended trivial name	Reaction
4.1.2.5		
L-Threonine acetaldehyde-lyase	Threonine aldolase	L-Threonine = glycine + acetaldehyde
[*Note: A pyridoxal-phosphate protein*]		
4.1.2.6		
L-Allothreonine acetaldehyde-lyase	Allothreonine aldolase	L-Allothreonine = glycine + acetaldehyde
[*Note: A pyridoxal-phosphate protein*]		
4.1.2.7		
Ketose-1-phosphate aldehyde-lyase	Ketose-1-phosphate aldolase NRN—Aldolase	A ketose 1-phosphate = dihydroxyacetone phosphate + an aldehyde
[*Note: Wide specificity*]		
4.1.2.8		
Indole-3-glycerolphosphate D-glyceraldehyde-3-phosphate-lyase	Indoleglycerol-phosphate aldolase	Indole 3-glycerolphosphate = indole + D-glyceraldehyde 3-phosphate
4.1.2.9		
D-Xylulose-5-phosphate D-glyceraldehyde-3-phosphate-lyase (phosphate acetylating)	Phosphoketolase	D-Xylulose 5-phosphate + orthophosphate = acetylphosphate + D-glyceraldehyde 3-phosphate + H_2O
[*Note: A thiamine-pyrophosphate protein*]		
4.1.2.10		
Mandelonitrile benzaldehyde-lyase	Hydroxynitrile lyase	Mandelonitrile = benzaldehyde + HCN
[*Note: A flavoprotein*]		
4.1.2.11		
p-Hydroxymandelonitrile hydroxybenzaldehyde-lyase	Hydroxynitrile lyase	p-Hydroxymandelonitrile = p-hydroxybenzaldehyde + HCN
4.1.2.12		
2-Oxopantoate formaldehyde-lyase	Ketopanto-aldolase	2-Oxopantoate = 2-oxoisovalerate + formaldehyde
4.1.2.13		
Fructose-1,6-diphosphate D-glyceraldehyde-3-phosphate-lyase	Fructosedi-phosphate aldolase NRN—Zymohexase, aldolase	Fructose 1,6-diphosphate = dihydroxyacetone phosphate + D-glyceraldehyde 3-phosphate
[*Note: Also acts on ketose monophosphates*]		
4.1.2.14		
6-Phospho-2-keto-3-deoxy-D-gluconate D-glyceraldehyde-3-phosphate-lyase	Phospho-2-keto-3-deoxy-gluconate aldolase	6-Phospho-2-keto-3-deoxy-D-gluconate = pyruvate + D-glyceraldehyde 3-phosphate

NRN—*non recommended name*

Table 4.   Enzymes: Classification and Reactions (continued)

Systematic name	Recommended trivial name	Reaction
4.1.2.15 7-Phospho-2-keto-3-deoxy-D-arabino-heptonate D-erythrose-4-phosphate-lyase (pyruvate-phosphorylating)	Phospho-2-keto-3-deoxy-heptonate aldolase	7-Phospho-2-keto-3-deoxy-D-arabinoheptonate + orthophosphate = phospho-enolpyruvate + D-erythrose 4-phosphate + H_2O
4.1.2.16 8-Phospho-2-keto-3-deoxy-D-octonate D-arabinose-5-phosphate-lyase (pyruvate-phosphorylating)	Phospho-2-keto-3-deoxy-octonate aldolase	8-Phospho-2-keto-3-deoxy-D-octonate + orthophosphate = phospho-enolypyruvate + D-arabinose 5-phosphate + H_2O
4.1.2.17 L-Fuculose-1-phosphate L-lactaldehyde-lyase	L-Fuculose-phosphate aldolase	L-Fuculose 1-phosphate = dihydroxyacetone phosphate + L-lactaldehyde
4.1.3 Ketoacid-Lyases **4.1.3.1** threo-D$_s$-Isocitrate glyoxylate-lyase	Isocitrate lyase NRN— Isocitrase, isocitritase, isocitratase	threo-D$_s$-Isocitrate = succinate + glyoxylate
4.1.3.2 L-Malate glyoxylate-lyase (CoA-acetylating)	Malate synthase NRN— Malate condensing enzyme, glyoxylate transacetase	L-Malate + CoA = acetyl-CoA + H_2O + glyoxylate
4.1.3.3 N-Acetylneuraminate pyruvate-lyase	N-Acetyl-neuraminate lyase NRN—N-Acetyl-neuraminic acid aldolase	N-Acetylneuraminate = 2-acetamido-2-deoxy-D-mannose + pyruvate
[Note: Also acts on N-glycolyl-neuraminate]		
4.1.3.4 3-Hydroxy-3-methylglutaryl-CoA acetoacetate-lyase	Hydroxymethyl-glutaryl-CoA lyase	3-Hydroxy-3-methylglutaryl-CoA = acetyl-CoA + acetoacetate
4.1.3.5 3-Hydroxy-3-methylglutaryl-CoA acetoacetyl-CoA-lyase (CoA-acetylating)	Hydroxymethyl-glutaryl-CoA synthase	3-Hydroxy-3-methylglutaryl-CoA + CoA = acetyl-CoA + H_2O + acetoacetyl-CoA
4.1.3.6 Citrate oxaloacetate-lyase	Citrate lyase NRN— Citrase, citridesmolase, citrate aldolase, citratase	Citrate = acetate + oxaloacetate

NRN—non recommended name

Table 4.   Enzymes: Classification and Reactions (continued)

Systematic name	Recommended trivial name	Reaction
4.1.3.7 Citrate oxaloacetate-lyase (CoA-acetylating)	Citrate synthase NRN— Condensing enzyme, citrate condensing enzyme, citrogenase, oxaloacetate transacetase	Citrate + CoA = acetyl-CoA + H_2O + oxaloacetate
4.1.3.8 ATP:citrate oxaloacetate-lyase (CoA-acetylating and ATP-dephosphorylating)	ATP citrate lyase NRN—Citrate-cleavage enzyme	ATP + citrate + CoA = ADP + orthophosphate + acetyl-CoA + oxaloacetate
4.1.3.9 2-Hydroxyglutarate glyoxylate-lyase (CoA-acylating)	2-Hydroxyglutarate synthase	2-Hydroxyglutarate + CoA = propionyl-CoA + H_2O + glyoxylate
4.1.3.10 n-Propylmalate glyoxylate-lyase (CoA-acylating)	n-Propylmalate synthase	n-Propylmalate + CoA = butyryl-CoA + H_2O + glyoxylate
4.2 Carbon-oxygen lyases		
4.2.1 Hydro-lyases		
4.2.1.1 Carbonate hydro-lyase	Carbonate dehydratase, carbonic anhydrase	H_2CO_3 (or H^+ + HCO_3^-) = CO_2 + H_2O
[Note: A zinc-protein]		
4.2.1.2 L-Malate hydro-lyase	Fumarate hydratase NRN—Fumarase	L-Malate = fumarate + H_2O
4.2.1.3 Citrate (isocitrate) hydro-lyase	Aconitate hydratase NRN—Aconitase	Citrate = cis-aconitate + H_2O
[Note: Also converts isocitrate into cis-aconitate]		
4.2.1.4 Citrate hydro-lyase	Citrate dehydratase	Citrate = cis-aconitate + H_2O
[Note: Does not act on isocitrate]		
4.2.1.5 D-Arabinonate hydro-lyase	Arabinonate dehydratase	D-Arabinonate = 2-keto-3-deoxy-D-arabinonate + H_2O
4.2.1.6 D-Galactonate hydro-lyase	Galactonate dehydratase	D-Galactonate = 2-keto-3-deoxy-D-galactonate + H_2O
4.2.1.7 D-Altronate hydro-lyase	Altronate dehydratase	D-Altronate = 2-keto-3-deoxy-D-gluconate + H_2O

NRN—*non recommended name*

Table 4. Enzymes: Classification and Reactions (continued)

Systematic name	Recommended trivial name	Reaction
4.2.1.8 D-Mannonate hydro-lyase	Mannonate dehydratase	D-Mannonate = 2-keto-3-deoxy-D-gluconate + H_2O
4.2.1.9 2,3-Dihydroxyacid hydro-lyase	Dihydroxyacid dehydratase	2,3-Dihydroxyisovalerate = 2-oxoisovalerate + H_2O
4.2.1.10 5-Dehydroquinate hydro-lyase	5-Dehydroquinate dehydratase	5-Dehydroquinate = 5-dehydroshikimate + H_2O
4.2.1.11 2-Phospho-D-glycerate hydro-lyase	Phosphopyruvate hydratase NRN—Enolase	2-Phospho-D-glycerate = phospho-enolpyruvate + H_2O
4.2.1.12 6-Phospho-D-gluconate hydro-lyase	Phosphogluconate dehydratase	6-Phospho-D-gluconate = 2-keto-3-deoxy-6-phospho-D-gluconate + H_2O
4.2.1.13 L-Serine hydro-lyase (deaminating)	L-Serine dehydratase NRN—Serine deaminase, cystathionine synthetase	L-Serine + H_2O = pyruvate + NH_3 + H_2O

[Note: A pyridoxal-phosphate protein. Also forms cystathionine from L-serine and L-homocysteine]

4.2.1.14 D-Serine hydro-lyase (deaminating)	D-Serine dehydratase	D-Serine + H_2O = pyruvate + NH_3 + H_2O

[Note: A pyridoxal-phosphate protein. Also acts, slowly, on D-threonine]

4.2.1.15 L-Homoserine hydro-lyase (deaminating)	Homoserine dehydratase NRN—Cystathionase homoserine deaminase	L-Homoserine + H_2O = 2-oxobutyrate + NH_3 + H_2O

[Note: A pyridoxal-phosphate protein. Also converts cystathionine into 2-oxobutyrate, NH_3 and cysteine]

4.2.1.16 L-Threonine hydro-lyase (deaminating)	Threonine dehydratase NRN—Threonine deaminase	L-Threonine + H_2O = 2-oxobutyrate + NH_3 + H_2O

[Note: A pyridoxal-phosphate protein]

4.2.1.17 L-3-Hydroxyacyl-CoA hydro-lyase	Enoyl-CoA hydratase NRN—Crotonase, enoyl hydrase	An L-3-hydroxyacyl-CoA = a 2,3-(or 3,4-)trans-enoyl-CoA + H_2O

[Note: Also acts (in the reverse reaction) on the cis-compounds]

NRN—non recommended name

Table 4.   Enzymes: Classification and Reactions (continued)

Systematic name	Recommended trivial name	Reaction
4.2.1.18 3-Hydroxy-3-methylglutaryl-CoA hydro-lyase	Methylglutaconyl-CoA hydratase	3-Hydroxy-3-methylglutaryl-CoA = $trans$-3-methylglutaconyl-CoA + H_2O
4.2.1.19 D-$erythro$-Imidazoleglycerolphosphate hydro-lyase	Imidazoleglycerol-phosphate dehydratase	D-$erythro$-Imidazoleglycerol phosphate = imidazoleacetol phosphate + H_2O
4.2.1.20 L-Serine hydro-lyase (adding indole)	Tryptophan synthase	L-Serine + indole = L-tryptophan + H_2O

[Note: A pyridoxal-phosphate protein. Glyceraldehyde phosphate can act instead of serine, and indoleglycerol phosphate instead of indole]

4.2.1.22 L-Serine hydro-lyase (adding hydrogen sulphide)	Cysteine synthase NRN—Serine sulphhydrase	L-Serine + H_2S = L-cysteine + H_2O

[Note: A pyridoxal-phosphate protein]

4.2.1.23 L-Serine hydro-lyase (adding methanethiol)	Methylcysteine synthase	L-Serine + methanethiol = S-methyl-L-cysteine + H_2O

[Note: A pyridoxal-phosphate protein]

4.2.1.24 5-Aminolaevulinate hydro-lyase (adding 5-aminolaevulinate and cyclizing)	Porphobilinogen synthase, aminolaevulinate dehydratase	2 5-Aminolaevulinate = porphobilinogen + 2 H_2O
4.2.1.25 L-Arabinonate hydro-lyase	L-Arabinonate dehydratase	L-Arabinonate = 2-keto-3-deoxy-L-arabinonate + H_2O
4.2.1.26 2-Amino-2-deoxy-D-gluconate hydro-lyase (deaminating)	Aminodeoxy-gluconate dehydratase	2-Amino-2-deoxy-D-gluconate + H_2O = 2-keto-3-deoxy-D-gluconate + NH_3 + H_2O

[Note: A pyridoxal-phosphate protein]

4.2.1.27 Malonate-semialdehyde hydro-lyase	Malonate semialdehyde dehydratase	Malonate semialdehyde = acetylene monocarboxylate + H_2O
4.2.1.28 Propanediol hydro-lyase	Propanediol dehydratase	Propanediol = propionaldehyde + H_2O

[Note: Contains coenzyme B_{12}. Also dehydrates ethylene glycol to acetaldehyde]

4.2.1.29 3-Indoleacetaldoxime hydro-lyase	Indoleacetaldoxime dehydratase	3-Indoleacetaldoxime = 3-indoleacetonitrile + H_2O

NRN—non recommended name

Table 4. Enzymes: Classification and Reactions (continued)

Systematic name	Recommended trivial name	Reaction
4.2.99 Other Carbon-oxygen Lyases		
4.2.99.1		
Hyaluronate lyase	Hyaluronate lyase NRN— Hyaluronidase (but cf. 3.2.1.35 and 36)	Hyaluronate = n 3(β-D-gluco-4,5-en-urono)- 2-acetamido-2-deoxy-D-glucose
4.2.99.2		
O-Phosphohomoserine phospho-lyase (adding water)	Threonine synthase	O-Phosphohomoserine + H_2O = threonine + phosphate
[Note: A pyridoxal-phosphate protein]		
4.2.99.3		
Poly-α-1,4-D-galacturonide lyase	Pectate lyase NRN— Pectate transeliminase	Eliminates Δ-4,5-D-galacturonate residues from pectate, thus bringing about depolymerization
[Note: Also acts on other polygalacturonides]		
4.2.99.4		
Poly-β-1,4-D-mannuronide lyase	Alginate lyase	Eliminates Δ-4,5-D-mannuronate residues from alginate, thus bringing about depolymerization
4.2.99.5		
Poly-1,4-D-glucuronide lyase	Polyglucuronide lyase	Eliminates Δ-4,5-D-glucoronate residues from polysaccharides containing 1,4-linked D-glucuronate, thus bringing about depolymerization
4.2.99.6		
Chondroitin-sulphate lyase	Chondroitin sulphate lyase NRN— Chondroitinase (but cf. 3.1.6.4)	Eliminates Δ-4,5-D-glucuronate residues, thus bringing about depolymerization
4.3 Carbon-nitrogen Lyases		
4.3.1 Ammonia-Lyases		
4.3.1.1		
L-Aspartate ammonia-lyase	Aspartate ammonia-lyase NRN—Aspartase	L-Aspartate = fumarate + NH_3
4.3.1.2		
L-threo-3-Methylaspartate ammonia-lyase	Methylaspartate ammonia-lyase	L-threo-3-Methylaspartate = mesaconate + NH_3
4.3.1.3		
L-Histidine ammonia-lyase	Histidine ammonia-lyase NRN— histidinase, histidine α-deaminase, histidase	L-Histidine = urocanate + NH_3

NRN—non recommended name

Table 4. Enzymes: Classification and Reactions (continued)

Systematic name	Recommended trivial name	Reaction
4.3.1.4 5-Formiminotetrahydrofolate ammonia-lyase (cyclizing)	Formiminotetra-hydrofolate cyclodeaminase	5-Formiminotetrahydrofolate = 5,10-methenyltetrahydrofolate + NH_3
4.3.1.5 L-Phenylalanine ammonia-lyase	Phenylalanine ammonia-lyase	L-Phenylalanine = trans-cinnamate + NH_3
4.3.1.6 β-Alanyl-CoA ammonia-lyase	β-Alanyl-CoA ammonia-lyase	β-Alanyl-CoA = acrylyl-CoA + NH_3
4.3.2 Amidine-Lyases		
4.3.2.1 L-Argininosuccinate arginine-lyase	Argininosuccinate lyase NRN—Argininosuccinase	L-Argininosuccinate = fumarate + L-arginine
4.3.2.2 Adenylosuccinate AMP-lyase	Adenylosuccinate lyase NRN—Adenylosuccinase	Adenylosuccinate = fumarate + AMP

[Note: Also acts on 5'-phosphoribosyl-4-(N-succinocarboxamide)-5-aminoimidazole]

4.4 Carbon-sulphur Lyases

4.4.1.1 L-Cysteine hydrogensulphide-lyase (deaminating)	Cysteine desulphhydrase NRN—Cysteine lyase	L-Cysteine + H_2O = pyruvate + NH_3 + H_2S

[Note: A pyridoxal-phosphate protein]

4.4.1.2 L-Homocysteine hydrogen-sulphide-lyase (deaminating)	Homocysteine desulphhydrase	L-Homocysteine + H_2O = 2-oxobutyrate + NH_3 + H_2S

[Note: A pyridoxal-phosphate protein]

4.4.1.3 S-Dimethyl-β-propiothetin dimethylsulphide-lyase	Dimethyl-propiothetin dethiomethylase	S-Dimethyl-β-propiothetin = acrylate + dimethyl sulphide
4.4.1.4 Alliin alkylsulphenate-lyase	Alliin lyase NRN—Alliinase	An S-alkyl-L-cysteinesulphoxide = 2-aminoacrylate + an alkyl sulphenate

[Note: A pyridoxal-phosphate protein]

4.4.1.5 S-Lactoyl-glutathione methylglyoxal-lyase (isomerizing)	Lactoyl-glutathione lyase NRN—Glyoxalase I	S-Lactoyl-glutathione = glutathione + methylglyoxal

[Note: Also acts on 3-phosphoglyceroylglutathione]

NRN—non recommended name

Table 4. Enzymes: Classification and Reactions (continued)

Systematic name	Recommended trivial name	Reaction
4.4.1.6 S-Alkyl-L-cysteine methylmercaptan-lyase (deaminating)	S-Alkylcysteine lyase	S-Methyl-L-cysteine = pyruvate + NH_3 + methyl mercaptan
4.5 Carbon-halide Lyases		
4.5.1.1 1,1,1-Trichloro-2,2-bis-(p-chlorophenyl)-ethane hydrogenchloride-lyase	DDT-dehydro-chlorinase	1,1,1-Trichloro-2,2-bis-(p-chlorophenyl)-ethane = 1,1-dichloro-2,2-bis-(p-chlorophenyl)-ethylene + HCl
4.99 Other Lyases		
4.99.1.1 Protohaem ferro-lyase	Ferrochelatase	Protoporphyrin + Fe^{2+} = protohaem + 2 H^+
5. ISOMERASES		
5.1 Racemases and epimerases		
5.1.1 Acting on Amino Acids and Derivatives		
5.1.1.1 Alanine racemase	Alanine racemase	L-Alanine = D-alanine
[*Note: A pyridoxal-phosphate protein*]		
5.1.1.2 Methionine racemase	Methionine racemase	L-Methionine = D-methionine
[*Note: A pyridoxal-phosphate protein*]		
5.1.1.3 Glutamate racemase	Glutamate racemase	L-Glutamate = D-glutamate
[*Note: A pyridoxal-phosphate protein*]		
5.1.1.4 Proline racemase	Proline racemase	L-Proline = D-proline
5.1.1.5 Lysine racemase	Lysine racemase	L-Lysine = D-lysine
5.1.1.6 Threonine racemase	Threonine racemase	L-Threonine = D-threonine
5.1.1.7 2,6-LL-Diaminopimelate 2-epimerase	Diaminopimelate epimerase	2,6-LL-Diaminopimelate = meso-diaminopimelate
5.1.1.8 Hydroxyproline 2-epimerase	Hydroxyproline epimerase	L-Hydroxyproline = D-allohydroxyproline
[*Note: Also interconverts D-hydroxyproline and L-allohydroxyproline*]		
5.1.2 Acting on Hydroxyacids and Derivatives		
5.1.2.1 Lactate racemase	Lactate racemase	L-Lactate = D-lactate
5.1.2.2 Mandelate racemase	Mandelate racemase	L-Mandelate = D-mandelate

Table 4.   Enzymes: Classification and Reactions (continued)

Systematic name	Recommended trivial name	Reaction
5.1.2.3		
3-Hydroxybutyryl-CoA 3-epimerase	3-Hydroxybutyryl-CoA epimerase	L-3-Hydroxybutyryl-CoA = D-3-hydroxybutyryl-CoA
5.1.3 Acting on Carbohydrates and Derivatives		
5.1.3.1		
D-Ribulose-5-phosphate 3-epimerase	Ribulosephosphate 3-epimerase NRN— Phosphoribulose epimerase	D-Ribulose 5-phosphate = D-xylulose 5-phosphate
5.1.3.2		
UDPglucose 4-epimerase	UDPglucose epimerase NRN— Galactowaldenase	UDPglucose = UDPgalactose
[Note: NAD acts as cofactor]		
5.1.3.3		
Aldose 1-epimerase	Aldose 1-epimerase, aldose mutarotase NRN—Mutarotase	α-D-Glucose = β-D-glucose
[Note: Also acts on L-arabinose, D-xylose, D-galactose, maltose and lactose]		
5.1.3.4		
L-Ribulose-5-phosphate 4-epimerase	Ribulosephosphate 4-epimerase	L-Ribulose 5-phosphate = D-xylulose 5-phosphate
5.1.3.5		
UDP-L-arabinose 4-epimerase	UDParabinose epimerase	UDP-L-arabinose = UDP-D-xylose
5.1.3.6		
UDPglucuronate 4-epimerase	UDPglucuronate epimerase	UDP-D-glucuronate = UDP-D-galacturonate
5.1.3.7		
UDP-2-acetamido-2-deoxy-D-glucose 4-epimerase	UDPacetyl-glucosamine epimerase	UDP-2-acetamido-2-deoxy-D-glucose = UDP-2-acetamido-2-deoxy-D-galactose
5.1.99 Acting on Other Compounds		
5.1.99.1		
Methylmalonyl-CoA racemase	Methylmalonyl-CoA racemase	D-Methylmalonyl-CoA = L-methylmalonyl-CoA
5.2 Cis-trans Isomerases		
5.2.1.1		
Maleate cis-trans-isomerase	Maleate isomerase	Maleate = fumarate
5.2.1.2		
4-Maleylacetoacetate cis-trans-isomerase	Maleylaceto-acetate isomerase	4-Maleylacetoacetate = 4-fumarylacetoacetate
[Note: Also acts on maleylpyruvate]		
5.2.1.3		
all-trans-Retinene 11-cis-trans-isomerase	Retinene isomerase	all-trans-Retinene = 11-cis-retinene
[Note: Light shifts the equilibrium towards the cis-isomer]		

NRN—non recommended name

Table 4. Enzymes: Classification and Reactions (continued)

Systematic name	Recommended trivial name	Reaction
5.2.1.4 3-Maleylpyruvate cis-trans-isomerase	Maleylpyruvate isomerase	3-Maleylpyruvate = 3-fumarylpyruvate
5.3 Intramolecular oxidoreductases		
5.3.1 Interconverting Aldoses and Ketoses		
5.3.1.1 D-Glyceraldehyde-3-phosphate ketol-isomerase	Triosephosphate isomerase	D-Glyceraldehyde 3-phosphate = dihydroxyacetone phosphate
5.3.1.2 D-Erythrose ketol-isomerase	Erythrose isomerase	D-Erythrose = D-erythrulose
5.3.1.3 D-Arabinose ketol-isomerase	Arabinose isomerase	D-Arabinose = D-ribulose
[Note: Also acts on L-fucose and, more slowly, on L-galactose and D-altrose]		
5.3.1.4 L-Arabinose ketol-isomerase	L-Arabinose isomerase	L-Arabinose = L-ribulose
5.3.1.5 D-Xylose ketol-isomerase	Xylose isomerase	D-Xylose = D-Xylulose
5.3.1.6 D-Ribose-5-phosphate ketol-isomerase	Ribosephosphate isomerase NRN—Phosphopentos-isomerase, Phosphoribo-isomerase	D-Ribose 5-phosphate = D-ribulose 5-phosphate
[Note: Also acts on D-ribose 5-pyrophosphate and D-ribose 5-triphosphate]		
5.3.1.7 D-Mannose ketol-isomerase	Mannose isomerase	D-Mannose = D-fructose
[Note: Also acts on D-lyxose and rhamnose]		
5.3.1.8 D-Mannose-6-phosphate ketol-isomerase	Mannosephosphate isomerase	D-Mannose 6-phosphate = D-fructose 6-phosphate
5.3.1.9 D-Glucose-6-phosphate ketol-isomerase	Glucosephosphate isomerase NRN—Phosphohexose isomerase, oxoisomerase, hexosephosphate isomerase	D-Glucose 6-phosphate = D-fructose 6-phosphate
5.3.1.10 2-Amino-2-deoxy-D-glucose-6-phosphate ketol-isomerase (deaminating)	Glucosamine-phosphate isomerase	2-Amino-2-deoxy-D-glucose 6-phosphate + H_2O = D-fructose 6-phosphate + NH_3
[Note: Acetylglucosamine 6-phosphate, which is not broken down, activates the enzyme]		

NRN—non recommended name

Table 4. Enzymes: Classification and Reactions (continued)

Systematic name	Recommended trivial name	Reaction
5.3.1.11		
2-Acetamido-2-deoxy-D-glucose-6-phosphate ketol-isomerase (deaminating)	Acetylglucosamine-phosphate isomerase	2-Acetamido-2-deoxy-D-glucose 6-phosphate + 2 H_2O = D-fructose 6-phosphate + NH_3 + acetate
5.3.1.12		
D-Glucuronate ketol-isomerase	Glucuronate isomerase NRN— Uronic isomerase	D-glucuronate = D-fructuronate
[Note: Also converts D-galacturonate to D-tagaturonate]		
5.3.1.13		
D-Arabinose-5-phosphate ketol-isomerase	Arabinose-phosphate isomerase	D-Arabinose 5-phosphate = D-ribulose 5-phosphate
5.3.1.14		
L-Rhamnose ketol-isomerase	L-Rhamnose isomerase	L-Rhamnose = L-rhamnulose
5.3.2 Interconverting Keto- and Enol-Groups		
5.3.2.1		
Phenylpyruvate keto-enol-isomerase	Phenylpyruvate tautomerase	Keto-phenylpyruvate = enol-phenylpyruvate
[Note: Also acts on other acylpyruvates]		
5.3.3 Transposing C=C Bonds		
5.3.3.1		
3-Ketosteroid Δ^4-Δ^5-isomerase	Steroid Δ-isomerase	A Δ^5-3-ketosteroid = a Δ^4-3-ketosteroid
5.3.3.2		
Isopentenylpyrophosphate Δ^3-Δ^2-isomerase	Isopentenyl-pyrophosphate isomerase	Dimethylallyl pyrophosphate = isopentenyl pyrophosphate
5.3.3.3		
Vinylacetyl-CoA Δ^3-Δ^2-isomerase	Vinylacetyl-CoA isomerase	Vinylacetyl-CoA = crotonoyl-CoA
[Note: Also acts on 3-methyl-vinylacetyl-CoA]		
5.4 Intramolecular Transferases		
5.4.1 Transferring Acyl Groups		
5.4.1.1		
Lysolecithin 2,3-acylmutase	Lysolecithin acylmutase NRN— Lysolecithin migratase	2-Lysolecithin = 3-lysolecithin
5.4.2 Transferring Phosphoryl Groups		
5.4.2.1		
D-Phosphoglycerate 2,3-phosphomutase	Phosphoglycerate phosphomutase	2-Phospho-D-glycerate = 3-phospho-D-glycerate
[Note: See also 2.7.5.3]		

NRN—non recommended name

Table 4. Enzymes: Classification and Reactions (continued)

Systematic name	Recommended trivial name	Reaction
5.4.99 Transferring Other Groups		
5.4.99.1		
L-*threo*-3-Methylaspartate carboxy-aminomethylmutase [*Note: Contains coenzyme B₁₂*]	Methylaspartate mutase	L-*threo*-3-Methylaspartate = L-glutamate
5.4.99.2		
Methylmalonyl-CoA CoA-carbonylmutase	Methylmalonyl-CoA mutase	Methylmalonyl-CoA = succinyl-CoA
5.5 Intramolecular lyases		
5.5.1.1		
4-Carboxymethyl-4-hydroxyisocrotonolactone lyase (decyclizing)	Muconate cycloisomerase	(+)-4-Carboxymethyl-4-hydroxyisocrotonolactone = cis-cis-muconate
[*Note: Also acts (in the reverse reaction), very slowly, on* cis-trans-*muconate*]		
5.99 Other isomerases		
5.99.1.1		
Benzyl-isothiocyanate isomerase	Isothiocyanate isomerase	$C_6H_5 \cdot CH_2 \cdot NCS = C_6H_5 \cdot CH_2 \cdot SCN$
6. LIGASES		
6.1 Forming C—O bonds		
6.1.1 Ligases Forming Amino-Acyl-RNA and Related Compounds		
6.1.1.1		
L-Tyrosine:sRNA ligase(AMP)	Tyrosyl-sRNA synthetase	ATP + L-tyrosine + sRNA = AMP + pyrophosphate + L-tyrosyl-sRNA
6.1.1.2		
L-Tryptophan:sRNA ligase(AMP)	Tryptophanyl-sRNA synthetase	ATP + L-tryptophan + sRNA = AMP + pyrophosphate + L-tryptophanyl-sRNA
6.1.1.3		
L-Threonine:sRNA ligase(AMP)	Threonyl-sRNA synthetase	ATP + L-threonine + sRNA = AMP + pyrophosphate + L-threonyl-sRNA
6.1.1.4		
L-Leucine:sRNA ligase (AMP)	Leucyl-sRNA synthetase	ATP + L-leucine + sRNA = AMP + pyrophosphate + L-leucyl-sRNA
6.1.1.5		
L-Isoleucine:sRNA ligase(AMP)	Isoleucyl-sRNA synthetase	ATP + L-isoleucine + sRNA = AMP + pyrophosphate + L-isoleucyl-sRNA
6.1.1.6		
L-Lysine:sRNA ligase(AMP)	Lysyl-sRNA synthetase	ATP + L-lysine + sRNA = AMP + pyrophosphate + L-lysyl-sRNA
6.1.1.7		
L-Alanine:sRNA ligase(AMP)	Alanyl-sRNA synthetase	ATP + L-alanine + sRNA = AMP + pyrophosphate + L-alanyl-sRNA

Table 4.   Enzymes: Classification and Reactions (continued)

Systematic name	Recommended trivial name	Reaction
6.1.1.9 L-Valine:sRNA ligase(AMP)	Valyl-sRNA synthetase	ATP + L-valine + sRNA = AMP + pyrophosphate + L-valyl-sRNA
6.1.1.10 L-Methionine:sRNA ligase(AMP)	Methionyl-sRNA synthetase	ATP + L-methionine + sRNA = AMP + pyrophosphate + L-methionyl-sRNA
6.1.1.11 L-Serine:sRNA ligase(AMP)	Seryl-sRNA synthetase	ATP + L-serine + sRNA = AMP + pyrophosphate + L-seryl-sRNA
6.1.1.12 L-Aspartate:sRNA ligase(AMP)	Aspartyl-sRNA synthetase	ATP + L-aspartate + sRNA = AMP + pyrophosphate + L-aspartyl-sRNA
6.1.1.13 D-Alanine:polyphosphoribitol ligase(AMP)	D-Alanyl-polyphos-phoribitol synthetase	ATP + D-alanine + polyribitolphosphate = AMP + pyrophosphate + O-D-alanyl-polyribitolphosphate

[Note: Involved in the synthesis of teichoic acids]

6.2 Forming C—S bonds

6.2.1 Acid-Thiol Ligases

6.2.1.1 Acetate:CoA ligase(AMP)	Acetyl-CoA synthetase NRN— Acetyl activating enzyme, acetate thiokinase	ATP + acetate + CoA = AMP + pyrophosphate + acetyl-CoA

[Note: Also acts on propionate and acrylate]

6.2.1.2 Acid:CoA ligase(AMP)	Acyl-CoA synthetase NRN— Fatty acid thiokinase (medium chain)	ATP + an acid + CoA = AMP + pyrophosphate + an acyl-CoA

[Note: Acts on acids from C_4 to C_{11} and on the corresponding 3-hydroxy- and 2,3- or 3,4-unsaturated acids]

6.2.1.3 Acid:CoA ligase(AMP)	Acyl-CoA synthetase NRN— Fatty acid thiokinase (long chain)	ATP + an acid + CoA = AMP + pyrophosphate + an acyl-CoA

[Note: Acts on acids from C_6 to C_{20}]

NRN—non recommended name

Table 4. Enzymes: Classification and Reactions (continued)

Systematic name	Recommended trivial name	Reaction
6.2.1.4 Succinate:CoA ligase(GDP)	Succinyl-CoA synthetase NRN— Succinic thiokinase	$GTP + succinate + CoA = GDP + orthophosphate + succinyl-CoA$
[Note: Itaconate can act instead of succinate and ITP instead of GTP]		
6.2.1.5 Succinate:CoA ligase(ADP)	Succinyl-CoA synthetase NRN— Succinic thiokinase	$ATP + succinate + CoA = ADP + orthophosphate + succinyl-CoA$
6.2.1.6 Glutarate:CoA ligase(ADP)	Glutaryl-CoA synthetase	$ATP + glutarate + CoA = ADP + orthophosphate + glutaryl-CoA$
[Note: GTP or ITP can act instead of ATP]		
6.2.1.7 Cholate:CoA ligase(AMP)	Choloyl-CoA synthetase NRN—Cholate thiokinase	$ATP + cholate + CoA = AMP + pyrophosphate + choloyl-CoA$

6.3 Forming C—N bonds

6.3.1 Acid-Ammonia Ligases (Amide Synthetases)

Systematic name	Recommended trivial name	Reaction
6.3.1.1 L-Aspartate:ammonia ligase (AMP)	Asparagine synthetase	$ATP + L\text{-Aspartate} + NH_3 = AMP + pyrophosphate + L\text{-asparagine}$
6.3.1.2 L-Glutamate:ammonia ligase (ADP)	Glutamine synthetase	$ATP + L\text{-glutamate} + NH_3 = ADP + orthophosphate + L\text{-glutamine}$
6.3.1.3 Ribosylamine-5-phosphate: glycine ligase(ADP)	Phosphoribosyl-glycine-amide synthetase NRN— Glycineamide ribonucleotide synthetase	$ATP + glycine + ribosylamine$ 5-phosphate $= ADP + orthophosphate + ribosyl\text{-glycineamide 5-phosphate}$

6.3.2 Acid-Amino-Acid Ligases (Peptide Synthetases)

Systematic name	Recommended trivial name	Reaction
6.3.2.1 L-Pantoate:β-alanine ligase (AMP)	Pantothenate synthetase NRN— Pantoate activating enzyme	$ATP + L\text{-pantoate} + \beta\text{-alanine} = AMP + pyrophosphate + L\text{-pantothenate}$

NRN—*non recommended name*

Table 4. Enzymes: Classification and Reactions (continued)

Systematic name	Recommended trivial name	Reaction
6.3.2.2 L-Glutamate:L-cysteine γ-ligase(ADP)	γ-Glutamyl-cysteine synthetase	ATP + L-glutamate + L-cysteine = ADP + orthophosphate + γ-L-glutamyl-L-cysteine
6.3.2.3 γ-L-Glutamyl-L-cysteine: glycine ligase(ADP)	Glutathione synthetase	ATP + γ-L-glutamyl-L-cysteine + glycine = ADP + orthophosphate + glutathione
6.3.2.4 D-Alanine:D-alanine ligase(ADP)	D-Alanylalanine synthetase	ATP + D-alanine + D-alanine = ADP + orthophosphate + D-alanyl-alanine
6.3.2.5	Phosphopanto-thenoyl-cysteine synthetase	CTP + 4'-phospho-L-panto-thenate + L-cysteine = unidentified products of CTP breakdown + 4'-phospho-L-pantothenoyl-L-cysteine

[Note: Cysteine can be replaced by some of its derivatives]

Systematic name	Recommended trivial name	Reaction
6.3.2.6 5'-Phosphoribosyl-4-carboxy-5-aminoimidazole: L-aspartate ligase(ADP)	Phosphoribosyl-aminoimidazole-succino-carboxamide synthetase	ATP + 5'-phosphoribosyl-4-carboxy-5-aminoimidazole + L-aspartate = ADP + orthophosphate + 5'-phosphoribosyl-4-(N-succinocarboxamide)-5-aminoimidazole
6.3.2.7 UDP-N-acetylmuramoyl-L-alanyl-D-glutamate: L-lysine ligase(ADP)	UDP-N-acetyl-muramoyl-alanyl-D-glutamyl-lysine synthetase	ATP + UDP-N-acetylmuramoyl-L-alanyl-D-glutamate + L-lysine = ADP + orthophosphate + UDP-N-acetylmuramoyl-L-alanyl-D-glutamyl-L-lysine
6.3.2.8 UDP-N-acetylmuramate: L-alanine ligase(ADP)	UDP-N-acetyl-muramoyl-alanine synthetase	ATP + UDP-N-acetylmuramate + L-alanine = ADP + orthophosphate + UDP-N-acetylmuramoyl-L-alanine
6.3.2.9 UDP-N-acetylmuramoyl-L-alanine:D-glutamate ligase(ADP)	UDP-N-acetyl-muramoyl-alanyl-D-glutamate synthetase	ATP + UDP-N-acetylmuramoyl-L-alanine + D-glutamate = ADP + orthophosphate + UDP-N-acetylmuramoyl-L-alanyl-D-glutamate
6.3.2.10 UDP-N-acetylmuramoyl-L-alanyl-D-glutamyl-L-lysine:D-alanyl-D-alanine ligase(ADP)	UDP-N-acetyl-muramoyl-L-alanyl-D-glutamyl-L-lysyl-D-alanyl-D-alanine synthetase	ATP + UDP-N-acetylmuramoyl-L-alanyl-D-glutamyl-L-lysine + D-alanyl-D-alanine = ADP + orthophosphate + UDP-N-acetylmuramoyl-L-alanyl-D-glutamyl-L-lysyl-D-alanyl-D-alanine

[Note: Involved with enzymes 6.3.3.4,7,8, and 9 in the synthesis of a cell-wall peptide]

Table 4. Enzymes: Classification and Reactions (continued)

Systematic name	Recommended trivial name	Reaction
6.3.2.11 L-Histidine: β-alanine ligase (AMP)	Carnosine synthetase	ATP + L-histidine + β-alanine = AMP + pyrophosphate + carnosine
6.3.3 Cyclo-Ligases		
6.3.3.1 5'-Phosphoribosyl-formylglycine-amidine cyclo-ligase(ADP)	Phosphoribosyl-aminoimidazole synthetase	ATP + 5'-phosphoribosyl-formylglycine-amidine = ADP + orthophosphate + 5'-phosphoribosyl-5-aminoimidazole
6.3.4 Other C—N Ligases		
6.3.4.1 Xanthosine-5'-phosphate: ammonia ligase(AMP)	GMP synthetase	ATP + xanthosine 5'-phosphate + NH_3 = AMP + pyrophosphate + GMP
6.3.4.2 UTP:ammonia ligase (ADP)	CTP synthetase	ATP + UTP + NH_3 = ADP + orthophosphate + CTP
6.3.4.3 Formate:tetrahydrofolate ligase(ADP)	Formyltetra-hydrofolate synthetase	ATP + formate + tetrahydrofolate = ADP + orthophosphate + 10-formyltetrahydrofolate
6.3.4.4 IMP:L-aspartate ligase (GDP)	Adenylosuccinate synthetase	GTP + IMP + L-aspartate = GDP + orthophosphate + adenylosuccinate
6.3.4.5 L-Citrulline:L-aspartate ligase(AMP)	Arginino-succinate synthetase	ATP + L-citrulline + L-aspartate = AMP + pyrophosphate + L-argininosuccinate
6.3.5 C—N Ligases with Glutamine as Amido-N-Donor		
6.3.5.1 Deamido-NAD:L-glutamine amido-ligase(AMP)	NAD synthetase	ATP + deamido-NAD + L-glutamine + H_2O = AMP + pyrophosphate + NAD + L-glutamate

[Note: NH_3 can act instead of glutamine]

6.3.5.2 Xanthosine-5'-phosphate: L-glutamine amido-ligase (AMP)	GMP synthetase	ATP + xanthosine 5'-phosphate + L-glutamine + H_2O = AMP + pyrophosphate + GMP + L-glutamate
6.3.5.3 5'-Phosphoribosyl-formyl-glycineamide:L-glutamine amidoligase(ADP)	Phosphoribosyl-formyl-glycineamidine synthetase	ATP + 5'-phosphoribosyl-formylglycineamide + L-glutamine + H_2O = ADP + orthophosphate + 5'-phosphoribosyl-formylglycineamidine + L-glutamate

Table 4.   Enzymes: Classification and Reactions (continued)

Systematic name	Recommended trivial name	Reaction
6.4 Forming C—C bonds		
6.4.1.1		
Pyruvate:carbon-dioxide ligase(ADP)	Pyruvate carboxylase	ATP + pyruvate + CO_2 + H_2O = ADP + orthophosphate + oxaloacetate

[*Note: A biotin-protein. The animal enzyme requires acetyl-CoA*]

6.4.1.2		
Acetyl-CoA:carbon-dioxide ligase(ADP)	Acetyl-CoA carboxylase	ATP + acetyl-CoA + CO_2 + H_2O = ADP + orthophosphate + malonyl-CoA

[*Note: A biotin-protein. Also catalyses transcarboxylation; the plant enzyme also carboxylates propionyl-CoA and butyryl-CoA*]

6.4.1.3		
Propionyl-CoA:carbon-dioxide ligase(ADP)	Propionyl-CoA carboxylase	ATP + propionyl-CoA + CO_2 + H_2O = ADP + orthophosphate + methylmalonyl-CoA

[*Note: A biotin-protein. Also carboxylates butyryl-CoA, and catalyses transcarboxylation*]

6.4.1.4		
3-Methylcrotonoyl-CoA: carbon-dioxide ligase(ADP)	Methyl-crotonoyl-CoA carboxylase	ATP + 3-methylcrotonoyl-CoA + CO_2 + H_2O = ADP + orthophosphate + 3-methylglutaconyl-CoA

[*Note: A biotin-protein*]

I. HISTAMINE

Biological Activities. The biological effects of histamine have been extensively reviewed.[7, 8, 9, 10, 11] In the cardiovascular system histamine has effects on both the capillaries and arterioles. It is a direct dilator on capillaries and the action on the arterioles varies with the species and dosage. For example, in the rabbit and rodents histamine is a constrictor of arterioles and causes an increase in blood pressure. On the other hand, it causes a dilitation of arterioles in the cat, dog, and man, resulting in a fall in blood pressure. Large doses are known to cause an increase in capillary permeability to plasma proteins and other large molecules which are thought to produce edema.[13] Large doses are also known to cause profound fall in blood pressure and lead to a production of shock-like state.

In the skin, histamine is involved with the so-called "triple response" of Lewis.[14] When histamine is injected in the skin one sees a localized red spot due to dilatation of minute blood vessels followed by a brighter red flush or flare which is caused by dilatation of neighboring arterioles as the result of an axon reflex, and finally, a localized edema which results from the release of histamine causing an increase in the permeability of capillaries. Small doses of histamine dilate cerebral blood vessels and can, in man, cause so-called "histamine headache" (0.1 mg parenterally). Histamine is also known to release catecholamines from the chromaffin cells of adrenal medulla. Histamine has a variety of effects on smooth muscle. These effects on smooth muscle cannot be generalized and must be examined with specific reference to the anatomical histological location of the effect and the species. A few of these effects will be listed here. In the guinea pig, histamine causes bronchial constriction and death when given in sufficient quantity and if the animal is sufficiently sensitive. Histamine also contracts the smooth muscle of the gut. The guinea pig ileum is sensitive and has been used as a bioassay procedure for histamine. The mechanism of action of histamine on smooth muscle is unknown. It apparently is independent of nervous innervation but may stimulate nervous elements of the system.[15, 16, 17, 18] Histamine is also noted to have effects on the potassium efflux from smooth muscle which results in an increased plasma level of potassium. In the cat, 75 μg intravenously will cause potassium to move from smooth muscle to the plasma. Histamine causes pronounced secretion of gastric juice. With histamine stimulation the gastric acidity increases. Histamine also stimulates a secretion of products from the pancreas mucous glands and other intestinal glands. It has also been noted to stimulate the production of tears from the lachrymal glands in man and several other species.

Antihistamines are effective only partially. An example is that many of the blood vessel effects and smooth muscle effects may be antagonized by antihistamines but the effect of histamine on gastric secretion does not seem to be influenced by antihistamines. Another thing to be considered with antihistamines is that many of these have intrinsic actions of their own such as a depression of the central nervous system.

Biosynthesis and Biotransformation. Histamine can be obtained from ingested food, synthesized by the decarboxylation of dietary histidine by intestinal flora, or formed in tissues by decarboxylation of histidine. The first two sources of histamine account for very little of histamine or its metabolites formed in urine. About 5% of dietary histamine taken orally is recovered in the urine. Much of the histamine in feces has its source from histamine formed by intestinal flora.

Most of histamine is synthesized within various cells by the action of histidine decarboxylase on histidine. Histidine decarboxylase has been found in most tissues including kidney, liver, pancreas, lungs, skin, stomach, and certain parts of CNS.[19]

Except for skin and certain parts of the CNS such as the hypothalamus, the histamine is stored in mast cells or basophils in the blood where histamine is bound to heparin.

The histidine decarboxylase activity of mast cells and mast cell tumors is different from 1-amino acid decarboxylase.[20] The enzyme has been purified 200 fold.[21] The enzyme of mast cells is readily dissociated from its pyridoxal phosphate cofactor.

A non mast cell histidine decarboxylase has an activity much lower than that associated with mast cells. This enzyme's activity can be increased by cold, burns, allergy, endotoxin, epinephrine, and norepinephrine.[22] It is believed to be a regulator in microcirculatory system.[23] Histidine decarboxylase activity in guinea pig and rat kidney seems to be due to the action of aromatic L-amino acid decarboxylase and of physiological importance since the Km is so high and the V max. so low.

Two major pathways of metabolism have been demonstrated.[25]

a. Histamine $\xrightarrow{1}$ methyl histamine $\xrightarrow{2}$ methyl imidazole
acetic acid

b. Histamine $\xrightarrow{3}$ imidazolacetaldehyde $\xrightarrow{4}$ imidazole
acetic acid
$\downarrow 5$
imidazole acetic acid
riboside

The histamine N-methyl transferase (1) transfers a methyl group from S-adenosylmethionine. This has been found in various parts of the central nervous system.[26] This appears to be the primary pathway of biotransformation in the brain.[27] About 4–8% of an injected dose in the human has been recovered.[24] This is suggested to be the principal route of biotransformation in the cat, dog, and man.[28] Most of the methyl histamine is further oxidized to methyl imidazole acetic acid by the action of histaminase or monoamine oxidase and aldehyde dehydrogenase (2). Histaminase has been purified 2,000 fold recently and characterized.[29, 30] Whether this is the same enzyme as diamine oxidase as described and characterized by Teller is yet to be clarified. Diamine oxidase has a pyridoxal phosphate cofactor. 42–47% of histamine given to humans is recovered in urine as such.[24]

The second pathway involves oxidative deamination by histaminase or monoamine oxidase (3) and then to imidazole acetic acid (9–11%) by the catalytic action of an aldehyde dehydrogenase (4) and to the imidazole acetic acid ribotide (16–23%) in the urine of humans.

Another pathway may involve the formation of acetyl histamine. There is little known about this.[25] Apparently 2–3% of an administered dose of histamine is excreted unchanged in man.[24]

Tissue and Blood Levels of Histamine. Histamine is found in most tissues such as skin, muscles, central and peripheral nervous systems, and parenchymal tissue, with the greatest amounts usually found in the skin, G-I tract, and the lungs.[9] The content varies greatly between species and within tissues of a species.[9, 10]

It is present in body fluids including lymph and sweat.[10] In man the blood level is 0.02–0.08 μg/ml. Much of histamine in blood is bound to white cells, but there is little correlation between histamine content and leucocytes in various animal species.

Histamine has been found in invertebrates, such as giant sponge (up to 100 μg/g in leather coral). It is also found in foods and plant.[10]

Physiological and Pathological Roles of Histamine. In anaphylactic reactions there is a liberation of histamine and its accompanying reactions which are associated with anaphylactic shock. Histamine release is associated with antigen-antibody reactions and allergic response. Other amines such as 5-HT and bradykinin may also be liberated.[10]

In mastocytosis, rare in man, but frequent in dog, there is an increased accumulation of mast cells of skin, liver, spleen, and skeletal systems. These mast cell accumulations have increased content of histamine and increased urinary excretion of free histamine.[31]

In certain cases of carcinoid (as opposed to those with a 5-HT imbalance) the histamine content in urine is increased. In severe burns, symptoms of shock have been correlated with increased liberation of histamine, increased histamine in blood and in urine.[16] In myeloid leukemia, values 300 times normal histamine have been associated with whole blood.[10] The fetus, especially of the rat and human, contains high amounts of histamine.[31]

BIBLIOGRAPHY

References:

1. Merck Index, 7th ed., 1960.
2. Urbach, K. F., "Nature and Probable Origin of Conjugated Histamine Excreted After Ingestion of Histamine," *Proc. Soc. Exptl. Biol. Med.*, 70:146, 1949.
3. Born, G. V. R., and J. R. Vane, "The Quantitative Determination of Diffusible Histamine in Blood," *Brit. J. Pharmacol.*, 7:298, 1952.
4. Code, C. F., and F. C. McIntire, "Quantitative Determination of Histamine," *Methods Biochem. Analy.*, 3:49, 1956.
5. Shore, P. A., A. Burkhalter, and V. H. Cohn, Jr., "A Method for the Fluorometric Assay of Histamine in Tissues," *J. Pharmacol. Exptl. Therap.*, 127:182, 1959.
6. J. Crossland, "X. Biologic Estimation of Histamine," *Methods Med. Res.*, 9: 186, 1961.
7. Goodman, L. S., and A. Gilman, *Pharmacological Basis of Therapeutics*, 3rd ed., p. 615, 1965.
8. de Palma, J. R., (ed.), *Drill's Pharmacology in Medicine*, 3rd ed., p. 763, 1965.
9. Wolstenholme, G. E. W., and C. M. O'Connor (eds.), *Histamine*, 1956.
10. Duner, H., and B. Pernon, in von Euler, U. S., and H. Heller (eds.), *Comparative Endocrinology*, Vol. 2, p. 239.
11. Ungar, G., "Physiological Functions of Histamine," *Symp. Fed. Proc.*, 24: 1293, 1965.
12. Dale, H. H., "Croonian Lectures on Some Chemical Factors in the Control of the Circulation," *Lancet i*, p. 1285, 1929.
13. Majno, O., G. E. Palade, and I. Butta, "Studies on Inflammation. II. The Site of Action of Histamine and Serotonin Along the Vascular Tree: a Topographic Study," *J. Biophys. Biochem. Cytol.*, 11:607, 1961.
14. Lewis, T., *Blood Vessels of Human Skin and Their Responses*, 1927.
15. Paton, W. D. M., and J. R. Vane, "An Analysis of the Responses of the Isolated Stomach to Electrical Stimulation and to Drugs," *J. Physiol.*, 165:10, 1963.
16. Daniel, E. E., "Effect of Drugs on Contractions of Vertebrate Smooth Muscle," *Pharmacol. Rev.*, 4:189, 1964.
17. Evans, D. H. L., H. O. Schild, and S. Thesleff, "Effects of Drugs on Depolarized Plain Muscle," *J. Physiol.*, 143:474, 1958.

18. Rocha, S., "On the Nature of the Receptors for Histamine," *Chemotherapia*, 3:544, 1961.

19. Werle, *Allergy and Asthma*, 3:335, 1957.

20. Udenfriend, S., "Amino Acid Decarboxylation Steps in the Biosynthesis of Norepinephrine, Serotonin, and Histamine," *Vitamins Hormones*, 22:445, 1964.

21. Hakanson, R., "Histidine Decarboxylase in Fetal Rat," *Biochem. Pharmacol.*, 12:1289, 1963.

22. Schayer, R. W., and O. H. Gangley, "Adaptive Increase in Mammalian Histidine Decarboxylase Activity in Response to Non-Specific Stress," *Am. J. Physiol.*, 197:721, 1959.

23. Schayer, R. W., "Significance of Induced Synthesis of Histamine in Physiology and Pathology," *Chemotherapia*, 3:128, 1961.

24. Schayer, R. W., and J. A. D. Cooper, "Metabolism of C^{14} Histamine in Man," *J. Appl. Physiol.*, 9:481, 1956.

25. Axelrod, J., and S. H. Synder, "Tissue Metabolism of Histamine C^{14} *in vivo*," *Symp. Fed. Proc.*, 24:774, 1965.

26. Brown, D. D., R. Tomchick, and J. Axelrod, "The Distribution and Properties of a Histamine-Methylating Enzyme," *J. Biol. Chem.*, 234:2948, 1959.

27. White, T., "Biosynthesis, Metabolism, and Function of Histamine in the Nervous System," *Symp. Fed. Proc.*, 23:1103, 1964.

28. Schayer, R. W., "Catabolism of Physiological Quantities of Histamine *in vivo*," *Physiol. Rev.*, 39:116, 1959.

29. Kapellar-Adler, R., "Histamine Catabolism *in vitro* and *in vivo*," *Symp. Fed. Proc.*, 24:775, 1965.

30. Zeller, E. A., "Identity of Histaminase and Diamine Oxidase," *Symp. Fed. Proc.*, 24:766, 1965.

31. Kahlson, G., "New Approaches to the Physiology of Histamine," *Perspectives Biol. Med.*, 5:179, 1962.

II. SEROTONIN

Biological Activities. The actions of serotonin (5-HT) are varied and complex. For an extensive discussion see references 10, 11, 12, 13. The cardiovascular effects vary with the species. Examples are the dog and cat in which there will first be seen a transient fall in blood pressure followed by a small rise in pressure, and then a prolonged fall. This variability is, to a certain extent, dependent upon the size of the dose and the animal. These effects are thought to be the result of chemoreflex, peripheral vasoconstriction, and finally, an inhibition of neurogenic vasoconstriction.[12] The pulmonary vessels are powerfully constricted in the cat, dog, and man when the 5-HT is injected intraarterially.[14] This is in contrast to the dilitation found when injected into the arterial system of the fore limb of the dog. In man, an infusion of 1–3 mg of 5-HT per minute resulted in an increased pulse rate and increased flow in the forearm. The blood pressure was found to be variable.[15] High doses of 5-HT have been noted to release histamine from cat skin.[16]

5-HT has an antidiuretic effect in dog, rat, and man.[10, 17] This effect is most marked in the rat and becomes less effective in dog and in man. The mechanism is not known but is speculated to be associated with a fall in renal plasma flow and selective constriction of glomerular arterioles.

The smooth muscle of the alimentary tract, uterus, urinary bladder, ureter, bronchial tract and nictitating membrane is contracted by 5-HT. 5-HT facilitates peristalsis in various parts of the gut and is believed by some to be involved with the regulation of peristalsis.[18, 19, 20]

In the central nervous system and peripheral nervous system 5-HT has been shown to be a potentiator of ganglionic transmission in the superior cervical and inferior mesenteric ganglia.[21] 5-HT does not readily cross the blood-brain barrier. If 5-HT is injected in cats, into the lateral cerebral ventricle a state of catatonia and shivering results.[18, 22, 23, 24] Microelectrode studies on single neurons in the brain have shown that 5-HT depresses the excitatory receptors of these neurons.[25] Reserpine depletes serotonin and other amines. This information coupled with the finding that monoamine oxidase inhibitors increase 5-HT content has led to the speculation that 5-HT may be a transmitter substance in the central nervous system.

Large doses of 5-HT protected against body X-irradiation in mice;[27] yet it has also been reported that 5-HT antagonists protected against body X-irradiation in mice.[28] The changes that occur in 5-HT content following X-irradiation are not yet clear. The evidence reported here is conflicting. Also, large doses of 5-HT have been noted to cause thrombocytosis[26] and teratogenic effects in mice.[27]

The administration of 5-hydroxytryptophan, a precursor of serotonin, has the following effects: tremors, ataxia, dilitation of the pupils, loss of light reflex, lachrymation, salivation, tachycardia, hyperpnoea, and stimulation of the gut in man.[30, 31] Larger doses can cause excitement and disorientation. These effects are believed to be the result of 5-HT which is synthesized from 5-hydroxytryptophan. It is believed that the 5-hydroxytryptophan penetrates the blood brain barrier and is then converted into 5-hydroxytryptamine in the brain itself.

Biosynthesis and Metabolic Pathways. The synthetic and metabolic pathways have been worked out for 5-HT[13, 31, 32] for neural and non-neural tissues according to the following scheme:

$$\text{tryptophan} \xrightarrow{\ \ 1\ \ } \text{5-OH tryptophan} \xrightarrow{\ \ 2\ \ } \text{5 HT} \xrightarrow{\ \ 3\ \ } \text{5 HIAA}$$

$$\downarrow 4$$

$$\text{N-acetyl-5-HT}$$

$$\downarrow 5$$

$$\text{N-acetyl-5-methoxytryptamine}$$
$$\text{(melatonin)}$$

Dietary tryptophan is hydroxylated to 5-OH tryptophan by an enzyme (1) which has not been studied in detail. Although 5-HT is found in many tissues, tryptophan hydroxylation has been demonstrated only in liver[33, 34] and most cell tumors.[35, 36] In bacterium, *Chromobacterium violaceum*, this hydroxylation has been demonstrated for L-tryptophan.[31]

5-hydroxytryptophan is decarboxylated by the action of an aromatic L-amino acid decarboxylase (2). This is the same enzyme which catalyzed the conversion of DOPA to dopamine. Its cofactor is pyridoxal phosphate. 5 HTP decarboxylase activity is found in most tissues, excepting blood. It is associated with particles which sediment with mitochondria and on further centrifugation with nerve endings,[37] although it has been reported to be in the supernatant fraction of the latter.[38]

5-HT is oxidatively deaminated to 5-hydroxy-3-indole aldehyde by the action of monoamine oxidase (MAO) (3). 5-HT is a good substrate for the enzyme.[39, 40] Its action is followed by that of aldehyde dehydrogenase to 5-hydroxy-3-indole acetic acid (5-HIAA) which may be the rate limiting step.[41] The enzyme (or group of enzymes) is widely distributed in tissues including brain and associated with the mitochondria fraction of subcellular fractions. An alternate pathway occurs in the pineal which contains 5-hydroxytryptamine-N-acetylase[42] (4) which forms the N-acetyl derivative of 5-HT and an hydroxyindole-O-methyl transferase (HIOMT) which converts this to melatonin.[43] 5-HT can be directly converted to 5-methoxytryptamine and then to 5-methoxy-indole-3 acetic acid by MAO. In urine of man 5-HIAA accounts for 30% of an injected dose of 5-HT.[44] The other principal metabolite is N-acetyl-5-HT up to 25%. Small amounts of O-glucuronide and 6-sulphate are excreted along with traces of 5-HT unchanged.[45]

Tissues and Blood Levels of 5-hydroxytryptamine. 5-HT is distributed throughout nature, being found in most animal species, (both mammalian and nonmammalian), and in plants.[13, 46, 47, 48] In the alimentary tract 5-HT is classically thought to be contained in the enterochromaffin cells of the mucosa. In the blood the 5-HT is contained in the platelets. Platelets cannot synthesize 5-HT and receive their stores mainly by concentrating the 5-HT from the plasma. At the time of coagulation serotonin or 5-HT seems to be released from the platelets. Other tissue sources of 5-HT in mammals are the mast cells. However, here we see an important species variability in that the mast cells of rats and mice contain high concentration of 5-HT whereas the mast cells of man, cat, dog, rabbit, guinea pig, and cow contain little 5-HT. The grey matter in the central nervous system is rich in 5-HT with the highest concentration being found in the hypothalamus, area postrema, septum pellucidum, caudate, nucleus, and midbrain; little is found in the cerebral cortex, cerebellum, or spinal cord. At a subcellular level 5-HT seems to be associated with the subcellular fractions containing the "pinched off nerve endings."

High concentration of 5-HT has been noted in malignant carcinoid syndrome in which there is a rise in secretion of 5-HT and 5-HIAA in the urine. The normal range is 3 to 14 mg of 5-HIAA for 24 hours. In malignancy several hundred mgs of 5-HIAA may be secreted for 24 hours. In phenylketonuria a concentration of blood and daily excretion of 5-HIAA is low. Wooley and Shaw have suggested that derangements of 5-HT metabolism are underlying causes of some naturally occurring mental disorders.[49]

Assay Procedures. 5-hydroxyindole compounds can be readily separated and detected on paper chromatograms.

Many solvent systems and reagents have been used for development of chromatograms.[2, 3] As quoted by Udenfriend et al.[2] several mean Rf values for 5-hydroxytryptamine have been noted as follows:

	Rf
Propanol- NH_3	0.65
Butanol-acetic acid- H_3O	0.42
20% KCl	0.39

5-HT can be assayed by means of ultraviolet absorption, colorimetrically, and fluorimetrically.[2] The fluorimetric methods are more specific and have greater sensitivity (0.1 μg).[2, 4] As low as 50×10^{-9}g. can be detected. The following bioassay procedures have been used for detection of 5-HT: constriction of perfused rabbit's ear,[5] cat's uterus,[6] rat colon,[7] clam heart,[8] and the fundic strip of rat's stomach.[9] The latter can measure amounts as low as 10^{-12} μg. However, these methods are somewhat tedious and not always specific.

BIBLIOGRAPHY

References:

1. *The Merck Index*, 7th ed., 1960.
2. Udenfriend, S., H. Weissbach, and B. B. Brodie, "Assay of Serotonin and Related Metabolites, Enzymes, and Drugs," *Methods Biochem. Analy.*, 6:95, 1958.
3. Jepson, J. P., in Smith, Ivor (ed.), *Chromatog. Techniques*, 1958.
4. Kuntzman, R., et. al., "Microanalytical Procedures for Fluorometric Assay of Brain Dopa-5HTP Decarboxylase, Norepinephrine and Serotonin, and a Detailed Mapping of Decarboxylase Activity in Brain," *J. Neurochem.*, 6:226, 1961.
5. Page, I. H., and A. A. Green, "II. Prefusion of Rabbit's Ear for Study of Vaso-constrictor Substances," *Methods Med. Res.*, 1:123, 1948.
6. Dalgliesh, E. C., C. C. Toh, and T. S. Work, "Fractionation of the Smooth Muscle Stimulants Present in Extracts of Gastro-Intestinal Tract. Identification of 5-Hydroxytryptamine and its Distinction from Substance P," *J. Physiol.*, 120:298, 1953.
7. Erspamer, V., *Arch. Intern. Pharmacodyn.*, 93:239, 1953.

8. Twarog, B. M., and I. H. Page, "Serotonin Content of Some Mammalian Tissues and Urine and a Method for its Determination," *Am. J. Physiol.*, 175: 157, 1953.

9. Vane, J. R., "A Sensitive Method for the Assay of 5-Hydroxytryptamine," *Brit. J. Pharmacol.*, 12:344, 1957.

10. Page, I. H., in Lewis (ed.), *5-Hydroxytryptamine*, 1957.

11. Goodman, L. S., and A. Gilman, *Pharmacological Bases of Therapeutics*, 3rd ed., p. 644, 1965.

12. Page, I. H., "Serotonin (5-Hydroxytryptamine); the Last Four Years," *Physiol. Rev.*, 38:877, 1958.

13. Stacy, R. S., and J. M. Robson, *Recent Advances in Pharmacology*, 3rd ed., p. 122, 1962.

14. Gingel, K. H., and S. R. Kottegoda, "Study of the Vascular Actions of 5-Hydroxytryptamine, Tryptamine, Adrenaline and Noradrenaline," *Quart. J. Exp. Physiol.*, 38:225, 1953.

15. Les Messurier, D. H., C. T. Schwartz, and R. F. Whelan, "Cardiovascular Effects of Intravenous Infusions of 5-Hydroxytryptamine in Man," *Brit. J. Pharmacol.*, 14:246, 1959.

16. Feldberg, W., and A. N. Smith, "Release of Histamine by Tryptamine and 5-Hydroxytryptamine," *Brit. J. Pharmacol.*, 8:406, 1953.

17. Erspamer, V., "Pharmacology of Indolealkylamines," *Pharmacol. Rev.*, 6: 425, 1954.

18. Bulbring, F., and Lin, "The Effect of Intraluminal Application of 5-Hydroxytryptamine and 5-Hydroxytryptophan on Peristalsis," *J. Physiol.*, 140:381, 1958.

19. Bulbring in Kety, S., and J. Elkes (eds.), *Regional Neurochemistry*, p. 437, 1961.

20. Bulbring and Crema, "Observations Concerning the Action of 5-Hydroxytryptamine on the Peristaltic Reflex," *Brit. J. Pharmacol.*, 13:444, 1958.

21.a. Trendelenburg, "The Action of Histamine, Pilocarpine and 5-Hydroxytryptamine on Transmission Through the Superior Cervical Ganglion," *J. Physiol.*, 135:66, 1957.

   b. Trendelenburg, "The Action of Morphine on the Superior Cervical Ganglion and on the Nicticating Membrane of the Cat," *Brit. J. Pharmacol.*, 12:79, 1957.

22. Feldberg, W., and S. L. Sherwood, "Injections of Drugs Into the Lateral Ventricle of the Cat," *J. Physiol.*, 123:148, 1954.

23. Domer, F. R., and W. Feldberg, "Tremor in Cats: The Effect of Administration of Drugs Into the Cerebral Ventricles," *Brit. J. Pharmacol.*, 15:578, 1960.

24. Feldberg, W., and K. Fleischhauer, *Brit. Med. Bull.*, 21:36, 1961.

25. Curtis, D. R., and R. Davis, "Pharmacological Studies Upon Neurones of the Lateral Geniculate Nucleus of the Cat," *Brit. J. Pharmacol.*, 18:217, 1962.

26. Steiner, F. A., et al., "Thrombozytone und Eosinophilie bei Adrenalektomierten Ratten Noch Einmaliger 5-Hydroxytryptamin-injection," *Experentia*, 13:500, 1957.

27. Paulson, E., J. M. Robson, and F. M. Sullivan, "Teratogenic Effect of 5-Hydroxytryptamine in Mice," *Science*, 141:717, 1963.

28. Lungendorff, H., and H. J. Melching, "Untersuchungen uber Einen Biologischen Strahlenschutz. XII. Mitteilung: Weitere Untersuchungen uber die Wirkungsmechanismus des 5-Hydroxytryptamin im Strahlenschutzversuch," *Strahlentherapie*, 110:505, 1959.

29. Feinstein, R. N., and J. E. Seaholm, "Pharmacological Studies with the Serotonin Precursor, 5-Hydroxytryptophan," *Proc. Soc. Exptl. Biol. & Med.*, 114: 247, 1963.

30. Davidson, J., et al., "Studies with the Serotonin Precursor, 5-Hydroxytryptophan, in Experimental Animals and Man," *J. Clin. Invest.*, 36:1594, 1957.
31. Udenfriend, S., "5-Hydroxytryptamine," *Symposium*, p. 43, 1958.
32. Sharman, D. F., *Brit. Med. Bull.*, 21:62, 1965.
33. Freedland, R. A., et al., "The Enzymatic Hydroxylation of Tryptophan," *Biochem. Biophys. Res. Comm.*, 5:94, 1961.
34. Renson, J., H. Weissbach, and S. Udenfriend, "Hydroxylation of Tryptophan by Phenylalanine Hydroxylase," *J. Biol. Chem.*, 237:2261, 1962.
35. Schindler, R., "The Conversion of ^{14}C-Labelled Tryptophan to 5-Hydroxytryptamine by Neoplastic Mast Cells," *Biochem. Pharm.*, 1:323, 1958.
36. Levine, R. J., W. Newenberg, and A. Sjoerdsma, "Hydroxylation of Tryptophan and Phenylalanine by Murine Neoplastic Mast Cells," *Fed. Proc.*, 23:563, 1964.
37. Rodriguez de Lores Arnais, G., and E. de Robertis, "5-Hydroxytryptophan Decarboxylase Activity in Nerve Endings of the Rat Brain," *J. Neurochem.*, 11:213, 1964.
38. Bogdanski, D. F., H. Weissbach, and S. Udenfriend, *J. Neurochem.*, 1:272, 1957.
39. Sjoerdsma, A., et al., "Metabolism of 5-Hydroxytryptamine (Serotonin) by Monoamine Oxidase," *Proc. Soc. Exptl. Biol.*, 89:36, 1955.
40. Zeller, E. A., J. Barsky, and E. R. Berman, "Amine Oxidases. XI. Inhibition of Monoamine Oxidase by 1-Isonicotinyl-2-Isopropylhydrazine," *J. Biol. Chem.*, 214:267, 1955.
41. Weissbach, H., B. G. Redfield, and S. Udenfriend, "Studies on the Effect of Vitamin B$_6$ on 5-Hydroxytryptamine (Serotonin) Formation," *J. Biol. Chem.*, 227:617, 1957.
42. Weissbach, H., B. G. Redfield, J. Axelrod, "Biosynthesis of Melatonin Enzymatic Conversion of Serotonin to N-acetylserotonin," *Biochim. Biophys. Acta*, 43:352, 1960.
43. Weissbach, and J. Axelrod, "Biosynthesis of Melatonin: Enzymic Conversion of Serotonin to N-Acetylserotonin," *Biochem. Biophys. Acta*, 43:352, 1960.
44. McIsaac, W. M., and I. H. Page, "The Metabolism of Serotonin (5-Hydroxytryptomine)," *J. Biol. Chem.*, 234:858, 1958.
45. Weissbach, H., et al., "*In vivo* Metabolism of Serotonin and Tryptamine: Effect of Monoamine Oxidase Inhibition," *J. Pharmacol. Exptl. Therap.*, 131:26, 1961.

III. CATECHOLAMINES

Biological Activities. The biological activities for the catecholamines are many and varied. One should examine the reviews for past literature.[6] The adrenal medulla contains both epinephrine and norepinephrine. In the human this is a ratio of 80% epinephrine to 20% norepinephrine. On the other hand, the sympathetic nerve endings contain only norepinephrine. Norepinephrine is believed to be a neurotransmitter of the peripheral sympathetic nervous system.

Cardiovascular effects. Norepinephrine, when given to man intravenously, produces an increase in the systolic and diastolic mean blood pressure system with an unchanged, or possibly, decreased cardiac output and an increased peripheral resistance. The blood flow to the kidney, brain, liver, and skeletal muscle is decreased while coronary flow is substantially increased. Due to a reflex increase in vagal tone the electrocardiograph pattern is sinus bradycardia. Nodal rhythms, A-V dissociation, bigeminal rhythm, ventricular tachycardia and fibrillation have been observed. These are the so-called α effects and are blocked by the α-blocking agents. Epinephrine, when given intravenously in man, in small doses of 0.1-0.4 μg/kg per minute produces a moderate increase in systolic pressure but a decrease in the diastolic pressure. Therefore the pulse pressure is increased but the mean blood pressure is not changed. The β-effect of epinephrine produces a decrease in peripheral resistance and results in an increase blood flow in skeletal muscle. Heart rate, cardiac output, and stroke volume are all increased due to the positive inotropic and positive chronotropic effect on cardiac muscle. These β effects have been thought by some to be due to the stimulation of epinephrine upon adenyl cyclase to produce 3',5'-adenosinemonophosphate. This activates phosphorylase.

Respiratory Effects. Epinephrine stimulates respiration briefly and dilates bronchi as a result of relaxation of smooth muscle of the bronchi. Norepinephrine is very weak in this action.

Metabolic Effects. Epinephrine activates adenyl cyclase to form cyclic adenylic acid (3',5'-adenosinemonophosphate) from ATP; this cyclic adenylic acid then activates phosphorylase to break down glycogen to glucose. Epinephrine also increases the free fatty acid content of blood. Norepinephrine is approximately one-sixth as active as epinephrine in the metabolic effects.

Smooth Muscle. The effect of epinephrine and norepinephrine on uterine muscle varies with the species and the phase of the sexual cycle in the dose given of catecholamines. For specific effects one is referred to basic texts of pharmacology. The gastrointestinal smooth muscle is generally relaxed by epinephrine.

Central Nervous System. Epinephrine administered to man causes restlessness, feelings of oppression, and anxiety. These are not seen with norepinephrine. In animals small doses of epinephrine cause arousal from natural sleep.

Biosynthesis of Catecholamines. The catecholamines are synthesized in the adrenal medulla and in the sympathetic nervous system. The following metabolic pathway has been explored and hypothesized as the main route of catecholamine synthesis.[15]

Phenylalanine

1 ↓

Tyrosine

2 ↓

Dihydroxyphenylalanine (dopa)

3 ↓

Dihydroxyphenylethylamine (dopamine)

4 ↓

Norepinephrine

5 ↓

Epinephrine

The enzymes involved in steps listed above:

1. Phenylalanine 4-hydroxylase—located in the liver, require pteridines as cofactor, O_2, reduced nicotinamide adenine dinucleotide.[16]

2. Tyrosine hydroxylase—demonstrated in brain, heart, adrenal—requires pteridines (also tetrahydropteridine and Fe^{++} increase activity). Believed to be rate limiting step.[17]

3. Aromatic amino acid decarboxylase—a pyridoxal-phosphate protein. Also acts on other aromatic amino acids including tyrosine, DOPA, histidine, tryptophan.[18] It is found in most tissue including liver, stomach, brain, kidneys.

4. Dopamine β-hydroxylase[19]-copper containing enzyme utilizing oxygen and ascorbic acid as cofactor, associated with the particulate matter of high speed homogenates of adrenal (chromaffin granules)[20] and tissues (granulated vesicles)[21]

5. Phenylethanolamine-N-methyl transferase[22] transfers the methyl group of S-adenosylmethionine to the nitrogen of norepinephrine. Highly localized in chromaffin granules, adrenal medulla and possibly brain and heart. It is associated with the supernatant fraction of high speed cellular fractions. Can methylate variety of natural derivatives and foreign phenylethanolamine derivatives.[15, 22]

Metabolic Alteration and Excretion. The major metabolites and enzymes involved in the biotransformation of the catecholamines have been characterized.[10, 12, 13, 15, 16, 17, 23, 24, 25] The metabolic pathway has been elucidated by Goodman and Gilman.[12] Most of the epinephrine and norepinephrine that enters circulation from the adrenal medulla or from exogenously or released rapidly from nerve endings is first methylated by catechol-o-transferase (COMT) to metanephrine or normetanephrine, respectively. Norepinephrine released slowly at nerve endings is initially deaminated by monoamine oxidase (MAO) to the corresponding aldehyde and then 3,4 dihydroxymandelic acid (vanilomandelic acid). MAO is believed to be associated with intraneuronal sites, possibly in the mitochondrial fractions of subcellular fractions.[26] It is a copper containing protein and acts on primary, secondary, and tertiary amines. It is found in highest concentrations in liver, kidney, and gastrointestinal tract. Inhibitors of MAO will increase norepinephrine, dopamine and 5 hydroxytryptamine stores in the brain and other tissues. Catechol-o-methyl transferase is present in most tissues including brain.[27] It is not present in skeletal muscle. It transfers a methyl group from S-adenosylmethionine to the meta hydroxyl group and requires Mg or other divalent ions as a cofactor. COMT inhibitors increase norepinephrine and epinephrine. COMT is localized in supernatant fraction of the cell. Small amounts of normetanephrine and metanephrine are conjugated to the corresponding sulfates or glucuronides and small portions of their aldehyde oxidation products are reduced to 3-methoxy phenylglycol.

The dopamine metabolite which has been found in the brain[28] and in the urine[29] is 3-methoxy-4-hydroxyphenylacetic acid (homovanillic acid). About 1.5–3.0% of infused norepinephrine or epinephrine is excreted in the urine unchanged. The rest is excreted as metabolites, the primary one being 3-methoxy-4-hydroxy mandelic acid. Daily urinary excretion of epinephrine is 2–5 μg and of norepinephrine 25–50 μg.[6a, 6b] Urinary excretion of catecholamines in vanilomandelic acid is markedly increased in conditions such as pheochromocytoma.

Tissue and Blood Levels. The concentrations of the hormones in the adrenal varies considerably with species.[6a, 6b, 30] The norepinephrine to epinephrine ratio varies with species as well.[6a, 6b] The total content varies from 0.12 to 14 mg/g tissue. The percent of norepinephrine ranges from 2% in rabbit to 80% in whale.[30] In man the adrenals contain 0.27–1 mg/g. Various factors, such as stress, will affect the concentration.[6b] Fetal adrenals contain less than adult.

Norepinephrine and epinephrine are found in most organs[6a, 6b, 30] including the brain.[31] The concentrations vary with tissue and with species; in the brain as high as 2 μg/g, in the heart, as high as 9 μg/g. The epinephrine content is approximately 15% of the total catecholamines in the brain and 10% in the peripheral tissues; it is considered to be associated with chromaffin cells. Dopamine is found in negligible quantity in the peripheral nervous system, but is found in greater quantities in the brain, especially in the basal ganglia where it is as high as 8 μg/g.[32] Representative figures can be found in the following references— adrenal,[6a, 6b, 30] brain.[31, 32] The concentration of norepinephrine in venous plasma under resting conditions seems to be less than 0.5 μg/l and for epinephrine less than 0.1 μg/l. This varies with investigator and physiological state.[6b]

In subjects with pheochromocytoma there are elevated blood levels of norepinephrine and epinephrine and the following metabolites have been excreted in elevated amounts: vanilomandelic acid,[29] metanephrine, normetanephrine.[33]

Patients with neuroblastoma increased excretion of vanilomandelic acid, metanephrine, dopamine, DOPA, and 4 hydroxy-3-methoxyphenyl-alanine, and 3 methoxytyramine have been seen.[34a, 34b, 34c]

Basal ganglia disorders including Parkinsonism have altered dopamine metabolism in the brain.[35, 36] Subnormal amounts of dopamine have been found in the caudate nucleus and subnormal amounts of dopamine excreted. Urinary dopamine is increased in hepatolenticular degeneration.[36]

Assay Procedures. Good separations can be made of catecholamines by descending filter paper chromatography using phenol as one developing solvent.

Rf Values

Constituent	Side Chain	Rf^3	Rf^4
Norepinephrine	$CHOHCH_2NH_2$	0.216	0.28
DOPA	$CH_2CHCOOHNH_2$	0.230	0.29
Dopamine	$CH_2CH_2NH_2$	0.320	0.43
Corbasil	$CHOHCH\ MeNH_2$	0.408	0.50
Epinephrine	$CHOHCH_2NHMe$	0.441	0.51
Epinine	CH_3CH_2NHMe	0.760	0.67

Good separations can be made in n-butanol-acetic acid.[5] Spots can be developed by spraying with potassium ferricyanide, iodine, and other oxidants. Ninhydrin gives strong color with noradrenaline, but not adrenaline. More successful methods in extraction and estimation have involved use of adsorption or ion exchange techniques.[6a, 6b, 7]

Norepinephrine and epinephrine are readily oxidized to their corresponding adrenochromes and in presence of alkali to their corresponding trihydroxyindole derivatives. The difference in the rate of oxidation of the 2 compounds in acid solution is used for their separation: at pH 4 epinephrine is completely oxidized and norepinephrine only slightly (approx. 10%): at pH 6 both are completely oxidized.[6a, 6b, 7, 8] Dopamine can be oxidized to fluorescent derivatives.[7]

a. Biological[6a, 6b, 7]
    by blood pressure in cat or rat
    (sens. 1–5 nanograms of norepinephrine)
    by relaxation of rat uterus
    (sens. nor. 75–300 times less than epi 1 μg)
    other methods using aortic strip, cat nicitating
    membrane, and rat colon
    no adequate bioassay for dopamine exists
b. Chemical
    colorimetrically[6a, 6b]
    fluorometrically,[6a, 6b, 7, 8, 9, 10]

BIBLIOGRAPHY

References:

1. *Merck Index*, 7th ed., 1960.
2. Lewis, G. P., "The Importance of Ionization in the Activity of Sympatho-mimetic Amines," *Brit. J. Pharmacol.*, 9:488, 1954.
3. James, W. O., "Demonstration and Separation of Noradrenaline, Adrenaline and Methyladrenaline," *Nature*, 161:851, 1948.
4. Crawford, T. B. B., "Derivatives of Adrenaline and Noradrenaline in an Extract of an Adrenal Medullary Tumour," *Biochem. J.*, 48:203, 1951.
5. James, W. O., and N. Kilbey, "Separation of Noradrenalin and Adrenalin," *Nature*, 166:67, 1950.
6.a. von Euler, U. S., *Noradrenaline*, 1956.
  b. von Euler, U. S., in Gray and Bacharach (eds.), *Hormones in Blood*, p. 515, 1961.
7. Callingham, B. A., and R. Cass, in Varley and Gowenlock (eds.), *The Clinical Chemistry of Monoamines*, p. 19, 1963.
8. Carlsson, A., and Waldeck, *Acta Physiol. Scand.*, 44:293, 1958.
9. Crout, J. R., in Seligson (ed.), *Standard Methods in Clinical Chemistry*, p. 62, 1961.
10. Udenfriend, S., *Fluorescence Assay in Biology and Medicine*, p. 125, 1962.
11.a. Anton, A. H., and D. F. Sayre, "A Study of the Factors Affecting the Aluminum Oxide-Trihydroxyindole Procedure for the Analysis of Catecholamines," *J. Pharmacol. Exptl. Therap.*, 138:360, 1962.
  b. Anton, A. H., and D. F. Sayre, "The Distribution of Dopamine and Dopa in Various Animals and a Method for their Determination in Diverse Biological Material," *J. Pharmacol. Exptl. Therap.*, 145:326, 1964.
12. Goodman, L. S., and A. Gilman, *Pharmacological Basis of Therapeutics*, 3rd ed., p. 477, 1965.
13. DiPalma, J. R. (ed.), *Drill's Pharmacology in Medicine*, 3rd ed., p. 463, 1965.
14. McNay, J. L., R. H. McDonald, Jr., and L. I. Goldberg, "Direct Renal Vaso-dilation Produced by Dopamine in the Dog," *Clin. Res.*, 11:248, 1963.
15. Axelrod, J., in Varley and Gowenlock (eds.), *The Clinical Chemistry of Monoamines*, p. 5, 1963.
16. Kaufman, S., "The Enzymatic Conversion of Phenylalanine to Tyrosine," *J. Biol. Chem.*, 226:511, 1957.
17. Nagatsu, T., M. Levitt, and S. Udenfriend, "Tyrosine Hydroxylase. The Initial Step in Norepinephrine Biosynthesis," *J. Biol. Chem.*, 239:2910, 1964.
18. Lowenberg, W., H. Weissbach, and S. Udenfriend, "Aromatic L-Amino Acid Decarboxylase," *J. Biol. Chem.*, 237:89, 1962.
19. Kaufman, S., and S. Friedman, "Dopamine-β-Hydroxylase," *Pharmacol. Rev.*, 17:71, 1965.
20. Levin, E. Y., B. Levenberg, and S. Kaufman, "The Enzymatic Conversion of 3,4-Dihydroxyphenylethylamine to Norepinephrine," *J. Biol. Chem.*, 235:2080, 1960.
21. Potter, L. T., and J. Axelrod, "Properties of Norepinephrine Storage Particles of the Rat Heart," *J. Pharmacol. Exptl. Therap.*, 142:299, 1963.
22. Axelrod, J., "Purification and Properties of Phenylethanolamine-N-Methyl Transferase," *J. Biol. Chem.*, 237:1657, 1962.
23. Armstrong, M. D., and A. McMillan, "Studies on the Formation of 3-Methoxy-4-Hydroxy-D-Mandelic Acid, a Urinary Metabolite of Norepine-phrine and Epinephrine," *Pharmacol. Rev.*, 11:394, 1959.

24. Axelrod , J., "The Metabolism of Catecholamines *in vivo* and *in vitro*," *Pharmacol. Rev.*, 11:402, 1959.

25. Goodall, McC., "Metabolic Products of Adrenaline and Noradrenaline in Human Urine," *Pharmacol. Rev.*, 11:416, 1959.

26. Blaschko, H., J. M. Hagen, and P. Hagen, "Mitochondrial Enzymes and Chromaffin Granules," *J. Physiol.*, 139:316, 1957.

27. Axelrod, J., and R. Tomchick, "Enzymatic O-Methylation of Epinephrine and Other Catechols," *J. Biol. Chem.*, 233:702, 1958.

28. Sharman, D. F., "A Fluorimetric Method for the Estimation of 4-Hydroxy-3-Methoxyphenylacetic Acid (Homovanillic Acid) and its Identification in Brain Tissue," *Brit. J. Pharmacol.*, 20:204, 1963.

29. Shaw, K. N. F., McMillan, and M. D. Armstrong, "The Metabolism of 3,4-Dihydroxyphenylalanine," *J. Biol. Chem.*, 226:255, 1957.

30. von Euler, U. S., in von Euler and Heller (eds.), *Comparative Endocrinology*, 1:258, 1963.

31. Vogt, M., "The Concentration of Sympathin in Different Parts of the Central Nervous System under Normal Conditions and after the Administration of Drugs," *J. Physiol.*, 123:451, 1954.

32. Carlsson, A., "The Occurrence, Distribution and Physiological Role of Catecholamines in the Nervous System," *Pharmacol. Rev.*, 11:490, 1959.

33. von Euler, U. S., and G. Strom, "Present Status of Diagnosis and Treatment of Pheochromocytoma," *Circulation*, 15:5, 1957.

34.a. von Studnitz, W., "Neuroblastoma and Catecholamine Excretion," *Lancet*, 2:215, 1961.

   b. von Studnitz, W., "Occurrence, Isolation and Identification of 3-Methoxy-4-Hydroxyphenylalanine," *Clin. Chem. Acta*, 6:526, 1961.

   c. von Studnitz, W., *Scand. J. Clin. Lab. Invest.*, supp. 48, 12:3, 1960.

35. Barbeau, A., C. F. Murphy, and T. L. Sourkes, "Excretion of Dopamine in Diseases of Basal Ganglia," *Science*, 133:1706, 1961.

36. Ehringer, H., and O. Hornykiewcz, "Verteilung von Noradrenalin und Dopamin (3-Hydroxytyramin) im Gehirn des Menschen und Ihr Verhalten bei Erkrankungen des extrapyromidalen Systems," *Klin. Wochenschrift*, 38:1236, 1960.

Addendum:

The recently published symposium of the II Catecholamine Congress held in Milan, 1965 is a highly recommended reference for the whole subject of Catecholamines *Pharmacological Reviews*, 18, Part 1:1–804, 1966.

IV. GAMMA AMINOBUTYRIC ACID

*Biological Activities.*The effects of GABA and related compounds have been reviewed recently.[12, 13] In man 5–100 mg of GABA administered intravenously cause transitory paraesthesias. In man, dogs, and rabbits there is variable and transitory bradycardia fall in blood pressure and respiratory rate.[12, 14, 15] Since GABA does not pass the blood-brain barrier, these effects are considered to be peripheral effects. GABA inhibits the isolated intestine and antagonizes the effects of nicotine and 5-hydroxytryptamine, but there are species differences and variability.[16] All these effects show tachyphylaxis. Doses of 0.3–10 mg/kg to cats reduce the amplitude of the lumbar extensor reflex and enhance flexor monosynaptic and polysynaptic reflexes of spinal cord.[17]

The effects of GABA and related compounds in spinal neurones and the brain have been studied with introcarotid injections, topical application and electrophoretically with the use of multibarrelled electrodes and in a variety of species and preparations. In general the effects of GABA are those which depress electrical activity of neurones both in the brain and spinal cord, and glutamic acid, on the other hand, excites neurones. See Curtis and Watkins[13] for an extensive discussion of the various conditions and various effects of these amino acids. GABA and glutamic acid are effective in non-mammalian systems.[12]

The roles of GABA as a possible inhibitory transmitter substance and L-glutamate as excitatory transmitter have been extensively discussed.[12, 13, 18, 28]

Biosynthetic Pathway, Biotransformation, Excretion. The following biosynthetic and metabolic scheme has been determined and reviewed for GABA.[12]

$$\alpha\text{-oxoglutarate} \xrightarrow{\;1\;} \text{glutamate} \xrightarrow{\;2\;} \text{GABA} \xrightarrow{\;3\;} \text{succinic semialdehyde} + \text{glutamate}$$

1. α-oxoglutarate produced by Krebs cycle is reduced by the action of glutamic dehydrogenase and combines with ammonia to form glutamate. This enzyme is located in mitochondrial fractions.

2. L-glutamate is decarboxylated by the action of glutamic decarboxylase (GAD). This enzyme occurs in mammalian organisms only in the central nervous system, almost entirely in the gray matter. The coenzyme of this decarboxylase is pyridoxal phosphate, loosely bound, and can be inhibited by thiosemicarbazide and phenylhydrazine. GAD is found in the supernatant fractions of high speed subcellular nerve ending fractions.[19]

3. Gamma amino butyric α-oxoglutarate transaminase action yields succinic semialdehyde + glutamate. This enzyme also contains pyridoxal phosphate as a coenzyme tightly bound; GAD and the transaminase levels parallel one another as well as both with GABA. It is associated with mitochondrial fractions of subcellular fractions as marked by succinic dehydrogenase.[19] Hydroxylamine will inhibit this enzyme.[5, 20]

Succinic semialdehyde can be oxidized to succinate[21] or reduced to 4-hydroxybutyrate,[22a, b] which appears to have biological activity of producing EEG sleep.[23] Whether this occurs in sufficiently high quantities in the brain has not yet been determined. Also γ-guanide butyric acid can be formed from brain homogenates incubated with GABA.[25]

For further discussions on the distributions of enzyme and metabolism of GABA and related amino acids see Elliott,[12] Roberts,[26] and Salganeff.[19] Exdogenously administered GABA can be metabolized by tissue other than the brain and labelled GABA-1-C[14] has been isolated from urine of cats as succinate.[20] Whether this occurs in the intact animal is not known.

Tissue and Blood Levels. GABA has not been detected in normal serum or in serum of patients with a variety of malignant and non-malignant diseases. GABA is distributed in brains of various animals in amount of 1.5–4 μ moles (or 150–400 μg) GABA/g. This varies considerably with species and strains within species.[12] It is formed from decarboxylation of L-glutamate also present in large amount (9–13 μ moles/g) by GAD. For a distribution of the GABA in various portions of the brain,[5, 18, 26, 27] GABA is associated with the supernatant fraction of subcellular nerve ending fractions much as is GAD.

Cerebral cortex contains 2–3 μ moles/g. Values as high as 9 μ moles/g have been found in beef substania nigra and dentate nucleus, and in general, greater amounts in gray matter than white. Trace amounts are found in cerebrospinal fluid.[56]

Inhibitors of GAD, such as thiosemicarbazide, will decrease content of GABA. The convulsant activity of thiosemicarbazide has been attributed to decreased GABA levels. Hydroxylamine inhibits the transaminase and increases GABA levels. This has been associated with increased convulsive thresholds. Reserpine will deplete GABA levels. GABA is found in crustacea in the central nervous system and in inhibitory nerves of the peripheral system.[9] GABA is found in bacteria, yeasts, fungi, chorella, and higher plants.

Assay Procedures. Most determinations of GABA have used standard paper chromatographic techniques. GABA is ninhydrin sensitive. A quantitative paper chromatographic procedure has been devised but is long and tedious.[2] Newer methods with paper electrophoresis and column chromatography have been devised.[3, 4] A specific spectrophotometric method for microdetermination of GABA using a bacterial system which converts GABA to succinate has been modified for brain extracts.[5] The measurement of the NADPH achieves both sensitivity and specificity; as little as 1 μg GABA in a sample of tissue extract can be determined.

Use of the inhibition of the crayfish stretch receptor organ has been made for bioassay determinations.[6, 7] Florey showed that extracts of brain exerted excitatory and inhibitory activity on discharges of the slow adapting neurons of the crayfish and called the inhibitory one, Factor 1.[8] This factor was later shown to be GABA.[9, 10, 11]

Table I. Chemical and Physical Properties of Biogenic Amines

	Chemical Name	Trivial Name	Empirical Formula	Molecular Wt.
Histamine	4-imidazolethylamine β-aminoethylglyoxaline	histamine ergamine	$C_5H_9N_3$ C–54.0% H–8.2% N–37.8%	111.2
Serotonin	5-hydroxytryptamine 5-hydroxy-3-β-aminoethyl indole	serotonin enteramine 5-HT	$C_{10}H_{12}N_2O$ C–68.2% H–69% N–59% O–9.1%	176.2
Norepinephrine	α-(aminomethyl)-3,4- dihydroxybenzyl alcohol	arterenol noradrenaline norepinephrine	$C_8H_{11}NO_3$ C–56.79% H–6.55% N–8.28% O–28.37%	169.2
Epinephrine	3,4-dihydroxy-α- (methylaminomethyl) benzyl alcohol	suprarenin adrenaline epinephrine adrenalin	$C_9H_{13}NO_3$ C–59.0% H–7.2% N–7.6% O–26.2%	183.2
Dopamine	3,4-dihydroxyphenyl- ethylamine	dopamine	$C_8H_{11}NO_2$ C–62.75% H–7.12% N–9.15% O–20.92%	153.18
Gamma aminobutyric acid	Gamma amino-n-butyric acid piperidic acid 4-aminobutanoic acid	GABA	$C_4H_9NO_2$ C–46.5% H–8.8% N–13.6% O–31.0%	103.1

	Melting point	Boiling point	pK
Histamine	83–83°	209–210 (18°)	5.0 (imidazole) at 30° C. 9.7 (NH_2) at 30° C.
Serotonin			
Norepinephrine	216.5°–218.0° HCl 146°		pK_1 (base) 8.73[2] pK_2 (base) 9.78[2]
Epinephrine	211–212° DL HCl 157°		pK_1 (base) 8.71[2] pK_2 (base) 9.90[2]
Dopamine			pK_1 (base) 8.87[2] pK_2 (base) 10.63[2]
Gamma aminobutyric acid	202° (decomp; rapid heating)		

Table I. Chemical and Physical Properties of Biogenic Amines (continued)

	Structure	Physical Form	Solubility
Histamine	$CH_2CH_2NH_2$ imidazole ring	white deliquescent needles from chloroform	freely soluble in water, alcohol, hot chloroform sparingly soluble in ether
Serotonin	HO— indole —$CH_2CH_2NH_2$	hygroscopic, light sensitive and unstable	s. H_2O
Norepinephrine	OH / HO—, HO— benzene ring —CH—CH_2—NH_2	white crystalline	sl. sol. H_2O, EtOH, eth. HCl—s. H_2O; sl. s. EtOH
Epinephrine	HO—, HO— benzene ring —$CHCH_2NHCH_3$ with OH	col. crystals browning on exposure to air	s. aq. solution mineral acids, NaOH, KOH i. EtOH, CH_3Cl_3, eth., acet., oils
Dopamine	HO—, HO— benzene ring —$CH_2CH_2NH_2$	white crystalline	
Gamma aminobutyric acid	$NH_2CH_2CH_2CH_2COOH$	leaflets from methanol + ether, needles from water + alcohol	freely soluble in water; insoluble or poorly soluble in other solvents

BIBLIOGRAPHY

References:

1. *Merck Index*, 7th ed., p. 53, 1960.
2. Roberts, E., and Frankel, "γ-Aminobutyric Acid in Brain: Its Formation from Glutamic Acid," *J. Biol. Chem.*, 187:55, 1950.
3. Hanson, A., and W. Studnitz, "Zur Bestimmung von γ-Aminobuttersaure und Glutaminsaure in biologischem Material mit Hilfe von Hochspannungs-electrophorese," *Acta Chem. Scand.*, 12:1332, 1958.
4. Berl, S. F., and H. Waelsch, "Determination of Glutamic Acid, Glutamine, Glutathione and γ-Aminobutyric Acid and Their Distribution in Brain Tissue," *J. Neurochem.*, 3:161, 1958.
5. Baxter, C. F., and E. Roberts, "Elevation of γ-Aminobutyric Acid in Rat Brain with Hydroxylamine," *Proc. Soc. Exp. Biol. Med.*, 101:811, 1959.
6. Elliott, K. A. C., and H. H. Jasper, "γ-Aminobutyric Acid," *Physiol. Rev.*, 39:383, 1959.
7. Florey, E., and K. A. C. Elliott, "Bio-Assay of Factor I," *Methods in Med. Res.*, 9:196, 1961.
8. Florey, E., "An Inhibitory and Excitatory Factor of Mammalian Central Nervous System, and Their Action on a Single Sensory Neuron," *Arch. Intern. Physiol.*, 62:33, 1954.
9. Bazemore, A., K. A. C. Elliott, and E. Florey, "Factor 1 and γ-Aminobutyric Acid," *Nature*, 178:1052, 1956.
10. Levin, E., R. A. Lovell, and K. A. C. Elliott, "The Relation of γ-Aminobutyric Acid to Factor I in Brain Extracts," *J. Neurochem.*, 7:147, 1961.
11. Lovell, R. A., and K. A. C. Elliott, "The γ-Aminobutyric Acid and Factor I Content of Brain," *J. Neurochem.*, 10:479, 1963.
12. Elliott, K. A. C., *Brit. Med. Bull.*, 21:70, 1965.
13. Curtis, D. R., and J. C. Watkins, "The Pharmacology of Amino Acids Related to γ-Aminobutyric Acid," *Pharmacol. Rev.*, 17:347, 1965.
14. Takahashi, H., *et al.*, "The Effect of γ-Aminobutyric Acid on Blood Pressure," *Japan J. Physiol.*, 5:334, 1956.
15. Elliott, K. A. C., and F. Hobbiger, "γ-Aminobutyric Acid: Circulatory and Respiratory Effects in Different Species; Re-Investigation of the Anti-Strychnine Action in Mice," *J. Physiol.*, 146:70, 1959.
16.a. Hobbiger, F., "Effects of γ-Aminobutyric Acid on the Isolated Mammalian Ileum," *J. Physiol.*, 142:147, 1958.
16.b. Hobbiger, F., "Antagonism by γ-Aminobutyric Acid to the Actions of 5-Hydroxytryptamine and Nicotine on Isolated Organs," *J. Physiol.*, 144:349, 1958.
17. Kuno, M., and A. Muneola, "Further Studies on Site of Further Action of Systemic Omega-Amino Acids in the Spinal Cord," *Japan J. Physiol.*, 12:397, 1962.
18. Wolleman, M., *Review Aggressologie*, 6:9, 1965.
19. Salganeff, L., and E. de Robertis, "Subcellular Distribution of the Enzymes of the Glutamic Acid, Glutamine and γ-Aminobutyric Acid Cycles in Rat Brain," *J. Neurochem.*, 12:287, 1965.
20. Roberts, E., Rothstein, and C. F. Baxter, "Some Metabolic Studies of γ-Aminobutyric Acid," *Proc. Soc. Exp. Biol. Med.*, 97:796, 1958.
21. Albers, R. W., and R. A. Salvador, "Succinic Semialdehyde Oxidation by a Soluble Dehydrogenase from Brain," *Science*, 128:359, 1958.

22.a. Bessman, S. P., F. J. Rossen and E. C. Layne, "γ-Aminobutyric Acid— Glutamic Acid Transamination in Brain," *J. Biol. Chem.*, 201:385, 1953.

22.b. Bessman, S. P., and W. N. Fishbein, "γ-Hydroxybutyrate in Mammalian Brain. Reversible Oxidation by Lactic Dehydrogenase," *J. Biol. Chem.*, 239:357, 1964.

23. Laborit, G., *Intern. J. Neuropharmacol.*, 3:433, 1964.

24. Drahontides, A. B., J. A. Schneider, and W. H. Funderburk, "Some Effects of Sodium γ-Hydroxybutyrate on the Central Nervous System," *J. Pharmacol. Exp. Therap.*, 135:275, 1962.

25. Honour, A. J., and H. McLennan, "The Effects of γ-Aminobutyric Acid and Other Compounds on Structures of the Mammalian Nervous System Which are Inhibited by Factor I," *J. Physiol.*, 150:306, 1961.

26. Roberts, E., in Elliott, K. A. C., I. H. Page, and J. H. Quastel (eds.), *Neurochemistry*, (2nd ed.), p. 636, 1962.

27. Baxter, C. F., and E. Roberts, "Demonstration of Thiosemicarbazide-Induced Convulsions in Rats with Elevated Brain Levels of γ-Aminobutyric Acid," *Proc. Soc. Exp. Biol. Med.*, 104:426, 1960.

28. Krnjevic, *Brit. Med Bull*, 21:10, 1965.

AMINO ACID AND PROTEIN HORMONES

I. INTRODUCTION

A detailed review of current advances in the biochemistry and physiology of each of the protein, peptide and amino acid hormones is clearly beyond the scope of the present chapter. Rather, it is intended to present accepted and reliable information on each hormone, and to provide an index to significant general reviews and papers which will permit readers to focus rapidly on a particular area of special interest. The bibliography is not intended to be exhaustive. References to original publications are not included when they are given in a listed general-review article. The hormones discussed are those selected by editorial consensus.

In general, the standard reference for information is *The Hormones*, edited by G. Pincus, K. V. Thimann, and E. B. Astwood, presently comprising five volumes. Valuable information concerning current problems in endocrinology may be found in the annual publications *Recent Progress in Hormone Research*, and *Vitamins and Hormones*. In addition, pertinent articles appear periodically in *Annual Reviews of Biochemistry*, *Annual Reviews of Physiology* and also in *Annual Reviews in Pharmacology*. Although reports bearing on problems in the field of endocrinology appear in a wide variety of scientific journals, those concerned specifically with this field are *Endocrinology*, *Journal of Endocrinology*, and *Acta Endocrinologica*.

II. SELECTED HORMONES

Luteinizing Hormone. (Interstitial Cell Stimulating Hormone) (LH:ICSH) A glycoprotein hormone secreted by the anterior pituitary gland which, in the female, causes luteinization of the ovarian follicles and, in the male, stimulates the testicular interstitial cells. The molecular weight of LH has been considered to be about 28,000, although recent studies suggest this value may be too high. The hormone contains about 25% carbohydrate. The amino acid and carbohydrate composition of ovine LH have been reported, as have studies on the —NH_2 and —COOH terminal amino acid of LH from a variety of species. The hormone is characterized by a low content of tryptophane, and relatively high content of proline and cystine. Optical rotatory studies suggest ovine LH is a non-helical protein. The isoelectric point of ovine LH has been reported to be pH 7.7, and of human LH, pH 5.5. A probable absence of sialic acid distinguishes LH from human chorionic gonadotropin (HCG) (an LH-like hormone), and from follicle stimulating hormone, its most tenacious contaminant. Sialic acid is required for the biological activity of the latter two gonadotropins. Pituitary LH fractions have been prepared from human urine, although with markedly low levels of biological activity. Assay of LH has been complicated by factors relating to distinguishing biological characteristics of heterologous LH's, and lack of a universally accepted reference standard. The most potent LH, however, appears to have a specific activity two to three times greater than NIH-LH-SI/mg, when measured in the ovarian ascorbic acid depletion assay. Immunological assays for LH have also been reported.

Follicle Stimulating Hormone. (FSH) A glycoprotein hormone secreted by the anterior pituitary gland, which, in the female, causes development of ovarian follicles, and in the male, causes stimulation of spermatogenesis. The molecular weight of FSH is about 30,000. The hormone contains about 10% carbohydrate. The isoelectric point of FSH has been reported to be acidic, about pH 5.0. It is not certain, however, that homogeneity has been achieved for any species of FSH, so that the significance of physical-chemical characterization is open to question. FSH is inactivated by neuraminidose, suggesting a requirement for sialic acid. Pituitary FSH is found in human urine, and purified preparations have been obtained from this source. Structural differences between heterologous FSH's have been implied on the basis of biological studies. A lack of FSH (and of LH) may result in Fröhlich's syndrome. The hormone is commonly assayed by its ability to promote ovarian growth in HCG-primed immature rats. The most potent preparations have activities of from 50 to 200 NIH-FSH-SI units/mg.

Thyroid Stimulating Hormone. (Thyrotrophin) (TSH) A glycoprotein hormone secreted by the basophil cells of the anterior pituitary gland, the physiological function of which is stimulation of the development of the thyroid gland and the secretion of the thyroid hormone. The molecular weight of TSH is about 30,000, containing about 8% carbohydrate. The isoelectric point of TSH apparently lies between pH 6 and pH 8. The amino acid composition of purified preparations has been reported. Excesses or deficiences of TSH will result in excess or deficiencies of thyroid hormones, with the corresponding physiological symptoms (see "L-thyroxin"). The most potent preparations have specific activities of about 30

USP units per mg. Biological assays of the hormone are based on its ability to promote uptake of P^{32} by immature chick thyroids, or to promote release of I-131 labelled thyroxine from chicken, mouse, or rat thyroid glands. An immunoassay for TSH has been reported.

Growth Hormone. (Somatotropin) (GH) A simple protein hormone, secreted by the anterior pituitary gland, whose action stimulates a large variety of physiological processes, resulting in increased tissue and skeletal growth, nitrogen retention, and fatty acid mobilization. Bovine and ovine GH have been shown to have two N-terminal amino acids, while those of other species, such as human, monkey and porcine, have only one.

Ox, sheep, pig and whale GH's have molecular weights ranging from 40,000–45,000, while monkey and human GH's appear to have a molecular weight of from 25,000–30,000. The isoelectric point of primate GH's is considerably more acidic than those of the lower species. Growth hormone is species-specific. Whereas GH from primates will exert an effect in the lower species, such as the rat, GH from the pituitaries of lower orders will not produce an effect in man or monkeys. Deficiency of GH results in dwarfism, while excess secretion results in acromegaly and, frequently, diabetes. A common bioassay for GH is based on the hormone's ability to promote body weight gain in hypophysectomized rats. A radioimmunoassay for GH has been reported, although there is some evidence to suggest that the portion of the GH molecule responsible for antigenicity is distinct from that required for biological activity.

Prolactin. (Lactogenic hormone, luteotrophin) (LTH) A simple protein hormone secreted by the anterior pituitary gland, whose physiological function is stimulation of the mammary glands in mammals, and maintenance of the corpus luteum in some species, including the rat and the mouse. Prolactin stimulates the crop sac in birds, an effect which is the basis for its biological assay. Purified preparations have been prepared

Figure I.   Amino Acid Sequence of Growth Hormones

Species	Molecular Weight	Isoelectric Point	—NH$_2$ Terminal	—COOH Terminal
Bovine	45,000	6.85	Phe-Ala-Thr⟍ Ala-Phe-Ala ⟋	Leu-Ala-Phe-Phe
Ovine	47,800	6.8	Phe —— Ala —— ⟹	Tyr-Ala-Phe
Porcine	41,600	6.3	Phe-Pro-Ala-Met-Pro-Leu—Leu-Phe-Ala-Phe	
Whale	39,900	6.2	Phe-Lys	Leu-Ala-Phe
Simian	25,400	5.5	Phe-Thr	Ala-Gly-Phe
Human	27,100	4.9	Phe-Pro-Thr-Leu-Asp-Leu—Leu-Phe	

from bovine, ovine and porcine pituitaries. Ovine Prolactin has a molecular weight of about 26,000. The N-terminal amino acid is threonine, while the C-terminal is ½ cystine, presumably indicating an interchain disulfide link at the C-terminus. The isoelectric point of Prolactin is acidic, ranging from pH 4.8 (porcine) to about pH 5.7 (ovine, bovine). The most potent preparations have potencies of about 30 I.U./mg.

Malanocyte Stimulating Hormone. (Intermedin) (MSH) A peptide hormone secreted by the intermediate zone of the pituitary gland, whose physiological function is associated with dispersion of melanin in the epidermal malanophores. Two types of MSH are known, α-MSH, a linear peptide containing 13 amino acid residues having the NH_2-terminal seryl residue blocked by an acetyl group and a valine amino at the -COOH terminus, and β-MSH, a linear peptide containing 18 amino acid residues with aspartic at either terminus. The structures of MSH from a variety of species are given in Figure 2.

Corticotrophin. (Adrenocorticotrophic Hormone) (ACTH) A peptide hormone secreted by the anterior pituitary gland whose physiological function is stimulation and secretion of adrenocortical hormones. Corticotrophin from human, porcine, ovine and bovine pituitary glands consists of 39 amino acids. The same amino acids, in identical sequence, occupy the first 24 and the last 7 positions in ACTH. Relatively minor species variations occur in the narrow range of amino acids between positions 25 to 32. Only the first 19 residues are required for biological activity, although the N-terminal serine residue is indispensable for activity. The structure of the ACTH's is given below. Deficiency of ACTH secretion results in Addison's disease, while hypersecretion occurs in Cushing's disease.

Insulin. A peptide hormone, formed in the β-cells of the islets of Langerhans, and secreted in response to hyperglycemic stimuli. Although the effects of insulin are many, its primary physiological role is to facilitate utilization of glucose, presumably by promoting its rate of entry into the body cells. Deficiency of insulin results in diabetes mellitus. The structure of insulins from a variety of species is shown in Figure 4.

Glucagon. A peptide hormone produced by the α-cells of the islets of Langerhans in the pancreas. It has a hyperglycemic effect, presumably due to a stimulation of heptatic glycogenolysis. Glucagon is a straight-chain polypeptide with a molecular weight of 3485. Its structure is shown in Figure 5.

Parathyroid Hormone. (Parathormone) A hypercalcemic factor secreted by the parathyroid gland in response to low levels of serum-α-MSH — Pig, Beef, Horse, Monkey

R-Ser-Tyr-Ser-Met-Glu-His-Phe-Arg-Try-Gly-Lys-Pro-Val-NH₂

β-MSH — Pig, Beef, Horse, Monkey

Pig..........	Asp-Glu-Gly-Pro-Tyr-Lys-Met-Glu-His-Phe-Arg-Try-Gly-Ser-Pro-Pro-Lys-Asp
Beef.........	Asp-Ser-Gly-Pro-Tyr-Lys-Met-Glu-His-Phe-Arg-Try-Gly-Ser-Pro-Pro-Lys-Asp
Horse........	Asp-Glu-Gly-Pro-Tyr-Lys-Met-Glu-His-Phe-Arg-Try-Gly-Ser-Pro-Arg-Lys-Asp
Monkey.......	Asp-Glu-Gly-Pro-Tyr-Arg-Met-Glu-His-Phe-Arg-Try-Gly-Ser-Pro-Pro-Lys-Asp

β-MSH — Human

Ala-Glu-Lys-Lys-Asp-Glu-Gly-Pro-Tyr-Arg-Met-Glu-His-Phe-Arg-Try-Gly-Ser-Pro-Pro-Lys-Asp

Figure 2. Amino Acid sequence of α-Malanocyte Stimulating Hormone and β-Malanocyte Stimulating Hormone

1 2 3 4 5 6 7 8 9 10 11 12 13 14 15 16 17 18 19 20 21 22 23

Ser–Tyr–Ser–Met–Glu (His, Phe–Arg–Try (Gly, Lys, Pro, Val, Gly) Lys–Lys (Arg, Arg, Pro, Val) Lys–Val–Tyr–

24 25 26 27 28 29 30 31 32 33 34 35 36 37 38 39
$$\overset{\displaystyle NH_2}{\underset{|}{}}$$
Pro–Asp–Ala–Gly–Glu–Asp–Glu–Ser–Ala–Glu–Ala–Phe–Pro–Leu–Glu–Phe

Proposed amino acid sequence of human ACTH

21 22 23 24 25 26 27 28 29 30 31 32 33 34 35 36 37 38 39

Human . . . . Lys–Val–Tyr–Pro–Asp–Ala–Gly–Glu–Asp–Glu–Ser–Ala–Glu–Ala–Phe–Pro–Leu–Glu–Phe
(NH₂ at 30)

Pig . . . . Lys–Val–Tyr–Pro–Asp–Gly–Ala–Glu–Asp–Glu–Leu–Ala–Glu–Ala–Phe–Pro–Leu–Glu–Phe
(NH₂)

Beef . . . . Lys–Val–Tyr–Pro–Asp–Gly–Glu–Ala–Glu–Asp–Ser–Ala–Glu–Ala–Phe–Pro–Leu–Glu–Phe
(NH₂)

Sheep . . . . Lys–Val–Tyr–Pro–Ala–Gly–Glu–Asp–Asp–Glu–Ala–Ser–Glu–Ala–Phe–Pro–Leu–Glu–Phe

COOH terminal sequences of corticotropins from various species

Figure 3.

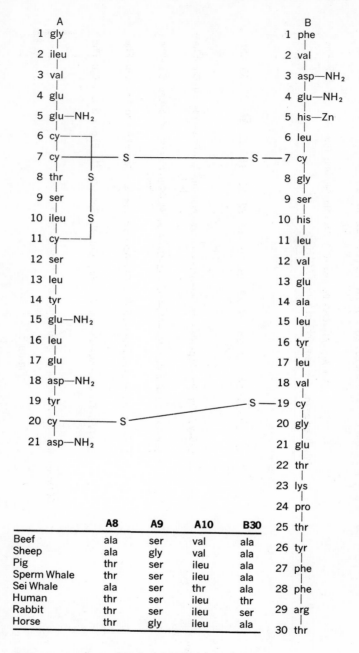

	A8	A9	A10	B30
Beef	ala	ser	val	ala
Sheep	ala	gly	val	ala
Pig	thr	ser	ileu	ala
Sperm Whale	thr	ser	ileu	ala
Sei Whale	ala	ser	thr	ala
Human	thr	ser	ileu	thr
Rabbit	thr	ser	ileu	ser
Horse	thr	gly	ileu	ala

Figure 4.   Amino Acid Sequence of Insulins.

His
|
Ser
|
Glu—NH₂
|
Gly
|
Thr
|
Phe
|
Thr
|
Ser
|
Asp
|
Tyr
|
Ser
|
Lys
|
Tyr
|
Leu
|
Asp
|
Ser
|
Arg
|
Arg
|
Ala
|
Glu—NH₂
|
Asp
|
Phe
|
Val
|
Glu—NH₂
|
Tyr
|
Leu
|
Met
|
Asp—NH₂
|
Thr

Figure 5.   Structure of Glucagon.

ionized calcium. Its physiological role is to maintain blood levels of calcium within narrow limits, about 10 mg per 100 ml which is accomplished by direct effects on bone, where it promotes dissolution of bone salts, and on kidney, where it acts to prevent losses of calcium into the urine. The amino acid composition of the hormone has been reported, and its amino acid sequence has been proposed. The endogenous hormone is believed to have a molecular weight of about 9,500 although biologically active fragments have been prepared having molecular weights of 3,800 and 5,200. A deficiency of parathyroid hormone leads to tetany, while excess secretion results most typically in osteitis fibrosa. Biological assay of parathyroid hormone is usually based on its ability to affect serum or urinary calcium or phosphate levels in parathyroidectomized rats. An immunoassay for the hormone has been described.

Oxytocin. A peptide hormone formed in the neurohypophysis, the physiological effect of which is to increase the rate and force of contraction of smooth muscle, especially of the uterus, as well as stimulation of milk ejection during lactation. The structure of oxytocin prepared from human, bovine and porcine sources is identical. Oxytocin is chemically related to vasopressin, its structure differing from ocytocin only in positions 3 and 8. (For details of structure see the following section.)

Vasopressin. (Antidiuretic Hormone) (ADH) A peptide hormone

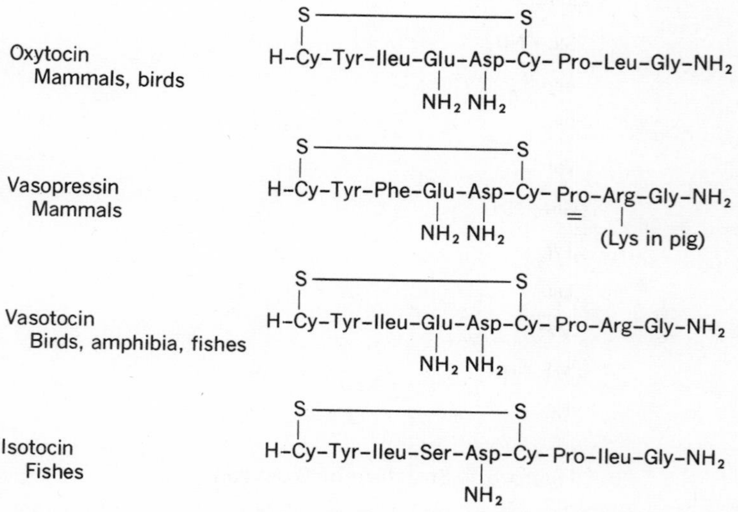

Figure 6. Amino Acid sequence of Oxytocin and Vasopressin.

formed in the neuronal cells of the hypothalamic nuclei, from which it migrates to, and is stored in, the nerve endings of the neurohypophysis. Its physiological effect is to increase blood pressure and to exert an anti-diuretic effect on the kidney. Species differences in the structure of vasopressin occur at position 8, and the nomenclature of vasopressin is based on the nature of this residue. (For example, in the porcine, where arginine is replaced by lysine, the hormone is "lysine vasopressin.")

Human Chorionic Gonadotropin. A glycoprotein hormone produced in the chorionic villi, the physiological effect of which is ovarian hyper-trophy with increased estrogen production. The hormone has been puri-fied from human pregnancy urine. It has a molecular weight of 30,000, containing 30% carbohydrate. The most potent preparations are about 10,000 I.U./mg.

L-Thyroxin. (T4) An amino acid hormone secreted by the thyroid gland in response to stimulation by thyrotrophin (TSH). It is stored in the thyroid gland in the iodized glycoprotein, thyroglobulin (MW 680,000) from which it is released, presumably through the action of a thyroid proteinase. The structure of L-Thyroxin is:

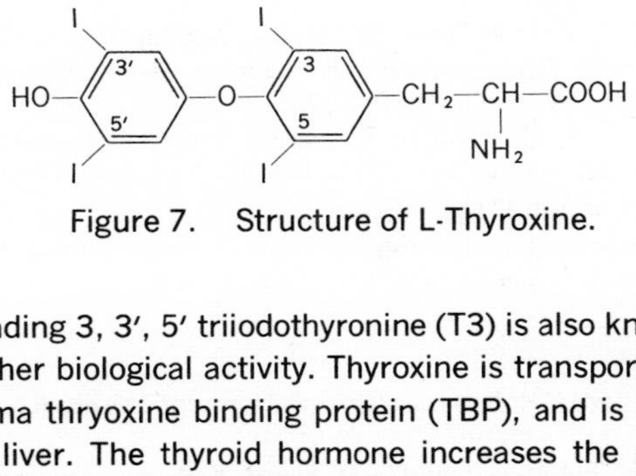

Figure 7.   Structure of L-Thyroxine.

The corresponding 3, 3', 5' triiodothyronine (T3) is also known and has a somewhat higher biological activity. Thyroxine is transported complexed with the plasma thryoxine binding protein (TBP), and is rapidly metab-olized in the liver. The thyroid hormone increases the rate of energy exchange and oxygen consumption of all normal tissue except the thyroid gland itself. Deficiency of thyroid hormone results in myxedema, while hyperthyroidism results in Graves' Disease.

Relaxin. A non-steroid hormone discovered in aqueous extracts of sow ovaries, but also found in blood of pregnant females of a variety of species, including man, and in placental and uterine tissue. Its physiologi-cal role is thought to be related to the pelvic relaxation of pregnancy and parturition, although a deficiency disease is not known. Relaxin appears to be a basic polypeptide having a molecular weight of about 9,000. It is inactivated by digestion with proteolytic enzymes, and by reagents which reduce disulfide linkages to sulfhydryl groups.

BIBLIOGRAPHY

Luteinizing Hormone:

(1) Bates, R. W., and P. G. Condliffe, "Assay and Biochemistry of Thyrotrophin," in S. W. Werner (ed.), *The Thyroid,* 2nd ed., p. 74, 1962.

(2) Cole, H. H. (ed.), *Gonadotropins: Their Chemical and Biological Properties and Secretory Control,* 1964.

(3) Dixon, H. B. F., "Luteinizing Hormone," *The Hormones,* 5:1, 1964.

(4) Li, C. H., and B. R. Starman, "Molecular Weight of Sheep Pituitary Interstitial Cell Stimulating Hormone," *Nature,* 202:291, 1964.

(5) Parlow, A. F., "Bio-Assay of Pituitary Luteinizing Hormone by Depletion of Ovarian Ascorbic Acid," in Albert, A. (ed.), *Human Pituitary Gonadotropins,* p. 300, 1961.

(6) Reichert, L. E., Jr., and N. S. Jiang, "Comparative Gel Filtration and Density Gradient Centrifugation Studies on Heterologous Pituitary Luteinizing Hormones," *Endocrinology,* 77:68, 1965.

(7) Reichert, L. E., Jr., "Characterization of Purified Heterologous Pituitary Luteinizing Hormones by Dinitrophenylation Digestion with Carboxypeptidase A and Hydrazinolysis," *Endocrinology,* 1966, In Press

(8) Reichert, L. E., Jr., and A. F. Parlow, "Partial Purification and Separation of Urinary Gonadotropins on Nonpregnant Humans," *J. Clin. Endocrinol. Metab.,* 24:1040, 1964.

(9) Ward, D. N., E. F. Walborg, Jr., and M. Adams-Mayne, "Amino Acid Composition and Electrophoretic Behavior of Ovine Luteinizing Hormone," *Biochim. Biophys. Acta,* 78:304, 1963.

(10) Walborg, E. F., Jr., and D. N. Ward, "The Carbohydrate Composition of Ovine Luteinizing Hormone," *Biochim. Biophys. Acta,* 78:304, 1963.

(11) Werner, S. W. (ed.), *Thyrotrophin,* 1963.

(12) Wolstenholme, G. E. W., and J. Knight (ed.), *Gonadotropins: Physico-Chemical and Immunological Properties,* 1965.

Growth Hormone:

(1) Knobil, E. and J. Hotchkiss, "Growth Hormone," *Ann. Rev. Physiol.,* 27:47, 1964.

(2) Marx, W., M. E. Simpson and H. M. Evans, *Endocrinology,* 30:1, 1942.

(3) Papkoff, H. and C. H. Li, "Chemistry of Hypophyseal Growth Hormone," *Metabolism,* 13:1082, 1964.

(4) Wilhelmi, A. E., "Comparative Biochemistry of Growth Hormone from Ox, Sheep, Pig, and Fish Pituitaries," in R. W. Smith, O. H. Gaebler and C. W. H. Long (ed.), *Hypophyseal Growth Hormone, Nature and Actions,* p. 59, 1955.

Prolactin:

(1) Dixon, J. S. and C. H. Li, "Chemistry of Prolactin," *Metabolism,* 13:1093, 1964.

(2) Li, C. H., "Biochemistry of Prolactin," in S. K. Kon and A. T. Cowie (ed.), *Milk: The Mammary Gland and its Secretions,* Vol. 1, p. 205, 1961.

(3) Li, C. H., "Hormones of the Anterior Pituitary," *Advan. Protein Chem.*, 12:269, 1957.

Malonocyte Stimulating Hormone:

(1) Albert, A. (ed.), *Human Pituitary Gonadotropins*, 1961.
(2) Hofmann, K. and H. Yajima, "Synthetic Pituitary Hormones," *Recent Progr. Hormone Res.*, 18:41, 1962.
(3) Lee, T. H., A. B. Lerner and V. Buettner-Janusch, "The Isolation and Structure of alpha- and beta- Malonocyte-Stimulating Hormones from Monkey Pituitary Glands," *J. Biol. Chem.*, 236:1390, 1961.
(4) Lerner, A. B., and T. H. Lee, "The Malonocyte Stimulating Hormones," *Vitamins and Hormones*, 20:337, 1962.

Follicle Stimulating Hormone:

(1) Butt, W. R., "Some Problems Related to the Investigation of the Immunological Properties of Human Pituitary Follicle Stimulating Hormone," in G. E. W. Wolstenholme and J. C. Knight (ed.), *Gonadotropins: Physico-Chemical and Immunological Properties*, 1965.
(2) Reichert, L. E., Jr., and A. F. Parlow, "Preparation of Highly Potent Human Pituitary Gonadotropins," *Proc. Soc. Exp. Biol. Med.*, 115:286, 1964.
(3) Roos, P. and C. A. Gemzell, "Preparation of Human FSH from Pituitaries and from Postmenopausal Urine," *Gonadotropins: Physico-Chemical and Immunological Properties*, 1965.
(4) Steelman, S. L. and A. Segaloff, "Recent Studies on the Purification of Pituitary Gonadotropins," *Recent Progr. Hormone Res.*, 15:115, 1959.
(5) Steelman, S. L. and F. M. Pohley, "Assay of Follicle Stimulating Hormone Based on the Augmentation with Human Chorionic Gonadotropin," *Endocrinology*, 53:604, 1953.

Thyroid Stimulating Hormone:

(1) Bates, R. W. and P. G. Condliffe, "Studies on the Chemistry and Bioassay of Thyrotrophins from Bovine Plasma," *Recent Progr. Hormone Res.*, 16:309, 1960.
(2) Condliffe, P. G., "Purification of Human Thyrotrophin," *Endocrinology*, 72:893, 1963.
(3) Odell, W., J. F. Wilbur and W. Paul, "Radioimmunoassay of Thyrotrophin in Human Serum," *J. Clin. Endocrinol. Metab.*, 25:1179, 1965.
(4) Pierce, J. G. and M. E. Carsten, "Preparation of Highly Purified Thyrotrophin," in S. C. Werner (ed.), *Thyrotrophin*, p. 216, 1963.
(5) Wynston, L. K., C. A. Free and J. G. Pierce, "Further Chromatographic Studies on Beef Thyrotrophin and a Comparison of Beef, Sheep and Whale Thyrotrophins," *J. Biol. Chem.*, 235:85, 1960.

Corticotrophin:

(1) Dixon, H. B. F., "Chemistry of Pituitary Hormones," *The Hormones*, 5:1, 1964.
(2) Hofmann, K., and H. Yajima, "Synthetic Pituitary Hormones," *Recent Progr. Hormone Res.*, 18:41, 1962.
(3) Hofmann, K. F., "Chemistry and Function of Polypeptide Hormones," *Ann. Rev. Biochem.*, 31:213, 1962.
(4) Leboritz, H. E., and F. L. Engel, "Relationship between the Structure and

Biological Activities of Corticotrophin and Related Peptides," *Metabolism,* 13:226, 1964.

(5)   Lee, T. H., A. B. Lerner, and V. Buettner-Janusch, "On the Structure of Human Corticotrophin," *J. Biol. Chem.*, 236:2070, 1961.

(6)   Li, C. H., "Synthesis and Biological Properties of ACTH Peptides," *Recent Progr. Hormone Res.*, 18:1, 1962.

Insulin:

(1)   Randle, P. J., "Insulin," in P. Karlson (ed.), *Mechanisms of Hormone Action,* 1965.

(2)   Randle, P. J., "The Physiological Role of Insulin," in G. Pimcus (ed.), *Recent Progr. Hormone Res.*, 1966, In Press.

(3)   Randle, P. J., "Insulin," *The Hormones,* 4:481, 1964.

(4)   Young, F. G., W. A. Proom and F. W. Wolff (ed.), *The Mechanism of Action of Insulin,* 1960.

(5)   Young, F. G., "On Insulin and Its Actions," *Proc. Roy. Soc.*, B157:1, 1962.

Glucagon:

(1)   Behrens, O. K., and W. W. Bromer, "Glucagon," *Vitamins and Hormones,* 16:263, 1958.

(2)   Foa, P. P., "Glucagon," *The Hormones,* 4:531, 1964.

(3)   Foa, P. P., G. Solansino and G. Pozza, "Glucagon-A Second Pancreatic Hormone," *Recent Progr. Hormone Res.*, 13:473, 1957.

Parathyroid Hormone:

(1)   Copp, D. H., "Parathyroids, Calcitonin and Control of Plasma Calcium," *Recent Progr. Hormone Res.*, 20:59, 1964.

(2)   Munson, P. L., P. F. Hirsch and A. H. Tashjian, Jr., "Parathyroid Gland," *Ann. Rev. Physiol.*, 25:325, 1963.

(3)   Potts, J. T., G. D. Aurbach and L. M. Sherwood, "Parathyroid Hormone-Chemical Properties and Structural Requirements for Activity," *Recent Progr. Hormone Res.*, Vol. 22, 1966, In Press.

(4)   Rasmussen, Howard and L. C. Craig, "The Parathyroid Polypeptides," *Recent Progr. Hormone Res.*, 18:269, 1962.

Oxytocin and Vasopressin:

(1)   Dixon, H. B. F., "Oxytocin and Vasopressin," *The Hormones: The Chemistry of Pituitary Hormones,* 5:1, 1964.

(2)   Hofmann, K., "Chemistry and Function of Polypeptide Hormones," *Ann. Rev. of Biochem.*, 31:213, 1962.

(3)   Sawyer, W. H., "Neurohypophyseal Hormones," *Pharmacol. Rev.*, 13:225, 1961.

Human Chorionic Gonadotropin:

(1)   Geschwind, I. I., "The Chemistry and Immunology of Gonadotropins," in H. H. Cole (ed.), *Gonadotropins: Their Chemical and Biological Properties and Secretory Control,* 1964.

Thyroxin:

(1)   Pitt-Rivers, R. and W. R. Trotter, *The Thyroid Gland,* Vol. 1, 2, 1965.

(2) Roll, J. E., J. Robbins and C. G. Lewallen, "The Thyroid," *The Hormones,*
5:159, 1964.

(3) Werner, S. C. (ed.), *The Thyroid,* 2nd ed., 1962.

Relaxin:

(1) Diczfalusy, E. and P. Troen, "Relaxin," in *Endocrine Functions of Human Placenta, Vitamins and Hormones,* 19:230, 1961.

(2) Frieden, E. H., N. R. Stone, and N. W. Laymen, "Nonsteroid Ovarian Hormones: The Properties of Relaxin Preparations Purified by Counter Current Distribution," *J. Biol. Chem.,* 235:2267, 1960.

(3) Steinmetz, B. G., V. L. Beach and R. L. Kroc, "Relaxin," in R. I. Dorfman (ed.), *Methods in Hormone Res.,* 2:559, 1962.

I. INTRODUCTION

Problems related to oxidation-reductions continue to occupy a central and highly active field in biochemical research. About 1780, the term *oxidation* was defined by Lavoisier as the addition of an oxygen atom to the substrate being oxidized, and *reduction* was defined as the opposite process— removal of oxygen from an oxide. For example:

$$2 \text{ HCHO} + O_2 \rightarrow 2 \text{ HCOOH}$$

On the other hand, many reactions which are termed oxidations do not involve oxygen, such as

$$Cl_2 + 2 \text{ FeCl}_2 \rightarrow 2 \text{ FeCl}_3$$

In this example, the ferrous ion has been "oxidized" to the ferric state, without using oxygen. Here oxidation involves the loss of an electron:

$$Fe^{++} \rightarrow Fe^{+++} + e(-)$$

In the same reaction, chlorine was reduced; it gained an electron. To accommodate this broader application of the terminology, we can state that oxidation refers to a decrease and reduction refers to an increase in the number of electrons possessed by a substance. It need not involve the removal of oxygen or the addition of hydrogen. According to this definition, a metal in the presence of its ion is an oxidation-reduction system; *i.e.*,

$$Ag \underset{\text{reduction}}{\overset{\text{oxidation}}{\rightleftharpoons}} Ag^+ + e(-)$$

The power of a substance as an oxidizing agent depends upon its ability to take up and hold electrons. Conversely, the power of a substance as a reducing agent depends upon the readiness with which it releases electrons to other substances. Thus oxidation-reduction is a relative process.

II. ELECTRON POTENTIAL OR PRESSURES

The oxidation-reduction potential is a measure of the tendency of a substance to accept or donate electrons. In order to establish a potential at

Table I. Oxidation-Reduction Indicator Dyes
E_0 values (potentials of half reduced dyes) at pH 7.0

Dye	E_0 (volts)
Hydrogen electrode (1 atmosphere pressure)	−0.421
Viologens	−0.400
Rosindone sulphonate No. 6	−0.385
Neutral red	−0.325
Induline scarlet	−0.299
Safranine-T	−0.289
Tetramethyl phenosafranine	−0.273
Dimethyl phenosafranine	−0.260
Phenosafranine	−0.252
2-Methyl-3, hydroxy-1: 4 naphthoquinone (phthicol)	−0.180
Brilliant alizarine blue	−0.173
Gallophenine	−0.142
Indigo disulphonate	−0.125
Indigo trisulphonate	−0.081
Methyl capri blue	−0.060
Indigo tetrasulphonate	−0.046
Ciba scarlet sulphonate	−0.036
Methylene blue	+0.011
Gallocyanine	+0.021
Cresyl blue	+0.047
Prune	+0.056
Thionine (Lauth's violet)	+0.063
Toluylene blue	+0.115
1-Naphthol-2-sulphonate indo-2: 6-dichlorophenol	+0.119
1-Naphthol-2-sulphonate indophenol	+0.123
m-Toluylenediamine indophenol	+0.125
2: 6-Dibromophenol indo-guanacol	+0.159
Thymol indophenol	+0.174
2: 6-Dichlorophenol indo-o-cresol	+0.181
o-Cresol indophenol	+0.191
m-Cresol indophenol	+0.208
2: 6-Dichlorophenol indophenol	+0.217
2: 6-Dibromophenol indophenol	+0.218
2: 6-Dichlorophenol indo-o-chlorophenol	+0.219
Phenol blue	+0.224
Bindschedler's green	+0.224
Phenol indophenol	+0.227
o-Bromophenol indophenol	+0.230
o-Chlorophenol indophenol	+0.233
Phenol-o-sulphonate-indo-2: 6-dibromophenol	+0.242
m-Bromophenol indophenol	+0.248
m-Chlorophenol-indo-2: 6-dichlorophenol	+0.254
Phenol-m-sulphonate-indo-2: 6-dibromophenol	+0.273

Reproduced by permission from *Oxidation Reduction Potentials in Bacteriology and Biochemistry*, L. F. Hewitt, 1950, by E. S. Livingstone, England.

an inert electrode, there must be an electronic transfer. To compare the potentials of different oxidation-reduction systems, it is necessary to refer all potentials to a common standard, to which an arbitrary value under specified conditions is assigned. The standard reference electrode (also called the normal hydrogen electrode) consists of a platinum elec-

Table II. Normal Oxidation-Reduction Potentials of Ionic Systems at 25° C

Oxidation-Reduction System	Electrode Reaction	Normal Potential E_0 (Volts)
Co^{+++}—Co^{++}	$Co^{++} \rightleftarrows Co^{+++} + \varepsilon$	+1.817
Ce^{++++}—Ce^{+++}	$Ce^{+++} \rightleftarrows Ce^{++++} + \varepsilon$	+1.55
Cl_2—Cl^-	$Cl^- \rightleftarrows 1/2Cl_2 + \varepsilon$	+1.3583
Sn^{++++}—Sn^{++}	$Sn^{++} \rightleftarrows Sn^{++++} + 2\varepsilon$	+1.256
Tl^{+++}—Tl^+	$Tl^+ \rightleftarrows Tl^{+++} + 2\varepsilon$	+1.211
Br_2—Br^-	$Br^- \rightleftarrows 1/2Br_2 + \varepsilon$	+1.0648
Hg_2^{++}—Hg^+	$1/2Hg_2^{++} \rightleftarrows Hg^+ + \varepsilon$	+0.9011
O_2(1 atm)—OH^- (pH 7)	$OH^- \rightleftarrows 1/2H_2O + 1/4O_2 + \varepsilon$	+0.810
Fe^{+++}—Fe^{++}	$Fe^{++} \rightleftarrows Fe^{+++} + \varepsilon$	+0.7477
MnO_4^-—$MnO_4^=$	$MnO_4^= \rightleftarrows MnO_4^- + \varepsilon$	+0.664
I_2—I^-	$I^- \rightleftarrows 1/2I_2 + \varepsilon$	+0.5345
$Fe(CN)_6^{4-}$—$Fe(CN)_6^{3-}$	$Fe(CN)_6^{4-} \rightleftarrows Fe(CN)_6^{3-} + \varepsilon$	+0.4866
Cu^{++}—Cu^+	$Cu^+ \rightleftarrows Cu^{++} + \varepsilon$	+0.455
Ti^{+++}—Ti^{++}	$Ti^{++} \rightleftarrows Ti^{+++} + \varepsilon$	+0.37
H_2 (1 atm)—H^+	$1/2H_2 \rightleftarrows H^+ + \varepsilon$	0.0000 (reference electrode)

trode, under one atmosphere of hydrogen pressure, immersed in a hydrogen ion solution containing an effec've activity of one symbol weight per 1,000 g solvent. The potential of the metal electrode, immersed in unit concentration of its ions, when connected with a normal hydrogen electrode, is called the "standard" or "normal" electrode potential of the metal. In an oxidation-reduction system, when the activity of the oxidized form is equal to that of the reduced form, the potential is designated by E_0. This is defined as the standard oxidation-reduction potential; it is used to compare oxidation-reduction systems with one another.

Oxidation-reduction potential depends on three conditions: 1) the innate tendency of a system to take up or give up electrons; 2) the ratio of the oxidant to the reductant; and 3) the hydrogen ion concentration.

Oxidation-reduction potentials can be determined by the use of indicators or by the electrometric method. For various reasons, indicators are less reliable in measurement of oxidation-reduction than for the measurement of pH. Therefore electrometric methods, which are much broader and more exacting, should be used whenever possible. The indicator method has proved of value in the study of living cells, but it has not as yet been possible to devise an electrode which would not injure the cell. Table I gives E_0 values for some of the oxidation-reduction dyes.

The potential of an oxidation-reduction system can be determined if that system can accept or yield electrons reversibly at metallic electrodes, and one-termed electromotively active systems. Table II gives the normal potential value for a number of ionic reversible oxidation-reduction systems and Table III gives ionization potentials of the elements.

Table III. Ionization Potentials of the Elements*

Element	I	II	III	IV	V
1 H	13.527	—	—	—	—
2 He	24.46	54.14	—	—	—
3 Li	5.363	75.26	121.8	—	—
4 Be	9.28	18.12	153.1	216.6	—
5 B	8.257	25.00	37.75	258.1	338.5
6 C	11.217	24.27	47.65	64.22	390.1
7 N	14.48	29.47	47.40	77	97.43
8 O	13.550	34.93	54.87	76.99	113
9 F	17.34	34.81	62.35	86.72	113.67
10 Ne	21.45	40.9	63.2	—	—
11 Na	5.12	47.06	70.72	—	—
12 Mg	7.61	14.96	79.72	108.9	—
13 Al	5.96	18.74	28.31	119.37	153.4
14 Si	8.12	16.27	33.35	44.89	165.6
15 P	10.9	19.56	30.0	—	64.70
16 S	10.30	23.3	34.9	47.08	63
17 Cl	12.952	23.67	39.69	53.16	67.4
18 A	15.68	27.76	40.75	~61	~78
19 K	4.318	31.66	46.5	—	—
20 Ca	6.09	11.82	50.96	69.7	—
21 Sc	~6.7	~12.8	24.61	~73.9	97.0
22 Ti	6.81	~13.6	~27.6	42.98	~99.6
23 V	6.71	14.1	~26.4	~48	~65
24 Cr	6.74	~16.6	—	—	~73
25 Mn	7.41	15.70	—	—	~76
26 Fe	7.83	16.16	—	—	—
27 Co	7.81	17.3	—	—	—
28 Ni	7.61	18.2	—	—	—
29 Cu	7.68	20.2	—	—	—
30 Zn	9.36	17.89	40.0	—	—
31 Ga	5.97	20.43	~30.6	63.8	—
32 Ge	8.09	15.86	34.07	45.5	93.0
33 As	10.5	20.1	28.0	49.9	62.5
34 Se	9.70	21.3	33.9	42.72	72.8
35 Br	11.80	19.1	25.7	—	—
36 Kr	13.93	~26.4	36.8	~68	—
37 Rb	4.159	27.36	~47	~80	—
38 Sr	5.667	10.98	—	—	—
39 Y	~6.5	12.3	20.4	—	—
40 Zr	6.92	13.97	24.00	33.8	—
41 Nb	—	—	24.2	—	49.3
42 Mo	7.35	—	—	—	60.8
45 Rh	7.7	—	—	—	—
46 Pd	8.3	19.8	—	—	—
47 Ag	7.54	21.4	35.9	—	—
48 Cd	8.96	16.84	38.0	—	—

* Values are expressed in volts. Uncertain values are indicated by ~.

Table III. Ionization Potentials of the Elements* (Continued)

Element	I	II	III	IV	V
49 In	5.76	18.79	27.9	57.8	—
50 Sn	7.30	~14.5	30.5	39.4	80.7
51 Sb	—	~18	24.7	44.0	55.5
52 Te	8.96	—	30.5	37.7	60.0
53 I	10.6	19.4	—	—	—
54 Xe	12.08	~21.1	32.0	~46	~76
55 Cs	3.87	23.4	~35	~51	~58
56 Ba	5.19	9.95	—	—	—
57 La	5.6	11.4	20.4	—	—
58 Ce	6.54	14.8	—	~36.5	—
62 Sm	—	11.4	—	—	—
63 Eu	5.64	11.4	—	—	—
76 Os	~8.7	—	—	—	—
78 Pt	8.88	—	—	—	—
79 Au	9.18	19.95	—	—	—
80 Hg	10.38	18.65	34.3	~72	82
81 Tl	6.07	20.32	29.7	50.5	—
82 Pn	7.38	14.96	~31.9	42.11	69.4
83 Bi	—	16.6	25.42	45.1	55.7
86 Rn	10.698	—	—	—	—
88 Ra	5.252	10.099	—	—	—
90 Th	—	—	29.4	—	—

*Values are expressed in volts. Uncertain values are indicated by ~.

Wendell M. Latimer, *The Oxidation States of the Elements and their Potentials in Aqueous Solutions*, © 1938. Reprinted by permission of Prentice-Hall, Inc., Englewood Cliffs, New Jersey.

The general expression for the oxidation-reduction potential is given by the equation: —

$$E = E_0 + \frac{Rt}{nF} \log e \frac{(Oxidant)}{(Reductant)}$$

E_0 + a constant, represents the electrode potential when:

$$\frac{(Oxidant)}{(Reductant)} = 1$$

Oxidant and Reductant are substituted for the oxidizing and reducing agents, respectively.

E = observed difference in potential (in volts)

R = the gas constant (8.314 absolute joules per degree per mole)

t = absolute temperature

n = number of electrons per gram equivalent

F = is the faraday (96,496 absolute joules per absolute volt equivalent) and is defined as the amount of electricity (in ampere seconds) required to liberate the one gram equivalent of a univalent element in electrolysis.

When H^+ is involved in the oxidation-reduction system, the electrode potential is given by the expression:

$$E = E_0 + \frac{Rt}{nF} \log e \frac{(oxidant)}{(reductant)} + \frac{Rt}{F} \log e (H^+)$$

Since $pH = -\log_{10} (H^+)$

$$E = E_0 = 2.303 \frac{Rt}{2F} \log_{10} \frac{(oxidant)}{(reductant)} - 2.303 \frac{Rt}{F} pH$$

Standard temperature and pressures are required for this determination. In Table IV, some of the pH relations of oxidation-reduction potentials are given for various types of oxidation-reduction systems. Table V gives the normal electrode potentials and designates E_0 for a number of metallic electrodes. Electrodes having higher electron pressure than the standard hydrogen electrode are negative, and those with lower electron pressures are positive.

III. BIOLOGICAL OXIDATION

The measurement of oxidation-reduction (redox) potentials has not proved to be a very convenient tool for biological investigations. Table VI shows the normal electrode potentials of some oxidation-reduction systems of biochemical interest and Table VII gives the electrode potentials of reversible systems occurring in biological fluids. Biological oxidations occur in water solutions, usually between pH 6 and 8, at relatively low temperatures. In its simplest term, physiological oxidation deals with the removal of hydrogen from the substrate and the combining of it with molecular oxygen to form water or hydrogen peroxide. It is doubtful whether the living cell carries out this process in such a simple direct fashion. Many investigations show that the oxidation process in tissues is often a long and complex chain phenomenon. Four different types of reaction systems are involved in cellular oxidations. Their fundamental role in biologic oxidation can be summarized as follows:

Dehydrogenases are specific enzymes activating the hydrogen of the substrate so that the hydrogen can be removed from its substrate to a proton acceptor.

A hydrogen transport system transfers the hydrogen removed from the substrate to the oxidase enzymes.

Table IV. pH Relations of Oxidation-Reduction Systems

n Valence Change or H Atoms Involved	k Cations Created by Dehydrogenation	Examples	Equation	Increase in E_0 per Unit Increase in pH (30°) (Volts)	Increase in E per Unit Increase in log $\frac{[ox]}{[red]}$ (Volts)
1	1	Cytochrome Fe⁺⁺—Fe⁺⁺⁺	$E = E_0 + \frac{RT}{F} \ln^* \frac{[ox]}{[red]}$	0.0	0.06
2	0	Quinone-hydroquinone (below pH 8)	$E = E_0 + \frac{RT}{2F} \ln \frac{[ox]}{[red]} + \frac{RT}{F} \ln[H^+]$	−0.06	0.03
2	1	Lactate-pyruvate (above pH 7) Yellow enzyme MB-MBH₂ (above pH 6) TPN; DPN** (below pH 9)	$E = E_0 + \frac{RT}{2F} \ln \frac{[ox]}{[red]} + \frac{RT}{2F} \ln[H^+]$	−0.03	0.03
2	−1	Acetaldehyde-acetate (above pH 7) MB-MBH₂ (below pH 5)	$E = E_0 + \frac{RT}{2F} \ln \frac{[ox]}{[red]} + \frac{3RT}{2F} \ln[H^+]$	−0.09	0.03
2	2	Sn⁺⁺—Sn⁺⁺⁺⁺	$E = E_0 + \frac{RT}{2F} \ln \frac{[ox]}{[red]}$	0.0	0.03
n	k	—	$E = E_0 + \frac{RT}{nF} \ln \frac{[ox]}{[red]} + \frac{[n-k]RT}{nF} \ln[H^+]$	$\frac{0.06[k-n]}{n}$	$\frac{0.06}{n}$

*n = log of n.

**TPN = triphosphopyridine nucleotide = coenzyme II.

DPN = diphosphopyridine nucleotide = coenzyme I.

$E_0' = E_0 +$ the factor involving H⁺.

Reproduced by permission from *Textbook of Biochemistry* by E. S. West and W. R. Todd, 1961, by Macmillan Company.

Table V. Standard Potentials of Some Typical Electrode Reactions at 25°

Electrode	Electrode Reaction	Standard Potential at 25°
Li^+, Li	$Li \rightarrow Li^+ + \varepsilon$	−2.9595
Rb^+, Rb	$Rb \rightarrow Rb^+ + \varepsilon$	−2.9259
K^+, K	$K \rightarrow K^+ + \varepsilon$	−2.9241
Ca^{++}, Ca	$Ca \rightarrow Ca^{++} + 2\varepsilon$	−2.763
Na^+, Na	$Na \rightarrow Na^+ + \varepsilon$	−2.7146
Mg^{++}, Mg (18°)	$Mg \rightarrow Mg^{++} + 2\varepsilon$	−1.866
(Pt); $PbSO_4(s)$, $PbO_2(s)$, $SO_4=$	$PbSO_4 + H_2O \rightarrow PbO_2 + 4H^+ + SO_4= + 2\varepsilon$	−1.685
(Pt); Ce^{+++}, Ce^{++++}	$Ce^{+++} \rightarrow Ce^{++++} + 2\varepsilon$	−1.609
(Pt); $MnO_2(s)$, MnO_4^-	$MnO_2 + 2H_2O \rightarrow MnO_4 + 4H^+ + 3\varepsilon$	−1.586
Pb; $PbO_2(s)$, Pb^{++}	$Pb^{++} + 2H_2O \rightarrow PbO_2 + 4H^+ + 2\varepsilon$	−1.467
Au; $Au_2O_3(s)$, H^+	$2Au + 3H_2O \rightarrow Au_2O_3 + 6H^+ + 6\varepsilon$	−1.36$_0$
(Pt); $MnO_2(s)$, Mn^{++}	$Mn^{++} + 2H_2O \rightarrow MnO_2 + 4H^+ + 2\varepsilon$	−1.236
(Pt); Hg_2^{++}, Hg^{++}	$Hg_2^+ \rightarrow 2Hg^{++} + 2\varepsilon$	−0.906
(Pt); Fe^{++}, Fe^{+++}	$Fe^{++} \rightarrow Fe^{+++} + \varepsilon$	−0.783
Zn^{++}, Zn	$Zn \rightarrow Zn^{++} + 2\varepsilon$	−0.7618
Fe^{++}, Fe	$Fe \rightarrow Fe^{++} + 2\varepsilon$	−0.441
(Pt); Cu^+, Cu^{++}	$Cu^+ \rightarrow Cu^{++} + \varepsilon$	−0.159
Sb; $Sb_2O_3(s)$, H^+	$2Sb + 3H_2O \rightarrow Sb_2O_3 + 6H^+ + 6\varepsilon$	−0.1445
Sn^{++}, Sn	$Sn \rightarrow Sn^{++} + 2\varepsilon$	−0.136
Pb^{++}, Pb	$Pb \rightarrow Pb^{++} + 2\varepsilon$	−0.122
Hg; HgO(s), OH^-	$Hg + 2OH^- \rightarrow HgO + H_2O + 2\varepsilon$	−0.0976
(Pt)$H_2(g)$; H^+	$H_2 \rightarrow 2H^+ + 2\varepsilon$	±0.0000
Cu^{++}, Cu	$Cu \rightarrow Cu^{++} + 2\varepsilon$	+0.3441
Pb; PbO(s), OH^-	$Pb + 2OH^- \rightarrow PbO + H_2O + 2\varepsilon$	+0.5785
Ag^+, Ag	$Ag \rightarrow Ag^+ + \varepsilon$	+0.7978
Hg_2^+, Hg	$2Hg \rightarrow Hg_2^+ + 2\varepsilon$	+0.7986
(Pt)$H_2(g)$; $H_2O(l)$, OH^-	$H_2 + 2OH^- \rightarrow H_2O + 2\varepsilon$	+0.8279
Au^{+++}, Au	$Au \rightarrow Au^{+++} + 3\varepsilon$	+1.36

Oxidase enzymes activate the oxygen in the tissue so that it will quickly oxidize the hydrogen supplied by the hydrogen transport system.

Peroxidases destroy the peroxide that may be formed. The processes of carboxylation and hydration are often important supplementary stages in biologic oxidation.

IV. ELECTRON TRANSPORT OF MITOCHONDRIA

It is clear that the major role of biological oxidations involves a series of oxidation-reduction systems arranged as an integrated chain in cell mito-chondria. Very recently, techniques have been developed to isolate the subunits of mitochondria called "electron-transport particles." Such procedures include sonic vibrations, dissolution with cholate, deoxycho-

Table VI. Normal Electrode Potentials of Some Oxidation-Reduction Systems of Biochemical Interest Values for pH 7

System	E_0'
Acetic acid + CO_2/pyruvic acid	-0.70
Succinic acid + CO_2/α-ketoglutaric acid	-0.67
Acetate + H^+/acetaldehyde	-0.60
Hydrogen/hydrogen ion	-0.420
Formate/carbon dioxide	-0.42
H^+/$1/2 H_2$	-0.42
Acetyl–S–CoA/acetaldehyde + HS–CoA ***	-0.41
Uric acid/xanthine	-0.36
Acetoacetic acid/β-hydroxybutyric acid	-0.35
Glutathione, G–S–SG/GSH*	-0.34
Pyruvic acid + CO_2/malic acid	-0.33
DPN^+/$DPN \cdot H + H^+$	-0.32
Diphosphopyridine nucleotide (oxidant)	-0.32
β-Hydroxybutyrate/acetoacetate	-0.293
1,3-Diphosphoglyceric acid/3-phosphoglyceraldehyde + Pi**	-0.29
Coenzyme I—reduced coenzyme I	-0.29
Riboflavin (oxidant)	-0.208
Alcohol/aldehyde	-0.20
Acetaldehyde/alcohol	-0.20
Pyruvic acid/lactic acid	-0.19
Lactate/pyruvate	-0.19
Phthiocol (oxidant)	-0.180
Oxaloacetic acid/malic acid	-0.17
Malate-oxaloacetate	-0.169
Malate-oxaloacetate	-0.166
Pyruvic acid + NH_4+/alanine	-0.13
Yellow enzyme (oxidant)	-0.123
Flavoprotein (old yellow enzyme) ox./red. ****	-0.12
Hemin Fe^{+++}/heme Fe^{++}	-0.114
Pyocyanine (oxidant)	-0.032
Cytochrome b Fe^{+++}/cytochrome b Fe^{++}	0.00
Succinate/fumarate	0.00
Methylene blue ox./red. ****	$+0.01$
Methylene blue (oxidant)	$+0.011$
Fumaric acid/succinic acid	$+0.03$
Myoglobin/metmyoglobin	$+0.046$
Ascorbic acid (reductant)	$+0.058$
Alloxan (oxidant)	$+0.062$
Dehydroascorbic acid/ascorbic acid	$+0.08$
Hemoglobin/methemoglobin	$+0.139$
Methemoglobin/hemoglobin	$+0.17$
Crotonyl–S–CoA/butyryl–S–CoA *****	$+0.19$
2,6-Dichlorophenolindophenol ox./red.****	$+0.22$
Ferrocytochrome c (reductant)	$+0.26$
Ferrocytochrome a (reductant)	$+0.29$
$1/2 O_2$/H_2O_2	$+0.30$
Ferricyanide/ferrocyanide	$+0.36$
Dopaquinone/dihydroxyphenylalanine	$+0.37$
3,4-Dihydroxy-L-phenylalanine (reductant)	$+0.38$
Epinephrine (reductant)	$+0.38$
NO^{3-}/NO_2^-	$+0.42$
Water/oxygen	$+0.815$
$1/2 O_2$/H_2O	$+0.82$

*G–S–S–G and GSH represent the oxidized and reduced forms, respectively.
**Pi represents inorganic phosphate, a mixture composed of $H_2PO_4^-$ and HPO_4^{--}.
***H–S–CoA represents coenzyme A. Crotonyl–S–CoA and butyryl–S–CoA, etc., represent the acyl derivatives of coenzyme A.
****Ox./red. represents oxidized form/reduced form.
*****H–S–CoA represents coenzyme A. Crotonyl–S–CoA and butyryl–S–CoA, etc., represent the acyl derivatives of coenzyme A.

Table VII. Electrode Potentials (at 50% Reduction) of Reversible Systems Occurring in Biological Fluids System is named by oxidant (o) or reductant (r). (pH = 7.0.)

System	Source	t(°C)	E_h at pH 7.0	E_h at pH 0
Hemocyanin (r)	Limulus polyphemus	?	0.54	—
Epinephrine (adrenaline) (r)	Adrenal medulla	30	0.38	0.809
3,4-dihydroxy-L-phenyl-alanine (r)	Intermediate, tyrosine to melanin	30	0.38	0.80
Cytochrome a (r)		20	0.29	—
Cytochrome c (r)	Beef heart	30	0.254	0.464
Homogentisic acid (r)	Urine of alkaptonuric	20	0.255	0.68
Urechrome	Urechis caupo	25	0.186	—
Methemoglobin (o)	Blood	30	0.139	—
Alloxan (o)	Possible component of animal tissues?	30	0.062	0.364
Ascorbic acid	Various fruits and animal tissues	30	0.058	0.390
Pigment of:	Penicillium phoeniceum	—	0.047	—
Metmyoglobin (o)	Horse heart	30	0.046	—
Juglone (o)	Walnuts	20	0.033	0.42
Raper's red substance (o)	Intermediate, tyrosine to melanin	17	0.033?	—
Hallachrome (r)	Halla parthenopea	19	0.026	0.44
Pigment of:	Arion rufus	—	0.025	—
Hermidin (r)	Mercurialis perennis	30	−0.032	0.366
Pyocyanine (o)	B. pyocyaneus	—	−0.034	see note
Vitamin K_1 (o)	Alfalfa	20	−0.04?	0.363
Cytochrome b (r)		20	−0.04	—
Toxoflavin	Bact. bongkrek	30	−0.049	0.337?
Phosphoriboflavin-protein		38	−0.06	0.37
Xanthine oxidase	Milk	—	−0.08 to −0.09	—
Pigment of:	Chromodoris zebra	30	−0.102	—
Chlororaphine (s.q.)	B. chlororaphis	29.5	−0.115	−0.274
Lawson (o)	Henna plant	20	−0.139	0.358
Phthiocol (o)	Tubercle bacillus	30	−0.180	0.299
Lapachol (o)	Variety of woods	30	−0.180	0.300
Lomatiol (o)	Seeds of Lomatia ilicifolia	30	−0.183	0.300
Riboflavin (o)	Animal and vegetable	30	−0.208	0.168?
A flavin	Liver	19.5	−0.209	0.177
Echinochrome	Arbacia punctulata	30	−0.221	0.200
Methyl flavin (lumiflavin) (o)	Action of light on riboflavin	30	−0.223	0.183
Hepatoflavin	Horse liver	30	−0.21	0.188

Reproduced by permission from Textbook of *Topics in Physical Chemistry*, by W. Mansfield Clark, 1952, by Williams and Wilkins Company.

late treatment with digitonin, extraction with organic solvents, and concentration by ultracentrifugation. The particles are about 1% the size of the intact mitochondria and many catalytic activities are lost during fragmentation (*e.g.*, the enzymes of the citric acid cycle). Even though many investigators, over a long period of time, have devoted their efforts to establishing its components and their mechanism of action, knowledge about the respiratory chain is still incomplete. But most of the components of the chain and their function appear to be rather well established, as shown in Figure 1.

Present research is concerned with the ultra structure of the respiratory chain. The position of the cytochrome c_1, c,a,a_3 and coenzymes system is well established. However, the relationship of the b system, composed of ferric ferroheme forms, to the electrode transport chain is uncertain.

V. OXIDATIVE PHOSPHORYLATION

At certain stages in the electron transport chain, some of the fine energy produced by oxidation is trapped and stored in the form of high-energy phosphates (ATP) for use in metabolic processes. This process has been termed *oxidative phosphorylation* and appears to be limited to the mitochondria. Its scheme is shown in Figure 1, where one mole of ATP is formed when FP oxidizes DPN · H. A second molecule is formed when cytochrome c^{+++} oxidizes cytochrome b^{++} through an intermediate carrier. A third molecule of ATP is formed in the oxidation of cytochrome c^{++}. In other words, one molecule of ATP can arise for each electron (or hydrogen) transferred between $NADH_2$ and flavoprotein, flavoprotein and cytochrome, and cytochrome c and oxygen. Measurements by various workers have confirmed the value 3 ATP per atom of oxygen. The quotient ATP formed per unit of oxygen consumed is commonly referred to as the P to O ratio. The P/O is 3 and applies only to substrates that are dehydrogenized by NAD. Succinate, oxidized directly by flavoprotein, yields only 2 moles, whereas cytochrome c yields only one mole of ATP. Surprisingly enough, it was found that the respiratory chain can run in the reverse direction with the consumption of ATP.

Various substances prevent the formation of ATP without interrupting the oxidative process. This phenomenon is termed the *uncoupling* of oxidative phosphorylation. There are many uncoupling agents, including methylene blue, brilliant cresyl blue, azide, dicoumarol, arsenite, pentachlorophenol and the antibiotics chlortetracycline, bacitracin and gramicidin. The most studied and frequently used uncoupling agent is 2,4-dinitrophenol (DNP).

$$\Delta E'_0 = 1.14 \text{ volts.} \quad -\Delta F^\circ = 1.14 \times 2 \times 96{,}500/4.18 = 52{,}636 \text{ cal. per mol of DPN} \cdot \text{H oxidized.}$$

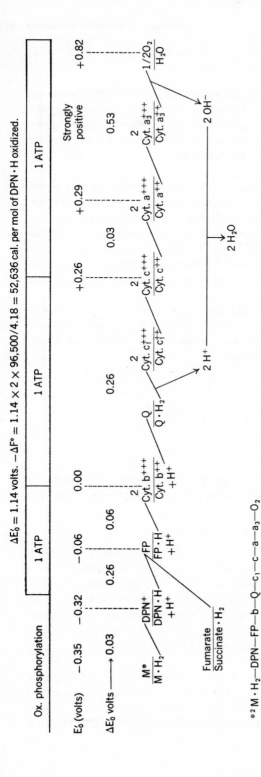

Figure 1

Diagram of the mitochondrial electron transport chain.

* The metabolite system, $M/M \cdot H_2$, indicated with an E'_0 of -0.35 volts, is oxaloacetate/malate. $Q/Q \cdot H_2$ represents the coenzyme Q system. $Cyt.b^{+++}$ represents ferricytochrome b and $cyt.b^{++}$ ferrocytochrome b. Representations for the other cytochromes are similar. The ferricytochromes are the oxidants of the systems and the ferrocytochromes the reductants. Two functional cytochrome groups are involved for each cytochrome system, since the oxidation of Fe^{++} to Fe^{+++} in the cytochromes is a one electron oxidation-reduction. The oxidation of succinate to fumarate in the chain is catalyzed by the enzyme succinic dehydrogenase, a flavoprotein, which also contains a protoheme group that appears to function as a part of the cytochrome b system. The electrons from succinate are accepted into the chain through the flavoprotein succinic dehydrogenase enzyme, which, thus, in its oxidized, FP, and reduced, $FP \cdot H_2$, forms constitutes an oxidation-reduction system. One molecule of ATP is formed in the oxidation of $DPN \cdot H$ by FP, another in the oxidation of ferrocytochrome b by ferricytochrome c, and a third in the oxidation of ferricytochrome c by either ferricytochrome a_3 or oxygen (uncertain). The oxidation of succinate in the chain forms only 2 molecules of ATP. The voltage difference between the oxygen and DPN systems (1.14 volts) represents 52,636 calories.

*² Simplified representation of the electron transport chain.

VI. OXIDOREDUCTASES

Oxidoreductases are the enzymes concerned with biological oxidation and reduction. They include dehydrogenases, oxidases, peroxidases, and hydroxylases, which introduce hydroxyl groups by means of a mechanism which is not fully established. The oxygenases introduce molecular oxygen in place of a double bond in the substrate.

Peroxidases or Hydroperoxidases.   The classical peroxidases are hemoproteins containing ferriprotoporphyrin IX (hemin) as the prosthetic group and are specific for peroxide. They use a wide range of substances as donors. They are common in plants and microorganisms, but their presence in animal tissues is rather limited. The peroxidases vary in molecular size but the presence of an iron atom is limited to one per mole. The coenzyme peroxidases are not hemoproteins; one, at least, is a flavoprotein.

Peroxidases oxidize many substrates including mono- and polyphenols, leucodyes, aromatic amines, cytochrome, nitrite, iodine, NADH and NADPH. An example of peroxidase action is the oxidation of hydroquinone by lacto peroxidase of milk.

Catalases.   The catalases are a specific type of hemin-containing hydroperoxidases, having the specific property of catalyzing the decomposition of hydrogen peroxide.

$$2\,H_2O_2 \rightarrow 2\,H_2O + O_2$$

Like other peroxidases, catalases form intermediate complexes during the composition of hydrogen peroxide. They are widely distributed in all living things, with the exception of some microorganisms. Crystalline catalases are prepared from such different sources as the liver of man, rat, pig, beef, horse, sheep, horse erythrocytes and kidney. Catalases have high activity rates; one catalase molecule decomposes over 2,000,000 molecules of hydrogen peroxide per minute.

Hydroxylases and Oxygenases.   Many—perhaps all—of the hydroxylases, unlike the oxygenases, require the presence of the reduced form of one of the co-enzymes, which is oxidized by molecular oxygen in the process. Details of the mechanism of this coupled oxidation are not well established. The hydroxylases are important in the metabolism of steroids and other cyclic compounds. The oxygenases, on the other hand, incorporate the whole oxygen molecule in the course of oxidative cleavage of a carbon-carbon double bond.

Oxidases. The oxidases are very often metalloproteins, containing metals such as iron, copper and molybdenum. Various oxidases are flavo-proteins; examples include xanthine, oxidase, aldehyde oxidase, and amino acid oxidase. Since the true oxidases catalyze oxidation of the sub-strate by molecular oxygen, they are also called *oxygenases*. Cytochrome oxidase may be the most important enzyme to react with oxygen, but it is not the only one. Today, three groups of enzymes are recognized which react with molecular oxygen.

1. Electron Transferoxidases.

There are many electron transferoxidases, such as uricase, xanthine oxidase, glucose oxidase, monamine oxidase, ascorbic oxidase and cyto-chrome oxidase. These enzymes act through a variety of prosthetic groups or cofactors, such as Fe, FAD, FMN, NADP, NAD, Mo and Cu. They catalyze the following reactions:

$$O_2 + 4e^- \rightarrow 2O^{--} \underset{}{\overset{+4H^+}{\rightleftharpoons}} 2H_2O$$

or

$$O_2 + 2e^- \rightarrow O_2^{--} \underset{}{\overset{+2H^+}{\rightleftharpoons}} H_2O_2$$

2. Oxygen Transferases.

These include pyrocatechase, homogentisate oxidase, tryptophan oxi-dase and indole oxidases, which oxidize various ring structures. For ex-ample: lipoxidase oxidizes methylene-interrupted, multiple-unsaturated fatty acids in which the double bonds have the *cis* configuration

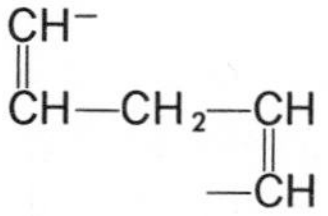

$$\begin{array}{c} CH^- \\ \| \\ CH-CH_2-CH \\ \quad \| \\ \quad -CH \end{array}$$

whereas homogentisate oxidase catalyzes the oxidation of homogentisic acid. The general reaction is:

$$A + O_2 \rightarrow AO_2$$

3. Mixed Function Oxidases.

These are commonly metalloproteins with prosthetic groups containing iron, copper, or manganese. Their activations are often inhibited by metal

Table VIII. Dehydrogenases that Catalyze Oxidation-Reduction Reactions between a Metabolite System and a Pyridine Nucleotide System

Enzyme and Source	Metabolite System	Specificity for DPN or TPN
Alcohol dehydrogenase		
(yeast)	CH_3CH_2OH/CH_3CHO	DPN
(liver)	$—CH_2OH/—CHO$	DPN
Aldehyde dehydrogenase		
(liver)	$—CHO/—COO^-$	DPN
(yeast)		$TPN > DPN$
Formaldehyde dehydrogenase (liver)	HCHO/Formate	DPN
Formic dehydrogenase (peas)	Formate/CO_2	DPN
Glucose dehydrogenase (liver)	D-Glucopyranose/D-Gluconolactone	DPN or TPN
Glucose-6-phosphate dehydrogenase	D-Glucopyranose-6-phosphate/6-Phospho-D-gluconolactone	TPN
Glutamic dehydrogenase	L-Glutamate/α-Ketoglutarate + NH‡	
(liver)		$DPN > TPN$
(higher plants)		DPN
(bacteria)		TPN
Glutathione reductase (plant and animal tissues)	Glutathione/Oxidized glutathione	$TPN > DPN$
Glyceraldehyde-3-phosphate dehydrogenase (muscle, yeast)	D-Glyceraldehyde-3-phosphate + phosphate/ D-1,3-Diphosphoglyceric acid	DPN
Glycerophosphate dehydrogenase (muscle)	L-α-Glycerophosphate/Dihydroxyacetone phosphate	DPN
Glyoxylic reductase (plants)	Glycolate/Glyoxylate	DPN
β-Hydroxyacyl-CoA dehydrogenase (liver)	L-β-Hydroxybutyryl-CoA/Acetoacetyl-CoA	DPN
β-Hydroxybutyric dehydrogenase (liver)	D-β-Hydroxybutyrate/Acetoacetate	DPN
β-Hydroxybutyryl-CoA dehydrogenase (liver)	D-β-Hydroxybutyryl-CoA/Acetoacetyl-CoA	DPN
Isocitric dehydrogenase	d-Isocitrate/Oxalosuccinate	
(heart)		TPN
(animal tissues)		DPN
(yeast)		DPN
Lactic dehydrogenase	L-Lactate/Pyruvate	
(heart)		$DPN > TPN$
(muscle, liver)		DPN
Malic dehydrogenase (muscle)	L-Malate/Oxaloacetate	$DPN > TPN$

Reproduced by permission from *General Biochemistry*, by Fruton and Simmons, 1961, by John Wiley and Sons, Inc.

binding agents. Two catalytic functions are performed by these enzymes: the reduction of an atom of oxygen to O^{--}, and the transfer of oxygen to the substrate. The operation of these oxidases thus requires not only O_2 but also an electron source, to reduce an atom of oxygen to O^{--}. Examples of mixed function oxidases are phenolase complex and imidazole acetic acid oxidase which are involved respectively in the formation of melanine and in the metabolism of histidine. The general reaction for this group is:

$$AH + DH_2 + O_2 \rightarrow AOH + D + H_2O$$

Here, AH is the substrate and DH_2, the hydrogen donor.

Dehydrogenases. Warburg's oxygen activation theory was followed by Wieland's hydrogen activation theory, which describes the activation of atoms of the metabolite by the dehydrogenase enzyme, and the removal of the active hydrogen by acceptors. Dehydrogenase enzymes are specific in their activity; most of the pyridine nucleotide-dependent dehydro-genases are relatively specific for the NAD system, and others are specific for NADP system; for some enzymes of this group, either nucleotide system is effective. Some of the more common dehydrogenases, together with the metabolite system with which they are usually associated, plus the specificity for the pyridine nucleotide system, are given in Table VIII.

The most important single property of these co-enzymes is their ability to undergo reversible oxido-reductions. In the presence of the specific dehydrogenase, hydrogen atoms are transferred between substrate and coenzyme. The process involves a direct transfer of one of the hydrogen atoms from the substrate to the pyridine nucleotide in a stereochemically specific manner. The other hydrogen is released in solution as H^+ ion.

$$\text{Substrate-}H_2 + NAD^+ \rightleftharpoons \text{Substrate} + NADH + H^+$$

BIBLIOGRAPHY

1. Adler, E., and M. Sreenivasaya, "Uber die Komponenten der Dehydrase-systeine," *Hoppe-Seylers Z.*, 249:24, 1937.
2. Andrews, L. V., and D. J. Brown, "The Oxidation Potential of the Alkaline Permanganate-Manganese Dioxide Electrode," *J. Am. Chem. Soc.*, 57:254, 1935.
3. Baldwin, E., *Dynamic Aspects of Biochemistry*, 1947.
4. Ball, E. G., "Studies on Oxidation-Reduction," *J .Biol. Chem.*, 118:219, 1937.
5. Ball, E. G., "Uber die Oxydation und Reduktion der drei Cytochrom-Kom-ponenten," *Biochem. Z.*, 295:262, 1938.
6. Ball, E. G., and T. T. Chen, "Studies on Oxidation-Reduction, Epinephrine and Related Compounds," *J. Biol. Chem.*, 102:691, 1933.
7. Barron, G., "Cellular Oxidation Systems," *Physiol. Rev.*, 19:184, 1939.
8. Barron, G., and Hastings, "Studies on Biological Oxidations, III. The Oxida-tion-Reduction Potential of the System Lactate-Enzyme Pyruvate," *J. Biol. Chem.*, 107:567, 1934.

9. Bary, H. G., and K. White, *Kinetics and Thermodynamics in Biochemistry,* 1957.

10. Brown, D. J., and H. A. Liebhafsky, "The Manganous-Manganese Dioxide and the Manganous-Permanganate Electrodes," *J. Am. Chem. Soc.,* 52:2595, 1936.

11. Brown, D. J., and R. F. Tefft, "The Manganese Dioxide-Permanganate Electrode," *J. Am. Chem. Soc.,* 48:1128, 1926.

12. Brown, D. J., and J. C. Zimmer, "The Oxidation Potential of Lead Dioxide Electrode in Perchloric Acid Solution," *J. Am. Chem. Soc.,* 52:1, 1930.

13. Bull, H. B., *Physical Biochemistry,* 1951.

14. Clark, N. M., *Topics in Physical Chemistry,* 1952.

15. Dakin, H. D., *Oxidations and Reductions in Animal Body,* 1912.

16. Dixon, M., and E. C. Webb, *Enzymes,* 1964.

17. Ernster, K., and Chaum-pu-Lee, "Biological Oxidations," *Ann. Rev. Biochem.,* 33:729, 1964.

18. Florkin, M., and H. S. Mason, *Comparative Biochemistry,* Vol. 1, 1960.

19. Friedhein, E. A. H., "Natural Reversible Oxidation Reduction Systems as Accessory Catalysts in Respiration," *Biochem. J.,* 28:180, 1934.

20. Fruton, J. S., and S. Simmonds, *General Biochemistry,* 1961.

21. Gerke, R. H., and M. D. Rourke, "The Potential of the Gold-Auric Oxide Electrode," *J. Am. Chem. Soc.,* 49:1855, 1927.

22. Green, D. E., *Mechanisms of Biological Oxidations,* 1941.

23. Green, D. E., J. G. Dewan, and L. F. Leloir, "The B-Hydroxybutyric Dehydrogenase of Animal Tissues," *Biochem. J.,* 31:934, 1937.

24. Hamer, W. J., "The Potential of the Lead Dioxide—Lead Sulfate Electrode at Various Temperatures," *J. Am. Chem. Soc.,* 57:9, 1935.

25. Hewitt, L. F., *Oxidation Reduction Potentials in Bacteriology and Biochemistry,* 6th ed., 1950.

26. Horowitz, N. H., and J. P. Baumberger, "Studies in Respiratory Pigment of Erechis Eggs," *J. Biol. Chem.,* 141:407, 1941.

27. Karlson, P., *Introduction to Modern Biochemistry,* 1963.

28. Laki, K., "Uber das Redoxpotential des Systems: Oxalessigsaure-1-Apfelsaure," *Hoppe-Seylers Z.,* 249:63, 1937.

29. Latimer, W. M., *The Oxidation States of the Elements and their Potentials in Aqueous Solutions,* 1938.

30. MacInnes, D. A., *The Principles of Biochemistry,* 1939.

31. Michaelis, L., and M. P. Schubert, "The Theory of Reversible Two-step Oxidation Involving Free Radicals," *Chem. Rev.,* 22:437, 1938.

32. Michaelis, L., and C. V. Smythe, "The Correlation Between Rate of Oxidation and Potential in Iron Systems," *J. Biol. Chem.,* 94:329, 1931.

33. Michaelis, L. and C. V. Smythe, "Biological Oxidations and Reductions," *Ann. Rev. Biochem.,* 7:1, 1938.

34. Noyes, A. A., and C. S. Garner, "Strong Oxidizing Agents in Nitric Acid Solution. I. Oxidation Potential of Cerous-Ceric Salts," *J. Am. Chem. Soc.,* 58:1265, 1936.

35. Popoff, S., J. A. Riddick, V. I. Wirth and L. D. Ough, "Oxidation-Reduction Potentials. III. The Mercuric-Mercurous Electrode," *J. Am. Chem. Soc.,* 53:1195, 1931.

36. Richardson, G. M., and R. K. Cannon, "The Dialuric Acid-Alloxan Equilibrium," *Biochem. J.,* 23:68, 1929.

37. Riegel, B., P. G. Smith and C. E. Schweitzer, "The Oxidation-Reduction Potential of Vitamin K," *J. Am. Chem. Soc.,* 62:992, 1940.

38. Roberts, E. J., and F. Fenwick, "The Antimony-Antimony Trioxide Electrode and its Use as a Measure of Acidity," *J. Am. Chem. Soc.,* 50:2125, 1928.

39. Rodkey, F. L., and E. G. Ball, "Oxidation-Reduction Potential of the Cytochrome c System," *J. Biol. Chem.*, 182:17, 1950.

40. Schlenk, Hellstrom and Eyler, "Desamino, Cozymase," *Ber. Chem. Ges.*, 71:1471, 1938.

41. Schumb, W. C. and S. B. Sweetser, "The Equilibrium of the Reaction Between Ferric Ion and Silver," *J. Am. Chem. Soc.*, 57:871, 1935.

42. Shaffer, P. A., "Catalysis of Ionic Oxidation-Reduction Reaction by Dyes to its Soluble Mechanism," *J. Phys. Chem.*, 40:1021, 1936.

43. Smith, D. F., and H. K. Woods, "The Free Energy and Heat of Formation of Lead Monoxide," *J. Am. Chem. Soc.*, 45:2632, 1923.

44. Stare, F. J., "A Potentiometric Study of Hepotoflavin," *J. Biol. Chem.*, 112:223, 1935.

45. Stern, K. G., "Oxidation-Reduction Potentials of Toxoflavin," *Biochem. J.*, 29:500, 1935.

46. Taylor, J. F., and A. B. Hastings, "Oxidation-Reduction Potentials of the Methemoglobin-Hemoglobin System," *J. Biol. Chem.*, 131:649, 1939.

47. Taylor, J. F., and V. E. Morgan, "Oxidation Reduction Potentials of the Metmyoglobin-Myoglobin System," *J. Biol. Chem.*, 144:15, 1942.

48. West, E. S., and Todd, W. R., *Text Book of Biochemistry*, 1961.

I. HISTORICAL INTRODUCTION AND NATURAL OCCURRENCE

I. Introduction.   Porphyrins exist in nature in free and combined states. In the free form they occur, usually in small amounts, in both the animal and vegetable kingdoms but do not appear to possess any significant biological function. As metal chelates, on the contrary, they give rise to the two essential groups of pigment of living matter: the hemes, iron-porphyrin complexes and the chlorophylls, magnesium porphyrin complexes.

The first reference to porphyrin was made by Scherer (1841)[1] who found that, upon addition of concentrated sulfuric acid to powdered hemoglobin, an iron-free residue could be obtained which acquired a bright red color by heating with alcohol. This red substance was called "iron-free hematin" by Mulder (1844)[2] and "Cruentine" by Thudichum (1867)[3]. Thudichum first described the absorption spectrum of this compound which Hoppe-Seyler soon designated "hematoporphyrin." In 1880, by treating chlorophyll with alkali, Hoppe-Seyler[4] obtained a substance with an absorption spectrum similar to hematoporphyrin, thus first suggesting the existence of a relationship between heme and chlorophyll.

Nencki and co-workers[5, 6] first crystallized hematoporphyrin by treatment of hemin with hydrobromic acid in glacial acetic acid. It was thus the first porphyrin to be isolated in relatively pure form. It is doubtful, however, that it had been fully purified. In the first few years after its recognition, it was thought to be isomeric with bilirubin and was regarded as the porphyrin of the excreta. Thus the terms "Hematoporphyria" or "Porphyrinuria" came to be widely applied to genetic and acquired disease states respectively. As is now well known, these terms are misnomers and hematoporphyrin is not encountered in nature. In 1901, Nencki and Zaleski[7] prepared mesoporphyrin by treating hemin with hydriodic acid. As noted below, the mesoporphyrins are of much importance in the classification of porphyrins but of minor significance in terms of natural occurrence.

In the early part of this century a series of basic studies carried out by a number of investigators (Nencki, Marchlewski, Küster, Willstätter, Fischer[8, 9, 10]) led to the elucidation of the chemistry of porphyrins and to the formulation of the basic tetrapyrrole structure of these compounds. Heme and chlorophyll were recognized as being iron and magnesium porphyrin complexes respectively (Willstätter).

Subsequent investigations, particularly by Fischer and co-workers,[9] on the composition of the side chains and their position relative to each other, laid the basis for the classification of porphyrins and their isomers.

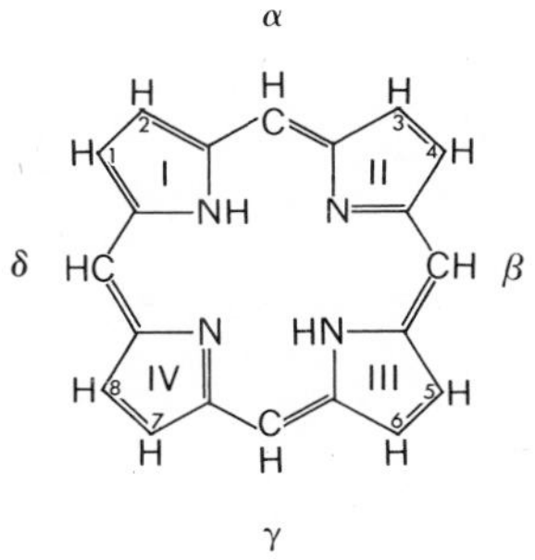

Porphin

Figure 1.　Structure of porphin.

II. Structures of Etioporphyrins I, II, III, IV.　All porphyrins are macrocyclic compounds derived from a porphin skeleton by substitution of some or all $\beta\beta'$ hydrogen atoms numbered 1–8, by various groups. As seen in Fig. 1, the synthetic porphin, a compound which has not been found in nature, is composed of four pyrrole derivatives (I, II, III, IV) joined together by four methene bridges (α, β, γ, δ). Porphin is composed of 20 carbon and 4 nitrogen atoms connected by alternating single and double bonds.

This configuration was actually first proposed by Küster[11] as early as 1912 but was held unlikely by others on the ground that such a large ring would be unstable. It was only in 1929 that Fischer and Zeile[12] conclusively proved it by the total synthesis of hemin. The presence of alternating single and double bonds in the aromatic ring provides a stabilizing resonating structure relatively resistant to chemical attack. Crystallographic studies have revealed that the porphyrin ring can be regarded as an essentially flat, almost square molecule, approximately 8.5 Å in diameter and 4.7 Å in thickness.[13]

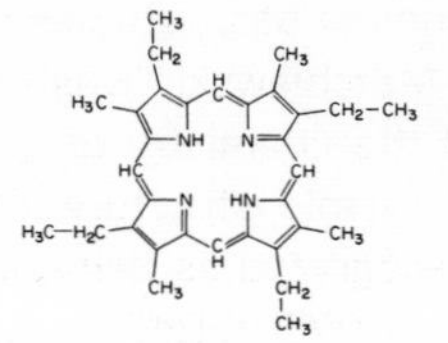

Etioporphyrin I

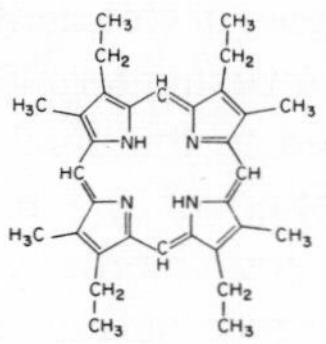

Etioporphyrin II

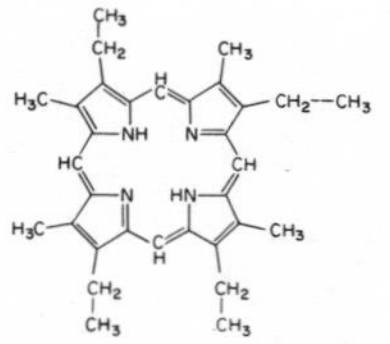

Etioporphyrin III

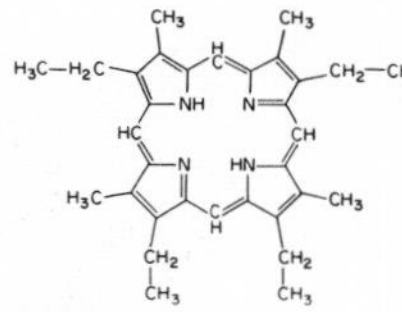

Etioporphyrin IV

Figure 2.   Structures of the four etioporphyrins.

Substitution of all β positions of porphin with two dissimilar groups results in the formation of four possible position isomers. Fischer synthesized the four isomers of a porphyrin having —CH_3 and —C_2H_5 β substituents and called them etioporphyrins, series I, II, III and IV (Figure 2). He suggested that all porphyrins be referred to these synthetic compounds, which do not occur in biological systems, for assignment of isomeric series. Any one of the four isomeric series may include more than one isomer type of a porphyrin with more than two dissimilar β substituents. Porphyrins with three unlike β radicals are designated with the appropriate Roman numeral for isomer type identification as is the etio- series. For example, of the 15 isomeric protoporphyrins (see below) type IX, series III, is that found in nature.

III. Structures of Uroporphyrin and Coproporphyrin I and III and Protoporphyrin IX (III).

H. Fischer first isolated uroporphyrin from the urine and coproporphyrin from the feces of a case of congenital porphyria. They were demonstrated to be series I porphyrins, while the protoporphyrin of this individual's hemoglobin, as in the normal, was Type IX(III). This was the basis of Fischer's "dualism" of the porphyrins in nature, subsequently shown to be of general significance.

The uroporphyrins and coproporphyrins are respectively tetraacetate, tetrapropionate porphin and tetramethyl tetrapropionate porphin (Figure 3). Although it was soon recognized, as mentioned above, that two of the four possible isomers are represented in nature (Series I and III),

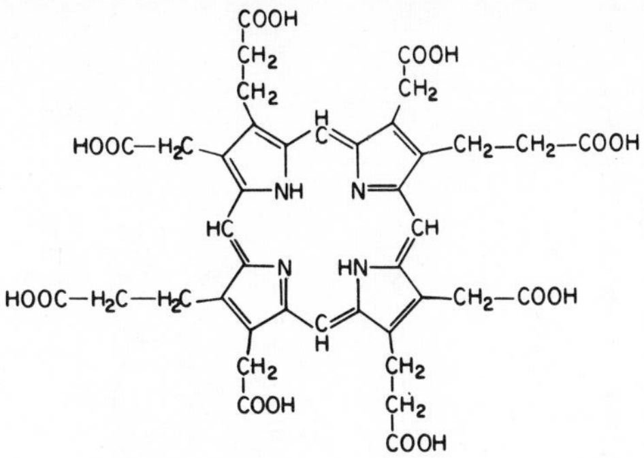

Uroporphyrin III

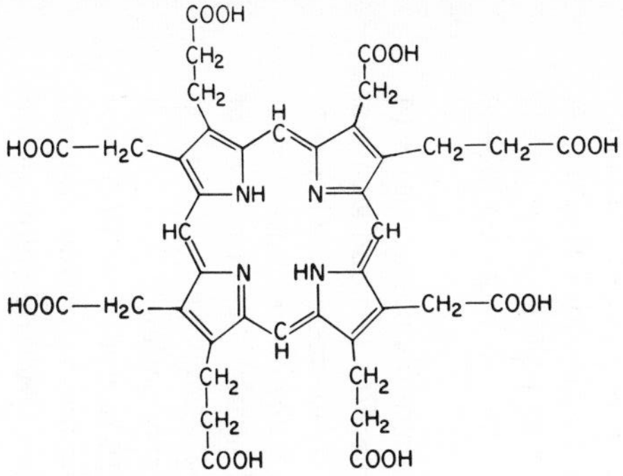

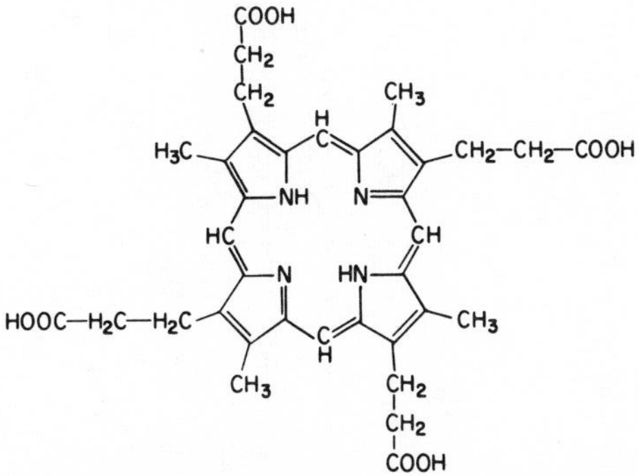

Uroporphyrin I

Coproporphyrin III

Coproporphyrin I

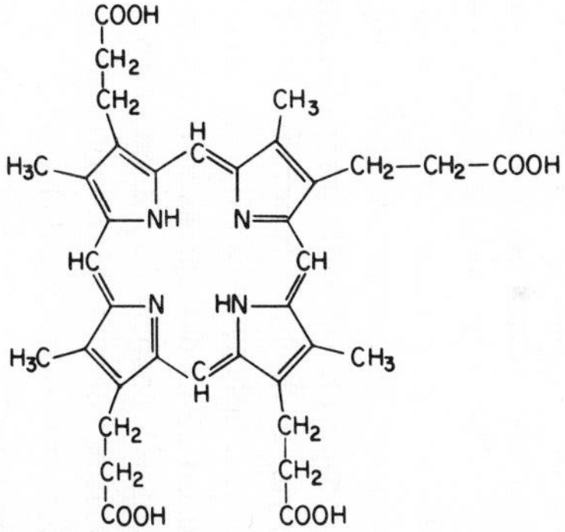

Figure 3.   Structures of uroporphyrins I and III and coproporphyrins I and III.

it later became apparent that all physiologically active tetrapyrroles belong to the etio- series III, the series I porphyrins being products of the biosynthetic pathway or the result of a derangement in the biosynthesis of porphyrins as in the genetic error represented by various forms of porphyria.

Fischer's choice of the prefixes uro- and copro- was based principally on the major site of occurrence or source of initial isolation. These terms, however, have become relatively unsatisfactory as neither porphyrin is limited in occurrence to urine and feces and both, in fact, are widely distributed in animal and plant kingdoms.[14, 15, 16]

Protoporphyrin with three dissimilar side chains in position 1–8 (4 methyls, 2 vinyls, 2 propionic acids), has 15 possible position isomers. However, only type IX (III) has been isolated or synthesized. Fischer synthesized 12 of the corresponding, more stable and easily prepared mesoporphyrins (containing 2 ethyl groups instead of the 2 vinyl groups of Proto) as reference material for isomeric type designation. Of the 15 mesoporphyrins, Types 1 and 2 belong to the etio- series 1; 3, 4, and 5 to the series II; 6–11 to the series III; and 12–15 to the series IV. Protoporphyrin is readily converted by catalytic reduction to mesoporphyrin, thus permitting ready identification on the basis of melting points of the methyl esters, chromatographic behavior and infra-red spectroscopy. The absorption spectra of the isomers are identical. Fischer found that the protoporphyrin obtained from the hemoglobin of various species

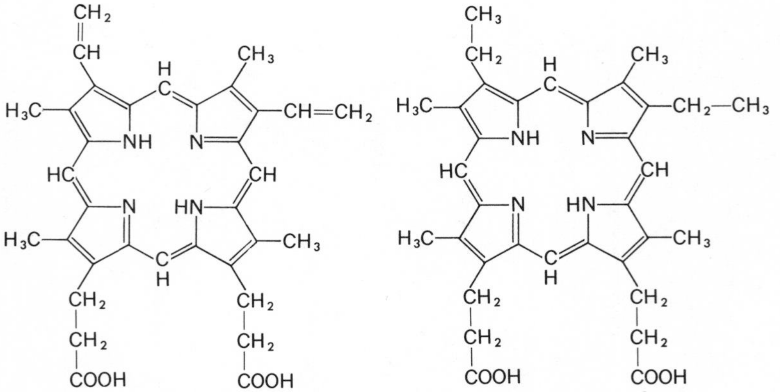

Protoporphyrin IX (III)   Mesoporphyrin IX (III)

Figure 4.   Structures of protoporphyrin 9 (III) and mesoporphyrin 9 (III) compared with etioporphyrin III.

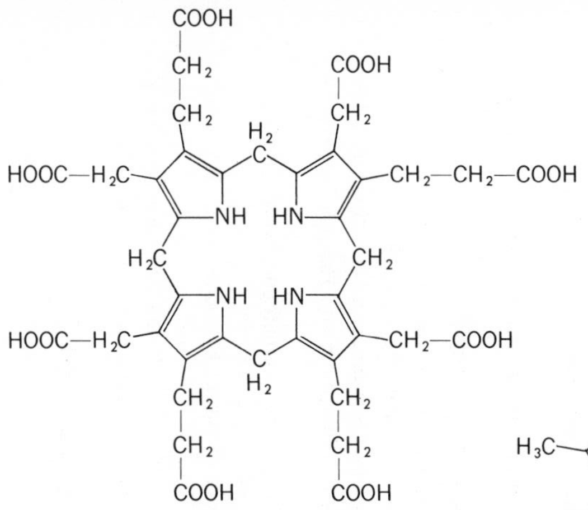

Uroporphyrinogen III

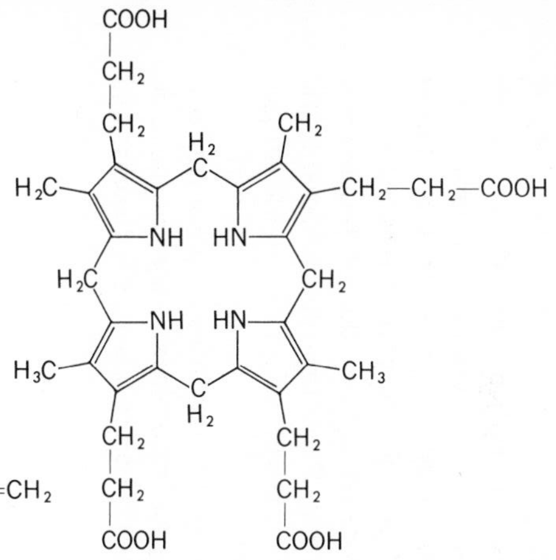

Coproporphyrinogen III

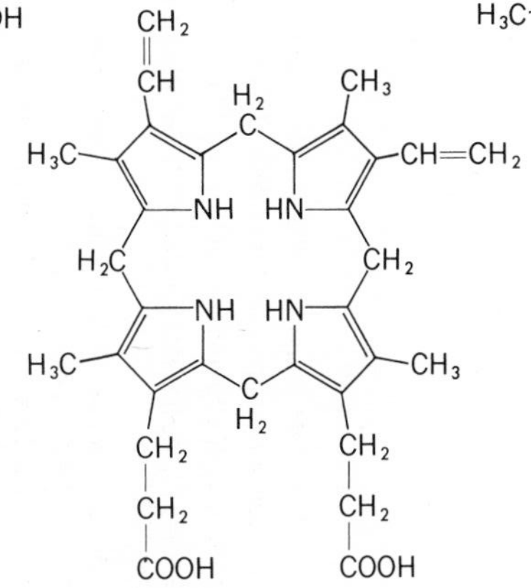

Protoporphyrinogen IX (III)

Figure 5. Structures of uro- and coproporphyrinogens III and protoporphyrinogen 9 (III).

invariably yielded mesoporphyrin IX, and it was therefore designated as protoporphyrin IX. As seen in Fig. 4, its configuration corresponds with that of the etio- series III porphyrins.

Reduction of various porphyrins with sodium amalgam or sodium borohydride results in the formation of the corresponding hexahydro-porphyrins or porphyrinogens in which the 4 pyrrole rings are linked together by 4 methylene bridges (Figure 5). Porphyrinogens are color-less compounds which do not fluoresce as they do not possess the aromatic structure of the porphyrin ring. They are readily oxidized to the corresponding porphyrins. Photo-oxidation is easily demonstrable *in vitro*, and may have significance *in vivo*.

The porphyrinogens are the actual intermediates in porphyrin bio-synthesis, hence of principal biological importance. They are found in various proportions with corresponding porphyrins in the tissues, bile and excreta.

BIBLIOGRAPHY

References:

1. Scherer, J., *Annal. D. Chem. U. Pharm.*, 40:1, 1841.
2. Mulder, J., "Ueber Eisenfreies Hamatin," *J. Prakt. Chem.*, 32:186, 1844.
3. Thudichum, J. L. W., *Report Med. Off. Privy Council 10*, 7:152, 1867.
4. Hoppe-Seyler, F., "Uber des Chlorophyll der Pflanzen," *Z. Physiol. Chem.*, 4: 193, 1880.
5. Nencki, M., and Sieber, "Untersuchungen uber den Blutfarbstoff," *Arch. Exp. Pathol.*, 18:401, 1884.
6. Nencki, M., and J. Zaleski, "Zur Kenntnis des Hamatoporphyrins," *Z. Physiol. Chem.*, 30:423, 1900.
7. Nencki, M., and J. Zaleski, *Z. Physiol. Chem.*, 34:997 (1901).
8. Willstätter, R., and A. Stool, *Investigations on Chlorophyll*, 1928.
9. Fischer, H., and H. Orth, *Die Chemie Des Pyrrols*, Bd. II, 1, 1937.
10. Lemberg, R., and J. W. Legge, *Haematin Compounds and Bile Pigments*, 1949.
11. Kuster, W. "Beitrage zur Kenntnis des Bilirubins und Hamins," *Z. Physiol. Chem.*, 82:463, 1912.
12. Fischer, W., and K. Zeile, "Synthese des Hamatoporphyrins, Protopor-phyrins und Hamins," *Ann. Chem.*, 468:98, 1929.
13. Crute, M. B., "The Crystal Structure of Nickel Etioporphyrin," *Acta Cryst.*, 12:24, 1959.
14. Goldberg, M. B., and C. Rimington, *Diseases of Porphyrin Metabolism*, 1962.
15. Watson, C. J., "Porphyrin Metabolism" in G. Duncan, *Diseases of Metabolism*, (5th Ed.), 1964.
16. Falk, J. E., *Porphyrins and Metalloporphyrins*, 1964.

II. CHEMISTRY OF DIPYRRL COMPOUNDS AND THE SYNTHESIS OF PORPHYRINS

Porphyrins are amphoteric. The protons attached to the nitrogens can be abstracted with sodium ethoxide in ethanol to yield the porphyrin dibase. Conversely, aqueous solutions of strong mineral acids can introduce two additional protons to yield the di-acid. Acidity and basicity of the porphyrins are strongly affected by alterations in the ring system and substituent groups. This property, coupled with the accompanying variation in solubility as a function of the polarity of solvents, has been used extensively as a method of fractionation and purification.

The protons attached to the nitrogen can be replaced by a number of metal ions. Small, symmetrical, divalent ions usually take up positions centered between the four nitrogens. In some cases, particularly when an external group is attached, the metal atom may be displaced somewhat above or below the plane of the ring.[1] Metal ions which are known to form complexes are: magnesium (Mg^{++}), vanadyl (VO^{++}), manganic (Mn^{+++}), manganous (Mn^{++}), ferric (Fe^{+++}), ferrous (Fe^{++}), cobaltic (Co^{+++}), cobaltous (Co^{++}), nickel (Ni^{++}), copper (Cu^{++}), Zinc (Zn^{++}), gallium (Ga^{++}) and stannous (Sn^{++}). Of these, the complex of magnesium is the weakest and vanadyl the strongest, as indicated by their resistance to cleavage by mineral acids.[2]

Depending upon the orbital energies, the complex may be ionic or covalent. In the latter case, the complex may be flat (sp^3) or octahedral (sp^3d^2), where external donors of electrons take up positions above and below and perpendicular to the porphyrin ring. A few typical configurations are illustrated by the following:

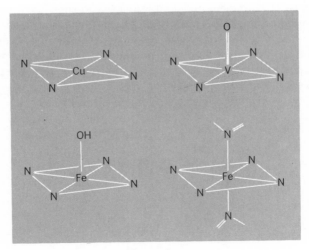

Figure 6.

The capacity of the metal to complex with groups external to the porphyrin ring is an important functional feature of enzyme systems containing, as their prosthetic groups, porphyrin metallo complexes.

Porphyrins exhibit a characteristic red fluorescence, a property which is functionally associated with their tendency to exist as stable free radicals. The unpaired electrons probably tend to center at the nitrogens of the II and III rings. At 25°C, measurements made by electron spin resonance indicate that several per cent of the molecules are in the metastable triplet state. In the di-acid and di-base, and in the metallo complexes with covalent bonding, unpairing of electrons is more difficult; consequently, these compounds do not exhibit fluorescence.

Hydrogenation of the porphyrin ring can take place progressively and in at least two different ways. Hydrogenation of the double bonds in the 1, 2 and 5, 6 positions does not interrupt the conjugation in the great ring. The dihydroporphyrins are often referred to as chlorins. They are widely distributed in nature, principally as the four major chlorophylls *a*, *b*, *c*, and *d*. Bacteriochlorophyll is a tetrahydroporphyrin or a dihydrochlorin. There are two distinct hexahydroporphyrins. One, purple in color, is believed to represent addition of hydrogen across the 3, 4 double bond. Although the conjugation of the microcyclic system is formally interrupted, several resonance forms can be drawn.[2] The other hexahydroporphyrin is the leuco base, structure A below. Here the conjugation is completely broken and the ring presumably puckers. A pink, highly unstable octohydroporphyrin is described, for which structure B below is proposed.[3]

The *in-vitro* synthesis of porphyrins is usually accomplished via the pyrroles. The complexity of the synthesis to a large extent depends upon the degree of asymmetry required in respect to substituent groups on the 1 through 8 and the α through δ positions. Syntheses which lead to a mixture of two or more porphyrin products usually are avoided. Routes for synthesis of single porphyrin products of varying asymmetry are illustrated by the following diagrams, where a quarter section represents a pyrrole ring and a key represents a methine bridge:

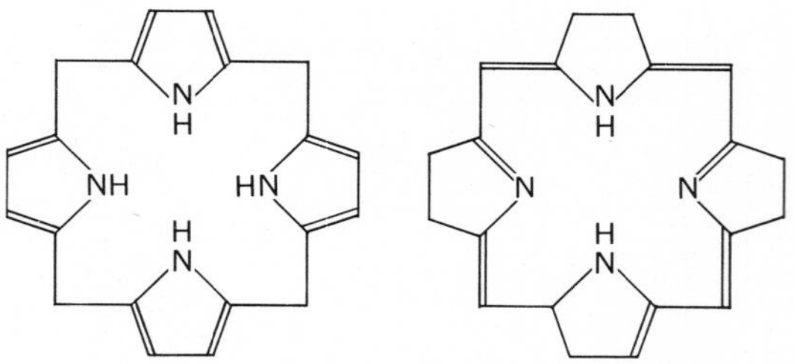

A   B

Figure 7.

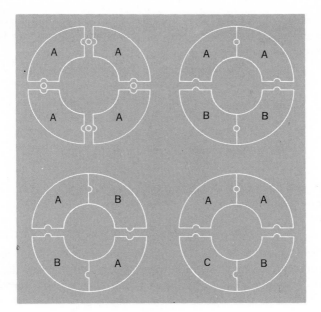

Figure 8.

The quarter circle diagram to the left involves a synthesis of a porphyrin direct from a pyrrole. An example is the synthesis of porphin, the unsubstituted parent of the porphyrin series, from pyrrole and formaldehyde.[4] The routes of synthesis illustrated by the three diagrams to the right proceed via α,α'-dipyrrylmethanes or α,α'-dipyrrylmethenes. Utilizing these combinations, unique syntheses have been achieved for most of the naturally occurring porphyrins and their derivatives, as well as their geometric isomers, *e.g.*, the four isomers of etio-, copro-, and uroporphyrin and the fifteen isomers of proto-, hemato-, meso- and deuteroporphyrin. In this trivial or common nomenclature, the isomer is designated by a Roman numeral following the name. The numeral one usually designates the arrangement of highest symmetry.

The dipyrrylmethanes and dipyrrylmethenes are related by the following reaction:

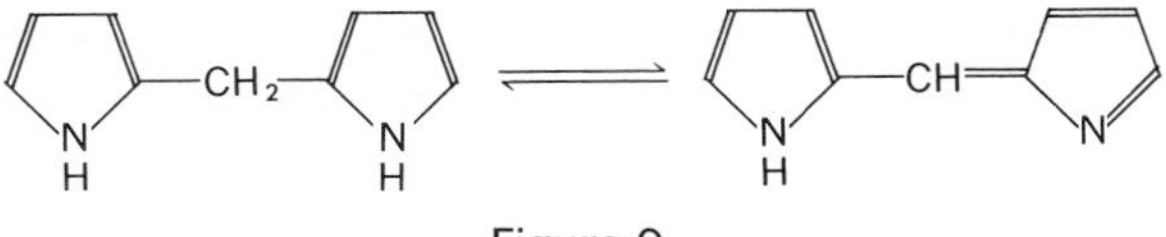

Figure 9.

The dipyrrylmethanes usually are without color and possess properties similar to the correspondingly substituted pyrroles. In the dipyrrylmethenes the two unsaturated 5-membered rings are in aromatic conjugation one to the other. They are "half porphyrins" both in structure and properties, being highly colored, amphoteric and readily forming metallo complexes:

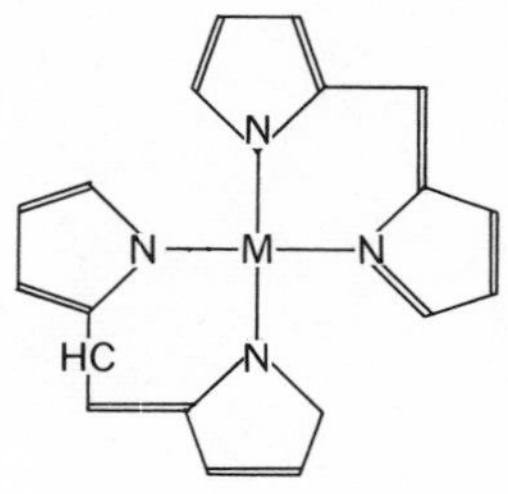

Figure 10.

The parent compound α,α'-dipyrrylmethane has been described.[5] Its alkyl-substituted derivatives, like those of the pyrroles, are extremely sensitive to oxidation. In further analogy with the pyrroles, introduction of electron-withdrawing groups such as carboxyl and carbalkoxy stabilizes the molecule. α,α'-Dipyrrylmethene can be prepared and along with its alkyl-substituted derivatives is quite stable to oxidation. The nomenclature for the dipyrrylmethanes and dipyrrylmethenes follows that of H. Fischer *et al.* His three-volume text, *Die Chemis des Pyrrols*[6] although now somewhat antiquated, remains the most comprehensive in the field.

The synthesis of α,α'-dipyrrylmethanes and α,α'-dipyrrylmethenes usually is accomplished by starting with the suitably substituted pyrroles. The pathway chosen depends upon the degree of asymmetry required in respect to the substituent groups. Some type reactions useful in porphyrin synthesis are seen in Figure 11.

Combining it with the dipyrrylmethene illustrating Type AA above yields etioporphyrin II. Combining it with the Type AA geometric isomer, 4,4'-dimethyl-3,3'-diethyl-5,5'-dibromo dipyrrylmethene hydrobromide yields etioporphyrin IV.

Combining two molecules yields etioporphyrin I.

Combining with Type AA above yields etioporphyrin III.

The above reactions are more complex than they appear as written, and anomalous results are occasionally encountered. For example, in the course of the aldehyde synthesis, the first dipyrrylmethene formed may react reversibly with yet unused α-free pyrrole to form a tripyrrylmethane intermediate. In the back reaction, owing to the effect of substituent groups, cleavage of another pyrryl-methane bond may take place to yield any of three dipyrrylmethenes.[11] The possibility of a similar rearrangement exists during the oxidation of dipyrrylmethanes to the corresponding dipyrrylmethenes.[12]

3,3'-dimethyl-4,4'-diethyl-5,5'-dibromo

dipyrrylmethene hydrobromide (Type AA)—

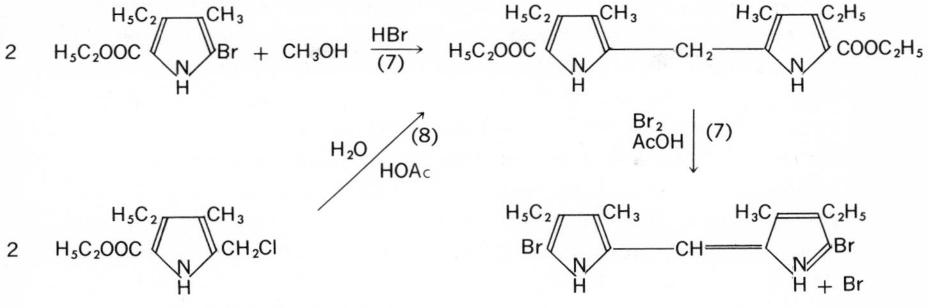

3,5,3',5'-tetramethyl-4,4'-diethyl

dipyrrylmethene hydrobromide (Type BB)—

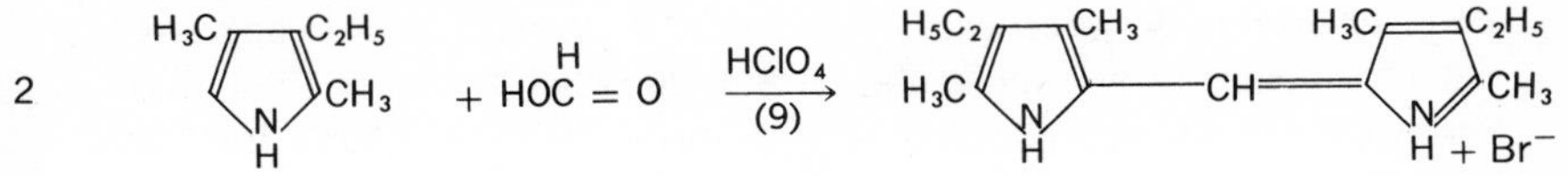

Figure 11

4,3',5'-trimethyl-3,4'-diethyl-5-

bromo dipyrrylmethene hydrobromide (Type AB)—

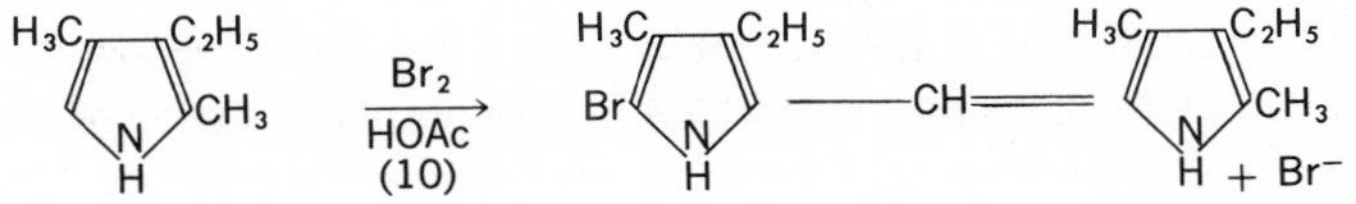

Figure 12

4,5,3',5'-tetramethyl-3,4'-diethyl

dipyrrylmethene hydrochloride (Type BC)—

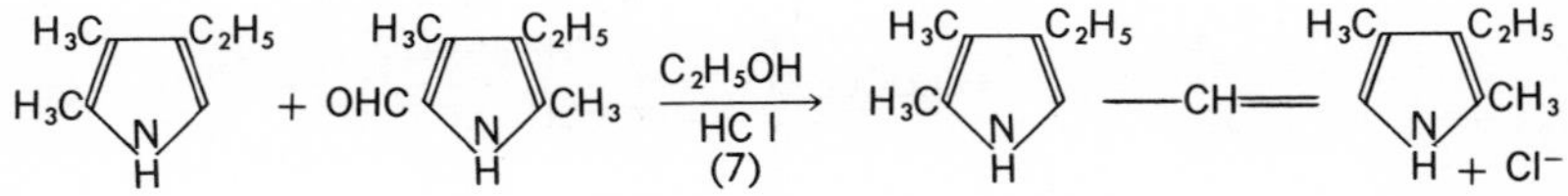

Figure 13

The reaction whereby two appropriate α,α'-dipyrrylmethanes or methenes are coupled to form a porphyrin is usually carried out as a one-step process, although stepwise coupling has been reported.[13] The reactions are seldom stoichiometric and may involve hydrolysis, dehydration, decarboxylation, dehydrogenation and dihydrobromination. With α,α'-dipyrrylmethanes, unique syntheses are frequently accomplished by a kind of 2AA or 2BB type of reaction. In the former, the α and γ carbon atoms are provided from the reaction medium, usually formic acid. Thus etioporphyrin II has been prepared from 4,4'-dimethyl-3,3'-diethyl dipyrrylmethane by reaction in boiling formic acid.[7] In the 2BB type of reaction, carbons are lost non-selectively from the 5 and 5' positions of dipyrrylmethanes containing carboxyl or carbethoxy groups. Conditions are dry thermal[14] or in HBr-acetic acid or strong alkali.[15] Condensation of the α,α'-dipyrrylmethenes is usually accomplished by heating in formic acid or by fusion in a melt of any of a variety of unsaturated dicarboxylic acids. A typical example is the 2AB preparation of etioporphyrin I by fusion of two molecules of 3,4'-dimethyl-3',4-diethyl-5-bromomethyl-5'-bromo dipyrrylmethene hydrobromide in a 190°C melt of maleic acid.[16] Yields vary from less than one to over 40%.

Among the more difficult porphyrins to synthesize are the chlorophylls and their derivatives. One of the least complicated of these is α-phylloporphyrin XV of 1,3,5,8,γ-pentamethyl-2,4-diethylporphin-7-propionic acid. This compound has been synthesized by an AB-A'B' type reaction, namely, the coupling of 3,5,3'-trimethyl-4-ethyl dipyrrylmethene-4'-propionic acid hydrobromide and 4,3'-dimethyl-3,5'-diethyl-5,4'-dibromo dipyrrylmethene hydrobromide in a tartaric acid melt.[17] As indicated by the reaction type, this is not a unique synthesis and the desired porphyrin has to be separated from three others, namely pyrroporphyrin XV (1,3,5,8-tetramethyl-2,4-diethyl-porphine-7-propionic acid), α,γ-dimethyl deuteroetioporphyrin II and mesoporphyrin XV. Despite these increasing difficulties, chlorophyll a- has been synthesized.[18]

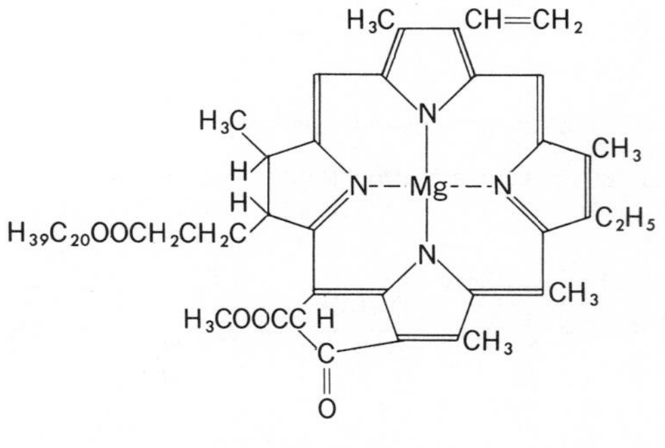

Figure 14

Table I. Physical Properties of a Few Typical α,α-Dipyrrylmethanes and α,α-Dipyrrylmethenes (5, 7, 10, 19, 20)

Compound	Melting Point °C	Color and Crystalline Form	Spectrum				Soluble In-	Insoluble In-
			λ max.	α mol. x10^{-4}	λ max.	α mol. x10^{-4}		
Dipyrrylmethanes								
parent compound i. e. unsubstituted	66	white platelets or needles					ether benzene	water aq. acid and alkali
3,3'-dimethyl-4,4'-diethyl-5,5'-dicarbethoxy-	148	white needles					alcohol	water
3,3'-dimethyl-4,4'-diethyl-5,5'-dicarboxy-	211 d.	white			291	2.8	alcohol aq. alkali	water
Dipyrrylmethenes								
3,5,3',5'-tetramethyl-4,4'-diethyl-	151	yellow-red platelets	442	2.09	(316	2.5)	dioxane alcohol	water
-perchlorate	d.	brown-red with green lustre needles	485	8.30	367	3.98	dioxane alcohol	
3,5,4',5'-tetramethyl-3,4'-diethyl-	80	yellow prismatic needles	444	2.55	—	—	dioxane alcohol	water
-hydrochloride	~200 d.	red-yellow with blue lustre	487	7.38	373	4.21	acetic acid chloroform ether hot alcohol	water
4,3,5'-trimethyl-3,4'-diethyl-5-bromo-	103	yellow	464	3.37	(345	4.38)	hot alcohol	water
-hydrobromide	215 d.	brown-violet prisms	483	4.32	373	6.15	hot alcohol	
3,3'-dimethyl-4,4'-diethyl-hydrobromide	~170 d.	yellow platelets	448	2.91	318	4.00	acetic acid	ether
3,3'-dimethyl-4,4'-diethyl-5,5'-dibromo-	175–176	red prisms	493	8.55	368	5.68	alcohol chloroform	water
-hydrobromide	200 d.							

BIBLIOGRAPHY

References:

1. Koenig, D. F., "The Crystal Structure of Chlorohemin, $C_{34}H_{32}N_4O_4FeCl$," *Dissertation*, 1962.

2. Erdman, J. G., J. W. Walter, and W. E. Hanson, American Chemical Society, *General Papers 2*, 1:259, 1957.

3. Eisner, U., "Some Novel Hydroporphyrins," *J. Chem. Soc.*, p. 3461, 1957.

4. Rothemund, P., "A New Porphyrin Synthesis, the Synthesis of Porphin," *J. Am. Chem. Soc.*, 58:625, 1936.

5. Hess, K., and F. Anselm, "Über das Di [*N*-Methyl-α-Pyrrolidyl]-Methan," *Ber.*, 54B:2310, 1921.

6. Fischer, H., and H. Orth, *Die Chemie des Pyrrols*, Vol. 1, 1934; 2(1), 1937: Stern, A., 2(2), 1940.

7. Fischer, H., and G. Stangler, "Synthese des Mesoporphyrins, Mesohämins und Über die Konstitution des Hämins," *Ann.*, 459:53, 1927.

8. Corwin, A. H., W. A. Bailey, Jr., and P. Viohl, "Structural Investigations upon a Substituted Dipyrrylmethane an Unusual Melting Point-Symmetry Relationship," *J. Am. Chem. Soc.*, 64:1267, 1942.

9. Fischer, H., P. Halbig, and B. Walach, "Über eine Neue Porphyrinsynthese, Oxydation von Porphyrinen und Einige Kleinere Beobachtungen," *Ann.*, 452:268, 1927.

10. Fischer, H., E. Bauman, and H. J. Riedl, "Über die Halogenierten Methene des Kryptopyrrols und Ihre Konstitution," *Ann.*, 475:205, 1929.

11. Corwin, A. H., and K. W. Doak, "Kinetics of the Condensation of Dipyrrylmethenes with an α-Free Pyrrole," *J. Am. Chem. Soc.*, 77:464, 1955.

12. Corwin, A. H., and K. J. Brunnings, "Rearrangements of Pyrrole Rings in the Oxydation of Dipyrrylmethanes," *J. Am. Chem. Soc.*, 64:2106, 1942.

13. Corwin, A. H., and E. C. Coolidge, "A Stepwise Porphyrin Synthesis," *J. Am. Chem. Soc.*, 74:5196, 1952.

14. Fischer, H., and A. Halbig, "Synthese des Iso-Ätioporphyrins, seines 'Hämins' und 'Phyllins,'" *Ann.*, 448:193, 1926.

15. Fischer, H., and A. Halbig, "Über Iso-Ätioporphyrin, sein Tetrabromderivat, seinen Oxydativen und Reduktiven Abbau, Sowie eine Synthese eines Iso-Mesoporphyrins und des Opsopyrrols," *Ann.*, 450:151, 1926.

16. Erdman, J. G., et al., "Synthesis and Properties of Porphyrin Vanadium Complexes," *J. Am. Chem. Soc.*, 78: 5844, 1956.

17. Fischer, H., and H. Helberger, "Synthese eines Phyllo-porphyrins, Phylloëtioporphyrins und Einiger Verwandten," *Ann.*, 480:235, 1930.

18. Woodward, R. B., et al., "The Total Synthesis of Chlorophyll," *J. Am. Chem. Soc.*, 82:3800, 1960.

19. Fischer, H., E. Sturm, and H. Friedrich, "Synthesen β-β'-Substituierter Pyrrole und Porphyrin-Synthesen aus Einfachen Pyrrolen," *Ann.*, 461:244, 1928.

20. Pruckner, F., and A. Stern, "Über die Absorptionsspektren der Pyrrolfarbstoffe," *Z. Physik. Chem.*, A180:25, 1937.

III. STRUCTURAL CHARACTERISTICS OF PORPHYRINS IN HEMOPROTEINS.

Protoheme as prosthetic group. The following hemoproteins contain proto-heme as their prosthetic group: hemoglobins, hemerythrins and eryth-rocruorins; myoglobins; cytochromes *b;* probably cytochrome *o*[1,2]; thyroid peroxidase; tryptophan pyrrolase; horseradish and other plant peroxidases, and catalases. Crystalline ox liver catalase also contains a proportion of non-functional oxidized product of protoheme which gives biliverdin on extraction with acid.[3] The structure of protoheme is given in Figure 1.

The protoheme molecule is almost planar[4,5,6]. In Figure 1, the iron atom is shown coordinated to pyrrole nitrogens by four nearly equivalent bonds. Not shown in Figure 1 are the fifth and sixth coordination bonds of the iron atom which are directed perpendicularly to the plane of the molecule, on either side. In hemoproteins one of the latter bonds is directed to a protein atom, the other also to protein or to H_2O, O_2, H_2O_2, etc.

Binding of heme to protein. Four types of linkage may be involved: (1) bonds to protein groups at the fifth or fifth and sixth coordination posi-tions of the iron atom, (2) electrostatic attraction between the nega-tively charged propionic acid side chains of the porphyrin and adjacent charged protein groups, (3) van der Waals and hydrogen bonding, and (4) covalent bonds between pyrrole β-substituents and amino acids of the protein. Linkages of types 1, 2 and 3 are probably involved in all hemoproteins whereas those of type 4 apply so far as is known only to milk peroxidase, myeloperoxidase, cytochromes *c* and cytochromoids (RHP, see below and also ref. 18).

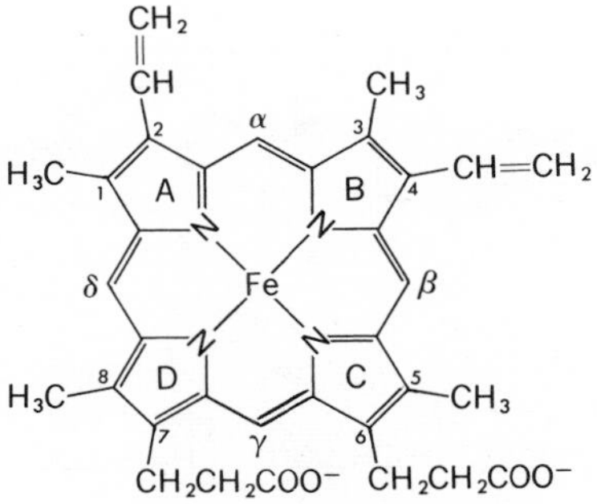

Figure 1.   Protoheme

The iron complex of protoporphyrin IX (ferriheme) showing the numbering of the pyrrole β-positions and the lettering of the methene carbon atoms linking the pyrroles ($\alpha,\beta,\gamma,\delta$) and of the pyrrole rings (A,B,C,D).

In linkages of type 1, binding of protein groups at both fifth and sixth positions of the iron atom gives rise to hemochromes (hemochromogens) which have strong, sharp, characteristic absorption bands (*e.g.*, cytochrome *c*). In hemoglobins, myoglobins, catalases, peroxidases, cytochromes a_3 and possibly cytochromes *d* (formerly a_2), the sixth position is occupied by a water molecule or, where appropriate, O_2 or H_2O_2 (see Table I).

In the cytochromes the precise nature of the iron-protein bonds, which may be affected by linkages of types 3 and 4 determines, in part, their redox potential, which is also influenced by the nature of pyrrole β-substituent. The nature of the protein-iron bonds and of the pyrrole β-substituents also determines the affinity of oxygen for hemoglobins and myoglobins and presumably, affects the reaction of catalases and peroxidases with H_2O_2. Linkages of type 4 are described below.

Prosthetic groups other than protoheme. The "parent" compound used below in the nomenclature of some hemes is deuteroheme which contains hydrogen atoms in place of the vinyls at positions 2 and 4 in Fig. 1.

Chlorocruoroheme (spirographis heme). 2-formyl, 4-vinyldeuteroheme is the prosthetic group of chlorocruorin which is the oxygen-carrying pigment of certain polychaete worms.[7]

Heme *c*. The prosthetic group of cytochromes of type *c* has been shown[8] to have the structure 2, 4, di-1'-(S-cysteinyl) ethyl deuteroheme IX (see Figure 2). In the cytochromoid, RHP (*Rhodospirillum* hemeprotein) from *Rhodospirillum* and other species of photosynthetic bacteria, the prosthetic group contains at least one S-cysteinyl residue as in heme *c* but the exact structure is uncertain.[9] It is also likely that in one of the two heme groups of RHP the sixth position of the iron atom is taken up by a water molecule instead of by a protein group.

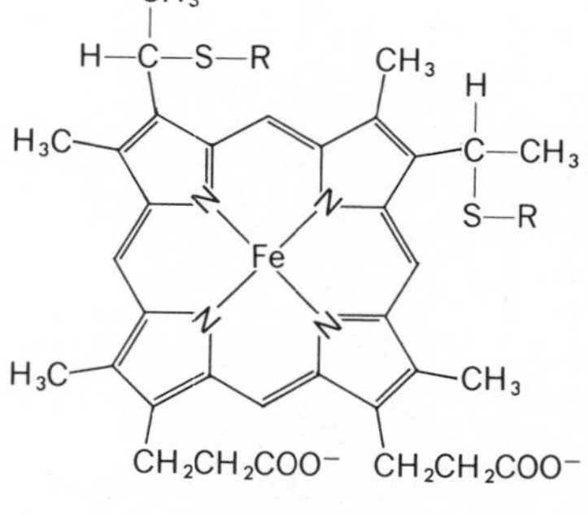

Figure 2.   heme *e*

where R = $-CH_2 = CH\ (NH_2)$ COOH

The term "heme *c*" is usually applied to the isolated compound shown in Figure 2. However, in cytochrome *c* the cysteinyl residues form part

of a peptide chain in which they are separated by two amino acid residues which vary according to the animal species.[10]

Heme *a*. Heme *a* is the only heme prosthetic group of mammalian
cytochrome a_+a_3 (cytochrome oxidase) and of cytochrome a_1 of certain
bacteria.[11, 12] Its structure is: 1, 3, 5-trimethyl-2, α-hydroxyalkyl-4-vinyl-
8-formylheme-6, 7-dipropionic acid[13] where the alkyl group is given[14] as
the saturated tri-isoprenyl shown in Figure 3. Since the catalytically hydrogenated compound was used for the determination of the structure
of the alkyl group, some unsaturation, suggested by spectral considerations, cannot be ruled out.[15]

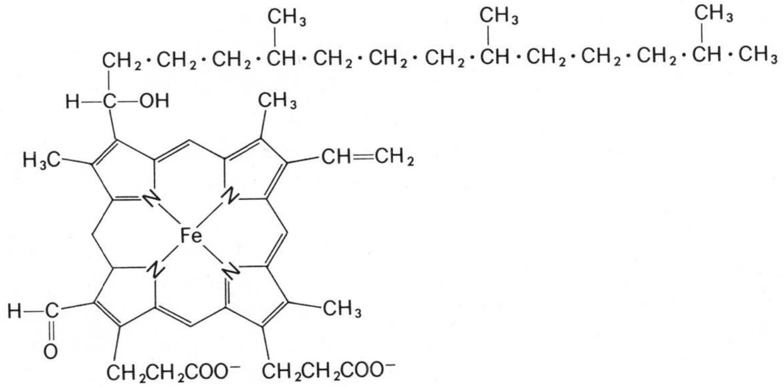

Figure 3.   heme *a*

Heme *d* (a_2). Heme *d* occurs as possibly the sole prosthetic group of
cytochrome *d* (*A. aerogenes* and certain other bacteria)[16] and, together
with heme *c*, as a prosthetic group of the cytochrome *c d* of a strain of
P. aeruginosa[17] (Enzyme Commission Nomenclature[18]). It is thought that
the heme *d* of cytochrome *c d* may be slightly different from that of cytochrome *d*; both are, however, iron complexes of chlorins. The possible
structures for the heme *d* of *A. aerogenes* are shown in Fig. 4.

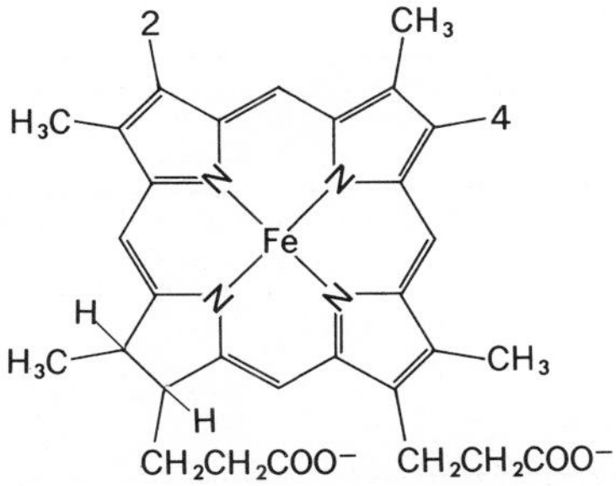

Figure 4.   heme *d*

The additional H atoms in positions 7 and 8 have been placed in ring D by analogy with chlorophyll a but may be in one of the other pyrroles.

Possible Substituents

Position 2	Position 4
$-CH{=}CH_2$	$-CHOH\ CH_3$
$-CHOH\ CH_3$	$-CH{=}CH_2$
$-CH{=}CH_2$	$-CH_2 \cdot CH_3$
$-CH_2 \cdot CH_3$	$-CH{=}CH_2$
$-CH{=}CH_2$	$-CH{=}CH_2$

Milk peroxidase heme. This peroxidase occurs in milk, salivary glands[19] and probably human eosinophils.[20] The heme prosthetic group has the same type of macro-ring conjugation as protoheme but differs from it in two known respects: (1) it is covalently bound to the enzyme protein probably by one or more ester linkages[21, 22] and (2) contains a conjugated unsaturated substituent more electrophilic than the two vinyl groups of protoheme together. Treatment by strong alkali renders the substituent less electrophilic.[21]

Myeloperoxidase (neutrophil peroxidase) heme. The peroxidase is produced only in neutrophils[20] (hence in pus[23]) and in neutrophilic tumors.[24, 25] The structure of the heme is not fully known but it contains three special structural entities: (1) the heme group is strongly covalently bound to the enzyme protein by other than thioether or ester bonds,[27, 30] (2) it contains a conjugated, strongly electrophilic, carbonyl substituent[26, 27] and possibly a second electrophilic substituent on a pyrrole opposite to that bearing the carbonyl[27] (3) and it contains an unknown structural entity labile to pyridine, responsible for the strong, sharp absorption maximum at 637 mμ of the reduced peroxidase.[27] This spec-

Table I.

Hemoprotein	Reactions showing valency states
Hemoglobins Myoglobins	$Fe^{2+} \cdot H\ OH + O_2 \rightleftharpoons Fe^{2+} \cdot O_2 + H_2O$
Catalases	$Fe^{3+} \cdot H\ OH + H_2O_2 \rightleftharpoons$ nominal* $Fe^{5+} + H_2O_2 \rightarrow Fe^{3+} \cdot H\ OH$ (Fe^{3+} · HOOH, $\qquad\qquad + H_2O + O_2$ Complex I)
Peroxidase (horseradish)	$Fe^{3+} \cdot H\ OH + H_2O_2 \rightleftharpoons$ nominal* $Fe^{5+} + AH^{\cdot} \rightarrow$ nominal* Fe^{4+} (Fe^{3+} · HOOH, $\qquad\qquad$ (Complex II) Complex I) $\qquad\qquad\qquad + A$ $\qquad\qquad\qquad\qquad\qquad\downarrow AH^{\cdot}$ $\qquad\qquad\qquad\qquad Fe^{3+} \cdot HOH + A$
Cytochromes in electron transport	$Fe^{3+} + e \rightleftharpoons Fe^{2+}$

* The word "nominal" indicates that the charge given may not be localized on the iron atom.

trum is similar in type to that of ferrosulfmyoglobin, ferrosulfcatalase and ferrosulfhemoglobin.[28]

Sulfhemoglobin heme. Sulfhemoglobin is found in erythrocytes in certain pathological states.[29] It can be formed *in vitro* by reaction of H_2S with the ferrihemoglobin (methemoglobin) peroxide complex (ferryl compound).[28] The structure of the heme group is unknown. It may not be able to retain its special structure when separated from the protein. The spectrum (sharp, strong band at 619 mμ, $\varepsilon_{mM} = 17$) is changed by pyridine to that of dipyridine ferroprotohemochrome. This reaction appears inconsistent with some structures which have been suggested.[28]

BIBLIOGRAPHY

References:

1. Taber, H. W., and M. Morrison, *Arch. Biochem. Biophys.*, 105:367, 1964.
2. Taniguchi, S., and M. D. Kamen, *Biochim. Biophys. Acta*, 96:395, 1965.
3. Lemberg, R., R. M. Norrie, and J. W. Legge, *Nature*, 144:551, 1939.
4. Crute, M. B., *Acta Cryst.*, 12:24, 1959.
5. Fleischer, E. B., *J. Am. Chem. Soc.*, 85:146, 1963.
6. Hodgkin, D. C., *Federation Proc.*, 23:592, 1964.
7. Fox, H. M., and G. Vevers, *The Nature of Animal Colours*, 1960.
8. Falk, J. E., *Porphyrins and Metalloporphyrins*, 1964.
9. Kamen, M. D., *Acta Chem. Scand.*, 17:S41, 1963.
10. Margoliash, E., and A. Schejter, "Cytochrome c," *Advan. Protein Chem.*, 21:113, 1966.
11. Morell, D. B., J. Barrett, and P. S. Clezy, *Biochem. J.*, 78:793, 1961.
12. Morrison, M., *et al.*, *J. Biol. Chem.*, 235:1202, 1960.
13. Lemberg, R., in Nord, F. F. (ed.), *Advances Enzymol.*, 23:265, 1961.
14. Grassl, M., *et al.*, *Biochem. Z.*, 238:771, 1963.
15. Lemberg, M. R., *Rev. Pure Appl. Chem.*, 15:125, 1965.
16. Barrett, J., *Biochem. J.*, 64:626, 1956.
17. Yamanaka, T., and K. Okunuki, *Biochem. Biophys. Acta*, 67:407, 1963.
18. "Enzyme Nomenclature," *International Union of Biochemistry*, 1965.
19. Morrison, M., *et al.*, *Arch. Biochem. Biophys.*, 111:126, 1965.
20. Archer, G. T., *et al.*, *Biochim. Biophys. Acta*, 99:96, 1965.
21. Morell, D. B., and P. S. Clezy, *Biochim. Biophys. Acta*, 71:157, 1963.
22. Hultquist, D. E., and M. Morrison, *J. Biol. Chem.*, 238:2843, 1963.
23. Agner, K., *Acta Chem. Scand.*, 12:89, 1958.
24. Schultz, J., H. Shay, and M. Gruenstein, *Cancer Res.*, 14:157, 1954.
25. Newton, N., D. B. Morell, and L. Clarke, *Biochim. Biophys. Acta*, 96:463, 1965.
26. Schultz, J., and H. W. Schmukler, *Biochemistry*, 3:1234, 1964.
27. Newton, N., *et al.*, *Biochim. Biophys. Acta*, 96:476, 1965.
28. Nicholls, P., *Biochem. J.*, 81:374, 1961.
29. Lemberg, R., and J. W. Legge, in *Haematin Compounds and Bile Pigments*.
30. Schultz, J., H. Schmukler, and A. Young, *Proc. Fifth Intern. Congr. Biochem.*, (Moscow, 1961), p. 60, 1962.

IV. PHYSICAL CONSTANTS OF PORPHYRINS

Ultraviolet, Visible, and Near Infrared Absorption Spectra. Certain useful generalizations can be made about porphyrin and metal porphyrin absorption in the ultraviolet, visible and near infrared regions.[1-5] Wavelengths of maximum absorption, the number of absorption bands, their relative intensities, and the band width at one-half maximum intensity can be related to the number, type, and distribution of substituents and the solvents. In metal complexes, these factors also depend upon the particular metal present, its oxidation and spin states, and axial ligands (if any).

a. Metal-free porphyrins, neutral species (Table I).

Porphyrins have an intense ($A_M > 10^5$) Soret band around 400 mμ and four (sometimes five) less intense absorption maxima fairly equally spaced in the visible region. The visible bands are frequently numbered I, (Ia), II, III, and IV from longer to shorter wavelengths (Figure 1). According to a more recent classification, bands I and II are designated as Q_x bands, bands III and IV as Q_y bands, the Soret band as Band B, and bands in the ultraviolet region as N, L, etc.[2] The wavelength positions and relative peak heights of these absorption maxima reflect both the interaction of individual substituents with the delocalized π-electron system of the porphyrin ring and the relative positions of the substituents on the ring.

Frequently, but not in all cases, the Soret and four visible region absorption maxima are shifted to longer wavelengths upon increasing the electron-withdrawing power of the substituents. Thus shifts to longer wavelengths are found on going from α-hydroxyethyl (hematoporphyrin IX) to vinyl (protoporphyrin IX) to formyl (chlorocruoroporphyin and porphyrin a). Changes in structure at positions "insulated" from the porphyrin ring have little or no effect on the spectrum. A marked shift to longer wavelengths results upon converting a ring-bound carboxylic acid salt to the free acid or an ester, whereas esterification or acidification of a more isolated carboxylic acid salt, e.g., propionic acid salts, results in little change in the spectrum.

The relative positions of substituents which interact similarly with the porphyrin π-electron system have little or no effect on the visible and Soret regions. Thus the isomeric coproporphyrins exhibit nearly identical spectra. On the other hand, the four isomeric tetramethyltetracarbethoxyporphyrins do have significantly different spectra because the methyl and carbethoxy groups interact quite differently with the porphyrin π-electron system; the most notable differences exhibited are in the relative intensities.[13]

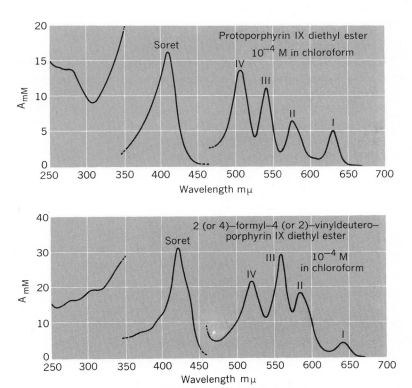

Figure 1.   Absorption spectra of 10⁻⁴M protoporphyrin IX diethyl ester and 10⁻⁴M 2(or 4)-formyl-4(or 2)-vinyldeuteroporphyrin IX diethyl ester in chloroform (6).

The visible spectra have been classified on the basis of the relative intensities of the four principal absorption bands. A spectrum in which the intensities follow the order IV > III > II > I is designated "etio-type." Included in this group are porphyrins having saturated alkyl or vinyl groups in all eight *beta* positions. The sequence IV > II > III > I is classified "phyllo-type" and is found among porphyrins with substituents on the meso positions and in a few other cases. "Rhodo-type" and "oxorhodo-type" spectra are cases where III > IV > II > I and III > II > IV > I are found, respectively.

b.   Metal-free porphyrins, protonated species (Table II).
On protonation, metal-free porphyrins exhibit an intensified Soret peak

and a shift from four to two major absorption maxima (bands I and II) in the visible region. The longer wavelength visible band (I) is at a shorter wavelength than band I of the corresponding neutral species and is less intense than band II.

c. Metal porphyrins (Table III).

Absorption spectra of the metal porphyrins are of several different types. The divalent metal complexes generally exhibit spectra with two principle maxima in the visible region, a sharp and intense Soret band,

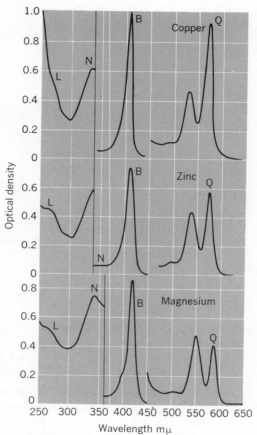

Figure 2. Absorption spectrum of metal protoporphyrin IX dimethyl esters in chloroform. Top: copper(II) (3.5 × 10⁻⁵M). Middle: Zinc(II) (2.7 × 10⁻⁵M). Bottom: Magnesium(II) (3.1 × 10⁻⁵M). Path length for visible and ultraviolet regions 1 cm, for Soret region 0.1 cm. Note change in horizontal scale at 350 mµ. (2).

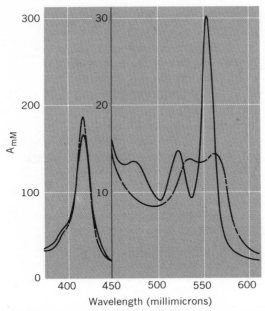

Figure 3.   Absorption spectra of dipyridine (—) and pyridine carbonyl (—) iron (II) protoporphyrin IX dimethyl esters in 0.2M pyridine in benzene (17).

and N, L, and other bands in the ultraviolet region (Figure 2). Effects due to differences in axial ligands are found, but usually they are relatively small (Figure 3). Spectra for trivalent metal porphyrins are considerably more complex. These spectra have more bands which are in many cases broad and poorly resolved (Figure 4). Furthermore, trivalent metal porphyrin spectra are usually quite sensitive to changes in the axial ligands and solvent as well as to the particular metal present.

Table I. Wavelengths and Intensities of Ultraviolet and Visible Absorption Maxima of Porphyrins

Wavelengths are given in nanometers (millimicrons) and intensities in millimolar absorptivity (A_{mM}), or molar absorptivity (ε).

		I [or $Q_x(0-0)$]	Ia	II [or $Q_x(0-1)$]	III [or $Q_y(0-0)$]	IV [or $Q_y(0-1)$]	Soret [or B]	UV [or N,L]	Refs.
Protoporphyrin IX									
dioxane	λ_{nm}	631		576	538	504			7
	A_{mM}	5.2		6.5	10.8	14.8			
Protoporphyrin IX dimethyl ester									
chloroform	λ_{nm}	630		576	541	506	407.5	275	6, 2
	A_{mM}	5.0		6.5	11.1	13.8	161.5	13.0	
pyridine	λ_{nm}	631	605	576	541	506	409		8
	A_{mM}	5.5	2.0	7.5	11.9	14.9	163		
dioxane	λ_{nm}	630	603	575	537	503			7
	A_{mM}	5.6	1.4	6.8	11.6	14.6			
Hematoporphyrin IX dimethyl ester									
chloroform	λ_{nm}	622		569	534	499	402	269	6
	A_{mM}	4.3		6.9	9.5	15.0	193	8.9	
pyridine	λ_{nm}	623	596	569	532	499	401		9
	A_{mM}	4.3	1.2	6.7	9.1	14.8	174		
Coproporphyrins I–IV and their tetramethyl esters									
dioxane	λ_{nm}	621	595	566	530	497	398		7, 4
	A_{mM}	5.4	1.4	7.2	10.3	15.4	177		
Uroporphyrins I–IV and their octamethyl esters									
chloroform	λ_{nm}	627		572	536	502	406		10
	A_{mM}	4.2		6.85	9.35	23.5	215		
dioxane	λ_{nm}	624	596	569	531	499			11
	A_{mM}	3.9	1.4	7.0	9.3	15.3			

Compound	Solvent									Ref.
Chlorocruoroporphyrin	dioxane	λ_{nm}	639	581	553	514				12
		A_{mM}	2.3	7.9	12.4	10.3				
Chlorocruoroporphyrin dimethyl ester	chloroform	λ_{nm}	644	584	558.5	518.5				35
	chloroform*	λ_{nm}	642	584	559	519	420	308	279	6
		A_{mM}	2.1	9.1	14.8	10.8	158	19.3	16.2	
Tetramethyltetracarbethoxyporphyrin I	chloroform	λ_{nm}	654	598	558	552	428	322	271	13
		A_{mM}	3.5	5.8	6.5	15.5	284	17.1	29.0	
Tetramethyltetracarbethoxyporphyrin II	chloroform	λ_{nm}	654	598	557	520	423	326	279	13
		A_{mM}	4.8	5.6	7.9	14.9	287	17.3	24.5	
Tetramethyltetracarbethoxyporphyrin III	chloroform	λ_{nm}	651	595	556	521	426.5	318	265	13
		A_{mM}	2.8	5.7	5.9	15.5	251	16.7	23.4	
Tetramethyltetracarbethoxyporphyrin IV	chloroform	λ_{nm}	648	595	556	523	427.5	317	266	13
		A_{mM}	1.8	5.7	5.2	15.6	247	16.2	24.6	

*A mixture of 2-formyl-4-vinyl and 4-formyl-2-vinyl isomers.

Table II. Wavelengths and Intensities of Absorption Maxima of Protonated Metal-free Porphyrins in the Visible and Soret Regions

Compound	Solvent		I or Q_X	II or Q_Y	Soret	Refs.
Protoporphyrin IX	1 M HCl	λ_{nm}	600	556	408	5, 14
		A_{mM}	5.6	13.5	241	
Hematoporphyrin IX dimethyl ester	1 M HCl	λ_{nm}	592	548	402	5
		A_{mM}	5.6	15.6	383	
Uroporphyrin III (and esters)	1 M HCl	λ_{nm}	593	552	406	10, 15
		A_{mM}	6.1	17.5	505	
Coproporphyrin III (and esters)	1 M HCl	λ_{nm}	591	548	401	5, 15, 7
		A_{mM}	6.5	17.5	470	

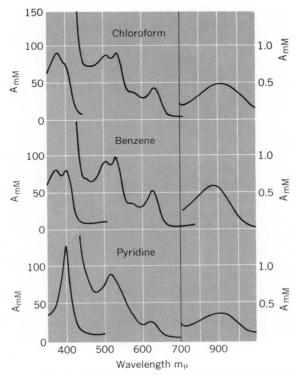

Figure 4. Absorption spectra of chloro iron(III) deuteroporphyrin IX dimethyl ester in chloroform (top), benzene (middle), and pyridine (bottom). Note ordinate scale in the visible region curve is $\frac{1}{10}$ the scale for Soret region curve (20, 28).

Table III. Absorption Spectra of Metal Porphyrins in the Soret and Visible Regions

Compound	Solvent											Ref
Chloro iron(III) protoporphyrin IX (hemin chloride)	dioxane	λ_{nm}		635.5			538.5	508				11
		A_{mM}		5.4			8.5	9.1				
	ether	λ_{nm}		638		585	539/40	512		407	381	16
		A_{mM}										
	ethanol-0.1N H$_2$SO$_4$(1:1, v/v)	λ_{nm}								398		27
		A_{mM}								131		
Chloro iron(III) protoporphyrin IX diethyl ester	chloroform	λ_{nm}	916	641			539	512			387	28
		A_{mM}	0.55	5.0			9.9	10.0			100	
	benzene	λ_{nm}	889	637			540	510			385	28
		A_{mM}	0.62	5.5			10.2	10.1			84	
	pyridine	λ_{nm}	928	632			525			409		28
		A_{mM}	0.44	3.3			10.0			121		
Methoxy iron(III) protoporphyrin IX dimethyl ester	chloroform	λ_{nm}	767			577				402		28
		A_{mM}				10.5				94		
	benzene	λ_{nm}	758		601	576				397		28
		A_{mM}	0.11		6.4	7.7				60		
	pyridine	λ_{nm}	753			570				407		28
		A_{mM}	0.18			9.7				81		
Acetato manganese(III) protoporphyrin IX dimethyl ester	pyridine	λ_{nm}	802	687		561			478		377	28
		A_{mM}	1.86	1.15		12.4			56		84	
Chlorohemin a	ether	λ_{nm}		660	600			505		416	370/80	16
Dipyridine iron(II) protoporphyrin IX	pyridine-aq. NaOH-Na$_2$S$_2$O$_4$, 25°	λ_{nm}				558	526.5		478	419		29
		A_{mM}				30.6	17.0		12.3	157		
Dipyridine iron(II) protoporphyrin IX dimethyl ester	0.1 to 1M pyridine in benzene	λ_{nm}				555	523		473	419		17
		A_{mM}				30.8	15.1		13.7	166		

Compound	Solvent	λ_{nm} / A_{mM} (or λ / ε)						Ref.
Pyridine carbonyl iron(II) protoporphyrin IX dimethyl ester	pyridine-benzene		564 / 14.3	534 / 13.8		417 / 172		17
Heme a	pyridine-aq. NaOH-$Na_2S_2O_4$		587 / 27.4					30
Chlorophyll a	ether	622 / 90.2	615 / 14.6	578 / 8.3	534 / 3.8	430 / 117.5	410 / 76.1	32, 33
	80% acetone	665 / 81.1	618 / 17.5	582 / 10.4	536 / 4.3	433 / 60.7		34
Chlorophyll b	ether	644 / 56.3	595 / 11.5	549 / 6.4	455 / 158.6	430 / 56.9	375 / 19.8	32, 33
	80% acetone	649 / 47.6	600 / 13			460 / 134.3		34

Table IV. Suggested Assignments for Absorption of Porphyrins in the Infrared[17, 18, 22]

Vibrational Assignments: 1800–635 cm^{-1}		Hydrogen Stretching Vibrations		
Ester carbonyl stretching vibration	1740–1725	Formyloxime	νOH	3367
Aromatic skeletal vibration	1675–1667	Pyrrole NH	νNH	3333–3300
Aromatic skeletal vibration	1625–1608	Acetyloxime	νOH	3330
Aromatic skeletal vibration	1597–1580	Methine (meso)	νCH	3125–3077
Aromatic skeletal vibration	1565–1550	Vinyl	νCH$_2$	3106–3077
Aromatic skeletal vibration	1540–1515	Vinyl	νCH	3012–2976
Aromatic skeletal vibration	1515–1498	Acetyl Methyl	ν_aCH$_3$	3003–2976
Aromatic skeletal vibration	1486–1475	Alkyl Methyl	ν_aCH$_3$	2985–2967
Aromatic skeletal vibration	1455–1440	Methyl Ester	ν_aCH$_3$	2959
Methyl ester CH$_3$ deformation	1443–1433	*Beta*-CH$_3$	ν_aCH$_3$	2941–2924
Symmetric *beta*-CH$_3$ deformation	1381–1359	Ethyl Ester	ν_aCH$_2$	2915–2907
Unassigned porphyrin ring deformation	1280–1250	Symmetric CH$_2$ and CH$_3$	νCH$_2$ + νCH$_3$	2890–2849
Unassigned porphyrin ring deformation	1235–1210	Formyl	νCH	2747–2740
Unassigned porphyrin ring deformation	1205–1185			
Methyl ester COC stretching vibration	1175–1156			
Pyrrole out of phase breathing deformation	1122–1103			
Unassigned porphyrin ring deformation	1075–1055			
In plane *beta*-CH deformation	1065–1045			
Unassigned porphyrin ring deformation	1035–1018			
In plane pyrrole NH deformation	990–975			
Out of plane *beta*-CH deformation	845–820			
In phase combination of out of plane pyrrole ring deformations	755–720			
Out of phase combination of in plane pyrrole ring deformations	720–690			
Out of plane pyrrole NH deformation	680–675			

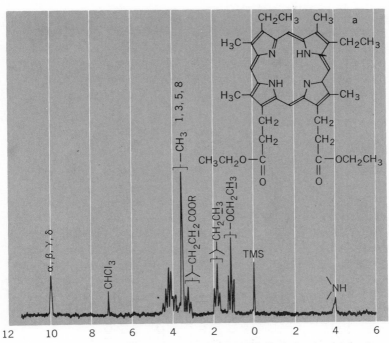

Figure 5.   NMR spectrum of mesoporphyrin IX diethyl ester in deutero-chloroform, 20 mg in 0.4 ml (31).

Table V. Porphyrin NMR Spectra[19, 22-26]

	Solvent	Proton	δ	Refs.
Protoporphyrin IX dimethyl ester	CDCl$_3$ (inf. diln.)	vinyl H$_1$ vinyl H$_2$ vinyl H$_3$	3.36 J_{12}= 12cps 6.34 J_{23}= 18cps 6.17	22
	2.5% F$_3$CCOOH in CDCl$_3$	vinyl H$_2$ vinyl H$_3$	6.44 J_{12}= 12cps 6.27 J_{23}= 18cps	22
Deuteroporphyrin IX dimethyl ester	CDCl$_3$ (inf. diln.) 2.5% F$_3$CCOOH in CDCl$_3$	2,4 H 2,4 H	9.12 9.43	22
2(and 4)-formyl-4(and 2)-vinyl-deuteroporphyrin IX dimethyl ester	2.5% F$_3$CCOOH in CDCl$_3$	formyl	11.59	22
Hematoporphyrin dimethyl ester	CDCl$_3$(inf. diln.)	α-hydroxyethyl CH α-hydroxyethyl CH$_3$	6.14 2.06	22
Mesoporphyrin IX dimethyl ester	CDCl$_3$ (inf. diln.) 2.5% F$_3$CCOOH in CDCl$_3$	2,4 ethyl CH$_2$ 2,4 ethyl CH$_3$ 2,4 ethyl CH$_2$ 2,4 ethyl CH$_3$	4.30 1.84 4.17 1.74	22
Uroporphyrin I	CDCl$_3$	propionic ester OCH$_3$ αCH$_2$ βCH$_2$ acetic ester OCH$_3$ CH$_2$	3.69 4.42 3.33 3.78 5.11	24

Table VI. Mössbauer Parameters for Hemin and Heme Compounds[21]

Compound	T(°K)	Quadrupole splitting ΔE (mm/sec)	Isomer shift δE^* (mm/sec)	Line Width Higher-energy	Lower-energy (mm/sec)†	Relative areas of the two lines (approx.)	Qualitative temperature transition (°K)
2,4-Diacetyldeuterohemin chloride dimethyl ester	298	0.89 ± 0.02‡	+0.09 ± 0.02	0.72	2.45	Equal	12–30
	77	0.81 ± 0.02	+0.05 ± 0.02	0.79	2.50	Equal	
	4.6	0.85 ± 0.02	−0.05 ± 0.02	0.47	0.47	Equal	
Mesohemin chloride dimethyl ester	298	0.94 ± 0.02	+0.07 ± 0.02	0.74	2.40	Equal	15–30
	77	0.89 ± 0.02	+0.04 ± 0.02	0.84	2.60	Equal	
	4.6	0.89 ± 0.02	−0.06 ± 0.02	0.48	0.48	Equal	
Protohemin chloride	298	1.06 ± 0.02	+0.20 ± 0.02	0.76	2.40	Equal	15–35
	77	1.04 ± 0.02	+0.11 ± 0.02	0.79	2.45	Equal	
	4.6	1.02 ± 0.02	−0.08 ± 0.02	0.48	0.48	Equal	
Bispyridine, 2,4-diacetyldeuteroheme dimethyl ester§	298	1.18 ± 0.02	+0.11 ± 0.02	0.40	0.40	Equal	No low-temperature transition
	77	1.11 ± 0.02	+0.05 ± 0.02	0.52	0.52	Equal	
	4.6	1.08 ± 0.02	−0.02 ± 0.02	0.52	0.52	Equal	
Bispyridine mesoheme dimethyl ester§	77	0.63 ± 0.02	+0.02 ± 0.02	0.55	0.55	Equal	No low-temperature transition
	4.6	0.65 ± 0.02	−0.08 ± 0.02	0.55	0.55	Equal	

* Isomer shifts are corrected for temperature differences between source and absorber.
† Standard error ± 0.02 mm/sec.
‡ Errors given are the resolution of the spectrometer. Somewhat greater errors (±0.04 mm/sec) are involved in the hemin parameters at 298°K and 77°K because the overlapping curves have different widths and the determination of their centroids is more difficult.
§ The bispyridine deuteroheme gives the same splittings in crystalline form or in frozen pyridine solution. The bispyridine mesoheme was examined only in frozen pyridine solution.

BIBLIOGRAPHY

References:

1. Fischer, H., and H. Orth, "Qualitative und Quantitative Nachweisreaktionen in der Porphyrinreihe," *Die Chemie des Pyrrols*, 2:579, 1937.
2. Caughey, W. S., et al., "Electronic Spectra of Substituted Metal Deuteroporphyrins," *J. Mol. Spectr.*, 16:451, 1965.
3. Gurinovich, G. P., A. N. Sevchenko, and K. N. Solov'ev, "The Spectroscopy of the Porphyrins," *Soviet Phys. Usp.*, 6:67, 1963.
4. Falk, J. E., *Porphyrins and Metalloporphyrins*, 1964.
5. "Criteria of Purity of Porphyrins and Related Compounds," in *Specifications and Criteria for Biochemical Compounds*, In Press.
6. Caughey, W. S., and W. Y. Fujimoto, Unpublished.
7. Stern, A., and H. Wenderlein, "Uber die Lichtabsorption der Porphyrine," *Z. Physik. Chem.*, A170:337, 1934.
8. Falk, J. E., and A. Johnson, Unpublished.
9. Granick, S., and L. Bogorad, and H. Jaffe, "Hematoporphyrin IX, a Probable Precursor of Protoporphyrin in the Biosynthetic Chain of Heme and Chlorophyll," *J. Biol. Chem.*, 202:801, 1953.
10. Mauzerall, D., "The Thermodynamic Stability of Porphyrinogens," *J. Am. Chem. Soc.*, 82:2601, 1960.
11. Stern, A., and H. Wenderlin, "Über die Lichtabsorption der Porphyrine (II)," *Z. Physik. Chem.*, 174:81, 1935.
12. Stern, A., and H. Molvig, "Uber die Lichtabsorption der Porphyrine (VIII)," *Z. Physik. Chem.*, 177:365, 1936.
13. Kleinspehn, G. G., A. E. Briod, and W. S. Caughey, *J. Org. Chem.*, In Press
14. Rimington, C., "Spectral-Absorption Coefficients of Some Porphyrins in the Soret-Band Region," *Biochem. J.*, 75:620, 1960.
15. Mauzerall, D., and S. Granick, "Porphyrin Biosynthesis in Erythrocytes. III. Uroporphyrinogen and its decarboxylase," *J. Biol. Chem.*, 232:1141, 1958.
16. Clezy, P. S., and D. B. Morell, "A Spectroscopic Study of Haematin Compounds. The Porphyrins," *J. Chem. Soc.*, p. 976, 1958.
17. Alben, J. O., and W. S. Caughey, Unpublished.
18. Mason, S. F., "The Infrared Spectra of N-Heteroaromatic Systems. Part I. The Porphyrins," *J. Chem. Soc.*, p. 976, 1958.
19. Caughey, W. S., and P. K. Iber, "Ring Nonplanarity and Aromaticity in Porphyrins. Nuclear Magnetic Resonance Spectra of Etioporphyrin II and its N-Alkyl Compounds," *J. Org. Chem.*, 28:269, 1963.
20. Caughey, W. S., and S. McCoy, in *International Symposium on the Biochemistry of Copper*, In Press, 1965.
21. Bearden, A. J., et al., *Proc. Natl. Acad. Sci. U.S.* 53:1246, 1965.
22. Caughey, W. S., et al., *J. Org. Chem.*, In Press.
23. Abraham, R. J., A. H. Jackson, and G. W. Kenner, "The Proton Magnetic Resonance Spectra of Porphyrins. Part I. The Effect of β-Substitution on the Proton Chemical Shifts of Porphyrins," *J. Chem. Soc.*, p. 3468, 1961.
24. Becker, E. D., R. B. Bradley, and C. J. Watson, "Proton Magnetic Resonance Studies of Porphyrins," *J. Am. Chem. Soc.*, 83:3743, 1961.
25. Caughey, W. S., and W. S. Koski, "Nuclear Magnetic Resonance Spectra of Porphyrins," *Biochemistry*, 1:923, 1962.
26. Abraham, R. J., et al., *Proc. Chem. Soc.*, p. 134, 1963.

27. Maehly, A. C., and A. Akeson, "Stabilization of Aqueous Hemin Solutions," *Acta Chem. Scand.*, 12:1259, 1958.

28. Gregg, C. A., B. D. McLees, and W. S. Caughey, Unpublished.

29. Gallagher, W. A., and W. B. Elliott, "The Formation of Pyridine Haemochromogen," *Biochem. J.*, 97:187, 1965.

30. Warburg, O., H. S. Gewitz, and W. Volker, "Uber Gewinnung und Abbau des Cytohämins," *Z. Naturforsch.*, 10b:541, 1955.

31. Caughey, W. S., Unpublished.

32. Smith, J. H. C., and A. Benitez, "Chlorophylls: Analysis in Plant Materials," *Modern Methods of Plant Analysis*, 4:142, 1955.

33. Anderson, A. H. F., and M. Calvin, "An Improved Method for the Separation and Purification of Chlorophyll A," *Nature*, 194:285, 1962.

34. Vernon, L. P., "Spectrophotometric Determination of Chlorophylls and Pheophytins in Plant Extracts," *Anal. Chem.*, 32:1144, 1960.

35. Parker, M. J., "The Cryptoporphyrin of Heart Muscle," *Biochim. Biophys. Acta*, 35:496, 1959.

INTRODUCTION

Purification and separation are essentially the same operation. Purification usually implies the separation of small amounts of impurities from a mixture which consists largely of one component. Since substances produced by living processes are almost never completely pure, an appropriate separation or purification technique must be employed in order to obtain a pure form. Some brief descriptions of purification procedures follow.

RECRYSTALLIZATION

Recrystallization consists of dissolving the substance to be purified in a suitable solvent, usually at the boiling point; filtering the hot solution to remove insoluble material; and allowing the hot solution to cool. Crystallization of the dissolved material then takes place. In the ideal situation, nearly all of the material being purified will separate in a crystalline form, and the soluble impurities will remain dissolved. An appropriate solvent is one in which the substance dissolves readily at the boiling point, but is insoluble at lower temperatures while the impurities remain in solution. If no recommendation exists concerning a suitable solvent, common solvents may be tested experimentally. Occasionally, a mixture of two solvents works better than any one alone. Such solvent-pairs are made up of two mutually soluble liquids, one which dissolves the substance readily and another which dissolves it sparingly. Examples are acetone-hexane and methanol-water systems.

When two or more components of a mixture are to be separated in a pure state, it is often necessary to perform a series of preliminary partial purifications. This technique is called fractional crystallization. One method involves separation into a series of fractions by cooling slowly to a selected temperature and collecting a first crop of crystals, then cooling the mother liquor to a lower temperature than before and collecting a second fraction of crystals, and so on. Another method is to bring the material into solution in one solvent and effect fractional crystallization by the stepwise addition of a second solvent. For example, the purification of water-soluble proteins involves their extraction from cells by water, followed by crystallization by adding organic solvents, or by altering the concentration of salts and/or hydrogen ions.

DISTILLATION

This procedure is very useful in the purification of volatile substances. Traces of impurities which are either non-volatile or slightly volatile are easily removed. In its simplest case, distillation is the volatilization of a liquid by the application of heat and the subsequent condensation of the vapor back to the liquid state. Although this is very efficient for the separation of mixtures of liquids whose boiling points are more than 80°C apart, it is not so efficient if the boiling points of the components are very close to each other. Fractional distillation can be employed to separate the latter type of mixture.

Fractional distillation consists of collecting fractions of the distillate as the boiling point of the mixture is progressively increased. The first fraction from a number of fractions will be richer in the more volatile component and the last fraction will contain the largest proportion of the less volatile component. Further concentration of the two components can be achieved by fractionally distilling each of the fractions collected and combining the more and less volatile parts of each with the appropriate portions of other fractions. This process can be repeated with steadily improved results, but the operation becomes time-consuming.

A much better method is to employ a fractionating column. This is a vertical column fitted with a "packing" in which the vapors can condense and flow back into the distilling flask. Before the liquid returns, it is revaporized. In this manner, a given portion of vapor on its way up the column is redistilled many times before it is finally collected. The degree of separation which is obtained depends on the efficiency of a given column, the difference in boiling points of components, and the heats of vaporization of the components of the mixture.

Frequently, two or more components form azeotropic mixtures of a definite and constant composition, which have a constant boiling point and behave like one homogeneous liquid. The components of such a mixture cannot be separated by fractional distillation.

Steam distillation consists of volatilizing an organic compound which is sparingly soluble in water, by passing steam into a mixture of the substance with a little water. The organic compound will distill with the steam and, since it is immiscible with water, is easily separated. This type of distillation is not always applicable, since all organic compounds do not steam easily. Where it can be used, however, it has certain advantages. It is an excellent way of separating a component from an aqueous mixture containing inorganic salts, or of separating a substance which is volatile with steam from other components which are not. Another advantage is that the temperature of this operation is always lower than the boiling point of water.

There are many substances which cannot be distilled satisfactorily in the ordinary way, either because they boil at such high temperatures that some decomposition occurs, or because they are sensitive to the oxygen in the air. In such cases, purification can be accomplished by distilling under diminished pressure (20 mm Hg or below). In this manner the boiling point is lowered and there is less chance of decomposition or oxidation. This is also called vacuum distillation.

Distillation at very high vacuum (0.001 mm Hg) is called either molecular distillation or evaporative distillation. A molecular still is any still in which the distance between the evaporating surface and the condenser surface is less than the mean free path of the vapor molecules. The simplest separation is the distillation of the desired substance from a residue of higher molecular weight. The degree of separation is comparable to that produced by the simple distillation of a two-component mixture when components differ in boiling point by 50°C or more. The great advantage is that the boiling point of high molecular weight and high-boiling substances is greatly reduced. This technique is particularly adapted to the purification of a substance which is difficult or impossible to distill at ordinary pressures. Numerous fractionations of fats and oils, fatty acids, sterols, vitamins, etc. have been successfully achieved by this technique.

ADSORPTION CHROMATOGRAPHY

Adsorption chromatography was developed by Tswett in 1906. This process is dependent on the differences in the degree to which the components of a mixture are adsorbed on the surface of some solid substance. The separation of the mixture depends on the adsorption tendencies of the components for the solid adsorbent and for the solvent.

A vertical column is prepared by packing with an anhydrous adsorbent (stationary phase). The column is saturated with whatever solvent will be employed, and the sample solution is poured on the column. The column is developed with either the same solvent or another one, whereupon the components of the mixture separate. The various constituents of the sample which form zones or bands can be removed either by extruding and manual separation, or by eluting with the solvent, one at a time.

The method was originally applied to colored substances, since they can be observed as unique bands on the column. However, any method which can be used to identify a substance, or to locate it on the column, can be employed. Fluorescence under ultraviolet irradiation and radioactivity have also been quite successful in locating bands. Another technique is to carry out an elution and follow the weight of the substance in each eluted fraction.

Some typical adsorbents and solvents employed in column adsorption chromatography are listed below:

SOLVENTS	ADSORBENTS
petroleum ether	starch, cellulose
carbon tetrachloride	sucrose
ethyl ether	talc
acetone	calcium carbonate
benzene	magnesium oxide
alcohol	silica gel
water	aluminum oxide

The adsorbent must not interact with the solute or solvent. Usually some knowledge of the sample constituents is required, if the proper adsorbent and solvent is to be selected.

The process of separating a mixture into a series of bands on a column is referred to as development. A chromatogram is the resulting pattern of bands which is produced, and the final step of washing out the bands is called elution. One of the greatest advantages associated with chromatographic techniques is the simplicity of the apparatus. This procedure can be used to remove small traces of impurities as well as to resolve complex mixtures of biochemical substances.

PARTITION CHROMATOGRAPHY

This technique is a form of column chromatography in which a solid adsorbent acts as a support for a stationary liquid phase. Such a phase is immiscible with the sample solvent. As the solutes pass through the column, they are continuously partitioned between the immobile liquid phase and the moving solvent phase. This produces a differential migration of the various constituents in the sample.

A mixture of amino acids may be chromatographed by placing it on a column of powdered starch saturated with water (stationary liquid phase), and separated by the use of certain solvents such as butanol (mobile liquid phase). The order of separation parallels the partition coefficients of the amino acids between the employed solvent and water. Since starch will take up much water, the amino acids dissolve in the water of the column, and the flowing solvent extracts the component amino acids in proportion to their relative solubilities in the two liquid phases. The solvent, in moving downward, tends to carry with it those acids which have the least tendency to dissolve in water, while the acids with the largest distribution coefficients are held more firmly by the column. In this way the mixture of acids can be collected separately as the acids are eluted from the column.

The operating techniques of partition chromatography are the same as for adsorption chromatography, only the mechanism for retarding the flow of solutes being different. Adsorption chromatography generally involves a relatively non-polar moving phase. This works best when the components to be separated are fairly non-polar. The advantages over partition chromatography are that larger amounts can be separated and that it is not necessary to control the temperature. Partition chromatography usually involves polar solvents and mixtures of fairly polar components such as amino acids or carbohydrates. Carefully controlled atmosphere and temperature are required.

PAPER CHROMATOGRAPHY

The use of filter paper for chromatographic purposes is a remarkable development because of its simplicity, its versatility, and its widespread applicability. The basic principle is very simple. A drop of solution containing a mixture of compounds is evaporated to dryness on a piece of filter paper. A suitable solvent is allowed to flow slowly along the paper over the spot, either by capillary action (ascending) or by gravity (descending). The substances in the initial spot are picked up by the moving solvent and carried along the paper to an extent which is related to their distribution between the water phase of the filter paper and the solvent. After the solvent has moved over a suitable distance, the paper is quickly dried. Suitable tests are then made on the filter paper in order to locate the various components. It is found that each component present has been carried away from the initial spot to a characteristic length and appears in a relatively small area on the paper. The ratio of the distance the compound moves along the paper to the distance covered by the solvent front is called the R_F value, which is characteristic for each component in the original mixture. The absolute value of R_F is dependent on the nature of the solvent, the temperature, and the presence of other substances which might influence distribution between water and solvent.

Two-dimensional chromatography is an improved procedure of paper chromatography. Here the spot containing the sample is placed in one corner of a square piece of filter paper. The solvent is run along the edge of the paper, distributing the components along the edge of the paper. After drying, the paper is rotated 90° and a second solvent is allowed to run across the paper at right angles to the direction of flow by the first solvent. In this way the various substances along the edge are moved to the middle regions of the paper. By the careful use of this technique, the compounds separated can be localized in a small area of the filter paper. This area may be cut out and the compound extracted from the paper.

Paper chromatography is one of the most effective means of resolving mixtures on a microscale. This fact, along with its simplicity and the relatively inexpensive apparatus required, is its greatest advantage. Since it is a partition technique with the stationary phase held on a piece of paper, it works best with polar developers and small amounts of polar substances.

GAS CHROMATOGRAPHY

A gaseous material is passed through a column containing a solid adsorbent (gas solid chromatography) or a liquid phase supported on an inert solid (gas liquid chromatography). When a liquid is used, the differences in the partition coefficients for the gaseous constituents between the gas and liquid phases are the basis of separation. The differences in adsorption coefficients are the basis when a solid adsorbent is employed.

The apparatus consists of a glass or metal tube, filled with a suitable packing. The column is enclosed in a thermostated oven. The intake end is provided with regulating valves for introducing the gas, and a sample injector. An inert carrier gas such as helium is passed through the column. The sample is introduced into the gas phase and carried through the column. The separated components are eluted in the gas phase and pass into a detector. Several types of detectors are available. The common types are thermal conductivity, ionization, and electron captive. The detector provides a signal which is proportional to the amount of a particular constituent being eluted. Through connection to an amplifier-reader system, it furnishes a peak for each eluted substance.

This technique can be utilized to separate the components of mixtures if they have at least some vapor pressure at a workable temperature. Commercially available preparative scale instruments can separate sample mixtures as large as 100 ml. The most important advantages are the high degree of resolution, and the small sample size requirement.

THIN-LAYER CHROMATOGRAPHY

Thin-layer chromatography is adsorptive in nature and combines the simplicity of paper chromatography with the speed of gas chromatography. Thin-layer chromatography is sometimes called 'thin-film,' 'open column,' or 'chromatoplate' chromatography. This is a type of adsorption chromatography where the adsorbent is a thin layer of a solid deposited on a glass plate support. Its operation is analogous to paper chromatography. The substance to be separated is placed a short distance from one end of the layer and is resolved by a solvent passing through the layer by capillary action. The development is carried out in a simple closed system but is much more rapid than paper chromatography. When the proper solvent mixtures are used, the technique can become a partition method. This method shows promise as a preparative one for quantities of one gram or less.

The use of this technique is now almost routine in natural product, pharmaceutical, and lipid laboratories. Although the applications to various aspects of non-lipid biochemistry have been hampered by the very polar molecules involved, these problems are being overcome, rather rapidly, by the introduction of new adsorbents.

Any finely divided material having the desired adsorptive structural properties can be used as the thin-layer solid. An area with potential for future development is the use of mixed adsorbents as thin layers.

ION EXCHANGE

This method resembles chromatography in that the liquid sample is allowed to pass through a column of granular solid material. The separation, however, is based on an entirely different principle and applies only to substances which are ionized. Two kinds of procedures exist. One is concerned with the exchange of cations and the other with the exchange of anions.

A cation exchanger consists of an insoluble polymeric resin with numerous negatively-charged functional groups. An example is RSO_3H, where R represents the polymeric portion. An exchange with a sodium ion can be illustrated as follows:

$$R-SO_3H + Na^+ \rightleftharpoons R-SO_3Na + H^+$$

The resin can be regenerated to original hydrogen form by washing it with a solution of acid. This action releases the sodium ion.

Similarly, resins which contain amine groups $(-NH_2)$ can act in an analogous manner exchanging anions, thus:

$$R-NH_3OH + Cl^- \rightleftharpoons RNH_3Cl + OH^-$$

The exchange proceeds by chemical equivalents, and the resin can be regenerated to the hydroxyl form by washing it with a strongly basic solution.

Since, in many cases, the differences between similarly charged ionic species are not large enough, a separation by ion exchange must be made by an elution or displacement chromatographic technique. The ions to be separated are adsorbed at the top of the column and eluted with a developing solvent. Elution results in a series of adsorptions and desorptions of the ionic species. If the differences in exchange potentials are great enough, it is possible to achieve a complete separation. A mixture of bases on a cation exchanger may be released individually by the use of elution solutions of various degrees of acidity.

MISCELLANEOUS METHODS

Solvent extraction is the selective dissolving of the soluble portion of a mixture with an appropriate solvent. This process depends on the difference in solubility of the various constituents in a sample. Liquid-liquid extraction is a physical partitioning process which depends on a favorable distribution of a particular substance between two immiscible solvents. Practical applications are mostly empirical, even though the theory is well known. Extraction procedures are widely accepted both in organic chemistry and biochemistry.

Ion exclusion is a process for the separation of ionic constituents from nonionic materials based on the distribution differences of these two types of solutes between a true aqueous solution and an ion-exchange resin. When an ion-exchange resin is in contact with a dilute water solution of an electrolyte, at equilibrium, the concentration of the electrolyte is greater in the solution than in the resin. When an ion-exchange resin is in contact with an aqueous solution of a non-electrolyte, at equilibrium, equivalent amounts of the non-electrolyte are dispersed in the water and resin phase. The absorption involved here is not an ion exchange. Alternate fractions of electrolytes and nonelectrolytes can be collected from a column packed with an ion-exchange resin, if one alternately pours sample solution and water through it. The resin is never exhausted, since no ion exchange is taking place.

Dialysis is a diffusion separation process in which there is a spontaneous flow of solute particles from a concentrated solution to a more dilute one through a semipermeable membrane. This is a common method of separating salts from colloidal suspensions. Synthetic membranes have been so refined that, for example, a separation of urea from glycerol can be accomplished without any difficulty. This method has found considerable application in the field of biochemistry.

Biological activity should not be overlooked as a method of separation or purification because such a process can be extremely selective. The metabolic selectivity of microorganisms, animals, and higher plants can be useful in separative or preparative work. Consider, for example, the metabolism of only one of a pair of optical isomers by some bacteria. A microorganism may also provide an enzyme for a specific reaction. This enzyme may then be employed either to remove impurities or convert the substance to be purified into some other suitable form which can, in turn, be more easily isolated.

BIBLIOGRAPHY

Berg, Eugene W., *Physical and Chemical Methods of Separation,* 1963.
Bobbitt, James M., *Thin-Layer Chromatography,* 1963.
Dal Nogare, Stephen, and Richard S. Juvet, Jr., *Gas-Liquid Chromatography,* 1962.
Wiberg, Kenneth B., *Laboratory Technique in Organic Chemistry,* 1960.

INSTRUMENTATION: THE DETERMINATION OF THE MOLECULAR STRUCTURE OF ORGANIC COMPOUNDS BY PHYSICAL METHODS

INTRODUCTION

Modern instrumental methods of analysis have greatly simplified the task of structure determination, both for the biochemist and for the organic chemist. In addition, these modern analytical tools have often been used to follow reaction rates and to determine reaction mechanisms.

Since modern analytical methods are of such importance to the chemist working with organic molecules, it is not surprising that a multitude of review articles and books have been written on various instrumental methods, within the last five years alone. The selection of references given below offers a fairly comprehensive overview of the field.

Many of the modern analytical techniques used in the determination of organic structures depend on the absorption or emission of electromagnetic radiation of various wavelengths. As shown in Table I, this range of wavelengths has an associated energy scale which is inversely proportional to the wavelength, i.e., the higher the wavelength, the lower the associated energy. In certain cases, the division of the spectrum into regions is artificial, since such divisions are determined by the available instrumentation.

Reference works discussing instrumental analytical methods of biochemical interest include:

Bentley, K. W. (ed.), *Technique of Organic Chemistry*, Vol. 11, Pt. 1, 1963.

Flett, M. St. C., *Physical Aids to the Organic Chemist*, 1962.

Katritzky, A. R. (ed.), *Physical Methods in Heterocyclic Chemistry*, Vol. 2, 1963.

Nachod, F. C., and W. D. Phillips (eds.), *Determination of Organic Structures by Physical Methods*, 1962.

Schwartz, J. C. P. (ed.), *Physical Methods in Organic Chemistry*, 1964.

Silverstein, R. M., and G. C. Bassler, *Spectrometric Identification of Organic Compounds*, 1963.

Table I. Associated Energy Scales

Region	Range	Normal Units	Approximate Energy $\left(\dfrac{Kcal.}{mole}\right)$	Type of Interaction of Radiation with Sample
X-ray	0.5–10A° $(5 \times 10^{-9}\text{–}10^{-7}\text{cm.})$	Ångströms	10^5	Since molecular dimensions are of the same size as the incident radiation diffraction phenomena are observed
Ultraviolet	185–400 mμ $(1.85 \times 10^{-5}\text{–}4.0 \times 10^{-5}\text{cm.})$	mμ	10^2	Electronic excitation of valence shell electron to an excited state is observed
Visible	400–700 mμ $(4 \times 10^{-5}\text{–}7 \times 10^{-5}\text{cm.})$	mμ	40	
Near-infrared	0.7–2.7 μ 14500–3700 cm.$^{-1}$ $(7 \times 10^{-5}\text{–}2.7 \times 10^{-4}\text{cm.})$	μ or cm^{-1}	10	Excitation of molecular vibration occurs
Infrared	2.5 $\times$ 35 μ 4000–300 cm.$^{-1}$ $(2.5 \times 10^{-4}\text{–}3.5 \times 10^{-3}\text{cm.})$	μ or cm^{-1}	1–5	

ULTRAVIOLET SPECTROSCOPY

The absorption of ultraviolet energy by an organic molecule results in an electron transition of a valence shell electron to an excited electronic state. For simple saturated organic molecules this type of excitation occurs below 185 mμ. Organic molecules containing non-bonding electrons or π electrons generally absorb light of a wavelength greater than 185 mμ; it is with these molecules that ultraviolet and visible spectroscopy find their application.

Single chromophores such as isolated double bonds and atoms with non-bonded electrons can often be identified by their absorption of ultraviolet energy in the vicinity of 200 mμ. Amines, sulfides and alkyl halides all show n $\rightarrow$ σ^* absorptions in this region. These n $\rightarrow$ σ^* absorptions are generally weak by comparison since their extinction coefficients (ε) rarely surpass 5,000. The intensity of the absorption is measured in terms of the extinction coefficient (ε) which is defined by the equation $\varepsilon = \dfrac{A}{bc}$, where A is the absorbance, b is the cell length in centimeters and c is the concentration in moles per liter. The maximum value possible for ε is somewhere between 10^5 and 10^6.

Simple non-conjugated olefins have characteristic end absorptions in the vicinity of 200 mμ due to a $\pi \rightarrow \pi^*$ electronic transition. These molecules have extinction coefficients of 10,000–20,000. Other isolated organic chromophores which contain π electrons also have characteristic absorptions. Among this group are included

$$-C{=}O, \quad -N{=}N-, \quad -C{=}S, \quad -N{=}O, \text{ and } -C{\equiv}N.$$

The most important application of ultraviolet spectroscopy is in the identification of conjugated π systems such as

$$\overset{|}{-}C{=}\overset{|}{C}{-}\overset{|}{C}{=}O \text{ and } \overset{|}{-}C{=}\overset{|}{C}{-}\overset{|}{C}{=}\overset{|}{C}{-}.$$

From the position of the absorption maximum and the peak intensity one can often identify the nature of the unsaturation and the molecular environment of the conjugated system. Application of Woodward's Rules is extremely useful in identifying the nature of conjugated unsaturation in structures such as are commonly found in steroid molecules. Several useful references are available:

Gilliam, A. E., and E. S. Stern, *Electronic Absorption Spectroscopy,* 1958.

Hershenson, H. M., *Ultraviolet and Visible Absorption Spectra-Index 1930–1959,* 1961.

Jaffé, H. H. and M. Orchin, *Theory and Applications of Ultraviolet Spectroscopy,* 1962.

Scott, A. I., *Interpretation of the Ultraviolet Spectra of Natural Products,* 1964.

INFRARED SPECTROSCOPY

Infrared spectroscopy might be described as the workhorse of the organic chemist because no other instrumental method can routinely supply as much information as fast. The absorption of infrared energy results in an excitation of the vibrational modes of the organic molecule. Since each functional group has a characteristic frequency at which it absorbs infrared radiation, the types of functional groups present in a molecule can generally be rapidly identified. The region of the spectrum from 2.5 to 7.0 μ is that where most of the functional groups show their fundamental stretching frequency; this has come to be known as the "functional group region." That portion of the spectrum from 7 to 15 μ is more characteristic of the molecule as a whole than of the functional groups. Since this region is different for every molecule it is commonly called the "fingerprint region." Infrared spectroscopy is quite useful in both the quantitative and the qualitative analysis of organic compounds.

Phenomena such as hydrogen bonding are readily studied by infrared methods. Such investigations can be carried out either with the fundamental stretching modes which occur in the regular infrared or with the first overtone of the fundamental stretching vibration which occurs in the near-infrared region of the spectrum. Rao has presented a survey of the chemical applications of infrared spectrosco[.].

Bellamy, L. J., *The Infra-red Spectra of Complex Molecules*, 1958.
Nakanishi, K., *Infrared Absorption Spectroscopy—Practical*, 1962.
Rao, C. N. R., *Chemical Applications of Infrared Spectroscopy*, 1963.
Szymanski, H. A., *IR—Theory and Practices of Infrared Spectroscopy*, 1964.

NUCLEAR MAGNETIC RESONANCE

Nuclear magnetic resonance (NMR) has had a greater impact on structural elucidation than has any other instrumental method in recent years. Although the general use of NMR is less than ten years old, the accumulated data is overwhelming.

When an organic molecule is placed in a strong magnetic field (14,000 gauss) the protons act like tiny magnets and orient themselves either with or against the applied field. When these protons are irradiated at a resonance frequency (generally 60 megacycles), transitions between alignment and non-alignment occur. Since there is a finite excess of nuclei in the lower energy state, this transition can be measured. Spectra are measured by holding the resonance frequency constant while making very small changes in the applied magnetic field. Since protons in different environments absorb a given radiofrequency at slightly different applied magnetic fields, a spectrum is obtained. The intensities of the peaks obtained in an NMR spectrum are proportional to the number of protons producing the peak. Thus NMR can be used to determine the molecular environments of protons and to count the number of protons in these different environments. In addition to peak position and intensity, the peak due to a given proton will show complex splitting patterns as a result of interactions with neighboring protons. This "spin-spin coupling" allows the assignment of proton positions in the molecule relative to each other.

In addition to elucidating the environment of nuclei, NMR is useful in establishing the presence of certain functional groups, determining conformation and configuration, and studying reaction rates, especially those of fast reactions.

Oxygen (O^{16}) and carbon (C^{12}) having spin numbers of zero do not give NMR signals. However, atoms with spin numbers other than zero do give NMR spectra. Thus the molecular environment of atoms such as B^{11}, C^{13}, N^{14}, N^{15}, O^{17}, F^{19}, Si^{29} and P^{31} can be determined by NMR. Detailed accounts of the theory and application of NMR spectroscopy can be found in most of the references listed below:

Bhacca, Norman S. and Dudley H. Williams, *Application of NMR Spectroscopy in Organic Chemistry*, 1963.

Jackman, L. M., *Applications of Nuclear Magnetic Resonance Spectroscopy in Organic Chemistry*, 1959.

Pople, J. A., and W. G. Schneider and H. J. Bernstein, *High-Resolution Nuclear Magnetic Resonance*, 1959.

Roberts, J. D., *An Introduction to the Analysis of Spin-Spin Splitting in High Resolution Nuclear Magnetic Spectra*, 1961.

Roberts, J. D., *Nuclear Magnetic Resonance*, 1959.

Varian Associates, *Varian NMR Spectra Catalog*, 1963.

POLARIMETRY AND OPTICAL ROTATORY DISPERSION

The ability of certain organic compounds to rotate plane polarized light has long been a recognized phenomenon of organic chemistry. In general, measurements have been made at a single wavelength (sodium D line) of materials in solutions. Normally the information obtained from molecular rotation is limited, but this type of measurement has been used to elucidate information about the relative and absolute configuration of asymmetric centers, conformation, and the identity and purity of known compounds.

When the optical rotation of an optically active compound is measured over a range of wavelengths, a curve is obtained. This is called an optical rotatory dispersion curve. When a chromophore such as a carbonyl group is present in the molecule, complex curves are obtained which can yield conclusive evidence for the assignment of absolute configuration. Three sources of further information are:

Djerassi, C., *Optical Rotatory Dispersion*, 1960.

Weissberger, A. (ed.), *Physical Methods of Organic Chemistry*, 3rd ed., Vol. 1, part 3, 1960.

Nachod, F. C., and W. D. Phillips (eds.), *Determination of Organic Structures by Physical Methods*, Vol. 2, 1962.

MASS SPECTROMETRY

One of the most rapidly developing methods of analysis is high-resolution mass spectrometry. This type of analysis is exceptionally useful in proving structures of natural products and in doing routine analysis because of the extremely small sample required ($10\,\mu g - 1$ mg).

Bombardment of the sample with an electron beam yields positively charged ions. These ions, which can either remain intact or fragment, are then accelerated along a circular magnetic path thus yielding a spectrum with peaks related to the mass to charge ratio of the products. This permits extremely accurate molecular weight determination. In addition, the fragmentation pattern of a given compound can often be used to deduce the complete structure of an unknown compound. Mass spectrometry is often the ideal method of analyzing products obtained from studies involving isotopic labelling. The major disadvantage of mass spectrometry is that instrumentation often costs in excess of $100,000.00.

Biemann, K., *Mass Spectrometry—Organic Chemical Applications*, 1962.

Budzikiewicz, H., C. Djerassi and D. H. Williams, *Interpretation of Mass Spectra of Organic Compounds*, 1964.

Budzikiewicz, H., C. Djerassi and D. H. Williams, *Structure Elucidation of Natural Products by Mass Spectrometry*, Vols. 1 and 2, 1964.

McLafferty, F. W., *Mass Spectrometry of Organic Ions*, 1963.

ELECTRON SPIN RESONANCE

Organic molecules having atoms with unpaired electrons are common intermediates in organic chemistry. These compounds are paramagnetic and thus electron spin resonance (ESR) signals can be obtained. These signals are a result of the quantized absorption of energy which occurs when the unpaired electron inverts its spin state in a magnetic field. In general, this technique is not extremely important to the biologically oriented chemist. However, some applications in biochemically interesting systems have been discussed.

Ingram, D. J. E., *Free Radicals as Studied by Electron Spin Resonance*, 1959.

Low, W. (ed.), *Paramagnetic Resonance*, Vol. 2, 1963.

I. ELEMENTAL ANALYSIS

Qualitative Tests. In biological material and organic compounds, elements commonly occurring along with carbon, hydrogen, and oxygen are nitrogen, sulfur, phosphorus, and the halogens (fluorine, chlorine, bromine, iodine). Besides some trace elements, one might expect to find sodium, potassium, calcium, iron, cobalt, zinc, and magnesium in such materials.

The detection of the nonmetallic elements can be accomplished by converting them to water-soluble compounds. This is easily done by fusing the organic material with certain metals. Sodium is used in the majority of cases. The obtained ions are then identified through a number of specific tests (see below).

Detection of N, S, and Halogens (X)
in Organic or Biological Material

$$C, N, S, X \xrightarrow[\text{Heat}]{\text{Na}} \begin{array}{l} \text{NaCN} \\ \text{Na}_2\text{S} \\ \text{NaX} \\ \text{NaCNS} \end{array}$$

Experimental Procedure. A piece of clean sodium metal (a cube with edges of about ½ cm) is placed in a small dry test tube and heated over a Bunsen burner until the metal melts. Very carefully, not more than 10 mg of the compound (or biological material) are added and the heating procedure is repeated until the bottom of the test tube becomes dark red. After cooling, some ethanol is added to destroy excess sodium, and continuously heated again. The test tube is then placed in a beaker containing 25 ml. of distilled water. The tube is broken by crushing its bottom with a glass rod. (Gloves and safety goggles are recommended precautions.) The resulting suspension is briefly heated and filtered. This process should yield a colorless solution, the stock solution, small portions of which are used for the identification tests.

1. Nitrogen. There exist several qualitative tests for the identification of nitrogen, but its detection is sometimes unsatisfactory. This is especially the case if the nitrogen in the original compound is present in the

form of a nitro group. A simple test is often more helpful than most of the more sophisticated color tests discussed below. Treating an organic compound which contains nitrogen with soda-lime very often results in the generation of ammonia. This gas can be detected by its odor or by means of the color change (red-blue) undergone by a moist piece of red litmus paper placed in the stream of gases leaving the test tube.

The cyanide ion can be easily detected by converting it into water-insoluble Prussian blue. An aqueous alkaline solution of this ion is gently heated with Fe^{2+} and Fe^{3+} ions (best as sulfates). After acidification with hydrochloric acid, iron hydroxide dissolves and the desired blue precipitate is left.

$$18 \, NaCN + 3 \, FeSO_4 + 2 \, Fe(SO_4)_3 \longrightarrow Fe_4[Fe(CH)_6]_3 + 9 \, Na_2SO_4$$

2. Sulfur. The sulfide ion is detected by acidifying the aqueous solution with acetic acid in a test tube. The top of the tube should be covered with a piece of moist filter paper saturated with a solution of lead acetate. In case the solution contains the sulfide ion, a dark brown-black spot develops on the filter paper.

If both nitrogen and sulfur are present in the original solution, one can obtain the CNS ion. Adding a small amount of Fe^{3+} ions to its aqueous solution produces a reddish color, due to formation of $Fe(CNS)_3$. It can be extracted into an ether-isoamylalcohol mixture. One observes then a bright red organic layer on top of the colorless aqueous layer.

3. The Halogens. A few milliliters of the stock solution are boiled for a short time after acidification with dilute nitric acid (to destroy CN and HS). A few drops of an aqueous silver nitrate solution when added to the solution will cause a fairly heavy precipitate. An opalescence usually does not indicate the presence of halide ions, it is due rather to the presence of impurities.

If the precipitate is white, only chlorine was present in the original material. A yellowish or yellow color of the precipitate indicates the presence of bromide and iodide as well.

To identify chlorine, bromide and iodine, one proceeds as follows:[1] A few milliliters of the original solution are gently heated for a short while after acidification with dilute sulfuric acid.

Iodine: A few drops of an aqueous sodium nitrate solution are added to a 1 ml sample of the stock solution, after cooling, and shaken with carbon tetrachloride. A violet color of the organic lower layer indicates the presence of iodine. After a positive iodine test, the whole stock solution is treated in this manner, to extract all iodine. One then proceeds to test for *bromine* as follows: A 1 ml sample of the iodine-free stock solution is shaken with chlorine water-carbon tetrachloride. A brown organic layer indicates presence of bromine. For identification of *chlorine*, dilute the original solution to about six times in volume and add 1 to 2 ml concentrated sulfuric acid and 0.5 g of potassium persulfate. After boiling this solution for several minutes, cool and add aqueous silver nitrate. A white precipitate indicates presence of chlorine. *Fluorine.* Since the fluoride ion does not give a precipitate with a silver ion, one can use the original stock solutions for its identification. A few ml are acidified with acetic acid and boiled for several minutes. If a drop of this solution is brought in contact with moist zirconium-alizarin test paper, a yellow coloration indicates presence of fluorine. *Beilstein Test for Halogens.* If a tiny quantity of the original material is placed into the loop of a clean copper wire and heated in the hot part of the flame of a Bunsen burner in the presence of halogens, a persisting green coloration of the flame will be observed.

4. Phosphorus. The organic or biological material is fused in a crucible containing KNO_3 and nitric acid. All organic-bound phosphorus is converted into ortho-phosphoric acid by this process. One dissolves the contents of the crucible in distilled water. A drop of this solution is placed on a piece of filter paper followed by a drop each of ammonium molybdate solution and of benzidine solution. The moist paper is placed over a dish filled with aqueous ammonia. Upon neutralization of the test spot, a blue color slowly develops due to simultaneous formation of molybdenum blue and benzidine blue. The test is very sensitive. It permits detection of 0.05 of P_2O_5. The dilution limit is 1:1,000,000.

Metals like iron, cobalt, zinc, etc., can be identified by normal analytical procedures after destruction of the biological material as indicated above. Since in biological material these cations occur only in minute amounts, attention is directed to analysis by "Spot Tests," a method pioneered and developed by F. Feigl[2] and extremely useful for qualitative detection of very small amounts of materials.

Quantitative Tests. 1. Carbon, Hydrogen, Nitrogen. After qualitative tests have confirmed the presence or absence of elements in a new or unknown compound, one still needs to know the relative amounts of those elements which are present. For carbon and hydrogen, a method is used which goes back to Liebig. The organic compound is heated to about 1000° in a slow stream of oxygen, and undergoes combustion to water and carbon dioxide. The combustion products are passed through an absorption train and the weight difference of the respective absorption tubes (one for water, one for CO_2) is determined by weighing the tubes before and after combustion.

Nitrogen is determined also by a combustion method which was introduced by Dumas also over a century ago. Any oxides of nitrogen which might be present in the combustion products are reduced by passing the gases through a column packed with short copper rods. The gases are then brought into the nitrometer and the volume of nitrogen is measured and reduced to normal conditions by noting temperature and barometric pressure.

2. Oxygen. Oxygen is usually determined indirectly by assuming it to be the difference between 100 per cent and the sum of the percentages of the other elements. It should be mentioned that rather satisfactory methods have recently been developed to permit the direct determination of oxygen. These methods are based upon thermal decomposition of samples at temperatures of about 1100°, the resultant gases being passed over pure carbon kept at the same temperature. All oxygen which was present originally in the compound is converted by this procedure to carbon monoxide. There are two ways in use to estimate the carbon monoxide. By a gravimetric procedure, the CO is oxidized to CO_2 by passing through a heated copper oxide column. The carbon dioxide is absorbed in a weighing tube filled with NaOH on asbestos. The volumetric method consists of determination of iodine formed according to the following equation:

$$5\,CO + I_2O_5 \xrightarrow{\;110°\;} 5\,CO_2 + I_2.$$

There are excellent fully-automated instruments for this type of analysis on the market.

During the last few years, a completely new concept for C, H, and N determination has been introduced by W. Walisch[3] and further developed by F. Korte[4] and collaborators. The composition of the gases is determined by heat conductivity. The advantage of this method seems to be its speed (10 minutes per C, H, N analysis) and the small amounts of material (0.3-1mg) necessary for such an analysis.

3. Sulfur, Halogens, or Phosphorus. In organic or biological material, each is determined quantitatively after conversion into ionized compounds. This can be achieved by heating a compound in a sealed tube with nitric acid (Carius method) or by fusing it with an excess of sodium peroxide in a steel bomb (Parr method). Hydrogen and carbon are burnt to water and carbon dioxide respectively, the halogens are converted into the corresponding sodium halides, sulfur and phosphorus undergo conversion into sodium sulfate and sodium phosphate. These anions are then determined according to usual quantitative procedures, i.e., volumetrically or gravimetrically.

II. MOLECULAR WEIGHT DETERMINATION

Molecular Weights of up to about 2000. Organic compounds, contrary to inorganic compounds, are not sufficiently identified by their empirical formula. As an example, the empirical formula CH_2O is the same for formaldehyde, acetic acid, lactic acid, glyceraldehyde, ribose, glucose, and fructose (and a great number of other carbohydrates). All of these compounds have different molecular formulas. That is, they have different numbers of atoms in the molecule and thus different molecular weights. The formulas for the mentioned compounds are CH_2O, $C_2H_4O_2$, $C_3H_6O_3$, $C_4H_8O_4$, $C_5H_{10}O_5$, and $C_6H_{12}O_6$.

The most common methods for molecular weight determination are the cryoscopic method and the ebullioscopic method. The first makes use of a depression of the freezing point of a known compound caused by the unknown, whereas the latter one makes use of the elevation of the boiling point of a pure compound caused by the presence of a dissolved unknown. The change of the boiling or melting point, Δt, depends on the number of particles (in most organic compounds this number is equal to the number of molecules) of solute dissolved. Thus one gram molecular weight of any substance (provided it does not dissociate either into ions or free radicals) dissolved in 1000 grams of solvent lowers the melting point by $K_{f.p.}$ degrees, or raises the boiling point by $K_{b.p.}$ degrees. If X grams of a substance of molecular weight M are dissolved in G grams of solvent, the following equation can be set up:

$$\Delta t = K \frac{X \cdot 1000}{M \cdot G}$$

$$M = \frac{K \cdot X \cdot 1000}{\Delta t \cdot G}$$

The solvents most widely used are acetic acid, benzene, and camphor; the experimentally determined values for $K_{f.p.}$ are 3.9, 5.1 and 39.7 respectively. The $K_{b.p.}$ values for the first two are 2.07 and 2.5, at 760 mm of mercury, respectively.

Experimentally, the molecular weight determination of an unknown is done by two exact temperature measurements, namely the determination of the boiling (freezing) point of the pure solvent, followed by a similar measurement of a solution of known concentration of the unknown. Since in many cases the changes in boiling (freezing) points are very small, a special thermometer, a Beckmann thermometer, is used; the apparatus is otherwise very simple (see figure 1).

Since, for camphor, the molecular depression of the freezing point (m.p. 178°) is large, an ordinary thermometer can be used. Using camphor as the solvent in determination of molecular weights is known as the Rast method. This method is very useful; it gives values which are exact within about 2–3%. It should be further noted that the value of 39.7 for the molar depression constant for camphor only can be used if the solution is at least 0.2 molar. Solutions of lower concentration give unreliable values.

Molecular Weight Between 2000–20,000. These are much more difficult to determine. The methods described above are not sensitive enough

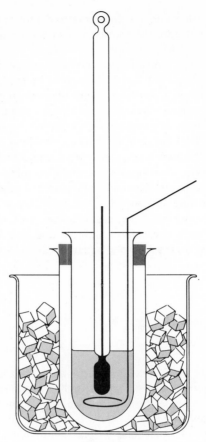

Figure 1.

without considerable (and often difficult) modifications. Furthermore, even if modified, they often are not applicable at all. One useful method for compounds falling in this molecular weight category is the so-called end-group assay. This method often is useful for molecular weight determination of condensation polymers. It has certain limitations, the most important of which are 1) the specific reaction which is used may be accompanied with simultaneous more or less rapid degradation, thus leading to low molecular weights; 2) side-reactions sometimes occur which might invalidate the results obtained; and 3) there has to be at least one characteristic end-group per 100 monohers, since with a lesser number of end-groups the accuracy decreases rapidly; 4) near the molecular weight of 20,000, incomplete reaction between the reagent and the functional group is the rule, thus also invalidating the results. Molecular weight of 20,000 and above afford specialized methods and techniques which are outside the scope of this chapter. A good write-up of methods applicable to this molecular weight range can be found in *Schwarz*.[5]

III. FUNCTIONAL GROUP ANALYSIS

Functional group analysis of organic compounds by chemical methods is now almost obsolete. Through the introduction of instruments, one can often quickly, conveniently and with very little substance measure infrared (IR), nuclear magnetic resonance (NMR), and ultraviolet (UV) spectra of unknowns. Determination and identification of functional groups which occur in a compound are done by correct interpretation of those spectra. The NMR spectrum yields information on the C-H bonds occurring in a compound. Via the IR spectrum of a compound, one can obtain information on the presence of practically all functional groups, in addition to valuable information on its carbon skeleton. To extract information about C-H bonds one needs a specialized knowledge on the interpretation of IR spectra; whereas identification of the other mentioned structural features can be done almost routinely, even by non-spectroscopists.

Ultraviolet spectra generally cannot be used so readily for detection of functional groups. They give information on the structure of the total chromophore (or π-electron system). The cause for this difference is to be found in the causes of these spectra. Whereas the IR spectrum is a molecular spectrum, the UV spectrum is electronic.

Infrared Spectra. In covalent compounds (and practically all organic compounds are covalent compounds) there is a constant stretching, bending, and rotation about the covalent bond. If irradiation by an outside source enters a solution or a mull of an organic compound and if it corresponds to the frequency of the molecular motions of the compounds, part of the outside irradiation is absorbed, thus changing the transmission of the irradiation. By plotting the percentage of transmittance versus frequency, one obtains an IR spectrum with absorption peaks (positions of low transmittance) corresponding to certain (functional) groups.

An IR spectrum can be obtained either from a pure liquid ("neat"), in solution, in suspension (mull), or from a disc. Here the sample is ground with KBr which is transparent in the IR region; this mixture then is formed into a disc or pellet by means of a press.

Solvents which are most commonly used are "nujol" (a purified mineral oil), carbon tetrachloride, chloroform, and carbon disulfide. These

Table I.   Preliminary Scanning Program

1. Absorption at 2.5 to 3.2 μ	O—H, N—H compounds
Check: a. 5.7–6.1	acids
b. 5.9–6.7	amides (usually two bands)
c. 7.5–10.0	—O— compounds
d. about 15.0	primary amines (broad)
2. Sharp absorption at 3.2–3.33	olefins, aromatics
Check: a. 5.0–6.0	benzenoid patterns (weak)
b. 5.95–6.10	olefins
c. 6.10–6.90	aromatics (two bands)
d. 11.0–15.0	aromatics (several very strong bands)
3. Sharp absorption at 3.35–3.55	aliphatics
Check: a. 6.7–7.0	—CH_2— —CH_3
b. 7.1–7.4	—CH_3
c. 13.3–13.9	—$(CH_2)_4$—
4. Two weak bands at 3.4–3.7	aldehydes
Check: 5.7–6.1	aldehydes and ketones
5. Absorption at 4.0–5.0	acetylenes, nitriles
6. Strong sharp bands at 5.4–5.8	esters, acyl halides (1 peak) anhydrides (2 peaks)
Check: 7.5–10.0	—O— compounds
7. Strong sharp bands at 5.7–6.11	aldehydes, ketones and acids
8. Strong bands at 7.5–10.0	—O— compounds (note: may be confused with skeletal bands)
9. Strong bands at 11.0–15.0	aromatics, chlorides

Reproduced by permission of The Macmillan Company from *Elementary Infrared Spectroscopy*, 1963, p. 116, by C. E. Meloan.

solvents are all fairly "empty" or clean in the infrared region, meaning that they are of relative great transparency.

If an infrared spectrum of an unknown is obtained, a quick preliminary scanning will very often provide useful information. Such a scanning program is outlined in Table I.

The results so obtained then should be carefully evaluated and checked against the infrared correlation chart found in Reference 7.

At this point of the structure evaluation of an unknown, one should have the results of elemental analysis and should know which elements other than C, H, and O are present; one also has the information provided by an ultraviolet spectrum. To further elucidate the structure of the unknown, one now should obtain a nuclear magnetic resonance spectrum. This type of spectrum yields information on the position of hydrogen atoms in a molecule, and on the relative number of hydrogen atoms in different environments.

NMR Spectra. If a molecule is placed between the poles of a powerful magnet and subjected to the radio-frequency of an oscillator, absorption of energy occurs. The absorption is connected with a transition of the nuclear spins of magnetically active nuclei. The most important of these, to the organic chemist and biochemist, are hydrogen nuclei. The frequency of the NMR absorption bands depends not only on structural features surrounding the hydrogen atom, but also on the field strength of the external field. The most commonly-used field strength is 14,100 gauss with a radio-frequency of 60 megacycles (Mc).

In order to obtain a NMR spectrum, two requirements have to be fulfilled. First, the sample has to be a liquid of low viscosity or has to be soluble in a suitable solvent to the extent of from 5 to 30 percent. Second, one has to have a reference as a standard against which one can measure the chemical shift. Of the several methods available for obtaining a reference point, the most commonly used is to co-dissolve tetramethylsilane, $(CH_3)_4 Si$, thus obtaining an internal standard. This substance absorbs energy at higher field strength than most other organic compounds. Two units for the chemical shift are in use. The first is delta, δ, which is defined as the chemical shift from the reference compound in cycles per second per million cycles of fixed frequency. δ for a chemical shift of 210 c.p.s. downfield from the resonance signal for the internal standard at a given frequency of the most commonly used instrument, namely 60 megacycles, is expressed as follows:

$$\delta \, Si(CH_3)_4 = \frac{210}{60} = 3.5 \text{ ppm (parts per million).}$$

The other is tau, τ, which is defined $10-\delta$. Thus, increasing values for δ correspond to decreasing field strength. These signals appear "downfield" from the internal standard tetramethylsilane, decreasing magnetic shielding of protons being responsible for the shift. If one uses the τ-scale, the majority of protons have positive τ-values. These values, contrary to the δ-values, increase with increasing magnetic shielding. The following table lists chemical shifts.

Besides chemical shifts, a NMR spectrum contains two more features which render it much more useful than IR spectra for structure identification. These are the *absorption peak area* and the *spin-spin coupling*.

The absorption intensities of protons of NMR spectra are independent of their environment and of their respective chemical shifts. By a simple integration of absorption peak areas, one can obtain extremely useful information about the ratio in which differently positioned protons occur in a compound.

Spin-spin coupling phenomena permit a further refinement in structure elucidation of an unknown compound on the basis of its NMR spectrum. Table III contains a compilation of more commonly encountered spin-spin coupling constants, ζ, which are very useful for structure determination.

Table II.

Functional Group	Example	Chemical Shift,* p.p.m. from tetramethylsilane
Enolic hydroxyl	$p\text{-}BrC_6H_4\overset{\displaystyle O\underline{H}}{C}{=}CH\text{—}\overset{\displaystyle O}{C}C_6H_4Br(p\text{-})$	16.61†
	$CH_3\overset{\displaystyle O\underline{H}}{C}{=}CH\text{—}\overset{\displaystyle O}{C}CH_3$	$ca.$ 15.4†
Carboxyl	$CH_3COO\underline{H}$	11.37†
Aldehyde hydrogen	$CH_3C\underline{H}{=}O$	9.80
	$C_6H_5C\underline{H}{=}O$	10.00
Aromatic hydrogen	C_6H_6	7.37
	Durene (ring hydrogens)	6.8
Trihalomethanes	$CHCl_3$	7.27
	$CHBr_3$	6.85
Olefinic protons	$C\underline{H}_2{=}C(CH_3)_2$	5.34
Nitro compounds	$CH_3CH_2C\underline{H}_2NO_2$	4.38
Phenols	$C_6H_5O\underline{H}$	4.24†
Diarylmethanes	$(C_6H_5)_2C\underline{H}_2$	3.92
Ethers	$\overset{\textstyle CH_2\text{—}CH_2}{\underset{\textstyle O}{\underset{\displaystyle \diagdown\diagup}{CH_2\quad CH_2}}}$	3.75
Alcohols	$C\underline{H}_3OH$	3.47
	$CH_3CH_2C\underline{H}_2OH$	3.58
Acetylenes	$C_6H_5C{\equiv}C\underline{H}$	3.05
	$CH_3C{\equiv}C\underline{H}$	1.80
Alkyl halides	$CH_3C\underline{H}_2Cl$	3.57
	$CH_3C\underline{H}_2Br$	3.43
	$CH_3C\underline{H}_2I$	3.20
Amines	$CH_3CH_2CH_2C\underline{H}_2NH_2$	2.70
Nitriles	$BrCH_2CH_2C\underline{H}_2CN$	2.58
Aldehydes and ketones	$CH_3COC\underline{H}_2CH_2$	2.47
	$CH_3CH_2C\underline{H}_2CHO$	2.42
Aromatic side chain	$C_6H_5C\underline{H}_3$	2.32
Alcohols	$CH_3C\underline{H}_2CH_2OH$	2.28†
	$(CH_3)_2CHO\underline{H}$	1.60†
	$CH_3O\underline{H}$	1.43†
Amides	$CH_3C\underline{H}_2CONH_2$	2.23
Hydrocarbons	$CH_3(C\underline{H}_2)_6CH_3$	1.27
Amines	$CH_3CH_2CH_2CH_2N\underline{H}_2$	1.10
Hydrocarbons	$C\underline{H}_3(CH_2)_6C\underline{H}_3$	0.88
Cyclopropane ring	$(C\underline{H}_2)_3$	0.22
Tetramethylsilane	$(C\underline{H}_3)_4Si$	0.00

*Where possible, the values are those from the Varian *NMR Spectra Catalog* and were obtained with 7% solutions in deuterochloroform. Copyrighted by Varian Associates and reproduced by permission.
†The position of this absorption is likely to be highly dependent on the solvent and concentration because of association and exchange.

Reproduced by permission from *The Systematic-Identification of Organic-Compounds* by Shriner, Fuson and Curtin, 5th edition, 1964, by John Wiley and Sons, Inc.

The spin-spin coupling constant between protons on adjacent carbon atoms (according to Karplus[15]) is a function of the dihedral angle between the two $\diagdown$CH—CH$\diagup$ bonds of such a system. ζ is largest with a dihedral angle of 0° and 180° and smallest (almost zero) with dihedral angles around 90°.

A very useful and additional feature of NMR spectroscopy is the fact

Table III. Spin-spin Coupling Constants

System	J (c/s)
$\diagup$C$\diagdown$ with H, H	12–15
=C$\diagdown$ with H, H	$-3 \cdot 2$ to $+1 \cdot 6$‡§
—CH$_2$—CH$_3$	$6 \cdot 7$–$7 \cdot 2$
$\diagdown$CH—CH$_3$	$5 \cdot 0$–$7 \cdot 0$
$\diagdown$CH—CH$\diagup$	$0 \cdot 0$–$14 \cdot 0$†
H$\diagdown$C=C$\diagup$ with H	$12 \cdot 0$–$18 \cdot 0$
H$\diagdown$C=C$\diagdown$ with H (acyclic)	$5 \cdot 0$–$12 \cdot 0$
(cyclic)	$3 \cdot 0$–$10 \cdot 0$
—CH=C$\diagdown$ with CH$\diagup$	$-3 \cdot 5$–$0 \cdot 0$§
$\diagdown$CH—CH=O	$0 \cdot 0$–$3 \cdot 0$
$\diagdown$CH—C≡CH	$2 \cdot 0$–$3 \cdot 0$
benzene ring, o	$7 \cdot 0$–$10 \cdot 0$
m	$2 \cdot 0$–$3 \cdot 0$
p	$0 \cdot 0$–$1 \cdot 0$

‡Dependent on β-substituents and dependency on tetrahedral angle. See ref. 15.
§It is sometimes possible to obtain the relative signs of coupling constants from the mathematical analysis of complete spin systems. Absolute signs are not known.

Reproduced by permission from *Physical Methods in Organic Chemistry* by Schwarz, J. C. P., 1964, by Oliver & Boyd Ltd., Scotland.

that one can detect exchangeable protons easily by taking a spectrum before and after shaking the solution with D_2O. Thus, for example, if the hydroxyl proton of an alcohol is exchanged by deuterium, the resonance peak caused by this particular proton will disappear. This happens, in spite of the fact that deuterium is perfectly able to give a NMR signal; however, its resonance frequency is of such a magnitude that it will not appear in the region at which the proton resonance shows up.

Solvents commonly used in NMR spectroscopy are CCl_4, $DCCl_3$, $D_3C—CO—CD_3$, $(CF_3CO)_2O$, $D_3C—SO—CD_3$. For the investigation of aliphatic compounds, benzene can be used; benzaldehyde is also a useful solvent for aliphatic compounds insoluble in those solvents mentioned above.

IV. DETERMINATION OF PHYSICAL PROPERTIES

Melting Point. The melting point of a compound is a property which is extremely useful for identification; it should be the first test run on a solid. The melting point also serves to check the purity of a sample. Generally, provided that it melts without decomposition, a pure compound should melt within a one-degree range. In order accurately to determine the melting point, one should take care that the rate of heating is such as to cause a rise in temperature of not more than 2° per minute. The temperature at which the sample starts to melt and that at which it is entirely molten—at this point, usually, the surface forms a meniscus—are recorded. These two readings represent the melting point range; if it is excessive—larger than 1°—one should recrystallize the sample for further purification. The entire process should be repeated until either the melting point does not rise further, or the range is not larger than one degree. Best results are often obtained by switching solvents. The melting point temperature should be corrected. To achieve this ones uses the simple apparatus as pictured in Figure 2.

Besides the melting point temperature, one also notes the temperature of the mercury thread by means of the auxilliary thermometer (t_2).

The stem correction is obtained by means of the equation

Correction, $C_1 = +N(t_1 - t_2) \times 0.000154$

where N = degrees of mercury thread above the level of the oil bath; t_1 = observed melting point, t_2 = average temperature of mercury thread. The value of C is added to the observed melting point.

If one uses the simple melting-point apparatus according to Figure 2, one should use cottonseed oil or high-boiling mineral oil, but never concentrated sulfuric acid as the bath liquid.

For compounds with a melting point above about 275° up to about

500°, the use of a more elaborate apparatus for determination is recommended: the Fisher-Jones melting-point apparatus is a widely used one.

Mixture Melting Points. The time-honored method, though not always a reliable one, for proof of identity of two solids with identical melting point, has been the investigation of a mechanical mixture of the two. Generally, but not always, non-identical compounds exhibit a melting point depression when thoroughly mixed. Since exceptions are not too infrequent, one always should prove or disprove identity of two compounds by other methods, *i.e.*, comparing UV spectra of the two compounds.

For investigation of special problems in connection with the melting of a compound, *i.e.*, phase changes and melting points of anisotropic liquids (liquid crystals), one should use a melting-point apparatus consisting of a microscope, a so-called heating table, and Polaroid inserts.

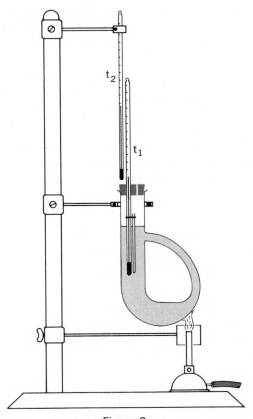

Figure 2.

Freezing Point. From 2 to 4 millimeters of the liquid are placed in a test tube fitted with a thermometer and a copper or nickel stirrer. The sample tube is inserted and fastened by means of a cork or rubber sleeve in a slightly wider test tube. This simple arrangement is cooled in a suitable bath (*i.e.*, ice, ice-salt or dry ice-acetone) while the sample is vigorously stirred. Upon formation of the first crystals, the cooling bath is removed. Stirring is continued while the temperature is being recorded.

A more or less pronounced rise in temperature will be noted. This rise is due to a supercooling effect. The freezing point is reached after this effect disappears.

Boiling Point. The boiling point of a liquid is an important constant which can be used to identify and characterize it. In addition, the boiling point range serves as an indicator of the purity of the sample. The boiling point can be determined easily and accurately enough if a sufficient quantity of *pure* liquid is available. It is necessary only to distill it carefully (to prevent superheating), and to record the temperature of the vapor of the center fraction. Distilling apparatus which permits the distillation of about 10 ml samples with reasonable accuracy is commercially available. If the true boiling point of a liquid is needed, a so-called Cottrell pump is used. (See Figure 3.)

Effect of Pressure on the Boiling Point. The boiling point of a liquid is the temperature at which the liquid and its vapor are in equilibrium. This equilibrium is pressure-dependent. Consequently, to report an accurate boiling point, one must report also the barometric pressure as well as the temperature.

If one wishes to convert boiling points at one pressure to those at a different pressure, one can use several equations.

The Clausius-Clapeyron equation is one of these, and

$$\text{Log } \frac{P_1}{P_2} = \frac{Hv}{2.3R} \frac{T_2 - T_1}{T_2 T_1}$$

is fairly accurate. In order to use it, one needs to know the heat of vaporization, ΔHv_1, which is usually not available. One can estimate it according to Trouton's rule:

$$\Delta Hv = 22T$$

The Trouton constant of 22 is an average value of the entropy of vaporization for a large variety of compounds. Little-associated hydrocarbons have a Trouton constant of 20 and a large one, namely 27, is more correct for the more associated compounds; i.e., acids; T is the boiling point in degrees Kelvin.

Density. The density which is defined as the weight of a unit volume (usually one milliliter) is one of the more conveniently determinable properties of a liquid. It is necessary to know it together with the refractive index if one wants to determine the molar refraction. (See below.)

The density of a liquid is determined by using a pycnometer. Its volume is obtained by filling the device up to the calibration mark with a reference liquid (water or mercury), and determining the weight difference, ΔW, between the empty and full pycnometer. ΔW divided by the known density of the used reference liquid (Table V) yields the volume of the vessel. The weight of the unknown liquid is determined by filling the pycnometer with it and reweighing. This weight, divided by the determined volume of the pycnometer, gives the density of the unknown liquid. Since density varies with temperature, it has to be recorded.

Refractive Index. The refractive index of a liquid is probably the property which is most easily determined. The refractive index is the ratio of

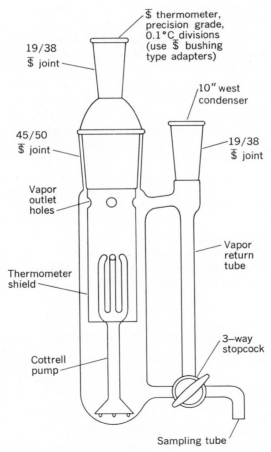

Figure 3.

the velocity with which light travels through it, to the velocity of light traveling in a vacuum. It is determined using an Abbe refractometer. Since the light source used most commonly is light of the wave-length of the sodium D line, the refractive index is usually taken at a temperature of 25° and is commonly referred to as $n_D{}^{25}$.

Molar Refraction. Molar refraction is a constant which expresses the polarizability of a compound. It can be calculated according to the Lorenz-Lorentz equation, provided density and refractive index are known:

$$M_D = \frac{n^2 - 1}{n^2 + 2} \frac{m}{d}$$

(n = refractive index, d = density, m = molecular weight)

The value of M_D determined in this way can be compared with a purely calculated one obtained by adding up group and atomic refractions.

Thus, by comparing the M_D value of an unknown compound obtained according to the Lorenz-Lorentz equation and one calculated by summing the appropriate values from Table VI, one should get almost identical values, if the assumed structure upon which the summation is based is correct. Using the appropriate values from Table VI for calculating M_D for the two isomeric acetylenes, $Cl—C \equiv C—CH_2—CH_3$ and $ClCH_2—C \equiv C—CH_3$, one obtains for the first a value of 21.02 and for the latter a value of 18.487. Since experimentally found values usually agree with the calculated ones (within ± 3%), it is evident that a decision covering the correct structure can be made.

Derivative Preparation. As indicated above, one recognizes the presence or absence of functional groups mainly by IR analysis. By adding information obtained from NMR and UV spectroscopy, one is able to obtain a fairly clear picture of the structure of an unknown. In the majority of cases the preparation of a derivative serves only to confirm unambiguously the structure of the unknown. Consequently, the procedures for the preparation of derivatives, which follow, constitute a check list only. This list follows closely one given in Shriner.[1]

CHECK LIST FOR DERIVATIVES

Derivatives for	Type of Derivative
Acids	Amides, p-nitrobenzyl ester, anilides, neutralization equivalents
	$= \dfrac{\text{weight of sample} \times 1000}{\text{volume of alkali (ml) N.F.}}$
Alcohols	Substitutes urethanes, p-nitrobenzoates, 3,5-dinitrobenzoates, 3-nitrophthalates

Aldehydes	Acids (by H_2O_2-oxidation), semicarbazones, 2,4-dinitrophenylhydrazones
Amides	α-Acylamidoxanthenes
Amines (prim. and sec.)	Substitutes amides, sulfonamides, substituted phenylthioureas, nitrosamines (sec. amines only)
Amines (tert.)	Quarternary ammonium salts, picrates, chloroplatinates
Amino acids	p-Toluenesulfonyl derivatives
Esters	Saponification equivalent

$$\frac{\text{weight of sample} \times 1000}{[\text{vol. of alkali (ml)} \times \text{N.F.}] - [\text{vol. of acid (ml)} \times \text{N.F.}]}$$

	Acid hydrazides, 3,5-dinitrobenzoates
Ethers (aromat.)	Bromination products, picrates
Ethers (aliphat.)	3,5-dinitrobenzoates
Alkyl halides	Alkylmercuric halides, anilides, S-alkyl isothiurea picrates
Aryl halides	Sulfonyl chlorides, sulfonamides
Aromatic hydrocarbons	Nitration, oxidation of side chains, aryl methyl ketones
Ketones	Oximes
Methyl ketones	Oximes, 2,4-dinitrophenyl hydrazones, semicarbazones, selective oxidation by means of NaOCP:$RCOCH_3 \rightarrow RCOOH$ $HCCl_3$ and subsequent identification of the acid
Nitriles	Amides, amines
Nitro compounds	Amines
Phenols	Aryloxyacetic acids, bromination
Sulfonamides	N-Xanthylsulfonamides
Sulfonic acids	Benzylthiuronium sulfonates, sulfonyl chlorides, sulfonamides, p-toluidine salts

BIBLIOGRAPHY

References:

1. R. L. Shriner, R. C. Fuson, and D. Y. Curtin, *The Systematic Identification of Organic Compounds*, 5th ed., 1964.

2. Feigl, F., *Spot Tests in Inorganic Analysis*, 1958.
3. Walisch, W., *Chem. Ber.*, 94:2314, 1961.
4. Weitkamp, H., R. Mayntz, and F. Korte, *Z. Analyt. Chem.*, 205:81, 1964.
5. Schwarz, J. C. P. (ed.), *Physical Methods in Organic Chemistry*, 1964.
6. Meloan, C. E., *Elementary Infrared Spectroscopy*, 1963.
7. Colthup, N. B., *J. Opt. Soc. Am.*, 40:397, 1950.
8. Pople, J. A., W. G. Schneider, and M. J. Bernstein, *High-Resolution Nuclear Magnetic Resonance*, 1959.
9. Jackman, L. M., *Applications of Nuclear Magnetic Resonance Spectroscopy in Organic Chemistry*, 1959.
10. Roberts, J. D., *Nuclear Magnetic Resonance*, 1959.
11. Silverstein, R. M., and G. C. Bassler, *Spectrometric Identification Organic Compounds*, p. 71, 1963.
12. Rogers, J. W., J. W. Knight, and A. R. Choppin, *J. Chem. Educ.*, 24:491, 1947.
13. Lange, A. N., *Handbook of Chemistry*, 7th ed., 1949.
14. Vogel, A. I., *Practical Organic Chemistry*, 1948.
15. Karplus, M., *Chem. Phys.*, 30:11, 1959.

THE SELECTION AND EVALUATION OF ANALYTICAL
CLINICAL CHEMICAL METHODS

I. INTRODUCTION

When the clinical chemist is faced with the problem of selection of a method for determination of a specific substance, the chief criteria he must use in the selection are that the method must be sufficiently specific (accuracy), sufficiently reproducible (precision) and sufficiently sensitive; at the same time, ideally, the method should be simple to perform and the cost of materials should be minimal. In most instances the final choice is a compromise, since perhaps very few ideal methods actually exist. For most substances there is a bewildering array of proposed analytical procedures with suggested modifications and modifications of the modifications. No analyst has the time to gain experience with all such variations of procedures and he must, therefore, be selective. If lucky and astute, he may be satisfied with his first or second choice of methods; if not, he may try several or end up creating a new "modification" or even a new approach. Yet, Chemist A and Chemist B may make entirely different first choices. Some of the justifiable reasons for this will be discussed subsequently. It must also be remembered, however, that chemists bring to such a problem their personal prejudices, valid or invalid, developed during their prior experience. Thus, Chemist A might avoid turbidimetric measurements if possible, and prefer spectrophotometric measurement to fluorometric measurement unless he needed the much greater sensitivity of the latter method.

II. SELECTION OF THE METHOD

There is, of course, a short-cut to the selection of a method for some substances: accepting the choice made either by someone else as published in a text, or by some quasi-official committee, e.g., the series of *Standard Methods of Clinical Chemistry* published by the American Association of Clinical Chemists, and the *Broadsheets* published by the Association of

Clinical Pathologists of Great Britain. Unfortunately, most of these "standard methods" do not appear to have become "standard" by the careful, step-by-step process used by the Association of Official Agricultural Chemists. These choices, therefore, cannot be regarded as infallible. For example, tributyrin was recommended as a substrate for lipase in Vol. I of *Standard Methods of Clinical Chemistry* but was superseded in Vol. II because of its inapplicability. In the case of choices made in texts on clinical chemistry, even if the author were infallible (which, of course, he isn't), he would be making a choice based on a set of circumstances which may not pertain in the particular situation at hand (instrumentation available, calibre of technicians, work load, etc.).

Assuming that no short-cut is to be taken, the actual process of arriving at a choice occurs in two steps; first, there must be an awareness of what methods are available (literature search) and, second, selection must be made after weighing all the pros and cons of each method against the specific requirements of the individual analytical situation.

Literature Search.   In some instances the chemist knows the particular field sufficiently well that he can proceed immediately to the process of selection. If not, he must do a "literature search." This is becoming an increasingly frightening task. A *complete* literature survey on any one analytical problem is just not possible. There are too many journals, published for too many years and in too many languages; furthermore, valuable analytical methods and data are often buried in publications whose primary subject is completely unrelated to methodology. To illustrate, the present author and two coworkers published a paper in 1959 titled *Determination of Bromsulfophthalein in Serum by Means of Acetone Precipitation of Proteins.*[1] It wasn't until several years later that, quite by accident, the present author found the same analytical technic buried in a paper published in 1947 in the *Am. J. Physiol.* It was entitled *The Relation Between the Esterase Activity of the Blood Plasma and of the Liver of the Dog.*[2]

Among the approaches available for a literature search are the following: (1) The bibliographies of texts on clinical chemistry. Very few of these books have significant bibliographies, even though they might discuss the available analytical technics. Furthermore, such texts are usually at least two years obsolete when they are published. (2) Reviews, such as those that appear in *Methods of Biochemical Analysis* and *Advances in Clinical Chemistry.* These are usually excellent sources. (3) Abstract journals, such as *Chemical Abstracts* and *Biological Abstracts. Index Medicus* and *Current List of Medical Literature* are also useful. (4) Bibliographies of original papers. For the most thorough job possible, one must go back to the papers listed in the bibliographies at hand, be they original publications, reviews or books, check the bibliographies of all these papers, and continue this review, step by step, to the end of the road.

III. POINTS TO CONSIDER IN THE SELECTION OF A METHOD

Accuracy. Everything else being equal, one would always choose the most accurate method available. In some situations, however, everything else is *not* equal, and this may lead to the selection of a less accurate method. For example, probably the most accurate technic for determination of total lipids in serum is that of Sperry and Brand,[3] yet the simpler gravimetric procedure of Pernokis *et al.*[4] is certainly sufficiently accurate for routine diagnostic purposes.

Precision. It is axiomatic that any useful method must be sufficiently precise. Since an increase in precision usually requires the expenditure of more effort, a corollary to the axiom might be that one should not be more precise than circumstances require. Precision requirements vary considerably. For example, if one accepts 4.1 to 5.6 meq/l as the normal range of serum potassium, then $\pm 16\%$ from the middle spans the entire range; whereas, if one accepts 131 to 150 meq/l as the normal range of serum sodium, then $\pm 7\%$ from the middle spans the range. The precision requirements thus are more stringent for sodium than for potassium. Faced with a choice between two methods for potassium, one of them simple with a precision of $\pm 6\%$ and the other complicated with a precision of $\pm 3\%$, the analyst would seem to be justified in choosing the former. This would not be true, however, if the methods were for sodium.

Sensitivity. A method should be sufficiently sensitive to permit use of the sample size desired without undue loss of precision. Sensitivity greater than that required ordinarily will not be advantageous unless, of course, the effect of possible interferences is diminished thereby.

Reagents. Of concern here are their availability, ease of preparation and stability. Most often it is their stability which may be critical. It is not a particularly welcome situation when a reagent must be made up fresh each time before use.

Sample stability. This is of concern only infrequently insofar as choice of methods is concerned, but it can be critical. Thus, ascorbic acid in serum or urine is reversibly oxidized to dehydroascorbic acid, which in turn degrades irreversibly to diketogulonic acid. One of the common methods of ascorbic acid analysis depends on decolorization of the dye 2,6-dichlorophenolindophenol by ascorbic acid. Another method depends on conversion of ascorbic acid to diketogulonic acid which forms a color upon coupling with 2,4-dinitrophenylhydrazine. Serum or urine cannot be stabilized for the dye method even by freezing, but oxalic acid effectively stabilizes serum for the 2,4-dinitrophenylhydrazine method, apparently preventing any change beyond the diketogulonic stage. Urine and serum can also be preserved for this method by freezing.

Level of technical skill required. This may in some instances influence the analyst's choice of a method. For example, the "wet ash" method for protein-bound iodine is technically more demanding than the "dry ash" method, and more skill is required to operate a Beckman Model DU Spectrophotometer than to operate a Klett filter photometer.

Equipment required. Before an investment in equipment is made, not only must the cost be considered, but also, in the case of mechanical or electronic equipment, thought should be given to the fact that yet another instrument is being placed in the laboratory which will undoubtedly break down from time to time to the utter frustration of the analyst. A sound philosophy to follow is not to buy an instrument unless it either (1) performs a unique and necessary function, or (2) pays for itself in a reasonable period of time, two years for example. Probably the most accurate and precise method available today for calcium determination in biologic fluids is atomic absorption spectrophotometry, yet it is hard to justify the purchase of a $6,000 instrument solely for routine calcium determinations.

Volume of tests. Frequently this a very important consideration, since some methods lend themselves more readily than others to economy in running large numbers of samples. With some methods it takes about 10 times as much time to run 10 tests as to run one test. With other methods it may take only two or three times as much time to run 10 as one. Thus, a technic which employs batch adsorption onto an adsorbent or ion exchange resin would be preferable to a method requiring column adsorption. Such considerations are relatively unimportant for the occasional single analysis, but it is a different story when many samples are to be run frequently.

Automation. The most widely accepted automated system of analysis today is the AutoAnalyzer manufactured by the Technicon Instruments Corporation, Chauncey, New York. Biochemical constituents are determined by this continuous-flow instrument which is capable of sample handling and presentation, delivery of reagent volumes in proper sequence, removal of interfering materials, heating or incubating reaction mixtures and measuring and recording of data. A large degree of flexibility is achieved because of its modular design. Many analytical technics have been adapted to this instrumental system but not all manual procedures are readily utilized, especially those which require handling of precipitates or involve multiple solvent extractions. Some methods that were developed for the AutoAnalyzer have not necessarily been considered ideal manual technics because of technical difficulties in performing these procedures manually. However, the AutoAnalyzer has successfully automated some of these technics as it is capable of carrying out every step in precisely the same way each time, with standards and specimens being treated similarly and exposed to the same conditions. Present-day technical developments have led to the automation of many technics that previously could not be determined by this instrumental system. The analyst can now choose from more than one method for measuring a given constituent. Besides the increased reliability achieved with automation, another obvious advantage is one of economy, *i.e.*, lower cost per analysis. No economy usually is effected by automation of one or two analyses performed at one time; usually at least six samples are needed for each batch. Furthermore, batteries of tests now become feasible, and it probably will become more economical to run *all* electrolytes on *all* serum samples than to run just those that are ordered for each sample. Aside from the factor of economy, there is another advantage to be derived from automation, namely increased reliability and precision of results. When the procedure is properly controlled, greater precision can be obtained on the AutoAnalyzer from *single* determinations than from the *means of duplicates* of manual analyses.

Special considerations.   Certain special considerations pertain to specific classifications of analytical technics.

Photometric methods

Of great concern is the question whether Beer's law is obeyed. It may be obeyed with an instrument of high resolution but not with a filter photometer. This situation is unwelcome when large numbers of tests are run because it takes longer to read them on the more complex instrument than on a simple filter photometer. Accurate work, of course, can be done when the relationship is curvilinear, rather than straight-lined, but more work is required. Stability of color is also important, providing more latitude in time as to when the color can be read. The effect of three commonly encountered sources of interference with photometric or spectrophotometric measurements must *always* be considered: turbidity, icterus and hemolysis. Whether or not these give significant interference may vary greatly from method to method.

Titrimetric methods

One must be certain that visual endpoints are equally apparent to all analysts involved. For example, not all analysts can detect the endpoints of EDTA titration for calcium with some of the indicators now in use. Furthermore, male color blindness is not rare.

Enzyme analyses

If a reaction can be made zero order, then a properly designed enzyme is zero order and gives results which are directly proportional to enzyme concentration. Furthermore, proper design calls for adequate control of all variables which affect the enzyme activity: pH, temperature, time and known activators. There are a great many poorly designed enzyme assay methods in the clinical chemistry literature, and particular care must be exercised in selection in this field.

IV. EVALUATION OF THE METHOD

Any analyst experienced in methodology research soon learns that he cannot expect to set up published methods and have them work right away just as the original authors claimed. In some instances, of course, this may be due to poor original work. More often, perhaps, it is because some subtle point in technic has not been adequately communicated by the written word. It should be standard procedure for a laboratory to check out a method before putting it into routine use. The following points should be checked, even if the original publication presented data on them. Unfortunately, in many instances the original publication gives no indication that some of these points ever were investigated.

Accuracy. If there is a generally recognized reference method for the substance in question, results by the new method under consideration can be compared with those yielded by the reference method. Examples of such reference methods are the uricase method for uric acid and Kjeldahl analysis for protein. Such a comparison should not be limited to a few normal samples but should be extended to pathologic samples. It is suggested that at least 25 comparisons be carried out. In many instances, of course, the lack of a reference method makes the establishment of accuracy difficult or impossible. If the substance is available as a standard in reasonably pure form, recoveries can be run by adding known amounts to unknown samples. Quantitative recovery of added pure substance, however, does not constitute proof of accuracy of results on unknowns.

Precision. This should always be determined for a method. What is really needed is the day-to-day reproducibility. If more than one analyst will be running the test, then the variability between analysts should be included in the estimate of precision. If a control chart of a pooled serum or urine is set up, the limits therefrom are valid estimates of the precision desired, provided, of course, that all analysts who will be running the test have contributed values to the control chart. Estimates of precision derived from running many replicates in one batch or from duplicate analyses of many unknown samples will be erroneously small.

Stability of reagents.   Evidence for stability is usually accumulated over a period of time after a test is put into routine use.

Stability of samples.   If not already known, it is necessary that stability of samples be established for the maximum temperature and maximum length of time to be encountered in routine practice. Again, this feature should be studied for abnormal as well as normal samples and for more than just a few samples. It cannot be assumed that samples will be more stable frozen or in the refrigerator than at room temperature. For example, serum lactic dehydrogenase is less stable in the frozen state than at room temperature.[5]

Photometric methods.   If the method is photometric it is usually helpful for the analyst to know the absorption curves of reagent blank vs. water, standard vs. water and standard vs. reagent blank. It is also wise to compare several curves of unknowns vs. reagent blank with that of standard vs. reagent blank. A check on obedience to Beer's law must be made for the entire range of absorbance to be used in practice and on the photometer or spectrophotometer which one contemplates using. Color stability should be checked and, if the cuvet compartment of the instrument to be used is one which becomes quite warm, the effect of temperature variation on color intensity should also be determined.

Enzyme methods.   The order of the reaction should be verified and, if the order is zero, then it should be verified that results are directly proportional to sample size. Thus, if the test calls for 1 ml serum, 0.5 ml should give one-half as much apparent activity, 0.25 ml one-fourth as much, etc. If an enzyme level is very high, it is frequently necessary to rerun the test with a smaller aliquot of sample. It must be remembered, however, that the assay was originally designed for a given aliquot and this may be important to final pH at incubation or to concentration of activators. Amylase requires a certain minimal level of chloride ion for full activity. If a smaller aliquot of urine is to be run, the decreased volume should be made up with physiological saline solution to assure adequate chloride.[6] In the case of some methods for serum alkaline phosphatase, if a smaller aliquot of sample is taken because of a very high level, the decreased volume must be made up with a normal serum so that the final pH is not too high.[7]

Normal values.   A thorough and adequate description of a normal range is an undertaking of major proportions since there are many variables to be taken into consideration. If the test being set up is one for which normals have not been established, the laboratory has no choice but to establish a normal range. (It should be emphasized that most normal ranges in the past have been calculated by improper statistics.)[8] If a normal range is already established, a small number of samples, perhaps six, from presumably normal individuals, should be run just as a crude check on whether or not the test is working. This is especially important when no reference method is available against which to check results. In a surprising number of instances, a new test seems to be working satisfactorily but, when normals are run, they fall outside the normal range claimed by the original authors.

V. SUMMARY

It is evident that there are quite a number of facets to the selection of a method of analysis—accuracy, precision, sensitivity, cost, etc. There is still one more which has not yet been identified directly and that is the ultimate *user* of the information the test provides, the clinician. It is he who should stipulate to the clinical chemist the test precision that is required. His help frequently is needed in the evaluation of the usefulness of tests. The clinical chemist is not certain what he is measuring with the thymol turbidity test; thus, "accuracy" here only has meaning relative to how well it correlates with liver disease. Furthermore, the clinical chemist should always keep the clinician in mind when changing methods if such a change involves a change in specificity or a change in the units reported. Proper communication by the chemist with the clinician prior to the change can avoid frustration on the part of the clinician and will obviate the risk of serious errors in interpretation.

References:

(1)   Henry, R. J., N. Chiamori, and A. G. Ware, "Determination of Bromsulfophthalein in Serum by Means of Acetone Precipitation of Proteins," *Am. J. Clin. Pathol.*, 32:201, 1959.

(2)   Brauer, R. W., and M. A. Root, "The Relation Between the Esterase Activity of the Blood Plasma and of the Liver of the Dog," *Am. J. Physiol.*, 149:611, 1947.

(3)   Sperry, W. M., and F. C. Brand, "The Determination of Total Lipids in Blood Serum," *J. Biol. Chem.*, 213:69, 1955.

(4)   Pernokis, E. W., M. R. Freeland and I. Kraus, "The Determination of Blood Lipids in Blood Dyserasias," *J. Lab. Clin. Med.*, 26:1978, 1941.

(5)   Kreutzer, H. H., and W. H. S. Fennis, "Lactic Dehydrogenase Isoenzymes in Blood Serum after Storage at Different Temperatures," *Clin. Chim. Acta*, 9:64, 1964.

(6)   Henry, R. J., and N. Chiamori, "Study of the Saccharogenic Method for the Determination of Serum and Urine Amylase," *Clin. Chem.*, 6:434, 1960.

(7)   Henry, R. J., and N. Chiamori, "Variation of pH of Clinical Samples as a Source of Error in Enzyme Determinations," *Clin. Chem.*, 5:402, 1959.

(8)   Henry, R. J., *Clinical Chemistry, Principles and Technics*, p. 144, 1964.

I. GENERAL CONSIDERATIONS

The development of a drug is a stepwise procedure during which a compound passes through many phases of experimentation and clinical evaluation toward its final introduction into medical practice. During this period, which often lasts for more than five years, the substance is evaluated by pharmacologists, chemotherapists and biochemists, who then pass responsibility on to the clinical pharmacologist and the clinical investigators. The toxicologist's contribution, however, is a continuous one. He works with each drug not only during the developmental phase but also long after it has been generally accepted by the medical profession.

Table I summarizes this long path toward acceptance. First, the acute toxicity studies must indicate that the compound has a satisfactory therapeutic margin. They are followed by subacute toxicity tests which should furnish reasonable assurance that well-supervised human tolerance and efficacy studies can be conducted with a minimum of risk to volunteers and the first patients. Once human tolerance is established and confidence is gained that the compound has the desired therapeutic potential, the toxicologist initiates an extensive program which should establish safety and anticipate possible toxic effects in all types of patients expected to be treated with the new drug, under any circumstances likely to occur in actual practice. These studies include the long-term chronic toxicity experiments and the determination of effects on fetal development, in addition to biochemical investigations on mechanism of action and biotransformation in man.

Only a small fraction of potential drugs survive the long and costly development procedures, mostly because of inadequate effectiveness and disturbing, subjective intolerance symptoms in man. But contrary to a widely-held belief, the toxicologic studies are rarely the cause for dropping a new compound. On the contrary, the better the toxicologist is able to determine the site and mechanism of untoward reactions, the more adequately can the clinician monitor the drug's use and prevent serious harm to the patients.

The conventional toxicologic procedures are adequate to eliminate most of the clearly dangerous substances and to safeguard the patients

Table I. Evaluation of Safety and Efficacy of a New Drug

Step	Safety	Efficacy
I	Acute toxicity testing ⟶	Pharmacologic screening
II	Subacute toxicity testing	Extended pharmacologic screening and drug metabolism in animals
III	Human tolerance	
IV		Human efficacy
V	Chronic toxicity testing and fetal toxicity testing	Drug metabolism in humans Extended clinical trials Studies on mechanism of action
		General use in humans
VI	Observation of unexpected side effects in man Attempt to reproduce unexpected side effects in animals	
VII		Final evaluation of indications, contra-indications and precautions

participating in the clinical evaluation. But even the most elaborate program is unable to predict many toxic reactions, once the drug is prescribed for a large patient population.[1] This is illustrated in Table II which shows that the predictive value of preclinical experiments and the various phases of clinical evaluation in man are dependent on the type and mechanism of the toxic drug reaction. It also indicates that the state of art in toxicology is not enough advanced to give the physician complete assurance that unexpected toxic effects will not occur, even if the drug has been conscientiously studied and has passed all requirements imposed by regulatory agencies.

Table II. Possibility to Recognize Various Types of Toxic Drug Reactions During Development of New Drugs (Adapted from Zbinden 1964[1])

Adverse Drug Effects	Animal Toxicity Tests	Extended Toxicol. Program*	Phase I	Phase II	Phase III	Recognized when Introduced on Market
	Recognized During Preclinical Evaluation		**Recognized During Clinical Trials****			
Exaggerated therapeutic effect	0	0	?	(+)	+	+ + +
Action on wrong target organ	0	+	+ +	+ +	+ + +	+ + +
Alteration of drug effect by pathologic conditions	0	?	?	?	+	+ + +
Alteration of drug effect by exogenous factors	0	+	0	0	+	+ + +
Direct toxic drug effects	+ +	+ +	+	+ + +	+ + +	+ + +
Direct toxic drug effect requiring a pathologic condition	0	?	?	?	+	+ + +
Direct toxic drug effect requiring exogenous factors	0	+	0	0	+	+ + +
Sensitization and allergies	0	0	0	(+)	(+)	+ + +
Idiosyncrasy and other unknown mechanisms	0	0	0	(+)	(+)	+ + +
Interference with absorption of nutrients	?	+	0	?	+	+ + +
Interference with natural defense mechanisms	0	+ +	0	?	+	+ + +
Deposition or precipitation of drug in tissue	+	+	0	0	+	+ +
Toxic effect on the fetus	(+)	(+)	0	0	0	+
Local irritation	+ +	+ +	+ +	+ + +	+ + +	+ + +
Toxic effects due to radioactivity of drug	+	+	0	0	0	+
Carcinogenic effect of drugs	+	+	0	0	0	?

0 useless
? questionable
(+) rarely
+ occasionally
+ + often
+ + + definitely

*includes special toxicity tests, drug metabolism and extended pharmacologic analysis
**Phase I = human tolerance
Phase II = preliminary efficacy studies
Phase III = broad clinical evaluation

Reference:

(1) Zbinden, G., "The Problem of the Toxicologic Examination of Drugs in Animals and their Safety in Man," *Clin. Pharmacol. Therap.*, 5:537–545, 1964.

II. EXPERIMENTAL DESIGN IN TOXICOLOGY

Acute Toxicity. The LD_{50}, the dose which is calculated to kill half of the animals, is determined in mice or rats. The drug is given orally or parenterally to groups of 5 to 20 animals starved for 16 hours at 3 or more dose levels which cause less than 100% mortality. The number of dead animals is recorded after 1, 2, 3 and 10 days. The LD_{50} is determined according to one of the graphic calculation methods described by Litchfield and Wilcoxon,[1] Miller and Tainter,[2] or DeBeer.[3] Observation of the acute symptoms gives valuable information as to the organs primarily affected by the drug. Death occurring within a few minutes or hours after drug administration is generally due to acute pharmacologic effects, e.g., respiratory or cardiovascular failure, CNS depression, etc., whereas delayed death often indicates irreversible organ damage such as bone marrow depression and hepatotoxicity.[4,5] Comparison of the oral and i.v. LD_{50}'s gives preliminary information about speed and completeness of enteric absorption. Acute toxicity experiments are also performed in rabbits, dogs and monkeys. The drugs are given to fewer animals, the dosage is repeated and increased daily. Minimal symptomatic dose, emetic, toxic and approximate lethal doses are determined. These studies are often supplemented by blood chemistry and autopsy.

The outcome of acute toxicity experiments is markedly influenced by environmental factors such as temperature,[6] housing conditions[7] and other stress factors.[8,9] There are also marked strain[10] and sex[11] differences which can often be explained by variations in the activity of the detoxifying enzymes.[12]

References:

(1) Litchfield, J. T., and F. Wilcoxon, "A Simplified Method Evaluating Dose-Effect Experiments," *J. Pharmacol. Exp. Therap.*, 96:99–113, 1949.

(2) Miller, L. C., and M. L. Tainter, "Estimation of the ED_{50} and its Error by Means of Logarithmic Probit Graph Paper," *Proc. Soc. Exp. Biol. Med.*, 57: 261–264, 1944.

(3) DeBeer, E. J., "The Calculation of Biological Assay Results by Graphic Methods. The All-or-None Type of Response," *J. Pharmacol. Exp. Therap.*, 85:1–13, 1945.

(4) Wheler, A. G., D. Dansby, H. C. Hawkins, H. G. Payne, and J. H. Weikel, Jr., "A Toxicologic and Hematologic Evaluation of Cyclophosphamide (Cytoxan®) in Experimental Animals," *Toxicol. Appl. Pharmacol.*, 4:324–343, 1962.

(5) Kutob, S. D. and G. L. Plaa, "A Procedure for Estimating the Hepatotoxic Potential of Certain Industrial Solvents," *Toxicol. Appl. Pharmacol.*, 4:354–361, 1962.

(6) Keplinger, M. L., G. E. Lanier and W. B. Deichmann, "Effects of Environmental Temperature on the Acute Toxicity of a Number of Compounds in Rats," *Toxicol. Appl. Pharmacol.*, 1:156–161, 1959.

(7) Greenblatt, E. N., and A. C. Osterberg, "Correlations of Activating and Lethal Effects of Excitatory Drugs in Grouped and Isolated Mice," *J. Pharmacol. Exp. Therap.*, 131:115–119, 1961.

(8) Renaud, S., "The Toxicity of Kanamycin and Bacitracin as Influenced by Stress and Sodium Chloride," *Toxicol. Appl. Pharmacol.*, 2:708–714, 1960.

(9) Weiss, B., V. G. Laties, and F. L. Blanton, "Amphetamine Toxicity in Rats and Mice Subjected to Stress," *J. Pharmacol. Exp. Therap.*, 132:366–371, 1961.

(10) Weaver, L. C., and T. L. Kerley, "Strain Difference in Response of Mice to d-amphetamine," *J. Pharmacol. Exp. Therap.*, 135:240–244, 1962.

(11) Munoz, C., S. Guerrero, C. Paeile and I. Campos, "Sexual Differences in Toxicity of Procaine in Rats," *Toxicol. Appl. Pharmacol.*, 3:445–454, 1961.

(12) Brodie, B. B., "Difficulties in Extrapolating Data on Metabolism of Drugs from Animal to Man," *Clin. Pharmacol. Therap.*, 3:374–380, 1962.

Subacute Toxicity.   As a prerequisite for human tolerance and efficacy studies, drugs must be given repeatedly to larger groups of animals and their effects on general development, behavior and vital organ systems must be investigated. The duration of these experiments depends on the scope of the projected human trials. It may thus range from 2 weeks for a limited human pharmacology test to 13 weeks for a more comprehensive evaluation of a drug's therapeutic potential. With the exception of its shorter duration, the design of the subacute toxicity test is identical to that of the test described for the chronic toxicity studies.

Chronic Toxicity.   Prolonged administration to large groups of animals is considered essential for evaluation of the toxic properties of those drugs which are to be introduced into medical practice. The detailed design of these studies has to take into consideration the projected circumstances of use, the therapeutic dose, the types of patients expected to be taking the drug, the route of administration, the chemical structure and the principal pharmacologic properties as well as the requirement of government agencies whose approval must be obtained before the substance may be released for general use. The ground rules for chronic toxicity testing require that the drug be given to 2 or 3 species of animals, most frequently rats and dogs, occasionally also monkeys or rabbits. Three dose levels are administered to groups of 20 to 50 rats or 5 to 10 animals of the other species. A control group of equal or even larger size must be included. The highest dose level should cause some toxic symptoms and the lowest level should be within the range of 2 to 10 times the proposed therapeutic dose. The route and frequency of administration should be the same as projected for therapeutic use in humans, but for reasons of convenience it is often permissible to mix the drugs in the rat diet, to administer the substances to dogs and monkeys in gelatin capsules or by stomach tube and to limit injections and oral applications to once a day five times a week. The duration of drug administration varies from 3 months to 2 years or more, depending on the type of drug and its projected duration of application in man. Comprehensive examination of general development and behavior, of blood cell count and urinalysis, and of liver and kidney function are required at regular intervals; autopsy and histologic examination of all vital organs are performed at the conclusion of the experiment. A more detailed description of chronic toxicity experiments is found in several reviews by Lehman et al.[1, 2], Barnes and Denz[3], Lehman[4], Boyd[5], Paget[6] and Zbinden.[7]

In certain cases it becomes necessary to deviate substantially from the above-summarized ground rules. For example, pharmacologic activities may not permit the use of higher than therapeutic dose levels; marked local irritation may necessitate early discontinuation of the testing of an injectable drug; cumulative irreversible toxicity may not permit prolonged administration at dose levels which initially were tolerated; drugs which are poorly absorbed from the intestinal tract may not cause any toxic symptoms, even at highly exaggerated dose levels; and compounds such as new hormones may be so difficult to synthesize that it would be impossible to make the large amounts necessary for a routine toxicity experiment.

Since in chronic toxicity studies toxic changes are purposely induced by prolonged administration of large quantities of drugs, it becomes necessary that the evaluation of these experiments be done with great care. In every case it must be discussed whether a toxic reaction represents a specific effect of the drug or merely a nonspecific consequence of malnutrition, spontaneous disease or general overloading of the excretory mechanisms. If the toxic reaction seems to be drug-related, the dose at which it occurred must be compared with the effective dose in the same animal species and the therapeutic dose in man, in order to estimate the therapeutic index. Furthermore, the possibility of species differences must be considered. Species differences are quite frequent and represent a most important limitation of the usefulness of the chronic toxicity testing done in laboratory animals. Many differences between drug effects observed in animals and those occurring in man are traced back to differences in drug metabolism.[8, 9] It therefore becomes essential that the pathways and speed of absorption, biotransformation and excretion be studied in animals as well as in man. It is a rule that during a drug's development any effect observed in animals must be especially looked for in subsequent human studies. But because of the possibility of species differences it is experience in man which must govern the final decision as to the significance of all toxic drug effects observed in animal experiments.

References:

(1)   Lehman, A. J., E. P. Lang, G. Woodard, J. H. Draize, O. G. Fitzhugh, and A. A. Nelson, "Procedures for the Appraisal of the Toxicity of Chemicals in Foods," *Food, Drug, Cosmetic Law Quart.*, 4:412–434, 1949.

(2)   Lehman, A. J., W. I. Patterson, B. Davidow, E. C. Hagan, G. Woodard, E. P. Lang, J. P. Frawley, O. G. Fitzhugh, A. R. Bourke, J. H. Draize, A. A. Nelson, and B. J. Vos, "Procedures for the Appraisal of the Toxicity of Chemicals in Foods, Drugs and Cosmetics," *Food, Drug, Cosmetic Law J.*, 10:679–748, 1955.

(3)   Barnes, I. M. and F. A. Denz, "Experimental Methods Used in Determining Chronic Toxicity," *Pharmacol. Rev.*, 6:191–242, 1954.

(4)   Lehman, A. J., "Control of Toxicity in Foods, Drugs and Cosmetics," *Federat. Proc.*, 19:13–16, 1960.

(5)   Boyd, E. M., "Toxicological Studies," *J. New Drugs*, 1:104–109, 1961.

(6)   Paget, G. E., "Toxicity Tests, A Guide for Clinicians," *J. New Drugs*, 2:78–83, 1962.

(7)   Zbinden, G., "Experimental and Clinical Aspects of Drug Toxicity," *Advances in Pharmacol.*, 2:1–112, 1963.

(8)   Brodie, B. B., "Difficulties in Extrapolating Data on Metabolism of Drugs from Animal to Man," *Clin. Pharm. Therap.*, 3:374–380, 1962.

(9)   Paget, G. E., "Correlations with Potential Toxicity in Man of Toxic Effects in Animals," *Clin. Pharm. Therap.*, 3:381–384, 1962.

Fetal Toxicity and Fertility.   The investigation of possible harmful effects on the developing fetus has become an integral part of the toxicologic evaluation of every drug which might be taken by women of childbearing age. But while there is considerable uniformity in the approach to chronic toxicity testing, no standard protocol for the investigation of teratogenic properties has yet attained overwhelming acceptance. At the present time the American Food and Drug Administration requires completion of the Litter Test which is a breeding experiment in drug-treated rats.* Two groups of 20 animals equally divided as to sex are given the drug at two dose levels, one of which is just below the dose causing toxicity. A control group receives the basal ration without the drug. After 60 days the animals are mated. On the 20th gestation day the offspring are taken by Caesarean section. Parameters to be observed are fertility, rate of pregnancy, absorption or implantation sites and teratogenic effects. In a second experiment, an equal number of rats receives the drug at two dose levels commencing with the initial mating period and continuing through two mating cycles. In the first litter the rats are carried to weaning. In the second litter half of the animals are sacrificed at birth and half at weaning, and one third of all animals are cleared for examination of the skeletons. The remaining rats are sectioned and examined for soft tissue changes. These experiments give a useful overall impression of a drug's toxic effect on fertility, fetal development, survival and growth rate, as well as lactation. Other experimental designs, followed mostly in European countries, differ from the Rat Litter Test in various respects; experiments are often conducted not only in rats but also in mice, rabbits or guinea pigs. The drugs are administered at two to three dose levels; the lowest dose corresponds to one- to tenfold the human therapeutic dose and the highest dose level is often chosen to cause clearcut toxicity to the mothers. The duration of drug administration is either from day of conception to term or only during the organogenetic phase, occasionally from 8 days before mating until term and sometimes from 60 days before mating until cop-

*On March 1, 1966, Dr. E. I. Goldenthal, Chief, Drug Review Branch, Division of Toxicological Evaluation, Bureau of Scientific Standards and Evaluation, Food and Drug Administration, Washington, D.C. 20204 released revised guidelines for testing of new drugs for their potential for producing adverse effects on the reproduction process. The proposed experimental procedure includes fertility and general reproduction studies in rats, a teratological study in two species (mouse, rat or rabbit) and a perinatal and postnatal study. A detailed protocol may be obtained from the Division of Toxicological Evaluation, Food and Drug Administration, Washington, D.C. 20204.

ulation. These are important differences, since the timing of drug administration has a marked influence on frequency and type of teratogenic drug effects.[1,2] The list of compounds known to cause disturbances of fertility and fetal malformations in animals is growing steadily and includes many widely used substances such as salicylates, caffeine, nicotine, insulin, many antibiotics, imipramine, meclizine, phenobarbital, etc., for which there is no evidence of teratogenic effects in man. On the other hand, known or strongly suspected teratogens, such as thalidomide, antimetabolites, alkylating agents, antitumor antibiotics, etc., can be recognized in these animal experiments. Whenever fetal malformations are induced in rodents, further experiments have to be conducted first in other strains of the same species, since strain differences are not infrequent.[2] The drug may then also be investigated in other animal species, including dogs, pigs, monkeys and in fertilized chicken eggs.[3] Additional information is gained from studies *in vitro* for effects on growth of embryonic tissue.[4] Other factors to be considered are the pharmacologic properties of the compound, its metabolism in the animal species in which the teratogenic effect was discovered as compared to that in man, and the dose necessary to produce fetal toxicity in relation to the pharmacologically active dose levels in man.[5] There are many nonspecific causes known to be responsible for teratogenesis in animals, among them anoxia,[6] hyperbaric oxygenation,[7] hypovitaminoses,[8] loss of amniotic fluid, external stresses, radiation, virus infections, etc.[2] It is therefore most important that an attempt be made to clarify the mechanism by which the drug may have caused the malformation, and if it can be determined that the effect was due to particular circumstances of the experiment which are not likely to be duplicated in man, the experimental finding will be of lesser concern. On the other hand, it must be kept in mind that a completely negative animal experiment does not prove absence of teratogenicity in man.

References:

(1) Wilson, J. G., "Embryological Considerations in Teratology," *Ann. N. Y. Acad. Sci.*, 123:219–227, 1965.

(2) Kalter, H., "Experimental Investigation of Teratogenic Action," *Ann. N. Y. Acad. Sci.*, 123:287–294, 1965.

(3) Landauer, W., "On the Chemical Production of Developmental Abnormalities and of Phenocopies in Chicken Embryos," *J. Cellular Comp. Physiol.*, 43:261–305, Suppl. 1, 1954.

(4) Fell, H. B., and E. Mellanby, "Metaplasia in Cultures of Chick Ectoderm by High Vitamin A," *J. Physiol.*, 119:470–488, 1953.

(5) Walker, B. E., "Cleft Palate Produced in Mice by Human-equivalent Dosage with Triamcinolone," *Science*, 149:862–863, 1965.

(6) Ingalls, T. H. and F. J. Curley, "Principles Governing the Genesis of Congenital Malformations Induced in Mice by Hypoxia," *New Engl. J. Med.*, 257:1121–1127, 1957.

(7) Ferm, V. H., "Teratogenic Effects of Hyperbaric Oxygen," *Proc. Soc. Exp. Biol. Med.*, 116:975–976, 1964.

(8) Warkany, J., "Disturbances of Embryonic Development by Maternal Vitamin Deficiencies," *J. Cellular Comp. Physiol.*, 43:207–236, 1954.

Local Irritation and Skin Sensitivity.   Drugs which are intended for topical administration are tested for their irritating and cytotoxic properties by single or repeated application to the skin, the penile and vaginal mucosa and the conjunctival sac of the eye of rabbits and guinea pigs. The evaluation is generally limited to gross observation. Injectables are tested by single and repeated subcutaneous, intramuscular and intravenous administration to rabbits with macroscopic and microscopic examination of the injection sites.[1,2] Another test uses a pain reaction after intradermal injection in dogs as endpoint.[3] Local tissue damage can also be determined by intradermal injection of a drug in white rabbits and subsequent intravenous administration of trypan blue. If the drug has caused tissue damage with increased vascular permeability, the trypan blue causes distinct discoloration of the skin which can be graded semiquantitatively.[2,4] Another method uses tissue cultures which are grown in presence of the test substance. Cytotoxic effects are determined by microscopic examination and estimation of the total purine and pyrimidine content.[5] Drugs which are intended for administration by inhalation are sprayed into closed chambers in which the animals, generally guinea pigs, are exposed to the material for periods of one hour to several days. Recently, open respiration systems have been constructed which permit more physiological conditions.[6] The irritating effect is judged by inspection of the respiratory tract and histopathologic examination of its mucosal lining. In all these experiments the drugs must be given at various concentrations and in the formulations intended for human use. Their effects must be compared with that of physiologic saline and, if possible, those of a few standard drugs whose local tolerance in humans is well known. Under these conditions, predictability of effects in humans is quite satisfactory.

The tests employed to detect skin-sensitizing properties of new drugs are much less reliable. The compounds are applied to the shaved skin surface or injected intradermally into guinea pigs for 10 days and the animals then retested 15 days after the last sensitizing dose.[1] Only highly reactive chemicals such as neosalvarsan, phenylhydrazine, primula extract, dinitrochlorobenzene and picryl chloride cause a typical contact sensitization.[7] The reasons for the difficulty in demonstrating sensitizing properties of other drugs are many. For example, the sensitivity reaction in man may not be due to the drug itself but to a metabolite which may not be formed in the animal; the drug-protein complex which is necessary to stimulate antibody production may not be formed under the conditions of the experiment, due either to a lack of specific proteins in the test animal or the inability of the drug to reach the site of complex formation.[8, 9] Various modifications of the animal tests are therefore tried, *e.g.*, injection of drug-protein complexes obtained by incubation of the drug with plasma or albumin; sensitivity testing with the major metabolites; combined injection of the test drug with a reactive compound such as picryl chloride which attracts antibody-producing cells and use of special pharmaceutical formulations which permit good penetration of the drug through the skin.[9] Although some progress has been made with these modifications, sensitivity testing in humans remains the only reliable method to evaluate the sensitizing properties of a new topically-applied drug. This is done with groups of 200 volunteers who are treated every second day for a total of 10 applications. The compound is administered to back or arm by patch. After a two-week rest period, the subjects are challenged with the compound which may be applied onto the surface of the skin by patch or given through scarification or by intradermal injection.[10]

A special procedure is necessary for testing the phototoxic and photoallergic properties. A drug which sensitizes the animals against the influence of light, such as methoxypsoralen, may be detected by severe toxic effects which occur if the drug-treated animal is exposed to U-V light.[11] The demonstration of photoallergic effects in animals, however, is even more difficult than the regular sensitivity reaction because the photoallergies are often due to species-specific metabolites which are formed in the skin under the influence of light.[12]

References:

(1) Draize, J. H., *Dermal Toxicity, in Appraisal of the Safety of Chemicals in Foods, Drugs and Cosmetics*, Association of Food and Drug Officials in the United States, pp. 46–59, 1959.

(2) Somers, G. F., "Testing Drugs for Dermal Toxicity," *J. Soc. Cosmetic Chemists*, 15:385–394, 1964.

(3) Hoppe, J. O., L. P. Duprey, S. Reznek, and F. P. Luduena, "Observations on the Use of the Trypan Blue and Skin-Twitch Tests for Measuring Local Tissue Toxicity," *Toxicol. Appl. Pharmacol.*, 1:73–86, 1959.

(4) Hoppe, J. O., E. B. Alexander and L. C. Miller, "Use of the Trypan Blue and Rabbit Eye Tests for Irritation," *J. Amer. Pharm. Assoc.*, 39:147–151, 1950.

(5) Schmidt, J. L., C. McIntire, D. L. Martin, M. A. Hawthorne and R. K. Richards, "The Relationship among Different *in Vivo* Properties of Local Anesthetics and Toxicity to Cell Cultures *in Vitro*," *Toxicol. Appl. Pharmacol.*, 1:454–461, 1959.

(6) Kinkel, H. J., "Inhalation and Toxicity Studies," *J. Soc. Cosmetic Chemists*, 15:395–409, 1964.

(7) Schild, H. O., "Mechanism of Development of Drug Sensitization of the Skin," *Proc. Roy. Soc. Med.*, 55:14–16, 1962.

(8) Paget, G. E., "Limitations of Animal Tests to Detect Sensitization Reactions in Man," *Proc. Roy. Soc. Med.*, 55:9–11, 1962.

(9) Davies, G. E., "Prospects for Animal Tests in Experimental Sensitization of Drugs," *Proc. Roy. Soc. Med.*, 55:11–14, 1962.

(10) Draize, J. H., "Dermal Toxicity," *Food, Drug, Cosmetic Law Journal*, 10:722–732, 1955.

(11) Hakim, R. E., R. G. Freeman, A. C. Griffin, and J. M. Knox, "Experimental Toxicologic Studies on 8-Methoxypsoralen in Animals Exposed to the Long Ultraviolet," *J. Pharmacol. Exp. Therap.*, 131:394–399, 1961.

(12) Burckhardt, W., and K. & M. Schwarz-Speck, "Photoallergische Ekzeme durch Nadisan," *Schweiz. Med. Wochschr.*, 87:954–956, 1957.

Special Toxicity Tests. The routine toxicity experiments described in the preceding five sections are often not well suited to demonstrate certain types of adverse reactions. It therefore becomes necessary to consider variations or special tests which may increase the probability of finding such toxic effects. From an unlimited choice of tests the toxicologist must

Table III. Some Special Toxicologic Procedures for the Demonstration of Adverse Drug Effects not Reliably Detected in Standard Toxicity Tests

Toxicologic Property	Experimental Procedure	Example Reference
Activation of gastric ulcer	Test in animals with experimental gastric ulcers (pylorus ligation, histamine, starvation)	1)
Hepatotoxicity	Test in animals with experimental liver damage (ligation of bile ducts, hepatotoxins, *e.g.*, ethionine, allyl alcohol, CCl_4, low protein diet)	2), 3), 4)
Bone marrow toxicity	Combination with irradiation or alkylating agents	5), 6)
Interference with resistance against infections	Test in artificially infected animals	7)
Physical dependence	Chronic administration followed by abrupt withdrawal or administration of specific antagonist. Test for ability to substitute for known dependence- producing drugs	8)
Displacement of bilirubin from albumin-binding sites and induction of kernicterus	Test in Gunn strain of rats (rats with congenital icterus)	9)
Nephrotoxicity	Test in animals with experimental kidney damage (pyelonephritis, nephrotoxic chemicals, choline deficiency)	10)
Toxic effect in hypo- or hyperthyreosis	Test in thyroidectomized, thiouracil- and thyroxine-treated animals	11)
Increased toxicity in various forms of malnutrition	Test in animals with vitamin or protein deficiency or various forms of nutritional imbalance	12)

make a selection which is based on the toxic properties known to be typical for compounds of similar pharmacologic activity or chemical structure. The details of most experimental procedures are not yet standardized and must be adapted for each drug. A few examples of special toxicity tests are listed in Table III. While these experiments may often indicate the presence of hidden toxic properties of a drug, it is mandatory that their evaluation be made with due regard for the often quite unphysiologic conditions under which the tests results are obtained.

References:

(1) Bonfils, S., J. P. Hardouin, and F. Delbarre, "Ulcération Gastrique du Rat blanc par Administration de Phényl butazone. Recherches sur le Mécanisme d'Action," *C. R. Soc. Biol.*, 148:881–883, 1954.

(2) Paget, G. E., "Correlations with Potential Toxicity in Man of Toxic Effects in Animals," *Clin. Pharmacol. Therap.*, 3:381–384, 1962.

(3) Popper, H., A. Dubin, C. Bruce, G. Kent, and D. Kushner, "Effects of Chlorpromazine upon Experimental Hepatic Injury," *J. Lab. Clin. Med.*, 49:767–773, 1957.

(4) Zbinden, G., and A. Studer, "Experimental Pathology of Iproniazid and Related Compounds," *Ann. N. Y. Acad. Sci.*, 80:873–884, 1959.

(5) Charipper, H. A., A. M. Slicher, and E. N. Grisewood, "The Use of Ionic Radiation in the Development of a Bioassay for Granulocytopenia," in A. Edelman, *Radioactivity for Pharmaceutical and Allied Research Laboratories*, pp. 27–48, 1960.

(6) Lu, F. C., W. A. Mannell, H. C. Grice, and M. G. Allmark, "The Effect of Agranulocytic and Nonagranulocytic Drugs in Rabbits Concurrently Treated with Busulfan (Myleran). III, Thiouracil, Morphine and Penicillin," *Toxicol. Appl. Pharmacol.* 2:171–182, 1960.

(7) Mills, L. C., B. F. Boylston, J. A. Greene and J. H. Moyer, "Septic Arthritis as a Complication of Orally Given Steroid Therapy," *J. Am. Med. Assoc.*, 164:1310–1314, 1957.

(8) World Health Organization, "Evaluation of Dependence-Producing Drugs," *World Health Organ. Tech. Rep. Ser.*, p. 287, 1964.

(9) Johnson, L., W. A. Blanc, J. F. Lucey and R. Day, "Kernicterus in Rats with Familial Jaundice," *Am. Med. Assoc. J. Diseases Children*, 94:548, 1957.

(10) Studer, A., G. Zbinden, and B. Fust, "Weitere Tierexperimentelle Untersuchungen zur Frage Schmerzmittelmissbrauch und Interstitielle Nephritis," *Schweiz. Med. Wochschr.*, 88:469–470, 1958.

(11) Sung, C. Y., and E. L. Way, "The Effect of Altered Thyroid Function on the Actions and Fate of d,1-Methadone," *J. Pharmacol. Exp. Therap.*, 108:1–10, 1953.

(12) Rosen, F., "The Relationship of Certain Vitamin Deficiencies to the Toxicity of Iproniazid," *Ann. N. Y. Acad. Sci.*, 80:885–894, 1959.

Carcinogenic Effects. The possibility that drugs may be a factor in human carcinogenesis is well recognized since many industrial chemicals and metals such as benzidine, coal tar, β-naphthylamine, dimethylaminoazobenzene, 2-acetylaminofluorene, nickel, arsenic and beryllium are known to be carcinogens in man. The recognition of a drug as a contributing or causative factor in human cancer is a most difficult problem since human beings are constantly exposed to a large variety of chemicals. Furthermore, carcinogenic action is characterized by a long latent period which, in man, may last 5 to 30 years.[1] Carcinogenetic properties of drugs may be detected in animals.[2] The usual procedures call for repeated oral, parenteral or combined oral and parenteral administration to male and female mice, rats, hamsters and occasionally dogs. Drugs are given to one large group at a tolerated dose level for 18 to 24 months, or even longer when dogs are used.[1, 3] Another group receives the drug at toxic dose levels and treatment is discontinued before too many animals die. The survivors are observed throughout the rest of their lives. Since spontaneous tumors are frequent, it is essential that large control groups be included and that animals of known and uniform strain be used. The tumor susceptibility of the available strain may be tested against urethan, which is a potent carcinogen.[3] The animal tests can be made more sensitive if the experiment is initiated in newborn animals or if a strain of mice is used which shows a high incidence of lung adenomas.[4] In all tests the animals are carefully observed for toxic symptoms and a detailed autopsy and histologic examination of all organs are mandatory. Types and incidence of tumors have to be recorded. The histological evaluation must also search for disturbances of cell and tissue organization which may represent the first steps toward tumor formation, *e.g.*, hyperplastic changes of the liver which may precede liver tumors or focal hyperplasia of the urinary tract epithelium which may develop into a carcinoma of the bladder.[4]

In evaluating the experimental results, one must keep in mind that strain and species differences are frequent and often striking.[1, 4, 5] Thus, it is probable that such drugs as griseofulvin, iron dextran, estrogenic hormone and isoniazid,[5 6] which cause tumors in animals, are not carcinogenic in man. However, the possibility still exists, and until evidence to the contrary is obtained by extensive epidemologic studies, any carcinogenic effect observed in animals must be considered as indicative of a potential risk in the drug's use in man. Among the drugs which often show carcinogenic effects in animals are the cancer chemotherapeutic agents, *e.g.*, the alkylating drugs, actinomycin D and N-isopropyl-α-(2-methylhydrazino)-p-toluamide hydrochloride.[7] The significance of these findings is particularly difficult to evaluate because of the generally limited survival time of patients requiring antitumor chemotherapy. The correlation between antitumor effect and carcinogenicity in animals, however, is so striking that tumor-inhibiting activity has been proposed as a fast preliminary screen for carcinogenic effects.[4] The same is true for mutagenic effects which may be tested in drosophila.[4] Radioactive substances represent another class of drugs which is strongly suspected of having carcinogenic potential in man. The classical example is Thorotrast (thorium dioxide) which causes widespread malignancies in many organs in humans. The situation is not yet clear with radioactive iodine which is used for the therapy of hyperthyreosis and has been accused of causing acute leukemia.[8]

The problem of chemical carcinogenesis is further complicated by the observation that compounds may act as co-carcinogens which means that they produce tumors only after the animals have received a sub-effective dose of a carcinogen.[1] While such combined effects have not yet been demonstrated in man, the possibility that similar phenomena may occur certainly exists. But in view of the multitude of possible interactions of chemicals, a meaningful screening for co-carcinogenic effects hardly appears feasible.

References:

(1) Berenblum, I., "The Experimental Basis for Carcinogenicity Testing," *Proc. Europ. Soc. f. Study of Drug Toxicity*, 3:7–13, 1964.

(2) Bourke, A. R., "Carcinogenicity." In Lehman, A. J. et al., "Procedures for the Appraisal of the Toxicity of Chemicals in Foods, Drugs and Cosmetics," *Food, Drug, Cosmetic Law J.*, 10:719–721, 1955.

(3) Della Porta, G., "The Study of Chemical Substances for Possible Carcinogenic Action," *Proc. Europ. Soc. f. Study of Drug Toxicity*, 3:29–37, 1964.

(4) Walpole, A. L., "The Properties in the Laboratory of Known Carcinogens," *Proc. Europ. Soc. f. Study Drug Toxicity*, 3:15–25, 1964.

(5) Modell, W., "Drug-Induced Diseases," *Ann. Rev. Pharmacol.*, 5:285–304, 1965.

(6) Roe, F. J. C., E. Boyland, and A. Haddow, "Chemotherapy of Tuberculosis," *Brit. Med. J.*, 1:1550, 1965.

(7) Kelly, M. G., R. W. O'Gara, K. Gadekar, S. T. Yancey, and V. T. Oliverio, "Carcinogenic Activity of a New Antitumor Agent, N-isopropyl-α-(2-methylhydrazino)-toluamide Hydrochloride (N SC-77213), *Cancer Chemother. Rep.*, 39: 77–80, 1964.

(8) Werner, S. C., and E. H. Quimby, "Acute Leukemia after Radioactive Iodine (I[131]) Therapy for Hyperthyroidism," *J. Am. Med. Assoc.*, 165:1558–1559, 1957.

III. TOXICOLOGIC INFORMATION GAINED FROM PHARMACOLOGIC AND BIOCHEMICAL STUDIES

Most of the adverse reactions to drugs occurring in man are functional in nature. Table IV shows that of the 25 most frequent side effects observed in a large patient sample, only the few cases of weight gain, skin rash and dermatitis are due to clearly demonstrable changes of tissue, while all others have no distinct anatomic substrate. Functional side effects, although mostly reversible, can seriously limit the usefulness of drugs and may endanger the lives of patients. Only in exceptional cases can they be predicted from routine toxicologic tests. It is important therefore that classical toxicity experiments be amended by a broad pharmacologic and biochemical analysis of the new compound. For example, cardiovascular studies may detect harmful drug effects on blood pressure, pulse rate, heart rhythm and autonomic control mechanisms; psychopharmacologic

Table IV. The 25 Most Frequently Reported Adverse Reactions to Drugs Observed in 11,115 Patients Treated with 77 Different Drugs or Drug Combinations (Summarized from 86 Recently Published Drug Evaluation Papers)

Drowsiness	426	Depression	23
Nausea	211	Anorexia	23
Dizziness	198	Increased appetite	21
Sedation	176	Tremor	21
Dry mouth	133	Perspiration	21
(Epi) gastric distress	98	Dermatitis	19
Nervousness	98	Increased energy	18
Incoordination	95	Vertigo	16
Headache	91	Palpitations	16
Vomiting	83	Nocturia	15
Weakness	61	Lethargy	15
Hypertension	57	Excitation	14
Nasal stuffiness	57	Abdominal distention	14
Insomnia	56	Frequency of bowel movements	14
Fatigue	55	Flatulence	14
Constipation	54	Stiffness	13
Tinnitus	49	Urticaria	13
Weight gain	39	Tachycardia	13
Hypotension	38	Lightheadedness	12
Dryness of nasopharynx	38	Somnolence	12
Heartburn	38	Pruritus	12
Diarrhea	30	Eructation	12
Skin rash	29		

tests may discover sedative or stimulant properties; studies of gastrointestinal function may uncover influences on gastric secretion, bile flow and gastrointestinal motility; and biochemical studies may reveal inhibition of important enzymes, malfunction of endocrine organs, disturbances of excretory functions, and depletion or accumulation of biogenic amines and other important substances in various organs. The goal of this extended evaluation is to learn as much as possible about mechanisms by which the drug acts. This information, together with the available knowledge about metabolic pathways, will often reveal much more of the compound's toxic potential than a routine toxicity experiment of many months' duration. It will often permit one to anticipate specific toxic effects which are related to a patient's pathologic condition due to disease or congenital abnormality. A useful notion as to contraindications and special precautions to be observed with a new drug may thus evolve before the substance has produced any harmful effect in man.

IV. TOXICOLOGY OF DRUG COMBINATIONS

The majority of today's patients are treated with more than one drug. It is thus not surprising that a certain number of untoward effects is due to an interaction of two or more pharmacologic agents.

True Potentiation.   In this case one drug prolongs and potentiates another agent's pharmacologic effect by sensitizing the organism, *e.g.*, potentiation of hypnotics by chlorpromazine.[1]

Inhibition of Drug Metabolism.   Some drugs block the microsomal enzymes which are involved in another drug's metabolism, thus leading to its accumulation with potentiation of its pharmacologic effect,[1, 2, 3] *e.g.*, potentiation of anticoagulants by monoamine oxidase inhibitors[4] and potentation of barbiturates and other sedatives by imipramine.[5]

Stimulation of Drug Metabolism.   Repeated administration of certain drugs such as phenylbutazone, aminopyrine or phenobarbital stimulates the drug-metabolizing liver enzymes. This may lead to accelerated breakdown of another drug causing diminution of activity and sometimes accumulation of metabolites.[6] The stimulation of aminopyrine metabolism by phenylbutazone is an example.[7]

Displacement of a Drug from its Binding Sites on Plasma Albumin.   This leads to a rapid increase of the unbound fraction in the blood and consequently to a rise in the tissue concentration with increased potential for tissue damage, *e.g.*, displacement of sulfonamides from their albumin binding sites by ethyl biscoumacetate, phenylbutazone, sulfinpyrazone, etc.[8]

Impairment of Organ Function.   A drug may depress an organ's function without causing untoward symptoms. However, if a second drug is given whose safety requires full responsiveness of that organ, adverse effects may ensue, *e.g.*, circulatory collapse after administration of anesthetics to patients in whom therapy with corticosteroids has induced adrenal insufficiency.[9]

If a fixed drug combination is developed, acute toxicity tests are performed in various animal species and the results are compared with the LD_{50}'s of the individual components. Furthermore, a subacute toxicity test in rats and dogs for 3 months' duration, using the drugs in a ratio contemplated for clinical use, is often done. In addition, metabolic studies are conducted to find out whether one component of the combination materially influences rate and pathways of metabolism of any of the others. Extensive pharmacology tests must be performed with the combination to rule out unexpected effects, particularly on blood pressure and its regulatory mechanisms. Drugs which are intended as single therapeutic agents may also be used frequently in combination with other substances in the clinic, *e.g.*, cardiovascular drugs are often given to patients treated with anticoagulants, and antiinfective agents will be used in combination with sulfonamides, antibiotics and/or antipyretics. The toxicologist must anticipate these possibilites and conduct at least some pilot experiments with drug combinations which are likely to be tried under clinical conditions and whose interaction might conceivably lead to untoward effects in man. Dangerous interactions are possible not only with other drugs but also with naturally occurring substances ingested in the diet. A typical example is the hypertensive crisis observed in patients on tranylcypromine after eating cheese with high tyramine content.[10] Moreover, hazardous effects of combination therapy are not limited to interactions of chemical substances; other methods of treatment sometimes enhance drug toxicity. For example, substances which depress the bone marrow will become much more toxic if they are administered in combination with radiotherapy. The increased use of bioelectric devices for diagnosis and therapy may cause many as yet unknown toxicologic problems, since drug therapy and concomitant electrical stimulation or depression of organ systems may result in a variety of complex interactions, not all of which will always be beneficial for the patient.

References:

(1) Fouts, J. R. and B. B. Brodie, "On the Mechanism of Drug Potentiation by Iproniazid (2-isopropyl-1-isonicotinyl Hydrazine)," *J. Pharmacol. Exp. Therap.*, 116:480–485, 1956.

(2) Axelrod, J., J. Reich enthal, and B. B. Brodie, "Mechanism of the Potentiating Action of β-diethylaminoethyl Diphenylpropylacetate," *J. Pharmacol. Exp. Therap.*, 112:49–54, 1954.

(3) Kato, R., P. Vassanelli and E. Chiesara, "A New Potent Inhibitor of Microsomal Drug-Metabolizing Enzymes, 2,4-dichloro-6-phenylphenoxyethalamine Hydrochloride (DPEA) (Lilly 32391)," *Biochem. Pharmacol.*, 12:353–356, 1963.

(4) Hrdina, P., M. Rusnakova, and V. Kovalcik, "Changes of Hypoprothrombinemic Activity of Indirect Anticoagulants after MAO Inhibitors and Reserpine," *Biochem. Pharmacol.*, 12 (Suppl.):855, 1963.

(5) Kato, R., E. Chiesara, and P. Vassanelli, "Mechanism of Potentiation of Barbiturates and Meprobamate by Imipramine," *Biochem. Pharmacol.*, 12:357–364, 1963.

(6) Conney, A. H., C. Davison, R. Gastel, and J. J. Burns, "Adaptive Increases in Drug-Metabolizing Enzymes Induced by Phenobarbital and Other Drugs," *J. Pharmacol. Exp. Therap.*, 130:1–8, 1960.

(7) Chen, W., P. A. Vrindten, P. G. Dayton, and J. J. Burns, "Accelerated Aminopyrine Metabolism in Human Subjects Pretreated with Phenylbutazone," *Life Sciences*, 2:35–42, 1962.

(8) Anton, A. H., "A Drug-Induced Change in the Distribution and Renal Excretion of Sulfonamides," *J. Pharmacol. Exp. Therap.*, 134:291–303, 1961.

(9) Elliott, H. W., "Influence of Previous Therapy on Anesthesia," *Clin. Pharmacol. Therap.*, 3:41–58, 1962.

(10) Asatoor, A. M., A. J. Levi, and M. D. Milne, "Tranylcypromine and Cheese," *Lancet*, 2:733–734, 1963.

I. INTRODUCTION

The science of nutrition deals with a series of interrelated and complex considerations. One must consider the kinds and amounts of nutrients an animal requires for maintenance, growth, and reproduction. In connection with these nutrient requirements it is necessary to consider not only the physiological roles played by the nutrients but also the results of an inadequate nutrient supply as well as an excess of nutrients.

Nutrition, then, may be defined as the sum of the processes by which a safe and adequate supply of essential substrate and cofactors (*i.e.,* nutrients) is presented, ingested, absorbed, metabolized, and disposed of by an organism so that growth, active life, and reproduction may occur. The kinds of food materials which will supply these nutrients must be of prime consideration and in this regard it is the basic purpose of this section to supply such information in tabular form.

Definitions of some of the terms which are commonly encountered in the science of nutrition are:

Metabolic balance—the procedure of determining quantitatively the difference between the intake (food) and the excretion (urine and feces) resulting in the degree of bodily gain or rentention *(positive balance)* or loss *(negative balance)*. With appropriate sequences of study and changed levels of intake, it is one valuable method for determining nutrient needs in animals of different physiological and pathological states.

Absorption is concerned with the quantity of the substance taken into the body, crossing the gastro-intestinal wall and when applied to actual values is the difference between intake and fecal excretion of, for example, nitrogen.

Deposition connotes the actual incorporation into body tissue.

Utilization indicates active participation in body activities.

Assimilation encompasses absorption, retention and utilization.

Accumulation or accretion refer to increments in deposition or storage over a period of time, as in growth.

Deficiency disease such as rickets, pellagra, scurvy, beriberi, etc., is caused by lack of some particular or specific nutrient in the body. Certain symptoms are identifiable in the body for each disease.

Limited nutrition—a condition brought on by restricted intake of a nutrient or nutrients, as opposed to no intake of a nutrient or nutrients, in which the body limits its processes or growth proportionately to the materials available.

Optimal nutrition—the result of a combination of food intake and its utilization that produces the best result in growth and development or maintenance of well-being.

Recommended Dietary Allowances—the amounts of nutrients recommended by the Food and Nutrition Board of National Research Council and considered adequate for maintenance of good nutrition in healthy persons in the United States. (The allowances are revised from time to time in accordance with newer knowledge of nutritional needs.)

Minimum Daily Requirements—the amounts of various nutrients that have been established by the Food and Drug Administration as standards for labeling purposes of foods and pharmaceutical preparations for special dietary uses. These are the amounts regarded as necessary in the diet for the prevention of deficiency diseases and generally are less than the Recommended Dietary Allowances.

Table I. Recommended Daily Dietary Allowances

Age years from to	Calories	Protein g	Calcium g	Iron mg.	Vita-min A value IU	Thia-mine mg.	Ribo-flavin mg.	Niacin equiv. mg.	Ascorbic acid mg.	Vitamin D IU
Men 18-35	2,900	70	0.8	10	*5,000	1.2	1.7	19	70	......
35-55	2,600	70	.8	10	5,000	1.0	1.6	17	70	......
55-75	2,200	70	.8	10	5,000	.9	1.3	15	70	......
Women 18-35	2,100	58	.8	15	5,000	.8	1.3	14	70	......
35-55	1,900	58	.8	15	5,000	.8	1.2	13	70	......
55-75	1,600	58	.8	10	5,000	.8	1.2	13	70	......
Pregnant (2d and 3d trimester)	+200	+20	+.5	+5	+1,000	+.2	+.3	+3	+30	400
Lactating	+1,000	+40	+.5	+5	+3,000	+.4	+.6	+7	+30	400
Infants 0-1	kg.x115 ±15	kg.x2.5 ±0.5	.7	kg.x1.0	1,500	.4	.6	6	30	400
Children 1-3	1,300	32	.8	8	2,000	.5	.8	9	40	400
3-6	1,600	40	.8	10	2,500	.6	1.0	11	50	400
6-9	2,100	52	.8	12	3,500	.8	1.3	14	60	400
Boys 9-12	2,400	60	1.1	15	4,500	1.0	1.4	16	70	400
12-15	3,000	75	1.4	15	5,000	1.2	1.8	20	80	400
15-18	3,400	85	1.4	15	5,000	1.4	2.0	22	80	400
Girls 9-12	2,200	55	1.1	15	4,500	.9	1.3	15	80	400
12-15	2,500	62	1.3	15	5,000	1.0	1.5	17	80	400
15-18	2,300	58	1.3	15	5,000	.9	1.3	15	70	400

*1,000, I.U. from preformed vitamin A and 4,00 I.U. from beta-carotene.

515

Notes to Table I

The allowance levels are intended to cover individual variations among most normal persons as they live in the United States under usual environmental stresses. The recommended allowances can be attained with a variety of common foods, providing other nutrients for which human requirements have been less well defined.

Entries on line for age range 18-35 years represent the 25-year age. All other entries represent allowances for the midpoint of the specified age periods, i.e., line for children 1-3 is for age 2 years (24 months); 3-6 is for age 4½ years (54 months) etc.

Niacin equivalents include dietary sources of the preformed vitamin and the precursor, tryptophan. 60 mg tryptophan represents 1 mg niacin.

The calorie and protein allowances per kg for infants are considered to decrease progressively from birth. Allowances for calcium, thiamine, riboflavin, and niacin increase proportionately with calories to the maximum values shown.

Table II. Standards for Enrichment: Minimum and Maximum Amounts of Required Nutrients Specified for Foods Labeled "Enriched"

| | Milligrams Per Pound of Product | | | | | | | | | |
| | Thiamine | | Riboflavin | | Niacin | | Iron | | Calcium | |
Item	Min.	Max.	Min.	Max.	Min.	Max.	Min.	Max.	Min.	Max.
	Mg.	Mg.	Mg.	Mg.	Mg.	Mg.	Mg.	Mg.	Mg.	Mg.
Bread, rolls, and buns, white	1.1	1.8	0.7	1.6	10.0	15.0	8.0	12.5	----	----
Cornmeal; corn grits	2.0	3.0	1.2	1.8	16.0	24.0	13.0	26.0	----	----
Cornmeal, self-rising	2.0	3.0	1.2	1.8	16.0	24.0	13.0	26.0	500	1,750
Farina	2.0	2.5	1.2	1.5	16.0	20.0	13.0	*	----	----
Flour, white	2.0	2.5	1.2	1.5	16.0	20.0	13.0	16.5	----	----
Flour, self-rising	2.0	2.5	1.2	1.5	16.0	20.0	13.0	16.5	500	1,500
Macaroni products; noodle products	4.0	5.0	1.7	2.2	27.0	34.0	13.0	16.5	----	----
Rice, milled	2.0	4.0	1.2	2.4	16.0	32.0	13.0	26.0	----	----

*No maximum level has been established.

Table III. Vitamin B6, Pantothenic Acid, Biotin, Folic Acid, Choline, and Inositol Content of Foods, Edible Portion.

FOOD	PORTION Amt.	Wt. gm.	VITAMIN B6 Wt. mcg.	Per cent	PANTOTHENIC ACID Wt. mg.	Per cent	BIOTIN Wt. mcg.	Per cent	FOLIC ACID Wt. mcg.	Per cent	CHOLINE Wt. mg.	Per cent	INOSITOL Wt. mg.	Per cent
Cereals and Bread Products														
Cereals, cooked, whole														
Barley, whole	½ c.	30(dry)	167.1	557	0.219	0.73	9.3	31.0	15	50.0	41.7	139.0	117.6	392.0
Corn, yellow	½ c.	20(dry)	93.4	467	0.128	0.64	4.2	21.0	5.3	26.5	12.2	61.0	10.0	50.0
Oats	½ c.	20(dry)	41.0	205	0.300	1.50	4.8	24.0	6.6	33.0	31.2	156.0	53.8	269.0
Rice, brown	½ c.	30(dry)	186.0	620	0.456	1.52	3.6	12.0	6.0	20.0	33.6	112.0	35.7	119.0
Wheat, whole	½ c.	30(dry)	158.4	528	0.411	1.37	4.8	16.0	14.7	49.0	28.2	94.0	110.0	370.0
Cereals, refined, cooked														
Cornmeal														
White	½ c.	20(dry)	(12.2)*	(61)	0.116	0.58	1.3	6.6	1.8	9.0	–†	–	10.2	51
Yellow	½ c.	20(dry)	–	–	0.138	0.69	–	–	1.8	9.0	2.0	10.0	–	–
Hominy, grits	½ c.	20(dry)	(1.2)	(6)	0.068	0.34	0.1	0.7	0.9	4.5	–	–	0.6	3
Rice														
Converted	½ c.	30(dry)	20.4	68	0.393	1.31	2.4	8.0	6.0	20.0	26.7	89.0	6.0	20
Parboiled	½ c.	30(dry)	30.0	100	0.411	1.37	3.0	10.0	5.7	19.0	29.4	98.0	7.5	25
White	½ c.	30(dry)	11.1	37	0.225	0.75	1.5	5.0	4.8	16.0	17.7	59.0	3.0	10
Cereal concentrates, raw														
Rice														
Bran	1 oz.	30(dry)	750.0	2500	0.831	2.77	18.0	60.0	43.8	146.0	51.0	170.0	138.9	463
Germ	1 oz.	30(dry)	480.0	1600	0.900	3.00	17.4	58.0	129.0	430.0	90.0	300.0	111.6	372
Polishings	1 oz.	30(dry)	600.0	2000	1.000	3.33	17.1	57.0	57.6	192.0	30.6	102.0	136.2	454
Wheat														
Bran	1 oz.	30(dry)	414.0	1380	0.900	3.00	4.2	14.0	58.5	195.0	42.9	143.0	–	–
Germ	1 oz.	30(dry)	275.4	918	0.660	2.20	–	–	91.5	305.0	121.8	406.0	231.0	770

*Data from Cheldelin and Williams (26), as only data available, even though they may not be comparable to figures obtained by other methods. Figures which are appreciably lower than other values available for similar types of foods are enclosed in parentheses.
†Dashes indicate that no representative value was found in the literature for particular constituent.

Food	Measure	Weight (g)												
Ready-to-eat, dark cereal														
Corn soya	1 c.	30	—	—	0.273	0.91	—	—	24.0	80.0	—	—	—	—
Oats	1 c.	25	—	—	0.230	0.92	—	—	5.6	22.4	—	—	—	—
Wheat														
Bran	1 c.	35	—	—	1.015	2.90	—	—	35.0	100.0	—	—	—	—
Flakes	1 c.	35	—	—	0.304	0.87	—	—	16.4	47.0	—	—	—	—
Shredded Wheat	1 bisc.	30	—	—	0.210	0.70	—	—	16.5	55.0	—	—	—	—
Ready-to-eat, white cereal														
Corn flakes	1 c.	25	(14.4)	—	0.047	0.19	—	—	1.4	5.5	—	—	—	—
Rice	1 c.	30	(48)	—	0.114	0.38	0.4	1.3	2.3	7.6	—	—	5.7	19
Bread														
White	1 sl.	23	23.0	100	0.101	0.44	0.3	1.1	3.4	15.0	—	—	11.7	51
Whole wheat	1 sl.	23	96.0	420	0.182	0.79	0.4	1.9	6.9	30.0	—	—	15.4	67
Flour														
White	1 c.	110	363.0	330	0.594	0.54	1.1	1.0	8.8	8.0	57.2	52	51.7	47
Whole wheat	1 c.	120	1116.0	930	1.296	1.08	10.8	9.0	45.6	38.0	—	—	132.0	110

Dairy Products

Food	Measure	Weight (g)												
Cheese														
Cheddar	1 oz.	30	(18.7)	(66)	0.114	0.40	1.0	3.6	4.5	16.0	13.6	48	7.0	25
Cottage	1 oz.	30	—	—	0.080	0.28	—	—	8.8	31.0	—	—	—	—
Processed	1 oz.	30	—	—	0.136	0.48	1.3	4.6	3.1	11.0	—	—	—	—
Egg														
Whole	1 med.	50	126.0	252	0.795	1.59	11.2	22.5	2.5	5.1	252.0	504	16.5	33
Yolk	1 med.	17	52.4	308	0.719	4.23	8.8	52.0	2.2	12.9	253.3	1490	—	—
White	1 med.	31	67.3	217	0.043	0.14	2.2	7.0	0.2	0.6	0.6	2	—	—
Milk														
Whole	1 c.	244	87.8	36	0.756	0.31	11.5	4.7	1.5	0.6	36.6	15	31.7	13
Evaporated reconstituted	1 c.	244	53.7	22	0.805	0.33	11.0	4.5	1.7	0.7	36.6	15	—	—
Non-fat dry reconstituted	1 c.	244	80.5	33	0.830	0.34	8.3	3.4	0.5	0.2	25.4	10.4	—	—

Fats, Oils, and Oily Foods

Food	Measure	Weight (g)												
Butter	1 Tbsp.	14	—	—	—	—	—	—	—	—	0.7	5	—	—
Lard	1 Tbsp.	14	—	—	—	—	—	—	—	—	0.7	5	—	—
Margarine	1 Tbsp.	14	—	—	—	—	—	—	—	—	0.7	5	—	—
Vegetable oils	1 Tbsp.	14	—	—	—	—	—	—	—	—	0.7	5	—	—

Table III. (continued) Vitamin B_6, Pantothenic Acid, Biotin, Folic Acid, Choline, and Inositol Content of Foods, Edible Portion

FOOD	PORTION		VITAMIN B_6		PANTOTHENIC ACID		BIOTIN		FOLIC ACID		CHOLINE		INOSITOL	
	Amt.	Wt.	Wt.	Per cent	Wt.	Per cent	Wt.	Per cent	Wt.	Per cent	Wt.	Per cent	Wt.	Per cent
		gm.	mcg.		mg.		mcg.		mcg.		mg.		mg.	
Fruits, fresh or frozen														
Apples, medium	1	130	39.0	30	0.130	0.10	1.2	0.9	2.6	2.0	—	—	31.2	24
Apricots	3 med.	100	71.0	71	0.290	0.29	—	—	3.3	3.3	—	—	—	—
Bananas	1 med.	100	320.0	320	0.310	0.31	4.4	4.4	9.7	9.7	—	—	34.0	34
Berries														
Blackberry	⅔ c.	100	—	—	0.260	0.26	—	—	13.7	13.7	—	—	—	—
Blueberry	⅔ c.	100	91.0	91	0.120	0.12	—	—	8.0	8.0	—	—	—	—
Raspberry, sweetened	¾ c.	100	38.0	38	0.210	0.21	—	—	5.0	5.0	—	—	—	—
Strawberry, sweetened	⅔ c.	100	61.0	61	0.160	0.16	4.0	4.0	9.0	9.0	—	—	60.0	60
Cantaloupe, diced	⅔ c.	100	36.0	36	0.260	0.26	3.1	3.1	6.8	6.8	—	—	120.0	120
Cherries, sour red, pitted	⅔ c.	100	85.0	85	0.070	0.07	—	—	6.0	6.0	—	—	—	—
Figs, small	3	114	148.2	130	0.388	0.34	—	—	16.0	14.0	—	—	—	—
Grapefruit, small	½	120	25.0	21	0.288	0.24	3.6	3.0	3.4	2.8	—	—	180.0	150
Grapes, 1 bunch	3½ oz.	100	85.0	85	0.050	0.05	1.6	1.6	5.2	5.2	—	—	—	—
Oranges, small	1	100	31.0	31	0.220	0.22	1.9	1.9	5.1	5.1	—	—	210.0	210
Peaches, sweetened	½ c.	100	20.0	20	0.120	0.12	1.7	1.7	4.0	4.0	—	—	96.0	96
Pineapple	3½ oz.	100	75.0	75	0.170	0.17	—	—	6.0	6.0	—	—	—	—
Rhubarb, sweetened	3½ oz.	100	29.0	29	0.070	0.07	—	—	4.0	4.0	—	—	—	—
Watermelon, diced	1 c.	150	49.5	33	0.450	0.30	5.4	3.6	0.9	0.6	—	—	96.0	64
Fruits, canned														
Apricots	½ c.	125	67.5	54	0.125	0.10	—	—	0.6	0.5	—	—	—	—
Blackberries	½ c.	125	30.0	24	0.100	0.08	—	—	17.5	14.0	—	—	—	—
Blueberries	½ c.	125	48.7	39	0.087	0.07	—	—	5.2	4.2	—	—	—	—
Cherries, sweet	½ c.	125	196.2	157	0.150	0.12	—	—	3.7	3.0	—	—	—	—
Peaches	½ c.	125	28.8	23	0.088	0.07	0.3	0.2	0.6	0.5	—	—	—	—
Pineapple	½ c.	125	88.7	71	—	—	—	—	1.0	0.8	—	—	—	—
Plums, purple	½ c.	125	33.7	27	0.100	0.08	—	—	1.2	1.0	—	—	—	—
Fruit, dried														
Apricots, small	6 halves	30	—	—	0.225	0.75	—	—	1.4	4.7	—	—	—	—
Dates, pitted	5	45	—	—	0.351	0.78	—	—	11.1	24.7	—	—	—	—
Figs, large	2	40	128.0	320	0.208	0.52	—	—	12.8	32.0	—	—	—	—
Prunes	5 med.	35	—	—	0.126	0.36	—	—	1.9	5.4	—	—	—	—
Raisins, seedless	3 Tbsp.	30	98.0	327	0.030	0.10	1.4	4.5	3.0	10.0	—	—	36.0	120

Fruit Juices

	Measure	g												
Canned fruit juice														
Apple	½ c.	120	42.0	35	—	—	—	—	0.2	0.2	—	—	—	—
Grapefruit	½ c.	120	15.6	13	0.204	0.17	1.0	0.8	2.3	1.9	—	—	120.0	100
Lemon	½ c.	120	61.2	51	—	—	—	—	0.2	0.2	—	—	—	—
Orange	½ c.	120	28.8	24	0.156	0.13	1.0	0.8	2.8	2.3	—	—	169.0	141
Pineapple	½ c.	120	115.2	96	0.120	0.10	—	—	1.1	0.9	—	—	—	—
Frozen or fresh														
Apple	½ c.	120	36.0	30	0.024	0.02	0.5	0.4	1.8	1.5	0.7	0.6	28.8	24
Grape	½ c.	120	25.2	21	0.048	0.04	0.4	0.3	3.6	3.0	—	—	—	—
Grapefruit	½ c.	120	16.8	14	0.192	0.16	0.8	0.7	1.6	1.3	—	—	120.0	100
Lemon, single	½ c.	120	46.8	39	0.108	0.09	—	—	1.2	1.0	—	—	—	—
Orange, fresh	½ c.	120	31.2	26	0.168	0.14	0.4	0.3	2.6	2.2	14.4	12	141.6	118
Orange, frozen	½ c.	120	26.4	22	0.168	0.14	0.4	0.3	2.6	2.2	14.4	12	110.4	92
Pineapple	½ c.	120	88.8	74	0.144	0.12	—	—	1.2	1.0	—	—	—	—

Legumes

	Measure (cooked)	dry												
Mung bean	½ c.	32	182.4	570	0.800	2.50	2.4	7.5	46.4	145	66.9	209	22.4	70
Cowpeas	½ c.	32	(67.2)	(210)	0.397	1.24	6.7	21.0	140.5	439	82.2	257	76.8	240
Garbanzos	½ c.	32	172.8	540	0.400	1.25	3.2	10.0	40.0	125	78.4	245	76.8	240
Lentils	½ c.	32	156.8	490	0.480	1.50	4.2	13.2	34.2	107	71.4	223	41.6	130
Lima beans	½ c.	32	176.0	550	0.416	1.30	3.1	9.8	41.0	128	—	—	54.4	170
Navy beans	½ c.	32	—	—	0.387	1.21	—	—	40.0	125	—	—	160.0	500
Kidney beans	½ c.	32	—	—	0.208	0.65	—	—	57.6	180	—	—	—	—
Split peas	½ c.	32	105.0	328	0.700	2.18	5.9	18.4	16.3	51	64.3	201	48.0	150
Soy beans	½ c.	32	204.8	640	0.538	1.68	19.5	61.0	71.7	224	108.8	340	64.0	200
Soy flour	1 c.	90	590.4	656	1.512	1.68	63.0	70.0	383.4	426	202.5	225	184.5	205

Meat and Poultry‡

	Measure	g												
Beef														
Ground	3½ oz.	100	460.0 #	460	0.440 #	0.44	—	—	6.9	6.9	—	—	—	—
Liver	2 oz.	57	378.5	664	5.324	9.34	54.7	96.0	167.6	294.0	290.7	510	29.1	51
Rib roast, lean	3 oz.	100	480.0 #	480	0.600 #	0.60	3.4	3.4	—	—	82.0	82	—	—
Round	3 oz.	100	495.0 #	495	0.520 #	0.52	2.6	2.6	10.5	10.5	68.0	68	11.5	11.5

‡Raw values, except where indicated.   #Cooked values.

Table III. (continued) Vitamin B6, Pantothenic Acid, Biotin, Folic Acid, Choline, and Inositol Content of Foods, Edible Portion.

FOOD	PORTION Amt.	PORTION Wt.	VITAMIN B6 Wt.	VITAMIN B6 Per cent	PANTOTHENIC ACID Wt.	PANTOTHENIC ACID Per cent	BIOTIN Wt.	BIOTIN Per cent	FOLIC ACID Wt.	FOLIC ACID Per cent	CHOLINE Wt.	CHOLINE Per cent	INOSITOL Wt.	INOSITOL Per cent
		gm.	mcg.		mg.		mcg.		mcg.		mg.		mg.	
					Meat and Poultry, concluded‡									
Lamb														
Leg	3 oz	100	320.0#	320	0.620#	0.62	5.9	5.9	3.3	3.3	84.0	84	58.0	58
Liver	2 oz	57	—	—	4.047	7.10	72.4	127.0	157.3	276.0	—	—	—	—
Loin chop	3 oz	100	330.0#	330	0.590#	0.59	—	—	—	—	76.0	76	—	—
Veal														
Chop	3½ oz	100	430.0#	430	0.550#	0.50	2.0	2.0	—	—	96.0	96	33.0	33
Leg	3½ oz	100	200.0	200	0.914	0.914	—	—	—	—	132.0	132	—	—
Shoulder	3½ oz	100	300.0	300	—	—	—	—	—	—	93.0	93	—	—
Stew meat	3½ oz	100	330.0	330	0.852	0.852	—	—	4.6	4.6	96.0	96	—	—
Pork														
Bacon	2 sl.	16	88.0#	550	0.070#	0.440	1.2	7.6	—	—	12.8	80	6.9	43
Ham	3½ oz	100	440.0#	440	0.640#	0.640	5.0	5.0	10.6	10.6	122.0	122	31.0	31
Liver	2 oz	57	—	—	3.994	7.008	57.0	100.0	126.0	221.0	314.6	552	—	—
Loin	3½ oz	100	480.0#	480	0.400#	0.400	5.2	5.2	2.4	2.4	77.0	77	45.0	45
Poultry														
Chicken														
Dark meat	3½ oz	100	(25.0)	(25)	0.692	0.692	10.0	10.0	2.8	2.8	—	—	47.0	47
White meat	3½ oz	100	(130.0)	(130)	0.804	0.804	11.3	11.3	3.0	3.0	—	—	48.0	48
Turkey	3½ oz	100	—	—	0.748	0.748	—	—	7.5	7.5	—	—	—	—
Bologna, A.P.	2 oz	57	—	—	—	—	—	—	—	—	—	—	—	—
Frankfurter, A.P.	1	50	65.0	130	0.212	0.425	—	—	—	—	34.2	60	—	—
Sausage, pork, A.P.	2 oz	57	108.3	190	0.321	0.563	—	—	6.5	11.5	28.5	57	—	—
Fish														
Halibut, canned	3½ oz	100	(110.0)	(110)	0.150	0.150	8.0	8.0	—	—	27.4	48	17.0	17
Mackerel, Pacific, canned	3½ oz	100	270.0	270	0.470	0.470	18.0	18.0	0.6	0.6	—	—	—	—
Salmon, canned	3½ oz	100	450.0	450	0.580	0.580	15.0	15.0	0.5	0.5	—	—	17.0	17
Tuna, canned	3½ oz	100	670.0	670	0.420	0.420	3.0	3.0	1.8	1.8	—	—	—	—
Sardines, Pacific, canned	3½ oz	100	280.0	280	0.600	0.600	24.0	24.0	0.5	0.5	—	—	—	—

‡Raw values, except as indicated.

#Cooked.

Shellfish, canned														
Clams	3½ oz.	100	83.0	83	0.590	0.590	—	—	2.0	2.0	—	—	—	—
Crabs	3½ oz.	100	364.0	364	—	—	—	—	0.4	0.4	—	—	—	—
Oysters	3½ oz.	100	37.0	37	0.490	0.490	8.7	8.7	11.3	11.3	—	—	44.0	44
Shrimp	3½ oz.	100	111.0	111	0.210	0.210	—	—	1.8	1.8	—	—	—	—

Nuts and Oily Fruits

Nuts, raw														
Almonds	12–15	15	15.0	100	0.087	0.578	2.7	18.0	6.7	45.0	—	—	—	—
Brazil nuts	2 med.	15	—	—	0.035	0.231	—	—	0.7	4.5	—	—	—	—
Cashews	6–8	15	—	—	0.174	1.62	—	—	—	—	—	—	—	—
Coconut, fresh	½ oz.	15	—	—	0.049	0.330	—	—	4.1	27.6	—	—	—	—
Filbert	10–12	15	—	—	0.172	1.146	—	—	10.0	66.6	—	—	—	—
Peanuts, roasted	15–17	15	45.0	300	0.320	2.137	5.1	34.0	8.5	56.5	24.3	162	27.0	180
Pecan halves	12	15	—	—	0.256	1.707	4.0	27.0	4.0	27.0	7.5	50	—	—
Walnut halves	8–15	15	144.0	960	0.146	0.970	5.5	37.0	11.5	77.0	—	—	—	—
Peanut butter	1 Tbsp.	16	48.0	300	0.400	2.500	6.2	39.0	8.5	56.5	23.2	145	28.8	180
Fruits, oily														
Avocado, Fuerte (cubed)	½ c.	75	457.5	610	0.675	0.90	4.1	5.5	22.5	30.0	—	—	—	—
Olive, ripe, mammoth	6	40	6.4	16	0.008	0.02	—	—	0.3	0.7	—	—	—	—

Vegetables

Vegetables, fresh or frozen														
Asparagus	3½ oz.	100	136.0	136	0.620	0.62	—	—	109.0	109.0	10.0	10.0	—	—
Beans, Lima	3½ oz.	100	170.0	170	0.450	0.45	—	—	34.0	34.0	—	—	—	—
Beans, snap, green	3½ oz.	100	63.0	63	0.200	0.20	1.9	1.9	27.5	27.5	42.0	42.0	21.0	21
Beets (diced)	⅔ c.	100	(37.0)	(37)	0.170	0.17	—	—	13.5	13.5	—	—	—	—
Broccoli	⅔ c.	100	171.0	171	1.290	1.29	—	—	53.5	53.5	—	—	—	—
Brussels sprouts	3½ oz.	100	162.0	162	0.720	0.72	2.4	2.4	49.0	49.0	23.0	23.0	95.0	95
Cabbage (fine shreds)	1 c.	100	120.0	120	0.260	0.26	2.4	2.4	32.3	32.3	23.0	23.0	26.4	48
Carrots (grated)	½ c.	55	66.0	120	0.150	0.27	1.4	2.5	4.4	8.0	7.0	13.4	95.0	95
Cauliflower (buds)	1 c.	100	177.0	177	1.010	1.01	17.0	17.0	22.2	22.2	—	—	—	—
Celery (diced)	1 c.	100	—	—	0.430	0.43	—	—	7.0	7.0	—	—	—	—
Corn	3½ oz.	100	222.0	222	0.890	0.89	6.0	6.0	28.0	28.0	—	—	55.0	55
Lettuce	¼ hd.	100	(71.0)	(71)	0.360	0.36	3.1	3.1	21.0	21.0	—	—	—	—
Mixed vegetables	3½ oz.	100	122.0	122	0.310	0.31	—	—	16.0	16.0	—	—	—	88
Onion (2½ in.)	1	110	(69.3)	(63)	0.187	0.17	3.8	3.5	11.0	10.0	—	—	96.8	88
Peas, cow	3½ oz.	100	118.0	118	0.400	0.40	21.0	21.0	41.0	41.0	97.0	97.0	240.0	240
Peas, green	3½ oz.	100	150.0	150	0.820	0.82	9.4	9.4	25.0	25.0	75.0	75.0	162.0	162
Potatoes, peeled	1 med.	100	220.0	220	0.400	0.40	—	—	6.8	6.8	29.0	29.0	29.0	29
Potatoes, sweet	½ med.	100	320.0	320	0.930	0.93	4.3	4.3	12.0	12.0	11.5	11.5	66.0	66

Table III. (continued) Vitamin B6, Pantothenic Acid, Biotin, Folic Acid, Choline, and Inositol Content of Foods, Edible Portion

FOOD	PORTION Amt.	PORTION Wt. (gm.)	VITAMIN B6 Wt. (mcg.)	VITAMIN B6 Per cent	PANTOTHENIC ACID Wt. (mg.)	PANTOTHENIC ACID Per cent	BIOTIN Wt. (mcg.)	BIOTIN Per cent	FOLIC ACID Wt. (mcg.)	FOLIC ACID Per cent	CHOLINE Wt. (mg.)	CHOLINE Per cent	INOSITOL Wt. (mg.)	INOSITOL Per cent
Vegetables, Concluded														
Squash, winter	3½ oz.	100	91.0	91	0.490	0.49	—	—	12.0	12.0	—	—	—	—
Squash, yellow	3½ oz.	100	63.0	63	0.390	0.39	—	—	17.0	17.0	—	—	—	—
Tomato	1 small	110	—	—	0.341	0.31	4.4	4.0	8.8	8.0	—	—	50.6	46
Mushrooms, fresh	2 oz.	60	(27.0)	(45)	1.626	2.71	9.6	16.0	14.4	24.0	—	—	10.2	17
Greens														
Beet	3½ oz.	100	—	—	0.260	0.26	2.7	2.7	60.0	60.0	—	—	21.0	21
Kale	3½ oz.	100	185.0	185	1.290	1.29	—	—	70.0	70.0	—	—	—	—
Mustard	3½ oz.	100	133.0	133	0.250	0.25	—	—	60.0	60.0	22.0	22.0	—	—
Spinach	3½ oz.	100	198.0	198	0.310	0.31	6.9	6.9	75.0	75.0	22.0	22.0	27.0	27
Turnip	3½ oz.	100	98.0	98	0.380	0.38	—	—	42.0	42.0	27.0	27.0	46.0	46
Vegetables, canned with liquid														
Asparagus, green	½ c.	120	90.0	75	0.240	0.20	2.0	1.7	32.4	27.0	—	—	—	—
Beans														
Lima	½ c.	120	97.2	81	0.132	0.11	—	—	15.6	13.0	—	—	—	—
Green string	½ c.	120	51.6	43	0.084	0.07	1.5	1.3	14.4	12.0	—	—	—	—
Beets (diced)	½ c.	125	67.5	54	0.125	0.10	—	—	3.5	2.8	—	—	—	—
Carrots (diced)	½ c.	125	51.2	41	0.137	0.11	1.9	1.5	4.1	3.3	—	—	—	—
Corn	½ c.	125	270.0	216	0.275	0.22	2.7	2.2	9.6	7.7	—	—	—	—
Mushrooms	½ c.	120	75.6	63	1.128	0.94	8.7	7.3	4.7	3.9	—	—	20.4	17
Peas														
Cow	½ c.	125	66.2	53	—	—	—	—	32.5	26.0	—	—	—	—
Green	½ c.	125	55.0	44	0.212	0.17	2.6	2.1	12.9	10.3	—	—	—	—
Spinach	½ c.	120	114.0	95	0.071	0.059	2.8	2.3	58.8	49.0	—	—	—	—
Tomatoes	½ c.	120	181.2	151	0.276	0.23	2.2	1.8	4.4	3.7	—	—	—	—
Tomato juice	½ c.	120	230.4	192	0.360	0.30	—	—	8.0	6.7	—	—	—	—

Miscellaneous

Food	Measure	gm													
Chocolate	1 oz.	28.4	(6.5)	(23)	0.054	0.19	9.0	9.0	32.0	28.1	99.0	—	—	24.1	85
Molasses	1 Tbsp.	20	(54.0)	(270)	0.092	0.46	1.8	16.0	9.0	1.9	9.5	17.2	86	30.0	150
Yeast, brewer's	1 Tbsp.	8	193.5	2419	0.880	11.0	16.0	200.0	161.8	2022.0	—	19.2	240	—	—
Food yeast, torula	1 Tbsp.	8	280.0	3500	0.800	10.0	8.0	100.0	240.0	3000.0	—	20.0	250	21.6	270
Honey	1 Tbsp.	20	2.0	10	0.012	0.06	—	—	0.6	3.0	—	—	—	—	—
Pollen, flower	—	1	9.0	900	0.027	2.70	0.3	25.0	—	—	—	—	—	—	—
Royal jelly	—	1	10.2	1020	0.320	32.00	4.1	410.0	0.5	50.0	—	—	—	0.1	10

Dairy Food Substitutes

Food	Measure	gm													
Soybean milk, commercial type															
Soyagen: infant, all-purpose, or malt-flavored powder		30	52.5	185.0	0.25	0.870	3.4	11.90	6.6	23.34	—	—		32.2	11.30
Reconstituted liquid	1 c.	240	57.5	24.0	0.27	0.112	3.7	1.54	7.2	3.00				35.3	1.47
Soyalac, infant, concentrated, liquid, reconstituted	1 c.	240	72.5	30.0	0.178	0.074	3.28	1.37	27.50	11.46	—			22.75	9.48

Prepared Plant Protein

Food	Measure	gm													
Gluten-type entrées															
Choplets	2 oz.	60	54.0	90.0	0.048	0.080	7.7	12.8	17.0	28.5		6.0	10.0	3.5	5.8
Dinner Cuts	2 oz.	60	36.0	60.0	0.032	0.054	3.0	5.0	13.2	22.0		9.5	12.5	3.0	5
Vegeburger	2 oz.	60	53.4	89.0	0.036	0.060	3.6	6.0	15.0	25.0		6.0	10.0	3.0	5
Weighted average‡	2 oz.	60	46.2	77.0	0.036	0.060	4.2	7.0	14.7	24.5		6.6	11.0	3.2	5.3
Nutmeat-type entrées															
Linketts	2 oz.	60	55.8	93.0	0.100	0.164	5.7	9.5	22.2	37.0		7.2	12.0	6.0	10
Nuteena	2 oz.	60	25.8	43.0	0.121	0.202	22.8	38.0	52.8	88.0		11.4	19.0	6.0	10
Patties	2 oz.	60	39.6	66.0	0.021	0.035	2.4	4.0	76.2	127.0		48.0	80.0	40.8	68
Proteena	2 oz.	60	43.2	72.0	0.125	0.208	13.2	22.0	19.2	32.0		6.9	11.5	6.6	11
Vegalinks	2 oz.	60	42.0	70.0	0.016	0.026	4.2	7.0	42.3	70.5		18.0	30.0	16.8	28
Weighted average‡	2 oz.	60	45.4	76.0	0.112	0.186	9.3	15.3	34.2	57.0		12.3	20.5	10.0	16.8

‡Weighted on the basis of sales per product per year.

Table IV.   Nicotinic Acid (Niacin) Requirements

Species	Reported requirement	Reference
Dog	0.2–0.5 mg/kg/day	1
	0.5–1.5 mg/kg/day	2
	10 mg semi-weekly[a]	3
	0.25 mg/kg/day	4
Monkey	2.5 mg/kg/day	5
Swine	13.7 mg/100 lbs/day[b]	6
	2 mg/kg/day[b]	7

[a] The dog used in this experiment weighed 7.25 kg.
[b] These values for swine represent levels of niacin fed as supplements to a purified diet and do not necessarily represent the minimum requirement for swine.

[1] Margolis, G., *et al., J. Nut.,* **16**, 541 (1938).
[2] Elvehjem, C. A., *et al., J. Biol. Chem.,* **123**, 137 (1938).
[3] Sebrell, W. H., *J. Nut.,* **16**, 355 (1938).
[4] Birch, T. W., *Id.,* **17**, 281 (1939).
[5] Harris, L. J., *Biochem. J.,* **32**, 1479 (1938).
[6] Hughes, E. H., *Hilgardia,* **11**, 595 (1939).
[7] Wintrobe, M. M., *Am. J. Physiol.,* **126**, 375 (1939).

Reproduced by permission from *Bioenergetics and Growth* by S. Brody, 1945, by Hafner Publishing Company.

Table V.   Pantothenic Acid Requirements

Species	Reported requirement	Reference
Mouse	30 mcg/day[a]	1
Rat	80 mcg/day[b]	2
	100 mcg/day[b]	3
	100 mcg/day	4
	50–75 mcg/day	5
	100 mcg/day at 3 weeks of age	6
	25 mcg/day at 10 weeks of age	6
Chick	1.4 mg/100 gm feed	7
	600 mcg/100 gm feed[c]	8
Dog	100 mcg/kg/day[d]	9
Swine	7.8–11.8 mg/100 lb/day[b]	10

[a] For growth of mice from 10 to 20 grams.
[b] For growth.
[c] A slight difference in the requirement for pantothenic acid was observed in different breeds.
[d] This amount is for growth; much less is required for adult animals.

[1] Sandza, J. G., and Cerecede, L. R., *J. Nut.,* **21**, 609 (1941).
[2] Unna, K., *J. Nut.,* **20**, 565 (1940).
[3] Henderson, L. M., *et al., Id.,* **23**, 47 (1942).
[4] Daft, F. S., *et al., Public Health Reports,* **55**, 1333 (1940).
[5] György, P., and Poling, C. E., *Science,* **92**, 202 (1940).
[6] Unna and Richards, G. V., *J. Nut.,* **23**, 545 (1942).
[7] Jukes, T. H., *J. Biol. Chem.,* **129**, 225 (1939).
[8] Bauernveind, J. C., *Poultry Sci.,* **21**, 142 (1942).
[9] Schaefer, A. E., *et al., J. Biol. Chem.,* **143**, 321 (1942).
[10] Hughes, E. H., and Ittner, N. R., *J. Animal Sci.,* **1**, 116 (1942).

Reproduced by permission from *Bioenergetics and Growth* by S. Brody, 1945, by Hafner Publishing Company.

Table VI.   Estimated Riboflavin Requirements

Species	Reported requirement	Requirement calculated to mcg/100 gm feed	Refer- ence
Rat	10 mcg/rat/day[a]	80–160	1
	18 mcg/rat/day[b]	144–288	2
Poultry:			
Chicks	290 mcg/100 gm feed[c]	290	3
Chicks	60 Sherman units/100 gm feed	150	4
Chicks	100–350 mcg/100 gm feed	100–350	5
Chicks	190–200 mcg/100 gm feed	190–200	6
Hens	230 mcg/100 gm feed	230	3
Egg production	100–130 mcg/100 gm feed	100–130	7
Hatchable eggs	245 mcg/100 gm feed	245	7
	2.5 mg/lb feed	573	8
	220–230 mcg/100 gm feed	220–230	6
Dog	200–400 mcg/100 gm feed[d]	200–400	9
	11.3 mcg/lb/day		10
Swine	1–3 mg/100 lb/day[e]	50–150	11
Man	35–60 mcg/kg/day[f]		12

[a] It is assumed that a growing rat will eat about 6–12 gm feed daily. The value 10 mcg/day was not reported as a minimum requirement; it merely represents the level fed in a purified diet which was used in studying a deficiency of pyridoxine.

[b] It is again assumed that a young rat will consume about 6–12 gm. feed daily. The value 18 mcg/day was the minimum amount of riboflavin which would support normal growth on a low-fat diet; it was not enough to support growth on a high-fat diet.

[c] 1 mcg = 0.4 Bourquin-Sherman Unit.

[d] Judging from Elvehjem's data and the fact that he fed the supplement only once a week, it is believed that the minimum riboflavin requirement of the dog is nearer to 200 than to 400 mcg/100 gm feed.

[e] It is assumed that a pig will eat about 2 kilograms of of feed per 100 lbs live weight per day.

[f] These values for man are based on the amount necessary to maintain normal levels of riboflavin in the urine. Sebrell states that the minimum daily requirement is nearer to 35 than to 60 mcg per kilogram of body weight.

[1] Supplee, G. C., et al., J. Nut., **20**, 109 (1940).
[2] Mannering, G. J., et al., Proc. Soc. Exp. Biol. & Med., **46**, 100 (1941).
[3] Norris, L. C., et al., Cornell Agr. Exp. Sta. Bull. 660, 1936.
[4] Jukes, T. H., Poultry Sci., **17**, 227 (1938).
[5] Heuser, G. F., et al., Id., **17**, 105 (1938).
[6] Hunt, C. H., et al., Id., **18**, 330 (1939).
[7] Davis, H. J., et al., Id., **17**, 87 (1938).
[8] Lepkovsky, S., et al., Hilgardia, **11**, 571 (1938).
[9] Axelrod, A. E., et al., Am. J. Physiol., **128**, 703 (1939).
[10] Street, H. R., and Cowgill, G. R., Am. J. Physiol., **125**, 323 (1937).
[11] Hughes, E. H., J. Nut., **20**, 233 (1940).
[12] Sebrell, W. H., et al., Public Health Repts., **56**, 510 (1941).

Table VII. Minimum Thiamine Requirements

Species	Reported requirement	Calculated requirement (mcg/100 gm diet)	Ref.
Mouse	10 mcg/mouse/day		1
Rat	80–100 mcg/100 gm diet	80–100	2
	12.5 mcg/rat/day[a]	125–250	3
Chicks	60 mcg/100 gm diet	60	4
Chicks & turkeys	60 mcg/100 gm diet	60	5
Chicks	130–150 mcg/100 gm diet	130–150	6
Dogs:			
Low-fat diet	75 mcg/100 gm diet	75	7
56.5%-fat diet	27.5 mcg/100 gm diet[b]	75	7
Swine	1 mcg/100 lbs/day[c]	50	8
	37 mcg/kg/day		9
	80–94 mcg/100 gm feed[d]	80–94	9
Man	0.22 mg/1000 Calories of diet[e]	88–110	10
Infant	80 units/day		11

[a] It is assumed that a growing rat will eat between 6 and 12 grams of feed daily.
[b] The author of the reference cited based this figure on 100 grams protein and carbohydrate of the high-fat diet.
[c] It is assumed that a pig weighing about 100 lbs will consume approximately 2 kg feed per 100 lbs live weight per day.
[d] The authors of this report estimate that their ration contained 75 per cent carbohydrate and protein; using this figure, they conclude that growing pigs require between 106 and 125 mcg thiamine per 100 grams carbohydrate and protein.
[e] It is assumed that 1 gram of diet is equivalent to 4 or 5 Calories.

[1] Houschildt, J. D., *Proc. Soc. Exp. Biol. & Med.*, **49**, 145 (1942).
[2] Arnold, A., and Elvehjem, C. A., *J. Nut.*, **15**, 429 (1938).
[3] Supplee. G. C., *et al.*, *Id.*, **20**, 109 (1940).
[4] Arnold and Elvehjem, *Id.*, **15**, 403 (1938).
[5] "Food and Life," U.S.D. Agr. Yearbook, p. 816, 1939.
[6] Jukes, T. H., and Heitman, H., *J. Nut.*, **19**, 21 (1940).
[7] Arnold and Elvehjem, *Am. J. Physiol.*, **126**, 289 (1939).
[8] Hughes, E. H., *J. Nut.*, **20**, 239 (1940).
[9] Van Etten, C., *et al.*, *Id.*, **20**, 607, 1940.
[10] Williams, R. D., *et al.*, *Arch. Int. Med.*, **69**, 721 (1942).
[11] Knott, E. M., *Proc. Soc. Exp. Biol. & Med.*, **45**, 765 (1940).

Table VIII. Minimum Vitamin A Requirements
(1 I.U. vitamin A = 0.6 mcg β-carotene = 0.21 mcg vitamin A)

Species	Reported requirement		Requirement (mcg/lb. body wt/day)		Ref.
	β-Carotene	Vitamin A	Carotene	Vit. A	
Rat	15–20 mcg/kg/day	4.6–5.3 mcg/kg/day	7–9	2–3	1
Dog		23–43 I.U./kg/wk		2–4	2
Poultry:					3
600-g. chick		150 I.U./100 gm feed			3
8 wks. old	125 mcg/100 gm feed		50		4
Chicks	50–100 mcg/100 gm feed	80–160 I.U./100 gm feed	15–30		5
Birth–12 wks.	125–150 mcg/100 gm feed		55–70		6
12 wks. maturity	200 mcg/100 gm feed		50		6
Laying hens	500 mcg/100 gm feed				6
Chicks	125–175 mcg/100 gm feed		30–42		7
Laying hens	450–600 mcg/100 gm feed				7
Turkeys	1000 mcg/100 gm feed				7
Laying hens	2.1 mg/lb. feed				8
Swine	4 mg/100 lbs/day		40		9
	25–39 mcg/kg/day	4.4–6.3 mcg/kg/day	11–18	2–3	1
	30 mcg/kg/day	50 I.U./kg/day	14	5	10
Sheep	25–35 mcg/kg/day	4.3–6.3 mcg/kg/day	11–16	2–3	1
Cattle	26–33 mcg/kg/day	5.1–6.4 mcg/kg/day	11–15	2–3	1
Dairy calves	11 mcg/lb/day		11		11
Reproducing	40–45 mcg/lb/day		40–45		12
Mature	66 mcg/kg/day				11
Horse	20–30 mcg/kg/day	4.2–5.3 mcg/kg/day	9–13	2–3	1
Man		20–30 I.U./kg/day		2–3	13
		25–55 I.U./kg/day		2–3	14

[1] Guilbert, H. R., Howell, C. E., and Hart, G. H., *J. Nut.*, **19**, 91 (1940).
[2] Grimm, P. D., and Short, D. M., *Am. J. Physiol.*, **118**, 477 (1936).
[3] Ringrose, R. C., and Norris, L. C., *Poultry Sci.*, **15**, 390 (1936).
[4] Sherwood, R. M., and Fraps, G. S., Texas Agr. Exp. Sta. Bull. 528, 1936.
[5] Record, P. R., *et al.*, *Poultry Sci.*, **16**, 25 (1937).
[6] Sherwood and Fraps, Texas Agr. Exp. Sta. Bull. 583, 1940.
[7] Sherwood, Proc. 7th Int. World Poultry Congress, page 123, Cleveland, 1939.
[8] Almquist, H. J., and Mecchi, *Poultry Sci.*, **18**, 129 (1939).
[9] Dunlap, G., *J. Agr. Sci. (Engl.)*, **25**, 217 (1939).
[10] Lund, A., *Nut. Abs. and Rev.*, **8**, 894 (1939).
[11] Brande, R., *et al.*, *Biochem. J.*, **35**, 693 (1941); Moore, L. A., *et al.*, *J. Nut.*, **26**, 649 (1943).
[12] Kuhlman, A. H., and Gallup, W. D., *Proc. Am. Soc. An. Prod.*, **33**, 67 (1940).
[13] Booher, L. E., "The vitamins," Am. Med. Ass. p. 111, 1939.
[14] Booher, *et al.*, *J. Nut.*, **17**, 317 (1939).

Table IX. Suggested Guide to Interpretation of Urinary Vitamin Excretion Data

	Deficient	Low	Acceptable	High
1. Adults (Males and Nonpregnant, Nonlactating Females)[1]				
Thiamine:				
μg/6 hours	<10	10–24	25–49	≥50
μg/g creatinine	<27	27–65	66–129	≥130
Riboflavin:				
μg/6 hours	<10	10–29	30–99	≥100
μg/g creatinine	<27	27–79	80–269	≥270
N′-Methylnicotinamide:				
mg/6 hours	<0.2	0.2–0.59	0.6–1.59	≥1.6
mg/g creatinine	<0.5	0.5–1.59	1.6–4.29	≥4.3
2. Children[2]				
Thiamine: μg/g creatinine:				
Age (years):				
1–3	<120	120–175	176–600	>600
4–6	<85	85–120	121–400	>400
7–9	<70	70–180	181–350	>350
10–12	<60	60–180	181–300	>300
13–15	<50	50–150	151–250	>250
Riboflavin: μg/g creatinine:				
Age (years):				
1–3	<150	150–499	500–900	>900
4–6	<100	100–299	300–600	>600
7–9	<85	85–269	270–500	>500
10–15	<70	70–199	200–400	>400

[1] The urinary values indicated above for adults are based on expected creatinine excretion of 1.5 gm daily for a reference man weighing 65 kg, for creatinine coefficient of 23.
[2] The guides offered here for children are based on considerably less extensive data than are the guides for adults.

	Trimester	Deficient	Low	Acceptable	High
3. Pregnant Women[3]					
Thiamine:	1	<27	27–65	66–129	≥130
μg/g creatinine	2	<23	23–54	55–109	≥110
	3	<21	21–49	50–99	≥100
Riboflavin:	1	<27	27–79	80–269	≥270
μg/g creatinine	2	<39	39–119	120–399	≥400
	3	<30	30–89	90–299	≥300
N′-Methylnicotinamide:	1	<0.5	0.5–1.59	1.6–4.29	≥4.3
mg/g creatinine	2	<0.6	0.6–1.99	2.0–4.99	≥5.0
	3	<0.8	0.8–2.49	2.5–6.49	≥6.5

[3] Based on observations in: The Vanderbilt cooperative study of maternal and infant nutrition. IV. Dietary, laboratory and physical findings in 2,129 delivered pregnancies. J. Nutrition 51, 565–598, 1953.

Table X. Amino Acids Indispensable for Growth

Amino acid	L. Mesenteroides	Drosophila Melanogaster Larva	Mouse	Rat (%)	Chick (%)	Salmon (%)	Pig (%)	Dog	Child
Arginine	+	+	–	0.2	1.2	+	0.2	+	–
Glycine	+	+	–	–	1.0	–	–	–	–
Histidine	+	+	–	0.4	0.2	+	0.2	+	+
Isoleucine	+	+	+	0.5	0.6	+	0.5	+	+
Leucine	+	+	+	0.8	1.4	+	0.6	+	+
Lysine	+	+	+	0.9	0.9	2.0	0.6	+	+
Methionine	+	+	+	0.5	0.5	+	0.3	+	+
Phenylalanine	+	+	+	0.7	0.9	+	0.3	+	+
Threonine	+	+	+	0.5	0.6	0.8	0.4	+	+
Tryptophan	+	+	+	0.2	0.2	+	0.2	+	+
Valine	+	+	+	0.7	0.8	+	0.4	+	+
Alanine	+	+	–	–	–	–	–	–	–
Aspartic acid	+	+	–	–	–	–	–	–	–
Cystine	+	+	–	–	–	–	–	–	–
Glutamic acid	+	+	–	–	–	–	–	–	–
Proline	+	+	–	–	–	–	–	–	–
Serine	+	+	–	–	–	–	–	–	–
Tyrosine	+	+	–	–	–	–	–	–	–
Hydroxy proline	–	–	–	–	–	–	–	–	–

Reprinted by permission of Burgess Publishing Company from *Elementary Biochemistry*, 1966, by Edwin T. Mertz.

Table XI. Quantitative Vitamin Unit Equivalents

Vitamin A is usually represented in I. U. (International Units) or U. S. P. units (identical with I. U. for vitamin A); thiamine and riboflavin in mg or in mcg (micrograms or gamma, which is 1/1000 mg or 1/1,000,000 g); ascorbic acid and nicotinic acid in mg. The equivalents are:

> 1 I. U. vitamin A = 1 U. S. P. unit = 0.6 mcg β-carotene.
> (The Sherman-Munsell unit of vitamin A, about 1.4 I. U. vitamin A, is defined by the amount needed to support growth in a "standard rat" for 8 weeks at the rate of 3 g per week.)
>
> 1 mg thiamine = 333 I. U.
>
> 1 U. U. thiamine = 3 mcg thiamine hydrochloride
>
> 2 ½ mg riboflavin = 1000 I. U.
> (1 Sherman-Bourquin unit riboflavin = 2.5 mcg or 1 mcg = 0.4 Sherman-Bourquin unit)
>
> 1 mg l-ascorbic acid = 20 I. U.
>
> 1 Sherman unit ascorbic acid = 10 to 15 I. U.
>
> 1 I. U. vitamin D = 0.025 mcg crystalline vitamin D, or
>
> 1 ·mcg vitamin D (calciferol) = 40 I. U.
>
> 1 Steenbock unit vitamin D = 3.3 I. U.

Reproduced by permission from *Bioenergetics and Growth* by S. Brody, 1945, by Hafner Publishing Company.

Table XII. Amino Acids Indispensable for Maintenance In Mature Animals

Amino acid	Rat and Dog[a]	Humans[b]
Arginine	0.0	0.0
Histidine	0.0[c]	0.0[c]
Isoleucine	4.2	0.70
Leucine	5.6	1.10
Lysine	5.0	0.90
Methionine	5.0[d]	1.10[d]
Phenylalanine	4.2	1.10
Threonine	3.0	0.50
Tryptophan	1.1	0.25
Valine	4.7	0.80

[a] Expressed as per cent of total dietary protein. Daily protein requirement not over 0.5 gm. per kg. body weight.
[b] Expressed as grams required per 24 hours.
[c] Gradual drop in hemoglobin occurs on diet devoid of histidine. Therefore required, but requirement very low.
[d] Cystine can replace 80–90% of the methionine required in humans. Replacement value not determined for rats and dogs.

Reprinted by permission of Burgess Publishing Company from *Elementary Biochemistry*, 1966, by Edwin T. Mertz.

Table XIII. Desirable Weights for Heights
(Home Economics Research Report No. 10, ARS, USDA)

Height,[1] inches	Weight[1] in pounds Men	Women
60		109 ± 9
62		115 ± 9
64	133 ± 11	122 ± 10
66	142 ± 12	129 ± 10
68	151 ± 14	136 ± 10
70	159 ± 14	144 ± 11
72	167 ± 15	152 ± 12
74	175 ± 15	

[1] Heights and weights are "without shoes and other clothing." Conversion factors: Inches × 2.54 = centimeters; pounds × 0.454 = kilograms. Adjustment of Calorie allowances for individuals whose weight and height differ from those of the reference man and woman is illustrated in the table below. A mean environmental temperature of 20°C and average physical activity are assumed.

Desirable weight Kilograms	Pounds	Calorie allowance[1] 25 years	45 years	65 years
		Men		
		(1)	(2)	(3)
50	110	2,300	2,050	1,750
55	121	2,450	2,200	1,850
60	132	2,600	2,350	1,950
65	143	2,750	2,500	2,100
[2]70	154	2,900	2,600	2,200
75	165	3,050	2,750	2,300
80	176	3,200	2,900	2,450
85	187	3,350	3,050	2,550
		Women		
		(4)	(5)	(6)
40	88	1,600	1,450	1,200
45	99	1,750	1,600	1,300
50	110	1,900	1,700	1,450
55	121	2,000	1,800	1,550
[2]58	128	2,100	1,900	1,600
60	132	2,150	1,950	1,650
65	143	2,300	2,050	1,750
70	154	2,400	2,200	1,850

[1] Rounded to nearest 50 calories.
[2] Reference man and woman (NRC).

Formulas

(1) 725 + 31W (2) 650 + 28W (3) 550 + 23.5W
(4) 525 + 27W (5) 475 + 24.5W (6) 400 + 20.5W
W = weight in kilograms.

Table XIV. Conversion Factors

Barrel = 31.5 gal.	**Gallon** = 4 quarts	**Ounce** = 28.3495 gm.
= 126 qt.	= 3.785 liters	= 0.0625 lb.
= 119 liters	= 8.345 lb. water	= 437.5 grains
	= 3.785 kg. water	
Bushel = 32 qt.		**Pint** = 0.5 qt.
= 77.7 lb. water	**Gram** = 0.035274 oz.	= 473.18 cc.
= 35.2 kg. water	= 0.002205 lb.	= 16.69 oz. water
	= 15.432 grains	= 1.043 lb. water
Can: #1 tall = 1 lb.		= 0.47318 kg. water
#2 = 1 lb. 4 oz.	**Kilogram** = 2.205 lb.	= 2 cups
#2½ = 1 lb. 12 oz.	= 35.274 oz.	= 32 tablespoons
#3 = 2 lb. 2 oz.		= 96 teaspoons
#10 = 6 lb. 10 oz.	**Liter** = 0.26418 gal.	
	= 1.0567 qt.	**Pound** = 16 oz.
Cup = 0.5 pint	= 35.275 oz. water	= 453.6 gm.
= 16 tablespoons	= 2.205 lb. water	= 0.4536 kg.
= 24 dessert spoons	= 1 kg. water	
= 48 teaspoons		**Quart** = 2 pt.
	Microgram = mcg. = μg	= 4 cups
Dessert spoon	= γ = gamma	= 946.4 cc.
= ⅔ tablespoon	= 0.001 mg.	= 64 tablespoons
= 2 teaspoons		= 192 teaspoons
= 120 drops		= 33.38 oz. water
		= 2.086 lb. water
		= 0.946 kg. water
Teaspoon		
= 5 cc.		**Tablespoon**
= 0.02 cups		= 0.0625 cup
= 60 drops		= 15 cc.
		= 1.5 dessert spoon
		= 3 teaspoons
		= 180 drops

I. INTRODUCTION

Radiation chemistry may be defined as the study of the chemical effects produced by the absorption of ionizing radiations, as from radio-active nuclei such as α, β and γ-rays, and X-rays; or from high-energy charged particles (electrons, protons, deuterons, etc.). Related to this is the study of the chemical effects which accompany nuclear reactions brought about by the decay of radio-active nuclei, particularly if the products are charged particles with excess kinetic energy.

The first definite observations of the chemical effects of ionizing radiations, now termed radiation chemistry, should be attributed to H. Becquerel. In 1894, he recorded the effect on a photographic plate of the penetrating rays given off by uranium compounds. Subsequently, after the isolation of radium compounds, it was found that water in which radium salts are dissolved undergoes some decomposition into its elements. However, relatively little attention was paid to these phenomena by either physicists or chemists. The field was left largely to the biologists who quite early found many important effects of these radiations, and who subsequently developed the so-called "hit" or "target" theory according to which the action of these radiations is likened to shooting at a target.

II. PHYSICO-CHEMICAL BASIS

Absorption of Radiation. It is obvious that the chemical effects must be related to the physical mechanism of energy absorption of these radiations. The physics of absorption of ionizing radiation is rather different from that governing light absorption leading to photochemical reactions. In the latter case, the absorption in the visible or UV region of the spectrum is specifically associated with a particular molecule or ion or even with a group within a molecule. The situation is rather different, however, in the absorption of ionizing radiation which is not associated with a certain bond structure but, to a first approximation, particularly for higher energies, is a mass effect. The reason for this is that the high-energy photons or particles are not selective: they have sufficient energy to interact with any of the electrons of the molecules present in the system. Thus this non-specific absorption process will depend only on the density of electrons in the systems. In general, absorption of ionizing radiation leads to excitation processes; this can be *excitation* to a discrete level (giving an excited state) or *ionization* when the electron is raised into the continuum.

Moreover, as each high-energy photon or particle, via secondary electrons, leads to excitation processes in a relatively large number of molecules lying in its path, the active species are distributed along the path of the ionizing particles. The rate of energy loss of the ionizing particle per unit path is given by:

$$-\frac{dE}{dx} = \frac{Nz^2}{v^2} f(v,\bar{I}) \tag{1}$$

where N is the number of electrons per cubic centimeter and z and v are the charge and velocity of the ionizing particles; $f(v,\bar{I})$ is a function of v and $\bar{I}$, the average ionization potential of the electrons of the absorber.

Direct and Indirect Effects. On the basis of the above discussion, it is clear that in dilute aqueous systems, most of the radiation energy will be absorbed by the solvent (water) and only a relatively small part by the solute. Therefore, in the case of aqueous systems, the majority of the primary active species is produced by the action of the radiation on the water and the radiation chemical processes are then due to the chemical reactions of these active species with the substances present in the aqueous system. This is the basis of the so-called "indirect effect" in contradistinction to the "direct" effect to which, in this case, some of the water molecules are subjected.

Closely related to this are two *kinetic effects* which may be of some relevance for the biological action. These are the *dilution* and *protection* effects. The dilution effect is associated with the observation that the yield of a given product produced by the ionizing radiation, *e.g.*, in an aqueous system, is, above a certain limit, independent of the concentration of the solute; this is due to the fact that if a certain number of active species are produced all of which can react with the solute, any further increase of the solute concentration will not lead to an increase in the yield.

The *protection effect* arises if there are *two* solutes present, both of which can act as scavengers for a particular active species. It is clear that, under these conditions, the active species will divide themselves between the two solutes, say A and B, according to their reactivities (k_A and k_B) and the actual concentrations of the solutes in the system; so that the ratio of their yields will be given by the expression:

$k_A [A]/k_B [B]$

Radiation Dosimetry. The number of molecules (M) transformed per ion pair, M/N_i, used as a measure of radiation chemical yields in the gas-phase, was also used when referring to yields in liquids, although in this case the number of ions (N_i) formed was not known and had to be calculated assuming a value for the mean energy required in forming an ion pair in the liquid; the value for air (32.5 eV) was sometimes taken, without any particular justification. A more satisfactory way of representing the yield is to relate it to the energy absorbed, which in principle can be measured directly. For this reason, the term G-value was introduced to denote the number of molecules changed per 100 electron-volts of energy absorbed. Thus G(X) refers to the number of molecules of a product X per 100 eV of energy absorbed and $G(-Y)$ refers in the same way to the loss of material Y that is destroyed on irradiation.

The use of G-values has the advantage that it does not imply any particular mechanism; these have now become the customary means of expressing radiation-chemical yields.

The unit of absorbed dose is the rad: 1 rad $=$ 100 ergs per gram. Sometimes the absorbed dose is given in units of electron volts per gram: 1 rad $= 6.24 \times 10^{13}$ eV/g. The absorbed dose is generally the quantity required when making dosimetric measurements, and is a direct measure of the energy transferred to the irradiated material. It is determined by the composition of the absorbing material as well as by the nature of the radiation.

In *chemical dosimetry,* which is used for greater convenience, the radiation dose is determined from the chemical change produced in a suitable system. Calculation of the dose requires a knowledge of the G-value for the reaction product and this can be found by comparing the chemical system with some form of absolute dosimeter. The quantity which is measured is the absorbed dose (or absorbed dose rate) in the material composing the dosimeter, which may be converted to the absorbed dose in other materials. In the *Fricke Dosimeter,* the reaction used is the radiation-induced oxidation of an acid solution of ferrous sulphate in the presence of oxygen.

III. WATER AND AQUEOUS SYSTEMS

From a biological point of view, aqueous systems are of primary interest; moreover, they also exemplify many general features of radiation chemistry.

Formation and reactions of OH Radicals and H Atoms. The first hypothesis, put forward essentially on an heuristic basis, was that, after the absorption of radiation, denoted by the symbol ($-\!\!\sim\!\!\rightarrow$), water is eventually split into hydrogen atoms and OH radicals:

$$H_2O \longrightarrow\!\!\!\!\!\sim\!\!\!\!\!\longrightarrow H + OH \tag{2}$$

which subsequently enter into chemical reactions.

Relatively stable free radicals have been known since the beginning of the century. More recently, free radicals have been shown to be transient intermediates in many reactions, including such diverse processes as autoxidation, electrolysis and polymerization. Consequently the properties and reactions of free radicals are well established.

Several methods based on physical measurements are available for the detection and identification of the radiation-produced free radicals. The most important from the point of view of radiation chemistry is electron paramagnetic resonance. Pulse radiolysis methods enable the absorption spectra of radicals and other transient intermediates to be obtained and also the measurement of the rates of their reactions with different molecules in the system.

The free radical hypothesis was successful in explaining the reaction in the presence of oxygen and/or at low pH. However, for reactions at higher pH's or in the absence of oxygen, certain difficulties manifested themselves in the interpretation of the results.

As these radiations also lead to *ionization,* it was to be expected that some of the radiation-produced primary species would be in the nature of ions. Although this seemed rather an obvious conclusion, it had been assumed earlier that any ionic species formed would be too short-lived to play any important part in the chemical reactions: namely, that in water they would almost instantly be decomposed according to:

$$(H_2O)^- \xrightarrow{\;aq\;} H + OH^- \tag{3}$$

$$(H_2O)^+ \xrightarrow{\;aq\;} OH + H^+ \tag{4}$$

leading again to OH and H, and that excited water molecules (H_2O^*) would at any rate undergo predissociation into free radicals:

$$H_2O^* \longrightarrow H + OH \tag{5}$$

However, with γ-rays or hard X-rays, only about 10% of the total radicals are formed by a process corresponding to reaction (5).

Both H atoms and OH radicals are very reactive, due essentially to the presence of the unpaired electron. They can undergo a back reaction:

$$H + OH \longrightarrow H_2O \tag{6}$$

The OH is a strong oxidizing agent, *i.e.*, by accepting an electron it is transformed into an OH^- ion, *e.g.*:

$$Fe^{2+} + OH \longrightarrow Fe^{3+} + OH^- \tag{7}$$

or dehydrogenates a molecule (RH) according to:

$$RH + OH \longrightarrow R\cdot + H_2O \tag{8}$$

Hydrogen atoms are generally strong reducing agents since they are capable of donating an electron and thereby being transformed into a hydrogen ion. However, under certain conditions they can also act as oxidizing agents, as by the dehydrogenation reaction:

$$RH + H \longrightarrow R\cdot + H_2 \tag{9}$$

and both will add easily to a double bond, for example according to:

$$\tag{10}$$

Formation and Reactions of Primary Ionic Species. When radiation is absorbed by the water, an electron will be "knocked out" from the medium, thus producing an electron and leaving behind a "hole." More recently, definite evidence has been produced to show that negative and possibly also positive ionic species are formed by the irradiation of water and that these are of considerable importance in the radiation chemistry of aqueous systems.

It was demonstrated that there are two reducing species present in irradiated water: hydrogen atoms and "electrons." The "electrons" were to be regarded as "self-trapped" in the polar medium, water. It was further suggested that these self-trapped electrons or "hydrated electrons" are similar to the "polaron," which was known from the behavior of electrons in polar crystals.

Some definite experimental confirmation of these views came from recent work by Hart and Boag and Keene. They showed that irradiation of water and of dilute aqueous solutions with short pulses of electrons (1.8 MeV) leads to a transient light absorption with a peak around 7000 Å, which the authors attribute to the electron in water.

It is clear that such a polaron is not to be pictured as an electron attached to a particular water molecule, but as an electron belonging collectively to a comparatively large number of water molecules with a "radius" of the order of 3 Å.

On the basis of these considerations, the self-trapped electron in water may be written as $(H_2O)_n^-$. For simplicity, it has been suggested to denote it as $(H_2O)^-$. In the literature it is frequently also designated by e_{aq}^-.

It is obvious that the polaron should be capable of interacting with suitably reactive centers (solutes) in the water, by which it can be "trapped" or annihilated. In the absence of any other "traps," the positive centers resulting from the removal of an electron from the solvent, which may be regarded as "positive polarons," $(H_2O)^+$, would react according to:

$$(H_2O)^+ + (H_2O)^- \longrightarrow 2H_2O \tag{11}$$

On account of reverse processes such as reactions (6) and (11), relatively very little decomposition of pure water takes place under the influence of ionizing radiation. Under these conditions, only relatively small amounts of H_2O_2 (molecular yields) are formed. This phenomenon is presumably due to the pair-wise interaction of two active species, *e.g.*, according to:

$$2(H_2O)^- \longrightarrow H_2 + 2OH^- \tag{12}$$

The situation is however rather different in the presence of suitable solutes (scavengers) which can react with the radiation-produced active species. If, for instance, there are a sufficient number of hydrogen ions in the solution, a competition to reaction (11) will be set up by a reaction of the negative polaron with the hydrogen ions, according to:

$$(H_2O)^- + H^+ \longrightarrow H + H_2O \tag{13}$$

leading to the formation of hydrogen atoms. Other reactions that have been studied are the reaction with hydrogen peroxide:

$$H_2O_2 + e_{aq}^- \longrightarrow OH + OH^- \tag{14}$$

and the reaction with molecular oxygen:

$$O_2 + e_{aq}^- \longrightarrow O_2^- \tag{15}$$

leading, in the first instance, to the anion of the HO_2 radical corresponding to the equilibrium:

$$O_2^- + H^+ \rightleftharpoons HO_2 \tag{16}$$

The HO_2 radicals lead to the formation of hydrogen peroxide, according to:

$$2HO_2 \longrightarrow H_2O_2 + O_2 \tag{17}$$

which has sometimes been regarded as one of the active agents in the biological effects of radiation.

Work on aqueous systems under different conditions has led to the investigation of several reactions of the negative polarons that may be of considerable biological interest. Carbon dioxide in solution reacts according to:

$$CO_2 + e_{aq}^- \longrightarrow CO_2^- \tag{18}$$

leading to the formation of the CO_2^- radical ion. Under suitable conditions, the CO_2^- radical ion can be built into the organic molecules with the formation of the corresponding carboxylic acids.

More recently, the rates of reaction of the hydrated electron in water

Table I. Rate Constants of the Hydrated Electron with Some Inorganic Molecules and Ions*

Reactant	Product	pH	Rate constant $(M^{-1} \cdot sec^{-1})$
H_3O^+	H		2.3×10^{10}
OH	OH^-		3.0×10^{10}
H_2O_2	$OH^- + OH$		3.0×10^{10}
O_2	O_2^-	7	1.8×10^{10}
NO	NO^-	7	3.1×10^{10}
N_2O	$N_2 + O^-$	7	8.7×10^9
CO_2	CO_2^-	7	7.7×10^9
$Fe(CN)_6^{3-}$	$Fe(CN)_6^{4-}$	7, 10, 3	3.0×10^9
Cu^{++}	Cu^+	7	3.3×10^{10}
Ag^+	Ag	7	3.6×10^{10}
Zn^{++}	Zn^+	7	1.7×10^9
Co^{++}	Co^+	7	1.35×10^{10}
Ni^{++}	Ni^+	7	2.3×10^{10}
Cd^{++}	Cd^+	7	5.5×10^{10}

*cf. Hart, E. J., Science *146*, 19 (1964).

Table II. Rate Constants of the Hydrated Electron with Various Organic Compounds in Aqueous Solution*

Compound	Rate constant $(M^{-1} \cdot sec^{-1})$
Aliphatic	
Acetaldehyde	3.5×10^9
Acetone	5.9×10^9
L-Cystine	3.4×10^9
Fumarate ion	7.5×10^9
Maleate ion	2.2×10^9
Pyruvate ion	6.8×10^9
Aromatic	
Benzene	$<7 \times 10^6$
Benzoquinone	1.2×10^9
Hydroquinone	$<1 \times 10^7$
Phenylalanine	$<1 \times 10^7$
Phthalate ion	2×10^9
Picric acid	3.5×10^{10}
Heterocyclic	
Adenosine	1.0×10^{10}
Cytidine	1.2×10^{10}
Hypoxanthine	1.7×10^{10}
5-Methylcytosine	1.0×10^{10}
Orotic acid	1.5×10^{10}
Purine	1.7×10^{10}
Pyridine	1.0×10^9
Thymine	1.7×10^{10}
Uracil	7.7×10^9
Thiophene	$\leq 6.5 \times 10^7$
Pyrrole	$\leq 6 \times 10^5$
Thiazole	2.5×10^9

*cf. Hart, E. J., Science, *146*, 19 (1964).

Table III. Reactivity of Various Solutes towards OH Radicals*

Solute	pH	Rate constant $(M^{-1} \cdot sec^{-1})$
Amino acids		
Alanine	5.5–6.0	4.6×10^7
Arginine	6.5–7.5	2.1×10^9
Aspartic acid	6.8–7.0	4.5×10^7
Glycine	5.8–6.0	1.0×10^7
	9.5–9.7	1.1×10^9
Histidine	6.0–7.0	3.0×10^9
Leucine	5.5–6.0	9.8×10^8
	9.7–9.9	2.2×10^9
	9.7–9.9	2.25×10^9
Methionine	5.5–5.7	4.9×10^9
Phenylalanine	5.5–6.0	3.5×10^9
Serine	5.5–6.0	1.9×10^8
Tryptophan	6.1–6.3	8.5×10^9
Peptides		
G-Glycine	5.5–6.0	1.3×10^8
G-G-Glycine	5.5–6.0	2.0×10^8
	8.5–8.7	1.05×10^9
G-G-G-Glycine	5.5–6.0	2.7×10^8
	7.7–7.9	7.1×10^8
	9.5–9.7	1.8×10^9
G-Alanine	5.5–6.0	2.1×10^8
G-Methionine	5.0–5.2	1.3×10^8
Histidyl histidine	5.5–6.5	5.4×10^9
Purines and Pyrimidines		
Thymine	5.0–5.5	3.0×10^9
	7.2–7.4	3.2×10^9
Uracil	5.0–5.2	3.1×10^9
	7.3–7.5	3.15×10^9
Cytosine	5.0–6.0	2.7×10^9
	7.4–7.6	2.95×10^9
Adenine	5.0–5.5	2.3×10^9
	7.3–7.5	3.0×10^9
Nucleosides		
Thymidine	5.0–5.2	3.0×10^9
	7.4–7.6	2.75×10^9
Cytidine	5.2–5.4	2.95×10^9
	7.2–7.4	2.75×10^9
Adenosine	5.0–5.2	2.3×10^9
	7.6–7.8	2.5×10^9
Nucleotides		
Thymidylic acid (Ammonium salt)	6.5–7.0	3.15×10^9
Deoxycytidylic acid	4.3–4.5	2.3×10^9
	6.7–7.0	3.0×10^9
Deoxyadenylic acid	6.4–6.6	2.1×10^9
Deoxyguanylic acid (Calcium salt)	6.5–7.0	4.1×10^9
Adenosine 5'-phosphate	5.2–5.5	1.8×10^9
Cytosine 5'-phosphate	7.4–7.6	2.65×10^9

*cf. Scholes, G., Shaw, P., Willson, R. L. and Ebert, M. in "Pulse Radiolysis," p. 155, ed. by Ebert, M., Keene, J. P., Swallow, A. J. and Baxendale, J. H. Academic Press London and New York (1965).

and of OH radicals with various substances of biological importance have been investigated. Tables I, II and III give some of the rate constants measured by pulse radiolysis techniques or by competition kinetics.

The experiments with simple or more complex molecules referred to above show quite clearly that the radiation-produced active species lead to some quite specific chemical reactions. From the results on simpler systems, it was clear that the degradation of biological macromolecules by radiation should not be looked upon as a physical process mediated somehow by the momentum of a charged particle, but rather that the biological effects of ionizing radiations would have a chemical and biochemical basis. In fact, it could be shown clearly that the effect of radiation on nucleic acid, for example, is basically a chemical effect.

BIBLIOGRAPHY

References:
1. Allen, A. O., *The Radiation Chemistry of Water and Aqueous Solutions*, 1961.
2. Spinks, J. W. T., and R. I. Woods, *An Introduction to Radiation Chemistry*, 1964.
3. Weiss, J. J., "Chemical Effects of Ionizing Radiations on Nucleic Acids and Related Compounds," *Progress in Nucleic Acid Research & Molecular Biology*, 3:103, 1964.
4. "Basic Mechanisms in the Radiation Chemistry of Aqueous Media," in Glassner, A., and E. J. Hart (eds.), *Radiation Research*, Suppl. 4, 1964.
5. *Advances in Chemistry Series*, 50:180, 1965.

When ionizing radiation enters living cells it deposits its energy in discrete bundles of ionizations along its track. These ionizations lead to chemical changes which can occur in any molecule along the path of the ray regardless of its structure. Since water is the most abundant substance in living cells the water molecule is the most likely one to be ionized and chemically changed. It has been estimated that 55% of the ionizations and excitations occur in water molecules.[1]

If the sole effect of the radiation attack on water molecules was to destroy water, this aspect of radiation action would be harmless since the total number of water molecules ionized is a minute fraction of those present in the cell. Assuming that water can diffuse freely through the cell a destroyed molecule would be easily replaced. However, the radicals formed from the breakdown of water will interact with nearby molecules, chemically altering them. Radiation damage to solute molecules resulting from the action of radicals from the radiolysis of water is referred to as indirect effect. Radiation damage to solute molecules resulting from direct ionization and excitation of those molecules is referred to as direct effect.

Since protein is the second most abundant substance in the cell, making up 50% to 80% of the dry weight, protein molecules are the second most likely targets of ionization and the most likely targets of attack by radicals from the breakdown of water. Proteins are capable of undergoing many chemical changes when altered by direct or indirect effect. There is good evidence that the injury to the protein following such attacks tends to localize on the glycine and cysteine or cystine moieties, producing radicals at the α-carbon of glycine and at the sulfur of cysteine or cystine.[2] The resulting chemical changes may or may not inactivate the protein.

It has been estimated that 1000 R, a dose sufficient to kill many types of cells, would damage 600 out of 4.7 million protein molecules in a hypothetical bacterial cell.[3] Since there are so many spare molecules of each protein and there is the machinery to make more, it is difficult to see how the effect on proteins could kill a cell. However, if the protein molecule destroyed is part of a critical structure such as the cell wall or

Table I. Radiation Effects on Proteins in Vitro

Protein	Effect Measured	G Value	Ref.
Albumin	Oxidation of thiol groups	3	21
Pepsin	Production of carbonyl groups	1.2	22
Cytochrome C	Oxidation	1.62	33
Cytochrome C	Oxidation of porphyrin double bonds	.045	33
Glyceraldehyde-3-P dehydrogenase	Thiol destruction	.23	25
Carboxypeptidase	Inactivation	.55	23
D-amino acid oxidase	Inactivation	.31	23
Ribonuclease	Inactivation	.09	23
Ribonuclease	Inactivation	.30	26
Trypsin	Inactivation	.077	23
Trypsin	Inactivation	.12- .44	29
Hexokinase	Inactivation	.033	23
Lysozyme	Inactivation	.03	23
Lysozyme	Inactivation	.44	28
Catalase	Inactivation	.009	23
Alcohol dehydrogenase	Inactivation	.06	24
Alcohol dehydrogenase	Inactivation	.06	26
Glyceraldehyde-3-P dehydrogenase	Inactivation	.06	24
Aldolase	Inactivation	.03	26
α Chymotrypsin	Inactivation	.14- .4	27
Pepsin	Inactivation	.006- .2	30
Pepsin	Inactivation	1.1	31
DNAase	Inactivation	.25- .80	32

nuclear membrane, or mitotic spindle, and if it could not be readily replaced, it is conceivable that protein damage might cause the cell to die or fail to reproduce.

In vitro irradiation of proteins does not reveal a very high radiosensitivity of this type molecule. If one measures change in function, as in enzyme activity, large doses of radiation are required for effect (Table I). Some chemical changes in the proteins require less radiation than does inactivation (Table I). Since function may depend on a single limited site on the molecule, function may not be impaired by multiple hits elsewhere in the molecule. And even the gross structural characteristics of the protein may not be greatly altered by one or two limited chemical alterations produced by radiation.

In vivo irradiation suggests a much greater radiosensitivity of protein function. Alteration of activity of some enzymes occurs in vivo at low doses (Table II). In most cases in vivo irradiation results in an increase in enzyme activity and this is probably secondary to other radiation-induced changes occurring in the cell. Enzyme release from a bound or blocked state could result in increase in activity and could destroy the cell. This is known as the "enzyme release hypothesis" of radiation death.[4]

In vivo irradiation produces changes in other proteins besides enzymes. Serum analyses show a fall in albumin and γ-globulin and an in-

Table II. Effects of Ionizing Radiation on Enzymes in Vivo

Enzyme	Tissue	Dose	Time After Radiation	Specific Activity % control	Ref.
Catalase	rat liver	600 R. W.B.	72 hr	30	34
Catalase	rat thymus nuclei	200 R. W.B.	1 hr	50	35
ATPase	rat spleen	100 R. W.B.	24 hr	188	36
ATPase	rat thymus	400 R. W.B.	24 hr	200	42
ATPase	mice spleen	640 R. W.B.	4 hr	112	37
			1–11 days	350	37
5-Nucleotidase	rat spleen	100 R. W.B.	72 hr	151	36
5-Nucleotidase	mice spleen	640 R. W.B.	4 hr	118	37
			1–11 days	200	37
5-Nucleotidase	rat thymus	400 R. W.B.	24 hr	250	42
β-glycerophosphatase	mice spleen	640 R. W.B.	4 hr	100	37
			1–11 days	200	37
DNAase II	mouse spleen	300 R. W.B.	24 hr	230	38
DNAase II	mouse thymus	300 R. W.B.	24 hr	375	38
DNAase II	rat spleen	750 R. W.B.	24 hr	200	39
DNAase II	mouse thymus	780 R. W.B.	24 hr	750	41
DNAase	mouse spleen	780 R. W.B.	24 hr	500	41
RNAase	rat thymus	1000 R. W.B.	4 hr	1600	40

Table III. Serum or Plasma Protein Changes after X-Irradiation

Species	Dose (R)	Time after exposure (days)	Effect	Reference
Rats	880	1–3	Fall in total protein, albumin and γ-globulin; α- and β-globulins increased	43
	800	7	Fall in albumin and γ-globulin; rise in β-globulin; no change in α-globulins.	44
	650	3	Fall in γ-globulins; rise in α_2-globulin.	45
	200–700	1–3	Fall in albumin; rise in α_1- and β-globulins.	46
Dogs	500	9–11	Fall in albumin. Fall in A/G ratio.	47
Mice	300	1–28	No change in albumin, α- and β-globulins; fall in γ-globulin.	48
Rabbits	1200	1	Albumin falls, α- and β-globulin rise, fibrinogen rises, γ-globulin unchanged.	49

crease in α- and β-globulins (Table III). These changes must be secondary to changes in various tissues responsible for synthesis of these proteins. Fall in specific antibody titres has also been observed but this too is a result of decreased synthesis and not a direct effect on the protein.[20]

Nucleic acids are the third most abundant substance in some cells. Because of their tremendous size they make particularly good radiation targets. They are also particularly sensitive to radiation; small doses of radiation produce marked structural and functional changes in DNA irradiated *in vitro* (Table IV) and *in vivo* (Table V). It has been estimated that 1,000 R would damage 186 out of 63,000 DNA and RNA molecules in a hypothetical bacterial cell.[3] Relatively minor alterations in DNA could be expected to have serious consequences in the cell because the vital function of each gene in the cell is presumably dependent upon the unique structure of its DNA. Since the number of each gene (therefore each type of DNA) per cell is limited in accordance with the cell ploidy, a critical disturbance in cell metabolism could result from an altered function of one, or at most a few, DNA molecules. Certain types of damage in DNA which are not immediately lethal to the cell could persist and be transmitted to the cell progeny, since DNA serves as the template for its own replication, *i.e.*, an altered purine or pyrimidine base in the nucleotide chain would code for a similar defect in the replicated DNA. The manifestation of radiation damage in DNA could vary in severity as well as in the rate of development. It is somewhat surprising that lethal effects are not observed at even lower doses of radiation than is found to be required. However, some of the radiation induced changes may occur in portions of the DNA molecule that are not essential to its coding function. It also seems probable from recent findings that at least some defects in the DNA of the irradiated cell are reparable through metabolic processes. Evidence for the importance of DNA damage as a cause of death in irradiated cells is discussed in a review by Kaplan.[6] Of special significance in this connection is the finding of an increased radio-sensitivity of cells in which 5-bromodeoxyuridine (BUdR), an analog of thymidine, has been incorporated exclusively into the cellular DNA.[7]

Table IV. Radiation Effect on DNA in Vitro

Radiation Effect	G Value	Reference
Sugar-phosphate rupture	0.45	50
Sugar-phosphate rupture	2.03	51
Double strand breaks	0.12–0.15	53
Base alteration	to 2	50
Cross linking	~0.08	53
Hydroperoxide formation	1	54
Single strand breaks	2–10	52
Decreased molecular weight	0.14–0.33	52
Hydrogen bond breakage	50–60	52
Inactivation of pneumococcus transforming principle	0.01–0.06	139
"Hydrogen bridge breakage"	3.8–24.1	138
Phosphomonoester release with esterase	0.8	55
Hydrogen bond break	6.6	55
Release of inorganic phosphate	.09	56
Release of ammonia	.47	56

Table V. Radiation Effect on DNA in Vivo

Tissue	Dose*	Time	Effect	Ref.
Rat thymus	1000 R. W.B.	Immed.	Decrease N/P ratios Decrease purine content	57
Rat thymus	1000 R. W.B.	24 hr	Disappearance of streaming birefringence. Viscosity reduction to 50%	57
Rat thymus	2000 R. W.B.	10 min	50% drop in viscosity	58
Rat spleen	2000 R. W.B.	10 min	50% drop in viscosity	58
Rat liver	2000 R. W.B.	10 min	50% drop in viscosity	58
Rabbit bone marrow	2000 R. W.B.	Immed.	No effect	60
Rabbit bone marrow	2000 R. W.B.	72 hr	30% reduction in high polymer fraction	60
Rabbit bone marrow	2000 R. W.B.	72 hr	80% reduction in viscosity	60
Pneumococcus	100,000 R.		Transforming ability little affected but cell viability down to 10%	59
Cultured leukemic lymphoblasts	1000 R.	Frozen until assay	Reduced priming activity for RNA and DNA polymerase from E. coli	61

* W.B. = Whole body radiation exposure.

Carbohydrates and lipids in the cell are not particularly sensitive to radiation. Chemical changes after *in vitro* irradiation can be identified and measured but they require large doses. *In vivo* chemical changes also require large doses of radiation. It does not seem that damage to these substances is cause for death of the cell except where they may form a part of a critical structure.

Significant changes in cell metabolism have been demonstrated in cells and tissues exposed to ionizing radiation, and the metabolic effects observed could account for many of the biological effects of radiation, including cell death. Mitochondrial oxidative phosphorylation has been reported to be depressed in a number of tissues in animals exposed to whole body irradiation (Table VI). This could be a secondary effect resulting from structural alterations which have been observed in the mitochondria by means of the electron microscope. Small, well defined, electron-lucent vacuoles between mitochondrial cristae are demonstrable in rat spleen as early as 75 minutes after 600 R whole body irradiation. Swelling of mitochondria, rupture and dissolution of their internal membranes have been observed.[11, 12] The question as to whether the loss of structural integrity of mitochondria might result from defects in the metabolic functions of the mitochondria remains unanswered. However, the functional state of the electron transport chain is apparently closely coupled to the active maintenance of the structure of the mitochondrion.[13] An abscopal effect involving endocrine activity has been reported to play an important role in the reduction of oxidative phosphorylation by mito-chondria after *in vivo* irradiation,[68] but the work of others[10, 69] fails to support this conclusion, suggesting rather that the observed effects are due to the localized action of the radiation. Inhibition of oxidative phos-phorylation can also be demonstrated in mitochondria exposed to *in vitro* irradiation but only if relatively high radiation doses are used (Table VI). The latter suggests that the radiosensitivity of mitochondria exposed to *in vivo* irradiation depends to a significant extent on effects which occur outside the organelle itself. One possibility is that hydrolytic enzymes are released from injured lysosomes and indirectly affect a variety of metabolic systems, including oxidative phosphorylation in mitochondria. In fact, one investigator found that the "apparent" defect in oxidative phosphorylation (lowered P/O ratios) by mitochondria from irradiated spleen could be explained by an increased activity of various phospha-tases present as contaminants, presumably released from lysosomes.[67]

Nuclear ATP synthesis is another cell process that is altered by radia-tion through an unknown mechanism. Only radiation-sensitive tissues such as thymus, spleen, intestinal mucosa and bone marrow show the effect (Table VII). Rats sacrificed 1 hour after 100 R total-body irradia-tion showed a complete suppression of high energy phosphate genera-tion in their cell nuclei. This is not an abscopal effect and is even more radiosensitive *in vitro*. Klouwen[19] discusses this phenomenon in some detail.

Inhibition of DNA synthesis is a radiation effect that has been widely studied, and the findings consistently show reduced incorporation of labeled precursors into the DNA of mitotically active cells after irradia-

Table VI. Effect of Radiation on Mitochondrial Oxidative Phosphorylation

Tissue	Substrate	Dose*	Time	P/O	Ref
Rat spleen	succinate	800 R. W.B.	1 hr	↓	62
Rat spleen	succinate	2000 R. in vitro		→	62
Rat thymus	succinate & pyruvate	800 R. W.B.	3 hr	↓	63
Mouse liver	succinate & pyruvate	700 R. W.B.		↓	64
Rat spleen	succinate or α ketoglutarate	1100 R. W.B.	4 hr	↓	65
Rabbit thymus	succinate	800 R. W.B.	4 hr	↓	66
Rabbit heart	succinate	800 R. W.B.	4 hr	↓	66
Rat spleen	succinate or α ketoglutarate	1000 R. W.B.	4 hr	→	67
Rat spleen	succinate	800 R. W.B.	24 hr	↓	68
Rat spleen	succinate	800 R head shielded	24 hr	→	68
Rat spleen	succinate	800 R. W.B.	24 hr	↓	69
Rat spleen	succinate	800 R head only	24 hr	→	69
Rat liver	succinate & β hydroxybutyrate	200,000 R in vitro		↓	70
Rat liver	pyruvate & citrate	840 R.	3 hr	↓	71

* W.B. = Whole body radiation exposure.

Table VII. Effect of Radiation of Nuclear ATP Synthesis

Tissue	Dose*	% Inhibition	Reference
Rat thymus	100 R. W.B.	100%	72
Rat spleen	100 R. W.B.	100%	72
Rat bone marrow	100 R. W.B.	100%	72
Rat lymph node	100 R. W.B.	100%	72
Rat thymus	44 R in vitro	100%	73
Rat spleen	44 R in vitro	100%	73
Rat thymus	200 R. W.B.	40%	74
Rat thymus	700 R. W.B.	38%	75
Human malignant tumors	25 R in vitro	50%	76

* W.B. = Whole body radiation exposure.

tion (Table VIII). Although these observations could be at least partially explained by a dilution of the labeled precursors with nonlabeled intermediates at some steps of the synthetic pathway, the effect appears to be a real one since net synthesis of DNA is also affected. The action of the radiation does not cause any obvious change in the essential components of the DNA synthesizing system. Radiation doses sufficient to inhibit DNA synthesis cause little effect on the template function of DNA (Table V). Kinases and polymerase are present in adequate amount, and no deficiency has been found in the required deoxynucleoside triphosphates. The latter finding suggests that the energy-yielding reactions necessary for synthetic processes are not seriously impaired. It now seems probable that the irradiation of actively dividing cells causes a decreased synthesis of DNA because of an inhibitory effect of radiation on the mitotic process. This general subject has been reviewed by Nygaard.[16]

An examination of radiation effects on RNA synthesis has yielded conflicting results (Table IX). The lack of uniformity in experimental findings is not entirely surprising, in view of the great chemical and metabolic heterogeneity of cellular RNA, plus the differences in results that might be expected from varied experimental methods used for the isolation, fractionation, and study of RNA. An important change in the synthesis of RNA could conceivably be limited to certain specific fractions which represent a very small proportion of the cell's total RNA; such an effect would probably be undetected by measurements of the incorporation of labeled precursors into total, unfractionated RNA. By use of autoradiographic and subcellular fractionation techniques, it is possible to localize the sites of active RNA synthesis and evaluate their relative radiosensitivities (Table IX). An inhibitory effect of radiation is most consistently found in tissues and cells that are mitotically active, and the cytoplasm and nuclei both show the effect. Changes in the nucleolus after irradiation include alterations in structural integrity,[91, 125] as well as a decreased uptake of tritiated cytidine.[91] Many explanations, all speculative, could

Table VIII. Effect of Radiation on DNA Synthesis

Tissue	Labeled Precursor	Dose	Time	Effect % Control	Ref
Rabbit bone marrow	Phosphate	1000 R abdomen	2 hr	56	77
Rat spleen	Phosphate	1000 R	2 hr	40	78
Mouse spleen	Phosphate	800 R	2 hr	21	79
Rat thymus	Phosphate	800 R	3 hr	47	81
Rat thymus	Phosphate	1000 R	.05 hr	49	82
Rabbit appendix	Phosphate	1000 R abdomen	2 hr	41	77
Mouse liver	Phosphate	800 R	2 hr	59	79
Rabbit kidney	Phosphate	1000 R	2 hr	77	77
Rat regenerating liver nuclei	thymidine	800 R (24 hr postop)	24 hr	34	83
Mouse intestine	thymidine	800 R	1 hr	100	80
Mouse spleen nuclei	thymidine	800 R	1 hr	60	84
Rat spleen	thymidine	125 R	½ hr	54	85
Rat small intestine	thymidine	125 R	½ hr	73	85
Rat regenerating liver	thymidine	600 R (before operation)	24 hr	30	86
Rat regenerating liver	thymidine	750 R (19 hr postop)	20 hr	50	87

Table IX. Effect of Radiation on RNA Synthesis

Tissue	Labeled Precursor	Dose	Time	Effect % Control	Ref
Rabbit bone marrow nuclei	Phosphate	1000 R abdomen	2 hr	56	77
Rat spleen	Phosphate	1000 R	2 hr	67	78
Rat thymus	Phosphate	800 R	3 hr	60	81
Rat thymus nuclei	Phosphate	1000 R	0.5 hr	72	82
Rat thymus cytoplasm	Phosphate	1000 R	0.5 hr	76	82
Rabbit thymus nuclei	Phosphate	1000 R abdomen	2 hr	100	77
Rabbit thymus cytoplasm	Phosphate	1000 R	2 hr	112	77
Mouse liver nuclei	Phosphate	600 R	2.5 hr	71	88
Mouse liver cytoplasm	Phosphate	600 R	2.5 hr	109	88
Rabbit kidney nuclei	Phosphate	1000 R abdomen	2 hr	146	77
Rabbit kidney cytoplasm	Phosphate	1000 R	2 hr	154	77
Rat thymus	Phosphate	300 R	3.5 hr	42	89
Rat liver total nuclear RNA	Phosphate	700 R	7.5 hr	120	89
Rat liver nuclei NaCl extractable RNA	Phosphate	700 R	7.5 hr	49	89
Rabbit appendix nuclei	Phosphate	2000 R In vitro	↓		90
HeLa cells nucleoli in culture	cytidine	300 R		30	91

Table X.   Effect of Radiation on Protein Synthesis

Tissue	Protein	Labeled Precursor	Dose	Time	Synthesis Effect	Ref.
Rabbit bone marrow	In vitro hemin globin	glycine-2-C^{14} glycine-2-C^{14}	800 R 800 R	Immed 48 hr	↑ ↑	92
Dog blood	hemin	glycine-2-C^{14}	500 R	1 hr	↑	93
Rat thymus	cytoplasmic protein	glycine-2-C^{14}	1000 R	2 hr	o-sl ↑	94
Rat liver	protein	acetate-C^{14}	950 R	6 hr	↑	95
Rabbit intestine	protein	glycine-1-C^{14}	800 R	5 hr	→	96
Jensen rat sarcoma	protein	methionine-S^{35}	2000 R	1 hr	→	97
Mouse pancreas	In vitro amylase		2000 R	24 hr	↑	98
Mouse muscle	In vivo protein	alanine-C^{14}	800 R	4 days	↓	99
Mouse liver	protein	alanine-C^{14}	800 R	4 days	↑	99
Rat serum	sheep erythrocyte agglutinin response to antigen		390 R	2–20 days	↓	100
T. pyrrhogaster embryo	actin myosin		500 R } 500 R }	20–90 hrs	↓ ↑	101 101
Rat serum	sheep erythrocyte hemolysin		175 R	1–3 days	↓	102
Regenerating rat liver	proteins of nuclei	leucine-C^{14}	900 R (2 or 6 hrs after exposure)	18 or 22 hr	↓	103
Rat thymus	proteins of nucleus	valine-H^3	1000 R	2 hr	↓	104
Nuclear suspensions	protein	valine-H^3	1000 R		↓	104
Rat thymus	nuclei	leucine-1-C^{14}	650 R	4 hr	↓	105
Rat thymus	microsome	leucine-1-C^{14}	650 R	4 hr	↓	
Rat thymus	ribosomes	leucine-1-C^{14}	650 R	6 hr	↓	
Mouse intestine	protein	leucine-C^{14}	2500 R	2 days	↓	106

be offered to explain the possible mode of action of radiation in inhibiting RNA synthesis. The effect could reasonably be attributed to radiation damage in DNA which must function as a template for RNA synthesis (Table V). A release of active hydrolytic enzymes from damaged lysosomes could be an important factor in accounting for this and other metabolic disturbances (Table II).

Radiation effects on protein synthesis have also been variable (Table X). Alterations in protein synthesis could be due to effects on DNA,[17] RNA, RNA synthesis, enzymes or ribosomes. The subject is briefly reviewed by Kelly.[14] More work is needed to elucidate the mechanism.

Although carbohydrates and lipids, *per se,* are radioresistant, the effects of radiation on carbohydrates and lipid metabolism are more radiosensitive. The mechanisms are unknown. Carbohydrate biosynthesis appears radioresistant but radiation produces a relative increase in lipid synthesis (Table XI). Increased lipid synthesis is seen only in fasted animals and apparently represents a reversal of decreased lipid synthesis seen in fasting animals. Anaerobic glycolysis appears to be suppressed by radiation but respiration is quite radio-resistant (Table XII). Complex polysaccharides such as hyaluronic acid are decomposed on irradiation *in vitro* or *in vivo.* The formation of lipid peroxides during *in vivo* irradiation has been extensively argued and its significance in radiation injury is unknown.

Structural damage has been discussed above in radiation effects on mitochondria and nucleoli with relation to effects on oxidative phosphorylation and RNA synthesis. A great many cytologic damages have been described (Table XIII). The increase in chromosomal aberrations is one of the most discussed effects, and is a good parameter of nuclear damage. However, a one-to-one relation between the production of any given chromosome aberration and cell survival has not been obtained.[15] The mechanisms of structural damage are unknown. It is still impossible to determine whether the structural changes lead to the biochemical changes or vice versa. It is not difficult to visualize a small structural defect releasing enzymes into a critical area or allowing entrance of ions or

Table XI. Effect of Radiation on Lipid Synthesis

Tissue	Precursor	Dose	Time	Effect	Ref.
Fasted mouse liver	P^{32}	510 R	30 min	↑	107
Fasted rat liver slices fatty acid	acetate-1-C^{14}	200 R	24 hr	↑	108
Fasted rat liver fatty acid	acetate-1-C^{14}	750 R	22 hr	↑	109
Fasted rat liver fatty acid	acetate-1-C^{14}	750 R	6 hr	↑	110
Fasted rat liver cholesterol	acetate-1-C^{14}	2400 R	24 hr	↑	111
Fasted rat liver slices cell free preparation cholesterol	acetate-1-C^{14}	2400 R	24 hr	↑	112
Fasted rat liver slices cholesterol, fatty acid	acetate-1-C^{14}	2400 R	Immed	↑	113
Fasted rat liver slices fatty acids	acetate-2-C^{14} butyrate-1-C^{14}	450 R	40 hr	↑	114
Force-fed rat liver fatty acids, cholesterol	acetate-1-C^{14}	1000 R	24 hr	→	115

Table XII. Effect of Radiation on Tissue Metabolism

Tissue	Assay System	Dose	Time	Effect	Ref.
Mouse spleen	lactic acid formation	640 R	1–9 days	—	116
Mouse liver	lactic acid formation	60,000 R	Immed	—	117
Rat liver slices	O_2 consumption	5 μc P^{32}/gm	24 hr*	23% ↓	118
Rat liver slices	anaerobic glycolysis	5 μc P^{32}/gm	24 hr*	60% ↓	118
Rat liver slices	pyruvate oxidation	5 μc P^{32}/gm	24 hr*	—	118
Yoshida ascites tumor	lactic acid production	20,000 R	Immed	50% ↓	119
Ehrlich ascites tumor	O_2 uptake	100,000 R		20% ↑	120
Ehrlich ascites tumor	anaerobic glycolysis	100,000 R		75% ↓	120
Yoshida ascites tumor	anaerobic glycolysis	20,000 R		↓	121
Yoshida ascites tumor	respiration	20,000 R		—	121
Ehrlich ascites tumor	anaerobic glycolysis	~2000 R	4 min	60% ↓	122

*24 hrs. after injection of P^{32}.

molecules which make the milieu of one sector of the cell unfit for its functions. If those functions are vital, the cell will die. The organization of the cell is so highly developed and functionally interdependent, it would not seem to take much alteration to disorganize and destroy it.

Many factors are capable of altering radiosensitivity and radioresistance. Some of these factors provide clues to the mechanism of radiation biochemical changes. For example the fact that cells are most radiosensitive during mitosis in partially synchronized cells indicates that the important radiation target may be unique structures and processes prevalent at that time. The fact that incorporation of halogenated derivatives into DNA increases cell radiosensitivity suggests that DNA may be a prime radiation target. The protective effect of sulfhydryl and disulfide protective agents, which appear to protect sulfur groups in proteins, suggests that protein sulfur groups are important radiation targets.

The ability of cells to repair radiation-induced damage further complicates the picture. Effects on radiosensitivity can be due to effects on repair mechanisms. Such mechanisms are capable of repairing DNA damage, chromosome breaks, inhibition of many biochemical processes. Even increased radiosensitivity of DNA subsequent to incorporation of

Table XIII. Effect of Radiation on Subcellular Structures

Structure	Tissue	Dose	Time	Effect	Ref
Cell membrane	mouse lymph node	400 R	48 hr	rupture increased	123
	human erythrocytes	4000 R	20 hr	K loss	124
	frog striated muscle	100,000 R	Immed	Increased K loss & Na uptake	129
Cytoplasm	HeLa cells	150 R	12 hr	vacuole formation	125
Endoplasmic reticulum	Mouse mammary tumor	1000 R	48 hr	dilation	123
	rat thyroid	2 μc I^{131}	3 days	clumped & denuded of ribosomes	128
Mitochondria	rat bone marrow	500 R	3 hr	Internal dis organization	126
	mouse lymph node	400 R	48 hr	swelling & rupture	123
	mouse mammary tumor	1000 R	48 hr	swelling & rupture	123
	rat spleen	600 R	75 min	vacuoles & swelling	127
Golgi Sacs	rat bone marrow	500 R	3 hr	vesicular degeneration	126
	HeLa cells	150 R	12 hr	excessive vesiculation	125
Lysosomes	rat spleen	1000 R	3 hr	fragility	130
	rat liver	10,000 R	Immed	release of enzymes	131
Nuclear membrane	Lebistes reticulatus R. testes	7500 R	6 hrs	altered reconstruction after meiosis	132
	rat spleen nuclei	25 R	1 hr	loss of Na and K	133
Nuclei	rat spermatid	10,000 R	3 days	reduced number of coiled microfibrils	134
	rat thymocytes	1500 R	6 hr	release of histones into cytoplasm	135
	tradescantia braetiata	200 R		chromosome breakage	136

halogenated derivatives can be explained on the basis of inhibition of repair mechanisms.[18]

Radiation biochemistry has accumulated much useful information on the effects of ionizing radiation in biological material. It remains largely for future research to answer many questions concerning the mechanism of radiation effects.

BIBLIOGRAPHY

References:

1. Kuzin, A. M., *Radiation Biochemistry*, translated by Halperin, Y., p. 117, 1964.
2. Gordy, W., and H. Shields, "Electron Spin Resonance Investigations of the Proteins," *Mem. Acad. Roy. Belg.*, 33:191, 1961.
3. Luse, R. A., "Basic Mechanisms in the Radiation Chemistry of Proteins and Nucleic Acids," *Radiation Res.*, suppl. 4, p. 192, 1964.
4. Bacq, Z. M., and P. Alexander, *Fundamentals of Radiobiology*, chapter IV, 2nd ed., 1961.
5. Guild, W. R., "The Radiation Sensitivity of Deoxyribonucleic Acid," *Radiation Res.*, suppl. 3, p. 257, 1963.
6. Kaplan, H. S., K. C. Smith, and P. Tomlin, "Radiosensitization of *E. Coli*

by Purine and Pyrimidine Analogues Incorporated in Deoxyribonucleic Acid," *Nature*, 190:794, 1961.

7. Djordjevic, B., and W. Szybalski, "Genetics of Human Cell Lines. III. Incorporation of 5-Bromo- and 5-Iododeoxyuridine in the Deoxyribonucleic Acid of Human Cells and its Effect on Radiation Sensitivity," *J. Exptl. Med.*, 112:509, 1960.

8. Boyce, R. P., and P. Howard-Flanders, "Release of Ultraviolet Light-Induced Thymine Dimers from DNA in *E. Coli* K-12," *Proc. Natl. Acad. Sci. U.S.*, 51: 293, 1964.

9. Setlow, R. B., and W. L. Carrier, "The Disappearance of Thymine Dimers from DNA: an Error-Correcting Mechanism," *Proc. Natl. Acad. Sci. U.S.*, 51: 226, 1964.

10. "Oxidative Phosphorylation in some Radiosensitive Tissues after Irradiation," *Ciba Found. Symp. on Ionizing Radiations and Cell Metabolism*, p. 77, 1956.

11. Goldfeder, A., "Cell Structure and Radiosensitivity," *Trans. N.Y. Acad. Sci.*, Series 2, 26(2):215, 1963.

12. Montgomery, P., R. C. Reynolds and D. H. Karney, "Subcellular Effects of X-Irradiation," *Lab. Invest.*, 12:858, 1963.

13. Lehninger, A. L., and C. L. Wadkins, "Oxidative Phosphorylation," *Ann. Rev. Biochem.*, 31:47, 1962.

14. Kelly, L. S., "Fundamental Aspects of Radiosensitivity," *Brookhaven Symp. in Biol.*, 14:32, 1961.

15. Wolff, S., "Radiation Effects as Measured by Chromosome Damage," *Cellular Radiation Biology*, 1965.

16. Nygaard, O. F., "Effects of Radiation on Nucleic Acid Metabolism," in Leone, C. A., (ed.), *Effects of Ionizing Radiations on Immune Processes*, 1962.

17. Novelli, G. D., T. Kameyama, and J. M. Eisenstadt, "The Effect of Ultraviolet Light and X-Rays on an Enzyme-Forming System," *J. Cellular Comp. Physiol.*, suppl. 1, 58:225, 1961.

18. Lett, J. T., et al., "Mechanisms of Sensitization to X-Rays of Mammalian Cells by 5-Bromo-Deoxyuridine," *Nature*, 203:593, 1964.

19. Klouwen, H. M., "Radiosensitivity of Nuclear ATP Synthesis and its Relation to Inhibition of Mitosis," *Cellular Radiation Biology*, 1965.

20. Taliaferro, W. H., L. G. Taliaferro, and B. N. Taroslow, *Radiation and Immune Mechanisms*, 1964.

21. Pavlovskaya, T. E., and A. G. Pasynskie, "The Protective Action of some Substances in the Irradiation of Protein Solutions," *Kolloidn. Zhur.*, 18:583, 1956.

22. Jayko, M. E., and W. M. Garrison, "Formation of C=O Bonds in the Radiation-Induced Oxidation of Protein in Aqueous Systems," *Nature*, 181: 413, 1958.

23. Barron, E. S. G., "The Effect of Ionizing Radiations on Systems of Biological Importance," *Ann. N.Y. Acad. Sci.*, 59:574, 1955.

24. Lange, R., A. Pihl, and L. Eldjarn, "The Inactivation of SH Enzymes by X-Rays," *Intern. J. Radiation Biol.*, 1:73, 1959.

25. Lange, R., and A. Pihl, "The Mechanism of X-Ray Inactivation of Phosphoglyceraldehyde Dehydrogenase," *Intern. J. Radiation Biol.*, 2:301, 1960.

26. Romani, R. J., and A. L. Tappel, "Anaerobic Irradiation of Alcohol Dehydrogenase, Aldolase and Ribonuclease," *Arch. Biochem. Biophys.*, 79:323, 1959.

27. Butler, J. A. V., A. B. Robins, and J. Rotblat, "The Inactivation of α-Chymotrypsin by Ionizing Radiation," *Proc. Royal Soc. Lodon*, A256:1, 1960.

28. Augenstine, L. G., "The Effects of Ionizing Radiation on Enzymes," *Advan. Enzymol.*, 24:359, 1962.

29. Augenstine, L. G., "Indirect Inactivation of Macromolecules in Solution by Ionizing Radiation, *Radiation Res.*, 10:89, 1959.

30. Bellamy, W., and E. Lawton, "Problems in Using High-Voltage Electrons for Sterilization," *Nucleonics*, 12(4):54, 1954.

31. Loken, M. K., et al., "Inactivation of Pepsin by Roentgen Radiation. II. Effect of Different Enzyme Concentrations or Various Organic Compounds," *Radiation Res.*, 11:72, 1959.

32. Robins, A. B., and J. A. V. Butler, "Effects of Oxygen on the Inactivation of Enzymes by Ionizing Radiations. I. Dilute Solutions of Trypsin and Deoxyribonuclease," *Radiation Res.*, 16:7, 1962.

33. Guzman Barron, E. S., and Veronica Flood, "Studies on the Mechanism of Action of Ionizing Radiations. IX. The Effect of X-Irradiation on Cytochrome C.," *Arch. Biochem. Biophys.*, 41:203, 1952.

34. Roth, J. S., et al., "Effect of Total Body X-Irradiation on some Enzymes of Rat Tissues," *Arch. Biochem. Biophys.*, 44:95, 1953.

35. Creasey, W. A., "The Enzymic Composition of Nuclei Isolated from Radiosensitive and Non-Sensitive Tissues with Special Reference to Catalase Activity," *Biochem. J.*, 77:5, 1960.

36. Kuzin, A. M., *Radiation Biochemistry*, translated by Halperin, Y., p. 117, 1964.

37. Ashwell, G., and J. Hickman, "Effect of X-Irradiation Upon the Enzyme Systems of the Mouse Spleen," *Proc. Soc. Exptl. Biol. Med.*, 80:407, 1952.

38. Pierucci, O., and W. Regelson, "Effect of Whole Body Irradiation on the Activity of Acid Deoxyribonuclease of Mouse Tissues," *Radiation Res.*, 24:619, 1965.

39. Ohada, S., et al., "The Effect of X-Ray Exposure on Deoxyribonuclease. II. Activity in Lymphoid Tissues," *Arch. Biochem. Biophys.*, 70:469, 1957.

40. Maor, Dalia and Peter Alexander, "Concerning the Mechanism of the Increased RNAase Activity in Lymphatic Cells Following Whole Body Irradiation, *Intern. J. Radiation Biol.*, 6:93, 1963.

41. Kurnich, N. B., B. W. Massey, and G. Sandeen, "The Effect of Radiation on Tissue Deoxyribonuclease," *Radiation Res.*, 11:101, 1959.

42. DuBois, K. P., and D. F. Peterson, "Adenosine Triphosphatase and 5-Nucleotidase Activity of Hematopoietic Tissues of Irradiated Animals," *Am. J. Physiol.*, 176:282, 1954.

43. Westphal, U., et al., "Influence of Whole Body X-Irradiation, Cold Exposure and Experimental Acidosis on Protein Composition and Azorubin-Binding Capacity of Rat Serum," *Am. J. Physiol.*, 175:424, 1953.

44. Fischer, M. A., M. Z. Magee, and E. P. Coulter, "Studies on the Serum Proteins of the X-Irradiated Rat," *Arch. Biochem. Biophys.*, 56:66, 1955.

45. Höhne, G., H. A. Künkel, and R. Anger, "Die Serum Elweisskörper der Ratte nach Roentgenganzbestrahlung mit 3000 R.," *Klin. Wochschr.*, 33:284, 1955.

46. Winkler, C., and G. Paschke, "Protein Content and Composition of Rat Serum as Related to Amount of Whole Body X-Irradiation," *Radiation Res.*, 5:156, 1956.

47. Cornatzer, W. E., O. Engelstad, and J. P. Davison, "Effect of Whole Body X-Irradiation on Blood Constituents," *Am. J. Physiol.*, 175:153, 1953.

48. Werder, A. A., C. A. Hardin, and P. Morgan, "The Experimental Effect of X-Irradiation and Cortisone on Serum Proteins," *Radiation Res.*, 7:500, 1957.

49. Kuzin, A. M., *Radiation Biochemistry*, translated by Halperin, Y., p. 167, 1964.

50. Scholes, G., J. F. Word, and J. Weiss, "Mechanism of Radiation-Induced Degradation of Nucleic Acids," *J. Mol. Biol.*, 2:379, 1960.

51. Peacocke, A. R., and B. N. Preston, "The Degradation and Denaturation of Sodium Deoxyribonucleate by Gamma Rays," *J. Polymer Sci.*, 31:1, 1958.

52. Cox, R. A., et al., "The Action of γ-Rays on Sodium Deoxyribonucleate in Solution," *Proc. Roy. Soc. London*, B149:511, 1958.

53. Lett, J. T., K. A. Stacey, and P. Alexander, "Crosslinking of Dry Deoxyribonucleic Acids by Electrons," *Radiation Res.*, 14:349, 1961.

54. Daniels, M., et al., "Chemical Action of Ionizing Radiations in Solution XVII. Degradation of DNA in Aqueous Solution by Irradiating with X-Rays," *J. Chem. Soc.*, 1957:226, 1957.

55. Collyns, B., et al., "Chain Scission and Hydrogen Bond Breakage on Irradiation of DNA," *Radiation Res.*, 25:526, 1965.

56. Scholes, G., and J. Weiss, "Chemical Action of X-Rays on Nucleic Acid, Purines, Pyrimidines, Nucleosides and Nucleotides by X-Rays and by Free Radicals Produced Chemically," *Biochem. J.*, 53:567, 1953.

57. Limperos, G., and W. A. Mosher, "Roentgen Irradiation of Desoxyribosenucleic Acid. II. Physicochemical Properties of Desoxyribosenucleic Acid From Irradiated Rats," *Am. J. Roentgenol.*,63:691, 1950.

58. Kuzin, A. M., *Radiation Biochemistry*, translated by Halperin, Y., 1964.

59. Drew, Ruth, "γ-Irradiation of Pneumococcus Deoxyribonucleic Acid," *Radiation Res.*, 3:116, 1955.

60. Kritskii, G. A., R. N. Safronova, et al., "Change in Properties of DNA of Bone Marrow Following X-Ray Irradiation," *Biokhimiya*, 29:701, 1964.

61. Harrington, H., "Effect of X-Irradiation on the Priming Activity of DNA," *Proc. Natl. Acad. Sci. U.S.*, 51:59, 1964.

62. Potter, R. L., and F. H. Bethel, "Oxidative Phosphorylation in Spleen Mitochondria," *Federation Proc.*, 11:270, 1952.

63. Thomson, J. F., W. W. Tourtellotte, and M. S. Carttar, "Some Observations on Effect of Gamma Radiation on the Biochemistry of the Rat Thymus," *Proc. Soc. Exptl. Biol. Med.*, 80:268, 1952.

64. Goldfeder, A., (ed.), *Progress in Radiobiology*, p. 69, 1956.

65. vanBekkum, D. W., et al., "The Oxidative Phosphorylation by Mitochondria Isolated From the Spleen of Rats After Total Body Exposure to X-Rays," *Brit. J. Radiol.*, 27:127, 1954.

66. Scalfe, J. F., and B. Hill, "Uncoupling of Oxidative Phosphorylation by Ionizing Radiation. II. The Stability of Mitochondrial Lipids and Cytochrome C.," *Can. J. Biochem.*, 41:1223, 1963.

67. Thomson, J. F., "Effects of Total Body X-Irradiation on Phosphate Esterification and Hydrolysis in Mitochondrial Preparations of Rat Spleen," *Radiation Res.*, 21:46, 1964.

68. Benjamin, T. L., and H. T. Yost, Jr., "The Mechanism of Uncoupling of Oxidative Phosphorylation in Rat Spleen and Liver Mitochondria after Whole-body Irradiation," *Radiation Res.*, 12:613, 1960.

69. vanBekkum, D. W., M. J. deVries, and H. M. Klouwen, "Biochemical and Morphological Changes in Lymphatic Tissues after Partial-body Irradiation," *Intern. J. Radiation Biol.*, 9(5):449, 1965.

70. Clarke, I. D., and J. Lang, "The Inactivation of Mitochondrial Enzymes by Gamma Radiation *In Vitro*," *Radiation Res.*, 24:142, 1965.

71. Goldstein, A. L., and J. C. Hall, "Role of Insulin and Other Compounds in Oxidative Phosphorylation after Wholebody Irradiation," *Arch. Biochem. Biophys.*, 109:442, 1965.

72. Creasey, W. A., and L. A. Stocken, "Biochemical Differentiation Between Radio-Sensitive and Non-Sensitive Tissue in the Rat," *Biochem. J.*, 69:17P, 1958.

73. Creasey, W. A., and L. A. Stocken, "The Effect of Ionizing Radiation on Nuclear Phosphorylation in the Radio-Sensitive Tissues of the Rat," *Biochem. J.*, 72:519, 1959.

74. Ord, M. G., and L. A. Stocken, "The Effects of 200 r of X-Radiation *In Vivo* on Phosphate Transfer Reactions in Nuclei from Rat Thymus Gland," *Biochem. J.*, 84:600, 1962.

75. Klouwen, H. M., and I. Betel, "Radiosensitivity of Nuclear ATP-Synthesis," *Intern. J. Radiation Biol.*, 6:441, 1963.

76. Fahmy, A. R., and W. F. Williams, "Effect of Radiation on Nuclear Phosphorylation in Human Malignant Tumours," *Brit. J. Cancer,*19:501, 1965.

77. Smillie, R. M. S., et al., "The Incorporation of Radioactive Phosphorus into the Nucleic Acids of Different Rabbit Tissues," *Biochem. J.*, 60:177, 1955.

78. Ord, M. G., and L. A. Stocken, "The Effects of X- and γ-Radiation on Nucleic Acid Metabolism in the Rat *In Vivo* and *In Vitro*," *Biochem. J.*, 63:3, 1956.

79. Kelly, L. S., et al., "Post-Irradiation Time and Dose-Response Studies on the Incorporation of p^{32} into DNA of Mouse Tissues," *Radiation Res.*, 2:490, 1955.

80. Sherman, F. G., et al., "DNA Synthesis, Cell Duplication and Migration in the Small Intestine of Normal and Irradiated Mice," *Federation Proc.*, 17:148, 1958.

81. Thomson, J. F., W. W. Tourtellotte, and M. S. Carttar, "Some Observations on Effect of Gamma Radiation on the Biochemistry of the Rat Thymus," *Proc. Soc. Exptl. Biol. Med.*, 80:268, 1952.

82. Ord, M. G., and L. A. Stocken, in deHevesy, G., A. Forssberg, and J. D. Abbott, (eds.), *Advances in Radiobiology*, 1957.

83. Lehnert, S. M., and S. Okada, "DNA-Synthesis in Nuclei from Regenerating Rat Liver after Whole-body Irradiation," *Intern. J. Radiation Biol.*, 5:323, 1962.

84. Fausto, N., A. O. Smoot, and J. L. Van Lancker, "Early Effects of X-Radiation on *In Vitro* DNA Synthesis in Mouse Spleen," *Radiation Res.*, 22:288, 1964.

85. Nygaard, O. F., and R. L. Potter, "Effect of Radiation on DNA Metabolism in Various Tissues of the Rat. IV. Early Effects," *Radiation Res.*, 16:243, 1962.

86. Fausto, N., T. Uchlyama, and J. L. Van Lancker, "Metabolic Alterations after Total Body Doses of X-Radiation. Effect of Irradiation of Normal Liver on DNA Synthesis after Partial Hepatectomy," *Arch. Biochem. Biophys.*, 106:447, 1964.

87. Looney, W. B., et al., "An Autoradiographic and Biochemical Study of the Effects of Radiation on DNA Synthesis in the Intact Animal," *Radiation Res.*, 24:312, 1965.

88. Payne, A. H., L. S. Kelly and C. Entenman, "Effect of Total Body X-Irradiation on the Relative Turnover of Nucleic Acid Phosphorus," *Proc. Soc. Exptl. Biol. Med.*, 81:698, 1952.

89. Klouwen, H. M., "Radiosensitivity of Nuclear RNA," *Biochem. Biophys. Acta*, 42:366, 1960.

90. Mori, K. J., and T. Morita, "Effects of X-Rays on Nuclear RNA of Lymphatic Cells," *Nature*, 200:1323, 1963.

91. Boudnitskaya, E. V., M. Brunfaut, and M. Errera, "Effects of X-Rays on RNA and RNA Metabolism in HeLa Cells," *Biochim. Biophys. Acta*, 80:567, 1964.

92. Richmond, J. E., K. I. Altman, and K. Salomon, "The Effect of X-Radiation on the Biosynthesis of Hemoglobin," *J. Biol. Chem.*, 190:817, 1951.

93. Nizit, A., et al., "Influence de l'Irradiation préalable sur la Synthèse de l'Hómine par les Hématies Jeunes *In Vitro*," *Arch. Intern. Physiol.*, 62:129, 1954.

94. Richmond, J. E., M. G. Ord, and L. A. Stocken, "The Effect of X-Radiation *In Vivo* on Protein and Nucleoprotein Metabolism in the Rat," *Biochem. J.*, 66:123, 1957.

95. Hevesy, G., "Effect of X-Rays on the Incorporation of Carbon-14 into Desoxyribonucleic Acid," *Nature.* 163:869, 1949.

96. Abrams, R., "Effect of X-Rays on Nucleic Acid and Protein Synthesis," *Arch. Biochem. Biophys.*, 30:90, 1951.

97. Holmes, B. E., and L. K. Mee, "The Incorporation of Methionine-S^{35} into the Proteins of Jensen Rat Sarcoma Cells after Irradiation of the Tumour," *Brit. J. Radiol.*, 25:273, 1952.

98. Hokin, M. R., and L. E. Hokin, "Protein Synthesis and Ribonucleic Acid Metabolism in Mouse Pancreas *In Vitro* after Whole Body Irradiation with X-Rays," *J. Biol. Chem.*, 219:85, 1956.

99. Hempelmann, L. H., et al., "Effect of Body Exposure to X-Rays on Rate of Incorporation of C^{14} Carboxyl-Labeled Alanine into Mouse Protein," *Federation Proc.*, 9:182, 1950.

100. Salerno, P. R., and H. L. Friedell, "A Comparison of the Effects of Radioactive Internal Emitters and X-Rays on Antibody Formation," *Radiation Res.*, 9:478, 1958.

101. Ogawa, Y., "Synthesis of Contractile Proteins in the X-Irradiated Embryo," *Nature*, 186:77, 1960.

102. Kohn, H. I., "Effect of X-Rays Upon Hemolysin Production in the Rat," *J. Immunol.*, 66:525, 1951.

103. Sestan, N., "Effect of Whole Body X-Irradiation on ^{14}C-Leucine Incorporation into Proteins of Cell Nuclei of Regenerating Rat Liver," *Nature*, 205: 615, 1965.

104. Smit, J. A., and L. A. Stocken, "The Effects of X-Irradiation on the Incorporation of Amino Acids into Proteins of Nuclei from Rat Thymus Gland," *Biochem. J.*, 91:155, 1964.

105. Herranen, A., "Effect of X-Irradiation on Amino Acid Incorporation into Thymus Cell Fractions," *Arch. Biochem. Biophys.*, 107:158, 1964.

106. Lipkin, M., H. Quastier, and F. Muggia, "Protein Synthesis in the Irradiated Intestine of the Mouse," *Radiation Res.*, 19:277, 1963.

107. Sherman, F. G., and A. B. Almeida, in deHevesy, G., A. Forssberg, and J. D. Abbott, (eds.), *Advances in Radiobiology*, p. 49, 1957.

108. Lerner, S. R., W. L. Warner, and C. Entenman, "Lipogenesis from Acetate-1-C^{14} by Liver Slices from X-Irradiated Rats," *Federation Proc.*, 12:85, 1953.

109. Coniglio, J. G., D. B. McCormick, and G. W. Hudson, "Biosynthesis of Fatty Acids in Liver and Intestine of Intact Normal Fasted and X-Irradiated Rats," *Am. J. Physiol.*, 185:577, 1956.

110. Coniglio, J. G., J. C. Kerschman, and G. W. Hudson, "Hepatic Glycogen, Lipogenesis and Glucose-6-Phosphatase in X-Irradiated and Control Rats," *Am. J. Physiol.*, 191:350, 1957.

111. Gould, R. G., L. V. Lotz, and E. M. Lilly, "Effect of X-Irradiation on Hepatic Cholesterol Synthesis," *Federation Proc.*, 15:264, 1956.

112. Bucher, W. L. R., A. V. Loud, and K. McGarrahan, "Cholesterol Biosynthesis in Liver Cell Fractions from X-Irradiated and Fasting Rats," *Federation Proc.*, 16:17, 1957.

113. Popjak, G., in Mitchell, J. S., B. E. Holmes, and C. L. Smith, (eds.), *Progress in Radiobiology*, p. 71, 1956.

114. Hansen, H. J. M., L. G. Hansen, and M. Faber, "The Effect of Whole-Body X-Irradiation on the Synthesis of Individual Fatty Acids in Liver Slices from Normal and Fasted Rats," *Intern. J. Radiation Biol.*, 9:25, 1965.

115. Pande, S. V., A. Ramalah, and T. A. Venkitasubramanian, "Effect of X-Irradiation on the Hepatic Synthesis of Fatty Acids and Cholesterol," *Biochim. Biophys. Acta*, 65:516, 1962.

116. Hickman, J., and G. Ashwell, "Effect of Irradiation by X-Ray Upon Anaerobic Glycolysis in Spleen Homogenates," *J. Biol. Chem.*, 205:651, 1953.

117. Lelièvre, P., "Etude de la Glycolyse Anaérobie dans les Tissue de Soures Irradiées à Fortes Doses de Rayons," *Compt. Rend. Soc. Biol.*, 151:412, 1957.

118. Irving, C. C., and J. D. Perkinson, Jr., "Biochemical Effects of Internal Irradiation," *Radiation Res.*, 12:597, 1960.

119. Höhne, G., et al., in deHevesy, G. A. Forssberg, and J. D. Abbot, (eds.), *Advances in Radiobiology*, 1957.

120. Caputo, A., and B. Giovanella, "The Action of Ionizing Radiations on the Respiration and on the Aerobic and Anaerobic Glycolysis of Ehrlich Mouse Ascites Cells," *Radiation Res.*, 13:809, 1960.

121. Maass, H., and G. Schubert, "Early Biochemical Reactions Following X-Irradiation," *Progr. in Nucl. Energy*, Series 6, 2:225, 1959.

122. Warburg, O., et al., "Partielle Anaerobiose der Krebszellen und Wirkung der Röntgenstrahlen auf Krebszellen," *Naturwiss.*, 46:25, 1959.

123. Goldfeder, A., and L. A. Miller, "Radiosensitivity and Biological Properties of Two Tumor Types Indigenous to the Same Host. VI. The Effects of X-Irradiation on Subcellular Units," *Intern. J. Radiation Biol.*, 6:575, 1963.

124. Shapiro, B., G. Kollmann, and J. Asnen, "Mechanism of the Effect of Ionizing Radiation on Sodium Uptake by Human Erythrocytes," *Radiation Res.*, 27:139, 1966.

125. Hendee, W. R., W. Zebrun, and F. J. Bonte, "Effects of X-Irradiation on Fine Structure of HeLa Cells," *Texas Rept. Biol. Med.*, 21:546, 1963.

126. Biryuzova, V. I., and V. G. Kondratenko, "Changes in Cell Elements in Irradiated Bone Marrow Cell Cultures," *Radiobiologiya*, 4:123, 1964.

127. Bari, W. A., and G. D. Sorenson, "Observations of the Early Effects of X-Irradiation on the Spleen in the Rat," *Lab. Invest.*, 12:856, 1963.

128. Sobel, H. J., "Electron Microscopy of I^{131}-Irradiated Thyroid," *Arch. Pathol.*, 78:53, 1964.

129. Portila, A., et al., "Radiation Damage in Muscle-Cell Membranes and Regulation of Cell Metabolism," *Exptl. Cell Res.*, 29:527, 1963.

130. Rahman, Y. E., "Effect of X-Irradiation on the Fragility of Rat Spleen Lysosomes," *Radiation Res.*, 20:741, 1963.

131. Desal, I. D., P. L. Sawant, and A. L. Tappel, "Peroxidative and Radiation Damage to Isolated Lysosomes," *Biochim. Biophys. Acta*, 86:277, 1964.

132. Follenius, E., "Effects of X-Rays on the Nuclear Membrane of Spermatocytes of Lebistes Reticulotus R Electron Microscope Study," *Compt. Rend.*, 257:1982, 1963.

133. Creasey, W. A., "Changes in the Sodium and Potassium Contents of Cell Nuclei after Irradiation, *Biochim. Biophys. Acta*, 38:181, 1960.

134. Lacy, D., and J. Rotblat, "Normal Structure of Spermatid Nuclei and Changes Caused by Ionizing Radiation," *Intern. J. Radiation Biol.*, 2:218, 1960.

135. Whitfield, J. F., H. Brohee, and T. Youdale, "The Effects of X-Irradiation on the Chromatin Structure and Histone Components of Rat Thymocyte Nuclei," *Exptl. Cell Res.*, 36:341, 1964.

136. Koller, P. C., "Symposium on Chromosome Breakage," *Progr. Biophys.*, 4:195, 1953.

137. Schwartz, E. E., "The Modification of Radiation Response," *The Biological Basis of Radiation Therapy*, 1966.

138. Hagen, U., and R. Wild, "Untersuchungen über die Strahlenempfindlichkeit der Desoxyribonukleinsäure Die Empfindlichkeit der Wasserstoffbrücken," *Strahlentherapie*, 124:275, 1964.

139. Guild, W. R., and F. M. De Filippes, "The Ionic Yield for Inactivation of Transforming Principle," (Abst). *Radiation Res.*, 5:481, 1956.

EXTINCTION COEFFICIENTS OF BIOLOGICAL SUBSTANCES

In Beer's Law, Optical Density = E (or A) = $-\log_{10}T$ = klc, where: T = Transmittance (I/I_0), c = Concentration, l = Length of optical path in cm, k = The specific extinction coefficient. When c is given in moles/liter, then k = ε = the molar extinction coefficient (or molar absorbtivity). Since the molecular weight of many proteins is known with substantial uncertainty, it is usual to express their optical constants in terms of specific extinction coefficients. In the table, l = 1 cm in all cases.

Substance	Wave Length, mμ	pH	Solvent	k	Concentration	References
1. N-acetyl-L-tryptophane	280 mμ	7	water	5900	1 M	1
2. Alcohol Dehydrogenase (horse liver)	280	7.5	0.1 M Na_2HPO_4	4.55	1%	2
3. Aldolase (Rabbit muscle)	280	7.4	10^{-4} M tris	9.10	1%	3
4. α-Amylase (B. subtilis)	280	7.0	acetate	25.6	1%	4
5. Brome Mosaic Virus	253.6	7.0	0.01 M phosphate	45	1%	5
6. Brome Mosaic Virus	260	7.0	0.01 M phosphate	48	1%	5
7. Bovine Serum Albumin (Nitrogen = 16%)	210	7.0	0.9% NaCl	203	1%	6
8. Bovine Serum Albumin	280	7.0	0.9% NaCl	6.6	1%	7
9. Catalase (Rat liver) (MW = 256,000)	407	7.0		436,000	1 M	8
10. p-Chloromercuribenzoic acid	232	4.6		16,900	1 M	9
11. p-Chloromercuribenzoic acid	234	4.5		17,400	1 M	9
12. Chymotrypsin	280			20.2	1%	10
13. Chymotrypsinogen	282			50,200	1 M	
14. Creatine transphosphorylase	280			8.4	1%	1
15. m-Cresol	270	7.0	water	1750	1 M	
16. Desoxyribonucleic acid	260	7.0	phosphate	210	1%	11
17. 2,4-Dinitroaniline	345	7.5	0.1 M tris	14,000	1 M	12
18. 2,4-Dinitrophenyl-L-alanine	265		1% $NaHCO_3$	8800	1 M	12
19. 2,4-Dinitrophenyl-L-alanine	361		1% $NaHCO_3$	17,100	1 M	12
20. S-DNP-cysteine	330		0.2 M acetic acid	9600	1 M	12
21. DNP-glycine	265		1% $NaHCO_3$	8800	1 M	12
22. DNP-glycine	361		1% $NaHCO_3$	17,100	1 M	12
23. DNP-glycine, methyl ester	260		ethanol	10,300	1 M	12
24. DNP-glycine, methyl ester	342		ethanol	17,200	1 M	12
25. DNP-glycylglycine	265		1% $NaHCO_3$	9,020	1 M	12
26. DNP-glycylglycine	353		1% $NaHCO_3$	16,000	1 M	12
27. ε-N-DNP-lysine	390		1 N HCl	10,200	1 M	13
28. ε-N-DNP-lysine	363	7.4	0.05 M phosphate	17,400	1 M	13
29. ε-N-DNP-lysine·HCl·H_2O	265		1% $NaHCO_3$	8,500	1 M	12

Extinction Coefficients of Biological Substances (Continued)

Substance	Wave Length, mμ	pH	Solvent	k	Concentration	References
30. ε-N-DNP-lysine-HCl·H_2O	361		1% $NaHCO_3$	17,700	1 M	12
31. ε-N-DNP-L-lysine, methyl ester	260		ethanol	8,300	1 M	12
32. ε-N-DNP-L-lysine, methyl ester	348		ethanol	16,650	1 M	12
33. di-DNP-L-lysine	263		1% $NaHCO_3$	15,850	1 M	12
34. di-DNP-L-lysine	355		1% $NaHCO_3$	30,850	1 M	12
35. DNP-phenylalanine	265		1% $NaHCO_3$	8,600	1 M	12
36. DNP-phenylalanine	361		1% $NaHCO_3$	17,200	1 M	12
37. DNP-L-phenylalanine, methyl ester	260		ethanol	9,700	1 M	12
38. DNP-L-phenylalanine, methyl ester	342		ethanol	17,200	1 M	12
39. 2,4-Dinitrothiophenol	408	10.5	0.05 M bicarbonate; EDTA	13,800	1 M	14
40. 2,4-Dinitrotoluene	242		95% ethanol	14,200	1 M	11
41. 5,5-Dithio-bis-2-nitro-benzoic acid	412	7.0		13,200	1 M	
42. N-ethylmaleimide	300	7.0	0.1 M phosphate	620	1 M	15
43. Gelatin	210			211	1%	
44. Gelatin	205			332	1%	
45. γ-Globulin (bovine)	291			15.2	1%	
46. γ-Globulin (chicken)	280	5.5	0.10 N NaOH	13.6	1%	16
47. γ-Globulin (equine)	277		0.25 N acetic acid	.0085	1 μg N/ml	17
48. γ-Globulin (human)	280		0.01 N HCl	13.6	1%	18
49. γ-Globulin (human)	280	7.6	0.5 M glycine	14.0	1%	19
50. γ-Globulin (rabbit)	210		0.9% NaCL	205	1%	
51. γ-Globulin (rabbit)	280		0.01 N HCl	13.5	1%	18
52. γ-Globulin (rabbit)	277		0.15 M KCl	13.8	1%	20
53. γ-Globulin (rabbit)	277		0.25 N Acetic acid	0.010	1 μg N/ml	17
54. γ-Globulin (rabbit) (A chain)	280		0.10 N HCl	13.7	1%	18
55. γ-Globulin (rabbit) (A piece)	280		0.01 N HCl	14.4	1%	18
56. γ-Globulin (rabbit) (B chain)	280		0.01 N HCl	11.8	1%	18
57. Glyceraldehyde-3-phosphate dehydrogenase (rabbit muscle)	280	6.7		14,300	1 M	21
58. Glyceraldehyde-3-phosphate dehydrogenase (rabbit muscle)	280	7.4	10^{-4} M tris	10.2	1%	21
59. Glycyl-L-tryptophane	280	7	water	5800	1 M	1
60. Glycyl-L-tyrosine	274	7	water	1280	1 M	1
61. Glycyl-L-tyrosyl-glycinamide	274	7	water	1480	1 M	1

No. Substance	λ (nm)	pH	Solvent	Value	Conc.	Ref.
62. Gramicidin	210		absolute ethanol	342	1%	6
63. Gramicidin	280		absolute ethanol	62	1%	6
64. m-Hydroxybenzoic acid	287	7	water	2100	1 M	1
65. m-Hydroxybenzaldehyde	311	7	water	2700	1 M	1
66. m-Hydroxybenzyl alcohol	272	7	water	1600	1 M	1
67. Indole	278	7	water	5600	1 M	1
68. Indole-3-acetic acid	279	7	water	7000	1 M	1
69. Indole-3-carboxylic acid	278	7	water	8400	1 M	1
70. Insulin	210			250	1%	22
71. Insulin	205			381	1%	22
72. Δ^5-3-Keto steroid isomerase	280	7.0	water	4.13	1%	23
73. β-Lactoglobulin	280	7		9.5	1%	7
74. Leucyl-L-tyrosine	274		water	1360	1 M	1
75. Methemoglobin (CN)	540		0.1 M NaOH	46,000	1%	24
76. Metmyoglobin (whale)	280	7.0	0.9% NaCl	18.0	1%	24
77. Metmyoglobin (whale)	280		0.1 N NaOH	17.9	1%	
78. Monoamine oxidase (plasma)	280	7.0	0.06 M phosphate	9.8	1%	24
79. apo-Myoglobin	280	7.0	0.9% NaCl	9.30	1%	24
80. apo-Myoglobin	280	7.0	0.1 M NaOH	9.2	1%	25
81. Myosin A	280		0.5 M KCl	5.60	1%	
82. o-Nitrophenylamine	410		NaCl	4510	1 M	11
83. p-Nitrophenylamine	370		NaCl	12,530	1 M	11
84. Ovalbumin (chicken)	280		water	7.35	1%	7
85. Ovalbumin N = 14.76%	280	7.0	NaCl	0.0053	1 μg N/ml	17
86. Ovalbumin	277		0.25 N acetic acid	0.0045	1 μg N/ml	17
87. Ovalbumin	210			215	1%	22
88. Ovalbumin	205			341	1%	22
89. Paramyosin (Pinna nobilis)	280	7.0	water	3.0	1 M	26
90. Phenol	268	7.0	phosphate, water, or NaCl	1500	1%	
91. Proteins (generally applicable)	$\Delta OD_{215-225}$	4–8	0.025 M phosphate	69.4	1 M	27
92. Ribonuclease	277.5	6.1		9800	1%	28
93. Ribonucleic acid	260	7.0	0.2 M NaCl	239	1 M	29
94. Ribonucleic acid	260	7.0	0.2 M NaCl	7940	1mM organic phosphorous	29
95. Ribonucleic acid (yeast)	260		0.01 M HCl	208	1%	30
96. Serum Albumin (human)	210		0.9% NaCl	203	1%	6
97. Serum Albumin (human)	280		0.9% NaCl	6.0	1%	6

Extinction Coefficients of Biological Substances (Continued)

Substance	Wave Length, mμ	pH	Solvent	k	Concentration	References
98. Siderophilin (human)	210		0.9% NaCl	200	1%	6
99. Siderophilin (human)	280		0.9% NaCl	14	1%	6
100. Southern Bean mosaic virus	253.6	7.0	0.01 M phosphate	55	1%	5
101. Southern Bean mosaic virus	260	7.0	0.01 M phosphate	58	1%	5
102. Taka-amylase	290		0.1 M NaOH	24.4	1%	31
103. Thyroglobulin (beef)	280	7.0	dil. salt	11.6	1%	32
104. Tobacco mosaic virus	253.6	7.0	0.01 M phosphate	30	1%	5
105. Tobacco mosaic virus	260	7.0	0.01 M phosphate	32	1%	5
106. Trinitrobenzenesulfonate	345	7.5		14,500	1 M	33
107. DL-tryptophaneamide	278	7.0	water	5500	1 M	1
108. L-tryptophane	278	7.0	water	6000	1 M	1
109. L-tryptophane ethyl ester	278	7.0	water	6000	1 M	1
110. Trypsin	280	8.0	tris-HCl	15.6	1%	34
111. Tyramine	274	7.0	water	1480	1 M	1
112. DL-Tyrosine	274	7.0	water	1520	1 M	1
113. L-Tryrosyl-glycine	274	7.0	water	1460	1 M	1

BIBLIOGRAPHY

References:

1. Cowgill, R. W., "Fluorescence and the Structure of Proteins," *Arch. Biochem. Biophys.*, 100:36, 1963.

2. Bonnichsen, R. K., "Crystalline Animal Alcohol Dehydrogenase 2," *Acta Chem. Scand.*, 4:715, 1954.

3. Baranowski, T., and T. Niederland, "Aldolase Activity of Myogen A," *J. Biol. Chem.*, 180:543, 1949.

4. Imanishi, A., K. Kakiuchi, and T. Isemura, "Molecular Stability and Reversibility of Denaturation of *Bacillus subtilis* α-Amylase," *J. Biochem.*, 54:89, 1963.

5. Brakke, M. K., "Photometric Scanning of Centrifuged Density Gradient Columns," *Anal. Biochem.*, 5:271, 1963.

6. Tombs, M. P., F. Souter, and N. F. Maclagan, "The Spectrophotometric Determination of Protein at 210 mμ," *Biochem. J.*, 73:167, 1959.

7. Fernandez Diez, M. J., D. T. Osuga, and R. E. Feeney, "The Sulfhydryls of Avian Ovalbumins, Bovine β-Lactoglobulin, and Bovine Serum Albumin," *Arch. Biochem. Biophys.*, 107:499, 1964.

8. Litwack, G., M. L. Sears, and T. I. Diamondstone, "Intracellular Distribution of Tyrosine-α-Ketogluterate Transaminase and 4-C[14] Hydrocortisone Activities During Induction," *J. Biol. Chem.*, 238:302, 1963.

9. Boyer, P. D., "Spectrophotometric Study of the Reaction of Protein Sulfhydryl Groups with Organic Mercurials," *J. Am. Chem. Soc.*, 76:4331, 1954.

10. Chervenka, C. H., "Ultraviolet Spectral Changes Related to the Enzyme Activity of Chymotrypsin," *Biochim. Biophys. Acta*, 31:85, 1959.

11. Eisen, H. N., and G. W. Siskind, "Variations in Affinities of Antibodies During the Immune Response," *Biochemistry*, 3:996, 1964.

12. Fletcher, C. M., A. G. Lowther, and W. S. Reith, "Studies on Determination of the Sequence of Amino Acids in Peptides and Proteins," *Biochem. J.*, 56:106, 1954.

13. Ando, T., and H. Fujioka, "Acetylation of the Amino Groups of Carboxypeptidase A," *J. Biochem.*, 52:363, 1962.

14. Sokolovsky, M., et al., "Nonenzymatic Cleavages of Peptide Chains at the Cysteine and Serine Residues Through Their Conversion to Dehydroalanine (DHAL). II. The Specific Chemical Cleavage of Cysteinyl Peptides," *J. Am. Chem. Soc.*, 86:1212, 1964.

15. Morell, S. A., et al., "Thiols of the Erythrocyte," *J. Biol. Chem.*, 239:2696, 1964.

16. Michaelides, M. C., R. Sherman, and E. Helmreich, "The Interaction of Muscle Phosphorylase with Soluble Antibody Fragments," *J. Biol. Chem.*, 239:4171, 1964.

17. McDuffie, F. C., and E. A. Kabat, "A Comparative Study of Methods Used for Analysis of Specific Precipitates in Quantitative Immunochemistry," *J. Immunol.*, 77:193, 1956.

18. Crumpton, M. J., and J. M. Wilkinson, "Amino Acid Compositions of Human and Rabbit γ-Globulins, and of the Fragments Produced by Reduction," *Biochem. J.*, 88:228, 1963.

19. Porath, J., and N. Ui, "Chemical Studies on Immunoglobulins," *Biochim. Biophys. Acta*, 90:324, 1964.

20. Gould, H. J., T. J. Gill, and P. Doty, "The Conformation and the Hydrogen Ion Equilibrium of Normal Rabbit γ-Globulin," *J. Biol. Chem.*, 239:2842, 1964.

21. Koeppe, O. J., P. D. Boyer, and M. P. Stulberg, "On the Occurrence Equilibria, and Site of Acylenzyme Formation of Glyceraldehyde-3-Phosphate Dehydrogenase," *J. Biol. Chem.*, 219:569, 1956.

22. Goldfarb, A. R., and L. J. Saidel, "The Ultraviolet Absorption Spectra of Proteins," *J. Biol. Chem.*, 193:397, 1951.

23. Kawahara, F. S., S. F. Wang, and P. Talalay, "The Preparation and Properties of Crystalline Δ^5-3-Ketosteroid Isomerase," *J. Biol. Chem.*, 237:1500, 1962.

24. Crumpton, M. J., and J. M. Wilkinson, "The Immunological Activity of Some of the Chymotryptic Peptides of Sperm-Whale Myoglobin," *Biochem. J.*, 94:545, 1965.

25. Small, P. A., W. F. Harrington and W. W. Kielley, "The Electrophoretic Homogenity of the Myosin Subunits," *Biochim. Biophys. Acta*, 49:462, 1961.

26. Bailey, K., et al., "Characterization of a Tryptic Fragment Isolated from the Insoluble Tropomyosin of *Pinna Nobilis*," *Biochim. Biophys. Acta*, 90:503, 1964.

27. Waddell, W. J., "A Simple Ultraviolet Spectrophotometric Method for the Determination of Protein," *J. Lab. Clin. Med.*, 48:311, 1956.

28. Bigelow, C. C., "Difference Spectra of Ribonuclease and Two Ribonuclease Derivatives," *Compt. Rend. Trav. Lab. Carlsberg*, 31:305, 1960.

29. Goldthwait, D. A., and J. L. Starr, "Chromatographic Characterization of Amino Acid Transfer and Microsomal Ribonucleic Acids Isolated from Yeast," *J. Biol. Chem.*, 235:2025, 1960.

30. Schmidt, G., in Colowick, S., and N. Kaplan (eds.), *Methods in Enzymology*, 3:689, 1957.

31. Takagi, T., and T. Isemura, "Necessity of Calcium for the Renaturation of Reduced Taka-Amylase A," *J. Biochem.*, 57:89, 1965.

32. Robbins, J., "Thyroglobulin Fractionation on Diethylaminoethyl Cellulose Columns," *J. Biol. Chem.*, 283:182, 1963.

33. Tonomura, Y., J. Yoshimura, and T. Ohnishi, "On the Active Site of Myosin A-Adenosine Triphosphatase," *Biochim. Biophys. Acta*, 70:698, 1963.

34. Green, N. M., "Competition Among Trypsin Inhibitors," *J. Biol. Chem.*, 205:535, 1953.

The primary reagent for immunological investigation is the specific antiserum. The antiserum represents the response of a suitable host to an antigenic stimulation, and is useful only if it has a usable high titre and a high degree of specificity.

Investigators in immunological methodology have often assumed that an antibody is readily obtained by the introduction of an antigen into a convenient animal. Actually, an antibody is not necessarily produced in this way. Factors in the antibody response include the chemical nature of the antigen (lipid, protein or polysaccharide), the route of injection, the dose of antigen used, the use of adjuvants, the species of recipient animal. The amount of antibody obtained, the breadth of specificity and the physical-chemical characteristic of the antibody will vary, depending on the time of bleeding of the animal following antigenic stimulation.

Since it is the purpose of this section to enumerate the methods and results obtained by attempts to produce antibodies in the rabbit for particular antigens for particular purposes, we will deal with classes of antigens and give several examples in each class.

There have been two major developments in immunological methods for biochemical and biological investigation. The first was the development of adjuvants (the Freund adjuvant is most commonly used), capable of greatly enhancing the immune response, often with the use of few injections and smaller quantities of antigens. The second important influence was the development of gel diffusion techniques for the demonstration of antigen-antibody reactions. Refinement of the gel diffusion techniques by Oudin and Ouchterlony was followed by the introduction of immunoelectrophoresis. Before the advent of the gel diffusion techniques, techniques which are not highly quantitative, the common procedures for estimating amounts of antibody were titration, quantitative precipitation, or the complement fixation test. The level of antibody obtained was reported in the form of titre or as antibody nitrogen. In some cases when enzymes were used as antigens, the specific antibody could be measured in terms of inhibition of the enzyme activity.

Antigen	Preparation	Test Method	Protocol	Result	Reference
1. Egg Albumin	alum precipitated	H.A.	1. 4 consecutive days each week I.V. week 1—0.5 mg/injection 2—1.0 mg/injection 3—1.5 mg/injection 4—2.0 mg/injection 8—2 mg—1 injection I.V. bleed 2–3 days after 8 week booster		1
2. Egg Albumin	Freund's adjuvant	quant. ppt.	2. injection 10–20 mg/animal subcutaneous bleed 30 days after injection	450 mg AbN/ml	2
3. Bovine gamma globulin	Freund's adjuvant	quant. ppt.	3. injection 10–20 mg/animal subcutaneous bleed 30 days after injection	410 mg AbN/ml	2
4. β-Lactoglobulin	Freund's adjuvant	quant. ppt.	4. injection 10–20 mg/animal subcutaneous bleed 30 days after injection	154 mg AbN/ml	2
5. Bovine plasma albumin	Freund's adjuvant	quant. ppt.	5. injection 10–20 mg/animal subcutaneous bleed 30 days after injection	910 mg AbN/ml	2
6. Human hemoglobin	Freund's—1.5 ml plus 1% hemoglobin—1 ml	ring ppt.	6. 2.5 ml Adj-Ag suspension/inj. subcutaneous in back region 1 time/week for 4–6 weeks; bleed periodically	1/10,000 with HbA	3

Abbreviations used in this table are found on page 587.

7. Calf cerebrospinal fluid	Freund's 1 ml antigen (25 mg prot/ml) Freund's: Ag = 1:1	gel. dif.	7. injection 0.3 ml/site in 6 sites in hind legs 1 x/month for total of 50 mg Ag (2 months)	not quantitative	4
8. Hela cells	4 day old monolayer culture 3 x 10^6 cells/ml ultrasound disrupt standardized at 30–40 mg prot N/ml	H.A.	8. 2 x 10^6 cells/injection I.V. 4 injections of 2 ml at 4 day intervals 1 week later 5 x 10^6 cells in Freund's Adjuvant subcutaneous and intra-muscular at many sites bleed 10 days after last injection	1/8, 192	5
9. Forssmann antigen	Boiled sheep erythrocyte stroma (1.35 mg N/ml)	Lysis	9. injection I.V. day 1, 0.22 ml 3, 0.4 ml 5, 1 ml 6, 1.25 ml 7, 2.5 ml 8, 2 ml 10, 2 ml 12, 2 ml 15, bleed	80,–100,000 AbH_{50} /ml	6
10. Human stratum corneum	ground callous shavings 30 mg in 4% Na alginate	H.A. gel. dif.	10. subcutaneous 1x/week for 6 weeks bleed 8 weeks	1×10^{-8}	7
11. Collagen: tail tendon		CF	11. 4 ml 0.1% collagen IP a. day 1, 2, 3, 4 of each week, 8–12 weeks b. rest 4 weeks c. boost 2–4 weeks d. repeat b & c for 3–6 months	max. 1/1024	8

Abbreviations used in this table are found on page 587.

Antigen	Preparation	Test Method	Protocol	Result	Reference
12. Human tumor tissue	Homogenized tumor 100 mg sediment/injection	gel. dif.	12. inject 3x/week—4 weeks bleed 1 week after last injection	not quantitative	9
13. Bovine spinal cord	4 g fresh bovine spinal cord homogenized in 4 ml saline Adj.—Freund's	Seek evidence of DDE ataxia, etc.	13. 250 mg/injection series .1 ml/foot pad, 4 foot pads one injection	not measured	10
14. Dentin	Dentin attached to tanned erythrocyte or dentin and Freund's Adj.—Freund's complete	H.A. gel. dif. fl.	14. total 8 ml prepared of RBC-Dentin in Adjuvant 1.5, 1.5, 2.0, 2.0 ml at 3 day intervals or 90–300 mg Dentin in 1 ml saline and 1 ml Adj. 4 weekly doses bleed weekly over 70 day period	max. by 7th week	11
15. Myelin	70 mg fresh rabbit spinal cord homogenized and emulsified with complete Freund's; total vol. 0.4 ml	agg. of myelin suspension	15. 1) 70 mgs in 0.4 ml with adj.: 1 inj. 2) 54 mg in Adj.; vol. 0.4 ml; 55 day rest then 35 mg. 3) 300 mg in Adj.; vol. 0.6 ml; 1 inj. 4) 300 mg spinal cord, no adjuvant; 1 inj. Intradermal in foot pads, each dose divided into 4 parts Bleed when showing clinical signs of demyelination	no quant. data demyelination (day of onset varied from 12–20 days) most effective was 300 mg with adj. (12–13 days) gravest clinical state	12

Abbreviations used in this table are found on page 587.

16. Ribonucleoprotein	ribonucleoprotein-rich fraction from chicken organs 11–15 mg/ml protein.	CF	16. 3 ml nucleoprotein, sub-cutaneous day 1, 2, 3, 13, 14, 15 bleed 10 days after last injection	0–½ with RNA 1/64–1/280 RNprotein DNprotein 1/16–1/128 DNA—⅛–1/32	13
17. Guinea pig leucocytes	G.p. leucocyte from peritoneum Freund's Adjuvant	Respiration, amino acid uptake, etc. physiology of leucocyte	17. 10^8 cells in 0.5 ml 0.85% saline + 0.5 ml adj. subcutaneous first injection with adj. subsequent 3 weekly injections 1 ml of 10^8 cells in saline Bleed one week after 4th injection	not quantitative	14
18. Mouse leucocytes and platelets	Mouse platelets and leucocytes Adj.—none	Aggl Lysis	18. Supernatant from 3 ml fibrinogen treated mouse blood suspended in 1 ml saline I.V. four groups of 3 daily injections bleed 6 days after last injection of group	anti RBC aggl. 1/2048 Lysis—1/512 RBC absorbed Ab aggl. leucocytes 1/128 and platelet 1/256	15
19. Rat tumor	Homogenates—10% in saline 10 ml homogenates: 9.7 ml Freund's Adj.	localization of I^{131} tagged Ag.	19. I M–2 ml/injection once each week for 4 weeks —divided between 2 thighs bleed 10 and 14 days after last injection	not quantitative	16
20. Ehrlich's Ascites tumor	Homogenate; 200 mg wet weight/ml	In vivo: inject Ab into mice—challenge with tumor or Ab as direct cause of death to mice 0.4 ml for 3 consecutive days measure % dead mice	20. 6 injections every other day IP total of 370–520 mg bleed 14 days after last injection		17

Abbreviations used in this table are found on page 587.

572

Antigen	Preparation	Test Method	Protocol	Result	Reference
21. Microsomes (guinea pig)	Microsomes and Ribosomes by differential centrifugation Ribosomes by deoxycholate treatment then lyophilized Freund's Adj.	gel. dif. ppt. H.A. anti Forssmann	21. 2 mg/ml saline: Freund's = 1:1 1 ml injection subcutaneous first series—1 time/week for 3 weeks 2nd series started 1 week after 1st series first series—bleed 1 week after last of 3 injections 2nd series—bleed 1 week after last of 3 injections	no quant. data	18
22. Plant incompatibility proteins	saline extracts of pollen from 5 genotypes 5% dry weight = 0.75% protein Adj.—alum (2 mg/ml of sol.) (for subcutaneous inj. only)	gel. dif.	22. Ranged from 0.5 to 2 ml/inj. I.V.—no alum 8 I.V. injections at weekly intervals 2 subcutaneous Bleed after 5th inj. Bleed 2 weeks after last inj.	8 lines found on immunoelectrophoresis	19
23. Chick embryo brain	homogenized brain—extracted in 0.9% saline supernatant from 20,000 g for 20 min. Adj.—Freund's complete	gel. dif.	23. 1 ml of Ag—Freund's (Ag concentration unknown) subcutaneous 4 sites day 1 day 30 day 37 bleed 10 days after last inj.	not quant.	20

Abbreviations used in this table are found on page 587.

	Preparation	Method	Immunization schedule	Results	Ref.
24. Slime mold spores *Dictyostelium mucoroides*	spore suspension Adj.—none	aggl. of spores ppt. Fl.	24. 1) 5 IV total 0.5 mg N 2) 1 IP total 1.2 mg N 4 IV 3) 1 IP total 2.2 mg N 2 IV within a series injection given on alternate days 13 injections given over 3 months bleed 7–8 days after last series		21
25. Plant: solanum (potato)	protein extracts, approx. 1 % Freund's Adj.	gel. dif. IE	25. 1 part plant protein: 3 parts adj. 1 ml into each thigh 1 time/week for 3 weeks I.V. of extract each day 1 ml, 1 ml, 2 ml, 2 ml 4 months later— day 1—1 ml I.V. " 3—1 ml " 5—2 ml " 7—2 ml " 9—5 ml " 11—5 ml " 16—bleed	no quant. data	22
26. Rat tissues	saline perfused, homogenized, lyophilized Adj.—none	gel. dif. precipitation *in vivo* effect	26. 200 mg resuspended (no stated vol.) IP 2 times/week for 3 months bleed: periodic	rabbit anti-rat kidney inj. into pregnant rats IV lead to malformation in 100% of fetuses	23
27. Rat mitochondria	liver and kidney fraction prepared Adj.—Freund's 2g mitochondria in 15 ml Adj.	CF: mitochondria Ag (0.05–0.20 mg protein/ml) aggl. of mitochondria; ppt.	27. 2 ml/injection subcutaneous week 1; adj. Ag week 2; adj. Ag week 4; adj. Ag week 6; booster—mitochondria in sucrose	anti-whole rat mitochondria 1/256–1/1,024	24

Antigen	Preparation	Test Method	Protocol	Result	Reference
28. Rat heart	hearts minced; rinsed in cold saline homogenized in 4 vol. saline for 3 days at 4° C. Adj.—Freund's	gel. dif.	28. 0.5 ml subcutaneous 0.5 ml IP	—	25
29. Rat tissues kidney, serum, RBC, adult liver, placenta, muscle, fetal skin, fetal liver, glomeruli	saline perfused organ grind in blender lyophilize—store at −20° C. Adj.—Freund's complete	gel. dif. ppt. in vivo effects	29. I M weekly for three weeks followed by monthly injections Bleed every other week		26
30. Amphibian embryos	homogenized, extracted water soluble nucleo-proteins mucoproteins lipoproteins	ppt.	30. IV 100 embryos injected days 1, 3, 5—100 embryos 15, 17, 19—200 ", 29, 31, 33—300 " Titers high by about 7th week	no quant. data given	27
31. Paramecium proteins	ammon. sulfate ppt. or homogenates in 1 ml saline Adj.—Freund's	gel. dif.	31. 2 x 10⁶ animals as anti-gen source—2.5 ml + 2.5 ml Freund's subcutaneous 3 injections 5 days apart bleed one week after last injection	not quant.	28
32. Sponge	stock 1.3 mg N/ml sponge suspension	precipitation reaggregation	32. 0.1 ml stock solution/ injection subcutaneous 9 injections over period of 3 weeks bleed 8 days after last injection	1/10,000 titer 0.5 ml extract 0.5 ml Ab	29

Abbreviations used in this table are found on page 587.

Animal	Antigen preparation	Method	Procedure	Results	Ref.
33. insects—hymenoptera	whole insect 2.5 g ground 20 ml saline— Adj.—Freund's	gel. dif. plates Agarose 1.2%	33. 1 ml of extract mixed with 3 ml adj. 0.6 ml/injection subcutaneous and I M 0.6 ml subcutaneous each side 2 weeks later 0.6 ml IM in each hind leg bleed 2 weeks after last injection bleed 4 weeks after last injection	no quant. data	30
34. mosquitoes; sand flies	extracts— 200 mg/2 ml Adj.—Freund's 1:1 antigen extract	agar gel	34. 0.1 ml of extract with 0.1 ml Freund's = 10 mg. total 120 mg. Route: thigh muscle injections 3 times week for 4 weeks bleed 10 days after last injection bleed 20 days after last injection		31
35. insect: may fly fly roach cricket silk worm	insect dried, ground, ether soluble parts discarded 1 g powder extracted overnight in 10 ml saline centrifuge—frozen spt considered as 1/10 Adj.—Freund's	Hemagglutination of tanned cells; hemagglutination inhibition gel. dif.	35. 4 ml of 1/10 in Freund's IM bleed 4 weeks after injection (may require 2nd course)	hem. titres may fly 1600 (3 lines) fly 10,240 (2 lines) cockroach 10,240 (6 lines) cricket 10,240 (4 lines) silk worm 25,600 (3 lines)	32

Abbreviations used in this table are found on page 587.

Antigen	Preparation	Test Method	Protocol	Result	Reference
36. insect protein (cuticle)	house fly larva extracted	ppt. (0.05 ml Ag dilution) Oudin (0.05 ml undil. Ab)	36. day 1 0.5 ml 3 1 ml 5 1.5 ml subcutaneous second and third series given bleed 7–10 days after last dose in each series —then start next series	10/39 animals produced Ab of at least 1/100 titre rest produced little or no Ab	33
37. insect blood proteins	saline extracts of cecropia homogenize in Waring blender centrifuge at 10,000 g dialyzed at 1.5° C. Adj.—none	Oudin tests	37. 2 ml of extract/inj. 1 presensitizing IV 3 weeks later—4 subcutaneous every other day 6–7 days after last injection, bleed	—	34

38. Schistosoma Mansoni cercariae	lyophilized—various prep. Adj.—Freund's	immuno-electrophoresis gel. dif.	38. 1 mg Ag/ml Freund's 0.125 ml emulsion (also 0.1 ml of same Ag in saline)
			Route: foot pad, ID, IV
			Injection day 1–0.125 in each of 4 foot pads
			   ,, 21–0.1 ml ID
			   ,, 28–0.1 ml IV
			   ,, 29–0.1 ml IV
			   ,, 30–0.1 ml IV
			bleed day 37
				no quant. data	35

39. Ascaris	whole worm—various preparations dried saline extract—Adj.—Freund's 1:1	gel. dif.	39. 20–32 mg dry antigen	no quant. data	36

Abbreviations used in this table are found on page 587.

Organism	Preparation	Method	Immunization	Result	Ref.
40. Sea urchin	extracts; homogenate of eggs and plutei lyophilized Adj.—none	Oudin; immuno electrophoresis	40. dose 2 ml injection 1) I.V. 2) rest for 3 weeks then 2 inj. subcutaneous every other day bleed 1 week after last inj. pool of 5 rabbits	no quant. data	37
41. Triturus	embryos homogenized 0.03 ml/embryo (saline extracted) centrifuged 4000 rpm 20 minutes	ouchlerlony	41. 50 mg/injection total 900 mg. lyophilizate given injection—every day for 2 weeks IP 1 week rest then 3–4 IP inj. 18 injections bleed 10 days after last inj.	—	38
42. Eye lens—Newt	lens ground with glass homogenizer conc. = 100 mg wet wt/ml saline 2500 rpm supernatant used Adj.—none	effect on lens regeneration	42. 1 ml IV injection—every other day 7 inj.	—	39
43. Newt eye lens	60 lenses were homogenized in 2 ml 0.15 M NaCl Adj.—Freund's	ppt. 1/4000 gel. dif., fluorescent AB immunoelectrophoresis	43. 1) 60 lenses subcutaneous 1 injection 2) 50 lenses, IP 2 weeks apart total 45 mg lens protein bleed 9 days after last inj.	—	40

Abbreviations used in this table are found on page 587.

Antigen	Preparation	Test Method	Protocol	Result	Reference
44. Rabbit eye lens	homogenized to 100 mg wet wt/ml in NaCl stored at −25° C. Adj.—Freund's	H.A.	1) 10 ml lens (100 mg wet wt/ml) route—1 ml total in 6 sites subcutaneous Schedule of Injections: day 1 — 50 mg; 9 — 50; 58 — 50; 88 — 50; 130 — 50; 220 — 50; 350 — 50. Schedule of bleeding: day 22, 32, 43, 68, 81, 96, 123, 138, 168, 227, 364	1/12,000–1/409,000 with adjuvant	41
45. Rabbit lens	33 mg N/ml 1:10 lens solution and equal vol. Adj. Adj.—Freund's		injection: 1) adj. subcutaneous 2) adj. IP 3) I.V. 3–6 injections	poor	42
46. Eye lens of vertebrates	ground, homogenized in saline centrifuge 2500 rpm for 15 minutes 1 mg N/ml of Ag	precipitation Ouchterlony react at 48 hrs. 37° C.	1 to 3 ml dose Route—I.V. every other day, total dose 33–40 mg	no titration used	43

Abbreviations used in this tables are found on page 587.

Antigen	Preparation	Test	Immunization	Results	Ref.
47. Adult human lens protein	lens homogenized in 0.9% NaCl centrifuge 8000—15,000 rpm at 4° C. 20 mg protein/ml 1 extract: 2 Freund's	gel. diffusion; immunoelectrophoresis	2 ml of emulsion/injection approx. 15 mg protein/injection total 90 mg protein subcutaneous in multiple sites weekly intervals for 6 weeks 2 weeks after last injection, bleed	7 precipitation lines obtained	44
48. Human cornea	cut cornea in fine slices ground in glass homogenizer; 7 ml saline Adj.—Freund's	Comp. fixation; H.A. gel. dif. ppt. H.A.I.	0.5 ml + 0.5 ml Freund's 2 per week for 8 weeks 5 days after last injection, bleed	CF 1/640 ppt. 1/409,000	45
49. Chicken lens and Iris	adult lens homogenized in saline centrifuge 3000 rpm for 20 min. extract standardized to 10 mg protein/ml by Biuret for test Adj.—Freund's	Precipitation	25 mg protein/ml 1 ml of mixture/site 5 sites 3:2 with Freund's Iris 10 mg/ml 4:1 with Freund's subcutaneous day 1, 11, 21 also weekly intervals 4–10 weeks bleed day 31, also 14 days after last booster	1/8000–1/16,000 anti-lens 1/600–1/1,000 anti-iris	46

Abbreviations used in this table are found on page 587.

Antigen	Preparation	Test Method	Protocol	Result	Reference
50. Chicken embryo skin	(1) 7 day epidermis; (2) feather homogenate Adj.—Freund's	CF	50. Epidermis 1 mg/injection 1 part Ag/1 pt. Freund's (1) 5 part Ag/1 pt. Freund's (2) inj. 3 times per week for 3 weeks 5 inj. foot pad 4 I.V. bleed 5, 15, 21 days after series booster doses needed—1 month later, then bleed 10 days later	anti-epidermis 1/640 feathers 1/640	47
51. Tobacco Mosaic Virus	Virus Adj.—none	gel. dif.	51. 10 mg; I.V. injections 6 times at weekly intervals bleed 10 days after last injection	not quant.	48
52. Vi Antigen	Acetone killed and dried bacteria Adj.—none	gel. dif.	52. I.V. 6 injections at 3-day intervals bleed 5 days after last inj.	—	49
53. Tetanus Toxoid	Toxoid—5 Lf.	protection	53. IM 1 inj.; 4 weeks rest; 1 injection bleed 4 weeks	0.06 units/ml (mean value)	50

Abbreviations used in this table are found on page 587.

Antigen	Material / Adjuvant	Method	Schedule / Dose	Results	
54. Properdin human		gel. dif.	54. 1000 units properdin/inj. in 2–5 ml solution I.V. 1st course 9–10 injections over 10–14 day period booster—6 weeks later bleed at daily intervals	—	51
55. Milk (Goats; cows) auto-immunization	skimmed rabbit milk Adj.—Freund's complete 1:1	CF	55. 2 ml; IM at 2 sites day 1; 3 weeks later; 8 weeks later bleeding samples weekly	no anti-rabbit produced anti-cow Ab appeared at 1 week anti-goat Ab appeared at 1 week goat and cow have 1 line in common on gel. dif.	52
56. phytohemagglutinins	crude extract of *phaseolus vulgaris* Adj.—Freund's complete	gel. dif. I.E.	56. 50 mg dry weight; IM—buttock pads days 1, 16, 31, 46 bleed day 56	8 lines found	53
57. Immunoconglutinin	Kaolin coated with fresh horse serum or with heated horse serum	immunoconglutinin H.A. CF	57. 1 ml Kaolin coated subcutaneous 1 ml/inj., IP 1 ml/injection., IM 1 ml or IV 1 ml days 1, 2, 3, bleed at 3–4 day intervals for 2 weeks after last inj.	H.A. titres 1/20,480	54
58. amylase—hog or human saliva	20–30 mg purified amylase Adj.—incomplete Freund's	E.I.	58. 20–30 mg ID in adj. 10–14 days later 10 mg in water repeat 10–14 day interval; maximum activity after 3–4 injections	—	55

Abbreviations used in this table are found on page 587.

Antigen	Preparation	Test Method	Protocol	Result	Reference
59. Urease	Jackbean urease	H.A.	59. from 0.5 unit/kg rabbits to 8 units/kg rabbit in final week (9 weeks) two times/week for 2 months	1/10–1/20,000	56
60. β-galactosidase	E. coli β-galactosidase by ammonium sulfate fractionation	—	60. 1000 lactase unit total	325 mg Ab N/ml	57
61. Bovine cream xanthine oxidase	purified Adj.—Freund's complete	Ouchterlony I.E. E.I.	61. total 3.3 mg enzyme, intradermal weekly for 4 weeks bleed 5th week	quant. test	58
62. RNAase	crystalline RNAase from Worthington further purified Adj.—Freund's (Difco) 1:1	I.E.	62. 10 mgs in phosphate buffer pH 7.6 2 ml of emulsion containing 5 mg RNAase subcutaneous or IM 1 inj.; 3 weeks later 2nd inj. same dose; or 3–4 weeks later— 3rd inj. if titre low; or 2 weeks later 3rd inj. if titre high; 3–4 weeks after 2nd dose bleed 1 time/month	—	59
63. Lactic dehydrogenase beef heart or skeletal muscle	Adj.—Freund's complete	—	63. 2.0 mg/injection series subcutaneous in hind foot pads day 1—primary day 22—booster with incomplete Freund's bleed 1 week after booster (day 29)	—	60

Abbreviations used in this table are found on page 587.

#	Antigen	Preparation / Adjuvant	Method	Test	Schedule / Dose	Page
64.	Human G-6-P-dehydrogenase (erythrocyte)	purified preparation 1×10^{-4} TPN (very necessary) Adj.–Freund's complete	E.I.	—	Total 10 mg enzyme/animal foot pads 2 series of injections—1 week apart into each of 3 foot pads	61
65.	Glucose 6-Phosphate dehydrogenase (yeast)	enzyme had 12 international units/mg Adj.–alumina	E.I.	—	12.8 mg enzyme total; IV or subcutaneous on alternate days for 2 weeks booster 2 mg IV 20 days after first series series repeated twice 10 days after last injection of series, bleed second bleeding 4 days after booster	62
66.	Alkaline Phosphatases (human)	partially purified from various organs Adj.–Freund's complete	reaction with isozyme	qualitative tests	0.5–1 mg/injection = 0.1–1 enzyme pNPP units subcutaneous day 1, 28, 35 bleed 38–45 days	63
67.	Human gonadotropic hormone	1 mg/ml HGH in saline Adj.–Freund's 1:1	disc electrophoresis gel. dif.	—	0.4 ml of mixture total dose 1 mg intradermal into foot pads; IP weekly intervals for 3 weeks 10 days later final IP inj. 0.8 ml bleed day 35	64
68.	Glucogon and insulin	Adj.–Freund's	Chromatographic method	non-precipitating non-flocculating	1 mg/ml Ag.; subscapula after the first; every 4 weeks for total of 3 injections bleed 12 weeks after 1st inj. (day 84)	65

Abbreviations used in this table are found on page 587.

Antigen	Preparation	Test Method	Protocol	Result	Reference
69. Bovine parathyroid hormone	extracts from parathyroid Adj.–Freund's complete	ppt. gel. dif.	69. 0.25 mg foot pad then bi-weekly IM 0.1 mg for 2 months then 0.2 mg monthly for a total dose of 1.5 mg/rabbit in 6 months or 25 mg in foot pad then in 1 month 10 mg, then 2–5 mg monthly–total 51 mg Bleed starting 1 month after initial injection (Ab 9–120 days following initial injection)	—	66
70. Human growth hormone	2 mg hormone Adj.–Freund's complete (Difco)	H.A. gel. dif. ppt.	70. 1) 2 mg subcutaneous in Adj./inj. week 1 and 3, 2 mg IP, week 5–total 10 mg 2) 1 mg subcutaneous in 1% potassium alum/inj. week 1 and 3 1 mg IP, week 5	H.A. titre 1/6,400–1/51,200	67

Abbreviations used in this table are found on page 587.

71. Insulin	beef insulin 22 or 27 units/mg pork insulin 22 units/mg Adj.—Freund's complete	BDB insulin—sheep cell hemolysis inhibition by insulin	71. approx. 7.5 mg alum precipitated insulin 1.5 ml + 10 ml Freund's 0.2 ml in each toe pad; 0.5 ml alum pt. I.V. 3–4 weeks later; 0.5 ml alum pt. I.V. 48–72 hours later blood sampled 7–19 days after booster #3	measured by extinction inhibition by 0.50 µg	68
72. ACTH (porcine)	Pork ACTH (Organum G) 0.025 mg emulsified in 0.25 mg adj. Adj.—Freund's complete	Bioassay radioimmunoassay	72. Group I day 1 subcut. Ag in adj. 22 " 43 " 64 " 0.25 mg in saline day 76 bleed Group II day 1 in 0.25 mg subcut. every 3–4 weeks—in adj. booster 8 days before bleeding repeat in Freund's till 19 months $\overline{w}$ 4–6 mg ribonuclease	—	69
73. Bovine Ribonuclease	crystalline from Armour and Sigma 2.5 ml sol. contained 30 mg ribonuclease Adj.—Freund's complete	E.I.	73. 6 subcut. in adj. over 3 months I.V. at 4–6 week interval bleed during period of adj. inj. bleed 4–5 days after each I.V. inj.	inhibitory capacity of Ab during the course of immunization varies—there is progression towards complete inhibitory Ab.	70

Abbreviations used in this table are found on page 587.

Antigen	Preparation	Test Method	Protocol	Result	Reference
74. Sheep erythrocytes	boiled sheep red cell stroma 1 mgN/ml	hemolysin titre 8.15×10^{-6} agglutination titre 44×10^{-3}	74. 1.0 ml I.V. 3 times/week for 4 weeks bleed 7 days after last injection	—	71
75. Cow's milk	whole milk 1:1 with Adj.—Freund's complete	gel. dif.	75. 1 ml of mixture subcutaneously 3 times/week for 4 weeks bleed 1 week later 1 ml booster subcutaneously bleed out 1 week later	—	72
76. Heart—rat —dog	minced, rinsed homogenized with 2 x vol. in cold phosphate pH 7.2 centrifuge 3000 rpm 10 minutes Adj.—Freund's complete	gel. dif. CF Latex aggl. P.C.A. H.A. H.A.I.	76. dose—0.5 ml emulsion (10 mg protein) 1) ID into foot pad 2) 3 to 4 weeks later 0.5 ml no adj.—subcut. or IM 3) 3 to 4 weeks later 0.5 ml no adj.—subcut. or IM 4) 1 week later—bleed	dog lines / rat lines: 1/320 0.20 CF; 1/160 20 latex; + — PCA; 1280 5120 HA	73
77. Leucocytes Porcine Bovine rabbit	Adj.—Freund's	CF HA gel. dif.	77. 2 mg/ml or 10 mg/ml or 20% suspension, ID 5 injections at weekly intervals bleed 1 week after 3rd inj. bleed 1 week after 5th inj.	H.A. = 1/800	74

Abbreviations used in this table are found on page 587.

A relatively recent technique which has demonstrated great versatility is the passive hemagglutination procedure: an antigen may be attached to a treated red cell in such a way that, as a result of the reaction between the antibody and the attached antigen, agglutination occurs. This hemagglutination reaction has a high degree of sensitivity.

It is evident that the results of immunization may be expressed in many ways. In many cases, no quantitative data are reported. In the present examples from relatively recent papers, there is a frequent use of adjuvants for immunization and of gel diffusion techniques for the estimation of a number of specific antibodies.

More general information on immunization can be obtained in the chapter by M. Cohn in *Methods in Medical Research*, Vol. V, and in Kabat, *Experimental Immunochemistry*, 2nd edition.

Abbreviations:

Ouch.	Ouchterlony
Oud.	Oudin
Gel. dif.	Gel diffusion
I. E.	Immunoelectrophoresis
C. F.	Complement fixation
H. A.	Hemagglutination
H. A. I.	Hemagglutination Inhibition
ppt.	Precipitation
aggl.	Agglutination
E. I.	Enzyme inhibition
Fl	Fluorescence
Route:	
IV	Intervenous
IM	Intramuscular
ID	Intradermal

BIBLIOGRAPHY

References:

1. Vaughan, J. H., et al., *J. Immunol.*, 84:258, 1960.
2. Pruzansky, J. J., et al., *J. Immunol.*, 85:588, 1960.
3. Chernoff, A. I., *Blood*, 8:399, 1953.
4. MacPherson, C. F. C., and M. Saffran, *J. Immunol.*, 95:629, 1965.
5. Garabedian, G. A., and J. T. Syverton, *Proc. Soc. Exp. Biol. Med.*, 105:632, 1960.
6. Spear, G. S., *Bull. Johns Hopkins Hospital*, 111:252, 1962.
7. Fisher, J. P., *J. Invest. Dermatology*, 44:43, 1965.
8. Rothbard, S., and Watson, R. F., *J. Exp. Med.*, 122:441, 1965.
9. Korngold, L., and R. Lipari, *Cancer Research*, 15:159, 1955.
10. Arnaki, M., and S. Weissbarth, *Proc. Soc. Exp. Biol. Med.*, 116:210, 1964.
11. Blechman, H., and M. Mori, *Ann. N.Y. Acad. Sci.*, 131(2):898, 1965.

12. Somers, J. E., *Neurology*, 14:232, 1964.
13. Jankovic, B. D., K. Isakovic, and J. Horvat, *Nature*, 190:1218, 1961.
14. Kritzman, J., and J. S. McCarthy, *J. Immunol.*, 92:299, 1964.
15. Morris, I. G., *J. Path. and Bact.*, 81:209, 1961.
16. Bale, W. F., I. L. Spar and R. L. Goodland, *J. Immunol.*, 80:482, 1958.
17. Levi, E., and A. M. Schechtman, *Cancer Res.*, 23:1566, 1963.
18. Whitbeck, E. G., and L. T. Rosenberg, *Immunology*, 7:363, 1964.
19. Mäkinen, Y. L. A., and D. Lewis, *Genetical Res.*, 3:352, 1962.
20. McCallion, D. J., and J. C. Trott, *J. Embryol. Exp. Morph.*, 12:511, 1964.
21. Takeuchi, I., *Developmental Biol.*, 8:1, 1963.
22. Gell, P. G. H., J. G. Hawkes, and S. T. C. Wright, *Proc. Roy. Soc. B.*, 151:364, 1960.
23. Brent, R. L., et al., *Proc. Soc. Exp. Biol. Med.* 106:523–526, 1961.
24. Davis, J. S., Jr. and A. J. Bollet. *J. Clin. Invest.* 41:2142. 1962.
25. Crawley, L. P., A. River, C. P. Hauser, *Nature.* 197:1307–1309. 1963.
26. Brent, R. L. *Am. J. Anat.*, 115:525. 1964.
27. Inoue, K., *Dev. Biol.*, 3:657–683. 1962.
28. Finger, I., C. Heller and J. P. Smith, *J. Mol. Biol.*, 6:182–189. 1963.
29. Spiegel, M., *Biol. Bull.*, 107:130–148. 1954.
30. O'Conner, R. and R. Erickson, *Annals of Allergy*, 23:151–157. 1965.
31. Fox, I., W. B. Knight, I. G. Bayona, *J. Allergy*, 34:196–202. 1963.
32. Pruzansky, J. A., R. Feinberg, G. Schick and S. M. Feinberg, *Proc. Soc. Exp. Biol. Med.*, 97:312–314, 1958.
33. Downe, A. E. R., *Canad. J. Zool.*, 40:957–967. 1962.
34. Telfer, W. H. and Williams, *J. Gen. Physiol.*, 36:389–413. 1953. See also *ibid.*, 37:539–558, 1954.
35. Kronman, B., *J. Immunol.*, 95:13. 1965.
36. Kagan, I. G., E. L. Jeska, and C. J. Gentzkow, *J. Immunol.*, 80:400, 1958.
37. Couffer-Kaltenbach, J., and P. Perlmann, *J. Biophys. Biochem. Cytol.*, 9:93, 1961.
38. Romanovsky, A., *Folia Biologia*, 8:276, 1962.
39. Ogawa, T., *Embryologia*, 8:146, 1964.
40. Takata, C., J. F. Albright and T. Yamada, *Developmental Biology*, 9:385, 1964.
41. Halbert, S. P., et al., *J. Exp. Med.*, 105:439, 1957.
42. Miller, W. J., *J. Exp. Zool.*, 137:463, 1958.
43. Ogawa, T., *Embryologia*, 7:201, 1962.
44. Leure du Pree, A., J. Little, and J. Langman, *Arch. Ophthalmol.*, 72:660, 1964.
45. Nelken, D., and E. Nelken, *Immunology*, 5:595, 1962.
46. Maisel, H., and C. Harmison, *J. Embryol. and Exp. Morph.*, 11:483, 1963.
47. Ben-Or, S., and E. Bell, *Develop. Biol.*, 11:184, 1965.
48. Kleczowski, A., *J. Gen. Microbiol.*, 16:405, 1957.
49. Whiteside, R. A., and E. E. Baker, *J. Immunol.*, 84:221, 1960.
50. Ipsen, J., *J. Immunol.*, 86:50, 1961.
51. Hinz, C. F., et al., *J. Immunol.*, 85:547, 1960.
52. Derbyshire, J. B., and Matthews, *J. Path. and Bact.*, 82:434, 1964.
53. Spitz, M., *Nature*, 202:902, 1964.
54. Ingram, D. G., *Canad. J. Microbiol.*, 8:307, 1962.

55. McGeachin, R. L., and J. M. Reynolds, *Ann. N.Y. Acad. Sci.*, 94:996, 1961.
56. Visek, W. J., M. E. Iwert, and W. Burrows, *Proc. Soc. Exp. Biol. Med.*, 109:54, 1962.
57. Cohn, M., and Torriani, *J. Immunol.*, 69:471, 1952.
58. Ultmann, J. E., and P. Fergelson, *Ann. N.Y. Acad. Sci.*, 103:724, 1963.
59. Siekevitz, P., *Ann. N.Y. Acad. Sci.*, 103:773, 1963.
60. Markert, C., and Appella, *Ann. N.Y. Acad. Sci.*, 103:915, 1963.
61. Marks, P. A., and E. A. Tsutsui, *Ann. N.Y. Acad. Sci.*, 103:902, 1963.
62. Bussard, A. E., *Ann. N.Y. Acad. Sci.*, 103:890, 1963.
63. Boyer, S. H., *Ann. N.Y. Acad. Sci.*, 103:938, 1963.
64. Fitschen, W., *Immunology*, 7:307, 1964.
65. Kaloglu, Y., et al., *Proc. Soc. Exp. Biol. Med.*, 112:518, 1963.
66. Williams, G. A., et al., *Proc. Soc. Exp. Biol. Med.*, 115:61, 1964.
67. Grumbach, M. M., S. L. Kaplan, and S. Solomon, *Nature*, 185:170, 1960.
68. Arquilla, E. R., and J. Finn, *J. Exp. Med.*, 118:55, 1963.
69. Imura, H., et al., *J. Clin. Endocrinol. Metabol.*, 25:1361, 1965.
70. Branster, M., and B. Cinader, *J. Immunol.*, 87:18, 1961.
71. Amiraian, K., and E. J. Leikhim, *J. Immunol.*, 87:301, 1961.
72. Grogan, F. T., and L. V. Crawford, *J. Immunol.*, 87:240, 1961.
73. Gery, I., and A. M. Davies, *J. Immunol.*, 87:351, 1961.
74. Colombani and Milgrom, F., *Vov Sanguinis*, 10:429, 1965.

SHIELDING AND ATTENUATION OF IONIZING RADIATION

I. INTRODUCTION

The intensity of radiation and thus the radiation dose at positions in the vicinity of any radiation source vary with the distance from the source and with attenuation due to intervening materials. The decrease in intensity with distance is due to divergence of the radiation emitted from the source. With regard to source distribution, the maximum variation with distance occurs with a point source of radiation for which the intensity varies inversely with the square of the distance from the source. The minimum variation occurs for infinite plane sources where there is no decrease with distance. When the distance from the source is fixed, as it is in most experimental situations, decreases in intensity and dosage can be achieved by interposing shielding material between the source and the position of interest. A brief description of the principles of radiation shielding for various types of radiation is given below, along with useful radiation shielding data.

II. NEUTRONS

Neutrons with energies above 10 keV are attenuated mainly through elastic collisions with nuclei and electrons in the shielding material. The average transfer of neutron energy (ΔE) to a particle is given by the following expression:

$$\Delta E = E \frac{2A}{(A + 1)^2}$$

where A is the mass of the particle in atomic mass units (amu) and E is the neutron energy. It should be noted that ΔE is a maximum when the mass of the particle equals the mass of the neutron (mass = 1 amu). Thus the hydrogen nucleus which consists of a single proton (mass = 1 amu) provides the greatest energy transfer per collision. Orbital electrons and nuclei having larger masses are less effective than the hydrogen nucleus.

Neutrons with energies less than 10 keV are best absorbed through their ability to transfer energy to a nucleus and to initiate nuclear reactions. In these cases, the products of the nuclear reactions may emit other types of radiation which present different shielding problems.

It should be noted that neutron sources usually have mixed energies and that the attenuation afforded by a given shield is generally least for the sources of highest energy. Therefore, the shielding required for the highest-energy neutrons will ordinarily provide adequate attenuation for the lower-energy neutrons. The reader with a neutron shielding problem is directed to the extensive coverage of such problems included in National Bureau of Standards Handbook 63, *Protection Against Neutron Radiation up to 30 Million Electron Volts.*

III. ALPHA PARTICLES

Alpha particles are attenuated with a high probability through inelastic collisions with orbital electrons resulting in the production of ionized or excited atoms. The range of the usual alpha particles available from radioactive isotopes is extremely short in most materials and amounts to only a few centimeters in air. As a result of this, shielding of these particles does not constitute a problem.

IV. ELECTRONS

Attenuation of electrons by shielding material occurs through elastic scattering of the electrons by nuclei and orbital electrons, by transfer of energy to orbital electrons, and by radiation of energy in the form of electromagnetic radiation. Elastic scattering, which changes only the direction of the electron, occurs mainly at low-electron energies and is generally effected by nuclei. The absorption of energy through transfer to orbital electrons is due to inelastic collision which results in the ejection of orbital electrons from the atom (ionization) or their transference from inner orbits to outer orbits (excitation). This type of electron attenuation is most important for low- and intermediate-energy electrons and for low atomic number shields. Higher-energy electrons are absorbed through radiative collision with nuclear fields. This process results in the production of a continuous energy spectrum of X rays (Bremsstrahlung) which is more difficult to attenuate than the electron beam which produced it. The probability of Bremsstrahlung production increases with energy of the electrons and with the square of the atomic number of the shielding material. The relative importance of radiative attenuation and attenuation by ionization (or excitation) is given by the following expression:

$$\frac{\text{Radiation}}{\text{Ionization}} = \frac{EZ}{820}$$

E is the electron energy in meV and Z is the atomic number of the absorber. Thus if one wishes to attenuate electron radiation appreciably, he should use shielding material of a low atomic number in order to avoid production of Bremsstrahlung.

Although electrons traverse involved paths in shielding material, a maximum range for a given electron energy or spectrum can be determined. Since this range, in most materials, is relatively small, shielding of electrons is ordinarily achieved by using a shield with a thickness equal to the maximum range. The maximum range of electrons in various materials is shown below.

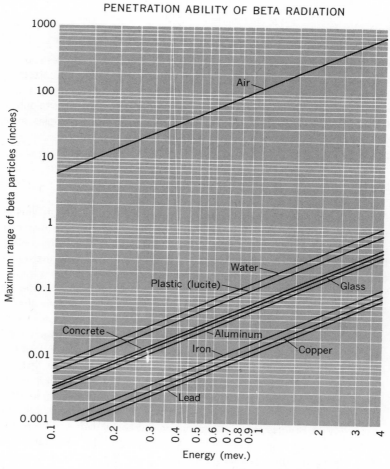

Figure 1. Shielding and Attenuation of Ionizing Radiation.

V. X RAYS AND GAMMA RAYS

Attenuation of X and gamma rays takes place by three distinct types of interaction of X and gamma ray photons with matter. Photoelectric effect designates an inelastic collision of the photon with an atom, resulting in a complete transfer of energy and the ejection of an electron from the atom. The probability of occurrence of photoelectric effect decreases rapidly with increasing energy ($\propto 1/E^3$) and increases rapidly with increasing atomic number of absorber ($\propto Z^3$). Scattering by atomic electrons is mainly an inelastic or incoherent scattering (Compton scattering) by lightly bound, essentially free, electrons in matter, with a partial transfer of energy to the electron which is ejected from the atom. A change in direction (scattering) of the photon also occurs. The probability of Compton scattering decreases with energy ($\propto 1/E$) and increases with electron density of the absorber. Also included in electron scattering interactions is coherent scattering, in which the photon direction is altered with no transfer of energy to the more tightly bound electrons responsible for the scattering. Pair production designates an interaction of the photon with the field of a nucleus in which an electron-positron pair is formed. In this interaction, a portion of photon energy (1.02 meV) is converted to the mass of the two particles and the remainder of the energy appears as kinetic energy of the particles. The probability of pair production occurrence increases rapidly with energy ($\propto E^2$ from 1.02 to 10 meV) and with atomic number ($\propto Z^2$). Subsequent to this process, the positron and electron annihilate within the absorber and release 1.02 meV in the form of two 0.51 meV photons which appear not unlike scattered photon radiation.

It should be noted that, in each of the above types of interaction, one or more electrons receive at least a portion of the photon energy; these electrons then transfer this energy to the absorber in the manner described previously for electrons.

Attenuation of monoenergetic X rays or gamma rays takes place according to the following equation:

$$I_x = I_0 e^{-\mu_m x}$$

where I_x is the intensity of radiation after passing through a thickness of absorber x (expressed in grams/cm^2), I_0 is the initial intensity, and μ_m is the mass absorption coefficient or probability of absorption per gram/cm^2 of absorber (units = cm^2/gram). The quantity μ_m is actually the *total* mass absorption coefficient and is simply the sum of the coefficients for photoelectric effect, scattering, and pair production, since these processes are independent of each other. Table I lists the total and component mass absorption coefficients for various photon energies in lead

Table I. Mass Absorption Coefficients in Lead

| Photon Energy | Scattering[a] | | Photo-Electric K, L & M Shells | Pair Production | | Total | |
| | With coherent | Without coherent | | Nucleus | Electron | With coherent | Without coherent |
Mev	Barns/atom[b]	Barns/atom	Barns/atom	Barns/atom	Barns/atom	cm²/g	cm²/g
0.01	1600	52.5	27500			84.6	80.1
.01307c	1200	51.8	13200			41.9	38.5
.01589d	980	51.3	45400			135	132
.02	750	50.7	24000			72.0	69.9
.03	450	49.0	7620			23.5	22.3
.04	310	47.4	3310			10.5	9.76
.05	230	46.0	1740			5.73	5.19
.06	180	44.8	1040			3.55	3.15
.08	127	42.4	444			1.66	1.41
.08823e	113	41.6	334			1.30	1.09
.08823e	113	41.6	2510			7.63	7.42
.10	100	40.4	1780			5.47	5.29
.15	64	36.4	596			1.92	1.84
.20	49	33.3	275			0.942	0.896
.30	36.2	29.0	93.4			.377	.356
.40	30.1	26.0	45.7			.220	.208
.50	26.3	23.7	26.1			.152	.145
.60	23.8	21.9	17.3			.119	.114
.80	20.3	19.27	9.5			.0866	.0836
1.0	18.0	17.32	6.2			.0704	.0684
1.5	14.4	14.07	3.0	0.55		.0522	.0512
2.0	12.2	12.00	2.0	1.72		.0463	.0457
3.0	9.51	9.44	1.1	3.93	0.001	.0423	.0421
4.0	7.91	7.87	0.80	5.76	.004	.0421	.0420
5.0		6.79	.60	7.25	.009		.0426
6.0		6.00	.49	8.47	.02		.0436

8.0	4.91	.35	10.5	.03	.0459
10	4.18	.28	12.3	.05	.0489
15	3.09	.18	15.7	.09	.0554‡
20	2.48	.13	18.3	.12	.0611
30	1.803	.09	21.9	.17	.0697
40	1.432	.07	24.4	.21	.0759
50	1.194	.05	26.2	.24	.0805
60	1.028		27.7	.27	.0843
80	0.810		29.8	.31	.0899
100	.672		31.3	.34	.0939

[a] Data in the first column is given by the sum of coherent scattering and of incoherent scattering from the Klein-Nishina formula corrected for binding effects. In the second column incoherent scattering is given by the Klein-Nishina formula for free electrons.

[b] Barns/atom $\times$ 0.002908 = cm^2/g.

[c] L_3 edge; at this and lower energies data for the M shell is given.

[d] L_1 edge; from this energy to the K edge energy data for the L and M shells is given.

[e] K edge; at this and higher energies data for the L, M and K shells is given.

‡ Energy region in which dipole absorption attains a maximum cross section.

From "X-Ray Attenuation Coefficients from 10 keV to 100 meV National Bureau of Standards Circular 583, United States Department of Commerce, April 30, 1957, Table 34.

Table II. Mass Absorption Coefficients in Concrete (0.56% H, 49.56% O, 31.35% Si, 4.56% Al, 8.26% Ca, 1.22% Fe, 0.24% Mg, 1.71% Na, 1.92% K, 0.12% S) ($\rho = 2.35$ g/cm³)

Photon Energy	Mass Absorption Coefficient	Photon Energy	Mass Absorption Coefficient	Photon Energy	Mass Absorption Coefficient
Mev	cm²/g	Mev	cm²/g	Mev	cm²/g
0.01	24.6	.30	.107	6.0	.0268
.015	7.68	.40	.0954	8.0	.0243
.02	3.34	.50	.0870	10.0	.0229
.03	1.10	.60	.0804	15	.0214
.04	.542	.80	.0706	20	.0209
.05	.350	1.0	.0635	30	.0209
.06	.267	1.5	0.0517	40	.0213
.08	.197	2.0	.0445	50	.0217
.10	.169	3.0	.0363	60	.0222
.15	.139	4.0	.0317	80	.0230
.20	.124	5.0	.0287	100	.0237

Coherent scattering is not included in the calculations.
The data were not revised.
From "X-Rays Attenuation Coefficients from 10 keV to 100 meV" National Bureau of Standards Circular 583, United States Department of Commerce, April 30, 1957, Table 39.

for so-celled narrow-beam conditions. Table II lists similar total mass absorption coefficients in concrete.

When a broad beam of radiation strikes an absorber, the attenuation due to scattering of photons is less than for a narrow beam since radiation is scattered *into* as well as *away from* central-beam positions and thus the dose beyond the absorber does not decrease as much as for a narrow beam. Most practical X and gamma ray shielding problems are concerned with beams which are relatively large in cross-section and thus do not follow narrow-beam absorption data. For this reason, and also since, in many calculations, we are dealing with either a continuous-energy spectrum (X rays) or multi-line spectrum (most gamma-emitters), empirical tables of absorption data are compiled and used.

For calculation of shielding requirements for usual collimated-beam X and gamma ray sources, Table III and Table IV should be used. It will be noted that tables give required lead and concrete shielding for various photon beams as a function of Workload, W (either milliampere—minutes/week for X rays or roentgens/week at 1 meter for gamma ray sources); Use Factor, U (the fraction of the Workload during which the beam will strike the particular shielding barrier); Occupancy Factor, T (the fraction of W $\times$ U during which the position protected by the shield is likely to be occupied); and the distance from the radiation source to the position of occupancy. Required barrier thicknesses are given for both Primary Barriers (barriers which can be struck by the "useful" or

Table III. X-Ray and Gamma-Ray Shielding Requirements for Controlled Areas[a]

The top block gives the distances (Ft.) for each WUT[b]; the bottom block gives the corresponding Thickness of Lead, mm, under the heading "Distance from Tube or Source to Occupied Area, Ft."

Potential, kV, or Isotope	Approximate HVL,[c] mm	Approximate TVL,[c] mm	Type of barrier	WUT[b]	Distance / Thickness →										
				40,000	5	7	10	14	20	28	40				
				20,000		5	7	10	14	20	28	40			
				10,000			5	7	10	14	20	28	40		
				5,000				5	7	10	14	20	28	40	
				2,500					5	7	10	14	20	28	40
				1,250						5	7	10	14	20	28
				625							5	7	10	14	20
				310								5	7	10	14
				155									5	7	10
100	0.2	0.7	Prim.		3.2	2.9	2.7	2.4	2.2	1.9	1.7	1.4	1.2	1.0	0.8
			Sec.		2.1	1.8	1.6	1.4	1.2	1.0	0.8	0.6	0.4	0.2	0.1
150	0.3	1.0	Prim.		4.1	3.8	3.5	3.3	3.0	2.7	2.4	2.1	1.8	1.6	1.3
			Sec.		2.6	2.3	2.0	1.8	1.5	1.2	0.9	0.7	0.5	0.3	0.1
200	0.5	1.7	Prim.		6.4	5.9	5.4	4.9	4.4	3.9	3.4	3.0	2.6	2.3	2.0
			Sec.		4.1	3.7	3.1	2.6	2.2	1.8	1.4	1.1	0.8	0.5	0.2
250	0.9	3.0	Prim.		11.3	10.4	9.5	8.6	7.7	6.8	6.0	5.2	4.4	3.6	2.8
			Sec.		6.4	5.7	5.0	4.2	3.5	2.8	2.2	1.6	1.2	0.8	0.3
300	1.7	5.6	Prim.		21.6	19.8	18.0	16.3	14.6	13.0	11.4	9.8	8.3	6.8	5.5
			Sec.		12.0	10.4	8.9	7.5	6.3	5.2	4.2	3.2	2.3	1.5	0.6
2000	12	4.0	Prim.					265	250	235	225	210	200	185	175
			Sec.					91	79	67	54	43	31	20	13
Cs-137	0.65	2.1	Prim.		112	105	99	93	86	80	74	67	61	55	48
			Sec.[d]		49	42	35	29	23	18	11	9	5	4	2
Co-60	1.20	4.0	Prim.		213	201	189	177	165	153	141	129	117	105	93
			Sec.[d]		93	82	71	60	47	34	20	10	0	0	0

[a] For a weekly design level of 100 mR; add one-tenth-value layer (TVL) for regions in the environs to reduce radiation to 10 mR/week.

[b] W = workload in ma-min/week for x-rays, R/week @ 1 meter for Gamma-rays; U = use factor; T = occupancy factor. T is equal to 1 for controlled areas and may be less than 1 for environs (see Text).

[c] These values are obtained at high filtration.

[d] Secondary barrier for Cs-137 and Co-60 are calculated for leakage radiation and 90° scatter.

Adapted from Tables IA and IB, in *Radiation Protection*, Braestrup and Wyckoff, 1958. Courtesy of Charles C Thomas, Publisher.

Table IV. X-Ray and Gamma-Ray Shielding Requirements for Controlled Areas[a]

Key — Distance from Tube or Source to Occupied Area, Ft. (WUT[b] vs. column)

WUT[b]	1	2	3	4	5	6	7	8	9	10	11
40,000	5	7	10	14	20	28	40				
20,000		5	7	10	14	20	28	40			
10,000			5	7	10	14	20	28	40		
5,000				5	7	10	14	20	28	40	
2,500					5	7	10	14	20	28	40
1,250						5	7	10	14	20	28
625							5	7	10	14	20
310								5	7	10	14
155									5	7	10

Thickness of Concrete (Density 147 lb/ft³)[d], in. (columns correspond to the key above)

Potential, kV, or Isotype	Approximate[c] HVL, in.	Approximate[c] TVL, in.	Type of barrier	1	2	3	4	5	6	7	8	9	10	11
100	0.6	2.0	Prim.	9.2	8.6	8.0	7.3	6.6	6.0	5.5	4.6	4.0	3.3	2.8
			Sec.	6.6	5.8	5.2	4.6	4.0	3.4	2.8	2.3	1.8	1.3	0.8
150	0.9	3.0	Prim.	13.3	12.4	11.5	10.6	9.7	8.9	8.1	7.2	6.5	5.8	5.1
			Sec.	9.1	8.2	7.3	6.4	5.5	4.6	3.7	2.9	2.2	1.7	1.2
200	1.1	3.6	Prim.	16.9	15.8	14.8	13.7	12.7	11.6	10.6	9.6	8.5	7.5	6.5
			Sec.	12.1	10.9	9.8	8.7	7.6	6.6	5.6	4.6	3.6	2.6	1.6
250	1.1+	3.8	Prim.	19.3	18.0	16.8	15.6	14.4	13.2	12.0	10.8	9.6	8.4	7.2
			Sec.	12.6	11.4	10.3	9.2	8.1	7.0	6.0	5.0	4.0	3.0	2.0
300	1.2	4.0	Prim.	21.7	20.5	19.3	18.1	16.9	15.7	14.5	13.3	12.1	10.9	9.7
			Sec.	13.4	12.2	11.0	9.8	8.8	7.8	6.8	5.8	4.8	3.8	2.8
2000	2.45	8.15	Prim.	56	53	50	47	45	42	40	40	37		
			Sec.	36.0	34.1	32.2	30.2	28.3	26.3	24.4	22.4	20.6	18.7	16.8
Cs-137	1.9	6.2	Prim.	19.1	17.7	16.3	14.9	13.4	12.0	10.6	7.8	6.4	5.0	3.7
			Sec.[e]											
Co-60	2.6	8.6	Prim.	45.1	42.7	40.3	37.8	35.4	32.9	30.5	28.0	25.6	23.1	20.6
			Sec.[e]	22.5	20.1	17.4	14.7	12.0	9.1	6.2	3.9	0.1	0	0

[a] For a weekly design level of 100 mR; add one-tenth-value layer (TVL) for regions in the environs to reduce radiation to 10 mR/week.

[b] W = workload in ma-min/week for x-rays, R/week @ 1 meter for Gamma-rays; U = use factor; T = occupancy factor. T is equal to 1 for controlled areas and may be less than 1 for environs (see Text).

[c] These values are obtained at high filtration.

[d] For other densities, the tabular values should be multiplied by 147/density.

[e] Secondary barrier for Cs-137 and Co-60 are calculated for leakage radiation and 90° scatter.

Adapted from Tables IA and IB, in Radiation Protection, Braestrup and Wyckoff, 1958. Courtesy of Charles C Thomas, Publisher.

"primary" radiation beam) and for Secondary Barriers (barriers against only secondary radiation, including leakage and scattered radiation). The tables are based upon protecting personnel in Controlled Areas (areas in which the occupational exposure of personnel to radiation or radioactive materials is under the supervision of an individual responsible for radiation protection) for which the Maximum Permissible Dose (MPD) is 100 milliroentgens/week. For Environs (areas immediately outside of controlled areas which may receive radiation from the controlled areas), the MPD is 10 mR/week; here, barriers must be increased by one Tenth-Value Layer (TVL) in order to reduce transmitted intensity and dose by a factor of 10. In using the tables, it should be noted that T should always be taken as 1 for controlled areas and that U should always be taken as 1 for secondary barriers. For more extensive X and gamma ray protection, calculations, and methods, see National Bureau of Standards Handbook 73 *(Protection Against Radiations From Sealed Gamma Sources)*, and National Bureau of Standards Handbook 76 *(Medical X-Ray Protection Up to Three Million Volts)*.

RADIATION ABSORBED DOSE FROM INTERNALLY DEPOSITED RADIONUCLIDES

I. INTRODUCTION

Absorbed dose calculations are used to evaluate the chronic exposure from environmental and industrial radioactive contaminants, from intentionally administered radionuclides used in nuclear medicine or biomedical research, and from accidents resulting from the deposition of radioactive materials in human beings. The last case may be treated by the methods applicable to one of the first two situations, depending upon the circumstances of the accident.

Physical factors which affect the absorbed dose calculations are usually known quite accurately for calculating the absorbed dose from intentionally-administered radiopharmaceuticals, but this unfortunately is not necessarily the case for chronic exposure to environmental or industrial sources of radiation. Such physical factors include the activity of the radionuclide, the chemical and physical state of the material, and the energy released and absorbed in tissue per disintegration of the radionuclide. The metabolic fate of the radioactive material is a biological factor, and consequently is associated with variability that usually can be evaluated only from limited data on experimental animals and a small number of human beings under various physiological and pathological conditions. Factors such as the route of entry of the radioactive material and the mass and shape of the target organ also enter into the absorbed dose calculations. In many cases, the radionuclide will not be homogeneously distributed throughout an organ, with the result that the absorbed dose may be very high in certain regions. Only the *average* absorbed dose for the total organ can be calculated. Little can be stated with respect to the absorbed dose at the cellular level.

The multiplicity of factors which must be taken into account when calculating the absorbed dose decreases the precision and accuracy of the calculation. In most instances, the calculated absorbed dose is only an estimate, and it is advisable, therefore, to determine an upper and lower value for this estimate based on the best available data.

II. MAXIMUM PERMISSIBLE DOSE

The maximum permissible doses (MPD) are the recommended maximum levels of radiation absorbed doses to an exposed population as set forth by the International Commission on Radiological Protection (ICRP)[1, 2] and the National Committee on Radiation Protection (NCRP).[3] It should be emphasized that these are maximum values, and the ICRP and NCRP recommend that all exposures be kept as low as possible, and that any unnecessary exposure be avoided. The exposed population is divided into the following three categories:

    A. Occupational exposure

    B. Exposure of special groups

        (a) Adults who work in the vicinity of controlled areas but who are not themselves employed on work causing exposure to radiation

        (b) Adults who enter controlled areas occasionally in the course of their duties, but are not regarded as radiation workers

        (c) Members of public living in the neighborhood of controlled areas

    C. Exposure of the population at large

The levels of exposure for these categories are given in Table I, and the original references[1, 2, 3] should be consulted for more detailed information.

Table I. Maximum Permissible Doses [1,2,3]

Exposed Part of the Body	Maximum Permissible Dose (rem) Exposure Group		
	A	B	C
Total body, gonads, and blood forming organs	5 (N–18)* rem 3 rem/13 weeks	1.5 rem/year** 0.5 rem/year†	0.05 rem/year
Skin, thyroid and bone	30 rem/year 8 rem/13 weeks	9 rem/year** 3 rem/year†	0.3 rem/year
Other single organs including the lens of the eye	15 rem/year 4 rem/13 weeks	4.5 rem/year** 1.5 rem/year†	0.15 rem/year
Hands, forearms, feet and ankles	75 rem/year 20 rem/13 weeks	—	—

*Cumulative maximum, where N is the individual's age in years.
**For groups B(a) and B(6)
†For group B(c)

III. CHRONIC EXPOSURE TO ENVIRONMENTAL AND INDUSTRIAL SOURCES OF RADIATION

The maximum permissible body burden, q (the maximum activity of a radionuclide that may be in the body at any point in time without exceeding the MPD) and the maximum permissible concentrations of a radionuclide in air, MPC_a and in water, MPC_w are based on the maximum permissible dose. The equations used to calculate q, MPC_a and MPC_w are given in references 1, 2, and 3 along with the assumptions and limitations as well as tabulated values for these parameters.

IV. ABSORBED DOSE FROM INTENTIONALLY ADMINISTERED RADIONUCLIDES

The first two equations given below are used to calculate the beta and gamma component of the absorbed dose, respectively. The third equation is used to calculate the gamma-ray exposure from internally administered radionuclides, and the absorbed dose may be approximated by using the roentgen-to-rad conversion factors given in NBS Handbook 85, Table |A|.[4]

$$\bar{D}_{\beta(\infty)} = 73.8E_\beta \sum_i C_{oi}T_{effi} \qquad \text{rads} \qquad (1)$$

$$\bar{D}_{\gamma(\infty)} = 73.8\left[\sum_i n_i E_i(AF)_i\right]\sum_i C_{oi}T_{effi} \qquad \text{rads} \qquad (2)$$

$$\bar{D}_{\gamma(\infty)} = 0.0346\rho\Gamma\bar{g}\sum_i C_{oi}T_{effi} \qquad \text{R.} \qquad (3)$$

where:

$\bar{D}_{\beta(\infty)}$ = average total beta component of the absorbed dose

$\bar{D}_{\gamma(\infty)}$ = average total gamma component of the absorbed dose

E_β = total local energy deposited per disintegration (Mev/dis)

C_{oi} = initial concentration of the jth component of the uptake or disappearance curve for a given organ (μc/gm)

T_{bi} = biological half-life of the jth component of the uptake or disappearance curve for a given organ (days)

T_{phy} = physical half-life of the radionuclide (days)

T_{effi} = effective half-life of the jth component of the uptake or disappearance curve for a given organ (days)

$$T_{effi} = \frac{T_{bi} \times T_{phy}}{T_{bi} + T_{phy}}$$

n_i = fractional number of photons per disintegration with energy E_i (Mev)

$(AF)_i$ = absorbed fraction

$$= \frac{\text{absorbed energy from a photon of energy } E_i}{\text{emitted energy from a photon of energy } E_i}$$

ρ = density of tissue under consideration (gm/cm^3)

Γ = specific gamma-ray constant (R-cm^2/mc-hr)

$\bar{g}$ = average geometrical factor (cm)

Equation 2 uses the method developed by Ellett, Callahan, and Brownell[5, 6] for calculating the gamma component of the absorbed dose. The use of equation 3 for calculating the gamma-ray exposure for internally administered radionuclides that emit low-energy photons has serious limitations because the method was developed for photon energies similar to those of radium (above 0.1 or 0.2 Mev) as pointed out by Quimby.[7] Equations 2 and 3 have been quantitatively compared by Ellett *et al.*,[5, 6] and by Smith.[8]

Table II contains nuclear data required in equations 1, 2, and 3. The term E_β has also been denoted by $\bar{E}_\beta$, E and $\bar{E}$ by various authors. This term includes all particulate radiations as well as photons whose energy is less than or equal to 11.3 kev. The calculation of E_β is covered in references[9, 10]. The photon yield, n_i, has been corrected for internal conversion of the photon unless otherwise noted.

Values of $\bar{g}$ Table III have been calculated by Focht *et al.*[14] based on methods developed by Bush[15] for cylinders containing a uniform distribution of a gamma-emitting radionuclide. The values in Table III are revised, since the values previously appearing in the literature were for a point source on the end surface of a cylinder rather than for a uniform distribution of a gamma emitter. The values in Table IV are for gamma-emitting radionuclides uniformly distributed in total body tissues.[9] Values of $\bar{g}$ for spheres of unit density which have a radius r of less than 10 cm may be approximated by equation 4.

$$\bar{g} = 3\pi r \qquad\qquad \text{cm.} \qquad\qquad (4)$$

The method of calculating g_p for a specified point inside, on the surface or outside a sphere is given by Loevinger *et al.*[9] The term g_p is the geometrical factor used when one wants to determine the gamma-ray exposure to a specified point from a specified source of radioactive material. In Figure 1, values of g_p are presented for the central axis of the standard human body containing a uniform distribution of a gamma-ray emitter. These values are useful in approximating the exposure of organs such as the thyroid, ovaries or testicles that lie near the central axis of the body from a uniform distribution of a gamma-emitting radionuclide in the body. The exposure calculated when $\bar{g}$ is used gives the average value, while values calculated using g_p give the maximum exposure.

Table II. Nuclear Data for Selected Radionuclides

Radio-Nuclide	Physical Half-Life Tphy.	Type of Decay	E_β (Mev/dis.)	Photons Type	Photons Energy E_i (Mev)	Photon Yield n_i No/100 dis.	Γ R-cm²/mc-hr.	References
H-3	12.26 yr	β^-	0.0055	–	–	none	–	11
C-14	5568 yr	β^-	0.050	–	–	none	–	11
F-18	110 m	β^+	g)¹ᵉ	γ^b	0.511	200	5.35ᵈ	13
Na-22	2.58 yr	β^+, E.C.	0.191ᵉ	γ^b / γ	0.511 / 1.277	180 / ≈100	≈13ᶜ	11
Na-24	14.97 hr	β^-	0.560	γ / γ / γ	1.368 / 2.754 / 3.85	100 / ≈100 / 0.0004	18.8ᶜ	11
P-32	14.22 hr	β^-	0.70	–	–	none	–	11
S-35	87.2 d	β^-	0.0492	–	–	none	–	11
Cl-36	3.03 × 10⁵ yr	β^-, E.C.	0.295ᵉ	x, K	≈0.002	≈0.1	≈0.25ᶜ	11
K-42	12.42 hr	β^-	1.42	γ / γ	0.320 / 1.53	≈0.20 / 20.	15.4ᶜ	11
Ca-45	164 d	β^-	0.077	–	–	none	–	11
Ca-47	4.7 d	β^-	0.51	γ / γ / γ	0.48 / 0.83 / 1.31	5 / 5 / 71	5.6ᶜ	12, 13
Sc-47	3.4 d	β^-		γ	0.160	70		12, 13
Cr-51	28.0 d	E.C.	0.0061	γ	0.323	9	0.15ᵈ	10
Mn-52	5.7 d	β^+, E.C.	0.072	γ / γ / γ / γ^b	1.46 / 0.94 / 0.73 / 0.511	100 / 100 / 100 / 70	19ᶜ	12
Mn-54	278 d	E.C.	0.0054	γ	0.838	100	4.6ᶜ	12, 13
Fe-55	2.6 yr	E.C.	0.0059	x, K	0.0059	100ᶠ	not appl.	12

Isotope	Half-life	Decay	E_β	Radiation	Energy (Mev)	Yield	Γ	Ref
Fe-59	45.3 d	β^-	0.118	γ	0.145	0.8		11
				γ	0.191	2.5		
				γ	1.099	56	} 6.3[c]	
				γ	1.29	44		
Co-57	267 d	E.C.	0.0229	γ	0.122	87.5	0.51 } 0.99[d]	10
				γ	0.136	8.8	0.48	
				γ	0.0144	8.6		
Co-60	5.26 yr	β^-	0.093	γ	1.173	≈100	} 13.3[c]	11
				γ	1.332	100		
Cu-64	12.8 hr	β^-, β^+, E.C.	0.13	x, K	0.0075	42[f]	1.1[c]	12
				γ	1.34	0.5[f]		
				γ^b	0.511	38		
Zn-65	244 d	E.C., β^+	0.0074[e]	x, K	≈0.008	37	5.0 } 8.1[c]	11
				γ^b	0.511	3.4	3.06	
				γ	1.114	49.3		
Ga-68	68 m	β^+, E.C.	h	γ^b	0.511	≈200	5.35[d]	13
				γ	1.24–1.88 (several)	Yields less than 0.5		
As-74	17.5 d	β^-, β^+	0.27	x, K	0.01	35[f]	4.7[c]	12
				γ	0.635	16[f]		
				γ	0.593	63[f]		
				γ^b	0.511	66		

a. E_β includes no component from K x-rays   b. Annihilation photons, 0.511 Mev photons from positron annihilation   c. Γ calculated for 0°C and 1 atm.   d. Γ calculated for 20°C and 1 atm.   e. Current N.B.S. value (Sept., 1964).   f. Not corrected for internal conversion of photon   g. F-18, $E_{\beta max} = 0.635 \pm 0.015$ Mev   h. Ga-68, $E_{\beta max} = 1.894$ Mev – 98.3/100 dis; $E_{\beta max} = 0.820$ Mev – 1.7/100 dis   i. Kr-85, $E_{\beta max} = 0.67$ Mev   j. Xe-133, $E_{\beta max} = 0.35$ Mev

Table II. Nuclear Data for Selected Radionuclides (continued)

Radio-Nuclide	Physical Half-Life Tphy.	Type of Decay	E_β (Mev/dis.)	Photons Type	Photons Energy E_i (Mev)	Photon Yield n_i No/100 dis.	Γ R-cm²/mc-hr.	References
Se–75	120 d	E.C.	0.0192	γ	0.265	53		10
				γ	0.280	28		
				γ	0.136	40	1.76^d	
				γ	0.121	13.2		
				γ	0.402	15.2		
				γ	0.097	3.3		
				others	–	4.7		
Br–82	35.8 hr	β⁻	0.135	γ	1.475	18^f		12
				γ	1.32	27^f		
				γ	1.044	30^f		
				γ	0.828	25^f	14.6^c	
				γ	0.777	82^f		
				γ	0.698	30^f		
				γ	0.619	48^f		
				γ	0.554	75^f		
Kr–85	10.3 yr	β⁻	i	γ	0.514	0.42	0.01^d	13
Rb–86	18.66 d	β⁻	0.66	γ	1.078	10	0.58^c	11
Sr–85	65 d	E.C.	0.0151	γ	0.514	99.2	2.69^d	10
Sr–87 m	2.8 hr	I.T.	0.081^a	x, K_α	0.014	9.8	0.25	10
				x, K_β	0.016	2.4	} 1.85^d	
				γ	0.388	78.2	1.60	
Sr–89	53 d	β⁻	0.56	–	–	none⁻	–	12
Sr–90	28.0 yr	β⁻	0.194	–	–	none	–	11
Y–90	64.03 hr	β⁻	0.93	–	–	none	–	11
Tc–99 m	6. hr	I.T.	0.014^a	x, K_α	0.0183	4.6	0.16	10
				x, K_β	0.0206	1.1	} 0.72^d	
				γ	0.140 + 0.142	90.4	0.56	
I–125	60.2 d	E.C.	0.0208	x, K_α	0.0274	112.6		10
				x, K_β	0.0311	24.2	1.23^d	
				γ	0.0354	7.		

Nuclide	Half-life	Decay mode	E_β	Radiation	Photon energy (Mev)	% per dis	Γ	Ref
I–131	8.07 d	β⁻	0.188	x, K	≈0.030	5	$\left.\begin{array}{l}0.21 \\ 2.26\end{array}\right\}2.47^d$	11
				γ	0.080	2		
				γ	0.284	6		
				γ	0.364	79		
				γ	0.638	9		
				γ	0.724	3		
I–132	2.33 hr	β⁻	0.49	γ	0.76	93^f	11.8^c	12
				γ	0.67	100^f		
				γ	0.97	23^f		
				γ	0.52	30^f		
				γ	1.41	13^f		
				γ	others	23^f		
Xe–133	5.27 d	β⁻	j	x, K	0.035	51	0.38^d	13
				γ	0.081	32.6		
Cs–131	9.7 d	E.C.	0.0074^a	x, Kα	0.0297	60	$\left.\begin{array}{l}0.56^d\end{array}\right.$	10
				x, Kβ	0.0337	15		
Cs–137	30 yr	β⁻	0.23	x, K	0.032	7.6	3.2^c	12, 13
				γ	0.662	85.^f		
Ir–192	74 d	β⁻, E.C.	0.17	γ	0.613 – 0.136	11 different photon energies	5.5^c	12
Au–198	2.696 d	β⁻	0.328	x, L	~0.009	1.3	$\left.\begin{array}{l}0.14 \\ 2.32\end{array}\right\}2.5^c$	11
				x, K	~0.070	2.7		
				γ	0.412	95		
				γ	0.676	0.82		
Au–199	3.15 d	β⁻	0.13		0.209	18^f	0.42^c	12
					0.159	78^f		
					0.05	5^f		
Hg–197	63.8 hr	E.C.	0.0794	x, Kα	0.0682	57	$\left.\begin{array}{l}0.31^d\end{array}\right.$	10
				x, Kβ	0.0778	18		
				γ	0.0773	19		
Hg–203	47.0 d	β⁻	0.099	x, Kα	0.0722	9.1	$\left.\begin{array}{l}1.20^d\end{array}\right.$	10
				x, Kβ	0.0824	3.6		
				γ	0.279	81.5		

a. E_β includes no component from K x-rays   b. Annihilation photons, 0.511 Mev photons from positron annihilation   c. Γ calculated for 20°C and 1 atm.   d. Γ calculated for 0°C and 1 atm.   e. Current N.B.S. value (Sept., 1964).   f. Not corrected for internal conversion of photon   g. F-18, $E_{\beta max}$ = 0.635 ± 0.015 Mev   h. Ga-68, $E_{\beta max}$ = 1.894 Mev – 98.3/100 dis; $E_{\beta max}$ = 0.820 Mev – 1.7/100 dis   i. Kr-85, $E_{\beta max}$ = 0.67 Mev   j. Xe-133, $E_{\beta max}$ = 0.35 Mev

Table III. Average Geometrical Factor, $\bar{g}$, for Cylinders Containing a Uniformly Distributed γ-Ray Emitter ($\mu = 0.028$)

Length of Cylinder (cm)	Radius of Cylinder (cm)										
	1	2	3	5	7	10	15	20	25	30	35
1	3.8	7.5	10.2	13.0	13.5	13.8	15.1	16.0	17.5	18.0	19.0
2	6.5	11.7	15.7	21.6	23.2	25.2	28.1	30.5	32.8	35.4	37.3
3	8.4	14.7	19.8	27.7	31.0	34.5	39.2	42.9	46.5	49.5	52.5
5	10.6	18.8	25.6	36.0	42.4	48.5	56.1	62.6	68.2	73.0	77.2
7	11.6	21.4	29.3	41.4	50.0	59.0	68.7	77.8	84.7	90.2	93.8
10	12.7	23.6	33.0	47.1	57.8	70.2	83.2	94.0	103	109	113
15	13.7	25.6	36.4	53.2	66.1	81.4	99.7	113	123	130	135
20	14.2	26.7	38.0	56.3	72.2	89.6	111	127	139	147	152
30	14.5	27.6	39.7	59.9	76.8	98.8	124	144	159	172	179
40	14.8	28.2	40.7	62.4	80.0	103	133	156	175	187	197
50	14.8	28.4	41.3	64.1	82.2	106	139	165	185	199	208
60	14.8	28.7	41.7	65.5	84.0	109	143	171	193	206	216
70	14.8	28.8	41.9	65.6	85.3	111	146	174	196	212	222
80	14.8	28.8	42.1	65.8	86.0	112	148	176	198	214	226
90	14.8	28.9	42.3	66.0	86.5	113	149	177	199	216	228
100	14.8	29.2	42.5	66.2	86.8	114	150	179	201	218	230

Reference: Focht, E. F., et al., *Radiology*, 85:151, 1965.

Table IV. Average Geometrical Factor, $\bar{g}$, for γ-Ray Emitter Uniformly Distributed in Total Body Tissues

Weight of patient, kg	Height of patient, cm						
	200	190	180	170	160	150	140
100	138	139	142	145	147	150	154
90	134	136	138	140	143	146	148
80	129	130	131	134	136	139	141
70	123	124	125	126	129	131	135
60	117	118	119	120	122	125	128
50	112	113	114	116	117	119	122
40	102	104	105	106	108	109	110

Reference: Hine and Brownell, *Radiation Dosimetry.*

The absorbed fraction (AF) is the ratio of the absorbed gamma-ray energy, and is calculated by means of a Monte Carlo type computer program as described by Ellett *et al.*[5, 6] The Monte Carlo method consists of repetitively tracing the path of a single photon through an absorbing medium using differential cross-section data to calculate the energy lost per interaction and the new scattering angle. After this process is repeated 40,000 to 60,000 times for a photon of a given energy, the average energy absorbed for that photon energy can be calculated for any geometrical shape described around the point source.

The AF has been calculated for various photon energies, phantom

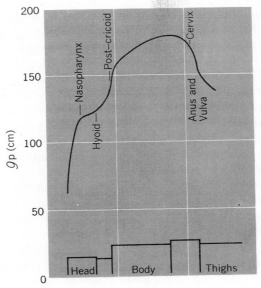

Figure 1.   Radio Absorbed Dose

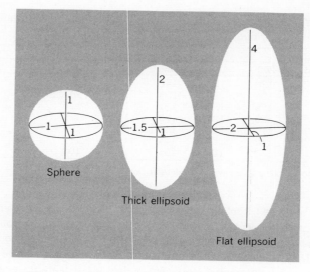

Figure 2.   Models for organs of various shapes.

Reference: *Brit. J. Radiol.*, 38:541, 1965.

masses and shapes as well as radionuclide distributions.[5, 6] The principal axes of the elliptical cylinders are in the ratio 1/1.8/6.19, and the principal axes of the ellipsoids are in the ratio 1/1.8/9.27. Figure 2 illustrates the geometrical relationship of other phantoms. Table V and VI give the AF for various photon energies for a central point source in phantoms of varying mass and shape. Table VII, VIII, and IX give similar data for a uniform distribution of activity.

The AF for a uniform distribution of a radionuclide varies between two-thirds and three-quarters of the AF for a central point source distribution, depending upon photon energy, phantom mass, and shape. This can be seen by inspecting Tables V through IX. The absorbed dose calculated for a central point source represents the maximum absorbed dose while the absorbed dose calculated for a uniformly distributed source calculates the average absorbed dose. This is similar to the maximum and average exposures calculated by using g_p and $\bar{g}$ respectively. One may use the central point source calculation to represent the maximum absorbed dose at the center of a phantom from a uniformly distributed source. In Table X, values of the AF for various point source locations along the central axis of elliptical cylinders are given. Also the AF given in Table X can be used to determine the maximum absorbed dose at points along the axis (*e.g.*, the gonadal absorbed dose) of an elliptical cylinder (the AF for point sources in elliptical cylinders and ellipsoids are almost identical) from a uniform distribution of activity.

Table V. Absorbed Fractions for Central Point Source Gamma Emitters in Elliptical Cylinders

Mass (kg)	MeV $E\gamma = 0.040$	$E\gamma = 0.080$	$E\gamma = 0.160$	$E\gamma = 0.364$	$E\gamma = 0.662$	$E\gamma = 1.46$	$E\gamma = 2.75$	Average radius (cm)
2·21	0·386	0·175	0·171	0·187	0·186	0·166	0·131	4·18
6·26	0·524	0·257	0·240	0·255	0·252	0·226	0·180	5·92
11·50	0·614	0·324	0·293	0·305	0·299	0·268	0·216	7·25
17·71	0·681	0·380	0·336	0·345	0·337	0·303	0·246	8·37
24·75	0·730	0·428	0·376	0·379	0·369	0·332	0·272	9·33
32·53	0·769	0·468	0·409	0·408	0·397	0·357	0·294	10·2
41·00	0·800	0·505	0·439	0·434	0·421	0·380	0·313	11·1
50·09	0·824	0·538	0·464	0·458	0·442	0·400	0·330	11·8
59·77	0·844	0·566	0·490	0·480	0·463	0·418	0·347	12·6
70·00	0·861	0·593	0·513	0·499	0·481	0·434	0·362	13·2
80·76	0·876	0·618	0·534	0·518	0·498	0·449	0·376	13·9
92·02	0·888	0·639	0·555	0·535	0·513	0·463	0·388	14·5
103·76	0·899	0·660	0·575	0·551	0·528	0·477	0·402	15·1
115·96	0·908	0·679	0·592	0·566	0·542	0·490	0·412	15·6
128·60	0·916	0·696	0·609	0·581	0·556	0·502	0·423	16·2
141·65	0·924	0·713	0·624	0·593	0·568	0·512	0·432	16·8
155·16	0·930	0·726	0·639	0·606	0·580	0·523	0·442	17·3
169·05	0·936	0·740	0·652	0·619	0·591	0·533	0·452	17·8
183·33	0·942	0·753	0·666	0·630	0·602	0·543	0·460	18·2
198·00	0·946	0·763	0·678	0·641	0·612	0·552	0·469	18·7

Reference: *Brit. J. Radiol.*, 37:45, 1964.

Table VI. Absorbed Fractions for Central Point Source Gamma Emitters in Ellipsoids and Spheres

Mass (kg)	$E_\gamma = 0.040$ MeV		$E_\gamma = 0.160$ MeV		$E_\gamma = 0.662$ MeV		$E_\gamma = 2.75$ MeV	
	Ellipsoid	Sphere	Ellipsoid	Sphere	Ellipsoid	Sphere	Ellipsoid	Sphere
2·21	0·382	0·566	0·169	0·249	0·182	0·250	0·129	0·177
6·26	0·521	0·743	0·237	0·360	0·249	0·343	0·178	0·245
11·50	0·611	0·831	0·290	0·443	0·296	0·408	0·214	0·294
17·71	0·678	0·890	0·334	0·512	0·333	0·457	0·244	0·333
24·75	0·727	0·923	0·373	0·567	0·364	0·498	0·268	0·367
32·53	0·767	0·944	0·406	0·616	0·392	0·538	0·290	0·396
41·00	0·798	0·959	0·436	0·661	0·416	0·571	0·309	0·419
50·09	0·823	0·968	0·462	0·698	0·437	0·600	0·326	0·444
59·77	0·842	0·975	0·486	0·729	0·457	0·626	0·343	0·464
70·00	0·860	0·981	0·510	0·755	0·475	0·651	0·357	0·483
80·76	0·875	0·985	0·531	0·777	0·492	0·672	0·372	0·501
92·02	0·888	0·987	0·552	0·799	0·508	0·693	0·385	0·516
103·76	0·898	0·990	0·572	0·817	0·523	0·710	0·397	0·532
115·96	0·907	0·992	0·590	0·836	0·537	0·728	0·408	0·547
128·60	0·916	0·994	0·606	0·850	0·551	0·743	0·419	0·561
141·65	0·923	0·995	0·621	0·862	0·563	0·756	0·429	0·574
155·16	0·929	0·995	0·636	0·874	0·576	0·769	0·439	0·586
169·05	0·936	0·996	0·650	0·885	0·586	0·782	0·449	0·598
183·33	0·941	0·997	0·663	0·895	0·597	0·793	0·457	0·609
198·00	0·946	0·998	0·676	0·903	0·607	0·804	0·466	0·619

Reference: *Brit. J. Radiol.*, 37:45, 1964.

Table VII. Absorbed Fractions for a Uniform Distribution of Activity in Ellipsoids

Mass (kg)	MeV $E_\gamma = 0.040$	$E_\gamma = 0.080$	$E_\gamma = 0.160$	$E_\gamma = 0.364$	$E_\gamma = 0.662$	$E_\gamma = 1.46$	$E_\gamma = 2.75$	Height (cm)
20	0·467	0·255	0·240	0·251	0·256	0·229	0·191	122·3
30	0·515	0·289	0·271	0·280	0·286	0·254	0·211	139·9
40	0·548	0·316	0·294	0·301	0·307	0·273	0·227	153·9
50	0·572	0·338	0·313	0·319	0·324	0·288	0·240	165·9
60	0·591	0·357	0·329	0·334	0·337	0·301	0·252	175·3
70	0·606	0·375	0·344	0·347	0·348	0·312	0·263	185·5
80	0·618	0·390	0·356	0·359	0·358	0·323	0·272	194·0
90	0·629	0·404	0·368	0·370	0·367	0·333	0·281	201·0
100	0·640	0·417	0·378	0·380	0·376	0·342	0·290	209·0
120	0·659	0·439	0·398	0·398	0·393	0·358	0·305	222·1
140	0·678	0·458	0·416	0·415	0·410	0·374	0·317	234·0
160	0·698	0·473	0·433	0·430	0·428	0·388	0·328	244·2

Reference: *Brit. J. Radiol.*, 38:541, 1965.

Table VIII. Absorbed Fractions for a Uniform Distribution of Activity in Small Spheres

Mass (kg)	MeV						
	$E_\gamma = 0.040$	$E_\gamma = 0.080$	$E_\gamma = 0.160$	$E_\gamma = 0.364$	$E_\gamma = 0.662$	$E_\gamma = 1.46$	$E_\gamma = 2.75$
0·3	0·195	0·088	0·090	0·102	0·100	0·094	0·078
0·4	0·216	0·098	0·100	0·111	0·112	0·101	0·085
0·5	0·234	0·106	0·107	0·119	0·120	0·107	0·090
1·0	0·295	0·138	0·133	0·146	0·147	0·128	0·107
2·0	0·366	0·177	0·167	0·179	0·178	0·157	0·129
3·0	0·412	0·205	0·192	0·203	0·200	0·179	0·145
4·0	0·445	0·227	0·212	0·222	0·219	0·196	0·159
5·0	0·471	0·247	0·229	0·238	0·234	0·210	0·171
6·0	0·492	0·264	0·244	0·252	0·246	0·222	0·180

Reference: *Brit. J. Radiol.*, 38:541, 1965.

Table IX. Absorbed Fractions for a Uniform Distribution of Activity in Flat Ellipsoids (see Fig. 1.)

Mass (kg)	MeV $E_\gamma = 0.080$	$E_\gamma = 0.160$	$E_\gamma = 0.662$	$E_\gamma = 2.75$
0·3	0·076	0·080	0·088	0·063
0·4	0·083	0·087	0·098	0·070
0·5	0·089	0·093	0·106	0·076
1·0	0·111	0·115	0·131	0·094
2·0	0·143	0·144	0·158	0·114
3·0	0·166	0·164	0·175	0·127
4·0	0·185	0·179	0·190	0·139
5·0	0·202	0·192	0·203	0·149
6·0	0·216	0·204	0·215	0·159

Reference: *Brit. J. Radiol.*, 38:541, 1965.

Table X. Absorbed Fractions for Point Sources Located at Distances $\frac{1}{2}$, $\frac{1}{6}$ and $\frac{1}{12}$, the Height of the Elliptical Cylinders of Table II

Mass (kg)	$E_\gamma = 0.080$ MeV Source distance $\frac{1}{2}$	$\frac{1}{6}$	$\frac{1}{12}$	$E_\gamma = 0.662$ MeV Source distance $\frac{1}{2}$	$\frac{1}{6}$	$\frac{1}{12}$	$E_\gamma = 2.75$ MeV Source distance $\frac{1}{2}$	$\frac{1}{6}$	$\frac{1}{12}$
2·21	0·175	0·167	0·156	0·186	0·175	0·160	0·131	0·122	0·111
6·26	0·257	0·247	0·227	0·252	0·240	0·219	0·180	0·170	0·158
11·50	0·324	0·314	0·285	0·299	0·283	0·261	0·216	0·204	0·189
17·71	0·380	0·370	0·334	0·337	0·320	0·297	0·246	0·232	0·215
24·75	0·428	0·418	0·380	0·369	0·350	0·325	0·272	0·259	0·240
32·53	0·468	0·458	0·420	0·397	0·377	0·351	0·294	0·281	0·259
41·00	0·505	0·495	0·455	0·421	0·403	0·376	0·313	0·299	0·277
50·09	0·538	0·429	0·489	0·442	0·425	0·394	0·330	0·317	0·295
59·77	0·566	0·558	0·517	0·463	0·444	0·412	0·347	0·334	0·310
70·00	0·593	0·585	0·543	0·481	0·462	0·429	0·362	0·348	0·323
80·76	0·618	0·610	0·568	0·498	0·479	0·443	0·376	0·363	0·337
92·02	0·639	0·632	0·590	0·513	0·494	0·459	0·388	0·376	0·348
103·76	0·660	0·653	0·612	0·528	0·510	0·475	0·402	0·388	0·360
115·96	0·679	0·673	0·631	0·542	0·524	0·488	0·412	0·400	0·371
128·60	0·696	0·690	0·648	0·556	0·538	0·502	0·423	0·410	0·381
141·65	0·713	0·707	0·666	0·568	0·552	0·515	0·432	0·421	0·391
155·16	0·726	0·722	0·681	0·580	0·564	0·527	0·442	0·430	0·400
169·05	0·740	0·736	0·696	0·591	0·575	0·537	0·452	0·440	0·410
183·33	0·753	0·749	0·710	0·602	0·586	0·547	0·460	0·448	0·418
198·00	0·763	0·760	0·721	0·612	0·595	0·556	0·469	0·457	0·427

Reference: *Brit. J. Radiol.*, 37:45, 1964.

Besides self-irradiation, organs within the central portion of the trunk of the body receive additional irradiation from the back-scatter of photons distributed throughout the body and from photons originating within the organ itself. The fractional increase in absorbed dose due to back-scattered radiation to a central region within a 70 kg phantom is given in Table XI. If the radioactivity is confined to a region of minimum body back-scatter, *e.g.* the head, the use of this factor is not appropriate.

Table XI. Back-scatter Increase Within a 70 Kg Phantom

MeV $E_\gamma = 0\cdot040$	$E_\gamma = 0\cdot080$	$E_\gamma = 0\cdot160$	$E_\gamma = 0\cdot364$	$E_\gamma = 0\cdot662$	$E_\gamma = 1\cdot46$	$E_\gamma = 2\cdot75$	200 kg phantom $E_\gamma = 0\cdot160$
$1\cdot14$	$1\cdot28$	$1\cdot17$	$1\cdot05$	$1\cdot04$	$1\cdot02$	$1\cdot01$	$1\cdot21$

Reference: *Brit. J. Radiol.*, 38:541, 1965.

The additional contribution to the absorbed dose at intermediate source locations can be estimated with sufficient accuracy for most applications by interpolating between the zero and maximum back-scatter case.

The evaluation of the AF by the method of Ellett *et al.*[5, 6] has been verified by Snyder *et al.*[16, 17] who are also using the Monte Carlo method, but employ a different approach to the problem which allows more freedom to specify the size and shape of phantoms, source, and target regions.

Depending on the frequency of data collection, the term $\sum_i C(t)_{oi} T_{effi}$ can be evaluated using either the method shown in Figure 3 or in Figure 4.[8] In Figure 3, the frequency of data collection is frequent enough so that the disappearance curve can be resolved into two components with initial concentrations C_{o1} and C_{o2} and effective half-lives T_{eff_1} and T_{eff_2}. In this case

$$\sum_i C(t)_{oi} T_{effi} = C_{01} T_{eff_1} + C_{02} T_{eff_2} \tag{5}$$

It should be remembered that in many instances the effective half-life

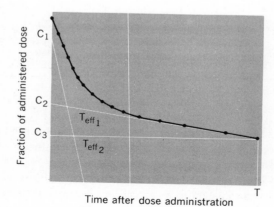

Figure 3.   Radio Absorbed Dose

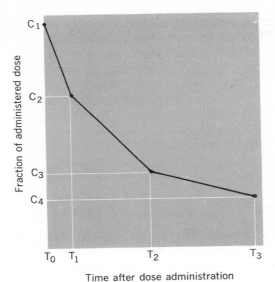

Figure 4.   Radio Absorbed Dose

used in absorbed dose calculations has no physiological significance. Moreover, the initial concentrations should not be indiscriminately used to calculate pool size.

When the last measurement (at time $= T$) was made in Fig. 3, the concentration of the radionuclide in the organ was C_3. However, one cannot be certain whether the remaining activity in the organ will disappear at a rate predicted by T_{eff2}, especially if one is using a long-lived radionuclide. For this reason, the concentration of the radionuclide remaining in the organ when the last measurement is made should be assigned an effective half-life equal to the physical half-life of the radionuclide. Then

$$\sum_i C(t)_{oi} T_{effi} = C_{01} T_{effi} + C_{02} T_{eff2}(1 - e^{-0.693T/T_{eff2}})$$

$$+ C_{02} T_{phy} e^{-0.693T/T_{phy}} \qquad (6)$$

When one has collected only limited biological disappearance data, Fig. 3 can no longer be used to calculate $\sum_i C(t)_{oi} T_{effi}$. Instead one must use Figure 4 to make an estimate of the absorbed dose. In this case, the area under the curve must be numerically integrated to obtain a value for $\sum_i C(t)_{oi} T_{effi}$. The activity in the organ after the last measurement should be given an effective half-time equivalent to the physical half-life of the radionuclide. Then

$$\sum_i C(t)_{oj} T_{effj} = 0.693 \left\{ (C_1 - C_2)\left(\frac{T_1}{2}\right) \right.$$

$$+ (C_2 - C_3)\left[T_1 + \left(\frac{T_2 - T_1}{2}\right)\right]$$

$$\left. + (C_3 - C_4)\left[T_2 + \left(\frac{T_3 - T_2}{2}\right)\right] + C_4 T_4 \right\}$$

$$+ C_4 T_{phy} e^{-0.693 T_3 / T_{phy}}$$

(7)

IV. ANATOMICAL DATA

Most of the anatomical data used in absorbed dose calculations are based on the standard man.[1] These data are given in Table XII. Table XII assumes spherical geometry for all organs including the total body. This assumption leads to an overestimation of the gamma-component of the absorbed dose for, *e.g.*, the total body.[5] The data in Table XIII relate to the intake and excretion of the standard man. However, if one uses the standard man as the sole guide in evaluating body weight, organ size, and metabolic activity, serious errors can be introduced into the absorbed dose calculations. Cook *et al.*[16] have discussed this problem, and the ICRP has had a task group working on a revision of the standard man.

Kereiakes *et al.*[17, 18] have considered the variation in the absorbed dose from various radiopharmaceuticals received by children ranging in age from infancy through adolescence and have compared these values with the absorbed dose a standard man would receive. Their work shows that the absorbed dose received by an infant or child can be twenty or more times greater than the absorbed dose received by a standard man from a given quantity of radionuclide because of differences in metabolic activity and anatomy (such as organ mass).

Table XIV gives the ICRP model for the gastrointestinal tract of the standard man. Hayes *et al.*[19] have evaluated the ICRP model based on fifty-four human subjects, and have found that on the average their results are roughly equal to standard man behavior. However, they found large variations within the group, and whether or not the radioactivity was ingested with a meal or between meals had a decided effect on the absorbed dose received, but age appeared to have little or no effect on the absorbed dose received. Garner[20] and Dolphin and Eve[21] have also evaluated the ICRP model. These studies, as well as the ICRP model, assume insoluble sources of radioactivity while in many cases one must

Table XII. Mass and Effective Radius of Organs of the Adult Human Body

	Mass, m (g)	Per cent of total body*	Effective radius, X (cm)
Total body*	70,000	100	30
Muscle	30,000	43	30
Skin and subcutaneous tissue†	6100	8.7	0.1
Fat	10,000	14	20
Skeleton			
Without bone marrow	7000	10	5
Red marrow	1500	2.1	
Yellow marrow	1500	2.1	
Blood	5400	7.7	
Gastrointestinal tract*	2000	2.9	30
Contents of GI tract			
Lower large intestine	150		5
Stomach	250		10
Small intestine	1100		30
Upper large intestine	135		5
Liver	1700	2.4	10
Brain	1500	2.1	15
Lungs (2)	1000	1.4	10
Lymphoid tissue	700	1.0	
Kidneys (2)	300	0.43	7
Heart	300	0.43	7
Spleen	150	0.21	7
Urinary bladder	150	0.21	
Pancreas	70	0.10	5
Salivary glands (6)	50	0.071	
Testes (2)	40	0.057	3
Spinal cord	30	0.043	1
Eyes (2)	30	0.043	0.25
Thyroid gland	20	0.029	3
Teeth	20	0.029	
Prostate gland	20	0.029	3
Adrenal glands or suprarenal (2)	20	0.029	3
Thymus	10	0.014	
Ovaries (2)	8	0.011	3
Hypophysis (pituitary)	0.6	8.6×10^{-6}	0.5
Pineal gland	0.2	2.9×10^{-6}	0.04
Parathyroids (4)	0.15	2.1×10^{-6}	0.06
Miscellaneous (blood vessels, cartilage, nerves, etc.)	390	0.56	

* Does not include contents of the gastrointestinal tract.
† The mass of the skin alone is taken to be 2000 grams.

deal with radioactive material which can pass back and forth across the gastrointestinal tract.

Table XV gives the ICRP model for particles in the respiratory tract of the standard man. Eve[22] discusses in detail the metabolism of inhaled and ingested insoluble radionuclides with specific reference to the ICRP model.

Table XIII. Intake and Excretion of the Standard Man

Water Balance			
Intake (cm³/day)		**Excretion (cm³/day)**	
Food	1000	Urine	1400
Fluids	1200	Sweat	600
Oxidation	300	From lungs	300
		Feces	200
Total	2500	Total	2500

Air Balance			
	O_2 (vol. %)	CO_2 (vol. %)	N_2 + others (vol. %)
Inspired air	20.94	0.03	79.03
Expired air	16	4.0	80
Alveolar air (inspired)	15	5.6	—
Alveolar air (expired)	14	6.0	—

Vital capacity of lungs   3–4 liters (men)
                                 2–3 liters (women)

Air inhaled during 8 hr work day	10^7 cm³/day
Air inhaled during 16 hr not at work	10^7 cm³/day
Total	2×10^7 cm³/day
Interchange area of lungs	50 m²
Area of upper respiratory tract, trachea, bronchi	20 m²
Total surface area of respiratory tract	70 m²

Total water in body = 4.3×10^4 g.
Average life span of man = 70 years.
Occupational exposure time of man = 8 hours/day; 40 hours/week; 50 weeks/year; 50 years total time.

Table XIV. Gastrointestinal Tract of the Standard Man

Portion of GI tract that is the critical tissue	Mass of contents (g)	Time food remains, τ (day)	Fraction from lung to GI tract, f_a	
			(sol.)	(insol.)
Stomach (S)	250	1/24	0.50	0.625
Small intestine (SI)	1100	4/24	0.50	0.625
Upper large intestine (ULI)	135	8/24	0.50	0.625
Lower large intestine (LLI)	150	18/24	0.50	0.625

Table XV. Particulates in Respiratory Tract of the Standard Man

Retention of particulate matter in the lungs depends on many factors, such as the size, shape and density of the particles, the chemical form and whether or not the person is a mouth breather; however, when specific data are lacking it is assumed the distribution is as shown below.

Distribution	Readily soluble compounds (%)	Other compounds (%)
Exhaled	25	25
Deposited in upper respiratory passages and subsequently swallowed	50	50
Deposited in the lungs (lower respiratory passages)	25 (this is taken up into the body)	25*

* Of this, half is eliminated from the lungs and swallowed in the first 24 hrs, making a total of $62\frac{1}{2}$ per cent swallowed. The remaining $12\frac{1}{2}$ per cent is retained in the lungs with a half-life of 120 days, it being assumed that this portion is taken up into body fluids.

BIBLIOGRAPHY

References:

1. Recommendations of the International Committee on Radiological Protection, I.C.R.P. Publication 2; Report of Committee II on Permissible Dose for Internal Radiation, 1959.
2. *Health Physics Journal*, Vol. 3, 1960.
3. *N.B.S. Handbook 69*, "Maximum Permissible Body Burdens and Maximum Permissible Concentrations of Radionuclides in Air and in Water for Occupation Exposure, Recommendations of the National Committee of Radiation Protection," U.S. Gov. Print. Office, 1959.
4. *N.B.S. Handbook 85*, (ICRU Report 10b), U.S. Gov. Print. Office, 1964.
5. Ellett, W. H., A. B. Callahan, and G. L. Brownell, "Gamma-ray Dosimetry of Internal Emitters—Monte Carlo Calculations of Absorbed Dose from Point Sources," *Brit. J. Radiol.*, 37:45, 1964.
6. Ellett, W. H., A. B. Callahan, and G. L. Brownell, "Gamma-ray Dosimetry of Internal Emitters, Part II Monte Carlo Calculations of Absorbed Dose from Uniform Sources," *Brit. J. Radiol.*, 38:541, 1965.
7. Quimby, E. H., and S. Feitelberg, *Radioactive Isotopes in Medicine and Biology—Basic Physics and Instrumentation*, p. 116, 1963.
8. Smith, E. M., "Calculating Absorbed Doses from Radiopharmaceuticals," *Nucleonics*, 24:33, 1966.
9. Loevinger, R., J. G. Holt, and G. J. Hine, "Internally Administered Radioisotopes," *Radiation Dosimetry*, 1958.
10. Smith, E. M., C. C. Harris, and R. H. Rohrer, "Calculation of Local Energy Deposition Due to Electron Capture and Internal Conversion," *J. Nuclear Medicine*, Vol. 7, 1966.
11. Slack, L., and K. Way, "Radiations from Radioactive Atoms in Frequent Use," *U.S.A.E.C.*, 1959.
12. Hine, G. J., "Tables of Data Useful for Dose Calculations," *Radiation Dosimetry*, p. 897, 1958.
13. *Nuclear Data Sheets*, Office of Technical Services, Washington, D.C.

14. Focht, E. F., E. H. Quimby, and M. Gershowitz, "Revised Average Geometric Factors for Cylinders in Isotope Dosage," *Radiology*, 85:151, 1965.

15. Bush, F., "The Integral Dose Received from a Uniformly Distributed Radioactive Isotope," *Brit. J. Radiol.*, 22:96, 1949.

16. Cook, M. J., and W. S. Snyder, "Estimation of Population Exposure," *Health Physics*, 11:810, 1965.

17. Seltzer, R. A., J. G. Kereiakes, and E. L. Saenger, "Radiation Exposure from Radioisotopes in Pediatrics," *New England J. Medicine*, 371:84, 1964.

18. Kereiakes, J. G., et al., "Radionuclide Doses to Infants and Children—a Plea for a Standard Child," *Health Physics*, 11:999, 1965.

19. Hayes, R. L., J. E. Carlton, and W. R. Butler, Jr., "Radiation Dose to the Human Intestinal Tract from Internal Emitters," *Health Physics*, 9:915, 1963.

20. Dolphin, G. W., and I. S. Eve, "Dosimetry of the Gastro-intestinal Tract," To be Published in *Health Physics*.

21. Garner, R. J., "A Model for Calculation of Radiation Doses to the Gastro-intestinal Tract of Ruminants," *Health Physics*, 10:297, 1964.

22. Eve, I. S., "An Outline of the Metabolism of Inhaled and Ingested Insoluble Radionuclides," *Brit. J. Radiol.*, 37:115, 1964.

I. INTRODUCTION

Viruses are a heterologous group of infectious agents with much variation in size, shape, chemical composition and biologic behavior. A precise definition is difficult to formulate, but should include the several traits which are common to plant, animal, insect and bacterial viruses: (1) small size, varying from 15 to 300 mμ; (2) ability to replicate or reproduce within susceptible living cells; (3) presence of a nucleic acid (RNA or DNA); and (4) a specific morphology, often with intricate fine structure.

Relatively few types of virus have been subjected to meticulous laboratory study, but the information available suggests that most agents are similar to those whose characteristics are tabulated in the accompanying Tables.

II. PHYSICAL AND CHEMICAL DESCRIPTION

Size. Determination of size or morphology of virus particles may be made by X ray diffraction or electron microscope studies; the latter method is more commonly employed. Multiple photographs of thin sections of virus-infected tissue, or suspensions of virus stained with phosphotungstic acid are carefully scrutinized. Shrinkage, distortion and other artifacts account for the range in values listed in Table I.

Structure and Composition. The simplest of viruses contains a central core of nucleic acid, either RNA or DNA, surrounded by a protein shell or coat. RNA is the nucleic acid found in all plant viruses, some animal disease agents and a few bacteriophages. DNA is present in the others. Table II indicates the variations among viruses in the proportion of nucleic acid. The more complex viral agents may also contain lipid or carbohydrates. Amino acid and nucleotide composition of several purified viruses has been determined (Cohen).

Morphology. The term *virion* refers to a complete infective particle. It is

Table I. Size of Representative Viruses

Group	Virus	Shape	Size (mμ)
Plant	Tobacco necrosis	Sphere	17–20
	Turnip yellow	Sphere	20–22
	Tomato bushy stunt	Sphere	20–22
	Bean mosaic, southern	Sphere	20–25
	Tobacco mosaic	Rod	280–300 × 15–17
	Orchid mosaic	Rod	12 × 480
	Potato X	Rod	600 × 10
Insect	Silkworm polyhedral	Rod	290 × 40
	Fir-shoot, granule	Rod	300 × 40
	Tipula iridescent	Sphere	130
	Antheraea mylitta	Sphere	30
	Sphinx ligustri	Sphere	12–15
	Sphinx populi	Sphere	80
Bacterial	T-even phage	Head	65 × 95
		Tail	25 × 100
	T-3, T-7	Head	47 diam.
		Tail	10 × 15
	ØX-174	Sphere	20–22 diam.
Animal	Vaccinia	Brick-shaped	200 × 350
	Influenza	Spheroid	80–100
	Herpes Simplex, capsid	Spherical	100
	with envelope		150–180
	Adenovirus	Spherical	70–80
	Polyoma	Spherical	45–50
	Poliovirus	Spherical	30
	Vesicular stomatitis	Rod-rounded end	165 × 65

Table II. Chemical Composition of Representative Viruses (Per Cent by Weight)

	Protein	Lipid	Nucleic Acid	Carbohydrate
Vaccinia	89	5.7	5.6	......
Influenza	69	24	1.0	7
Herpes Simplex	70	22	6.5	1.6
Adenovirus (type 2)	87	......	13	......
Poliovirus	78	......	22	......
Equine Encephalomyelitis	49	43	4.4	4.0
Tobacco Mosaic	94.2	......	5.8	1.0
Turnip Yellow	63	......	37	......
T-2 phage	50	2.6	40	10
Silkworm Polyhedral	86	......	14	......
Tipula Iridescent	82	5	12	......

Table III. Viruses with Icosahedral Symmetry

Number of Capsomeres	Virus
12	Bacteriophage ØX-174
42	Polyoma
	Human Wart
92	? Wound Tumor
162	Herpes Simplex
	Varicella
	Herpes Zoster
252	Adenovirus
	Canine Hepatitis
	Gallus adeno-like (GAL)
812	Tipula Iridescent

composed, in its simplest form, of a core of nucleic acid surrounded by a protein coat or *capsid*. The *capsid* may be made up of a number of morphologically similar subunits or *capsomeres* placed symmetrically around the central core. In some viruses, such as herpes simplex, a loose sac or envelope invests the capsid and the enclosed nucleic acid. The entire infective particle with envelope in such cases is called the virion, and the inner capsid and nucleic acid are designated the *nucleo-capsid* or *nucleoid*. Additional terms—*head, tail, collar*, etc.—are applied to appropriate parts of the bacteriophage.

The simpler virus particles have either helical or icosahedral symmetry, while the architecture of larger forms may be very intricate. The precise morphology of several viral agents is still to be determined. The number of capsomeres in a virus particle having icosahedral symmetry can be calculated with the formula $10 \times (n-1)^2 + 2$, where $x = 1$ (or rarely 3, as with turnip yellow virus) and $n =$ the number of capsomeres along one edge (Table III).

III. CLASSIFICATION

Viruses are traditionally separated, according to the host affected, into four major families: plant, animal, insect, and bacterial (Tables IV & V). The rationale for this classification is not clear especially since many similarities exist between members of different families. Icosahedral symmetry is seen in adenoviruses (animal) as well as in the tipula iridescent virus (plant) and ØX-174 (bacterial), for example; and helical symmetry occurs in plant, insect, and animal viruses.

The taxonomy of vertebrate or animal viruses is further advanced than that of the other families and is summarized in Table V. Type of nucleic acid, symmetry, number of capsomeres, susceptibility to physical or chemical agents, host infected and protein antigens form the basis for the classification.

Table IV. General Characteristics of Viruses Infecting Plants, Insects, and Bacteria

Virus Family	Nucleic Acid	Shape	Symmetry
Plant	RNA	Rods	Helical
		Spheres	Icosahedral
Insect			
Polyhedrosis			
Nuclear	DNA	Rods	Helical
Cytoplasmic	RNA	Spheres	Icosahedral
Granulosis	DNA	Rods	Helical
Cytoplasmic	DNA	Spheres	Icosahedral
Bacterial	DNA	Tail-head	Complex
	RNA-DNA	Spheres	Icosahedral

IV. METHODS OF STUDY

A. Ultracentrifugation, either preparatory or analytical, is a commonly used tool for the separation of virus from host material. In combination with density gradients prepared from cesium chloride, sucrose or tartrate, centrifugation permits the quantitative measurement of the rate of virus sedimentation and provides information relative to the purity of the preparation. (See Markham)

B. Electron microscopy, especially since the development of the negative staining technique (see Wildy and Horne), and improved methods for thin sectioning, has provided a tremendous amount of new information concerning virus morphology and virus behavior. The electron microscope will also prove a rapid and accurate aid in clinical diagnosis of virus infection.

C. X-ray diffraction patterns provided the initial indications of the shape and structure of virus particles which were later confirmed by electron microscope studies. The use of x-ray diffraction is limited by the large amount of crystalline virus required.

D. Electrophoresis has been used to determine the homogeneity of virus preparations or to obtain separation of the various components. Polyacrylamide, agar or starch are the commonly used gel systems.

E. The isolation of viral agents from clinical specimens is a complicated procedure best conducted by special laboratories or regional health departments. The methods employed vary with the agent being sought. Agents detected must be specifically identified by serologic procedures. Table VI illustrates the general approach to isolation of viral agents.

V. VIRAL DISEASES

A wide variety of clinical syndromes can be produced by the same agent or group of agents, and although agents tend to multiply in certain tissues

Table V. A Classification of Some of the Common Animal Viruses

Group-Typical Examples	Structure	Nucleic Acid	Inhibition by Actinomycin	Host
1. Poxvirus (200-300 mμ diameter) Smallpox, vaccinia	Complex, largest of viruses Nucleoid enclosed in envelope of lipid & protein	DNA	Yes	Man
2. Herpes virus (120-150 mμ diameter)	Icosahedral with envelope		Yes	Man
a. Herpes simplex, varicella, herpes zoster				Monkey
b. B virus				Swine
c. Pseudorabies				Man, mice, guinea pigs
d. Cytomegalovirus				
3. Adenovirus (70-90 mμ diameter) Human 28 types	Icosahedral, no envelope	DNA	Yes	Primates, carnivores rodents, birds, ungulates
4. Myxovirus				
a. Influenza A,B,C (80-120 mμ)	RNA coil in lipid envelope	RNA	Yes	Man*, swine, horse, birds
b. Parainfluenza, mumps ±, NDV (120-150 mμ)	RNA coil in lipid envelope	RNA	No	Man, mouse, monkey, cattle
c. Measles, distemper, rhinderpest	RNA coil in lipid envelope	RNA	No	Human, dog, cattle
5. Papovaviruses (40-50 mμ) Papilloma, Polyoma Vacuolating	Icosahedral, no envelope Similar to small polyhedral plant viruses and RNA phage	DNA	Yes	Rabbit, monkey, mice
6. Arbovirus (30-50 mμ) Western equine, Dengue Yellow Fever, St. Louis	? Helical symmetry Lipid envelope	RNA	No	Vertebrates & arthropods
7. Picornavirus (25-35 mμ)	Icosahedral, no envelope	RNA, single strand	No	Inhabit alimentary tract of many cattle, pigs, birds, etc.
8. Reovirus (70-80 mμ)	Icosahedral, no envelope	RNA, double strand	Yes	Man, mice, cattle

±Mumps has been isolated only from man.

* Influenza B and C have been isolated only from man.

Table VI. Guide for the Isolation of Viral Agent from Properly Collected Specimens*

Virus Suspected	Method for Detecting Virus					
	Tissue culture	Suckling mice	Adult mice	Chick embryo	Guinea pig	Rabbit
Polio	+ + + +[1]					
Coxsackie A	+[1]	+ + + +				
B	+ + +[1]	+ + +				
ECHO	+ + + +[1]	±				
Arboviruses	+[2]	+ + + +		+ +	+	
Rabies	+[2]	+ + + +	+ + + +	+ +	+ + +	+ +
Herpes Simplex	+ + + +	+ + + +	+	+ + + +	+	+ + +
Varicella, Herpes Zoster	+ + + +[3]					
Adenovirus	+ + + +[1]					
Influenza	+ +[4]			+ + + +		
Mumps	+ +[1]	±		+ + + +		
Measles	+ + +[1,3]					
Vaccinia, Variola	+ + + +[1,3]			+ + + +	+ + +	

*Number of pluses indicates relative preference for a particular method.
(1) Monkey kidney, Hep2, Hela
(2) Hamster kidney or Duck embryo
(3) Human Fibroblast or Amnion cultures
(4) Primary monkey kidney

of the body, the symptoms produced may vary from none to very marked. This is perhaps best illustrated by the enterovirus family (Table VII). Other agents (chicken pox or measles) rarely infect a host without producing the classical clinical manifestations of disease.

BIBLIOGRAPHY

Andrews, C. H., "Classification of Viruses of Vertebrates," *Advances in Virus Research*, 9, Smith, K. M., and M. A. Lauffer, Editors, 1962.

Bawden, F. C., *Plant Viruses and Virus Diseases*, 4th Ed., 1964.

Burnet, F. M., and W. M. Stanley, *The Viruses*, 1, 2, 3, 1962.

Cohen, S. S., "Comparative Biochemistry and Virology," *Advances in Virus Research*, 3, Smith, K. M., and M. A. Lauffer, Editors, 1955.

Lennette, E. H., Editor, *Diagnostic Procedures for Viral and Rickettsial Disease*, 3rd Ed., 1964.

Markham, R., "Ultracentrifugation of Plant Viruses," *Advances in Virus Research*, 9, Smith, K. M. and M. A. Lauffer, Editors, 1962.

Wildy, P., and R. W. Horne, *Prog. Med. Virol.*, 5:1, 1963.

Table VII. Various Clinical Syndromes Resulting from Infection with Common Virus Agents*

VIRUS AGENT (Group)	Encephalitis Aseptic Meningitis	Febrile Illness	Diarrhea	Exanthem	Respiratory Infection, Pneumonia	Pharyngitis	Paralysis	Other
1. Poliovirus (3 known types)	+ + +	+ +	+				+ + +	
2. Coxsackie A (24 known types)	+ +	+	?	+	+ +	+ +	+	Pleurodynia,
3. Coxsackie B (6 known types)	+ + + + +	+			+ +		+	Myocarditis
4. ECHO (32 known types)	+ + + + +	+ + + +	+?	+ +	+ +		+	Hemorrhagic Fever
5. Arbovirus (160 known types)	+ + + +	+ + +						Stomatitis,
6. Herpes Virus (one known type)	+ +	+		+ + +				Conjunctivitis
7. Adenovirus (28 known types)		+ + +			+ +	+ + +		Conjunctivitis
8. Influenze (3 known types)		+ +			+ + +			
9. Parainfluenza (3 known types)		+ +			+ + +		±	Croup
10. Mumps (one known type)	+ +				+ +			Parotitis,
11. Measles (one known type)	+	+ + + +		+ + + + +		+		Orchitis

*See a textbook of infectious diseases for more complete information. Number of pluses indicates frequency of occurence of each sign or symptom.

I. INTRODUCTION: WORKING CONCEPTS OF CONTROL

Many biophysical processes, as indicated elsewhere in this *Handbook*, have some inherent self-regulation or control to the extent that, if the input level changes, the dynamic response of the process tends to a new but not greatly different steady-state. As an example, when the fluid-flow rate into a tank having a small escape pipe at the bottom is increased, a new higher equilibrium level eventually results because of the inherent physical processes by which the increased level "feeds back" negatively as an increased outlet flow to balance the new inflow. In contrast, there are some processes whose inherent feedback effects are positive or regenerative; in such cases, an input disturbance tends to grow, at least over a certain range, before saturation effects occur. Such a process is termed unstable. The current growth of population, knowledge, and cities exemplify the effect.

Such inherent control is called *passive*, as distinct from the *active* control which is discussed below. Active control can be functionally defined by a general structure involving a closed-loop of subsystems, each having identifiable roles (see Figure 1). Further, control of this type can be more precise.

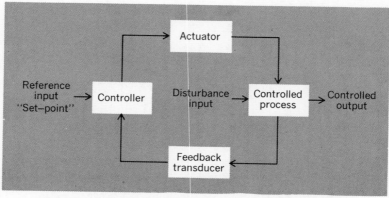

Figure 1. Basic Structure of Feedback Control System

Such an analytic scheme presupposes a meaningful casualty from input to output, and implies that a feedback control system only exists when viewed in this light. Certainly the mathematical equations for a given system cannot define whether it is a *feedback* control system or not. For example, mutually-causal systems such as those of predator:prey populations involve the same mathematical analysis. By way of illustration, the warm-blooded animal uses a complicated active control scheme to maintain an essentially constant internal temperature over a wide range of environmental disturbances. Its consequent release from the many behavioral constraints of the cold-blooded animal (which has passive control only and also a slightly unstable heat balance process) has apparently provided a significant selective advantage in evolution.

Biological control was initially perceived in regulatory or *homeostatic* terms, that is, the actuation of mechanisms to bring such variables as temperature, pressure and concentrations back to their normal "setpoints" after having been dislocated by system disturbances. The *servomechanism* is another type having the additional primary function that the system output shall "track," or follow faithfully, a varying reference input, with power amplification almost always being required between input and output. An example is the power steering of various vehicles. Neuro-muscular control seems to fit this functional definition well, especially noteworthy being the multivariable sophisticated servomechanism by which eye movement is controlled both in tracking visual targets and compensating against body disturbances.

II. STRUCTURE OF CONTROL

Dynamic analysis requires mapping of information flows within the system, and this is aided by *block diagram* representation which reticulates the system into blocks (subsystems) connected by arrowed lines (input and output variables). Since energy and material flows are mostly modulated as dependent variables, they are not usually shown explicitly. The structure of control can be studied as a closed-loop of four main subsystems (see Figures 1 and 3).

The *Controlled Process*, H, viewed causally, is the reason for the whole system's existence. The mammalian thermoregulation system illustrates the idea very well, the body presumably being a biochemical plant which operates most efficiently in a narrow temperature range about 37°C. (Figure 2). In detail, however, the problem of mathematically modelling the body for this heat-flow situation is not trivial, nor indeed inferring exactly which variables are being controlled. Contemporary models include at least three separate "lumps"—the core, muscles and skin—thus involving a third-order differential equation.

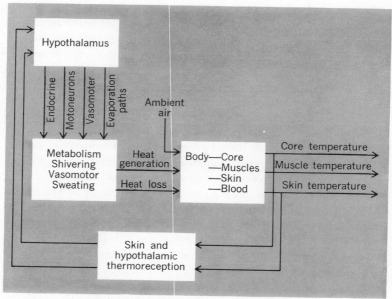

Figure 2.   Thermoregulatory Control System

The *Controller*, G, determines the commands to be sent to the controlled process via the actuators, based upon comparison of the desired outputs (set-points) and the actual outputs, as signalled by the feedback transducers. In thermoregulation, the hypothalamus provides this function, but as in many homeostats there is no clear evidence for input set-points. However, this raises no practical problem, provided that the closed-loop somewhere implements the sign inversion of negative feedback which is necessary for static stability; consequently the comparator concept may still validly be used since it has analytical convenience. This defines the error variable(s),

$$E(t) = R(t) - C(t) \tag{1}$$

which appears explicitly in Figure 3 when $F = 1$.

The *Actuators*, A, provide the highpower-level *manipulated variables* M(t) to operate upon the controlled process. In thermoregulation, these include increased metabolism and muscle shivering for heat production, evaporation to increase heat loss, and vasomotor action to modulate blood and hence heat flow to the skin. The system's disturbances arise from ambient conditions and may be viewed as heat flows, thus algebraically combined with actuator outputs.

The *Feedback Transducers*, F, feed back information on the actual system outputs, usually also converting into another energy domain. Thus, skin thermoreceptors feed back through afferent neurons information on the insulating lump of the controlled process, while the hypothalamus region itself effectively measures the core temperature. Biological receptors typically have *adapting* characteristics; that is, they signal urgently when changes occur. Dynamically, this fact helps to make a fast but stable loop, an action nominally provided by G in the conventional configuration of Figure 3.

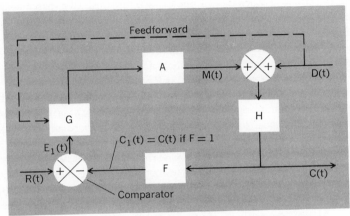

Figure 3.   Stylized Linear Feedback Control System

III. DYNAMICS OF CONTROL

Control system dynamics are studied through their description of differential equations, which in practice are often complicated and non-linear, requiring computer solutions. However, most basic dynamic patterns can be revealed from analysis of idealized linear systems, especially knowing the Laplace transform technique of expressing output:input ratios as *Transfer Functions*, here G, A, H and F. In consequence, the closed-loop transfer functions are, Figure 3,

$$\frac{C}{R} = \frac{GAH}{1 + FGAH} \quad \text{and} \quad \frac{C}{D} = \frac{H}{1 + FGAH} \quad (2)$$

Input

time

Unit   Step Input

The *steady-state* responses, for example to unit step changes in the reference and disturbance inputs, characterize one basic closed-loop property. Here the transfer functions typically become simple *gains*, and taking $F = H = 1$ for convenience, then the *loop gain* GA equals a constant value K, and the so-called *proportional* control is being implemented. Then,

$$C_R(t \to \infty) = \frac{K}{1 + K}, \text{ and } C_D(t \to \infty) = \frac{1}{1 + K} \tag{3}$$

Thus only if $K \to \infty$ does $C_R \to 1$ and $C_D \to 0$, the desirable responses, for which the system error is zero, Eq. (1). Unfortunately, an infinite static loop gain K would make practical loops unstable, but the effect can be achieved dynamically by using *integral* or "follow-up" control. As an example of this, one can always position a finger exactly over a point by continuing to take corrective action as long as visual error persists.

The dynamic response should be as fast as possible, but adequately stable and not requiring expensively large amounts of a manipulated variable (*e.g.*, muscle force, heat flow); these are normally conflicting demands. The stability limit is specified directly from Eq. 2, for if the common denominator, the *characteristic function* equals zero, namely, if FGAH $= -1$, then the static configuration of negative feedback is converted dynamically into a configuration of positive feedback just sufficient to sustain growth or oscillations. In this regard, rate-sensitive (adapting) transducers are important because they provide *derivative* control action which can stabilize the system. As an extreme example, the vestibular system provides such action to help stabilize the human's upright posture as an inverted pendulum (another example of an inherently unstable controlled process).

IV. PROGRAMMING AND OPTIMIZING THE CONTROL

Biologically, a number of techniques have evolved to specify quantitatively the system operation within the structure so far discussed.

Information Aspects. These generally seem to obviate the need for use of the relatively slow feedback path, that is to program open-loop control. Open-loop control can in fact always be at least as fast, stable, and economical as closed-loop control, and is therefore desirable when unknown disturbance and internal parameter changes are small. Thus, in human operator work, the alert driver anticipates the effect of oncoming gradient changes (a disturbance input) by adjusting engine power before the car's speed changes; and in autonomous systems, for example, an increased ventilation and blood circulation appear before the undertaking of a heavy muscular task. Another major implementation is the *preprogramming* presumably involved in learning fast, skilled tasks such as piano playing and ball throwing. Thus the iterative learning task should involve establishing a program of actuator forcing without the corrective benefit of the feedback path which is now too slow for the speed of action required. The penalty paid for this fast open-loop control is that occasional unpredicted disturbances and mistakes in executing the actuator program will result in unsatisfactory outputs.

Energetic Aspects. The ongoing penalty of such autonomous systems as walking and breathing is significant, and since energy acquisition is expensive to an organism, minimization of its demand in these systems should provide a selective advantage. These systems usually have at least two manipulated variables to actuate (here frequency and size of pace or lung volume), so that an optimal combination should be available. Indeed experimental data confirm this under various system loadings for both walking and breathing. Unfortunately, the information pathways which effect such a slow adaptive or optimizing control are not yet identified biologically, and the task illumines the fascinating current problems of understanding biological control systems.

BIBLIOGRAPHY

References:
1. Grodins, F. S., *Control Theory and Biological Systems,* 1963.
2. Milsum, J. H., *Biological Control System Analysis,* 1966.
3. Yamamoto, W. S., and J. R. Brobeck, *Physiological Controls and Regulation,* 1965.
4. Riggs, D. S., *The Mathematical Approach to Physiological Problems,* 1963.
5. *Models and Analogues in Biology,* 1960.
6. *Homeostasis and Feedback Mechanisms,* 1964.
7. *Automatic Control,* Scientific American, Inc., 1955.

TELEMETERING OF BIOLOGICAL SIGNALS: BIO-TELEMETRY

I. INTRODUCTION

Bio-telemetry is the technique for measuring and transmitting biological information from a living organism and its environment to a location where this information can be observed or recorded. It is a means of communication between a living system and an observer.

The essential blocks of a bio-telemetering system are shown in Figure 1. The transducer converts the biological variable into signals that can be processed. (The properties of transducers are discussed in several of the general references.) The signal conditioner amplifies and modifies the signal to make it suitable for transmission or recording. The modification of signals may include the filtering of certain bands of component frequencies, altering the shapes of the signal pulses, etc. The transmission link connects the signal input blocks to the readout device. Readout or display devices include oscilloscopes, mercury columns, etc., or recorders utilizing ink or photographic film. The blocks or components shown may be interchanged or combined; in some systems, one or more may be eliminated. For example, in the radio-transmitted EKG system, the electrode is the transducer; the amplifier and filter are the conditioner; the radio transmitter and receiver are the transmission linkage; and the recorder is the readout device.

In telemetering, the major concern is in the conditioning and the transmission of the signal, although the total system includes both transducers and readout. The conditioner depends on the type of transducer and the characteristic of the signal. Transmission is accomplished either by direct connection of wires or cables, or by wireless linkage using radio, ultrasonics, and optics. Sometimes telemetry is used to designate wireless transmission exclusively, since radio linkage is most commonly used.

The requirements for bio-telemetry are more than mere communication from the subject to the observer. In order to minimize constraint of and interference with the living system the following problems must be considered in addition to the usual concern with bandwidth and signal and noise levels.

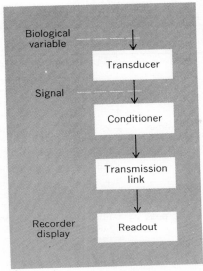

Figure 1.   Block diagram of a typical bio-telemetry system.

1   Weight and size limitation: the generally accepted limit for animals is from 1 to 5 percent that of subject.

2   Long-term power supply of the unit.

3   Physiological and psychological reactions. The compatibility of the potting material to living tissues, the effect of the telemetering unit on the subject body and on its behavior should be considered.

4   Stability and reliability.

5   Packaging and installation techniques, *i.e.*, harness or implant.

A brief survey of the physiological parameters that have been telemetered and the characteristics of these signals is given in Table I. The telemetering system should be selected to transmit these signals with maximum fidelity and simplicity. The most commonly used technique of radio telemetry is discussed in the next section.

II.   RADIO TELEMETERING SYSTEMS

The block diagram of a typical radio telemetering system is as shown in Figure 2.
The transducer, signal conditioner, and transmitter may be either mounted on the surface of the subject or implanted inside the body. With

Table I. Characteristics of Physiological Signals Telemetered

Physiological Signal	Amplitude Range	Frequency Range	Transducer	Ref.
Electrocardiogram (EKG)	0.75–4mv. p-p.	0.1–100 cps.	Electrodes	1
Phonocardiogram		30–100 cps.	Piezoelectric pickup, micro-phone.	2
Electromyogram (EMG)	0.1–4mv. p-p.	2–10^5 cps. (10–500 cps. clinical)	Electrodes	1
Electroencephalo-gram (EEG)	10–$75\mu v$	0.5–200 cps.	Electrodes	1
Electrogastrograph	$10\mu v$–$350\mu v$	0.05–0.2 cps.	Surface electrodes	3
Nerve potentials	3mv. peak	up to 1000 pulses/second rise time $0.3\mu s$	Electrodes	4
Blood pressure	0–400 mm Hg	0.5–100 cps.	Strain gage on artery. Hydraulic coupling to transducer	1 7
Blood flow	1–300 cm/sec.	1–20 cps.	Electro-magnetic flowmeter. Electro-sonic flowmeter.	5 6
Gastrointestinal pressure	20–100 cm H_2O	0–10 cps.	Variable inductance	8
Bladder pressure	to 100 cm H_2O	0–10 cps.		9
Temperature	90°–110°F	0–0.1 cps.	Thermistor thermal expansion	1
Respiration rate		0.15–6 cps.	Electrode impedance; piezoelectric devices; pneumograph	1
Tidal volume	50–1000 ml per breath	0.15–6 cps.	Impedance pneumograph	1
Stomach pH	3–13	0–1 cp min.	Glass electrode; Antimony electrodes	10
Intestinal forces	1–40 grams	0–1 cps.	Strain gages	11

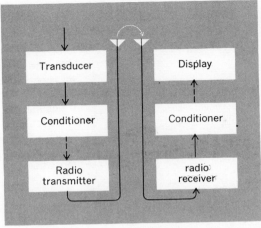

Figure 2.   Block diagram of a typical radio telemetry system.

micro-electronic techniques, the complete unit can be made to weigh less than a gram. When implanted in a mouse, it will transmit a single channel of information for almost any desired length of time.

Figure 3 shows the three popular circuits used for bio-telemetry.

With integrated circuit technology, weight and size limitations are not serious for subjects weighing more than 50 g. The K-5 transmitter shown in Figure 4 weighs 0.4 g without a battery. The long-term power supply is a major problem in bio-telemetry. Studies show that miniature telemetering units may be powered by the body energy of the subject, as expressed in heart beats, blood flow, respiration, body motion, electrochemical energy, etc.; or through its environment, as in temperature difference, electromagnetic field of a radio wave, intense light, etc. Of the latter, radio fields have been shown to be operational. Applications include radio power-charged storage batteries, rectified continuous radio power,[16] pulsed radio power, and the alternative receiving and transmitting of signals at the same frequency.[10]

The body reaction to a surface unit is not serious, but the effect of implanted telemetric apparatus is a problem not completely investigated. It is known that Teflon and medical grade Silastic (Dow No. 382) have little effect on body tissues. They can be used to coat the telemetering unit to reduce the reaction. The size and shape of the implant seem to have an effect on the long term body reaction.[17] The psychological reaction to an implant has not yet been studied to any significant extent.

In order to protect the telemetering unit from handling and body environment, the unit should be packaged. The problem again is more serious for an implanted unit than a surface unit. For implant transmitters

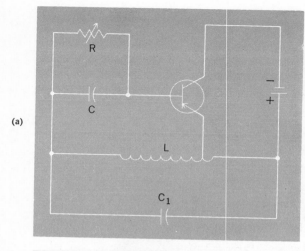

(a) Pulsed carrier oscillator-modulator. Carrier frequency may be modulated by the motion of magnetic rod in coil L or by the microphonic action of C_1. The pulse rate of carrier trains may be varied by the value of R.C., such as by using a thermistor for R to transmit temperature information.[12]

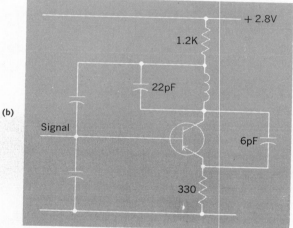

(b) C. W. FM oscillator-modulator. It is a common base collector to an emitter-coupled oscillator. The input signal varies the base emitter voltage, and therefore the base emitter capacitor, to produce frequency change on the carrier.[14]

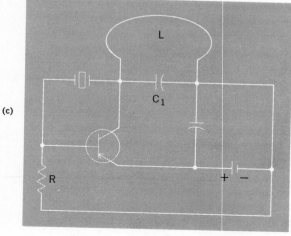

(c) Crystal-controlled oscillator for animal tracking. The tank coil, L, is the harness on the animal. The circuit may be made to give a pulsed carrier by adding a capacitor in parallel with R.[15]

Figure 3. Three oscillator-modulator circuits for bio-telemetry.

there has not been found any single material which is satisfactory in sealing off the body fluid to prevent corrosion, providing mechanical protection, and at the same time being compatible to body tissue. The present preferred approach is to use several layers of potting material to obtain all the three functions.

Because of the extreme requirements of circuit simplicity and size and weight, the transmitting part of a telemetering system is usually designed with very little margin of operation. The stability and reliability become problems for long term operation. Special circuits and electronic techniques have to be developed both in the design of the transmitter and the

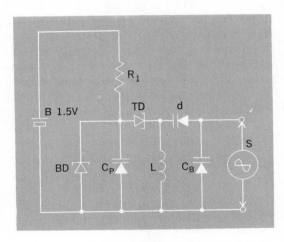

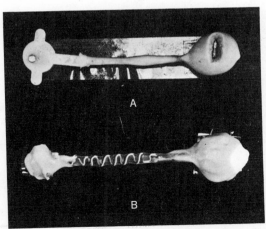

Figure 4. The circuit diagram and photographs of K-5 implant transmitters.

operation of the receiving equipment. By using solid-state electronic devices, the possible life of these telemetering systems can be longer than the natural life span of the subject.

As an example of the telemetering system, the construction and operation of K-5 systems developed at Case Institute is summarized.[16] The circuit of K-5 is shown in Figure 4.

The transmitter is mounted on an 8 mm diameter printed circuit board. On one side is a spiral coil, serving as oscillator coil as well as antenna; on the other side, the diodes and resistors are mounted. The over-all size of the transmitter is 8 mm diameter by 3 mm thick. It weighs 0.44 g. A 40-hour battery (RM-312) weighs 1 g, and has a size of 12 mm diameter by 5 mm thick. The unit can be used to transmit signals from 5 microvolts up and has a frequency band from 0.01 cps to 20 KC. The input impedance is from 100 kilo-ohms to several megohms. It operates at 100 to 300 MC. The power supply may be a battery and a miniaturized magnetic switch, or may be a radio-wave power detector. The detector is a sphere of 1 cm diameter; it can replace the battery and supply power to the transmitter from an RF induction field of 5 to 10×10^{-5} webers/meter^2.[16]

BIBLIOGRAPHY

General:

"Bio-telemetry," [special issue], *Bio-Science*, February, 1965.
Caceres, C. A., *Biomedical Telemetering*, 1965.
Geddes, L. A., "A Bibliography of Biological Telemetry," *Amer. J. of Med. Electronics*, 1:294–298, 1962.
Murray, W. E., et al., *Biomedical Sciences Instrumentation*, Vols. 1, 2, 1963, 1964.
Nichols, M. H., *Radio Telemetry*, 1957.
Slater, L. E., *Bio-Telemetry*, 1963.
Telemetry Transducers Handbook, n.d.

References:

(1) Sullivan, G. H., C. Hoefener, and V. W. Bolie, "Electronic Systems for Biological Telemetry," in L. Slater (ed.), *Biotelemetry*, 1963.
(2) Ginsburg, S. J., L. Gerstley III, R. M. Rauch, and J. M. Benjamin, "A Fetal Phonocardiotachometer for Use in Labor," *IEEE Trans. on Bio-Medical Eng.*, Vol. BME-11(1 and 2):35, 1964.
(3) Sobakin, M. A., M. D., F. P. Smirnov, and L. N. Mishin, "Electrogastrography," *IRE Trans. on Bio-Medical Electronics*, Vol. BME-9(2):129, 1962.
(4) Suckling, E. E., *Bioelectricity*, 1961, p. 200–201.
(5) Joachim, K. E., "Development of the Electromagnetic Blood Flowmeter," *IRE Trans. on Bio-Medical Electronics*, Vol. BME-9(4):228, 1962.
(6) Franklin, D. C., D. W. Baker, and R. F. Rushmer, "Pulsed Ultrasonic Transit Time Flowmeter," *IRE Trans. on Bio-Medical Electronics*, Vol. BME-9(1):44, 1962.

(7)   Shirer, H. W., "Blood Pressure Measuring Methods," *IRE Trans. on Bio-Medical Electronics,* Vol. BME-9(2):116, 1962.

(8)   Farrar, J. T., and James S. Bernstein, "Recording of Intraluminal Gastro-intestinal Pressures by a Radio Telemetry Capsule," *Gastroenterology,* 35(6): 603, 1958.

(9)   Gleason, D. M., and John K. Lattimer, "A Miniature Radio Transmitter which is Inserted into the Bladder and which Records Voiding Pressures," *J. Urol.,* 87(3):507, 1962.

(10) Nagumo, J., et al., "Echo Capsule for Medical Use, (A Batteryless Endora-diosonde)," *IRE Trans. on Bio-Medical Electronics,* Vol BME-9(3):195, 1962.

(11) Ko, W. H., C. J. Slabinski, and E. T. Yon, "An Implant Telemetering System for Measure of Internal Stress and Strain," to be published.

(12) Mackay, R. S., "Radio Telemetering from within the Human Body," *Science,* 134:1196–1202, 1962.

(13) Slater, L. E., *Some Facts about Bio-Telemetry,* 1964.

(14) Sperry, C. J., et al., "Miniature Subcutaneous FM Transmitter for Brain Po-tentials," *Science,* 134:1421, 1961.

(15) Southern, W. E., *Equipment and Techniques for Using Radio Telemetering in Wildlife Studies,* 1963.

(16) Ko, W. H., "RF Induction Power Supply for Implant Circuits," and "Minia-ture FM Implant Bio-telemetering Transmitters," International Conference on Med. Elec. and Bio. Eng., Tokyo, Japan, Aug. 1965.

(17) Oppenheimer, B. S., et al., "Further Studies of Polymers as Carcinogenic Agents in Animals," *Cancer Res.,* 15:333, 1955.

I. ACOUSTICAL TERMINOLOGY

General

Sound. 1. An oscillation in pressure, stress, particle displacement, particle velocity, etc., in a medium with internal forces (*e.g.*, elastic, viscous), or the superposition of such propagated oscillations; 2. an auditory sensation evoked by the oscillation described above.

> Note 1: In case of possible confusion, the term "sound wave" or "elastic wave" may be used for concept (1) and the term "sound sensation" for concept (2). Not all sound waves can evoke an auditory sensation; *e.g.*, ultrasound.

> Note 2: The medium in which the sound exists is often indicated by an appropriate adjective; *e.g.*, air-borne, water-borne, structure-borne.

Acoustics. The science of sound, including its production, transmission, and effects; the acoustics of a room are those qualities that together determine its character with respect to distinct hearing.

Acoustic, Acoustical. The qualifying adjectives mean containing, producing, arising from, actuated by, related to, or associated with sound. Acoustic is used when the term being qualified designates something that has the properties, dimensions, or physical characteristics associated with sound waves; acoustical is used when the term being qualified does not designate explicitly something that has such properties, dimensions, or physical characteristics.

> Note 1: The following examples qualify as having the "properties or physical characteristics associated with sound waves" and hence would take acoustic: impedance, inertance, load (radiation field), output (sound power), energy, wave, medium, signal, conduit, absorptivity, transducer.

> Note 2: The following examples do not have the requisite physical characteristics and therefore take acoustical: society, method, engineer, school, glossary, symbol, problem, measurement, point of view, end-use, device.

Note 3: As illustrated in the preceding notes, usually the generic term is modified by acoustical, whereas the specific technical implication calls for acoustic.

Oscillation. The variation, usually with time, of the magnitude of a quantity with respect to a specified reference when the magnitude is alternately greater and smaller than the reference.

Vibration. An oscillation wherein the quantity is a parameter that defines the motion of a mechanical system.

Periodic Quantity. An oscillating quantity whose values recur for certain increments of the independent variable.

Note 1: If a periodic quantity v is a function of t, then
$$v = f(t) = f(t + T)$$
where T, a constant, is a period of v.

Note 2: In general, a periodic function can be expanded into a series of the form
$$y = f(t) = A_0 + A_1 \sin(wt + a_1) + A_2 \sin(2wt + a_2) + \cdots,$$
where w, a positive constant, equals 2π divided by the period T, and the A's and a's are constants which may be positive, negative, or zero.

Primitive Period (Period). The primitive period of a periodic quantity is the smallest increment of the independent variable for which the function repeats itself.

Note: If no ambiguity is likely, the primitive period is simply called the period of the function.

Cycle. The complete sequence of values of a periodic quantity that occur during a period.

Frequency. Frequency of a function periodic in time is the reciprocal of the primitive period. The unit is the cycle per unit time and must be specified. Internationally, the cycle per second is called the hertz (Hz).

Angular Frequency (Circular Frequency). The angular frequency of a periodic quantity, in radians per unit time, is the frequency multiplied by 2π. The usual symbol is ω.

Basic Frequency. The basic frequency of an oscillatory quantity having sinusoidal components with different frequencies is the frequency of the component considered to be the most important.

Note: In a driven system, the basic frequency would in general be the driving frequency, and in a periodic oscillatory system, it would be the fundamental frequency.

Audio Frequency. Any frequency corresponding to a normally audible sound wave.

Note: Audio frequencies range roughly from 15 to 20,000 cycles per second (Hz).

Ultrasonic Frequency. A frequency lying above the audio frequency range.

The term is commonly applied to elastic waves propagated in gases, liquids, or solids.

Note 1: The term "ultrasonic" may be used as a modifier to indicate a device or system intended to operate at an ultrasonic frequency.

Note 2: "Supersonic" was a term once used in acoustics synonymously with ultrasonic; such usage is now deprecated.

Infrasonic Frequency. A frequency lying below the audio frequency range.

Peak-to-Peak Value of an oscillating quantity is the algebraic difference between the extremes of the quantity.

Simple Harmonic Motion. A motion such that the displacement is a sinusoidal function of time.

Phase of a Periodic Quantity. For a particular value of the independent variable, the fractional part of a period through which the independent variable has advanced, measured from an arbitrary reference.

Wave. A disturbance which is propagated in a medium in such a manner that at any point in the medium the quantity serving as measure of disturbance is a function of the time, while at any instant the displacement at a point is a function of the position of the point.

Any physical quantity that has the same relationship to some independent variable (usually time) that a propagated disturbance has, at a particular instant, with respect to space, may be called a wave.

Wavelength. A periodic wave in an isotropic medium is the perpendicular distance between two wave fronts in which the displacements have a difference in phase of one complete period.

Harmonic. A sinusoidal quantity having a frequency that is an integral multiple of the frequency of a periodic quantity to which it is related.

Subharmonic. A sinusoidal quantity having a frequency that is an integral sub-multiple of the fundamental frequency of a periodic quantity to which it is related.

Signal. A disturbance used to convey information; the information to be conveyed over a communication system.

Noise. Any undesired sound. By extension, noise is any unwanted disturbance within a useful frequency band, such as undesired electric waves, a transmission channel or device; an erratic, intermittent, or statistically random oscillation.

Note: If ambiguity exists as to the nature of the noise, a phrase such as "acoustic noise" or "electric noise" should be used.

Background Noise. The total of all sources of interference in a system used for the production, detection, measurement, or recording of a signal, independent of the presence of the signal.

Note 1: Ambient noise detected, measured, or recorded with the signal becomes part of the background noise.

Note 2: Included in this definition is the interference resulting from primary power supplies, that separately is commonly described as hum.

Random Noise. An oscillation whose instantaneous magnitude is not specified for any given instant of time. The instantaneous magnitudes of a random noise are specified only by probability distribution functions giving the fraction of the total time that the magnitude, or some sequence of magnitudes, lies within a specified range.

Reverberation. 1. The persistence of sound in an enclosed space, as a result of multiple reflections after the sound source has stopped; 2. the sound that persists in an enclosed space as a result of repeated reflection or scattering, after the source of the sound has stopped.

Echo. A wave that has been reflected or otherwise returned with sufficient magnitude and delay to be detected as a wave distinct from that directly transmitted.

Modulation. The variation in the value of some parameter characterizing a periodic oscillation. Thus, amplitude modulation of a sinusoidal oscillation is a variation in the amplitude of the sinusoidal oscillation.

Beats. Periodic variations that result from the superposition of two simple harmonic quantities of different frequencies f_1 and f_2. They involve the periodic increase and decrease of amplitude at the beat frequency $(f_1 - f_2)$.

Distortion. An undesired change in waveform. Noise and certain desired changes in waveform, such as those resulting from modulation or detection, are not usually classed as distortion.

Static Pressure. At a point, the pressure that would exist at that point in the absence of sound waves.

Microbar, Dyne per Square Centimeter. A unit of pressure commonly used in acoustics. One microbar is equal to 1 dyne per square centimeter.

Note: The term "bar" properly denotes a pressure of 10^6 dynes per square centimeter. Unfortunately, the bar was once used in acoustics to mean 1 dyne per square centimeter, but this is no longer correct.

Sound Pressure. At a point, the total instantaneous pressure at that point in the presence of a sound wave minus the static pressure at that point.

Peak Sound Pressure. For any specified time interval, the maximum absolute value of the instantaneous sound pressure in that interval.

Note: In the case of a periodic wave, if the time interval considered is a complete period, the peak sound pressure becomes identical with the maximum sound pressure.

Effective Sound Pressure (Root-Mean-Square Sound Pressure). At a point, the root-mean-square value of the instantaneous sound pressures, over a time interval at the point under consideration. In the case of periodic sound pressures, the interval must be an integral number of periods or an interval that is long compared to a period. In the case of nonperiodic sound pressures, the interval should be long enough to make the value obtained essentially independent of small changes in the length of the interval.

Note: The term "effective sound pressure" is frequently shortened to "sound pressure."

Particle Velocity. In a sound field, the velocity of a given infinitesimal part of the medium, with reference to the medium as a whole, due to the sound wave.

Wave Velocity (Propagation Velocity). A vector quantity that specifies the speed and direction with which a sound wave travels through a medium.

Volume Velocity. The rate of alternating flow of the medium through a specified surface due to a sound wave.

Note: Expressed mathematically the volume velocity V is:

$$V = \int_s v d\sigma$$

where v is the component of particle velocity normal to the element of surface $d\sigma$; the integration is performed over surface S through which the medium is oscillating.

Sound Energy. A given part of a medium is the total energy in this part of the medium minus the energy which would exist in the same part of the medium with no sound waves present.

Sound-Energy Density at a point in a sound field is the sound energy contained in a given infinitesimal part of the medium divided by the volume of that part of the medium.

Note 1: The terms "instantaneous energy density," "maximum energy density," and "peak energy density" have meanings analogous to the related terms used for sound pressure.

Note 2: In speaking of average energy density in general, it is necessary to distinguish between the space average (at a given instant) and the time average (at a given point).

Acoustic Radiation Pressure. A unidirectional, steady-state pressure exerted upon a surface exposed to an acoustic wave.

Sound-Energy Flux. The average rate of flow of sound energy for one period through any specified area.

Note: In a medium of density, ρ, for a plane or spherical free wave having a velocity of propagation, c, the sound-energy flux through the area, S, corresponding to an effective sound pressure, p, is

$$J = \frac{p^2 S}{\rho c} \cos \theta$$

where θ = the angle between the direction of propagation of the sound and the normal to the area S.

Sound Intensity (Sound-Energy Flux Density) (Sound-Power Density). In a specified direction at a point, the average rate of sound energy transmitted in the specified direction through a unit area normal to this direction at the point considered.

Note 1: The sound intensity in any specified direction, a, of a sound field is the sound-energy flux through a unit area normal to that direction. This is given by the expression

$$I_a = \frac{1}{T} \int_0^T pv_a dt$$

where

T = an integral number of periods or a time long compared to a period

p = the instantaneous sound pressure

v_a = the component of the instantaneous particle velocity in the direction a

t = time

Note 2: In the case of a free plane or spherical wave having the effective sound pressure, p, the velocity of propagation, c, in a medium of density, p, the intensity in the direction of propagation is given by:

$$I = \frac{p^2}{pc}$$

Sc is called characteristic impedance.

Sound Power of a Source. The total sound energy radiated by the source per unit of time.

Sound Absorption. The change of sound energy into some other form, usually heat, in passing through a medium or on striking a surface.

Damping. The dissipation of energy with time or distance.

Relaxation Time. The time taken by an exponentially decaying quantity to decrease in amplitude by a factor of $1/e = 0.3679$.

Strength of a Sound Source (Strength of a Simple Source). The maximum instantaneous rate of volume displacement produced by the source when emitting a wave with sinusoidal time variation.

Note: The term is properly applicable only to sources of dimensions small with respect to the wavelength.

Levels

Level. In acoustics, the level of a quantity is the logarithm of the ratio of that quantity to a reference quantity of the same kind. The base of the logarithm, the reference quantity, and the kind of level must be specified.

Note 1: Examples of kinds of levels in common use are electric power level, sound-pressure-squared level, voltage-squared level.

Note 2: The level as here defined is measured in units of the logarithm of a reference ratio that is equal to the base of logarithms.

Note 3: In symbols,

$$L = \log_r (q/q_0)$$

where

L = level of kind determined by the kind of quantity under consideration, measured in units of log,r

r = base of logarithms and the reference ratio

q = the quantity under consideration

q_0 = reference quantity of the same kind

Note 4: Differences in the levels of two like quantities q_1 and q_2 are described by the same formula because, by the rules of logarithms, the reference quantity is automatically divided out:

$$\log_r (q_1/q_0) - \log_r (q_2/q_0) = \log_r (q_1/q_2)$$

Bel. A unit of level when the base of the logarithm is 10. Use of the bel is restricted to levels of quantities proportional to power.

Decibel. One tenth of a bel. Thus, the decibel is a unit of level when the base of the logarithm is the tenth root of ten, and the quantities concerned are proportional to power.

Note 1: Examples of quantities that qualify are power (any form), sound pressure squared, particle velocity squared, sound intensity, sound-energy density, voltage squared. Thus the decibel is a unit of sound-pressure-squared level; it is common practice, however, to shorten this to "sound pressure level" because ordinarily no ambiguity results from so doing.

Note 2: The logarithm to the base the tenth root of 10 is the same as ten times the logarithm to the base 10: *e.g.*, for a number X^2, $\log_{10} 1/10 \, X^2 = 10 \log_{10} X^2 = 20 \log_{10} X$. This last relationship is the one ordinarily used to simplify the language in definitions of sound pressure level, etc.

Neper. A unit of level when the logarithm is on the Napierian base e. Use of the neper is restricted to levels of quantities analogous to electric current.

Note: Examples of quantities that qualify are voltage, current, particle velocity, sound pressure.

Power Level. In decibels, 10 times the logarithm to the base 10 of the ratio of a given power to a reference power. The reference power must be indicated.

Note: In sound recording, for example, a reference electric power often used is the milliwatt, and the symbol dbm is employed to indicate both the unit of power level, the decibel, and the reference power, the milliwatt.

Sound Pressure Level. In decibels, of a sound, 20 times the logarithm to the base 10 of the ratio of the pressure of this sound to the reference pressure. The reference pressure shall be explicitly stated.

Note 1: The following reference pressures are in common use:

(a) 2×10^{-4} mibrobar

(b) 1 microbar

Reference pressure (a) is in general use for measurements concerned with hearing and with sound in air and liquids, while (b) has gained widespread acceptance for calibration of transducers and various kinds of sound measurements in liquids.

Note 2: Unless otherwise explicitly stated, it is to be understood that the sound pressure is the effective (rms) sound pressure.

Note 3: It is to be noted that, in many sound fields, the sound pressure ratios are not the square roots of the corresponding power ratios.

Sound Level. A weighted sound pressure level, obtained by the use of metering characteristics and the weightings A, B, or C specified in American Standard Sound Level Meters for Measurement of Noise and Other Sounds, Z24.3–1944. The weighting employed must always be stated. The reference pressure is 0.0002 microbar.

Note: A suitable method of stating the weighting is, for example, "The A-sound level was 43 db."

Noise Level. The level of noise, the type of which must be indicated by further modifier or context.

Note: The physical quantity measured (*e.g.*, voltage), the reference quantity, the instrument used, and the band width or other weighting characteristic must be indicated.

Overload Level of a component or system is that level at which operation ceases to be satisfactory as a result of signal distortion, overheating, etc. In an acoustical system, sound pressure level is to be understood, unless otherwise specified.

Peak Level. The maximum instantaneous level that occurs during a specified time interval. In acoustics, peak sound pressure level is to be understood, unless some other kind of level is specified.

Velocity Level. In decibels, of a sound, 20 times the logarithm to the base 10 of the ratio of the particle velocity of the sound to the reference particle velocity. The reference particle velocity shall be stated explicitly.

Intensity Level (Sound-Energy Flux Density Level). In decibels, of a sound, 10 times the logarithm to the base 10 of the ratio of the intensity of this sound to the reference intensity. The reference intensity shall be stated explicitly.

Note 1: A common reference sound intensity is 10^{-16} watt per square centimeter in a specified direction.

Note 2: In a free progressive plane or spherical wave, there is a known relation between sound intensity and sound pressure, so that sound intensity level can be deduced from a measurement of sound pressure level. In general, however, there is no simple relation between the two, and a measurement of sound pressure level should not be reported as one of intensity level.

Power (Level) Gain. In decibels, the amount by which the output power level in decibels exceeds the input power level in decibels. By reason of the properties of logarithms, it is also 10 times the logarithm to the base 10 of the ratio of the output power to the input power.

Note: Ordinarily the name of this quantity can be shortened, without ambiguity, to power gain in decibels.

Voltage (Level) Gain. In decibels, the amount by which the output voltage-squared level in decibels exceeds the input voltage-squared level in decibels. By reason of the properties of logarithms, it is also 20 times the logarithm to the base 10 of the ratio of the output voltage to the input voltage.

Note 1: Ordinarily the name of this quantity can be shortened, without ambiguity, to voltage gain in decibels.

Note 2: Voltage level gain is not always equal to power level gain.

Oscillation, Vibration, and Shock

Forced Oscillation (Forced Vibration). The oscillation of a system is forced if the response is imposed by the excitation. If the excitation is periodic and continuing, the oscillation is steady-state.

Resonance. Resonance of a system in forced oscillation exists when any change, however small, in the frequency of excitation causes a decrease in the response of the system.

Resonance Frequency (Resonant Frequency). A frequency at which resonance exists.

Antiresonance. For a system in forced oscillation, antiresonance exists at a point when any change, however small, in the frequency of excitation causes an increase in the response at this point.

Natural Frequency. The frequency of free oscillation of a system. For a multiple-degree-of-freedom system, the natural frequencies are the frequencies of the normal modes of vibration.

Mode of Vibration. In a system undergoing vibration, a characteristic pattern assumed by the system, in which the motion of every particle is simple harmonic with the same frequency. Two or more modes may exist concurrently in a multiple-degree-of-freedom system.

Fundamental Frequency. Of a periodic quantity, the frequency of a sinusoidal quantity which has the same period as the periodic quantity; of an oscillating system, the lowest natural frequency. The normal mode of vibration associated with this frequency is known as the fundamental mode.

Logarithmic Decrement. The natural logarithm of the ratio of any two successive amplitudes of like sign, in the decay of a single-frequency oscillation.

Viscous Damping. The dissipation of energy that occurs when a particle in a vibrating system is resisted by a force that has a magnitude proportional to the magnitude of the velocity of the particle and direction opposite to the direction of the particle.

Critical Damping. The minimum viscous damping that will allow a displaced system to return to its initial position without oscillation.

Shock Pulse. A substantial disturbance characterized by a rise and decay of acceleration from a constant value in a short period of time. Shock pulses are normally displayed graphically as curves of acceleration as a function of time.

Duration of Shock Pulse. The time required for the acceleration of the pulse to rise from some stated fraction of the maximum amplitude and to decay to this value.

Pulse Rise Time. The interval of time required for the leading edge of a pulse to rise from some specified small fraction to some specified larger fraction of the maximum value.

Transmission-Propagation

Sound Field. A region containing sound waves.

Wave Front. Of a progressive wave in space, a continuous surface which is a locus of points having the same phase at a given instant; of a progressive surface wave, a continuous line which is a locus of points having the same phase at a given instant.

Compressional Wave. A wave in an elastic medium which causes an element of the medium to change its volume without undergoing rotation.

   Note 1: Mathematically, a compressional wave is one whose velocity field has zero curl.

   Note 2: A compressional plane wave is a longitudinal wave.

Longitudinal Wave. A wave in which the direction of displacement at each point of the medium is normal to the wave front.

Shear Wave (Rotational Wave). A wave in an elastic medium which causes an element of the medium to change its shape without a change of volume.

   Note 1: Mathematically, a shear wave is one whose velocity field has zero divergence.

   Note 2: A shear plane wave in an isotropic medium is a transverse wave.

   Note 3: When shear waves combine to produce standing waves, linear displacements may result.

Transverse Wave. A wave in which the direction of displacement at each point of the medium is parallel to the wave front.

Plane Wave. A wave in which the wave fronts are everywhere parallel planes normal to the direction of propagation.

Spherical Wave. A wave in which the wave fronts are concentric spheres.

Cylindrical Wave. A wave in which the wave fronts are coaxial cylinders.
Rayleigh Wave. A surface wave associated with the free boundary of a solid, such that a surface particle describes an ellipse whose major axis is normal to the surface, and whose center is at the undisturbed surface. At maximum particle displacement away from the solid surface, the motion of the particle is opposite to that of the wave.

> Note: The propagation velocity of a Rayleigh wave is slightly less than that of a shear wave in the solid; the wave amplitude of the Rayleigh wave diminishes exponentially with depth.

Wave Interference. The phenomenon which results when waves of the same or nearly the same frequency are superposed and is characterized by a spatial or temporal distribution of amplitude of some specified characteristic differing from that of the individual superposed waves.

Standing Wave. A periodic wave having a fixed distribution in space which is the result of interference of progressive waves of the same frequency and kind. Such waves are characterized by the existence of nodes or partial nodes and antinodes that are fixed in space.

Stationary Wave. A standing wave in which the net energy flux is zero at all points.

> Note: Stationary waves can only be approximated in practice.

Node. A point, line, or surface in a standing wave where some characteristic of the wave field has essentially zero amplitude.

> Note: The appropriate modifier should be used before the word "node" to signify the type that is intended; *e.g.*, displacement node, velocity node, pressure node.

Antinode (Loop). A point, line, or surface in a standing wave where some characteristic of the wave field has maximum amplitude.

Doppler Effect. The phenomenon evidenced by the change in the observed frequency of a wave in a transmission system caused by a time rate of change in the effective length of the path of travel between the source and the point of observation.

> Note: The effect is described quantitatively by:

$$f_r = \frac{(1 + v_r/c)}{(1 - v_s/C)} f_s$$

where

f_r = observed frequency

f_s = frequency at source

v_r = component of velocity (relative to the medium) of observation point toward source

v_s = component of velocity (relative to the medium) of source toward observation point

c = speed of sound in a stationary medium

Doppler Shift. The change in the observed frequency of a wave, due to the Doppler effect.

Transmission Loss. The reduction in the magnitude of some characteristic of a signal, between two stated points in a transmission system.

Note 1: The characteristic is often some kind of level, such as power level or voltage level; in acoustics the characteristic that is commonly measured is sound pressure level. Thus, if the levels are expressed in decibels, the transmission level loss is likewise in decibels.

Note 2: It is imperative that the characteristic concerned (such as the sound pressure level) be clearly identified because in all transmission systems more than one characteristic is propagated.

Absorption Loss. That part of the transmission loss due to the dissipation or conversion of sound energy into other forms of energy (*e.g.*, heat), either within the medium or attendant upon a reflection.

Divergence Loss. That part of the transmission loss due to the divergence on spreading of the sound rays in accordance with the geometry of the system (*e.g.*, spherical waves emitted by a point source.)

Refraction Loss. That part of the transmission loss due to refraction resulting from nonuniformity of the medium.

Scattering Loss. That part of the transmission loss due to scattering within the medium or due to roughness of the reflecting surface.

Streaming (Acoustic). The name given to unidirectional flow currents in a fluid that are due to the presence of acoustic waves.

Acoustic Dispersion. The change of speed of sound with frequency.

Acoustic Refraction. The process by which the direction of sound propagation is changed due to spatial variation in the speed of sound in the medium.

Diffraction. That process that produces a diffracted wave.

Diffracted Wave. A diffracted wave is one whose front has been changed in direction by an obstacle or other nonhomogeneity in a medium, otherwise than by reflection or refraction.

Acoustic Scattering. Acoustic scattering is the irregular reflection, refraction, or diffraction of a sound in many directions.

Acoustic Impedance. Of a fluid medium on a given surface lying in a wave front, the complex ratio of the sound pressure (force per unit area) on that surface to the flux (volume velocity, or particle velocity multiplied by the area) through the surface. When concentrated rather than distributed impedances are considered, the impedance of a portion of the medium is based on the pressure difference effective in driving that portion and the flux (volume velocity). The acoustic impedance may be expressed in terms of mechanical impedance divided by the square of the area of the surface considered.

Note 1: Velocities in the direction along which the impedance is to be specified are considered positive.

Note 2: The real part of an acoustic impedance is acoustic resistance and the imaginary part is acoustic reaction.

Mechanical Impedance. The impedance obtained from the ratio of force to velocity during simple harmonic motion.

Note 1: The ratio of force to displacement is sometimes also called mechanical impedance; this usage is deprecated.

Note 2: If the force and velocity are measured at the same point, the ratio is designated driving point impedance; if they are measured at different points, the ratio is designated transfer impedance.

Specific Acoustic Impedance (Unit Area Acoustic Impedance). At a point in the medium, the complex ratio of sound pressure to particle velocity.

Characteristic Impedance (Intrinsic Impedance). The impedance of a medium is the ratio of the effective sound pressure at a given point to the effective particle velocity at that point in a free plane progressive sound wave.

Note 1: The characteristic impedance is equal to the product of the density and the speed of sound in the medium.

Note 2: The characteristic impedance of an acoustic medium is analogous to the characteristic impedance of an infinitely long transmission line.

Acoustic Resistance. The real component of the acoustic impedance.

Specific Acoustic Resistance. The real component of the specific acoustic impedance.

Acoustic Reactance. The imaginary component of the acoustic impedance.

Specific Acoustic Reactance. The imaginary component of the specific acoustic impedance.

Acoustic Ohm (CGS). An acoustic resistance, reactance, or impedance has a magnitude of one acoustic (cgs) ohm when a sound pressure of 1 microbar produces a volume velocity of 1 cubic centimeter per second.

Acoustic Stiffness. The quantity which, when divided by 2π times the frequency, gives the acoustic reactance.

Acoustic Compliance. The reciprocal of acoustic stiffness.

Transducers and Instruments and Their Parameters

Transducer. A device capable of being actuated by waves from one or more transmission systems or media and of supplying related waves to one or more other transmission systems or media.

Note: The waves in either input or output may be of the same or different types (*e.g.*, electric, mechanical, or acoustic).

Electroacoustic Transducer. A transducer for receiving waves from an electric system and delivering waves to an acoustic system, or vice versa.

Variable-Resistance Transducer. A transducer that depends for its operation upon sound-actuated variation in electrical resistance.

Electrostatic (Capacitor) (Condenser) Transducer. A transducer that consists of a capacitor and depends upon interaction between its electric field and the change of its electrostatic capacitance.

Piezoelectric (Crystal) (Ceramic) Transducer. A transducer that depends for its operation on the interaction between the electric charge and the deformation of certain asymmetric crystals having piezoelectric properties.

Note: Some ceramics can have induced piezoelectric properties due to the application of an electric field during manufacturing.

Electrostriction Transducer. A transducer that depends for its operation upon the production of an elastic strain in certain symmetric crystals proportional to the square of the dielectric displacement.

Magnetostriction Transducer. A transducer that depends for its operation on the interaction between the magnetization and the deformation of a material having magnetostrictive properties.

Electrokinetic Transducer. A transducer that depends for its operation on the dielectric polarization in certain liquids resulting from viscous shearing stress that accompanies flow through porous materials.

Hot-Wire Transducer. A unilateral transducer that depends for its operation on the change in resistance of a hot wire produced by the cooling or heating effects of a sound wave.

Sound Probe. A device that responds to some characteristic of an acoustic wave (*e.g.*, sound pressure, particle velocity) and that can be used to explore and determine this characteristic in a sound field without appreciably altering that field.

Split Transducer. A directional transducer in which electroacoustic transducing elements are so divided and arranged that each division is electrically separate.

Acoustic Radiometer. An instrument for measuring acoustic radiation pressure by determining the unidirectional steady-state force resulting from reflection or absorption of a sound wave at a boundary.

Directional Response Pattern (Beam Pattern). The directional response pattern of a transducer used for sound emission or reception is a description, often presented graphically, of the response of the transducer as a function of the direction of the transmitted or incident sound waves in a specified plane and at a specified frequency.

Note 1: A complete description of the directional response pattern of a transducer would require three-dimensional presentation.

Note 2: The directional response pattern is often shown as the response relative to the maximum response.

Directivity Factor of a transducer used for sound emission is the ratio of the sound pressure squared, at some fixed distance and specified direction, to the mean-square sound pressure at the same distance averaged over all directions from the transducer. The distance must be great enough so that the sound appears to diverge spherically from the effective acoustic center of the sources. Unless otherwise specified, the reference direction is understood to be that of maximum response.

The directivity factor of a transducer used for sound reception is the ratio of the square of the open-circuit voltage produced in response to sound waves arriving in a specified direction to the mean-square voltage that would be produced in a perfectly diffused sound field of the same frequency and mean-square sound pressure.

Note 1: This definition may be extended to cover the case of finite frequency bands whose spectrum may be specified.

Note 2: The average free-field response may be obtained in various ways, such as

1) By the use of a spherical integrator

2) By numerical integration of a sufficient number of directivity patterns corresponding to different planes, or

3) By integration of one or two directional patterns whenever the pattern of the transducer is known to possess adequate symmetry.

Beam Width of a directional transducer, at a given frequency in a given plane including the mean axis, is the angle included between the two directions, one to the left and the other to the right of the axis, at which the angular deviation loss has a specified value.

Note: Beam widths are commonly spec. ied for an angular deviation loss of 3, 6, or 10 decibels, the choice depending upon the directivity of the transducer or upon its intended application. The particular angular deviation loss can be indicated conveniently by use of a term such as "3-db beam width."

Free-Field Voltage Sensitivity (Receiving Voltage Response). The free-field voltage sensitivity of a transducer used for sound reception is the ratio of the output open-circuit voltage to the free-field sound pressure in the undisturbed sound field. The frequency and direction of incidence must be specified.

Note 1: The ratio may be expressed, for example, in microvolts per microbar.

Note 2: Unless otherwise specified, the undisturbed free field is understood to mean a plane progressive wave.

Transmitting Voltage Response. Of an electroacoustic transducer used for sound emission, the ratio of the sound pressure apparent at a distance of 1 meter in a specified direction from the effective acoustic center of the transducer to the signal voltage applied across the electric input terminals.

Note: The sound pressure apparent at a distance of 1 meter can be found by multiplying the sound pressure observed at a remote point (where the sound field is spherically divergent) by the number of meters from the effective acoustic center of the transducer to that point.

Free Impedance. Of a transducer, the impedance at the input of the transducer when the impedance of its load is made zero.

Note: The approximation is often made that the free electric impedance of an electroacoustic transducer designed for use in water is that measured with the transducer in air.

Loaded Impedance. Of a transducer, the impedance at the input of the transducer when the output is connected to its normal load.

Sonics

Sonics. The technology of sound in processing and analysis. Sonics includes the use of sound in any noncommunication process.

Ultrasonics. The technology of sound at frequencies above the audio range.

Note: Supersonics is the general subject covering phenomena associated with speed higher than the speed of sound (as in the case of aircraft and projectiles traveling faster than sound). This term was once used in acoustics synonymously with "ultrasonics"; such usage is now deprecated.

Macrosonics. The technology of sound at signal amplitudes so large that linear approximations are not valid.

Note: Processing techniques usually involve macrosonics.

Flaw Detection. The process of locating imperfections in solid materials by observing internal reflections or a variation in transmission through the materials as a function of sound-path location.

Agglomeration. The union of small particles suspended in a fluid medium into larger aggregates by the action of sound waves.

Sonic Cleaning (Degreasing). The cleaning of contaminated materials by the action of intense sound in the liquid in which the material is immersed, usually involving cavitation.

Drilling. The process of cutting or shaping materials with an abrasive slurry driven by a reciprocating tool usually attached to an electromechanical transducer.

Soldering (Sonic). The method of joining metals by metallic bonding alloys through the use of mechanical vibrations to break up the surface oxides.

Sonic Surgery. The use of focused ultrasound to produce precisely circumscribed alterations at predetermined sites within the tissue.

Cavitation. Sonically induced cavitation in a liquid is the formation, growth, and collapse of gaseous and vapor bubbles due to the action of intense sound waves.

Cavitation Noise. The noise produced in a liquid by gaseous or vaporous cavitation.

Oseen Force. A steady force exerted on a suspended particle by second-order velocity effects resulting from second harmonic content in a distorted wave.

Sonoluminescence. The luminescence produced in liquids by sonically induced cavitation.

Sonic Viscometry. The determination of the coefficients of viscosity of liquids or slurries by measurement of the acoustic properties of a transmitted wave, or by the reaction of such a medium on a transducer.

Molecular Relaxation. The equalization of energy among the degrees of freedom of a molecule following a disturbance that produces deviations from the equilibrium distribution law.

Piezoelectricity. The property exhibited by some asymmetrical crystalline materials which when subjected to strain in suitable directions develop electric polarization proportional to the strain. Inverse piezoelectricity is the effect in which mechanical strain is produced in certain asymmetrical crystalline materials when subjected to an external electric field; the strain is proportional to the electric field.

Electrostriction. The phenomenon wherein some dielectric materials experience an elastic strain when subjected to an electric field, this strain being independent of the polarity of the field.

Magnetostriction. The phenomenon wherein ferromagnetic materials experience an elastic strain when subjected to an external magnetic field. Also, magnetostriction is the converse phenomenon in which mechanical stresses cause a change in the magnetic induction of a ferromagnetic material.

Schlieren Method. The technique by which light refracted by the density variations resulting from sound waves is used to produce a visible image of a sound field.

Sonic Applicator, Medical. A sonic applicator is a self-contained electromechanical transducer designed for local application of sound for therapeutic purposes.

Pressure Gain Factor. The factor of a focusing transducer is the ratio of the peak pressure amplitude at the focus to the peak pressure amplitude at the radiating surface.

Image Converter. A device for making acoustic field configurations optically visible.

II. EFFECTS OF INTENSE, NONCAVITATING ULTRASOUND ON THE MAMMALIAN CENTRAL NERVOUS SYSTEM

Ultrasound has not been studied as a naturally occurring phenomenon, exclusive of the relatively low-frequency, low-intensity-level emanations of animal origin.[1] Thus all pertinent information has been obtained in laboratory environments, almost entirely in animal experiments. The most comprehensive treatment of the effects of intense noncavitating ultrasound on animals has been studies on the central nervous system— primarily cat and mouse, with the results of a detailed histological investigation available on the cat.[2] Although studies of the effects of ultrasound on other anatomic structures have been undertaken, none thus far have reached the stage of sufficient completeness for tabular presentation. The human brain has been modified at localized sites by intense ultrasound, but thus far insufficient material has accumulated for a detailed histologic study.[3] However, the dosage conditions employed to induce functional changes and the histologic results available indicate that the effects on the human brain are the same as those observed on the cat. Therefore, the reader is referred to the animal experiments which summarize the results obtained from a histologic study of *small* gray and *small* white matter lesions following single ultrasonic exposures.[4] Table I lists physical acoustic properties of various tissues (all mammalian, and including human tissues for which data is available) which can be employed for the determination of certain effects accompanying sound wave propagation, such as the fraction of the incident energy reflected at an interface and the time rate of heat production per unit volume resulting from absorption.[5]

The following remarks summarize the results of research efforts to identify the physical factors responsible for the "selective" changes produced by intense ultrasound in tissue (in particular, the mammalian central nervous system), but which do not lend themselves readily to tabular organization.

The basic work concerned with investigating the physical mechanism(s) by which high intensity ultrasound selectively affects the tissue structure of the central nervous system has been carried out on frogs[15, 16] and young mice,[17, 18, 19, 20, 21, 22] irradiated at the lumbar enlargement of the spinal cord with paralysis of the hind legs as the endpoint. Animals have been irradiated at a considerable number of sets of identical values for the acoustic field variables for various periods of time and at different base temperatures. From the data obtained, the exposure time required for 50% of the animals to become paraplegic has been determined for each of a number of values of the acoustic intensity. The dosage curves thus obtained exhibit a linear relationship between the reciprocal of the exposure time and the square root of the intensity. The slopes of the dosage lines depend upon the base temperature of the animal, increasing with an increase in the base temperature. It has been found that the temperature rise produced in the tissue by the absorbed acoustic energy is not sufficient by itself to cause the observed alterations in the tissue. Further, it was shown that the effect of short repetitive exposures, which individually do not produce paralysis, can sum to

Table I. Physical Acoustical Properties of Mammalian Tissues.

Tissue	T (°C)	Density (gm/cm³)	Sound Speed (cm/sec)	Acoustic Impedance (gm/cm²sec)	Amplitude Absorption Coefficient (cm⁻¹)	Heat Capacity (cal/gm°C)	Ref.
Central Nervous System (cat, rat) (a, b, c)	37	1.03	1.51	1.56	0.11		6, 7
Young Mouse (a, b, c, f) 24 hrs. after birth	2				0.02	0.81	8, 9
	10				0.05	0.81	8, 9
	28				0.10	0.81	8, 9
	40				0.11	0.81	9
	45				0.12	0.81	9
Muscle (skeletal) (a, b, c, d)	37	1.07	1.57	1.68	0.13	0.82	10
Fat (a, b)	37	0.97	1.44	1.40	0.05	0.71	10, 11, 12
Skull Bone (human)	37	1.7	3.36	6.0		0.3	10, 12, 13
							10, 12, 14
Fre- quency (Mc) ⟵ e ⟶							⟶
0.6					0.4		
0.8					0.9		
1.2					1.7		
1.6					3.2		
1.8					4.2		
2.25					5.3		
3.5					7.8		

a) Values tabulated for acoustic parameters are for 1 Mc.
b) Absorption coefficient value is proportional to frequency.
c) Average value for adult animal. In the cat the absorption coefficient for white matter is 9/5 that of gray matter.
d) Absorption coefficient varies with direction of sound propagation relative to fiber orientation (average value listed).
e) Temperature unknown, believed to be in the range 15–25°C.
f) Absorption coefficient is independent of acoustic intensity to at least 200 w/cm².

produce an irreversible change. In the latter experiments, the temperature was allowed to return to the base value between exposures, and the maximum temperature rise is considerably less than that resulting from a single exposure at the same sound level which is of appropriate duration to produce paralysis.

Acoustically-induced cavitation has been eliminated as a primary factor by producing lesions, as well as motor deficits, under a hydrostatic pressure sufficiently great to prevent tension forces from occurring in tissue.[16, 23, 24]

Appropriate dosages of high intensity ultrasound produce physiologic changes which are observable immediately after a minimum dosage required to produce an effect is delivered.[2, 17, 18, 19] This has been demonstrated to be within a few tenths of a second as indicated by observations of changes in motor activity in the unanesthetized human.[25] No evidence for delayed effects has appeared, as in the case for ionizing radiation, indicating that ultrasound acts at a level of structure which is closely associated with physiologic function.

The effects of high intensity ultrasound on tissue structure at dosages which produce selective irreversible changes, are produced at submicroscopic sites, as shown by detailed histologic studies.[4] The changes which are produced cannot be seen in stained tissue sections until after a time interval varying from minutes to an hour after irradiation, depending upon the dosage.[4] The secondary changes which follow the primary actions are then observable as visible lesions.

The two important findings stated above, namely, that physiologic changes are evident immediately after exposure but that histologic changes do not begin to appear until later, have led to investigations of the possible interaction of intense, noncavitating ultrasound and biologically important molecular species in solution. As a result, it has been shown that DNA is degraded, principally as backbone scission, in noncavitating ultrasonic fields and that the rate of degradation is intensity-dependent.[26] However, a preliminary study has shown that the enzymatic activity of specific proteins irradiated in solution in the absence of cavitation is not reduced.[27]

It has been shown that there is a break-down of the blood-brain barrier within ultrasonically-produced lesions.[28] Trypan blue passes the blood-brain barrier at the site of the lesion if injected soon after ultrasonic exposure, but it does not stain the lesion region if injected later than 72 hours postirradiation.

Precisely-placed ultrasonic lesions have been produced in a number of deep brain structures in man (ansa lenticularis; globus pallidus; substantia nigra; corpus Luysii; subthalamic fasciculus; Forel fields; ventral, posterior, lateral, and medial nuclei; and the central nucleus of the thalamus) for treatment and relief of the signs and sensations associated with hyperkinetic, hypertonic and intractable pain disorders.[3, 29, 30]

III. EFFECTS OF CAVITATING ULTRASOUND ON CELLS AND MICROORGANISMS

The effect of ultrasound on cells and microorganisms in liquid suspensions has been studied largely in the presence of cavitation. Although cavitation is by no means the only mechanism by which effects of ultrasound are manifested,[5] the text of this section is restricted to effects occurring in the presence of cavitation. Reviews on this topic, together with extensive bibliographies, are available.[31, 32] The tabulations below are extracted from the extensive literature on this subject to illustrate, by example only, the dependencies of the observed effects upon the physical parameters of importance.

The threshold of cavitation varies with the geometrical configuration of the sound field, frequency, chemical composition of the suspending fluid, temperature, viscosity and pressure.[5] However, the relative rates at which different types of biological cells are destroyed is invariant over a wide frequency range for specified values of the other parameters.[33, 34] Studies show that so long as 1% of the population remains undamaged, the rate of destruction is described by $dN/dt = -RN$, where N is the cell concentration, t is time, and R, the rate constant, can be considered a measure of cell fragility, provided the physical conditions are maintained invariant. Table II[34, 35] shows typical values of relative fragility of some biological cells, normalized so that human red blood cells are unity. It is noted that the large cells tend to be more fragile, although no simple relationship exists between size and fragility.

Although the relative rates of cell destruction are the same at most frequencies, at certain frequencies some cells exhibit greatly increased sensitivities to destruction by ultrasound, i.e., rupture occurs more readily at particular characteristic frequencies.[33, 34, 35,] This has been

Table II.[34, 35] Ultrasonic Fragilities of Various Cells

Cell Type	Relative Fragility	Average Diameter (microns)
Paramecium aurelia G's	16	80
Paramecium caudatum	4	150
Trichomonas foetus	2	12
Human rbc	1	6
Rabbit sperm	0.7	5
Amoeba proteus	0.4	200
T-2 bacteriophage	0.2	0.01
Escherichia coli	0.15	1

Table III.[33, 34, 35,] Variation of Optimum Destructive Ultrasonic Frequency with Size.

Cell Type	Maximum Diameter (microns)	Minimum Diameter (microns)	Optimum Freq. (kc)
Paramecium caudatum	223	63	1.2
Paramecium bursaria	118	51	1.7
Paramecium aurelia G's	124	29	3.3
Paramecium trichium	80	38	4.1
Amphiuma rbc	45	10	16.5

interpreted as a resonance phenomenon and the dependence of the optimum frequency of destruction upon cell type and cell size is shown in Table III.

For sufficiently high intensities, the effectiveness of the ultrasonic action depends upon the concentration. Table IV shows the effect of concentration for microbial cells[36] and Table V shows the effect of concentration upon hemolysis.[36] It is seen that the higher the concentration, the less effective the irradiation.

The production of heat during irradiation apparently plays a secondary role in the production of the observed effects. However, the survival of the microorganism depends upon the temperature of the irradiated medium,[37] reflecting the decrease in cavitation threshold with increasing temperature[5] (see Table VI).

Table IV.[36] Effect of Concentration on Destructive Ability of Ultrasound on *Trypanosoma gambiense.*

Concentration (Specimens/mm)	Time for Complete Destruction (sec)
14,100	20
48,000	75

Table V.[36] Effect of Concentration on Hemolysis of Erythrocytes by Ultrasound

Dilution in Isotonic Saline	Time for Complete Hemolysis (min)
1:5	75
1:25	7

Table VI.[37] Survival of *Bac. prodigiosum vs* Temperature of Suspending Medium (4.5 w/cm^2, 800 kc, 20 min.)

Survival %	T (°C)
50	6
15	20
2	40

Table VII.[38] Percentage of Microorganisms Failing to Grow Following Exposure to 9 kc Ultrasound

Species	pH	Exposure time (min)	Temperature (°C)			
			15	25	35	45
Escherichia coli	4	10	44	60	48	71
		20	55	43	65	82
	5	10	35	39	46	47
		20	61	62	73	67
	7	10	41	49	40	49
		20	65	65	55	63
Serratia marcescens	4	5	26	24	36	71
		7.5	38	22	38	77
		10	41	42	51	83
	5	5	31	30	33	39
		7.5	39	37	48	52
		10	44	43	55	65
	7	5	27	29	24	33
		7.5	42	45	37	46
		10	47	52	49	59
Pseudomonas aeruginosa	4	10	44	51	79	55
		20	60	66	79	89
	5	10	46	41	58	72
		20	71	71	79	91
	7	10	46	51	63	75
		20	67	72	77	87

Table VIII.[38, 39] Percentage of *Micrococcus varians* Destroyed Following 80 minute Exposure to 9 kc Ultrasound

pH	Temperature (°C)	Cells Destroyed (%)
4	15	59
	25	56
	35	71
	45	99
5	15	28
	25	36
	35	48
	45	80
7	15	48
	25	39
	35	52
	45	59

The effect of ultrasonic irradiation time, temperature and pH of the medium upon different microorganisms is shown in Tables VII[38] and VIII.[38, 39] It is seen that at pH 7, little effect is produced on rate of destruction in the case of *Escherichia coli* and *Serratia marcescens*. For *Pseudomonas aeruginosa,* destruction increases with increasing temperature while the pH level (within the range considered) appears to have no effect. For the three other microorganisms, increased destruction is observed at pH and 45° C.

Table IX.[31]   Effect of Composition of Suspending Medium on Complete Destruction of Gonococci by Ultrasound.

Suspending Medium	Time for Complete Destruction (min)
Twice distilled water	4–5
Physiological saline	5–6
Blood serum	10
Peptone bouillon	40–50

A relationship exists between the composition of the suspending liquid and the destructive effect of ultrasound, wherein it appears that proteins inhibit destructive effects more than do lipoids and carbohydrates[31] (see Table IX). This also reflects, to some extent, the increase in cavitation threshold with increasing viscosity of the suspending medium.[5]

The effect of ultrasound on living organisms is dependent upon position in a standing wave field. Table X shows that injury to Spiroyra filaments is markedly more pronounced at acoustic pressure nodes than at antinodes.[40]

A demonstration of the fact that cavitation is not necessary for the production of reversible or irreversible effects in microorganisms is found in an experiment in which rotifers are exposed to ultrasound in the frequency range 200 Mc to 600 Mc.[41, 42] Here, the threshold of cavitation is many orders of magnitude greater than the sound intensities available.[5]

IV. ULTRASONIC TECHNOLOGY

Ultrasonic instrumentation for cavitation-type experiments is available from commercial sources. Descriptions of important features of such instrumentation and the important acoustic parameters have been treated adequately in the literature.[43, 44] Discussions of cavitation phenomena are also treated in the literature.[5, 45, 46]

Instrumentation for the determination of the ultrasonic propagation parameters (velocity and absorption) in liquid and liquid-like media have reached a high degree of sophistication[47, 48] and are available from commercial sources.

Instrumentation for the generation and detection of intense (noncavitating) ultrasound (focussed and unfocussed fields) is not readily available and the experimenter must construct and calibrate his own apparatus. A discussion of the important features of such instrumentation including design criteria has been prepared.[5]

Table X.[40] Injury to Spirogyra *vs* Position in Ultrasonic Field in Water and in Agar

Relative Intensity	Injury in Water				Injury in Agar				Agar Concentration (%)
	Exposure Time (sec)	% Injured		Exposure Time (min)	% Injured			
		Node	Antinode		Node	Antinode		
1	10	74	80	5	49	0		1
1	10	95	100	40	74	0		4
1	25	56	75	50	40	0		2
1	30	85	65	24	30	0		2
2	5	70	78	0.41	17	0		2
2	15	83	100	0.25	47	7		1

BIBLIOGRAPHY

References:

1. Busnel, R. G. (ed.), *Acoustic Behaviour of Animals*, 1963.

2. Fry, W. J., "Intense Ultrasound in Investigations of the Central Nervous System," *Advances in Biological and Medical Physics*, 6:281, 1958.

3. Fry, W. J., and R. Meyers, "Ultrasonic Method of Modifying Brain Structures," *Confin. Neurol.*, 22:315, 1962.

4. Barnard, J. W., *et al.*, "Small Localized Ultrasonic Lesions in the White and Gray Matter of the Cat Brain," *A.M.A. Arch. Neurol. Psychiat.*, 75:15, 1956.

5. Fry, W. J., and F. Dunn, in Nastuk, W. L. (ed.), *Physical Techniques in Biological Research*, 4:261, 1962.

6. Fry, W. J., and R. B. Fry, "Temperature Changes Produced in Tissue During Ultrasonic Irradiation," *J. Acoust. Soc. Am.*, 25:6, 1953.

7. Barnard, J. W., *et al.*, "Effects of High Intensity Ultrasound on the Central Nervous System of the Cat," *J. Comp. Neurol.*, 103:459, 1955.

8. Dunn, F., "Temperature and Amplitude Dependence of Acoustic Absorption in Tissue," *J. Acoust. Soc. Am.*, 34:1545, 1962.

9. Dunn, F., in Kelly, E., *Ultrasonic Energy*, p. 51, 1965.

10. Guttner, W., *Acustica.*, 4:547, 1954.

11. Colombati, S., and S. Petralia, *Riceica Sci.*, 20:71, 1950.

12. Goldman, D. E., and T. F. Hueter, "Tabular Data of the Velocity and Absorption of High-Frequency Sound in Mammalian Tissues," *J. Acoust. Soc. Am.*, 28:35, 1956.

13. Theisman, H., and Pfander, "Uber die Durshlassigkeit des Knochens fur Ultraschall," *Strahlentherapie*, 80:607, 1949.

14. Hueter, T. F., "Messung der Ultraschallabsorption im Menschlichen Schadelknochen und Ihre Abhangigkeit von der Frequenz," *Naturwissenschaften*, 39:21, 1952.

15. Fry, W. J., *et al.*, "Physical Factors Involved in Ultrasonically Induced Changes in Living Systems: I. Identification of Non-Temperature Effects," *J. Acoust. Soc. Am.*, 22:867, 1950.

16. Fry, W. J., *et al.*, "Physical Factors Involved in Ultrasonically induced Changes in Living Systems: II. Amplitude Duration Relations and the Effect of Hydrostatic Pressure for Nerve Tissue," *J. Acoust. Soc. Am.*, 23:364, 1951.

17. Fry, W. J., and F. Dunn, "Ultrasonic Irradiation of the Central Nervous System at High Sound Levels," *J. Acoust. Soc. Am.*, 28:129, 1956.

18. Dunn, F., "Comments on 'Mechanical Mechanism of Destructive Effects of Sound on Tissue,'" *J. Acoust. Soc. Am.*, 29:395, 1957.

19. Dunn, F., and W. J. Fry, in Kelly, E. (ed.), "Ultrasound in Biology and Medicine," *Amer. Inst. Biol. Sci.*, p. 226, 1957.

20. Dunn, F., "Physical Mechanisms of the Action of Intense Ultrasound on Tissue," *Am. J. Phys. Med.*, 37:148, 1958.

21. Ballantine, H. T., *et al.*, "Focal Destruction of Nervous Tissue by Focused Ultrasound: Biophysical Factors Influencing its Application," *J. Exper. Med.*, 104:337, 1956.

22. Hueter, T. F., H. T. Ballantine, and W. C. Cotter, "Production of Lesions in the Central Nervous System with Focused Ultrasound: A Study of Dosage Factors," *J. Acoust. Soc. Am.*, 28:192, 1956.

23. Hug, O., and R. Pape, "Nachweis der Ultraschallkavitation im Gewebe," *Strahlentherapie*, 94:79, 1954.

24. Rajewsky, B., O. Hug, and R. Pape, "Zur Frage der Ultraschall-Kavitation im Gewebe," *Naturforsch.*, 9b:10, 1954.

25. Fry, W. J. (unpublished data).

26. Hawley, S. A., R. M. Macleod, and F. Dunn, "Degradation of DNA by Intense, Noncavitating Ultrasound," *J. Acoust. Soc. Am.*, 35:1285, 1963.

27. Macleod, R. M., and F. Dunn (unpublished data).

28. Bakay, L., *et al.*, "Ultrasonically Produced Changes in the Blood-Brain Barrier," *A.M.A. Arch. Neurol. Psychiat.*, 76:457, 1956.

29. Fry, W. J., *et al.*, "Topical Differentia of Pathogenetic Mechanisms Underlying Parkinsonian Tremor and Rigidity as Indicated by Ultrasonic Irradiation of the Human Brain," *Trans. Am. Neurol. Assn.*, Vol. 16, 1958.

30. Meyers, R., *et al.*, "Early Experiences with Ultrasonic Irradiation of the Pallidofugal and Nigral Complexes in Hyperkinetic and Hypertonic Disorders," *Neurosurg.*, 16:32, 1959.

31. El'piner, I. E., *Ultrasound: Physical, Chemical and Biological Effects*, 1964.

32. Grabar, P., "Biological Actions of Ultrasonic Waves," *Advances in Biological and Medical Physics*, 3:191, 1953.

33. Ackerman, E., in "Proc. Third International Conf. on Medical Electronics," *Intern. Fed. for Med. Elect.*, p. 437, 1960.

34. Ackerman, E., *Biophysical Science*, 1962.

35. Ackerman, E., "Cellular Fragilities and Resonances Observed by Means of Sonic Vibrations," *J. Cell. Comp. Physiol.*, 39:167, 1952.

36. Schoenaors, F., "Contribution a l'etude de l'action des Ultrasons sur Les Trypanosomes," *Comp. Rend. Soc. Biol.*, 142:182, 1948.

37. Fuchtbauer, H., and H. Theismann, "Zur Wirkung des Ultraschalls Auf Bakterien," *Naturwissenschaften*, 36:346, 1949.

38. Ackermann, E., *et al.*, *WADC Technical Report*, p. 53, 1953.

39. Kinsloe, H., E. Ackerman and J. J. Reid, "Exposure of Microorganisms to Measured Sound Fields," *J. Bacteriol.*, 68:373, 1954.

40. Goldman, D. E., and W. W. Lepeschkin, "Injury to Living Cells in Standing Sound Waves," *J. Cell. Comp. Physiol.*, 40:255, 1952.

41. Hawley, S. A., and F. Dunn, "UHF Acoustic Interaction with Biological Media," *Naturwissenschaften*, 51:555, 1964.

42. Dunn, F., and S. A. Hawley, in Kelly, E. (ed.), *Ultrasonic Energy*, p. 66, 1965.

43. Hueter, T. F., and R. H. Bolt, *Sonics*, 1955.

44. Crawford, A. E., *Ultrasonic Engineering*, 1955.

45. Esche, R., *Akust. Beih.*, 4:208, 1952.

46. Flynn, H. G., in Mason, W. P. (ed.), *Physical Acoustics*, 1b:58, 1964.

47. Seki, H., A. Granata, and R. Truell, "Diffraction Effects in the Ultrasonic Field of a Pistion Source and Their Importance in the Accurate Measurement of Attenuation," *J. Acoust. Soc. Am.*, 28:230, 1956.

48. McSkimin, H. J., in Mason, W. P. (ed.), *Physical Acoustics*, 1a:272, 1964.

ABSTRACTING, INDEXING, AND ALERTING SERVICES FOR BIOCHEMISTRY AND BIOPHYSICS

I. INTRODUCTION

To provide the bioscientist with access to the primary biochemical and biophysical literature, both with respect to current awareness and retrospective search capability in specific areas, abstracting, indexing, and alerting services[1, 2] play a vital role. The purpose of this section is to describe the nature and scope of these services and to list a number of them whose coverage lies within the range of interest of biochemists and biophysicists.

II. ABSTRACTING AND INDEXING SERVICES

Abstracting and indexing services are combined for the purposes of this discussion but it should be recognized that the two do not always go hand in hand. All abstract compilations are indexed to some degree or another but all indexing services are not necessarily associated with abstracts. Several of the larger services are briefly described with references to addresses for correspondence.

Chemical Abstracts (CA) is published biweekly by Chemical Abstracts Service[3] of the American Chemical Society. Over 194,000 abstracts of articles and patents in 74 defined fields of chemistry and chemical engineering published in 1965 make it the largest English-language scientific abstracting service in the world. The journal is available in complete form or as separates in five specialized areas, one of which is the Biochemical Sections in which over 60,000 abstracts were published in 1965.

Abstracts of papers of biochemical interest can be found in other sections of *CA*, as well as in the Biochemical Sections. For example, various organic chemistry sections contain information on the laboratory synthesis of compounds of biochemical interest. The reader is alerted to these entries through the issue keyword index and through a cross-reference system.

The indexes to *CA* are of two basic types, the issue indexes and the volume indexes, and cover the complete issue of the journal, not the separates alone. Each issue of the complete journal contains a keyword index, a numerical patent index, a patent concordance relating equivalent patents issued in different countries, and an author index. Each issue of the separates contains the keyword index to the complete journal. Volume indexes are prepared by subject and author, and the numerical patent index and patent concordance are cumulated by volume. These volume indexes are cumulated into 5-year collective indexes.

CA issues are available in microfilm form. A photocopy service for Russian chemical journals is provided.

Biological Abstracts (BA)[4] is published semi-monthly and in 1965 published over 110,000 abstracts under 83 major subject headings including biochemistry and biophysics and numerous related areas. The semi-monthly issues contain an author index, a biosystematic index based on taxonomic categories, and a cross index relating abstracts which have common interests in two or more categories of *BA*. A subject index (called Biological Abstracts Subject in Context—B.A.S.I.C.) is published separately for each issue of *BA*; it is in the form of a Keyword-In-Context index based on the titles of the articles abstracted in the issues. An annual cumulative index to *BA* includes the cumulative subject (B.A.S.I.C.), author, biosystematic, and cross indexes. Readers of B.A.S.I.C. who do not have reasonable access to current issues of *BA* may obtain abstracts of interest through a service provided by Biological Aids.[4] Certain regular, specialized information services in all areas of the life sciences can be provided for individuals or special interest groups.

Index Medicus[5] is published monthly by the National Library of Medicine and represents a publication phase of the first large-scale, computer-based information storage and retrieval system in the United States. The monthly publication contains a subject and a name (author) section (index). The subject section consists of a listing of article titles, authors, and bibliographic references under an extensive subject category classification system. Included in the monthly journal is the "Bibliography of Medical Reviews" under the same subject classification system and with its own name (author) index.

Excerpta Medica[6] is a comprehensive medical science monthly abstracting service. The *Excerpta Medica* series consists of twenty-five separate subject-oriented publications. *Excerpta Medica Section II B—Biochemistry* is offered as a separate. Most monthly issues contain author and subject indexes. Cumulated indexes vary with the section; the Biochemistry separate contains monthly subject and author indexes which are cumulated into annual indexes.

Chemisches Zentralblatt. This German-language article and patent abstract journal[7] is published weekly and includes the general category of biological chemistry. Indexing patterns have changed over the years. Presently there are annual subject and formula indexes and semiannual patent and author indexes.

Referativnyi Zhurnal is a family of about 40 Russian abstracting journals, one of which is *Referativnyi Zhurnal Biologicheskaya Khimiya.*[8] This journal publishes semi-monthly abstracts in Russian of biochemical articles from the world's literature. There are issue author and patent indexes, annual author, subject, patent, and formula indexes, and an annual index of organic reactions.

Science Citation Index[9] is a comprehensive directory of cited references appearing in the bibliographies or footnotes of articles published in over 1060 source publications and in U.S. patents. The index is issued quarterly and includes a patent citation and corporate index. It represents a new approach to the building of a bibliography.

III. ALERTING SERVICES

Although abstracts themselves have an alerting function, a number of services have been designed specifically as current-awareness tools to alert readers before the publication of the abstract or, in many cases, before the article itself is published.

Chemical Titles (CT)[3] is a biweekly computer printout of titles of articles recently published or to be published in 650 domestic and foreign journals, many of which are top producers of biochemical and biophysical literature. A permuted Keyword-In-Context format is augmented by bibliographic information and an author index. *CT* is offered as a computer tape rental service and a custom search service of the tapes is available on a subscription basis.

Chemical-Biological Activities (CBAC)[3] is a biweekly, computer-produced alerting service designed to present in concise digest form specific information which relates organic chemical structure to biological activity in animal, plant, and microorganism systems. Like *CT*, it is available in journal form or as computer tape or custom search services. The journal contains Keyword-In-Context, author, and molecular formula indexes to the digest (informational) section of the publication. The three indexes are cumulated semiannually.

BioResearch Titles[4] is a monthly computer-based publication presenting a permuted title index to articles published in the life sciences. In addition to the permuted title (subject index), the publication has a bibliographic section and an author index.

Current Contents[9] is a weekly presentation of the contents, in their original format, of foreign and domestic research journals. It is issued in two series: *Space, Electronic, and Physical Sciences* and *Chemical, Pharmaco-Medical, and Life Sciences* with some degree of overlap between the two. An author index and address directory accompanies each issue. An article tear sheet service is available.

Who's Doing What in Biomedicine[10] is a monthly guide to current research in biomedicine. The format includes a subject index, and investigator-location index, an alphabetical index of investigators, and a title listing section. Index entries are cumulated annually.

Service	Address Reference	Frequency	Indexes	Comments
Abstracts of Bioanalytic Technology	11	q.		clinical chemistry
Abstracts of Bulgarian Scientific Literature. Biology and Medicine, English Edition	12	q.	q.a.A.	abstracts of Bulgarian journals
Abstracts of Bulgarian Scientific Literature. Chemistry and Chemical Technology, English Edition	12	sa.	sa.a.A.	abstracts of Bulgarian journals
Abstracts of Selected Articles from Soviet Bloc and Mainland China Technical Journals	13	m.		Series II: Chemistry and chemicals
Aerospace Medicine and Biology: An Annotated Bibliography	14	sa.	v.A.C.S.	aerospace medicine and bioastronautics
Analytical Abstracts	15	m.	a.A.S.	
Annual of Czechoslovak Medical Literature	16	a.	a.S.	biochemistry and pharmacology
Bibliography of Agriculture	17	m.	m.A.; a.A.S.	National Agriculture Library
Biological Abstracts	4	sm.	sm., q.c., a.A.S.	see text
BioResearch Titles	4	m.		see text
Bulletin Signaletique Section 12: Biophysique. Biochimie. Chimie analytique biologique.	18	m.	m.A.; a.S.A.	biophysics and biochemistry
Chemical Abstracts	3	bw.	see text	
CA—Biochemical Sections	3	bw.	see text	
Chemical-Biological Activities	3	bw.	see text	
Chemical Titles	3	bw.	see text	
Chemisches Zentralblatt	7	w.	see text	
Current Contents of Chemical, Pharmaco-Medical and Life Sciences	9	w.	see text	
Current Contents of Space, Electronic and Physical Sciences	9	w.	see text	

Abbreviations: w.—weekly; bw.—biweekly; sm.—semimonthly; m.—monthly; bm.—bimonthly; sa.—semiannual; a.—annual; S.—subject index; A.—author index; C.—corporate index; Cl.—collective (cumulative) index.

Service	Address Reference	Frequency	Indexes	Comments
Dairy Science Abstracts	19	m.	m.A.; a.A.S.	dairy biochemistry
Excerpta Medica	6	m.	see text	
Index Medicus	20	m.	see text	National Library of Medicine
International Abstracts of Biological Sciences	21	m.	q.S.A.	
Kagaku Gijutsu Bunken Sokuhō: Kagaku, Kagaku Kōggō Hen. [Scientific and Technical Bibliography Express Report: Chemistry and Chemical Engineering].	22	sm.		biochemistry
Lab World	23	m.	a.S.	Journal-Ease section
Novinsky Zahranicnf Literatury. Zdravotnictvf.	24	10./a.		titles in original languages
Nuclear Science Abstracts	25	sm.	sm.A, C, report no., S.; q., sa., a., 5-year Cl.	Atomic Energy Commission
Nutrition Abstracts and Reviews	26	q.	q.A.; a.A.S.	
Nutrition Information Abstracts	27	sm.	sm.S.	
Physics Abstracts (Science Abstracts. Section A)	28	m.	m.A.; a.A.S.	biophysics
Physics in Medicine and Biology (Section on Abstracts and Reviews of Books)	29	q.	a.A.S.	biophysics
Referativnyf Zhurnal: Biologicheskaya Khimiya	8	sm.	a.A.S.	see text
Revista de Referate din Literatura Sovietica de Specialitate: Stiinte Medico-Biologice	30	bm.	A.	abstracts from 25 Soviet journals
Science Abstracts of China: Biological Sciences	31	bm.		
Sheng Wu Hua Hsueh Wen Chai—K'ang Sheng Su Teng Pu Fen. [Biochemical Abstracts:Antibiotics Section]	31	m.		translation of Referativnyi Zhurnal: Biologicheskaya Khimiya

Service	Address Reference	Frequency	Indexes	Comments
Studii si Cercetari de Biochimie [Recenzii Section]	32	q.		300 abstracts per year from world's literature
Tampakushitsu, Kakusan, Koso. Protein Nucleic Acid Enzyme	33	m.		biochemistry
U. S. Government Research Reports	34	sm.	sm.AD, number, and S.; bm. title	nonclassified government report literature
Wu Li Lun Wen So Yin [Index to Physics Articles]	31	m.		translation of Physics Abstracts' Section A.

Abbreviations: w.—weekly; bw.—biweekly; sm.—semimonthly; m.—monthly; bm.—bimonthly; sa.—semiannual; a.—annual; S.—subject index; A.—author index; C.—corporate index; Cl.—collective (cumulative) index.

REFERENCES AND ADDRESSES

1. *A Guide to the World's Abstracting and Indexing Services in Science and Technology, Report 102.* National Federation of Science Abstracting and Indexing Services, Washington, D.C., 1963.

2. *A Directory of Information Resources in the United States—Physical Sciences, Biological Sciences, Engineering.* National Referral Center for Science and Technology, Superintendent of Documents, U. S. Govt. Printing Office, Washington, D.C. 20402, Jan., 1965.

3. Chemical Abstracts Service
   The Ohio State University
   2540 Olentangy River Road
   Columbus, Ohio 43210

4. BioSciences Information Service of Biological Abstracts
   3815 Walnut Street
   Philadelphia, Pennsylvania 19104

5. Superintendent of Documents
   U. S. Government Printing Office
   Washington, D.C. 20402

6. Excerpta Medica Foundation
   Herengracht 119–123
   Amsterdam-C, The Netherlands
           or
   Excerpta Medica Foundation
   Academy of Medicine Building
   2 East 103rd Street
   New York, N.Y. 10029

7. Akademie-Verlag, GmbH
   Leipziger Str. 3–4
   Berlin, W 8
   Germany

8. Izdatel'stvo Akademii Nauk SSSR.
   Shubinskii Per. D. 10
   Moscow, C-99, USSR

9. Institute for Scientific Information
   325 Chestnut Street
   Philadelphia, Pennsylvania 19106

10. Center for Information Resources, Inc.
    2431 K Street N.W.
    Washington, D.C. 20037

11. American Association of Bioanalysts
    2000 P Street N.W.
    Washington, D.C. 20006

12. Bulgarian Academy of Sciences, Centre of Scientific and Technical Information and Documentation
    1, Rue 7 Noemvri
    Sofia, Bulgaria

13. Office of Technical Services
    U. S. Department of Commerce
    Washington, 25, D.C.

14. Science and Technology Division
    Library of Congress
    Washington, 25, D.C.

15. Society for Analytical Chemistry
    14 Belgrave Square
    London S.W.I., England
       published by
    W. Heffer & Sons, Ltd.
    4 Petty Cury
    Cambridge, England

16. Státní Lékařská Knihovna
    Sokolská 31
    Prague 2, Czechoslovakia

17. U. S. Department of Agriculture
    c/o Superintendent of Documents
    U. S. Government Printing Office
    Washington, 25, D.C.

18. Centre de Documentation du Centre National de la Recherche Scientifique
    (C.N.R.S.)
    15 quai Anatole-France
    Paris 7, France

19. Commonwealth Bureau of Dairy Science and Technology
    Shinfield, Reading, England
       published by
    Commonwealth Agricultural Bureau
    Farnham Royal, Bucks, England

20. National Library of Medicine
    c/o Superintendent of Documents
    U. S. Government Printing Office
    Washington, 25, D.C.

21. Pergamon Press
    122 E. 55th Street
    New York 22, N.Y.
       and
    Pergamon Press Limited
    Headington Hill Hall
    Oxford, England

22. Japan Information Center of Science and Technology
    15–5 Ichiban-cho
    Chiyodaku, Tokyo, Japan

23. Sidale Publishing Company
    672 South Lafayette Park Place
    Los Angeles, 57, California

24. Státní knihovna ČSSR,
    Prague 1–190
    Czechoslovakia

25. U.S. Atomic Energy Commission
    Division of Technical Information Services Extension
    P. O. Box 62
    Oak Ridge, Tennessee

26. Commonwealth Bureau of Animal Nutrition
    Rowett Research Institute
    Bucksburn, Aberdeen, Scotland

27. Nutrition Information Centre
    Vitamins Ltd.
    Upper Mall
    London W. 6, England

28. Institution of Electrical Engineers
    Savoy Place
    London W.C. 2, England

29. Taylor and Francis, Ltd.
    Red Lion Court
    Fleet Street
    London E.C. 4, England
      (Agents for U.S.A. and Canada)
    Academic Press Inc.,
    111 Fifth Avenue
    New York 3, N.Y.

30. Academia Republicii Populare Romîne
    Institutul de Studii Romîno-Sovietic
    str. Gutenberg 3 bis
    Bucharest, Rumania

31. Institute of Scientific and Technical Information of China
    117 Chao Yang Men Street
    Peking, China

32. Academia Republicii Populare Romîne.
    Institutal de Biochimie
      Order from
    "Cartimex" I.S.C.E.
    str. Aristide Briand 14
    Bucharest, Rumania

33. Kyoritsu Shuppan Company
    3–9 Kanda Surugadai
    Chiyoda-ku
    Tokyo, Japan

34. Office of Technical Services
    U.S. Department of Commerce
    c/o Superintendent of Documents
    U. S. Government Printing Office
    Washington, 25, D.C.